CHEMICAL TECHNOLOGY OF PETROLEUM

Chemical Technology of Petroleum

WILLIAM A. GRUSE

Retired, Mellon Institute
Lecturer, Engineering and Mines
University of Pittsburgh

DONALD R. STEVENS

Assistant Administrative Fellow
Mellon Institute

Third Edition

McGRAW-HILL BOOK COMPANY, INC.

New York   Toronto   London

1960

CHEMICAL TECHNOLOGY OF PETROLEUM

25089

THE MAPLE PRESS COMPANY, YORK, PA.

Preface

The first edition of this book (1928) described the science and technology of an industry which had changed little in principle since 1855, when Benjamin Silliman, Jr., outlined the basic products and the way to make them. The second edition (1942) was rewritten completely to describe the new industry, based on thermal cracking, solvent separation, and the beginnings of chemical synthesis of products. The experiences of the war period, 1940–1945, leading to the subsequent adoption of catalytic methods and the wide development of synthesis, have prompted the authors to write their book again, as the best way of presenting the striking developments made since that time.

The purpose of the book remains unchanged: to supply a chemical introduction to the science and technology of petroleum for advanced students and young research workers and to point the way into the voluminous literature on which the new science and technology are based.

The authors gratefully acknowledge support and encouragement from Gulf Research & Development Company, which has for many years sponsored their research at the Mellon Institute. They are much indebted to their collaborators, who have contributed six chapters. And, finally, they extend sincere thanks to the many friends who have given help, information, and judicious criticism; notably to Harold M. Smith, D. B. Taliaferro, J. Bennett Hill, William I. Gilbert, J. B. McKinley, R. G. Hay, William A. Horne, R. C. Odioso, R. C. Zabor, John Pellegrini, Helen Thayer, William E. Hanson, M. A. Hanna, Paul Cornell, T. L. Cantrell and associates, L. U. Franklin, Jerry McAfee, R. G. Capell, A. M. Henke, F. D. Rossini, T. W. Warren, W. G. Lovell, Bruce Walsh, H. C. Hunter, H. A. Ambrose, F. H. Garner, S. W. Ferris, W. A. Wright, E. J. Barth, A. C. Miller, Arnold Mallis, Alex Lewis, Jr., K. C. Heald, G. V. McGurl, M. J. Hill, J. W. Early, J. G. Erdman, and Paul Weaver.

William A. Gruse
Donald R. Stevens

Contents

Contents

Contents

CHEMICAL TECHNOLOGY OF PETROLEUM

CHAPTER I

Production, Classification, and Description of Crude Oils

References to the occurrence and properties of bituminous materials resembling petroleum are found scattered throughout classical and more modern literature. The descriptions by Herodotus, Plutarch, the Scriptural writers, Strabo, Pliny, and others are well summarized by Peckham[1] and Redwood.[2] The early history of the modern development has been outlined by Engler[3] and from an American standpoint by Bacon and Hamor.[4]

The wide distribution of petroleum in many parts of the world is in harmony with modern geological thinking. It appears that, within wide regions recognizable as sedimentary basins—such as the American Mid-Continent, the Alberta Basin in Canada, or the Persian Gulf area—the occurrence of oil is the rule rather than the exception, and the problem is not the finding of petroleum as such but finding it in commercial quantities.

PRODUCTION

I-1. Drilling. There is apparently no confirmation of the stories that petroleum was produced from drilled wells in antiquity, specifically in China.[5] It seems more likely that early production was by dipping up seeped material or by enlarging a seepage area by digging, until it became a hand-dug well. The drilling of cased wells in the United States has

---

[1] "Technology and Uses of Petroleum," U.S. Census, 1880. See also Forbes, "Bitumen and Petroleum in Antiquity," E. J. Brill, N. V. Leiden, Netherlands, 1936.

[2] "Petroleum," 4th ed., p. 2, Charles Griffin & Co., Ltd., London, 1922.

[3] "Das Erdöl," vol. I, p. 3, S. Hirzel Verlag, Leipzig, 1909.

[4] "American Petroleum Industry," vol. I, p. 197, McGraw-Hill Book Company, Inc., New York, 1916.

[5] General statement, *Petroleum (Berlin)* **26**(6):171 (1930).

been by two methods, the so-called cable tool and the rotary method. The first has been employed in the Eastern part of the country, and in general for shallow wells; the technique involves breaking the rock at the bottom of the hole by striking repeated blows with a bit suspended at the end of a cable. At intervals the tools are withdrawn and the shattered rock is bailed out as mud, after which the striking is resumed. The rotary method is more suited to soft rock, such as occurs in the Mid-Continent and Gulf Coast areas. A hole is drilled by a bit in rotary motion and the cuttings are continuously washed up out of the hole by a stream of drilling mud pumped down the hollow drill stem under pressure. The general methods of arranging the outer casing and the concentric inner tubing, as well as the methods of completing the well, are essentially the same by both methods.

The circulating mud employed in rotary drilling is important and its properties are critical.[1] It is essentially a suspension of clay in water, suitably modified by additives. It must be gel-like and viscous enough to carry the rock cuttings out of the hole; heavy enough (10 to 18, or more, lb per gal) so that a column of mud the depth of the well will counterbalance the rock or gas pressure; thixotropic enough to hold rock fragments in suspension if circulation should stop, but nonviscous enough to pump readily and to drop its burden when flowing very slowly. In addition, it must cool the bit and seal off the rock formations penetrated, neither flowing into the coarser strata nor filtering into the finer structures.[2] These objectives are attained by using heavy materials like barium sulfate to confer weight; bentonites to hold them in suspension; gums and starches to increase viscosity and thixotropy; specially prepared cellulose derivatives; starches and soluble silicates to avoid flocculation by well brines; alkaline tannates (quebracho) and sodium phosphates as reducers of viscosity; and water-soluble alcohols and ketones as antifoam agents.

A fairly recent development is the use of oil-base and oil-in-water emulsion muds;[3] these have certain advantages in operation, connected with their filtering and flushing properties. Oil-base muds have sometimes been employed preferentially in cases where the formation temperature is above the boiling point of water; the absence of water in the mud is not important, however, since the operating pressure is usually high enough to keep the water in liquid phase.

[1] See Rogers, "Composition and Properties of Oil Well Drilling Fluids," The Gulf Publishing Company, Houston, 1953.

[2] Paxton, *J. Inst. Petrol.*, **39**:2 (1953). Oxford and Chisholm, *World Oil*, **138**(1):107; (2):116 (1954).

[3] *Oil Gas J.*, **50**(44):102 (1952). Crittenden and Trimble, *Oil Gas J.*, **53**(52):83 (1955). *Chem. Eng. News*, **34**(39):4702 (1956).

I-2. Logging. One of the difficulties encountered in drilling is recognition of the possible oil and gas content of formations penetrated while sinking the well. Such recognition is possible by examining cores taken from the well[1] but this is usually prohibitively slow and expensive. Within recent years, methods have been developed for securing equivalent information by electrical logging of the formations encountered.[2] Electrical resistivity and self-potential data were first employed to differentiate sand or shale beds, to estimate bed thickness, and to plot underground structure contours. It was later found that oil-bearing formations frequently showed higher resistivity than did surrounding strata. Still later came recognition that electric logs were useful (particularly when employed with core data) in determining figures of value for reservoir engineering purposes, such as connate water salinity, water saturation, and the porosity and fluid permeabilities[3] of the formation. Quantitative interpretation of electric log data has been so successful that such logging is an almost universal accompaniment of oil well drilling. Acoustic methods of logging have been studied and some success has been attained in making logs by recording the natural gamma radiation of the formations.[4] An alternative is to introduce into the bore hole a source of neutrons and then to log by measuring the induced gamma radiation;[5] a miniature Van de Graaff generator has been described for the purpose.

I-3. Fracturing and Acid Treating. Once a producing horizon has been located, it can usually be isolated by cementing behind the casing; the well casing and cement can then be perforated at the proper depth and the oil withdrawn. It often happens that oil flow from the rock is obstructed by clogging of one sort or another. The free surface of the rock face can be increased in several ways. A method developed in the early days involved exploding a charge of nitroglycerin or similar violent brisant material at the well bottom. A less drastic means, effective in limestones and lime-bonded sandstones, is treatment of the rock face

---

[1] Henderson, Gove, Ledbetter, and Griffith, *Trans. AIME*, **198**, *Tech. Publ.* 3501, 1952. Pollard and Reicherz, *Bull. Am. Assoc. Petrol. Geologists*, **36**:230 (1952). Logging by visual inspection of well cuttings is not fully informative or precise.

[2] Wyllie, *World Petrol. Congr., Proc. 3rd Congr., Hague*, **2**, p. 378, 1951. "Fundamentals of Electric Log Interpretation," Academic Press, Inc., New York, 1954. Martin, *Oil Gas J.*, **54**(5):145 (1955). Uren, "Petroleum Production Engineering. Oil Field Development," 3d ed., pp. 630ff., McGraw-Hill Book Company, Inc., New York, 1946.

[3] Uren, *op. cit.*, pp. 14–15, 677–687.

[4] Kokesh, *Oil Gas J.*, **50**(12):284 (1951).

[5] Fearon and Mardock, *World Petrol. Congr., Proc. 3rd Congr., Hague*, **2**:418 (1951); *Bull. Am. Assoc. Petrol. Geologists*, **36**:312 (1952). Wyllie, *Geophysics*, **17**:790 (1952). Atkins, *Oil Gas J.*, **54**(63):88 (1956). See also, *Symposium on Nuclear Technology in the Petroleum Industry*, ACS Meeting, Miami, April, 1957; Caldwell and Sippel, p. 5; Youmans and Buck, p. 23.

with relatively dilute hydrochloric acid suitably inhibited against metal corrosion.[1] Another successful mechanical technique depends on the application of hydraulic pressure to split the rock strata apart. Drilling mud, crude oil, or nonviscous distillate, carrying suspended sand as a propping material, is pumped into the formation under high pressure. The liquid penetrates the rock along the bedding planes, spreading the strata apart; the sand entrained in the fracturing liquid holds the layers apart after the pressure is released, thus increasing drainage surface. The process is known as hydraulic fracturing.[2]

I-4. Reservoir Engineering.[3] Within recent years the technology involved in maintaining conditions for maximum oil recovery from a field has been studied intensively under the name of reservoir engineering. Perhaps the most important requirement is the maintaining of pressure in the reservoir. In the undisturbed formations, the pressure is due to gas associated with the oil (in solution, with or without additional gas separated at the top of the formation—gas cap) or to water at the bottom or sides of the oil body in the reservoir, or to both. If wells penetrate this system and are allowed to flow unchecked, the natural pressure is likely to be dissipated while there is still a good deal of oil unproduced.[4] This situation can be helped by control of the rate and method of oil removal; it is important that oil be withdrawn at such a rate that natural water at the edges of the formation will have time to keep orderly pace with production. Another way of increasing recovery involves judicious introduction of extraneous gas or water into the formation. Intelligent control depends in any case on adequate information. Necessary basic data on the equilibrium behavior of hydrocarbon mixtures under reservoir conditions have been supplied by American Petroleum Institute Research Project 37.[5] Knowledge of the composition and viscosity of the reservoir fluid, the temperatures and pressures, with their distribution in the for-

---

[1] Sherman and Fry, *Ind. Eng. Chem.*, **26**:921 (1934); on selective acid treatment, Shelton and Clark, *Petrol. Engr.*, **17**(8):235 (1946); on use of radioactive tracers to locate zones of action, *Oil Gas J.*, **50**(18):55 (1951).

[2] Clark, *Oil Gas J.*, **47**(24):76 (1948). Padgett, *World Petrol. Congr., Proc. 3rd Congr., Hague*, **2**:618 (1951). Clark, *Oil Gas J.*, **52**(19):122 (1953); **53**(18):109 (1954).

[3] Pirson, "Elements of Oil Reservoir Engineering," McGraw-Hill Book Company, Inc., New York, 1958. Muskat, "Physical Principles of Oil Production," McGraw-Hill Book Company, Inc., New York, 1949.

[4] See Muskat, *Ind. Eng. Chem.*, **45**:1401 (1953), for estimates of percentages which may remain; sometimes these are high.

[5] See the reports of this project over some twenty-five years; also Sage and Lacey, "Volumetric and Phase Behavior of Hydrocarbons," Stanford University Press, Stanford, Calif., 1939; Reprint, Gulf Publ. Co., Houston, Tex., 1949. It should be remembered that carbon dioxide and hydrogen sulfide are often present in petroleum gases; they can be quite important in the equilibrium picture; *Ind. Eng. Chem.*, **41**:475 (1949). Finally, see Eilerts, "Phase Relations of Gas Condensate Fluids," Monograph 10, Bureau of Mines, American Gas Association, New York, 1957.

mations, the relative permeability[1] of the rock to oil, gas, and water, and the relative viscosity of these phases are of great value in reservoir studies. Adequate information of the sort outlined makes it possible to treat a reservoir system by the known laws of vapor-liquid equilibrium and to predict its history under certain schedules of production.[2]

Within recent years deeper drilling to zones of higher pressure and temperature has led to discovery of reservoirs from which a single phase can be withdrawn containing large proportions of normally gaseous hydrocarbons with much lower amounts of very light crude oils; the latter might be present up to, say, 4 gal per 1,000 cu ft. An early example of this reservoir type is the Kettleman Hills field in California;[3] most of those known in the United States are located on the Gulf Coast of Lousiana and Texas. The product is distinguished from ordinary gas-cap fluids by the fact that the light oil content is recoverable as condensate when pressure is reduced on the sample; this is, of course, contrary to the usual separation of liquid from a homogeneous vapor-gas mixture (existing under less severe conditions) when pressure is increased. The reservoirs are therefore known as "condensate" reservoirs. Adequate information is not available in all cases on the actual nature of the oil deposit. There is not much doubt that the single phase withdrawn exists as such in the reservoir, since this can be confirmed by laboratory duplication. Some cases are oil bodies in communication with gas caps, at such high pressure and temperature that retrograde condensation of liquid hydrocarbons occurs when pressure is reduced on the gas-cap material.[4] Other cases may represent gas caps physically separated from their accompanying liquid oil, or even complete reservoirs of abnormally light crude oil vaporized into large proportions of gaseous hydrocarbons. The common factor in all these possible cases is the very high pressure and temperature which induce the existence of a single phase containing rather nonvolatile hydrocarbons which condense as liquid when pressure is reduced. Since decreasing pressure allows condensation, it is important that pressure be maintained during exploitation. This can be done by withdrawing gas-phase material, recovering the condensate liquid, and returning the stripped gas to the formation; the process is known as recycling.[5]

[1] Uren, *op. cit.*, pp. 14–15, 677–687.

[2] Muskat, *J. Appl. Physics*, **16**:147 (1945). On reservoir volume to be drained by one well, see Miller and Higgins, *U.S. Bur. Mines Rept. Invest.* 3479, 1939.

[3] Kennedy, *Petrol. Engr.*, **11**(9):117; (11):77 (1940).

[4] Dodge, "Chemical Engineering Thermodynamics," p. 545, McGraw-Hill Book Company, Inc., New York, 1944; Uren, "Petroleum Production Engineering. Oil Field Exploitation," 3d ed., p. 16, McGraw-Hill Book Company, Inc., New York, 1953.

[5] *AIME, Petrol. Div., Tech. Paper* 1969, 1946. *World Oil*, **126**(11):32; (12):130 (1947). *Oil Gas J.*, **46**(47):158 (1948). Stevens and Boots, *J. Inst. Petrol.*, **35**:309 (1949).

Since the prevailing formation pressure represents the energy available for producing oil from a reservoir, the conserving of such pressure is for this second reason highly important.   It is more desirable to maintain such pressure than to restore it.   However, where operating pressure has declined, it can usually be built up again by pumping in enough gas; in extreme cases a single phase condition can be restored.[1]   It will be obvious that in most cases the gas from the formation, stripped of liquid hydrocarbons, will be employed.[2]

When pressure is well dissipated and production has become difficult, secondary recovery methods may be applied.   While the repressuring just described qualifies under this head,[3] the more familiar method is water flooding.   This involves establishing or renewing water pressure to displace oil from the rock pores while pushing the oil to recovery wells.[4] It is important that the composition of the water be controlled to avoid precipitation of insoluble materials and the swelling of bentonite clays, followed by their dispersal in the formation, where they might interfere with flow of oil.   Bacterial contamination of certain kinds is also undesirable.[5]

Over a period of years, attempts have been made to improve the results of water flooding by including additive agents in the water injected. Many of these were doomed to failure by disregard of the elementary inorganic chemistry of the formations and of the water contained.   More recently water-soluble detergents, particularly of the non-ionic type,[6] have given moderate improvements in recovery.   It has been pointed out

[1] Katz and Williams, *Bull. Am. Assoc. Petrol. Geologists*, **36**:342 (1952).

[2] Tignor, Nabors, Jennings, and Krause, *U.S. Bur. Mines Rept. Invest.* 4690, 1950; Dobyns, Ayers, and Lewis, *U.S. Bur. Mines Rept. Invest.* 4892, 1952.   Use of inert gases such as nitrogen and gasoline engine exhaust is described in *Oil Gas J.*, **52**(27):94 (1953).

[3] Actually, repressuring involves the idea of restoring reservoir pressure derived from gas dissolved in the oil; secondary recovery implies only a push toward recovery wells by a fluid applied from outside.   Successful applications of the latter method will depend pretty largely on the relative permeability of the reservoir rock to oil, gas, and water and on the relative viscosities of the phases.

[4] Grandone, *U.S. Bur. Mines Rept. Invest.* 3761, 1944; Keithly and Jennings, *U.S. Bur. Mines Rept. Invest.* 3783, 1944; Grandone and Holleyman, *U.S. Bur. Mines Rept. Invest.* 4600, 1949; Powell and Johnston, *U.S. Bur. Mines Rept. Invest.* 4831–2, 1952.   Powers, *Petrol. Engr.*, **23**(7):A33 (1951); also, *Trans. AIME Tech. Publ.*, **189**:2939 (1950); **195**:3279 (1952).   For theory, see Calhoun, *Oil Gas J.*, **50**(20):308 (1951).   For detailed discussion, see Spencer, "Secondary Recovery of Oil," Pennsylvania State College, 1949.

[5] Watkins, Willet, and Arthur, *U.S. Bur. Mines Rept. Invest.* 4930, 1952.   Reichelt, *Erdöl u. Kohle*, **7**(4):227 (1954).

[6] Dunning, Hsiao, and Johansen, *U.S. Bur. Mines Rept. Invest.* 5020, 1953.   Dunning, Gustafson, and Johansen, *Ind. Eng. Chem.*, **46**:591 (1954).   Dunning and others, *Oil Gas J.*, **54**:19, 115 (1955).   Barnes, *Oil Gas J.*, **52**(27):67 (1953).   Botset, *World Oil*, **143**(4):176, (1956).

by Muskat[1] that the real function which additives might perform is the lowering of the interfacial tension between water and oil. It is sometimes supposed that the tension between oil and rock is the significant one; actually, in most reservoirs the rock is water-wet rather than oil-wet.

In order to overcome difficulties of producing some of the heavy, very viscous oils known, or the heavier materials left in spent reservoirs, it has been proposed that such heavy oils can be heated to a less viscous condition and pushed ahead to output wells by *in situ* combustion of part of the oil; air or oxygen is fed down certain wells with the idea that an advancing combustion wave can be maintained in the rock, moving toward recovery wells.[2] It has been suggested that burning of less than 15 per cent of the oil in place will be sufficient to produce the rest. The project is related to underground gasification of oil and coal, which has been under study for some years.[3]

Any formation producing a wax-bearing oil, and the well piping carrying such oil, may be exposed to clogging by deposited wax. This is encouraged by the change in concentration resulting from evaporation of light fractions and by the probable drop in temperature the evaporation involves. The wax will carry with it any silt or other solid particles suspended in the oil. There is likely also to be a good deal of resinous and asphaltic material in the deposit. It is not unlike the rod wax of the early days of the industry.[4] Control methods include mechanical scraping, use of solvents, and application of heating.[5] Wax content varies a great deal from one crude to another, and the wax-clogging problem may be serious in one location and nonexistent in others.

A common obstruction forming in piping under critical conditions of temperature, pressure, and composition is caused by hydrocarbon hydrates. These are complexes, presumably clathrate in nature, between water and the lower paraffins, up to butane; they are relatively stable at low temperatures and high pressures.[6] The remedies are dehydration,

---

[1] *Ind. Eng. Chem.*, **45**:1401 (1953).

[2] Kuhn and Koch, *Oil Gas J.*, **52**(14):92 (1953). Buffum, *Petrol. Engr.*, **26**(6):399 (1954).

[3] The U.S. Bureau of Mines, with industrial cooperation, has been active in this area. Sheinman and others, *Petrol. Engr.*, **10**(3):27 (1938); **11**(5):91 (1939). Elder and others, *U.S. Bur. Mines Rept. Invest.* 4808, 1951.

[4] Wood, Young, and Buell, *Oil Gas J.*, **26**(4):149 (1928).

[5] Comprehensive discussion by Reistle, *U.S. Bur. Mines Tech. Paper* 414, 1928. Calhoun, *Oil Weekly*, **121**(1):42 (1940). Williams, *Petrol. Engr.*, **12**(12):93, (1941). Pryor, *Petrol. Engr.*, **15**(5):122 (1944). Grant, *World Oil*, **127**(13):142 (1948). Crumley, *Bull. Geol. Soc. Am.*, **1**:307 (1949).

[6] Hammerschmidt, *Ind. Eng. Chem.*, **26**:851 (1934). Frost and Deaton, *Oil Gas J.*, **45**(12):170 (1946). McKetta and Katz, *Trans. AIME*, **170**, *Tech. Publ.* 2123, 1947. Reamer, Selleck, and Sage, *Trans. AIME*, **195**, *Tech. Publ.* 3376, 1952. Scauzello, *Chem. Eng. Progr.*, **52**:324 (1956).

injection of compounds like the lower alcohols, or heating at critical points of accumulation.

I-5. Emulsions and Emulsion Breaking.   Practically all petroleum *in situ* is in contact with so-called connate water dispersed in the pores of the reservoir, and at least a little of this brine, or perhaps edge or bottom water, is produced simultaneously with the oil.   Larger proportions of water may encroach, particularly as the reservoir pressure drops, and when this happens, the water is very likely to come to the surface emulsified with the oil.   It seems probable that the emulsions are formed by the agitation involved in the production—pumping, or flowing through small orifices, and anything which minimizes such agitation reduces the extent of emulsification.[1]

It is a matter of observation that emulsions practically never occur with light gravity paraffinic oils, but are common with those of heavy asphaltic type.   Poineer work on the nature of the emulsions was done by Sherrick.[2] He was able to show that they are always of the water-in-oil type and that in his samples the water particles were negatively charged.   He suggested that the emulsifying and stabilizing agents are silt particles carrying films of adsorbed asphaltic material.   He also studied the influence of salt content in the water on the nature and size of the electric charge on the water particles.   It was later shown[3] that an emulsion can practically always be broken by removing the asphalt by one means or another.   The importance of asphaltic constituents was indicated by the observation[4] that the oil recovered from an emulsion was more viscous, of heavier gravity, and showed a higher carbon residue value than the unemulsified part of the same oil; this would indicate accumulation of asphalt from the crude into the emulsion.

Recent work on surface active and film-forming materials in crude oils[5] serves to broaden slightly the concept of asphaltic material as the universal emulsifier.   It is suspected that such interphase films may contain high-molecular-weight waxes (not very soluble in oils), resins, and protein materials, all stabilized by metal complexes of porphyrin character.

The water content of emulsions may reach 60 per cent, but usually ranges from 3 to 20 per cent.   The water droplets varied, for certain occurrences studied, from 0.00001 to 0.2 mm in diameter; in this case they were positively charged, but the sign was easily reversed.[6]

[1] Dow, *U.S. Bur. Mines Rept. Invest.* 2683, 1925.

[2] *Ind. Eng. Chem.*, **12**:133 (1920); **13**:1010 (1921).

[3] Lottermoser and Calantar, *Kolloid Z.*, **48**:362 (1929).

[4] Dow and Reistle, *U.S. Bur. Mines Rept. Invest.* 2692, 1925.   See also, *ACS. Abstracts of Papers*, 20-I, 21-I, ACS Meeting, Miami, April, 1957.

[5] Dodd, Moore, and Denekas, *Ind. Eng. Chem.*, **44**:2585 (1952).

[6] Abozeid, *AIME Tech. Publ.* 345, 1930.

Breaking of crude oil emulsions follows the same general lines as for other emulsion types. These are[1] gravity settling or centrifuging; contact breaking—filtering; electrical precipitation; heating; chemical treatment.

These differ in effectiveness from one emulsion to another. Gravity settling can be accelerated by centrifuging;[2] contact breaking is effected by percolating the emulsion through a mass of wood shavings or other coalescing material of high surface area; a contact mass wetted selectively by the internal phase of the emulsion seems to be preferred. Electrical separation depends on the Cottrell principle; the emulsion (warmed to, say, 160°F) is exposed to a high voltage (e.g., 16,000 volts or even higher) alternating current. The water particles line up in chains and coalesce to droplets large enough for gravity settling.[3] Heating usually takes the form of pumping through a heated pipe coil and discharging to an evaporator. Care must be taken to avoid depositing dry salt in the heating tubes; the water should not be allowed to vaporize until it reaches the evaporator.[4] Most crude oil emulsions are broken by chemical treatment.[5] This ordinarily follows the principle of supplying an agent which, if added alone, would form an emulsion of type opposite that prevailing in the system. Thus, to an emulsion of water in oil, one should add a sodium soap, which tends by itself to form an oil-in-water dispersion. Methods of this sort have been applied extensively and successfully, although the matter is usually more complicated in details.[6] One difficulty is that emulsifiers of the oil-in-water type are usually not soluble in the oil, normally the outside phase, so that it is necessary to include a carrier which will help distribute the active agent where it is needed.[7]

An early successful emulsion breaker of this general type analyzed in percentage as sodium oleate 83.0, sodium silicate 5.0, sodium resinate 5.5, phenol 4.0, water 1.0.[8] Later similar products employed sulfonated oleic acid; a wide variety of sulfonated organic complexes have been

[1] Dow, *U.S. Bur. Mines Bull.* 250, 1926. Shea, *U.S. Bur. Mines Bull.* 417, 1939.

[2] Ayres, *Ind. Eng. Chem.*, **13**:1011 (1921).

[3] Wyant, *Natl. Petrol. News*, **20**(42):119 (1928). Eddy and Eddy, *Ind. Eng. Chem.*, **13**:1016 (1921). Pearce, *Brit. J. Appl. Phys.*, **5**:136 (1954).

[4] On performing the evaporation in vacuum, see *Petrol. Engr.*, **2**(6):182 (1931).

[5] DeGroote, "Science of Petroleum," vol. I, p. 616, Oxford University Press, New York and London, 1938. *Oil Gas J.*, **44**(11):116 (1945). Kirkpatrick, *Petrol. Refiner*, **27**(11):142, 622 (1948).

[6] A different theory is propounded by Blair, to the effect that the demulsifying agent is adsorbed at the phase interface and exerts a strong spreading pressure. Ultimately the original emulsifying film collapses. *ACS Abstr.*, 21-I, ACS Meeting, Miami, April, 1957.

[7] Dodd, *Chem. & Met. Eng.*, **28**:249 (1923).

[8] Matthews and Crosby, *Ind. Eng. Chem.*, **13**:1015 (1921). Mead and McCoy, *Colloid Symp. Monograph*, **4**:44 (1926).

patented for the purpose.[1]   These chemical reagents are generally applied as dilute water solutions, with the aid of gentle warming and mixing. A classification and discussion of emulsion breaking methods have been presented by D. B. Dow.[2]   The breaking treatment must be applied at or near the point of production because pipeline requirements for oil to be accepted for transportation prescribe a water content of not over 2 per cent.

Crude oil emulsions are often confused with what are known as "bottom settlings."[3]   There is, however, a clear distinction; bottom settlings are the sediments accumulated in storage tanks and usually represent the heavier remains of years of repeated filling of the tanks.   They ordinarily contain a high proportion of emulsified water, which is very firmly held; in addition, there is almost always a good deal of inorganic material, silt and sand, some asphalt, and some amorphous wax which has separated during cold weather.   These mixtures are extremely refractory to breaking and have been most successfully attacked by chemical methods.

I-6. Inorganic Constituents.   The ash content of a normal crude oil is of the order of 0.01 to 0.05 per cent.   Some of this may be present as truly oil-soluble compounds, but much is probably carried dissolved in water droplets dispersed in the oil, or as solid particles of suspended inorganic matter.   While many analyses of recovered ash have been published,[4] the investigators have not always taken the precaution of filtering or preferably centrifuging to remove suspended material.[5]   There is in consequence real doubt whether many of the trace elements are real or adventitious constituents of the crudes in which they have been found. There is also the possibility that volatile constituents may have been lost during dry ashing[6] or elements gained from the reagents used in wet ashing.   The major components are likely to be silicates and sulfates of calcium, magnesium, and sodium, with oxides of iron and aluminum. The high content of iron suggests that it was derived from steel tanks and piping, while the silicates could represent suspended clay.   The less

[1] See numerous U.S. patents of DeGroote on this subject.

[2] *U.S. Bur. Mines Bull.* 250, 1926.

[3] See McCoy, Shidel, and Trager, *Mining Met. Bull.*, **152**:1513 (1919); discussion, **153–156**:3168 (1919).

[4] Shirey, *Ind. Eng. Chem.*, **23**:1151 (1931).   Wells, *U.S. Geol. Survey Bull.* 950, 1946.   Katchenov, *Doklady Akad. Nauk. S.S.S.R.* **62**:361 (1948); *C.A.*, **43**:2139 (1949); **45**:7339 (1951).   Southweck, Thesis, Massachusetts Institute of Technology, June, 1951.   Jones and Hardy, *Ind. Eng. Chem.*, **44**:2618 (1952).   For methods of determining these traces, see Karchmer and Gunn, *Anal. Chem.*, **24**:1733 (1952). Milner, Glass, Kirchner, and Yarick, *Anal. Chem.*, **24**:1728 (1952).   Gamble and Jones, *Anal. Chem.*, **27**:1456 (1955).

[5] See Russell, *Div. Phys. Inorg. Chem.*, 5P, ACS Meeting, New York, 1951, for analysis of ash from a centrifuged crude and from the sludge removed by centrifuging.

[6] Gamble and Jones, *loc. cit.*

plentiful elements recognized seem to cover a considerable portion of the Periodic Table, and the number to be found is probably limited chiefly by the sensitiveness of the analytical method applied. A typical list of elements found, in the order of decreasing percentage present (reading downward), is

Iron	Copper	Molybdenum
Calcium	Manganese	Lead
Magnesium	Strontium	Tin
Silicon	Barium	Sodium
Aluminum	Boron	Potassium
Vanadium	Cobalt	Phosphorus
Nickel	Zinc	Lithium

and still others, ending in silver and gold. In this tabulation, sodium comes quite low, although most investigators have recognized it as a major component. It will be evident that such results cannot easily have much general significance; the composition of the earth's crust is highly variable and it is easy to believe that a petroleum which has migrated even a short distance underground could bring up at least traces of almost any known element. A recent, less comprehensive but more systematic study[1] of 23 crudes (spectrographic analyses of dry ash samples after the oils had been water-washed and filtered) gave the following

Maximum percentage of ash	*Elements*
10–100 per cent	Na, Ca, Fe, V, Ni, Cu
1–10 per cent	Zn, K, Mg, Al
0.1–1.0 per cent	Zr, Sr, Pb, Nd, Mo, La, Co, Ca, Ba, B, As, Mn, Ti

Actually the results were weighted by the number of crudes showing these ranges for each element listed, but the tabulation will serve to give at least a rough idea of the elements present. The presence of elemental sulfur in petroleum, although long doubted, has been well established by Eccleston, Morrison, and Smith.[2] The matter is discussed more fully in Chap. II.

Desalting. Crude oil as produced is likely to contain appreciable amounts of salt, up to a maximum 0.1 per cent by weight (roughly 300 lb/1,000 bbl). This is composed mostly of the mixed chlorides of sodium, calcium, magnesium, and iron.[3] It is likely to be present as

[1] Ball, Wenger, Hyden, Horr, and Myers, *ACS, Div. Petrol. Chem.*, ACS Meeting, Dallas, April, 1956.

[2] *Anal. Chem.*, **24**:1745 (1952).

[3] For analyses of brines, see Illinois Geological Survey, *Illinois Petroleum*, **66**:5 (1952). Ohio, *Div. Geol. Survey, Rept. Invest.*, No. 11, p. 1, 1952. Rall and Wright, *U.S. Bur. Mines Rept. Invest.* 4974, 1953.

droplets of concentrated brine, with perhaps some free salt crystals. Even after an emulsion-breaking treatment a recognizable salt content may persist.   Salt is objectionable because it brings about corrosion of steel equipment, particularly during refining operations; the chlorides (chiefly magnesium) hydrolyze when heated, to set free hydrogen chloride. This will dissolve in any liquid water present—usually in condensers at the point where steam is converted to water—and cause rapid corrosion. Another difficulty is that a dry salt deposit may be formed on evaporator tube surfaces.   For such reasons it is desirable to reduce the salt content of crude oil to not more than 5 or 10 lb per 1,000 bbl.

Desalting is effected by the application of familiar methods.[1]   Electrical precipitation,[2] as with emulsions, contact separation by percolation, centrifuging to aid gravity settling, and heat-and-pressure treatment, may be employed.   The most common practice is to wash the crude with 10 or 15 per cent of hot water, sometimes under pressure and at temperatures up to 250°F.   To separate the salt solution, contact coalescence,[3] demulsifying chemicals[4] or centrifuging[5] may be applied.   Sometimes it is advantageous to separate the existing brine solution, as by electrical precipitation, and then to wash the dry crude with fresh water, separating the wash solution by another dehydration.

I-7. Composition.[6]   Much of the early study of the composition of petroleum was concerned with analyses of whole crudes for percentages of elements present.   While the physical nature of the oils and the variable losses during production make such analyses somewhat uncertain, the results are surprisingly uniform.   Thus Bushong[7] summarized data for American crude oils of his day and found the following:

Carbon	83.9–86.8
Hydrogen	11.4–14.0
Sulfur	0.06–1.75
Nitrogen	0.11–1.70

Engler, a year later,[8] presented similar figures for foreign crudes, and like results are obtained for oils that seem to have little in common except a fluid nature and a subterranean origin.   The explanation is due to

[1] Christianson and Horne, *U.S. Bur. Mines Rept. Invest.* 3422, 1938.

[2] *Petrol. Engr.*, **19**(2): 98 (1947).

[3] *Trans. AIChE*, **42**:413 (1946).

[4] *Petrol. Refiner*, **27**(1): 142 (1949).

[5] *Oil Gas J.*, **44**(46):81 (1946).

[6] For references to early literature on the composition of various crude oils, see the second edition of this book, p. 1, 1942.

[7] *Univ. Kansas Geol. Survey*, **9**:303 (1908).

[8] "Das Erdöl," vol. I, p. 3, S. Hirzel Verlag, Leipzig, 1909.

C. F. Mabery[1] who proposed that petroleums are composed of many members of a few homologous series of hydrocarbons. He pointed out that differences in the proportion of each series and in the extent to which individual members of each series are present would make little difference in the composition of the total mixture; the net result is that the elementary composition of any one petroleum is remarkably like that of any other petroleum. This concept is of great value for scientific study, but its development permits serious variation in technical properties. A moderate amount of asphaltic material may have little or no effect on the elementary composition of a crude oil, but may increase considerably the difficulty of producing good lubricants from it. Likewise, a 10 per cent increase of aromatics in a kerosene fraction may not alter very much the analytical figures for either the kerosene cut or the crude itself, but may alter markedly the feasibility of making refined kerosene. In other words, within the narrow limits of the elementary composition of petroleums, there is room for all the wide differences known to exist in both crude oils and petroleum products.

The view that petroleum is essentially a mixture of hydrocarbons has proved to be a correct one. Even the other elements found are present, except for sulfur, which may be present as the element, not as simple derivatives, but almost certainly as relatively complex substances, predominantly hydrocarbon in character and differentiated from pure hydrocarbons only by a small content of oxygen, sulfur, nitrogen, and, in rare cases, phosphorus. The chemical nature of both types of materials is discussed in Chap. II.

Conventional crude oils may be described qualitatively as brownish-green to black liquids of specific gravity from, say, 0.810 to 0.985[2] and having a boiling range from about 75 to above 700°F, where active decomposition occurs when distillation is attempted. They will contain from none to 35 or more per cent of gasoline and varying proportions of kerosene hydrocarbons and higher-boiling constituents, up to the highly viscous and nonvolatile compounds present in steam-engine cylinder lubricants and the asphalts.

The actual composition of the fluid (gas and liquid) delivered by the well is highly variable, depending on the original composition of the "oil" *in situ*, the manner of production, and the stage reached in the life of the well or reservoir. For a newly opened formation and under ideal conditions the proportions of gas may be so high that the fluid is really a solution of liquid in gas, which leaves the reservoir rock so completely that a core will not show any visible content of liquid oil. A rough

---

[1] A leading early investigator of American petroleum; for biography, see *Ind. Eng. Chem.*, **15**:314 (1923).

[2] The reservoir fluid is usually much lighter.

indication of this situation is a high ratio of gas to oil produced. This
ratio may be essentially zero for fields where the rock pressure has been
dissipated and oil must be pumped out, to a few hundred cubic feet per
barrel in more normal cases, and to as much as 50,000 or more cu ft per
bbl for so-called "condensate" reservoirs, where a very light crude oil—
say, 0.80 sp gr or lighter—exists as vapor in a body of gas at high pressure and usually rather high temperature.[1] It must be remembered that
when temperature and pressure are sufficiently high, even a fairly normal
crude and its accompanying gas may exist in the reservoir as a single
phase, and would be classified as a condensate. The composition of the
reservoir fluid, the gas separated, and the residual liquid from such a
condensate well are,[2] in mole per cent, as follows:

Component	Separated gas	Separated liquid	Well fluid
Nitrogen	1.00	0.03	0.96
Carbon dioxide	2.80	0.98	2.73
Methane	86.42	16.43	83.61
Ethane	6.00	6.87	6.03
Propane	2.34	7.17	2.54
Butanes	0.92	7.25	1.18
Pentanes	0.29	6.21	0.51
Hexanes	0.23	9.53	0.61
Heptanes +	....	45.53	1.83

As mentioned above, a condensate reservoir may in some cases represent
a gas cap from a complete reservoir, physically separated from the main
body of liquid oil, and thus existing by itself in a somewhat abnormal
condition.   It is sometimes possible to estimate from the fluid composition and the circumstances surrounding a condensate discovery that it is
or was recently in contact with a body of liquid oil
      The composition of a bottom-hole sample—presumably the whole
reservoir fluid—from a well in Oklahoma has been reported by Lindsly.[3]
The well pressure, shut in and not flowing, was 2,829 lb per sq in. and
the temperature 149°F.   The fluid composition was, in mole per cent:

$$
\begin{aligned}
\text{Methane} &\quad 32.8 \\
\text{Ethane} &\quad 14.89 \\
\text{Propane} &\quad 3.93 \\
\text{Butanes} &\quad 3.75 \\
\text{Pentanes} &\quad 2.79 \\
\text{Hexanes} &\quad 3.58 \\
C_7 + &\quad 38.16
\end{aligned}
$$

[1] See discussion earlier in this chapter.
[2] Unpublished data from the authors' laboratory.
[3] *Petrol. Engr.*, **7**(5):34 (1936).

A similar study of a bottom-hole sample taken from a well in the Gulf Coast area of Louisiana gave[1] the following (all mole per cent):

Methane	21.78
Ethane	2.96
Propane	1.69
Butanes	1.52
Pentanes	1.09
Hexanes	1.51
C_7+	69.45

The reservoir fluid analyzed had a density of 0.8001 g per ml at 173°F and under the bottom-hole pressure of 2,952 lb per sq in. Such figures are of course highly variable with the particular formation and the conditions of production. Crude oils are ordinarily examined and described in terms of the liquid remaining after gaseous constituents have been separated. The work of the U.S. Bureau of Mines has been invaluable in making available inspection analyses of the crude oils of the world.[2]

I-8. Classification. No successful method of classification for petroleum oils has yet been devised. Systems based on a superficial inspection involving some physical property, such as specific gravity, are easily applied, and specific or Baumé gravity (API gravity; see Chap. IV) is actually used to a large extent in expressing the quality of crude oils. Such a system is approximately indicative of the general character of a crude oil so long as materials of one general type are under consideration. Thus among crudes from one area, an oil of 35° gravity (0.85) is usually more valuable than one of 30° gravity (0.876), because it will contain more light fractions (gasoline, etc.) and less of the heavy asphaltic constituents which are likely to render it less suited for making refined products.[3]

A more rational basis of classification is found in some expression of the composition of the oils. In American practice, crude oils have long been roughly classified as paraffin base, asphaltic base, or, if they contain both paraffin and asphalt, mixed-base. A fourth class, known as "hybrid base," including naphthenic oils which carry a small amount of wax, was suggested by N. A. C. Smith.[4] This system was devised on the basis of

---

[1] Unpublished data from the authors' laboratory.

[2] No comparable body of information on crude petroleums has been published anywhere else; see *U.S. Bur. Mines Rept. Invest.* 4289, May, 1948, and particularly, *Infor. Circ.* 7470, June, 1948, for a bibliography of 115 Bureau reports on the subject.

[3] Since heavy gravity may also be caused by a high content of naphthenic and aromatic groupings, this statement needs some qualifications; a heavy crude oil low in asphaltic materials is desirable because it will supply cracking stocks which yield, on cracking, gasolines of high octane number.

[4] *U.S. Bur. Mines Rept. Invest.* 2806, 1927. Smith and Lane, *U.S. Bur. Mines Bull.* 291, 1928.

differences in the nature of the residuum left by nondestructive distillation —waxy, asphaltic, or mixed. The "asphalt" may, of course, vary widely in character, so that the asphalt-base class is broadly inclusive. This system is of the highest value to the refiner, since it indicates almost at once in a general way the nature of the products, the system of refining required, and the probable difficulties to be encountered. These considerations are discussed later. A logical development of Smith's suggestion was advanced by Lane and Garton.[1] A crude oil is subjected to a standardized analytical distillation, first at atmospheric pressure and then in vacuum. Fractions are collected over intervals of 25°C in boiling point, and classification is based on the API gravity of two key fractions: No. 1 from 250 to 275°C at atmospheric pressure in the kerosene range, and No. 2 from 275 to 300°C at 40 mm pressure in the lubricating oil range. If key fraction 1 is of gravity 40° or lighter (0.825), the lower-boiling portions of the crude are considered to be paraffinic; if 30° or heavier (0.860), they are naphthenic; and if between 33 and 40°, they are intermediate. Likewise, if the gravity of key fraction 2 is 30° or lighter, the higher-boiling fractions of the crude are paraffinic; if 20° or heavier (0.934), they are naphthenic; and if between 20 and 30°, they are intermediate. This permits a classification of crude oils into types as follows:

TABLE I-1. KEY FRACTIONS FOR CHARACTERIZING CRUDE OILS

	Key fraction 1	Key fraction 2
Paraffin	40° or lighter	30° or lighter
Paraffin—intermediate	40° or lighter	20 to 30°
Intermediate—paraffin	33 to 40°	30° or lighter
Intermediate	33 to 40°	20 to 30°
Intermediate—naphthene	33 to 40°	20° or heavier
Naphthene—intermediate	33° or heavier	20 to 30°
Naphthene	33° or heavier	20° or heavier
Paraffin—naphthene	40° or lighter	20° or heavier
Naphthene—paraffin	33° or heavier	30° or lighter

The last two possible cases have not been recognized in any known crude oil. A crude so examined can be characterized further as wax-bearing or wax-free. This serves to emphasize the fallacy of the one-time belief that only paraffinic crudes are wax-bearing. It is true that commercial wax recovery is limited to paraffinic crudes, but not all paraffinic crudes contain wax suitable for recovery; furthermore, wax is known to occur in a number of naphthenic crudes. The method is, unfortunately, not very critical.

[1] *U.S. Bur. Mines Rept. Invest.* 3279, 1935.

The above methods of classifying oils are based on physical measurements which give an indication of chemical composition. They have the scientific disadvantage of resting on one-point, or at most two-point, characterization. With the more exacting demands of a technically educated market (octane numbers, cetane numbers, viscosity indices), direct chemical information is desirable. This is supplied more adequately by the Bureau of Mines correlation index,[1] which involves assign-

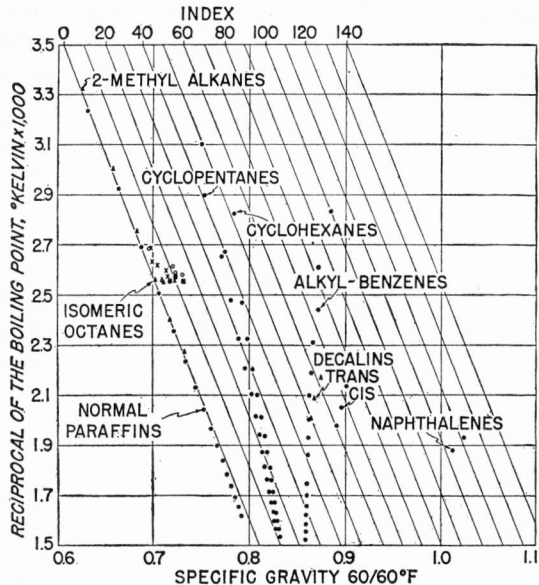

FIG. I-1. Reference frame for correlation index numbers of crude oil fractions. (*From Smith and McKinney, Cuba Petroleum News Digest, Special Edition, November 1, 1956, Fig. I.*)

ing a number to each distillate fraction obtained in the customary Bureau of Mines Hempel distillation. The number is obtained by plotting the reciprocal of the volumetric average boiling point of the particular fraction against the specific gravity of that fraction. A reference framework is first provided by performing this operation for individual members of classes of hydrocarbons—n-paraffins, i-paraffins, etc., down to condensed aromatics. This provides a line for each class of hydrocarbons on a chart,[2] Fig. I-1, arranged in order from n-paraffins on one side to

[1] Smith, *U.S. Bur. Mines Tech. Paper* 610, 1941.

[2] Smith and McKinney, *Cuba Petroleum News Digest, Special Edition*, Nov. 1, 1956, Fig. I. A slightly less complete chart is given in Smith, *op. cit.*, Fig. 3. See this reference for simplified equations by which the correlation index can be calculated directly.

condensed aromatics on the other.   These lines define zones within which points may be set down for corresponding fractions of the crude oil under study.   Since the line for *n*-paraffins is numbered zero and that for benzene 100, each fraction then has an index number (low for paraffins, high for aromatics) expressing its chemical composition.   The comparison of these numbers for the successive fractions of a crude will show how the chemical composition shifts with rising boiling point.   A few typical numbers are:

Sample	Boiling point of fraction, °C	Correlation Index
Bradford, Pennsylvania............	75–100	14
	175–200	21
	250–275	22
Kern County, California...........	75–100	23
	175–200	32
	250–275	33
Goldsmith, West Texas............	75–100	
	175–200	27
	250–275	31

The number rises with increasing cyclic character of the hydrocarbons present; the known increase of cyclic components with increase of boiling point is evident in the trend of the numbers.   The correlation index is soundly based, and yields much information in compact form.   Unfortunately, as set up, it is limited to distillable materials.   While perhaps the scale could be shifted to a molecular-weight basis and applied to residua, much of the convenience and the applicability to accumulated assay distillation figures would be lost.

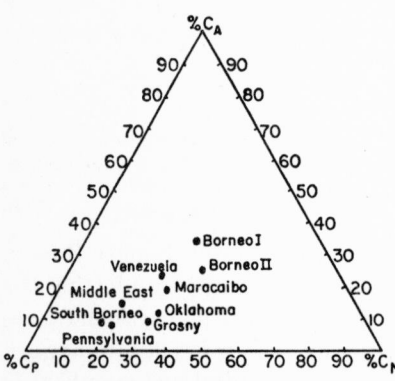

Fig. I-2. Typical crude oils on a quantitative composition diagram.   (*From Van Nes and Van Westen,* "*Aspects of the Constitution of Mineral Oils,*" *p. 7, Elsevier Press, Inc., Houston, Tex., 1951.*)

A similar means of describing an oil in terms of the composition of successive fractions is the carbon distribution spectrum of Van Nes and Van Westen.[1]   They employed first a quantitative plot resembling a qualitative triangular diagram described in a previous edition of the present book (see 2d ed., p. 7, 1942).   By physical property correlations

[1] "Aspects of the Constitution of Mineral Oils," pp. 7ff., Elsevier Press, Inc., Houston, Tex., 1951.

they determined the percentage of the total carbon in certain crude oils, distributed, respectively, as paraffins, naphthenes, and aromatics. This measurement permitted them to locate a point for each crude so analyzed on a triangular diagram in which the apices are 100 per cent each of the three hydrocarbons classes (see Fig. I-2). This is, of course, an improvement on previous one-point characterizations, but suffers from the disadvantages of that type. They next applied this technique to successive fractions obtained in a true-boiling distillation and plotted both the true-boiling curve and the analyses of the fractions on a common diagram. The result is a chemical picture of the successive fractions and the residuum of a whole crude, which they call the carbon distribution spectrum.

DESCRIPTION

There is no doubt about the technical merit of a curve method of describing a crude oil. However, where many crudes are to be compared, the results may be clumsy to handle and a qualitative description has advantages. Chemical study, even though somewhat sketchy and incomplete, has made it obvious that the main constituents of the average petroleum, particularly for the high-boiling and nonvolatile portions, are the cyclic compounds, naphthenes and aromatics. The chemical relation of these to paraffins, through hydrogen addition, is known and a similar relation, in the other direction, to asphalts by hydrogen removal can be assumed for discussion. (It is probably not far wrong.) These relations can be expressed by a diagram (Fig. I-3). It is not the intention to suggest that the constituents of a crude oil have shifted among

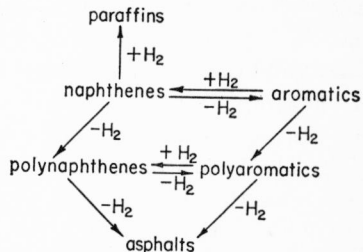

Fig. I-3. Chemical relations of crude oil constituents. Asphalts, of course, contain other elements, such as sulfur and nitrogen; see Chap. XV. Their position in the diagram is oversimplified.

themselves according to this diagram. What little is known about genesis of petroleum indicates rather that the composition of an oil is determined largely by the raw materials from which it was made and the chemical conditions under which the conversion occurred. Nor is the diagram intended as a suggestion that the hydrocarbon constituents of a crude oil are in equilibrium.[1] It serves, however, to show how these constituents are

---

[1] Such quantitative work as has been done indicates the contrary. The isomers of some of the lower paraffins are not present in the proportions called for by equilibrium constants known for the temperatures prevailing in the reservoirs and presumably in the source beds lying nearby. Rossini, ACS Southwest Regional Meeting, Houston, December, 1947. Smith and Rall, *Ind. Eng. Chem.*, **45**:1495 (1953).

related one to another; it serves further to emphasize that the bulk of the hydrocarbons in average crudes are cyclic, with free paraffinic and truly asphaltic constituents as somewhat unusual extremes. A distinction must be drawn between paraffinic molecules present as such and paraffinic chains attached to cyclic molecules. The former are in general low and the latter rather high in quantity. The uncombined aromatics and the predominantly aromatic molecules are also relatively low (in the average crudes); by difference the naphthenes and mixed naphthene-aromatics can be regarded as the major constituents. With these presumptions it is possible to make a case for describing a crude oil on the basis of some expression of its chemical composition, such as averaged Bureau of Mines correlation index figures for its middle portions. A diagram (Fig. I-4)[1] has been constructed along this principle. Each oil tabulated is characterized by certain averaged properties of its middle fractions, as determined in the Bureau of Mines assay,[2] as follows:

1. The horizontal axis bar represents a progression from paraffinic oils on the left to aromatics on the right; the scale is that of the Bureau of Mines correlation index, with zero at the left of the diagram and 100 at the right, representing the extremes from *n*-paraffins to benzene. The position of a crude on this bar is fixed by the averaged correlation index for its fractions boiling between 200°C at atmospheric pressure and 275°C at 40 mm. It serves to express directly the paraffinic or cyclic nature of the fractions examined, and hence of the bulk of the crude.

2. The length of the vertical bar for each crude above the horizontal indicates the wax content of the heavy gas oil and light lubricating fractions of that crude; it has been made proportional to the averaged cloud point of the portion of the crude boiling above 275°C at 760 mm and below 275°C at 40 mm. From this figure the crystalline wax content of the crude can be judged.

3. The length of each bar below the horizontal is a measure of the carbon residue value (Conradson) of the undistilled residuum from each crude at 275°C under 40 mm. It thus serves to indicate the asphalt content of each residuum and, hence, of each crude.

This method of diagramming crude oils to show chemical relations has certain positive advantages:

a. The necessary data are available, since they are derived from assay examinations by the Bureau of Mines, performed and published for hundreds of oils.

---

[1] The authors are greatly indebted to Harold M. Smith of the U.S. Bureau of Mines, who suggested the principle of the plotting, made the first sketches, and assisted in the development of a satisfactory presentation.

[2] *U.S. Bur. Mines Bull.* 207, 1922; 291, 1928; *U.S. Bur. Mines Tech. Paper* 610, 1941.

b. The method shows for the first time a relationship based on quantitative figures for a considerable number of crude oils.

The inherent disadvantages are:

a. The horizontal axis should ideally be based on naphthene-aromatic ratio; the correlation index actually employed is influenced by the paraffin content of the fractions examined.

b. The estimate of paraffinic content (vertical block upward) does not include paraffins present in the residuum.

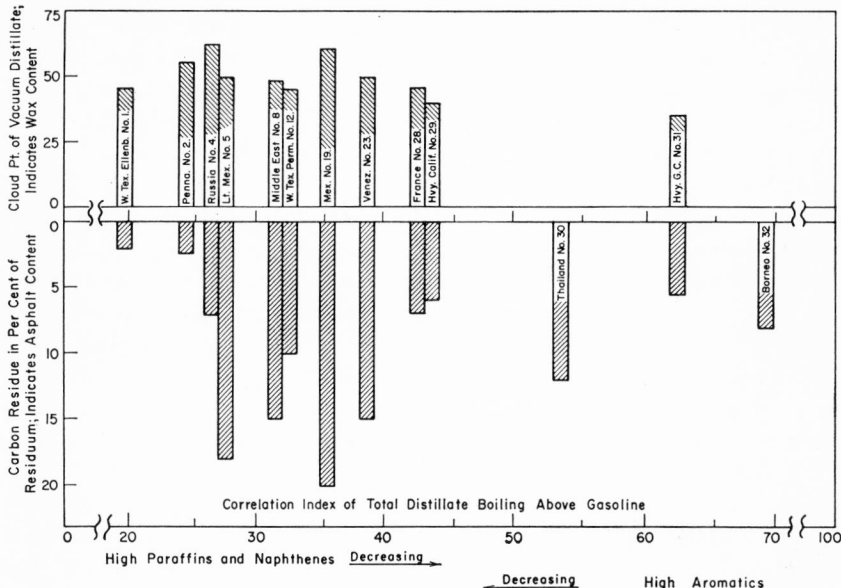

FIG. I-4. Relation between all known types of crude oils. (*After H. M. Smith.*)

c. The carbon residue value (vertical downward) is influenced not only by asphalt content, but also by high-molecular-weight hydrocarbons which crack to coke. Thus the carbon residue percentage for Bradford, Pennsylvania, oil is 2.4, although the crude is essentially free of what may be called asphalt.

d. Since the plotting is based on distillate content only, crudes high in nonvolatile content may not be placed and represented correctly.

The oils corresponding to the numbers used in Figs. I-4 and I-5 are listed in Table I-2.

It will immediately be apparent that the bulk of the crudes charted are of intermediate character as to chemical make-up; this is expressed by the fact that out of 32 oils tabulated, 17 have correlation index numbers falling between 30 and 40. This result might have been caused by arbitrary choice, but an effort has been made to select examples by geo-

TABLE I-2. CRUDE OILS PLOTTED IN FIGS. I-4 AND I-5

	Reference	CI	Cloud, °F	CCR, per cent
1. West Texas, Ellenberger.........	BM RI 4959*	19	46	1.9
2. Bradford, Pennsylvania..........	BM RI 4289	24	60	2.4
3. Grass Creek (light), Wyoming....	BM RI 4289	25	66	3.3
4. Grosny, Russia.................	BM Bull 401†	26	62	7.1
5. Poza Rica, Mexico..............	US BM‡	28	48	13.0
6. Palembang, Sumatra............	BM Bull 401	29	65	6.7
7. Adams County, Michigan........	BM RI 4289	29	46	15.4
8. Kirkuk, Iraq...................		32	53	14.8
9. Nienhagen, Germany............	US BM	32	46	7.6
10. Seminole, Oklahoma.............	BM RI 4289	32	45	15.4
11. San Jaoquin, Venezuela..........	US BM	33	100+	5.2
12. Goldsmith, West Texas..........	BM RI 4289	33	44	10.0
13. Haft Kel, Iran.................	BM Bull 401	33	53	11.9
14. East Heidelberg, Mississippi.....	BM RI 4687	33	51	20.0
15. Sudr, Egypt...................	US BM	33	60	21.6
16. East Texas..	BM RI 4289	34	60	10.0
17. North Belridge, California.......	BM RI 4289	35	60	8.3
18. Surakhany, Russia..............	BM Bull 401	35	30	1.8
19. Ezequil, Mexico................	US BM	36	44	15.0
20. Golden Spike, Alberta...........	US BM	37	49	8.0
21. Light Oficina, Venezuela.........	US BM	37	47	12.7
22. Yenangyuang, Burma............	BM Bull 401	39	73	4.3
23. Heavy Oficina, Venezuela........	US BM	39	48	14.9
24. Stettler, Alberta...............	US BM	39	50	13.9
25. Grass Creek, Wyoming (hvy)....	BM RI 4289	40	36	15.4
26. Miri, Borneo..................	BM Bull 401	41	68	2.5
27. Vinton, Texas..................	BM RI 4289	43	28	5.6
28. Lacq, France...................	US BM	43	46	15.7
29. Huntington Beach, California....	BM RI 4289	44	41	5.8
30. Ampurfang, Thailand...........	US BM	54	<0	11.7
31. Lolita, Texas..................	BM RI 4289	63	34	5.6
32. Tarakan, Borneo...............	BM Bull 401	70	<5	8.1

* U.S. Bureau of Mines Reports of Investigations.
† U.S. Bureau of Mines Bulletins.
‡ Private communication from U.S. Bureau of Mines.

graphical distribution and by quantitative importance. The unusual oils of the Far East occur in relatively small quantities, while those of the North American Mid-Continent, of Venezuela, and of the Middle East, all produced on a large scale, fall directly into the 30 to 40 range. In order to show the relations of these several oils, a supplementary diagram (Fig. I-5) presents the characteristics of sixteen crudes with CI values between 32 and 39.

By combining the chemical indications of Fig. I-4 or I-5 with a qualitative expression of the results achieved by conventional refining, a fair picture can be obtained of a crude oil in relation to both composition and application. This is more rational than it sounds, because results of refining are dependent on and reflect chemical composition. Thus Pozo Rica crude from Mexico (No. 5 in Fig. I-4) is high in both wax and asphalt; the Mexican crudes have in the past been worked mostly for gasoline, fuel oil, and paving asphalt, and the straight-run gasolines

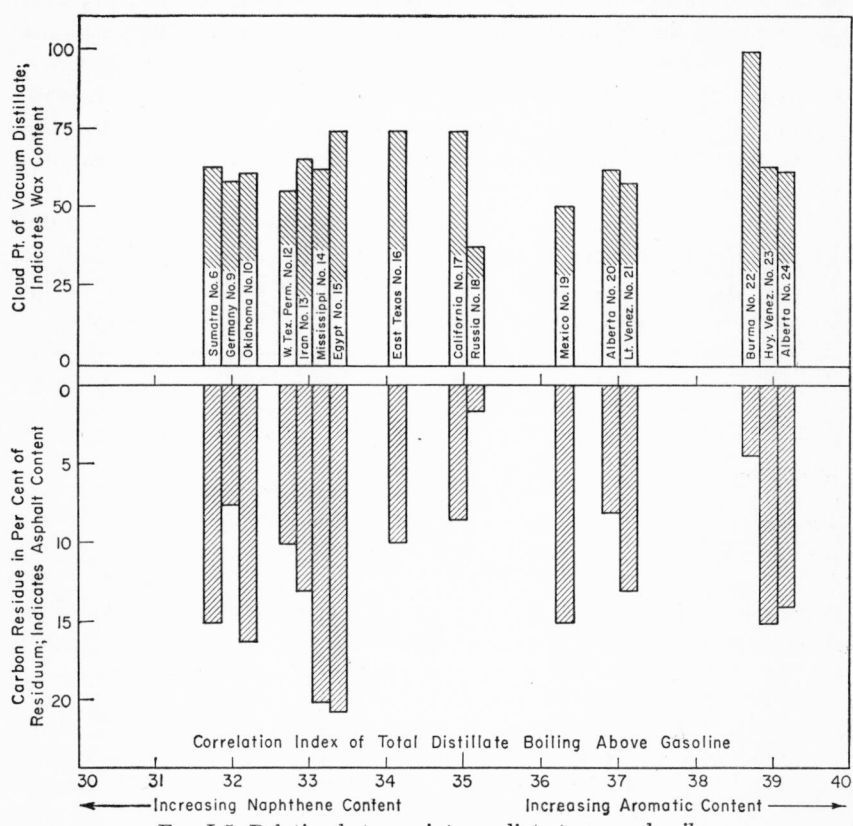

Fig. I-5. Relation between intermediate-type crude oils.

recovered have been rather low in octane number. Pennsylvania crudes have for a hundred years been known for production of wax and a high yield of excellent lubricating stock; the diagram indicates these (No. 2 in Fig. I-4) by showing a low correlation index, a high cloud point, and a carbon residue value suggesting very little asphalt. The conventional crudes of West Texas and of the Middle East are more or less alike. The diagram shows this (Kirkuk, Iraq, No. 8, and Goldsmith, West Texas, No. 12), but it does not show that the West Texas crudes contain corrosive sulfur compounds, while the Middle East oils are less objectionable in this respect.

The association of particular kinds of oil with particular producing areas has been approximately valid since the oil industry spread from Pennsylvania into other regions. Exceptions may occur at any time as drilling is extended beyond the depths at which the characteristic production of an area had previously been encountered. Thus, the deep Ordovician formations in West Texas have been found to yield sweet, highly paraffinic oil in regions previously known for rather asphaltic crudes of corrosive sulfur content. Similarly, the Texas Gulf Coast, until the last few years an area of naphthenic production, has recently been referred to as an outstanding reserve of paraffinic oil. In other words, depth must be considered as a third dimension in geographical distribution of petroleum.[1]

The rapid rise in production occurring since about 1950 has increased considerably the variety of crudes to be included in an over-all picture. H. M. Smith[2] has numbered 330 typical crudes in the United States, falling into eight area groups as follows:

	Per cent of U.S. production		Per cent of U.S. production
Appalachian..........	1.0	Gulf Coast..........	22.2
Michigan.............	0.9	West Texas..........	21.1
Mississippi..........	1.9	Rocky Mountain.....	4.5
Mid-Continent.......	32.8	California...........	15.5

There is a good deal of difficulty in setting down a brief description of the crudes from each area because of the diversity of types just mentioned. A tabulation has been made under the following headings:[3]

[1] Dr. W. E. Hanson has pointed out the desirability of grouping crude oils by sedimentary basins, rather than by geographical regions. Such an arrangement would bring into order some of the inconsistencies just pointed out in the text.

[2] *Ind. Eng. Chem.*, **44**:2577 (1952).

[3] The analytical data used in the tabulation have been drawn from a variety of sources, as follows:

UNITED STATES

McKinney and Blade, *U.S. Bur. Mines Rept. Invest.* 4289, 1948. Blade and Garton, *U.S. Bur. Mines Rept. Invest.* 4687, 1950. Espach and Fry, *U.S. Bur. Mines Rept. Invest.* 4768, 1951. Garton and McKinney, *U.S. Bur. Mines Rept. Invest.* 4959, 1953; 5249, 1956. Hughes and Blade, *U.S. Bur. Mines Inform. Circ.* 7470, 1948. H. M. Smith, *Ind. Eng. Chem.*, **44**:2577 (1952); U.S. Bureau of Mines, private communication of H. M. Smith; *World Petrol. Congr., Proc. 3rd Congr., Hague*, **6**:319 (1951). Lindsley, *U.S. Bur. Mines Rept. Invest.* 5055, 1954; also Wenger and Lanum, *Petrol. Engr.*, **26**(7):C-43 (1954). Wendland, *Oil Gas J.*, **52**(50):204 (1954). Pope

Specific gravity.   This gives a rough picture of the proportion of light and heavy, volatile and high-boiling, hydrocarbons, and when correlated with actual volatility, of the proportions of cyclic hydrocarbons and asphaltic materials.

Gasoline distillate; kerosene distillate.   These define at once the value of the crude as a source of these important materials of commerce.

Sulfur, percentage on crude.   This will give an indirect indication of the refining value of the oil; the value rises as sulfur content drops.

Asphalt content.   This serves to indicate the feasibility of making valuable heavy lubricating oils, or alternatively, the less valuable heavy fuel oil and road oils or paving asphalts.

The figures taken together serve to indicate the approximate value of the oil in question for general-purpose refining.

---

and Wilber, *Petrol. Engr.*, **28**(12):C-19 (1956).   Wenger and others, *U.S. Bur. Mines Rept. Invest.* 5309, 1957.

CANADA

Chantler, Seely, and Goodspeed, Dept. of Mines, Mines Branch, Ottawa, 1951. McKinney and Smith, *Petrol. Processing,* **7**:1270 (1952).   Nelson, *Oil Gas J.*, **34**(51): 137 (1956).

MEXICO

Kramer and Calkins, *U.S. Bur. Mines Tech. Paper* 346, 1925; *Petrol. Processing,* **8**:875 (1953).   Private communication from H. M. Smith, U.S. Bureau of Mines.

VENEZUELA

Nelson, Martorano, and Fombana, *World Petrol. Congr., Proc. 3rd Congr., Hague,* **6**:336 (1951).   Hedberg, Sass, and Funkhouser, *Bull. Am. Assoc. Petrol. Geologists,* **31**:2089 (1947).

TRINIDAD

Morton and Richards, *J. Inst. Petrol.*, **31**:159 (1945).

COLOMBIA

Smith, *World Petrol. Congr., Proc. 3rd Congr., Hague,* **6**:331 (1951); *Oil Gas J.*, **53**(45):123 (1955).

PERU

Smith, *World Petrol. Congr., Proc. 3rd Congr., Hague,* **6**:331 (1951).   Rassmuss, *Oil Gas J.*, **53**(34):238 (1954).

RUSSIA

Kraemer and Lane, *U.S. Bur. Mines Bull.* 401, 1937.   Gal'pern and Musaev, *Petrol. Engr.*, **15**(1):98 (1943).

RUMANIA

Edeleanu, *Petroleum Z.*, **4**:1281 (1926).   Kraemer and Lane, *U.S. Bur. Mines Bull.* 401, 1937.   Hlauschek, *Bull. Am. Assoc. Petrol. Geologists,* **34**:755 (1950).   Rosu, *Oil Forum,* **8**(2):55 (1954).

GERMANY

Louis and Bienner, *Rev. inst. franc. pétrole Ann.*, **8**:239 (1953).   Private communications from H. M. Smith, U.S. Bureau of Mines, and Dr. Gunther Schlicht, Deutsche Erdöl, A.G.

I-9. North America

United States. As of 1958, the United States produced about 37.5 per cent of the world's total supply of petroleum. The characteristics of the various oils are discussed, by regions, below. The figures are for volume per cent.

APPALACHIAN. Pennsylvania is the classical area for these oils, but they have also been produced in quantity in West Virginia and New York. The general characteristics are:

Specific gravity	Gasoline	Kerosene	Sulfur	Asphalt*
0.80–0.90	30–40	15	<0.25	<5

* The term "asphalt" is somewhat indefinite, depending on the analytical procedure applied in its determination. For this tabulation the word refers to the residual content of asphaltic material of 100 penetration at 77°F (ASTM D 5). Since this value is rarely measured in a routine examination of a crude oil, it has been estimated by the method of H. M. Smith [*Ind. Eng. Chem.*, **44**:2578 (1952); Stanfield and Hubbard, *U.S. Bur. Mines Tech. Paper* 717, 1949], in which the Conradson carbon value for the entire crude oil is multiplied by 4.9. This gives a fair approximation, although it may be somewhat misleading for crude oils analytically very low in asphaltenes, such as Cabin Creek, West Virginia (Appalachian), or West Texas Ellenberger production. In these cases the carbon residue value is attributable to true hydrocarbons of high molecular weight which, because of their nonvolatile character, crack to coke in the test.

The typical oil is perhaps that from Bradford:

Specific gravity	Gasoline	Kerosene	Sulfur	Asphalt
0.803	35	17	0.11	Trace

These crudes are the first ever produced in quantity (1859) and fortunately for the early industry, they are easy to refine; they are highly paraffinic, although within recent years still more paraffinic oils have

---

FRANCE

Private communications from H. M. Smith, U.S. Bureau of Mines, Dr. Eduard Thomas, Paris, and Esso Research & Engineering Co. *Industrie petrole*, **24**(8):46 (1956).

MIDDLE EAST

Smith, *World Petrol. Congr., Proc. 3rd Congr., Hague*, **6**:319 (1951). Marot, *World Petrol. Congr., Proc. 3rd Congr., Hague*, **6**:353 (1951). *Rev. inst. franc. petrole et Ann.*, **8**:437 (1953); **9**:503 (1954). Private communications from Refineries Department, British Petroleum Co.

EGYPT

Private communication from H. M. Smith, U.S. Bureau of Mines.

FAR EAST

Central Sumatra. Private communication from California Crude Oil Sales Co. Lerik and Talang, Standard Vacuum Oil Co.

been encountered in Louisiana and West Texas. The gasoline is of low octane value. The kerosene is good (it was for many years the world's standard), and the lubricating oils excellent as to stability, viscosity index, and low volatility for a given viscosity. Oils from northwestern Ohio and eastern Kentucky represent transition from the Pennsylvania type to the more cyclic, heavier gravity, higher sulfur, more asphaltic crudes of the Mid-Continent. The Illinois production represents still another step in the same direction.

MICHIGAN. This development is a relatively recent one. The crude oils are of intermediate character, suitable for general-purpose refining, that is, for preparation of cracking stocks and fuel oil. They are distinguished by the fact that the paraffin content of the gasolines contained is exceptionally high in normal compounds; the gasolines themselves are thus hard-knocking and octane numbers near zero are quite possible.

	Specific gravity	Gasoline	Kerosene	Sulfur	Asphalt
Light	<0.80	<40	20	<0.5	<5
Coldwater	0.781	41	21	0.3	2–3
Heavy	0.80–0.90	25–35	18	0.5–1.0	>25
Adams	0.859	22	21	0.6	25

MISSISSIPPI. Discovery and development of this area are recent. The light oils are of intermediate character, suited for general-purpose refining:

	Specific gravity	Gasoline	Kerosene	Sulfur	Asphalt
	0.80–0.87	25–40	20	<0.75	5–25
Cranford	0.821	35	19	0.10	6

The heavy crudes, however, are suited for little else than heavy fuel oil:

	Specific gravity	Gasoline	Kerosene	Sulfur	Asphalt
	0.87–0.95	5–25	5–10	1.0–2.0+	>25
Baxterville	0.966	5	12	3.0	70

THE MID-CONTINENT. Production in the Mid-Continent became important about 1910. It developed rapidly and was, until the rise of the Middle East, the most prolific oil-producing region in the world, and is still one of the most interesting and most varied. It embraces Oklahoma, Kansas, eastern Colorado, and except for West Texas and the Gulf Coastal area, all of Texas and Louisiana. The crudes produced are quite varied; the average type is fairly high in volatile content, contains both wax and asphalt in fair amounts, and is best suited for general-purpose refining. It is easy, however, to find high-quality, paraffinic exceptions suitable for manufacture of wax and good lubricating oils;

for instance, some of the products of the long-lived and prolific East Texas field. Examples of typical oils, historically rather than currently important, are:

	Specific gravity	Gasoline	Kerosene	Sulfur	Asphalt
Light	0.80–0.85	30–45	10–15	<0.5	10–15
East Texas	0.836	34	15	0.36	10
Cushing	0.824	36	15	0.25	6
				Mostly	Mostly
Heavy	0.85–0.90	5–25	5–15	<0.5	10–15
Healdton	0.857	23	14	0.77	13
El Dorado	0.853	25	16	0.27	14
Morel	0.891	15	13	0.67	31

GULF COAST. This area stretches along the coasts of Texas and Louisiana. It was until recent years characterized by the production of oils of heavy gravity, free of wax, and low in gasoline content, with a compensating high content of distillates in the kerosene and gas oil range. These crudes were, in earlier days, much used for the manufacture of low pour-point lubricating oils. However, the steep viscosity-temperature curves and relative instability under oxidizing conditions put them at a disadvantage in competition with paraffinic oils. The freedom from wax varied, and sometimes only a haze of ceresin could be observed on chilling the lubricating distillates. The gasoline from such crudes is high in naphthenes and isoparaffins and of good octane number. The gas oil is well suited for catalytic cracking, and the gasolines so produced are high in aromatics. Within recent years deeper drilling has produced oils of higher gasoline content and of more paraffinic character. Some of the recent discoveries are condensate fields. Typical crudes, both historical and current, are:

	Specific gravity	Gasoline	Kerosene	Sulfur	Asphalt
Older heavy oils	0.85–0.90	5–10	15–25	<0.25	<5
Barbers Hill	0.856	5	8	0.15	<5
Lolita	0.856	6	10	0.15	3
Fannett	0.870	16	25	0.21	2
Lighter deep production:					
Lovell's Lake	0.835	25	20	<0.10	0.5
Aransas Pass	0.817	32	25	<0.10	1

WEST TEXAS. The West Texas Permian Basin has been a prolific source of intermediate-type oils; the gasoline content is usually high and often naphthenic, and thus of good octane number. The asphalt content is rather high, and the most characteristic feature of these oils is the content—typically 1.5 per cent—of "sour" corrosive sulfur compounds. In some cases there is as much as 0.5 per cent of elemental sulfur (McElroy crude).   In general, these oils are best suited for general-purpose refining.   However, deeper drilling into older formations has located sweet, highly paraffinic crudes of Pennsylvania type.   The Ordovician Ellenberger crude is an example.   Typical products of the area are:

	Specific gravity	Gasoline	Kerosene	Sulfur	Asphalt
Older high-sulfur					
production	0.85–0.90	30–40	5–10	1.0–2.0	10–25
Goldsmith	0.854	27	15	1.9	12
McElroy	0.869	27	13	2.4	15
Newer sweet crudes:					
Monahans (Ellenberger)	0.817	37	15	0.16	3

ROCKY MOUNTAINS.   The earlier production of these fields was of the "black oil" type, highly asphaltic and rather high in sulfur content.   Better intermediate-base oils were located; these carry a large content of relatively high melting point wax.   Lubricating oil manufacture has been successful with these better crudes.   The products of the recently developed Williston Basin are of the lighter type.

Typical crudes are about as follows:

	Specific gravity	Gasoline	Kerosene	Sulfur	Asphalt
Black oils	0.85–0.90	20–30	5–10	1.0–2.0	15–40
Elk Basin	0.868	27	12	1.7	21
Grass Creek	0.90	16	12	2.7	25
Lighter paraffinic oils:					
Lance Creek	0.81	36	14	<0.1	5

CALIFORNIA.   The character of the production in California has varied somewhat with time.   The first wells, dating from the earlier years of the century, were drilled in fields inland and north of Los Angeles.   The formations were rather shallow, the oils heavy, naphthenic, and mostly high in sulfur.   For example:

	Specific gravity	Gasoline	Kerosene	Sulfur	Asphalt
Cat Canyon	0.957	11	10	3.8	50
Lompoc	0.933	18	13	3.6	41
McKettrick	0.943	5	15	0.7	21

All were producing from about 2,800 ft.   In the Los Angeles area, early shallow production was also heavy and asphaltic:

	Specific gravity	Gasoline	Kerosene	Sulfur	Asphalt
Placerita*	0.927	17	14	1.30	65
* At 1,800 ft.					

Deeper drilling in the same regions has disclosed oils of much lighter gravity, higher gasoline content, and lower percentage of sulfur, although often still high in asphaltic materials:

	Specific gravity	Gasoline	Kerosene	Sulfur	Asphalt
Oak Canyon	0.857	37	10	0.59	20
Potrero	0.790	64	16	0.33	2–3

Both of these are from depths of 5,000 to 7,000 ft. The lighter crudes have been of more intermediate character, wax-bearing but yielding naphthenic gasolines. The untreated products are often rather unstable, so that extensive chemical refining is required. Only certain selected crudes are suitable for lubricating oil manufacture, but the gasolines are rather uniformly high in octane number. The instability may be due to nitrogen compounds, perhaps of the pyrrole type. Most recent deep California production tends to be of high-grade intermediate character and low sulfur content. Condensate reservoirs, yielding crudes very high in gasoline, have been encountered.

Canada. There was a very small production of light crude oil of Pennsylvania type in New Brunswick and somewhat more of a crude resembling that of the Lima, Ohio, field, in Ontario forty or more years ago. The development in Alberta began about 1925, but has increased a great deal since 1950. Prior to that time gas and condensate fields were more important and the normal crude oils resembled those of Montana and Wyoming. More recently intermediate-base waxy oils resembling the average output of the Mid-Continent and suitable for general-purpose refining have been discovered and produced. The gas accompanying some of the current production is quite high in hydrogen sulfide, as, for instance, that of Pincher Creek. Characteristics of typical crudes are:

	Specific gravity	Gasoline	Kerosene	Sulfur	Asphalt
Alberta:					
Campbell	0.85	30	10	0.85	11
Leduc	0.82	35	10	0.4	7
Stettler	0.87	25	5	1.5	25
Pincher Creek	0.82	37	20	0.27	4
Saskatchewan:					
Lloydminster	0.98	—	—	3.0	53

Canada supplies, as of 1958, about 2 per cent of the world output.

Mexico. The Mexican oil fields lie near the eastern coasts of the country, from Tampico southward. The early flush production, 1910–1920, was very heavy, highly asphaltic, high in sulfur, and low in volatile content, which latter was, however, paraffinic. Refining was very simple, involving distillation to yield gasoline and some kerosene, leaving fuel oil and residual asphalt. Typical of this was:

	Specific gravity	Gasoline	Kerosene	Sulfur	Asphalt
Panuco	0.98	3.5	6.0	5.4	60 to 80

More recently lighter oils, both paraffinic wax-bearing and naphthenic, have been predominant in the output, for example:

	Specific gravity	Gasoline	Kerosene	Sulfur	Asphalt
Vera Cruz:					
Poza Rica	0.881	20	11	1.8	22
Ezequil Ordonez	0.938	13	8	3.2	35

Although lighter by comparison, they are still asphaltic and not suitable for lubricating oil manufacture. Still more recent production is quite paraffinic and high in volatile content:

	Specific gravity	Gasoline	Kerosene	Sulfur	Asphalt
Tabasco:					
Colombo	0.794	47	30	0.11	Trace
Tamaulipas:					
Reynosa	0.744	79	16	<0.10	Trace

The latter would appear to be condensates rather than normal crudes. Mexican production is about 1.3 per cent of the world supply.

I-10. South America

Venezuela. Oil production began in Venezuela about 1920, and now constitutes about 14 per cent of the world output. About two-thirds is derived from fields around Lake Maracaibo and the rest from the Orinoco basin. The crudes are nearly all black oils, with a family resemblance to the intermediate-base oils of Los Angeles County, California. The Maracaibo output is represented by:

	Specific gravity	Gasoline	Kerosene	Sulfur	Asphalt
Lagunillas	0.948	7	19	2.2	55
Mara (light)	0.87	22	12	2.0	30*

* Residue above 900°F.

Those from the Orinoco area by:

	Specific gravity	Gasoline	Kerosene	Sulfur	Asphalt
Oficina (light)	0.84	35	5	0.5	12
Oficina (heavy)	0.87	25	5	0.8	20

The more cyclic oils show higher sulfur and asphalt content and are lower in wax. By and large the gasolines are naphthenic, the kerosene poor, and the lubricating stocks unsuitable for use as such. Deeper drilling has made available rather more paraffinic crudes.

Trinidad. This island can be regarded as a geological extension of Venezuela, and as a matter of fact, the oils produced resemble those of Venezuela and the intermediate California crudes. The fields are close to the pitch lake and there is probably a genetic relation between the two. An unusually light gravity oil is:

	Specific gravity	Gasoline	Kerosene	Sulfur	Asphalt
Tabaquite	0.80	30	25	0.3	Very low

Colombia. The oils are black and asphaltic, resembling heavy California production, of high viscosity and low wax content. This latter makes possible manufacture of lubricating distillates of low pour-point temperature. Colombian production is 0.75 per cent of the world total.

	Specific gravity	Gasoline	Kerosene	Sulfur	Asphalt
LaCira	0.93	12	20	1.0	30
Casabe	—	5	10	1.0	30 to 40

Peru

	Specific gravity	Gasoline	Kerosene	Sulfur	Asphalt
La Brea	0.83	38	—	0.1	6
	0.85	34	—	0.1	8

The first above is wax-bearing, the second wax-free; both are of intermediate-naphthene base.

I-11. Russia. There is a long history of oil production in Russia and during the period up to about 1910 it was a major competitor of the United States for the world's kerosene markets. However, the industry has not, until recently, been developed as intensively as in North America. Most of the producing area (75 per cent at present) has always lain between the Black and Caspian Seas and to the northeast of that area.[1] There is prospect of good production far to the east, in central Asia, north and east of the Caspian. In general, the oil-bearing formations resemble those of the United States, but about one-third of the promising areas lie to the far north, where operation may be quite difficult for climatic reasons. Information is not available on the nature of recent Russian production. The older Baku oils were of mixed base, low in sulfur and rather high in resins and asphalts; gasoline content was low but it contained a good deal of naphthene-isoparaffin material. Grosny oil (Volga-Ural Basin) is higher in gasoline, kerosene, and wax. Not many Russian crudes are suitable for lubricating oil manufacture. The recent central Asian production is reported to be of mixed base, low in sulfur and gasoline, and not useful for lubricants. The data tabulated are not recent, but it may be supposed that the description of the older production is more or less valid for the present. Distribution of production among Russian fields is not known, but as a whole the Russian bloc accounted in 1958 for 14 per cent of the world supply. Of this, Rumania furnished over 1.2 per cent and Hungary, Yugoslavia, Albania, Poland,

[1] The oil seeps and eternal gas fires of Baku have been known since classical times.

and Czechoslovakia enough to make up 0.2 per cent for the satellite countries.

	Specific gravity	Gasoline	Kerosene	Sulfur	Asphalt
Ural-Gorodsky	0.95	25	0	5.0	45
Grosny	0.85	25	16	0.1	10
Baku-Surakhany	0.85	19	5	<0.1	3
Emba-Dossor	0.86	16	6	0.1	3
Ferghana	0.84	32	9	0.25	14

I-12. Europe

Rumania. The Rumanian oil fields are generally divisible into two classes, based on the formations which they tap. Certain Orchiuri, Baicoi, and some Moreni oils have been drawn from Dacic formations, and the Campina, Runcu-Mislea, and Boldesti crudes from Meotic structures. The Dacic oils, about one-third of the production, are naphthene-intermediates, rather asphaltic. The Meotic crudes, making up most of the rest, are wax-bearing and more nearly intermediate in character. Both are quite aromatic. It was the aromatic content of Rumanian kerosene distillates which led Edeleanu to devise sulfur dioxide extraction, the first differential solvent process to be applied industrially in petroleum refining.[1] Examples of prewar Rumanian production are as follows:

	Specific gravity	Gasoline	Kerosene	Sulfur	Asphalt
Moinesti	0.867	15	20	—	40 Asphaltic residuum
Moreni	0.85	27	12	0.2	10
Campina	0.86	19	13	0.3	7
Runcu-Mislea	0.82	46	5	0.15	7

Poland

	Specific gravity	Gasoline	Kerosene	Sulfur	Asphalt
Boryslaw	0.87	19	10	0.3	10
Drohobycz	0.85	24	10	0.4	10

These earlier Polish oils resembled those of Rumania, to which they were related geologically. They can be compared to intermediate base oils of the United States.

Germany. The German oil fields are located in the northwestern part of the country, east of Belgium and Holland. Production was very small until about 1950; although developed rapidly, it is still less than 0.5 per cent of the world total.

	Specific gravity	Gasoline	Kerosene	Sulfur	Asphalt
Holstein Hannover Weser Ems	0.85	20	10	0.6–1.2	7 to 12

[1] German Patent 216,459.

These oils are very much alike, intermediate in type, but vary in wax content from 1.0 to 5 per cent.

	Specific gravity	Gasoline	Kerosene	Sulfur	Asphalt
Emsland	0.91	10	7	1.0	5

This last crude contains as much as 10 per cent wax. An oil of exceptionally high wax content—20 per cent—has been encountered in the upper Rhine Valley. This is perhaps related to the wax-bearing Pechelbronn oil in the French part of the Rhine valley.

France. Known oil reserves in France have been very small until the past five years, when discoveries in the Aquitaine Basin (most recently in the Paris Basin) made a substantial addition. Actual production is still not much more than 0.1 per cent of the world total. Representative crudes are

	Specific gravity	Gasoline	Kerosene	Sulfur	Asphalt
Lacq	0.923	16	7	4.3	42

This is a rather low-grade oil, accompanied by large amounts of natural gas of high hydrogen sulfide content—H_2S, 18 per cent, CO_2, 12 per cent.[1]

	Specific gravity	Gasoline	Kerosene	Sulfur	Asphalt
Parentis	0.857	30	15	0.4	—
Pechelbronn	0.88	9	20	Rather high	—

Pechelbronn is an old field in northeastern France, notable because it has in the past produced a small yield of rather nonvolatile oil by mining operations. Lacq and Parentis are in the southwestern region, not far from Bordeaux.

There is an appreciable production of natural gas in Italy, some of which carries vapors of light hydrocarbons, thus suggesting existence of distillate fields.[2] In Sicily there is an established production of an asphaltic oil low in wax content.

	Specific gravity	Gasoline	Kerosene	Sulfur	Asphalt
Ragusa	0.94	7	15	2.4	30

A similar oil is encountered in Hungary[3] and there is a small production of general-purpose crude in Austria.

I-13. Middle East. This is now the most prolific oil-producing area in the world and so far perhaps the most homogenoeus as to general character of output. The important fields are located in the sedimentary basin at the head of the Persian Gulf. The oldest in age of production

[1] *Industrie pétrole,* **24**(8):46 (1956).
[2] *Chem.-Ingr. Tech.,* **27**(8/9):465 (1955).
[3] *Brennstoff-Chem.,* **37**(15/16):244 (1956).

are those of Iran, followed by Iraq, Bahrein, Saudi Arabia, Kuwait, and Qatar in the order given. The reservoir conditions are favorable to high production per well, and by careful control it has in some fields been possible to maintain the character of the crude oil essentially constant over many years.[1] The reservoir gas is high in hydrogen sulfide; the oils in production are all more or less alike, of mixed base, rather asphaltic, containing 1 to 2 per cent sulfur and upward of 25 or 30 per cent gasoline. The sulfur content is not highly corrosive, and by using modern refining procedures it is possible to manufacture satisfactory kerosene, lubricating oils, and wax. However, the average crudes are of middle to low grade and more suited to general-purpose refining. The following types are fairly representative of current production.

	Specific gravity	Gasoline	Kerosene	Sulfur	Asphalt
Iran	0.852	30	20	1.4	18
Iraq:					
Kirkuk	0.844	32	22	2.0	16
Zubair	0.847	30	20	1.9	18
Qatar	0.823	39	5	1.3	8
Kuwait:					
Burgan	0.867	27	17	2.5	25
Saudi Arabia	0.84	30	15	1.3	15
Egypt, Sinai:					
Asl	0.921	8	13	2.0	45
Sudr	0.918	14	9	2.0	53

Early production in Egypt was from the Hurghada area, yielding a heavy mixed-base oil of high wax content; the present small production is of the same character. Recent discoveries in North Africa and the Sahara Desert indicate the presence of important oil deposits.

It should be remembered that several of the Middle Eastern fields contain productive horizons at several depths and that there is appreciable variation in properties among the oils of these horizons. This is true in Kuwait and in Zubair; for the latter there are four "pays" or producing horizons and the oils become lighter in gravity with increasing depth, about as follows:

	Gravity	S, Per cent
First	0.934	4.5
Second	0.898	3.8
Third	0.849	—
Fourth	0.810	—

The Middle East contains a high proportion of the known reserves of the world, and production is increasing rapidly. In 1958 Iran yielded

[1] King, *Petrol. Engr.*, **10**(1):161 (1938).

4 per cent, Iraq almost 4, Kuwait about 8, Qatar 0.9, and Saudi Arabia 6 per cent of the world supply.

I-14. Far East. Prior to the war damage of 1942–1945, the oil production of the Far East amounted to about 2 per cent of the world total, derived chiefly from Borneo and Sumatra, with smaller contributions from Java, Burma, and Assam. Rehabilitation has not been completed in all cases, but some local increases of output have occurred and an area in New Guinea has been added; production now amounts to 2.8 per cent of the total output.

	Specific gravity	Gasoline	Kerosene	Sulfur	Asphalt
Sumatra, southwest:					
Djambi	0.84	27	10	0.03	5
Talang	0.88	17	13	0.08	10
Tandjung	0.90	15	13	0.08	8
Sumatra, central:					
Minas	0.85	20	11	0.06	10

This last crude is highly paraffinic; the untreated kerosene distillate has good burning qualities, and there is a valuable wax content.[1]

	Specific gravity	Gasoline	Kerosene	Sulfur	Asphalt
Lirik	0.85	12	20	0.19	12

This crude is so waxy as to be solid at ordinary temperatures.

	Specific gravity	Gasoline	Kerosene	Sulfur	Asphalt
Sumatra, southeast:					
Talang Akar-Pendopo	0.84	30	30	0.08	7
Borneo, North:					
Seria, waxy	0.85	37	19	0.05	Trace
Miri:					
Nonwaxy	0.90	20	—	<0.1	Trace
Waxy	0.82	50	—	<0.1	Trace

The gasoline from these crudes is naphthenic and of good octane number; the kerosene, when present, is poor.

	Specific gravity	Gasoline	Kerosene	Sulfur	Asphalt
Borneo, East:					
Tarakan	0.94	None*	14	0.13	10

* 25 per cent heavy naphtha.

This crude is often not distilled, but sold as produced, for fuel oil purposes.

	Specific gravity	Gasoline	Kerosene	Sulfur	Asphalt
Keotoi	$\begin{Bmatrix} 0.80 \\ 0.90 \end{Bmatrix}$	20–35	30–40	—	—

[1] Data by courtesy of California Crude Sales Co.

The volatile fractions of these oils are highly aromatic.

	Specific gravity	Gasoline	Kerosene	Sulfur	Asphalt
New Guinea:					
Klamono	0.94	6	11	1.0	30
Burma:					
Yenangyuang	0.83	33	None	0.1	2.5

These crudes contain high-melting wax.

	Specific gravity	Gasoline	Kerosene	Sulfur	Asphalt
India, Assam:					
Digboi	0.85	29	4	0.1	8

These oils were in the prewar period the source of the high-melting Rangoon paraffin wax.

These Far Eastern crudes fall more or less into one class. They are derived mostly from Miocene and Pliocene formations, are low in sulfur and asphalt, and are quite high in wax content. Most of them are high in naphthenes and aromatics, which implies gasolines of high octane number and kerosenes of poor burning quality. The shallower production is sometimes so low in volatile content as to permit sale as fuel oil without distillation. Deeper reservoirs yield oils higher in gasoline, kerosene, and wax. Such crudes are often selected for more complete refining.

There has been a small oil production in China since about 1940. The earlier fields lay (1) in Szechuan, roughly a thousand miles west of Shanghai and five hundred miles north of the China Sea, and (2) at the border between Kansu and Sinkiang, about a thousand miles northwest of the center of Szechuan. The former were, when last described, largely gas-producing, while the Kansu-Sinkiang area supplied a few hundred barrels a day of light paraffinic oil containing about 15 per cent paraffin wax—valuable but troublesome to produce.[1] More recently discoveries have been reported in the Wuzu and Tsungaria areas of northern Sinkiang.[2] It is now variously reported that Chinese production is as low as 30,000 and as high as 500,000 bbl per day; in other words, 0.15 or 2.5 per cent of the world total.

[1] Gavin, *Petrol. Engr.*, **17**(1):181 (1945). Small, *Petrol. Engr.*, **18**(1):98 (1946).
[2] *Oil Gas J.*, **54**(67):103 (1956).

CHAPTER **II**

Composition of Petroleum and Petroleum Products

by BEVERIDGE J. MAIR, PH.D.

American Petroleum Institute Research Project 6
Carnegie Institute of Technology

HYDROCARBON COMPONENTS OF NATURAL PETROLEUM

It is desirable to distinguish between the composition of naturally occurring petroleum materials and that of the finished products which result from conversion operations such as thermal and catalytic cracking, reforming, alkylation, isomerization, and polymerization. These latter contain compounds not present in the original crude petroleum or present in insignificant amounts. It has been estimated[1] that about 60 per cent of modern gasoline consists of molecules not to be found in the original crude oil. This figure is now too low.

Natural petroleum is composed of hydrocarbons together with smaller amounts of organic compounds of sulfur, oxygen, and nitrogen and still smaller amounts of compounds containing metallic constituents, particularly vanadium, nickel, iron, and copper. The purely hydrocarbon content may be as high as 97 or 98 per cent for Pennsylvania petroleums and as low as 50 per cent for a few heavy crude oils from Mexico or Mississippi. Of course, even crudes with 50 per cent of nonhydrocarbon components retain most of the hydrocarbon characteristics—the molecules containing one or perhaps two atoms of elements other than carbon and hydrogen. The nonhydrocarbon constituents are usually concentrated in the higher-boiling portions of the crude. The carbon and hydrogen content is approximately constant from crude to crude even though the amounts of the various hydrocarbon types and of the individual isomers may vary widely. Thus, the hydrogen content is usually between 83 and 87 per cent, and the carbon content between 11 and 14 per cent.

---

[1] Wilson, *Advances in Chem. Ser.*, No. 5, p. 1, 1951.

This constancy is explained by the fact that variation in the amounts of each series of hydrocarbons does not have a profound effect on over-all composition.[1]   The ratio of carbon to hydrogen increases somewhat from the low- to the high-molecular-weight fractions; this is attributable to an increase in the content of polynuclear aromatics and multiring cycloparaffins in these higher-boiling fractions.

Study of the nature of the individual hydrocarbon constituents in petroleum began about a century ago.   In 1856, three years before the historic Drake well came into production, de La Rue and Miller[2] reported the presence of several alkylbenzenes in a Burma petroleum.   The method used involved the preparation of the barium salts of the alkyl benzene sulfonic acids and fractional crystallization to separate the salts of the individual acids.   Other early investigators include Schorlemmer,[3] Silliman,[4] and Engler.[5]   Around the turn of the century and during the first two decades following there may be mentioned Markownikoff,[6] Aschan,[7] Young,[8] Fortey,[9] and Mabery.[10]   In this early work chemical methods were relied on very heavily.   For example, Markownikoff,[11] by treatment of a Caucasian petroleum fraction (boiling near 70°C) with dilute nitric acid, obtained a nitro compound which he found to be identical with one obtained in a similar manner from synthetic methylcyclopentane. Aschan used treatment with chlorosulfonic acid to obtain normal paraffins, since this acid destroyed other types of hydrocarbons quite rapidly. Benzene and toluene were usually determined by nitration.   Distilling columns were employed in some of this early work; the separation by Fortey of a good sample of cyclohexane (freezing point +4.7°C compared with +6.55°C for the pure compound) by crystallization of the distillate fractions into which it had been concentrated is an example of what could be accomplished at that early date.

As a result of the work of these men and others, it was recognized (probably first by Mabery) by 1925 or somewhat earlier that the hydro-

[1] The net result is to convey an impression of simplicity which is not borne out by the facts.   The number of possible isomers of the paraffinic hydrocarbon $C_{40}H_{82}$ has been calculated as 62×10^{12} [Henze and Blair, *J. ACS*, **53**:3077 (1931); **54**:1538 (1932)].

[2] *Proc. Roy. Soc. (London)*, **8**:221 (1857).

[3] *Ann.*, **127**:331 (1863).

[4] *Am. Chemist*, **2**:18 (1871–1872).

[5] *Ber.*, **12**:2187 (1879); **18**:2234 (1885).

[6] *Ann.*, **234**:97 (1886); *Ber.*, **28**:577 (1895); *Ann.*, **30**:974 (1897); **33**:1908 (1900).

[7] *Ber.*, **31**:1801 (1898).

[8] *J. Chem. Soc.*, **71**:440 (1897); **73**:920 (1898); **75**:172 (1899).

[9] *J. Chem. Soc.*, **73**:932 (1898); **75**:873 (1899).

[10] *Proc. Am. Acad. Arts Sci.*, **31**:341 (1895); *Am. Chem. J.*, **18**:230 (1896); **19**:482 (1897); *J. ACS*, **24**:165 (1902).

[11] *Ann.*, **307**:343 (1899).

carbons in petroleum belonged to several series, including normal paraffins, branched paraffins, cycloparaffins, and aromatics. For the cycloparaffins, the presence of both five- and six-membered ring compounds was established. There was, however, at that time, no reasonably complete analysis of even the lower-boiling part of the gasoline fraction of any crude petroleum and the manner in which the content of the individual constituents varied from crude to crude was virtually unknown.

The situation has changed markedly since 1925. Since then investigation has produced a literature too voluminous to cite in detail. The American petroleum industry, through the American Petroleum Institute, has sponsored and supported several research projects to investigate the composition of petroleum. These include API Research Projects 6, 48, and 52, concerned, respectively, with hydrocarbon, sulfur, and nitrogen components of petroleum.[1]

The chemical methods used in the early work on the composition of petroleum are now regarded with suspicion, since they may produce changes in structure or even the complete destruction of certain hydrocarbon components. More recent progress has depended in part on the development of improved physical fractionating processes and in part on the development of new spectrographic methods of recognition. For the distillation, laboratory columns of new design containing up to 200 theoretical stages of separation have become available.[2] Such columns are capable of giving a fairly complete separation of hydrocarbons boiling about 1.5 to 2°C apart. Improved procedures for azeotropic distillation have been developed.[3] Of these, one involving the use of

[1] The work of Project 6 (which has continued for almost thirty years) is summarized by Rossini, Mair, and Streiff, "Hydrocarbons from Petroleum," Reinhold Publishing Corporation, New York, 1953; that of Project 48 (dating from 1948) by Ball, Bordwell, Smith, Waddington, and Seyfried, *Proc. API*, **32**(1):139 (1954); and that of Project 52 (established in 1953) by Ball, VanderWerf, Waddington, and Lake, *Proc. API*, **34**(6):152 (1954). Many other laboratories have contributed. Approximately twenty-five years' work on the composition of the higher-boiling fractions of petroleum at the University of Delft and in the laboratory of the Bataafsche Petroleum Maatschappi is summarized by Van Nes and Van Westen, "Aspects of the Constitution of Mineral Oil," Elsevier Press, Inc., Houston, 1951. Investigations of the hydrocarbon constituents in the lower-boiling fractions have been conducted at the Petroleum Refining Laboratory of the Pennsylvania State University [Fenske and Tongberg, *Ind. Eng. Chem.*, **24**:832 (1932); Tongberg, Quiggle, and Fenske, *Ind. Eng. Chem.*, **28**:201 (1936)] and in the laboratories of the U.S. Bureau of Mines [Smith and Rall, *Ind. Eng. Chem.*, **45**:1491 (1953); Smith, *Ind. Eng. Chem.*, **44**:2577 (1952)]. There should also be mentioned the work of Birch [*J. Inst. Petrol.*, **39**:185 (1953); Birch, Callum, Dean, and Denyer, *Ind. Eng. Chem.*, **47**:240 (1955)] on sulfur compounds; that of Bailey ["Science of Petroleum," vol. II, p. 1047, Oxford University Press, New York and London, 1938] on nitrogen compounds; and that of Von Braun [*ibid.*, p. 1007, 1938] and of Lochte [*Ind. Eng. Chem.*, **44**:2597 (1952)] on the carboxylic acids.

[2] Willingham and Rossini, *J. Research Natl. Bur. Standards*, **37**:15 (1946).

[3] Mair, Glasgow, and Rossini, *J. Research Natl. Bur. Standards*, **27**:39 (1941).

certain perfluorochemicals alternately with polar organic compounds containing hydroxyl, carboxyl, keto, cyanide, or similar groups as azeotrope-forming substances is particularly effective for the separation of branched paraffins from cycloparaffins—one of the most difficult separations encountered in the analysis of petroleum fractions.[1] Adsorption methods have been developed for separating aromatic hydrocarbons quantitatively from paraffins and cycloparaffins; the same procedures will break down aromatic mixtures into mononuclear, dinuclear, and trinuclear portions. In certain cases, adsorption may be employed to separate isomers, particularly aromatic isomers. An extension of the method of partition chromatography, which makes use of certain fluorochemicals as the mobile phase, is also effective for separating paraffins (particularly branched paraffins) from cycloparaffins.[2] The same classes can also be separated using a partition chromatographic method with liquid displacement.[3] A crystallization procedure for sorting out normal and branched paraffins, cyclic, and aromatic hydrocarbons has come into wide use.[4] This process depends on the formation of solid molecular compounds of the normal paraffins with urea, the separation of these compounds from the remaining liquid, and the regeneration of the normal paraffins. For hydrocarbons in the range from about C_8 to C_{17}, fairly satisfactory recovery of the normal compounds may be achieved; above this range significant amounts of other hydrocarbons (for instance, branched paraffins with unsubstituted chains longer than C_8) form solid molecular compounds with urea and the separation becomes less satisfactory. Fractionation by thermal diffusion has been applied to petroleum fractions, particularly in the higher-boiling gas oil and lubricating oil ranges.[5] The separation in this case appears to depend, in part at least, on the shapes of the component molecules. Where aromatics are absent, the separation is approximately according to cycloparaffin ring content and resembles that obtained with solvent extraction. Countercurrent solvent extraction has also been employed principally as a means of separating the higher-boiling fractions according to hydrocarbon type. This process offers great promise of further development.

Within recent years molecular spectroscopy has been applied successfully to determining quantitatively the percentage of each hydrocarbon

[1] Mair, *Anal. Chem.*, **28**:52 (1956).

[2] Mair, Montjar, and Rossini, *Anal. Chem.*, **28**:56 (1956).

[3] Sauer, Washall, and Melpolder, *Anal. Chem.*, **29**:1327 (1957).

[4] Benzen, German Patent Application No. O.Z. 12,438, March 18, 1940. Zimmerschied, Dinnerstein, Weitkamp, and Marschner, *Ind. Eng. Chem.*, **42**:1300 (1950). Redlich, Gable, Dunlop, and Millar, *J. ACS*, **72**:4153 (1950). Schlenk, *Ann.*, **565**:216 (1949).

[5] Jones, *Ind. Eng. Chem.*, **45**:2689 (1953); **47**:212 (1955). Melpolder, Brown, Washall, Doherty, and Young, *Anal. Chem.*, **26**:1904 (1954). Sullivan, Ruppel, and Willingham, *Ind. Eng. Chem.*, **47**:208 (1955).

in mixtures containing up to about 10 components where the components are known and where pure samples of all the components are available for comparison.   These restrictions, of course, limit this particular application to material in the lower-boiling part of the gasoline fraction.   In some cases, spectroscopic methods may be employed to determine hydrocarbon types.   For example, ultraviolet spectroscopy may determine aromatics, and mass spectroscopy the content of paraffins, cycloparaffins, olefins, and aromatics in straight-run or cracked fractions in the gasoline range.[1]   Even for fractions from lubricating oil distillates (preferably separated as far as practical by other methods) high-temperature mass spectrometry may give useful information concerning the amounts of certain types of hydrocarbons and sulfur compounds.[2]   Infrared spectroscopy has also been applied in this molecular-weight range to give values of, for example, the content of methyl groups, as well as of methylene groups in long chains and in cycloparaffin rings.[3]

In spite of these rather impressive advances in separating techniques and in spectroscopic methods, analysis for the individual hydrocarbon components is still a very formidable task.   Nearly all the hydrocarbons in the paraffin, cyclopentane, cyclohexane, and benzene series theoretically possible (a total of about 500) are actually present in the gasoline fraction, at least in small amounts.   In the kerosene and gas oil fractions the complexity is much greater.   Very few of the large number of hydrocarbons probably present have been isolated from fractions of virgin petroleum boiling above 132°C.

II-1. Gasoline Fraction.   Of the investigations mentioned above, aimed at determining the composition of even the gasoline fraction of a crude oil, the most thoroughgoing and systematic has been that carried on by Project 6 of the American Petroleum Institute.   Below a boiling point of 132°C for paraffins, cyclopentanes, and cyclohexanes and below 180°C for aromatics, nearly all the possible members of these series were found in a Ponca City, Oklahoma (Mid-Continent), petroleum.[4]   A few possible branched paraffins and alkylcyclopentanes were not found, but they may have been present in traces only.   It seems probable that the same situation may exist for the higher-boiling fractions of the gasoline;

[1] Brown, *Anal. Chem.*, **23**:430 (1951).

[2] O'Neal, Conference on Applied Mass Spectrometry, Hydrocarbon Research Group, Institute of Petroleum, London, October, 1953.   Melpolder, Brown, Washall, Doherty, and Young, *Anal. Chem.*, **26**:1904 (1954).   Lumpkin and Johnson, *Anal. Chem.*, **26**:1719 (1954).   Lumpkin, *Anal. Chem.*, **28**:1947 (1956).

[3] Hastings, Watson, Williams, and Anderson, *Anal. Chem.*, **24**:612 (1952).   Francis, *Anal. Chem.*, **25**:1466 (1953).

[4] Table II-29 gives a tabulation of all the paraffins, cycloparaffins, and aromatics found by the Project in this crude oil; they number 151 and cover a boiling range up to 389°C.

all possible isomers of all the possible classes may be present, most of them in small amounts or in traces. In any case, it is true that the bulk of the material is made up of only a few compounds. This is illustrated by Fig. II-1, which shows that 5 compounds make up 29 per cent and 20 compounds 59 per cent of the entire gasoline fraction.

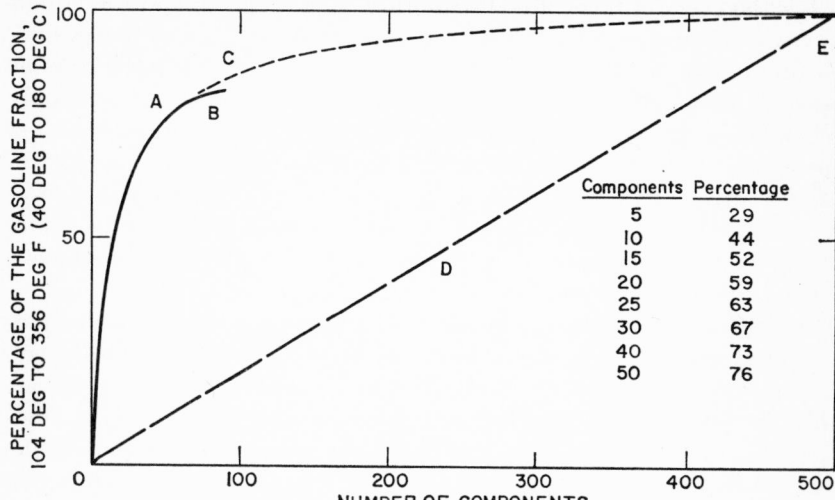

Components	Percentage
5	29
10	44
15	52
20	59
25	63
30	67
40	73
50	76

Fig. II-1. Number of components, counted in order of decreasing abundance, and the percentage of the gasoline fraction constituted by them. Curve *OAB* gives the results so far obtained for the Ponca crude; *ACE* the expected shape of the curve for the (approximately) 500 components which are possible. *ODE* gives the results which would be obtained if each of the 500 components occurred in equal amount.

The highly branched paraffins which are particularly valuable as aviation- and motor-fuel components are, unfortunately, not the principal paraffinic constituents of the gasoline fraction of any natural petroleum so far examined. This is shown for the paraffinic constituents, C_6 to C_8, of the Ponca crude in Table II-1; the normal, singly, doubly, and triply branched paraffins in that range are present approximately in the ratio of 100:59 to 13:0.25.

TABLE II-1. AMOUNTS OF PARAFFIN TYPES IN PONCA CRUDE

Type of paraffin	Amount in the crude oil, volume per cent			
	Hexanes	Heptanes	Octanes	Total
Normal................	1.80	2.3	1.9	6.0
Singly branched.........	0.72	1.30	1.49	3.51
Doubly branched........	0.12	0.25	0.44	0.81
Triply branched.........	....	0.00	0.015	0.015

Examination of the amounts of the monomethyl pentanes, hexanes, heptanes, octanes, and nonanes confirms the fact that, in general, the 2-methyl isomers are the most abundant.　This may be regarded as part of the general tendency to produce long uninterrupted chains of carbon atoms rather than those interrupted by branching.

For the cyclopentanes, the distribution is:

	Per cent of crude
None or one substituent group:	
None—cyclopentane	0.05
Methyl	0.87
Ethyl	0.16
n-Propyl	0.06
Two carbon atoms in alkyl chains:	
One substituent group	0.16
Two substituent groups	1.72
Three carbon atoms in alkyl chains:	
One group	0.07
Two groups	0.33
Three groups	0.92

Analogous figures for cyclohexanes are:

	Per cent of crude
None or one substituent group:	
None—cyclohexane	0.71
Methyl	1.6
Ethyl	0.37
Two carbon atoms in alkyl chains:	
One group	0.37
Two groups	1.41

In both cases the preference is for several short side chains rather than one long substituent, thus differing from the over-all trend among the paraffins.

The results and conclusions for the benzenes are similar to those for the cyclopentanes and cyclohexanes.　For the series from benzene to n-propylbenzene, the amounts of the individual components are: benzene, 0.15; toluene, 0.51; ethylbenzene, 0.19; and n-propylbenzene, 0.09. According to the degree of substitution of the benzene ring the amounts for the C_8 alkylbenzenes are as follows: one substituent, 0.19; two substituents, 0.88.　For the C_9 alkylbenzenes, the corresponding values are as follows: one substituent, 0.16; two substituents, 0.33; three substituents, 0.82.

The only member of the cycloheptane class so far isolated from petroleum is cycloheptane itself, present in extremely small amount (0.01 per cent).　As already noted, the first member of the class (for cyclopentanes, cyclohexanes, and benzenes) is present in smaller amount than higher members.   Assuming this to be true for the cycloheptanes, somewhat larger amounts of this class may be found in the upper part of the gasoline fraction; however, cycloheptanes are not expected to constitute an important part of this material.

Only five bicycloparaffins have so far been isolated from the Ponca crude and only three of these have been identified—*cis*-bicyclo-[3.3.0]-octane boiling at 136.5°C, bicyclo-[3.2.1]-octane at 138°C, and *trans*-bicyclo-[4.4.0]-decane (*trans*-decahydronaphthalene) boiling at 187.25°C. The first consists of two cyclopentane rings joined through two adjacent carbon atoms, the second, a cyclohexane ring fused to a cyclopentane ring through nonadjacent carbon atoms, and the third, two cyclohexane rings condensed through adjacent carbon atoms.   A tricycloparaffin (adamantane) with unusual properties (melting point, 268°C; density, 1.07 g per ml) was found by Landa and Machacek[1] in the distillate boiling near 192°C from a Hodonin crude oil.   The structure of this hydrocarbon, confirmed through synthesis by Prelog and Seiwerth,[2] showed that it contained three cyclohexane rings arranged as follows:

$$CH_2 \longrightarrow CH \longrightarrow CH_2$$
$$CH \qquad CH_2 \qquad CH$$
$$CH_2 \longrightarrow CH \longrightarrow CH_2$$

These few compounds provide our principal clues to the structures of the polycycloparaffins.   On the basis of this rather fragmentary evidence, it appears probable that, as with the monocycloparaffins, only five- and six-membered ring systems of this class will be found in significant amounts.   Many additional members probably exist in the higher-boiling part of the gasoline fraction; the class constitutes a very important part of the kerosene and still higher-boiling fractions.

Gasolines from natural petroleum vary widely in hydrocarbon composition, depending on the type of crude from which they are derived.   Those from Pennsylvania are high in paraffins (both normal and branched); those from California and the Gulf Coast are high in cycloparaffins. Low-boiling distillates high in aromatic content (above 20 per cent) are obtained from some Gulf Coast and West Texas crudes and notably those from the Far East.   A few unusual naphthas are high in branched paraffins, Winkler, Texas, for example.   Michigan provides naphthas rich in normal paraffins.

[1] *Coll. trav. chim. tchèques.*, **5**:1 (1933).
[2] *Ber.*, **74**:1644 (1941).

Table II-2 shows the considerable variation in aromatic content, from 4.9 to 27.6 per cent, for seven domestic naphthas investigated by Project 6. The variation in content of normal paraffins, branched paraffins, cyclopentanes, and cyclohexanes for the paraffin-cycloparaffin

TABLE II-2. AROMATIC CONTENT OF STRAIGHT-RUN GASOLINES
WITH END POINTS NEAR 177°C

Gasoline	Volume per cent
Ponca, Oklahoma	9.8
East Texas	10.4
Bradford, Pennsylvania	8.3
Greendale-Kawkawlin, Michigan	7.2
Winkler, Texas	4.9
Midway, California	8.0
Conroe, Texas	27.6

From Forziati, Willingham, Mair, and Rossini, *J. Research Natl. Bur. Standards*, **32**:11 (1944).

portion, from 40 to 102°C, of these seven naphthas is given in Table II-3. The *n*-paraffin content varies from 63.1 per cent for the Greendale-Kawkawlin distillate to 9.5 per cent for that from Winkler, Texas, the branched paraffin content from 61.6 per cent for Winkler to 13.2 per cent for Greendale-Kawkawlin. The Midway gasoline is richest in cyclopentanes (41 per cent), and that from Conroe in cyclohexanes (44.2 per cent).

TABLE II-3. AMOUNTS OF HYDROCARBON TYPES IN THE PARAFFIN-CYCLOPARAFFIN
PORTION (40 TO 102°C) OF STRAIGHT-RUN GASOLINES

Gasoline	Volume per cent			
	Normal paraffins	Branched paraffins	Cyclo-pentanes	Cyclo-hexanes
Ponca, Oklahoma	35.7	20.5	23.4	20.4
East Texas	24.7	27.3	26.0	22.0
Bradford, Pennsylvania	34.4	32.2	13.4	20.0
Greendale-Kawkawlin, Michigan	63.1	13.2	8.0	15.7
Winkler, Texas	9.5	61.6	8.4	20.5
Midway, California	10.0	21.5	41.0	27.5
Conroe, Texas	18.2	20.3	17.3	44.2

From Forziati, Willingham, Mair, and Rossini, *J. Research Natl. Bur. Standards*, **32**:11 (1944).

Gasolines from most crudes show a decrease in paraffin and an increase in cycloparaffin and aromatic content with increase in molecular weight, but this is not invariably the case. Table II-4 shows results reported by

Smith[1] for three naphthas.   For Yates the paraffin content decreases and that of cycloparaffins increases markedly with increase in boiling point. On the other hand, Slaughter and Wasson naphthas show slight and irregular variations in content of these types; for both naphthas a maximum in aromatic content is found in the 200 to 242°F fraction, with some decrease in the higher-boiling portions.

TABLE II-4. PARAFFINS, CYCLOPARAFFINS, AND AROMATICS FOR SEVERAL
BOILING RANGES OF THREE NAPHTHAS

Boiling range, °F at 1 atm	Volume per cent								
	Slaughter			Wasson			Yates		
	Paraffins	Cyclo-paraffins	Aromatics	Paraffins	Cyclo-paraffins	Aromatics	Paraffins	Cyclo-paraffins	Aromatics
100–200	49.9	30.4	19.7	55.1	34.4	10.5	81.6	18.4	0
200–242	31.9	37.9	30.2	35.5	37.6	26.9	29.1	70.9	0
242–285	35.1	40.2	24.7	34.5	41.0	24.5	38.0	61.0	1.0
285–320	43.1	38.6	18.3	44.6	34.5	20.9	34.1	62.5	3.4

From Smith, "Science of Petroleum," vol. V, part I, p. 3, Oxford University Press, New York and London, 1950.

In spite of these large variations in composition, the distribution of the components within a given class is not random but follows a well-defined pattern.   From the results for the seven naphthas studied by Project 6[2] it was concluded that the differences between naphthas depend on the relative amounts of the five classes, normal paraffins, branched paraffins, cyclopentanes, cyclohexanes, and benzenes, but that within any one of these classes the relative amounts of the individual constituents are of the same magnitude.   This point is illustrated in Table II-5 which shows the ratio of the dimethylbutanes to the methylpentanes in the seven naphthas.   Additional evidence in support of this conclusion comes from the results reported by Smith and Rall[3] for 21 domestic and 11 foreign naphthas.   They extended the generalization further, observing that, except for a few unusual naphthas (Michigan, Winkler, Yates, and Monument), the ratio of normal to branched paraffins is also approximately constant.   Obviously, it is possible to estimate the amount of a

[1] "Science of Petroleum," vol. V, part 1, p. 3, Oxford University Press, New York and London, 1950.
[2] Forziati, Willingham, Mair, and Rossini, *J. Research Natl. Bur. Standards*, **32**:11 (1944).
[3] *Ind. Eng. Chem.*, **45**:1491 (1953).

TABLE II-5. AMOUNTS OF DIMETHYLBUTANES AND METHYLPENTANES
IN THE BRANCHED HEXANE PORTION OF SEVEN GASOLINES

Gasoline	Volume per cent	
	Dimethylbutanes	Methylpentanes
Ponca, Oklahoma..........................	14	86
East Texas................................	13	87
Bradford, Pennsylvania....................	10	90
Greendale-Kawkawlin, Michigan.............	14	86
Winkler, Texas............................	12	88
Midway, California........................	16	84
Conroe, Texas.............................	16	84

From Forziati, Willingham, Mair, and Rossini, *J. Research Natl. Bur. Standards,*
32:11 (1944).

given hydrocarbon in a naphtha if the amount of the class to which it
belongs is known.

II-2. Kerosene and Gas Oil Fractions. Kerosene is produced from
petroleum distillates boiling in the approximate range from 180 to 275°C;
it is composed chiefly of hydrocarbons containing about 11 to 15 carbon
atoms per molecule. Gas oil consists of material boiling between the
kerosene and lubricating oil distillates, comprising chiefly hydrocarbons
with from 15 to about 25 carbon atoms per molecule; this corresponds
approximately to a boiling range of from 275 to 400°C at 1 atm.

After the exploratory work of Mabery, the earliest chemical study
of an American (Mid-Continent) kerosene was by Wagner.[1] Extraction
with liquid sulfur dioxide at −10°C was followed by distillation, separately, of the soluble and insoluble portions. From empirical formulas
and some physical properties of the distillate fractions from the soluble
portion, Wagner suggested, among other possibilities, that they contained
substituted tetrahydronaphthalenes. More recent research has confirmed that aromatic cycloparaffins, including tetrahydronaphthalenes,
are constituents of the kerosene fraction.

The examination of Ponca crude oil by API Research Project 6 has
been extended into the kerosene range. Types of hydrocarbons differing
from those making up the bulk of the gasoline have been encountered.
Dicycloparaffins, which constitute a very minor part of the gasoline
fraction, occur in appreciable amounts in kerosene, as do dinuclear
aromatics; tricycloparaffins and trinuclear aromatics become important
in gas oils. Mixed-type hydrocarbons containing both aromatic and
cycloparaffin rings in the same molecule are also present in both kero-

[1] *Ind. Eng. Chem.,* **16**:135 (1924).

senes and gas oils.   These include, for example, the indanes and the tetrahydronaphthalenes with, respectively, five- and six-membered cycloparaffin rings.   In the case of the dinuclear aromatics the predominant type of structure appears to be that in which the aromatic rings are condensed, as in naphthalene and its homologues.   However, at least a small amount of material with two single aromatic rings is present, since biphenyl has been isolated from the Ponca oil and both biphenyl and 3-methylbiphenyl have been found in West Edmond crude.[1]   From a correlation of certain physical properties of the aromatic portion, Martin and Sankin[2] report that the trinuclear aromatics are predominantly of phenanthrene rather than of anthracene structure; spectroscopic evidence supports this conclusion.[3]   However, 10 homologues of anthracene have been isolated from a Kuwait oil, establishing that this class is also present, at least in small amount.[4]

An aromatic with four rings, 1-methylchrysene, has been isolated from a Mid-Continent petroleum.[5]   With the exception of some normal paraffins, this appears to be the highest-molecular-weight pure hydrocarbon thus far isolated from natural petroleum.

TABLE II-6. COMPOSITION OF KEROSENE AND GAS OIL FRACTIONS
FROM THE PONCA PETROLEUM

Types of hydrocarbon	Amount in given boiling range, volume per cent	
	180 to 230°C at 1 atm	230 to 300°C at 1 atm
Normal paraffins..............	23	22
Branched paraffins............	16	8
Monocycloparaffins............	32	29
Dicycloparaffins...............	11	17
Tricycloparaffins..............	0	4
Mononuclear aromatics*.......	15	12
Dinuclear aromatics...........	3	8

* Includes both alkyl benzenes and aromatic-cycloparaffin types.

The approximate amounts of the several classes of hydrocarbons in the Ponca crude for two fractions in the kerosene and light gas oil ranges are given in Table II-6.[6]   An increase in content of dicycloparaffins and dinuclear aromatics with increase in boiling point is indicated.

[1] Adams and Richardson, *Anal. Chem.*, **25**:1073 (1953).
[2] *Anal. Chem.*, **25**:206 (1953).
[3] Charlet, Lanneau, and Johnson, *Anal. Chem.*, **26**:861 (1954).
[4] Carruthers, *J. Chem. Soc.*, 1956, p. 603.
[5] Moore, Thorpe, and Mahoney, *J. ACS*, **75**:2259 (1953).
[6] Rossini and Mair, *Advances in Chemistry Ser.*, No. 5, p. 334, 1951.

The aromatic and cycloparaffin content of gas oils from crudes of the United States is outlined in Tables II-7 and II-8.[1] These show how the

TABLE II-7. DISTRIBUTION OF AROMATICS IN GAS OILS FROM CRUDE OILS
OF THE UNITED STATES

Aromatic content, volume per cent	Per cent of total production in specified areas								
	California	Rocky Mountain	West Texas	Gulf Coast	Mid-Continent	Mississippi	Michigan	Appalachian	United States
>30	33	...	5	35	2	...	...	...	15
25–30	45	24	27	20	...	20	...	...	18
20–25	...	63	43	33	54	6	16	...	41
15–20	...	13	17	12	40	74	32	100	32
<15	22	...	8	...	4	...	52	...	4

TABLE II-8. DISTRIBUTION OF CYCLOPARAFFIN RINGS IN PARAFFIN-CYCLOPARAFFIN
PORTION OF GAS OILS FROM CRUDE OILS OF THE UNITED STATES

Cycloparaffin ring content, weight per cent	Per cent of total production in specified areas								
	California	Rocky Mountain	West Texas	Gulf Coast	Mid-Continent	Mississippi	Michigan	Appalachian	United States
>50	5	...	...	1	...	...	...	...	1
40–50	29	...	3	25	1	...	..	...	10
30–40	64	36	17	22	6	...	...	...	22
20–30	2	64	72	46	86	86	16	...	59
<20	...	...	8	6	7	14	84	100	8

gas oils from crudes of each producing area are distributed on the basis of their content of aromatics and cycloparaffins. For example, of the gas oils from the crude oils produced in the Gulf Coast region, 35 per cent contain more than 30 per cent of aromatics, $35 + 20 = 55$ per cent contain more than 25, and $35 + 20 + 33 = 88$ per cent contain at least 20 volume per cent of aromatics.

II-3. Lubricant Fractions. Since lubricating oils are distinguished from other portions of crude oil chiefly by a high viscosity, opinions as to their constitution are complicated by speculations on the structures which confer viscosity. The viscosity of known pure hydrocarbons has been established by the synthetic work of Mikeska[2] and by that spon-

---

[1] Smith, *Ind. Eng. Chem.*, **44**:2577 (1952).

[2] *Ind. Eng. Chem.*, **28**:970 (1936).

sored by the American Petroleum Institute;[1] but the matter was a good deal of a mystery when Mabery established (by elementary analyses which were none too accurate)[2] the marked deficiency of hydrogen, based on the C_nH_{2n+2} formula of n-paraffins, in the lubricating fractions of various crudes.   The existence, in the same raw fraction, of oils high and low, respectively, in hydrogen, with corresponding differences in properties, was well established by Smith[3] who effected his separations by distillation and solvent extraction.   The same approach was applied by Davis and McAllister[4] who established reference frameworks of physical properties for known hydrocarbons and then fitted the oil fractions into these frameworks; they then calculated the number of carbon atoms present in cycloparaffin rings.   No method for aromatic rings was available, and the results were thus fragmentary, but the general method has proved fruitful as more of the necessary facts have become available.

   Some lubricating oils are manufactured from steam or vacuum distillates, some from residual stocks, and some are blends of distillates and residua.   Distillates suitable for the production of lubricating oils are comprised principally of hydrocarbons containing from 25 to 35 or possibly 40 carbon atoms per molecule.   In residual stocks hydrocarbons with 50 to 60 and more (up to 80 or so) carbon atoms per molecule may be present.   The composition of a finished lubricating oil will usually differ markedly from that of the lubricant fraction from which it is derived since wax (high in normal paraffin content, at least in distillate stocks) is removed, and refining by solvent extraction and adsorption preferentially removes nonhydrocarbon constituents, polynuclear aromatics, and possibly some of the multiring cycloparaffins.

   The individual normal paraffins up to C_{36} have been isolated from petroleum and their purities determined by mass spectroscopy.[5]   Apart from these no compound approaching a pure hydrocarbon has so far been isolated from the lubricant fraction of petroleum.   Even after extensive separation by all the methods available, the resulting fractions contain components representing several types of hydrocarbon.

   Two rather different methods of approach have been used in the analysis of products in the lubricating oil range.   In a rather empirical procedure, initiated by Waterman and his associates in Holland,[6] oils

---

[1] Research Project 42 at Pennsylvania State University; other interesting properties and their correlations with viscosity have also been studied.

[2] For his final work, see *Ind. Eng. Chem.*, **15**:1233 (1923), but his earliest speculations were made twenty-five years earlier.

[3] *U.S. Bur. Mines Tech. Paper* 428, 1928; 477, 1930.

[4] *Ind. Eng. Chem.*, **22**:1326 (1930).

[5] Schaerer, Busso, Smith, and Skinner, *J. ACS*, **77**:2017 (1955).

[6] Van Nes and Van Westen, "Aspects of the Constitution of Mineral Oils," Elsevier Press, Inc., Houston, 1951. See chap. IV of the present work.

are considered to be composed of a mixture of "structural" units: aromatic rings, cycloparaffin rings, and paraffinic side chains plus free paraffins. Methods so based give the percentages of the total carbon atoms present contained in each group. Analyses are made from correlations of simple physical properties such as refractive index, density, and molecular weight (n-d-M method) or viscosity, refractive index, and density.[1] Additional correlations have been developed by Kurtz, Martin, and associates.[2]

Table II-9 gives results for carbon distribution obtained by the n-d-M method for several refined oils of high, medium, and low viscosity index. As might be expected the oils of low viscosity index give the highest values for per cent of carbon atoms in aromatic rings.

These methods may be applied to oils which have not been subjected to extensive fractionation; they are relatively very rapid; their main disadvantage is the lack of information concerning the arrangement of the structural groups within the component molecules.

By the second approach the lubricant fraction is first of all separated as completely as feasible into its component classes of hydrocarbons, using, in proper sequence, all the physical fractionating processes available (distillation at very low pressures, adsorption, formation of solid molecular compounds with urea, solvent extraction, and thermal diffusion). The fractions so obtained are then examined to determine the completeness of separation and the amounts of the subtypes in the main classes. Within recent years spectroscopy, particularly mass spectroscopy, has proved effective for this purpose. Methods based on this approach are time-consuming and costly so that comparatively few data of this type are available.

The paraffin-cycloparaffin portion of a dewaxed lubricating oil from mixed crude has been investigated by Melpolder, Brown, Washall, Doherty, and Headington.[3] The oil was separated by distillation at low pressures and by adsorption to give narrow boiling fractions of paraffin-cycloparaffin material. A heart cut (molecular weight, 474) was then separated by thermal diffusion to give 43 fractions which were analyzed by the mass spectrometer. Results for fractions 1, 22 and 43, and for the composite material, given in Table II-10, show that fraction 1 was very rich in branched paraffins and fraction 43 in multiring cycloparaffins. The high proportion of branched paraffins (26 per cent) in the composite material may be noted. Of course, the normal paraffins had been

---

[1] Boelhouwer and Waterman, *J. Inst. Petrol.*, **40**:116–121 (1954).

[2] Martin and Sankin, *Anal. Chem.*, **25**:206 (1953). Kurtz and Sankin, *Ind. Eng. Chem.*, **46**:2186 (1954). Kurtz, King, Stout, and Peterkin, *ACS, Div. Petrol. Chem.*, ACS Meeting, Atlantic City, September, 1956.

[3] *Anal. Chem.*, **28**:1936 (1956).

removed with the wax, and the aromatics by the adsorption treatment. Spectrometric analyses of fraction 1 indicated the presence of some paraffins with single methyl side chains near the fourth carbon as well as some more highly branched material. A long extrapolation from the

TABLE II-9. ANALYSES OF SEVERAL REFINED OILS

Type of oil*	Viscosity data		Carbon distribution by the n-d-M method		
	SSU at 210°F	Visc. index	Aromatic carbon atom %	Cycloparaffinic carbon atom %	Paraffinic carbon atom %
HVI aviation oils from:					
Venezuelan crude 1...	99	+ 96	5	25	70
Venezuelan crude 2...	101	+100	4	29	67
Middle East crude 1..	99	+ 97	4	28	68
Middle East crude 2..	99	+ 96	5	27	68
West Texas crude.....	96	+105	6	24	70
HVI motor oils from:					
Venezuelan crude 1...	65	+ 98	6	27	67
Venezuelan crude 3...	66	+ 99	5	26	69
Mid-Continent crude..	49	+100	5	29	66
Pennsylvania crude...	51	+107	10	25	65
MVI motor oils from:					
U.S. coastal crude....	63	+ 70	5	39	56
Venezuelan crude 4...	60	+ 44	9	33	58
LVI oils from:					
Venezuelan crude 4...	62	0	21.5	30	48.5
Borneo crude.........	61	0	32	26	42
N.E. Borneo crude....	45	<0	34	33	33
Medicinal oil from:					
Venezuelan crude 4...	48	+ 73	0	42	58

* All the high viscosity index (HVI) and medium viscosity index (MVI) oils except the Pennsylvanian oil have been solvent extracted; the low viscosity index (LVI) oils have only been acid treated. The medicinal oil has undergone heavy acid and oleum treatments.

From Van Nes and Van Westen, "Aspects of the Constitution of Mineral Oils," Elsevier Press, Inc., p. 404, Houston, 1951.

gasoline fraction indicates that molecules carrying relatively long straight chains may be the principal components of the branched paraffin portion. The results given in Table II-10 show that the cycloparaffins with one to five rings per molecule are the more abundant but that small amounts with up to ten rings per molecule are also present. Evidence, again from the mass spectrometric examination, indicated that the multiring components are highly substituted with relatively short side chains.

TABLE II-10. COMPOSITION OF THE PARAFFIN-CYCLOPARAFFIN PORTION OF A LUBRICATING OIL FROM MIXED CRUDE

Type of hydrocarbon	Volume, per cent			
	Fraction 1	Fraction 22	Fraction 43	Total Fraction 1 to 43
Branched paraffins	70	22		26
Monocycloparaffins	20	7		8
Dicycloparaffins	9	22		15
Tricycloparaffins	1	24		15
Tetracycloparaffins		14	5	13
Pentacycloparaffins		8	28	11
Hexacycloparaffins		3	24	7
Heptacycloparaffins			17	3
Octacycloparaffins			13	1
Nonacycloparaffins			9	1
Decacycloparaffins			4	

From Melpolder, Brown, Washall, Doherty, and Headington, *Anal. Chem.*, **28**:1936 (1956).

TABLE II-11. APPROXIMATE ANALYSIS OF C_{25}-C_{35} PART OF LUBRICANT FRACTION, PONCA CRUDE

Types of Hydrocarbon*		Volume per cent
Normal paraffins		13.7
Branched paraffins		8.3
Monocycloparaffins	18.4 ⎫	
Bicycloparaffins	9.9 ⎬	44.8
Tri- and higher cycloparaffins	16.5 ⎭	
Mononuclear aromatics with cycloparaffin rings		10.5
Dinuclear aromatics with cycloparaffin rings		8.1
Trinuclear aromatics with cycloparaffin rings		6.6
Multiring aromatics, very low in hydrogen, with bulk of nonhydrocarbon material		8.0
Total		100.0

* Including, as appropriate, necessary paraffin side or connecting groups.
From Mair and Rossini, *Ind. Eng. Chem.*, **47**:1062 (1955).

Extrapolation of the results for the cycloparaffins in the gasoline fraction of the Ponca petroleum supports this conclusion.

Results for the composition of the lubricant fraction of the Oklahoma petroleum investigated by API Research Project 6[1] are given in Table II-11. The lubricant fraction was separated by distillation at very low pressures and then by reflux solvent extraction in tall columns to give several series of "homogeneous" fractions. Conclusions concerning the composition were obtained from a correlation of physical

[1] Mair and Rossini, *Ind. Eng. Chem.*, **47**:1062 (1955).

properties including molecular weights and carbon-hydrogen ratios before and after hydrogenation of the aromatics to the corresponding cycloparaffins, as well as from a cooperative spectroscopic investigation of certain key fractions by fifteen laboratories in the petroleum industry. The results show that the lubricant fraction contains a greater proportion of cycloparaffins, aromatics, and nonhydrocarbon components and a smaller proportion of normal and branched paraffins than the lower-boiling portions of this petroleum. The branched paraffins amount to 15.8 per cent of the branched paraffin-cycloparaffin portion, somewhat less than that found (26.2 per cent) by Melpolder and associates for the same portion of the oil which they examined. The mass spectroscopic examination indicated that, for the polycycloparaffins in the Ponca petroleum, somewhat more than half the rings appear to be in condensed structures. Both cyclopentyl and cyclohexyl nuclei are present. In noncondensed structures mass spectroscopy indicates a ratio of cyclopentyl to cyclohexyl groups of nearly 2:1, but this point is not supported by infrared data and remains in doubt.

The infrared spectral data for fractions from the branched paraffin-cycloparaffin portion of the Ponca crude indicated that the paraffinic CH_2 groups are contained principally in unsubstituted chains at least four carbon atoms in length. It seems plausible to assume, on the basis of a long extrapolation of the results for the branched paraffins and cycloparaffins in the gasoline fraction of this crude, that these long alkyl chains are contained principally in the branched paraffins and that the cycloparaffin rings are highly substituted with relatively short side chains.

Mono-, di-, and trinuclear aromatics are the main constituents of the aromatic portion, but undoubtedly material with more, possibly five or more, aromatic nuclei per molecule is present in small amounts. For the dinuclear aromatics, most of the material consists of condensed rings (naphthalene types). This has been established by careful hydrogenation of the dinuclear aromatic portion to the corresponding cycloparaffin material (10 not 12 atoms of hydrogen are taken up per molecule),[1] by physical property correlations,[2] and by spectroscopic examination. For the trinuclear aromatics the phenanthrene type of structure rather than that of anthracene predominates.[3]

It is also indicated that the greater part of the aromatics occur as mixed aromatic-cycloparaffin compounds; a fraction from the mononuclear aromatic portion of the Ponca crude contained only 11 per cent alkylbenzenes, the rest being composed of mixed-type components.[4]

---

[1] Mair, Willingham, and Streiff, *J. Research Natl. Bur. Standards*, **21**:565 (1938).
[2] Martin and Sankin, *Anal. Chem.*, **25**:206 (1953).
[3] Charlet, Lanneau, and Johnson, *Anal. Chem.*, **26**:861 (1954).
[4] Mair and Rossini, *loc. cit.*

The composition of the lubricant fraction of crudes from different sources varies widely, but detailed information is lacking. In the lubricant fraction of some Californian and coastal crude oils normal paraffins are missing or are present in only trace amounts. Presumably the branched paraffin content is also very low. Cycloparaffins and aromatics are the principal constituents. Table II-12 shows the considerable variation in aromatic content of the light lubricant fraction from several crude oils.

TABLE II-12. AROMATIC CONTENTS OF LUBRICANT FRACTIONS

Crude	Volume per cent
East Texas	25.7
Michigan	29.0
Webster, Texas	29.5
Mirando, Texas	49.3

From Lipkin, Hoffecker, Martin, and Ledley, *Anal. Chem.*, **20**:130 (1948).

NONHYDROCARBON COMPONENTS OF PETROLEUM

Nonhydrocarbons occur in petroleum to a greater extent than is perhaps generally realized. Sulfur and oxygen are not often present in amounts greater than 2 per cent and a nitrogen content of more than 0.5 per cent is rather uncommon. This does not suggest a high content of corresponding compounds, but it must be remembered that the molecular weight of these complexes is probably near that of the accompanying hydrocarbons. If a lubricating oil contains 1 per cent of sulfur, and if the molecular weight of the sulfur-carrying compound is of the order of 300, then the lubricating oil may contain 10 per cent of sulfur compounds. Similar considerations apply to other nonhydrocarbon constituents.

Such substances, in spite of the presence of a foreign element, are still made up largely of carbon and hydrogen and retain many hydrocarbon characteristics.

II-4. Sulfur Compounds. Practically all known crude oils contain sulfur. The amount varies from, perhaps, 0.04 per cent for a Pennsylvania oil to about 5.0 per cent for a heavy Mississippi crude. The results of a recent survey (1950) of the sulfur content of crude oils, in terms of the percentage produced in different geographical areas of the United States, is given in Fig. II-2.

Nearly all the crude produced from the Appalachian and Gulf Coast areas had a sulfur content of less than 0.25 per cent by weight; on the other hand, for the Mississippi area, 35 per cent contained more than 2 per cent. Crudes from South America, including Trinidad, and those from the Near and Middle East have, on the average, somewhat more sulfur; those from Eastern Europe, the U.S.S.R., the Far East, India,

Pakistan, and Burma, somewhat less than the average for North America.[1] However, it should be remembered that the sulfur content of crude oils produced from broad geographical regions will vary with time, depending on the composition of newly discovered fields, particularly those in different geological environments.

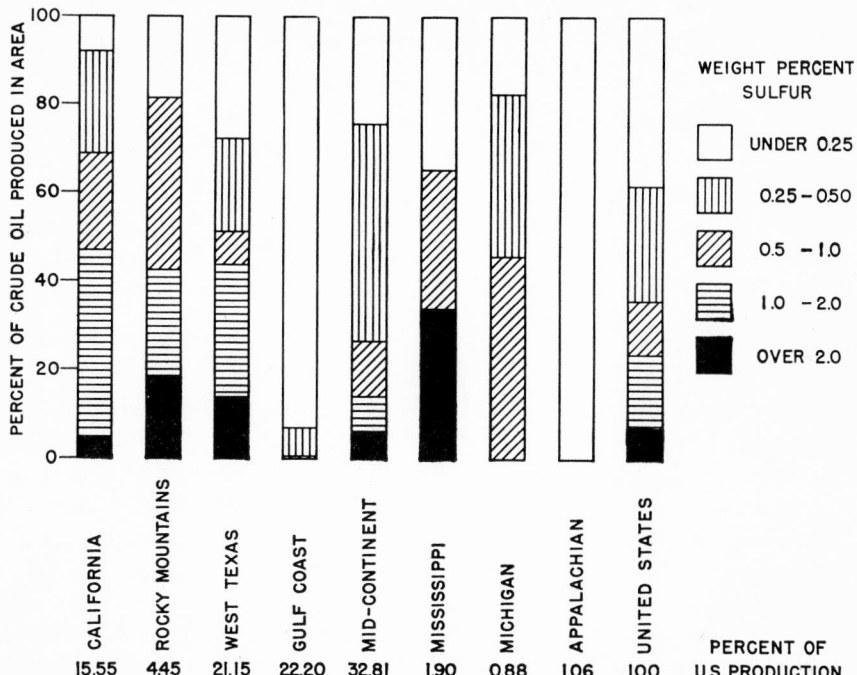

Fig. II-2. Distribution of sulfur in crude oils of the United States. [*From Smith, Ind. Eng. Chem.*, **44**:2577 (1952).]

The distribution of sulfur in the various fractions of crude oils has been studied many times beginning with Mabery[2] in 1891. It is generally true that the proportion of sulfur increases with the boiling point, but Sissingh[3] pointed out that when (as is usual) decomposition occurs during the distillation, the middle fractions may contain more sulfur than do the last, contrary to the usual distribution. The distribution of sulfur compounds among the products of conventional refinery distillation for several crudes is given in Table II-13.[4] Obviously, 95 per cent of the sulfur or better is contained in the gas oil and residual portions.

[1] Tait, *Advances in Chem. Ser.*, No. 5, p. 151, 1951.

[2] *Am. Chem. J.*, **13**:232 (1891).

[3] *Brennstoff-Chem.*, **6**:22 (1925).

[4] Tait, *loc. cit.* See also Nelson, Fombano, and Cordera, *Petroleum Times*, **59**:456 (1955).

TABLE II-13. SULFUR DISTRIBUTION IN PRODUCTS OF DISTILLATION

Crude	Sulfur content of crude, per cent weight	Sulfur in product, lb per 100 lb of sulfur in crude			
		Gasoline and naphtha	Kerosene	Gas oil	Residue
Far East............	0.15	0.3	3.6	38.6	57.5
East Texas.........	0.36	0.9	1.3	15.4	82.4
East Venezuela.....	0.55	0.5	1.7	15.5	82.3
Iran...............	1.4	1.1	1.5	12.6	84.8
West Texas........	2.0	1.8	4.2	14.8	79.2
West Venezuela....	2.2	0.05	0.55	6.6	92.8
Kuwait............	2.45	0.1	0.8	9.5	89.6

From Tait, *Advances in Chemistry Ser.*, No. 5, p. 153, 1951.

A high sulfur content is generally considered to be harmful in most petroleum products and the removal of sulfur compounds or their conversion to less deleterious types has long constituted an important part of refinery practice.   In gasoline, the presence of sulfur compounds is sometimes said to promote corrosion of engine parts, especially under winter conditions, when water containing sulfur dioxide from the combustion may accumulate in the crankcase.[1]   In addition, mercaptans in hydrocarbon solution are directly corrosive to copper and brass in the presence of air.   Mercaptans also affect unfavorably lead susceptibility and color stability.   Free sulfur, if present, is also corrosive.[2]   Sulfides, disulfides, and thiophenes are less corrosive but are directly detrimental in lowering octane number response to tetraethyl lead (see Chap. XI). Federal specifications which formerly limited the sulfur content of gasoline to 0.1 per cent have been abandoned; however, the safe upper limit is still the subject of debate.   Millions of barrels of gasoline with a sulfur content between 0.2 and 0.5 per cent have been sold in the Western United States without obvious harmful effect[3] and in Europe motor fuels of still higher sulfur content have been common.[4]   In diesel fuels sulfur compounds increase wear and may contribute to the formation of engine deposits; the wear can be minimized by proper engine design and control of jacket temperatures.[5]   High content of sulfur can sometimes

[1] Mougey, *Ind. Eng. Chem.*, **20**:18 (1928); crankcase ventilation is of considerable help in minimizing such trouble.

[2] Ormandy and Craven, *J. Inst. Petrol. Technologists*, **9**:133 (1923).

[3] Lowry and Egloff, *Oil Gas J.*, **40**(31):52 (1941).

[4] Kalichevsky and Stagner, "Chemical Refining of Petroleum," Reinhold Publishing Corporation, New York, 1942.

[5] Tait, *loc. cit.*

be tolerated in industrial fuel oils (this is changing in heavily populated areas) but the situation for lubricating oils is different; small additions of sulfur compounds may be useful in preventing metal corrosion, but high natural content of sulfur compounds seems to lower resistance to oxidation and asphaltene deposition.

The removal of sulfur content has been discussed to some extent in Chap. VII on chemical refining. The direct extraction of mercaptans from distillates by alkaline reagents is of some interest and has received a good deal of attention.

Indications that sulfur from conventional sources may not be able to supply the future demand, together with motives of economy, have resulted in a growing recovery of this material from natural and refinery gases.[1]

Some of the sulfur compounds in petroleum undergo thermal reactions at relatively low temperatures. Newton and Leach[2] distilled on a large scale a Crane County (West Texas) crude of 2.03 per cent sulfur content. Nearly half of the total sulfur was recovered as hydrogen sulfide from the various fractions, and the fractions themselves contained the following percentages of sulfur:

	Per cent
Gasoline	0.34
Heavy naphtha	0.57
Kerosene	0.60
Gas oil	0.68–1.04
Lubricating distillates	1.5–2.5
Coke	3.1

Most of the hydrogen sulfide was released during a definite period in the distillation, at oil temperatures between 330 and 400°F. Recently, API Project 48 has studied the thermal stability of sulfur compounds in several crudes and also the stability of one crude (Bradford, Pennsylvania) to which elemental sulfur was added. For a Wasson, Texas, crude, the first pronounced evolution of hydrogen sulfide was observed between 300 and 425°F; the evolution became rapid at 550°F. On the other hand, for a Wilmington, California, crude, little release of hydrogen sulfide even at 550°F was observed, indicating a basic difference in the sulfur compounds present in the two oils. This difference has been made the basis of routine refinery tests of crude oils. Where elemental sulfur is present, a reaction with the evolution of hydrogen sulfide begins at about 300°F and is very rapid at 425°F.[3]

[1] *Petrol. Processing*, **6**:1248 (1951).   McCabe, *Ind. Eng. Chem.*, **47**(4):99A (1955).
[2] *Oil Gas J.*, **27**(42):100 (1929).
[3] Ball, Rall, Waddington, and Smith, *ACS, Div. Petrol. Chem.*, ACS Meeting, Cleveland, April, 1951.

Hydrogen sulfide is a readily recognizable constituent of many crude oils. Some (Iran, Iraq, West Texas) with sulfur content between 1 and 2 per cent are accompanied by gas high in hydrogen sulfide content[1] and large quantities of hydrogen sulfide occur in the natural gas from many fields. The presence of elemental sulfur was reported by several early investigators.[2] However, it is debatable whether the sulfur was present in the original petroleum or was produced by air oxidation of hydrogen sulfide. Recently, Eccleston, Morrison, and Smith[3] report the presence of sulfur in samples of several West Texas crudes, collected at the well head and very carefully protected from contact with air. Thus, although surprising, it seems definite that some crude oils contain elemental sulfur as they issue from the ground; much unpublished work supports this conclusion.

The constitution of the sulfur compounds in petroleum has been the subject of many investigations, beginning with those of Mabery from 1891 to 1906.[4] Within recent years important contributions to our knowledge have come principally from two sources—studies by Birch and those of Project 48, American Petroleum Institute. Birch's investigations pertain to the sulfur compounds recovered from caustic soda wash and the acid sludges from distillates of Iranian crudes; the compounds identified are not necessarily those present in the original crude. Yet, many of the compounds obtained by Birch have also been isolated and identified by Project 48, operating at temperatures too low to cause thermal reactions, and otherwise protecting the integrity of the original structures.

Table II-14 lists the 43 sulfur compounds isolated by Project 48 from a Wasson, Texas, crude. Divided according to type, they are as follows: 17 alkane thiols (mercaptans), 3 cycloalkane thiols, 14 alkane sulfides, and 9 cyclic sulfides. For the cyclic sulfides and cyclic thiols, constituents with both five- and six-membered rings are present. Among the open-chain thiols, the most prevalent type, the secondary thiols, decrease with increasing carbon content of the molecule and become of negligible importance at 12 to 13 carbon atoms; the primary thiols disappear at 5 to 6 carbon atoms, and the tertiary thiols are very minor components throughout.[5]

A number of bicyclic sulfides have been isolated from the acid sludge of an Agha Jari (Iranian) kerosene distillate and tentatively identified;[6]

[1] Devine and Wilhelm, *U.S. Bur. Mines Rept. Invest.* 3128, 1931.

[2] Richardson and Wallace, *J. Soc. Chem. Ind.*, **21**:316 (1902). Thiele, *Chem. Ztg.*, **26**:896 (1902).

[3] *Anal. Chem.*, **24**:1745 (1951).

[4] *Am. Chem. J.*, **13**:232 (1891); Mabery and Quayle, *Am. Chem. J.*, **35**:404 (1906).

[5] Ball, Bordwell, Smith, Waddington, and Seyfried, *Proc. API*, **32**(1):139 (1954).

[6] Birch, *J. Inst. Petrol.*, **39**:185 (1953). Birch, Cullum, and Dean, *ACS, Div. Petrol. Chem.*, ACS Meeting, Atlantic City, September, 1956.

TABLE II-14. SULFUR COMPOUNDS IDENTIFIED IN WASSON, TEXAS, CRUDE OIL
AND ESTIMATED PER CENT BY WEIGHT PRESENT WHENEVER KNOWN

Name	Boiling point, °C	Weight per cent in Wasson, Tex. crude oil
Methanethiol......	5.96	0.00240
Ethanethiol............................	35.0	0.00530
2-Thiapropane...	37.31	0.00088
2-Propanethiol.......	52.56	0.00199
2-Methyl-2-propanethiol....................	64.22	0.00055
2-Thiabutane	66.65	0 00222
1-Propanethiol.......	67.5	0.00041
3-Methyl-2-thiabutane.....................	84.81	0 00064
2-Butanethiol......	85.15	0.00386
2-Methyl-1-propanethiol....	88.72	0.00003
3-Thiapentane............................	92.10	0 00075
2-Thiapentane............................	95.52	0 00030
1-Butanethiol............................	98.4	Trace
2-Methyl-2-butanethiol....................	99.0	0.00064
3,3-Dimethyl-2-thiabutane...................	99.0	
2-Methyl-3-thiapentane.....................	107.4	
3-Methyl-2-butanethiol...	109.8	
2-Pentanethiol..........................	112.9	0.0014
3-Pentanethiol..........................	113.9	0.00057
4-Methyl-2-pentanethiol.....		
3-Methyl-3-pentanethiol......,...........		
3-Thiahexane............................	118.50	0.00012
2,4-Dimethyl-3-thiapentane......	120.02	0.00053
2,2-Dimethyl-3-thiapentane..................	120.41	0.000058
Thiacyclopentane.........................	121.12	0.000077
2-Thiahexane............................	123.2	0 000077
2-Methyl-3-thiahexane......	132.05	0.000078
Cyclopentanethiol..	132.2	
2-Methylthiacyclopentane.......	133.23	0.0023
4-Methyl-3-thiahexane.........	133.65	0.00050
3-Methylthiacyclopentane.................	138.67	0.00046
2-Hexanethiol............................	138.9	0.0028
Thiacyclohexane..........................	141.75	0.00032
trans-2,5-Dimethylthiacyclopentane.............	142.0	0.0025
cis-2,5-Dimethylthiacyclopentane........	142.28	0.0024
3-Thiaheptane.......................... .	144.24	0.000078
2-Methylthiacyclohexane........	153.04	0.0029
3-Methylthiacyclohexane.................	158.04	0.000024
4-Methylthiacyclohexane...................	158.64	0.000048
Cyclohexanethiol........................	158.8	0.0012
3-Hexanethiol*..........		
cis-2-Methylcyclopentanethiol*		
2-Octanethiol*............................		

* Tentatively identified.

From Ball, Bordwell, Smith, Waddington, and Seyfried, *Proc. API,* **34**(VI):106 (1954).

these include compounds with two condensed five-membered rings, e.g., *cis*-2-thiabicyclo-[3,3,0]-octane, and those with a five- and a six-membered ring, e.g., 2-thiabicyclo-[4,3,0]-nonane. The interesting tricyclic sulfide, thia-adamantane, was also isolated:

$$CH_2 \text{---} CH \text{---} CH_2$$

$$CH \qquad CH_2 \qquad CH$$

$$S$$

$$CH_2 \text{---} CH \text{---} CH_2$$

As has already been discussed, hydrocarbons with analogous structures are found in petroleum (compare the previous section in this chapter).

Brown and Meyerson[1] also report the presence of polycyclic sulfides with condensed five- and six-membered rings in the acid sludge from a West Texas kerosene distillate.

Several thiophenes have been reported in the acid sludge from the Agha Jari kerosene distillate as follows: 2,3,4-trimethylthiophene, 2,3-dimethyl-4-ethylthiophene, 2,3,4,5-tetramethylthiophene, and 2,3,4-tri-methyl-5-ethylthiophene.

The presence of benzothiophenes in the higher-boiling fractions of the Wasson crude has been reported by Project 48.[2] This work, involving separation of the sulfur compounds by adsorption on alumina and a mass spectrometric examination of the fractions produced, indicates that at least 11 per cent of the crude boiling above the gasoline range consists of sulfur compounds and that 65 per cent of these compounds are benzothio-phenes, containing 1, 2, and 3 rings per molecule. For the highest-boiling part of the Wasson crude this means that at least 20 per cent and perhaps much more is composed of polycyclic benzothiophenes. Lump-kin and Johnson[3] used similar procedures to separate and examine the sulfur compounds in lubricating oil. They report that the majority of the sulfur compounds in this range are of the condensed aromatic-thiophene type. Thiophenes have been reported in cracked naphthas from California crudes as follows: thiophene, 2-methylthiophene, 3-methyl-thiophene, 2-ethylthiophene, 2,3-dimethylthiophene, and 3,4-dimethyl-thiophene.[4] The presence of significant amounts of thiophenes in cracked naphthas is probably attributable to the breakdown of alkylated or aromatic thiophenes similar to those found in the higher-boiling frac-

[1] *Ind. Eng. Chem.*, **44**:2620 (1952).
[2] Thompson, Coleman, Rall, and Smith, *Anal. Chem.*, **27**:175 (1955).
[3] *Ind. Eng. Chem.*, **26**:1719 (1954).
[4] McKittrick, *Ind. Eng. Chem.*, **21**:585 (1929).

tions of the Wasson and other crude oils. However, small amounts of low-molecular-weight thiophenes exist in some virgin petroleums, since both thiophene and 2-methylthiophene have been identified in a Wilmington, California, crude; in this case the distillate was prepared by very mild thermal treatment (100°C for 30 sec).[1]

Benzenethiol, 2-methyl-1-benzenethiol, and 4-methyl-1-benzenethiol have been reported[2] in cracked gasoline from Texas crude. Here again, it would seem that thermal decomposition is the reason for the presence of these compounds in the gasoline fractions.

Disulfides have been found in the spent caustic used in treating gasoline distillates from Iranian crudes;[3] these probably result from the oxidation of mercaptans and are not regarded as constituents of the original petroleum.

The distribution of the various types of sulfur compounds varies markedly among crudes of diverse origin. The subject has been studied by Project 48[4] for the naphtha fraction of seventeen domestic and foreign crudes. The types of sulfur compounds determined and the method of analysis were as follows:

Type	*Method of Analysis*
Hydrogen sulfide..........	Titration with silver nitrate
Free sulfur..............	Removal with mercury and determination of difference in sulfur content
Mercaptans.............	Titration with silver nitrate
Disulfides..............	Reduction with zinc and acetic acid followed by titration with silver nitrate
Sulfides I................	Extraction with mercurous nitrate and determination of difference in sulfur content
Sulfides II...............	Extraction with mercuric nitrate and determination of difference in sulfur content
Residual sulfur...........	Sulfur compounds remaining after complete procedure has been carried out

The crudes were distilled under reduced pressure to give naphthas with end points corresponding to 482°F (250°C) at atmospheric pressure. Results are given in Fig. II-3.

Two of the naphthas (Goldsmith and Yates) contain elemental sulfur. Sulfur compounds from the Deep River, Michigan, naphtha are rich in mercaptans and disulfides, the latter probably originating from the mercaptans, whereas at the other extreme, sulfur compounds from the Schuler, Velma, Hawkins, Wilmington, Heidelberg, Santa Maria, and

---

[1] Thompson, Coleman, Nikkelsen, Yee, Ward, and Rall, *Anal. Chem.*, **28**:1384 (1956).

[2] Henderson, Ayres, and Ridgeway, *Oil Gas J.*, **38**(46):114 (1940).

[3] Birch and Norris, *J. Chem. Soc.*, **127**:898 (1925).

[4] Hale Thompson, Barker, Smith, and Ball, *Anal. Chem.*, **23**:287 (1951).

Rangely naphthas contain very small quantities of the mercaptan-disulfide group and large quantities of sulfides.

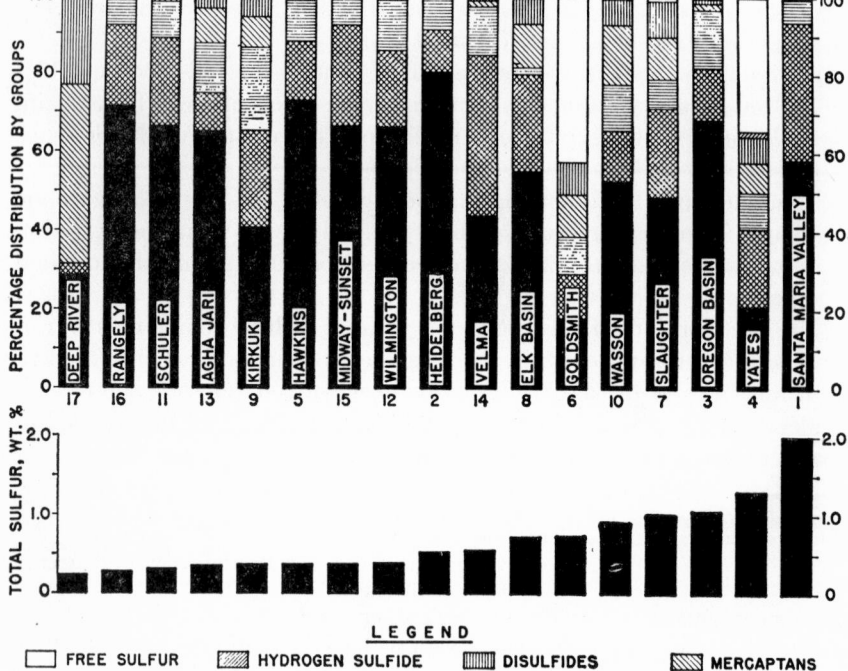

Fig. II-3. Group sulfur analyses of naphthas from vacuum distillations. [*From Hale, Thompson, Barker, Smith, and Ball, Anal. Chem.,* **23**, 287 (1951).]

II-5. Oxygen Compounds. The total oxygen content of petroleum oils is generally low—up to 2 per cent. Larger amounts have been reported, but these results, particularly in the case of older work, were often taken from analyses by difference after carbon and hydrogen had been estimated directly. This procedure allows other elements, especially nitrogen and sulfur, to appear as oxygen. In cases where the oxygen content is authentically high, it is usually found that the oil has been exposed to prolonged atmospheric oxidation, either during or after production. It was pointed out by Markownikoff and Oglobin[1] and also by Mabery[2] that the oxygen content of the oils increases with the boiling point of the fractions examined; this has been confirmed many times for fractions produced by conventional refinery distillation. The resinous and asphaltic materials which may be separated from the residues and

[1] *Ber.,* **16**:1873 (1883).
[2] *J. Franklin Inst.,* **162**:113 (1900).

higher-boiling fractions have oxygen contents up to 8 per cent by weight and perhaps occasionally somewhat higher.

Though these high-molecular-weight compounds contain most of the oxygen in petroleum almost nothing is known concerning their structure; those of lower molecular weight have been investigated with more success and have been shown to contain carboxylic acids and phenols.

The presence of acid substances in petroleum first appears to have been reported in 1874 by Eichler[1] and by Hell and Medinger[2] in Russian and Rumanian oils, respectively. Nine years later Markownikoff and Oglobin[3] established that these substances contained carboxyl groups and were indeed real acids.

Since the first acids obtained were derivatives of the monocycloparaffins (naphthenes), they were termed "naphthenic acids." Although alicyclic (naphthenic) acids appear to be the more prevalent, it is now well known that aliphatic acids are also present; many members of both classes have been isolated in the past twenty years.[4]

In addition to the carboxylic acids, alkaline extracts from petroleum, particularly cracked distillates, contain, in smaller amounts, mixtures of phenols.[5] The two classes may be separated by selective neutralization since the phenols are the weaker acids. In one method, the alkaline extracts are acidified to liberate both carboxylic acids and phenols. The carboxylic acids are brought back into solution with sodium carbonate; phenols, together with hydrocarbon impurities which were imperfectly separated in the first extraction, remain undissolved. Redissolving the phenols in dilute sodium hydroxide serves to separate them from the remaining hydrocarbons. Extraction procedures at controlled values of the hydrogen ion concentration of the aqueous phase have also been found effective for separating carboxylic acids from phenols.[6] The carboxylic acid content of typical American and Russian crudes has been determined by Shipp.[7] Results are given in Table II-15. The high content of acids in the naphthenic oils examined is striking, but it must be remembered that hundreds of crudes have not yet been examined in this way so that this conclusion can only be tentative.

As the result of a long series of investigations begun in 1928 von Braun[8]

[1] *Bull. soc. naturalistes Moscou,* **46**:274 (1874).

[2] *Ber.,* **7**:1216 (1874).

[3] *J. Russ. Phys.-Chem. Soc.,* **13**:34 (1883).

[4] Lochte, *Ind. Eng. Chem.,* **44**:2597 (1952). "Petroleum Acids and Bases," Chemical Publishing Company, Inc., New York, 1955.

[5] Story and Snow, *Ind. Eng. Chem.,* **20**:359 (1928). Tanaka and Kobayashi, *J. Fac. Eng., Tokyo Imp. Univ.,* **17**:125 (1927).

[6] Gallo, Carlson, and Biribauer, *Ind. Eng. Chem.,* **44**:2610 (1952).

[7] *Oil Gas J.,* **34**(44):56 (1936).

[8] *Ann.,* **490**:100 (1931).

TABLE II-15. NAPHTHENIC ACIDS IN AMERICAN AND RUSSIAN CRUDE OILS

Crude	Type	Fraction	Naphthenic acid, per cent
American crude oils			
Pennsylvania.....................	Paraffinic	Kerosene	0.006
Pennsylvania.....................	Paraffinic	Gas oil	0.010
East Texas.......................	Intermediate	Kerosene	0.009
Mid-Continent (pipeline mixture).....	Intermediate	Kerosene	0.009
California.........................	Naphthenic	Naphtha	0.01
		Kerosene	0.06
		Gas oil	0.36
Texas heavy......................	Naphthenic	Kerosene	0.075
		Gas oil	0.35
Russian crude oils			
Balakhany light..................	Naphthenic	Whole crude	1.05
		Kerosene	0.5
Balakhany heavy.................	Asphaltic	Whole crude	1.10
		Kerosene	0.5
Binagady........................	Asphaltic	Whole crude	0.85
		Kerosene	0.5
Ramain..........................	Intermediate	Whole crude	0.40
		Kerosene	0.20
Surakhani........	Intermediate	Whole crude	0.20
		Kerosene	0.20

From Shipp, *Oil Gas J.*, **34**(44):56 (1936).

came to the conclusion that the carboxylic acids in petroleum with less than eight carbon atoms per molecule are almost entirely aliphatic in nature; monocyclic acids begin at C_6 and predominate in the range from C_9 to C_{13}, and bicyclic acids begin at C_{12} and predominate above C_{14}. This seems to indicate that the structures of the carboxylic acids correspond with those of the hydrocarbons with which they are associated in the crude oil; that is, in the range where paraffins are the prevailing type of hydrocarbon, the aliphatic acids may be expected to predominate; similarly, in the ranges where the monocycloparaffins and dicycloparaffins prevail one may expect to find principally monocyclic and dicyclic acids, respectively.

Many of the individual acids have been isolated.[1] Lochte used a

[1] Tchitchibabine, *Chim. & ind. (Paris)*, Spec. No. 306-18, 1932. Nenitzescu, Isacescu, and Volrap, *Ber.*, **71B**:2055 (1938). Lochte, *Ind. Eng. Chem.*, **44**:2597 (1952). Lochte and Littmann, "Petroleum Acids and Bases," Chemical Publishing Company, Inc., New York, 1955.

commercial mixture of acids from the gasoline and kerosene fractions of a Signal Hill, California, crude produced in such a manner that phenols were absent. Branched-chain acids through C_6 and normal acids through C_9 were isolated, the latter in greater amount; they may occur also above C_9. Indeed, Tanaka and Kuwata[1] report the presence of myristic, palmitic, stearic, and arachidic acids in a Japanese gas oil. Among the cyclic acids those with both five- and six-membered rings were isolated. The former include cyclopentane carboxylic, 2-methylcyclopentane carboxylic, 3-methylcyclopentane carboxylic, cyclopentylacetic, 3-methylcyclopentyl acetic, 2,3-dimethylcyclopentyl acetic, and 1,2,2-trimethylcyclopentane carboxylic acids; the latter cyclohexane carboxylic, *p*-methylcyclohexane carboxylic, and *cis*- and *trans*-2,2,6-trimethylcyclohexane carboxylic acids. It will be noted that acids are present with the carboxyl group attached directly to the ring as well as those in which it is separated by one carbon atom.

In addition, dimethylmaleic anhydride has been isolated, both by Lochte[2] and by Nenitzescu.[3] Traces of aromatic acids have also been found by Lochte in the acid mixtures from California.

Very little is known concerning the structure of the polycyclic acids. Goheen[4] converted a mixture recovered from a Gulf Coast petroleum, averaging 20.7 carbon atoms per molecule, to the corresponding hydrocarbons, and, by the methods for hydrocarbon ring analysis, found that they contained on the average 2.6 rings per molecule. It seems probable that acids with 4, 5, and perhaps more rings per molecule will be found in the higher-boiling fractions where the corresponding cycloparaffins are known to occur.

The presence of phenols in cracked distillates was first recognized by Brooks and Parker;[5] traces had been noticed by Story and Snow in straight-run gasoline, but since the distillation was carried on at atmospheric pressure, it is not certain that the compounds were present as such in the parent oil. It is certain, however, that cracked fractions contain more phenols and it is assumed that they are formed from higher-molecular-weight substances (perhaps resins) during pyrolysis.

Phenol is present in minor proportions; of the cresols the ortho form is the most abundant. As in coal tar, no evidence for the presence of 2,6-dimethylphenol has been found but the other five xylenols appear in various amounts. The following occurrences have been noted: pseudocumenol in the higher-boiling cresylic acids in a cracked California

[1] *Chem. Zentr.*, 1929, I, p. 960.
[2] Hancock and Lochte, *J. ACS*, **61**:2448 (1939).
[3] Nenitzescu, Isacescu, and Volrap, *Ber.*, **71B**:2055 (1938).
[4] *Ind. Eng. Chem.*, **32**:503 (1940).
[5] *Ind. Eng. Chem.*, **16**:587 (1924).

distillate,[1] di- and triethyl phenols in a Japanese kerosene distillate,[2] β-naphthol in a Polish oil,[3] traces of di- and trihydroxy benzenes,[4] trimethyl hydroquinone in a cracked distillate from a Gulf Coastal gas oil.[5]

According to Field, Dempster, and Tilson,[6] the quantitative distribution of phenols in the California distillate studied by them is as shown in Table II-16.

TABLE II-16. COMPOSITION OF CRESYLIC ACIDS FROM PETROLEUM AND COAL TAR

	Boiling point of fraction			
	Petroleum acids			Coal-tar acids
	196 to 222°C	215 to 235°C	228 to 258°C	206 to 245°C
Phenol	2.26	0.02	.....	1.78
o-Cresol	28.92	2.01	0.68	12.67
m-Cresol	7.53	1.08	0.33	16.64
p-Cresol	5.45	0.79	0.24	9.43
2,5-Dimethylphenol	34.22	31.20	4.74	10.82
2,4-Dimethylphenol	16.25	14.92	2.28	12.76
2,3-Dimethylphenol	0.08	4.48	0.67	
3,5-Dimethylphenol	.....	7.79	2.55	12.17
3,4-Dimethylphenol	.....	3.47	1.42	8.43
Isopseudocumenol	.....	10.43	26.17	
2-Methyl-5-ethylphenol	.....	.....	.....	6.28
Per cent of fraction accounted for	94.71	76.19	39.08	90.98

Gallo, Carlson, and Biribauer[7] found that the alkaline extracts from catalytic naphthas yield cresylic acids (plus some sulfur compounds) almost entirely, whereas those from thermal naphthas contain major proportions, up to about 70 per cent, of carboxylic (fatty) acids. The cresylic acid content of several naphthas, thermal and catalytic, is given in Table II-17. Obviously, the heavy catalytic naphthas are richest in cresylic acids. As indicated in Table II-18, the distribution of the components within the cresylic acid portion is not greatly different in thermal and catalytic naphthas.

[1] Field, Dempster, and Tilson, *Ind. Eng. Chem.*, **32**:489 (1940).
[2] Tanaka and Kobayashi, *J. Fac. Eng., Tokyo Imp. Univ.*, **17**:125 (1927); *C.A.*, **22**:1032 (1928).
[3] Holzmann and Pilot, *Brennstoff-Chem.*, **11**:409 (1930).
[4] Catlin, *Ind. Eng. Chem.*, **18**:1743 (1926).
[5] Potts and Marrow, *Ind. Eng. Chem.*, **31**:1270 (1939).
[6] *Ind. Eng. Chem.*, **32**:489 (1940).
[7] *Ind. Eng. Chem.*, **44**:2610 (1952).

TABLE II-17. AMOUNTS OF CRESYLIC ACIDS IN SEVERAL NAPHTHAS

Type	Naphtha		Cresylic acids, volume per cent
	Origin	Final boiling point, °F	
Catalytic.............	West Texas	300	0.023
Catalytic.............	Louisiana	325	0.020
Catalytic.............	West Texas	370	0.051
Catalytic.............	Texas	370	0.070
Catalytic.............	Louisiana	405	0.15
Catalytic.............	West Texas	426	0.14
Catalytic.............	Texas	440	0.37
Catalytic.............	West Texas	446	0 14
Catalytic.............	Texas	450	0.22
Thermal.............	Texas	275	0.002
Thermal.............	Texas	430	0 040

From Gallo, Carlson, and Biribauer, *Ind. Eng. Chem.*, **44**:2610 (1952).

TABLE II-18. COMPOSITION OF THE CRUDE CRESYLIC ACIDS FROM CRACKED NAPHTHAS (C_5 TO 450°F)

Compounds	Volume per cent	
	Catalytic	Thermal (Venezuelan)
Phenol...............	20	15
Cresols...............	45	35
C_8+ phenols.........	25	45
Impurities............	10	10

From Gallo, Carlson, and Biribauer, *Ind. Eng. Chem.*, **44**:2610 (1952).

In addition to the carboxylic acids and phenolic compounds, the presence of esters, anhydrides, or lactones of what are probably aliphatic acids has been reported by Kraemer[1] as existing in the soft paraffin of Hanover and Galician petroleum; only the presence of acid anhydrides in petroleum has been confirmed. Indirect chemical evidence for the existence of alcohols and ketones (or possibly aldehydes) in heavy lubricating oil is given by Marcusson.[2] This has not been confirmed.

Small amounts of two crystalline compounds have recently been obtained by chromatographic separation of the sulfur dioxide extract of a lubricating oil distillate.[3] One of these with a formula near $C_{21}H_{30}O$

[1] *Chem. Ztg.*, **31**:676 (1907).
[2] *Chem. Ztg.*, **47**:35 (1923).
[3] Carruthers and Cook, *J. Chem. Soc.*, 1954, p. 2047.

was found by both chemical and spectroscopic tests to contain no carbonyl or hydroxyl groups. The evidence indicated a tetracyclic structure, with one of the rings aromatic, the others cycloparaffin; the oxygen was believed to be present in an ether grouping. This suggests that some of the oxygen in petroleum is contained in compounds analogous to the benzothiophenes which occur in the higher-boiling fractions. The other compound, with a formula near $C_{28}H_{44}O_2$, exhibited a distinct band at a typical carbonyl frequency but failed to give chemical reactions characteristic of carbonyl.

The recovery of naphthenic acids from petroleum is of some commercial importance, annual production amounting to about 40 million pounds in 1955.[1] They are used in the form of their metal salts, lead naphthenates being the most important. The lead salts are applied as extreme pressure lubricants and as paint driers along with cobalt and manganese naphthenates. Copper naphthenates are applied as wood preservatives and in various paints. Other salts are employed in greases and to gel inflammable liquids.

The increasing demand for phenol and the cresols in resins, plasticizers, adhesives, coatings, flotation agents, and as disinfectants, germicides and fungicides may be met in part from petroleum sources.[2]

II-6. Nitrogen Compounds. The nitrogen content of crude oils is generally low. Early analyses indicating up to 2 per cent nitrogen for some crudes appear to be in error; the maximum reported in recent work is 0.88 weight per cent for an Oxnard, California, crude. Most California crudes and some from other areas contain from 0.1 to 0.7 per cent; however, crudes with no detectable nitrogen or only trace amounts are not uncommon. In general, the more asphaltic the oil, the higher its nitrogen content. A correlation between nitrogen content and carbon residue of the crude oil has been established; the higher the carbon residue, the higher the nitrogen content.[3]

The presence of nitrogen in petroleum is of much greater significance in refinery operations than might be expected from the small amounts present. Nitrogen compounds can be responsible for the poisoning of cracking catalysts;[4] they contribute also to the formation of gums in such products as domestic fuel oil.[5] The trend in recent years toward cutting deeper into the crude to obtain stocks for catalytic cracking has

---

[1] Hatch, *Petrol. Refiner*, **34**(10):121 (1955).

[2] Gallo, Carlson, and Biribauer, *Ind. Eng. Chem.*, **44**:2610 (1952).

[3] Ball, Whisman, and Wenger, *Ind. Eng. Chem.*, **43**:2577 (1951).

[4] Maxted, *J. Soc. Chem. Ind. (London)*, **67**:93 (1948). Mills, Boedeker, and Oblad, *J. ACS*, **72**:1554 (1950).

[5] Mapstone, *Petrol. Refiner*, **28**:111 (1949). Thompson, Chenicek, Druge, and Symon, *Ind. Eng. Chem.*, **43**:935 (1951).

accentuated the harmful effects of the nitrogen compounds, which are concentrated largely in the higher-boiling portions.

Nitrogen compounds have been found in petroleum distillates boiling as low as 225°C; however, of the total nitrogen in 12 crudes examined, 85 to 100 per cent was found in residues boiling above 300°C at 30 mm.[1] Others have confirmed the nonvolatile nature of most of the nitrogen compounds in petroleum.[2] Nitrogen compounds in virgin crudes or in residual fractions may be concentrated in the asphaltic portion. For example, by precipitation with pentane, a virgin Wilmington, California, crude oil containing 0.65 per cent nitrogen gave an asphaltic portion, representing 5.7 per cent of the entire crude, which contained 2.4 per cent nitrogen. Adsorption on florisil is also effective in concentrating nitrogen compounds; they tend to be more strongly adsorbed than the other components.[3]

Nitrogen compounds in petroleum may be classed arbitrarily as "basic" or "nonbasic"; the relative amounts depend on the procedure used. Bases of relatively low molecular weight may be extracted with dilute mineral acids; equally strong bases of higher molecular weight may remain unextracted because of unfavorable partition between the oil and aqueous phases. A method has been developed in which the nitrogen compounds are classified as basic or nonbasic, depending on whether they can be titrated with perchloric acid in a 50-50 solution of glacial acetic acid and benzene.[4] Application of this method showed that the ratio of "basic" to total nitrogen is approximately constant, irrespective of the source of the crude, varying only from 0.25 to 0.34 for 14 crudes investigated. Further, the ratio of basic to total nitrogen was found to vary only moderately throughout the entire range of distillate and residual fractions.

As a result of the work of Bailey[5] from 1929 to 1941 and the more recent work of Lochte[6] considerable information is available concerning the constitution of the nitrogen compounds extractable with dilute mineral acids from petroleum distillates. These extracts were found to contain both quinolines and pyridines carrying alkyl substituents, as well as a few pyridines in which the substituent was a cyclopentyl or

---

[1] Ball, Whisman, and Wenger, *Ind. Eng. Chem.*, **43**:2577 (1951).

[2] Richter, Caesar, Meisel, and Offenhauer, *Ind. Eng. Chem.*, **44**:2601 (1952).

[3] Smith, Smith, and Dinneen, *Anal. Chem.*, **22**:867 (1950). Helm, Latham, Ferrin, and Ball, **17**:21, *ACS, Div. Petrol. Chem., Abstracts of Papers*, p. 85, Atlantic City, September, 1956.

[4] Richter, Caesar, Meisel, and Offenhauer, *loc. cit.*

[5] "Science of Petroleum," vol. II, p. 1047, Oxford University Press, New York and London, 1938.

[6] Lochte, *Ind. Eng. Chem.*, **44**:2597 (1952). Lochte and Littmann, "Petroleum Acids and Bases," Chemical Publishing Company, Inc., New York, 1955.

cyclohexyl group. In this category are included 3-cyclopentyl pyridine, 4-cyclopentyl pyridine, and 2-(2,2,6-trimethylcyclohexyl)-4,6-dimethyl pyridine. A list showing the compounds (about 50) so far isolated and identified has been prepared.[1]

In addition, isoquinoline and 1- and 3-methylisoquinolines have been isolated from a California cracked petroleum stock.[2]

A little information is available concerning those compounds which cannot be extracted with dilute mineral acids; these contain the greater part of the nitrogen in petroleum. Sauer, Melpolder, and Brown[3] used adsorption fractionation to concentrate the nitrogen compounds in two heating oil distillates, i.e., catalytically cracked and straight-run oils from a Kuwait crude. Examination of the concentrates by mass spectrometry indicated the presence of carbazoles, indoles, and pyrroles, in addition to the basic pyridines and quinolines. For the straight-run distillate, the distribution of the several types in the nitrogen concentrate is as follows:

Type	Per cent
Pyridines	43.9
Carbazoles	29.5
Indoles	9.4
Pyrroles	8.9
Quinolines	8.3

Porphyrins (nitrogen-metal complexes) are also constituents of the nonbasic nitrogen portion. They have been found in several European and North American crude oils.[4] Both nickel porphyrins[5] and vanadium porphyrins[6] have been recognized in California crude oils (see below).

II-7. Metallic Constituents. The ash content of crude oils has been discussed in Chap. I. As there stated, doubt exists about the extent to which most of the elements found are really native to an oil; however, vanadium, copper, nickel, and some part of the iron found seem to be in a different class, present as oil-soluble compounds. Arguments from possible genesis indicate that they may have persisted from the source materials. These metals are capable of complexing with pyrrole pigment compounds derived from chlorophyll and hemoglobin to form remarkably stable, oil-soluble compounds. Since chlorophyll and hemoglobin are almost certain to have been present in plant and animal source materials, it is easy to surmise that the metals in question are present in such form, ending in the ash content. Evidence for the presence of several other

---

[1] Ball, VanderWerf, Waddington, and Lake, *Proc. API*, **34**(VI):152 (1954).

[2] Hackman, Wibaut, and Gitsels, *Rec. trav. chim.*, **62**:229 (1943).

[3] *Ind. Eng. Chem.*, **44**:2606 (1953).

[4] Treibs, *Ann.*, **510**:42 (1934); *Ann.*, **517**:172 (1935).

[5] Dunning, Moore, and Denekas, *Ind. Eng. Chem.*, **45**:1759 (1953).

[6] Skinner, *Ind. Eng. Chem.*, **44**:1159 (1952).

metals in oil-soluble form has been given by Dodd, Moore, and Denekas.[1] They found that certain metal-containing compounds were surface active and were adsorbed at water-oil interfaces; consequently, they could be concentrated in water-spray columns. The metal-containing extracts obtained in this way appeared to be soluble in oils and in organic solvents; zinc, titanium, calcium, and magnesium compounds were thus found in addition to vanadium, nickel, iron, and copper.

An analysis of a number of crudes for iron, nickel, vanadium, and copper is given in Table II-19. The relatively high vanadium content

TABLE II-19. MINERAL CONTENT OF VARIOUS CRUDES IN PARTS PER MILLION

Crude	Fe	Ni	V	Cu
East Texas............	3.2	1.7	1.2	0.4
West Texas............	5.1	4.8	7.9	0.4
Mirando..............	7.6	1.9	1.4	0.5
Jackson...............	4.4	1.8	0.9	0.2
Scurry County.........	3.4	1.0	0.8	0.2
Wilmington...........	28	46	41	0.6
Santa Maria...........	17	97	223	0.3
Kettleman.............	24	35	34	0.4
Ventura...............	31	33	49	1.1
Tibu-Petrolea..........	1.6	9.0	60	0.9
Kuwait...............	0.7	6.0	22.5	0.1
Mid-Continent.........	3.8	4.2	7.9	0.3
Kansas...............	5.8	5.8	20.8	0.4
Morocco..............	....	0.8	0.6	0.1
Redwater.............	3.4	10.6	4.5	<0.1

From Milner, Glass, Kirchner, and Yurick, *Anal. Chem.*, **24**:1728 (1952).

in some of these crudes, particularly that from the Santa Maria, California, field, is apparent. Heavy Mara, Venezuela, oil has an even higher vanadium content, about 1,000 ppm. Usually the vanadium content exceeds that of nickel, but the reverse is sometimes found. For example, crude oils with a low total metal content, from deep production in West Texas, are richer in nickel than vanadium. This is also true for certain Trinidad asphalts.

Distillation in the refinery concentrates the metallic constituents in the residues though some appear in the higher-boiling distillates; in part, the latter may be due to entrainment. However, evidence is accumulating that some portion of the metallic constituents enter petroleum distillates by actual volatilization of the organometallic compounds present in the original petroleum. Wrightson[2] observed that as the per-

[1] *Ind. Eng. Chem.*, **44**:2585 (1952).
[2] *Anal. Chem.*, **21**:1543 (1949).

centage overhead obtained by vacuum distillation of a reduced crude is increased, the amount of metallic constituents in the overhead oil is also increased. Woodle and Chandler[1] distilled a blend consisting of a small proportion of a highly colored nonvolatile residue with a light-colored distillate. From the color of the fractions produced, it appeared that entrainment was not significant and that the metal content of the distillate was attributable to actual volatilization. Further, their data indicate that vanadium exists in crude oil in a family of compounds of widely varying molecular weight; the less volatile concentrate in the residue, those of somewhat lower molecular weight, pass into the distillate. It has also been shown[2] that synthetic nickel, vanadium, iron, and copper tetraphenyl porphyrins (not naturally occurring in petroleum) may be sublimed under reduced pressure without decomposition. The matter of volatility is supported by direct experiments on the sublimation of metalloporphyrin compounds at temperatures of the order of 220 to 300°C.[3]

The greater part of the vanadium, nickel, iron, and (presumably) copper in residual stocks may be precipitated along with the asphaltenes by propane or similar solvents. For residual fuels from several crudes, Sacks[4] found that removal of the asphaltenes with n-pentane reduced the vanadium content of the oil by 83 to 95 per cent. Large reductions in the amounts of iron and nickel were also observed. Skinner[5] precipitated an asphaltic portion from a dry Santa Maria, California, crude oil with propane and then extracted the asphaltic portion with a succession of solvents in the following order: n-pentane, n-hexane, n-heptane, 2,2,4-trimethylpentane, cyclohexane, benzene, and pyridine. Some of the metallic constituents were sparingly soluble in the propane-oil portion but all tended to be concentrated in the asphaltic portion. Although vanadium (0.02 per cent by weight in the original petroleum) was present in all fractions, the greater part was found in the cyclohexane and benzene extracts. The nature of the organometallic compounds is of interest. Porphyrins were identified in certain petroleums and asphalts by Treibs.[6] His general results have been verified, although some of his methods and structure identifications have been revised.[7] Spectroscopic evidence was also employed by Skinner,[5] who arrived at the conclusion that vanadium

[1] *Ind. Eng. Chem.*, **44**:2591 (1952).

[2] Horeczy, Hill, Walters, Schutye, and Bonner, *Anal. Chem.*, **27**:1899 (1955).

[3] Erdman, Ramsey, and Hanson, *Science*, **123**:502 (1956).

[4] *Can. J. Technol.*, **29**:492 (1951).

[5] *Ind. Eng. Chem.*, **44**:1159 (1952).

[6] *Ann.*, **509**:103 (1934); **510**:42 (1934); **517**:172 (1935).

[7] Erdman, Ramsey, Kalenda, and Hanson, *ACS, Div. Petrol. Chem.*, ACS Meeting, Dallas, April, 1956.

compounds from petroleum of the Santa Maria Valley field in California exist as porphyrin complexes. Both vanadium and nickel derivatives of the porphyrins have been identified spectroscopically in water-spray extracts of petroleum from the North Belridge, California, field by Dunning, Moore, and Myers.[1] It has also been suggested that some of the oil-soluble components may be present as salts of the carboxylic acids which occur in petroleum in small quantities; there seems to be no experimental evidence to support this proposition.

The occurrence of metallic constituents in crude oil is of considerably greater interest to the petroleum industry than might be expected from the very small amounts present. Even minute amounts of iron, copper, and particularly nickel and vanadium in the charging stocks for catalytic cracking affect the activity of the catalyst and result in increased gas and coke formation and reduced yields of gasoline.[2] In high-temperature power generators, such as oil-fired gas turbines, the presence of metallic constituents, particularly vanadium in the fuel, may lead to ash deposits on the turbine rotors, thus reducing clearances and disturbing their balance. More particularly, damage by corrosion may be very severe.[3]

The ash resulting from the combustion of fuels containing sodium and especially vanadium reacts with refractory furnace linings to lower their fusion points, and so cause their deterioration.[3]

HYDROCARBON COMPONENTS OF THERMAL AND CATALYTIC GASOLINES

The quantity of gasoline which can be obtained from petroleum, by distillation alone, is not sufficient to supply the demand. Also, the hydrocarbon molecules which predominate in natural petroleum do not in most cases possess the structure necessary for a fuel of the antiknock quality required. For these reasons, the petroleum industry has developed a number of refining processes which change the size and structure of the original molecules to increase both the yield and quality of gasoline obtainable.

The process by which material boiling in the gasoline range is produced from higher-boiling distillates and residual stocks is known as cracking. In this operation, the larger molecules are split into fragments of lower molecular weight by the application of heat and pressure alone (thermal cracking), or by contact with a catalyst at elevated temperatures (catalytic cracking). Where material already boiling in the gasoline range is upgraded to give a product of better antiknock quality,

[1] *Ind. Eng. Chem.*, **46**:2000 (1954).
[2] Mills, *Ind. Eng. Chem.*, **42**:182 (1950).
[3] Jones and Hardy, *Ind. Eng. Chem.*, **44**:2615 (1952).

the process is known as reforming.   As with cracking, both thermal and catalytic reforming processes may be employed.

Very substantial quantities of gaseous paraffin hydrocarbons result from catalytic reforming; cracking and thermal reforming yield gaseous hydrocarbons of high olefin content; some of these may be converted by polymerization or alkylation to yield high-grade material boiling in the gasoline range.

The term polyforming is applied to a process which may be regarded as a combination of thermal reforming and thermal polymerization.   In this case, the C_3 and C_4 hydrocarbons which are produced are recycled with additional C_3 and C_4 hydrocarbons when available.   In addition to the reactions characteristic of thermal reforming, both polymerization and alkylation occur.

The processes and the chemistry involved in the foregoing hydrocarbon transformations are discussed in Chap. X.

II-8. Cracked Gasolines.   Since the first catalytic cracking process was introduced about 1936, the improved antiknock quality of gasolines obtained by catalytic cracking over those produced by thermal treatment (for equal yields) has resulted, to a considerable extent, in the replacement of thermal by catalytic methods.   However, some thermal gasoline is still produced with the older equipment; moreover, the thermal process may be employed to advantage with certain refractory catalytic cycle stocks.[1]

The composition of gasolines produced by catalytic cracking depends on a number of variables, including the nature of the feed stock and the operating conditions (temperature, pressure, space velocity, ratio of catalyst to oil, nature of catalyst, etc.).   Similar factors (except those pertaining to catalyst) affect the composition of thermal gasolines, with high temperature and low pressures causing a shift in the composition to a higher content of aromatics and olefins.   The effect of cracking severity on the composition of catalytic naphthas produced from paraffinic- and naphthenic-type stocks has been studied by Starr, Tilton, and Hockberger.[2]   Some of their results are shown in Table II-20.   Naphthas 1, 2, and 3 show the effect of increasing the severity of cracking for a paraffinic type (Tinsley, Mississippi) gas oil.   A moderate increase in severity results in an increase in the content of both olefins and aromatics (properties given in columns 1 and 2); with an additional increase in cracking severity, the content of aromatics rises still higher, while the olefin content declines (compare properties given in columns 2 and 3).   The

[1] Hirsch and Fisher in Brooks, Boord, Kurtz, and Schmerling (eds.) "The Chemistry of Petroleum Hydrocarbons," vol. II, p. 27, Reinhold Publishing Corporation, New York, 1955.

[2] *Ind. Eng. Chem.*, **39**:199 (1947).

influence of type of feed stock may be seen by comparing the data shown in columns 2 and 4; more aromatics and less olefins are obtained, at equal cracking severities, from the naphthenic-type coastal gas oil.

TABLE II-20. EFFECT OF CRACKING SEVERITY AND TYPE OF STOCK
ON COMPOSITION OF CATALYTIC NAPHTHAS

Boiling range, yield, and composition	No. 1, from Tinsley gas oil, temperature 800°F, conversion 49 volume per cent	No. 2, from Tinsley gas oil, temperature 975°F, conversion 65 volume per cent	No. 3, from Tinsley gas oil, temperature 975°F, conversion 80 volume per cent	No. 4, from light coastal gas oil, temperature 975°F, conversion 65 volume per cent
200 to 250°F fraction, yield, volume per cent on feed................	4.7	4.8	4.2	5.6
Aromatics, volume per cent........	13	31	59	44
Cycloparaffins, volume per cent....	35	30	18	35
Paraffins, volume per cent.........	52	39	23	21
Olefins, volume per cent...........	28	40	16	28
250 to 300°F fraction, yield, volume per cent on feed................	4.7	5.2	5.3	6.7
Aromatics, volume per cent........	36	66	87	83
Cycloparaffins, volume per cent....	35	15	1	10
Paraffins, volume per cent.........	29	19	12	7
Olefins, volume per cent...........	19	21	4	11

Adapted from Starr, Tilton, and Hockberger, *Ind. Eng. Chem.*, **39**:199 (1947).

A comparison of the composition of catalytic (Houdry fixed-bed), thermal, and virgin gasoline is given by Bates, Rose, Mills, and Kurtz.[1] Results for the hexanes are given in Table II-21. The catalytic product

TABLE II-21. COMPOSITION OF THE HEXANES FROM A CATALYTIC,
THERMAL, AND STRAIGHT-RUN GASOLINE

Components	Volume per cent		
	Type of gasoline		
	Houdry catalytic	Thermal	East Texas straight-run
n-Hexane....................	9	63	51
Branched hexanes.............	91	37	49

From Bates, Rose, Kurtz, Mills, *Ind. Eng. Chem.*, **34**:147 (1942).

is much richer in branched hexanes than either the thermal or the straight-run material. Additional results showing the distribution of molecular

[1] *Ind. Eng. Chem.*, **34**:147 (1942).

type with respect to boiling range for the catalytic and thermal gasoline are given in Fig. II-4.   The low olefin content of the catalytic distillate is typical of products from two-pass fixed-bed operations (see the discussion of Table II-24).   Compared with the thermal, the catalytic product is very rich in aromatics, particularly in the higher-boiling portion.   The better antiknock quality of catalytic gasoline is attributable to the higher content of branched rather than normal paraffins (and branched olefins) in the lower-boiling portion and to the higher content of aromatics in the higher-boiling part.

To eliminate as far as possible the effects of starting material, Cady, Marschner, and Cropper[1] compared the composition of the C_5 and C_6 fractions of three gasolines, respectively, virgin, thermal, and catalytic, produced from the same Mid-Continent petroleum (Table II-22).   To

TABLE II-22. COMPOSITION OF VIRGIN AND "HYDROGENATED" CRACKED NAPHTHAS

Carbon atoms per molecule	Hydrocarbon type	Volume per cent		
		Virgin	"Hydrogenated" thermal	"Hydrogenated" catalytic
5	n-Alkane	53	57.3	20.0
	Methylalkane	42.1	37.9	77.3
	Cycloalkane	4.9	4.8	2.7
6	n-Alkane	38.7	41.1	5.3
	Methylalkane	28.1	36.4	69.4
	Dimethylalkane	1.0	1.7	16.3
	Cycloalkane	31.2	19.5	8.1
	Aromatic	1.0	1.3	0.9

From Cady, Marschner, Cropper, *Ind. Eng. Chem.*, **44**:1859 (1952).

show clearly the differences in extent of branching, all the olefins in both the thermal and catalytic gasolines are considered as though completely hydrogenated.   The virgin and thermal gasolines appear to be quite similar; on the other hand, the catalytic gasoline contains a much higher proportion of branched constituents.   The results are in accord with the conclusion that isomerization is much more extensive with catalytic than with thermal cracking.

Streiff and Rossini[2] found that the distribution of ethylbenzene, p-xylene, m-xylene, and o-xylene was nearly constant in the C_8 alkylbenzene portion from five different catalytic refining processes (Table II-23).   Moreover, the relative amounts were about what would be

[1] *Ind. Eng. Chem.*, **44**:1859 (1952).
[2] *J. Research Natl. Bur. Standards*, **39**:303 (1947).

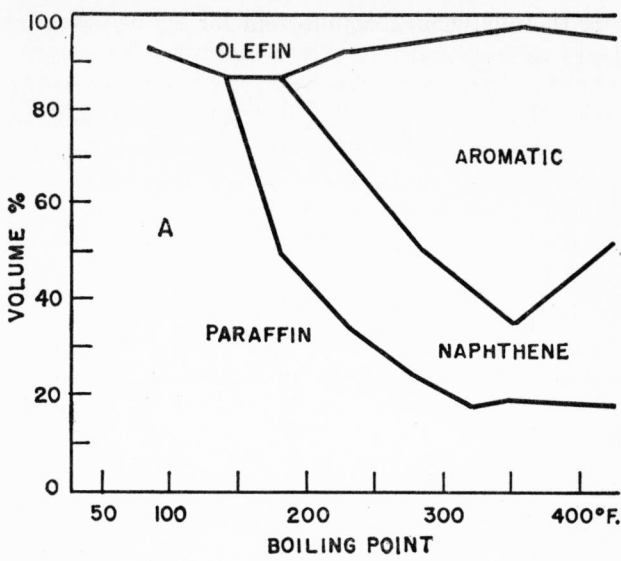

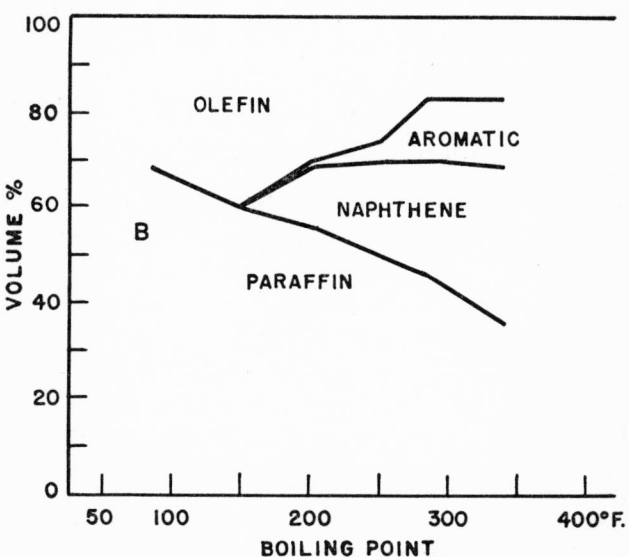

FIG. II-4. Composition of gasolines with respect to boiling point. (*Top*) Catalytic gasoline (Houdry) from light gas oil from mixed-base crude. (*Bottom*) Thermal gasoline from light gas oil from mixed-base crude. [*From Bates, Rose, Mills, and Kurtz, Ind. Eng. Chem.,* **34**:147 (1942).]

expected at thermodynamic equilibrium for the temperature at which the material was produced.

TABLE II-23. AMOUNTS OF THE FOUR C$_8$ ALKYLBENZENES

Sample*	Tempera-ture, °F	Volume per cent			
		Ethyl-benzene	p-Xylene	m-Xylene	o-Xylene
Hydroforming...........	925	11.6	17.7	46.5	24.2
Two-pass fixed bed.......	867	13.2	17.7	48.1	16.6
Three-pass fixed bed.....	875	8.6	20.3	52.2	18.9
Low-temperature fluid....	800	12.9	17.4	45.5	24.2
High-temperature fluid...	975	12.6	19.8	49.6	18.0

* These five samples were produced as follows:

Hydroforming: Material in the gasoline range is reformed in the presence of hydrogen over a catalyst to give a product of nearly the same boiling range but of higher aromatic content.

Two-pass fixed bed: Gas oil or heavier distillate is cracked in the presence of a catalyst; the gasoline fraction from the first operation is passed through a similar catalyst bed.

Three-pass fixed bed: Heavy naphtha or kerosene accumulated from the two-pass fixed-bed process is repassed through a similar operation.

Low-temperature fluid and high-temperature fluid: Kerosene or gas oil is cracked in a process in which fluid catalyst is moved continuously through a reactor and regenerator.

From Streiff and Rossini, *J. Research Natl. Bur. Standards*, **39**:303 (1947).

Somewhat different results were obtained by Melpolder, Brown, Young, and Headington[1] for the content of ethylbenzene in a naphtha produced from a fluid catalytic cracking unit operating at 900°F. Their values for the relative amounts of the C$_8$ alkylbenzenes observed and computed from thermodynamic data are as follows:

	Volume per cent	
	Actual	Calculated
Ethylbenzene..........	19.8	9.7
p-Xylene..............	15.5	22.6
m-Xylene.............	42.5	46.7
o-Xylene..............	22.2	21.0

Obviously, the content of ethylbenzene is about twice the equilibrium value; the amounts for the xylenes are in fair accord with those calculated.

[1] *Ind. Eng. Chem.*, **44**:1142 (1952).

Results for the analysis of two gasolines, made, respectively, by the Houdry fixed-bed (two-pass) and fluid catalytic methods are given in Table II-24. The product from the Houdry process is characterized by a low olefin content and is typical of fixed-bed processing, where the output from the initial cracking is subsequently contacted with fresher catalyst. This results in treating by hydrogen exchange to yield a relatively saturated product. Currently, by far the greater production is by the fluid catalytic method; a gasoline of higher olefin content results.

TABLE II-24. COMPOSITION IN VOLUME PER CENT OF TWO
CATALYTICALLY CRACKED GASOLINES

Type of hydrocarbon	Houdry fixed-bed (two-pass)*	Fluid catalytic at 900°F†
Normal paraffins..........	4.4 ⎱	24.7
Branched paraffins.........	42.7 ⎰	
Cycloparaffins.............	16.8	10.0
Aromatics.................	31.9	24.0
Olefins...................	4.2	41.3

* From Glasgow, Willingham, and Rossini, *Ind. Eng. Chem.*, **41**:2292 (1949).
† From Melpolder, Brown, Young, and Headington, *Ind. Eng. Chem.*, **44**:1142 (1952).

II-9. Reformates. In thermal reforming, which is essentially a cracking operation, the improvement in antiknock quality is due largely to a decrease in size of the molecules, whereas with catalytic reforming, the improvement is due principally to changes in the structure of the molecules without much reduction in size. Thermal reforming was the first process used commercially (beginning about 1931). Larger yields are obtained for a given improvement in antiknock quality with catalytic than with thermal processing, and the greater the improvement in this quality, the greater the difference in yield becomes. Data given by Egloff[1] show that in reforming a gasoline with octane number of 37 (F-1 Research Method) to a product with octane number of 60, yields of 90 and 96 per cent were obtained with the thermal and catalytic methods, respectively. With more severe treating to an octane number of 90, the corresponding yields were 47 and 84 per cent.

A number of catalytic reforming methods are in commercial use; they differ in such matters as the nature of the catalyst, the method of contacting, and the procedure used to regenerate the catalyst; all operate in the presence of recycle hydrogen. In general, aromatics are produced by dehydrogenation of cyclohexanes; cyclopentanes are isomerized to cyclohexanes and these are, in turn, dehydrogenated to aromatics; highly

[1] *J. Inst. Petrol.*, **41**:69 (1955).

branched paraffins result from hydrocracking and isomerization of the normal and less highly branched paraffins. Aromatics also result from the dehydrocyclization of paraffins. This reaction is favored by severe conditions and is important in the reforming of paraffinic stocks. Data for the reforming of two heavy naphthas, from Venezuela and Kuwait, respectively, under conditions of varying severity, show that aromatic production from the naphthenic Venezuela naphtha may be attributed principally to the dehydrogenation of cycloparaffins. On the other hand, the production of aromatics from the paraffinic Kuwait naphtha was from 140 to 157 per cent of that potentially available from the cycloparaffin conversion, showing that dehydrocyclization played a considerable part in the high aromatic yield.[1] The nature of the catalyst affects the results. For example, a catalyst containing small amounts of platinum on an acid base (platforming catalyst) is reported to be excellent in promoting the isomerization of cyclopentanes to cyclohexanes, a reaction desirable for maximum aromatic production.[2] The platinum catalyst is also reported to give low carbon deposition and to have a long life without regeneration.

Since the increase in aromatics usually results largely from the conversion of cycloparaffins, it is obvious that the nature and boiling range of the feed stock will affect the aromatic content and the relative amounts of the individual aromatics. An example of the effect of boiling range of feed stock on the content of individual aromatics, or groups of aromatics, is given in Table II-25.

TABLE II-25. EFFECT OF BOILING RANGE OF FEED STOCK ON AMOUNTS
OF AROMATICS PRODUCED BY HYDROFORMING

	Boiling range of feed stock	
	200–275°F	250–350°F
Benzene, volume per cent...............	0.9	0.6
Toluene, volume per cent................	29.1	3.6
C_8, volume per cent....................	9.3	25.4
C_9, volume per cent....................	0.7	16.6
C_{10} and higher, volume per cent..........	0.2	6.2

From Love and Pfennig, *Advances in Chem. Ser.*, no. 5, p. 299, 1951.

A comparison of the composition of a Pennsylvania straight-run gasoline, and two gasolines produced from it, one by thermal reforming, the other by catalytic reforming, is given by Haensel and Sterba.[3] The

[1] Egloff, *loc. cit.*
[2] Fowle, Ciapetta, Pitts, and Leum, *Advances in Chem. Ser.*, no. 5, p. 77, 1951.
[3] *Advances in Chem. Ser.*, no. 5, p. 60, 1951.

thermal gasoline is characterized by a large percentage of aliphatic olefins in the lower-boiling and some cyclic olefins in the higher-boiling portion, the catalytic gasoline by a high content of paraffins in the lower-boiling and of aromatics in the higher-boiling fraction (see Fig. II-5).

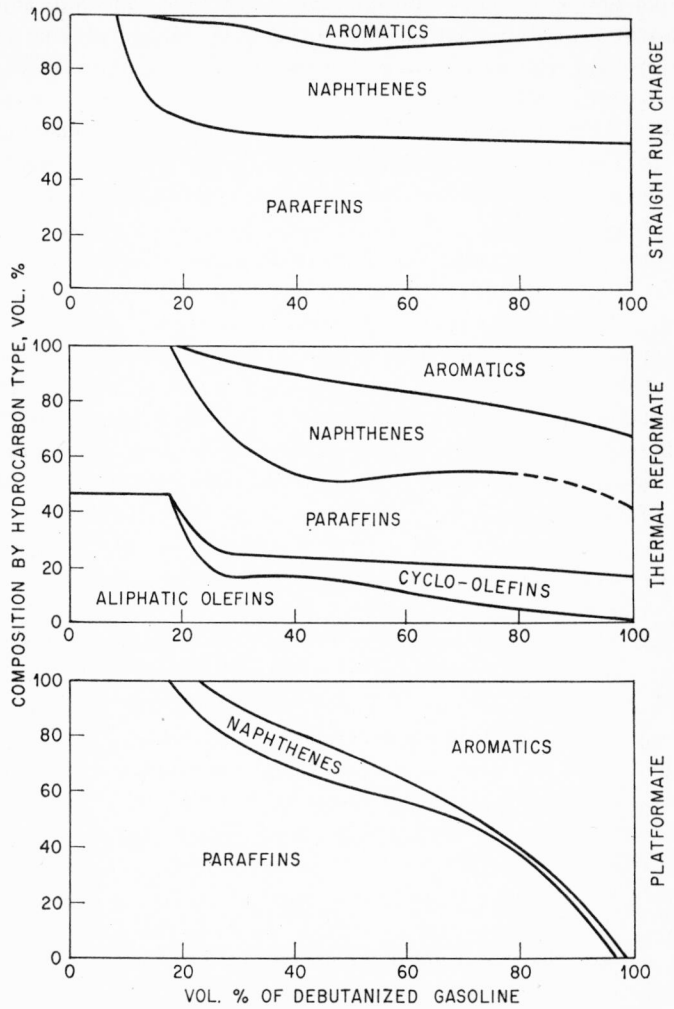

Hydrocarbon–Type Content of Debutanized Pennsylvania Straight-Run Gasoline, Platformate, and Thermal Reformate

Fɪɢ. II-5. (*From Haensel and Starba, Advances in Chem. Ser., no. 5, p. 60, 1951.*)

With thermal reforming, the original paraffins and cycloparaffins are cracked and dehydrogenated to produce lower-boiling paraffins and olefins; a small part of the cycloparaffins are dehydrogenated to give cyclic olefins, and a still smaller part to give aromatics. On the other hand, with catalytic reforming, Haensel and Sterba concluded that the paraffins are hydrocracked and isomerized with a consequent reduction in boiling range; the cyclopentanes are isomerized to cyclohexanes, and, together with the original cyclohexanes, converted by dehydrogenation to aromatics having a somewhat higher boiling point than the original components.　These reactions account for the concentration of paraffins in the lower-boiling portion and of aromatics in the higher-boiling portion of the catalytic reformate.

II-10. Polymer Gasoline.　From the early investigations of Bertholet (1860–1870) and Butlerow (1870–1880) to the more recent researches of Ipatieff (1930–1950) the subject of the polymerization of gaseous olefins (both thermally and catalytically) has been studied many times.

Incentive for the conversion of gaseous hydrocarbons, containing both saturates and olefins, to motor fuels was provided by the large volumes of these gases which became available from the cracking of petroleum about thirty years ago.　The first commercial polymerization process using heat and pressure alone began operation in 1931.[1]　Saturated hydrocarbons in the feed gas were cracked or dehydrogenated to olefins and these together with olefins already present were simultaneously polymerized to liquid fuels.　Shortly thereafter (1934), the cold acid process for the polymerization of isobutene was announced.[2]　Sulfuric acid was used as the catalyst to give a product consisting almost entirely of 2,4,4-trimethylpentene-1 and the corresponding pentene-2; hydrogenation of the mixture yielded nearly pure 2,2,4-trimethylpentane ("isooctane").　Later both hot sulfuric acid and solid phosphoric acid (a calcined composite of phosphoric acid and kieselguhr) were used as catalysts to polymerize butenes (normal and branched) to give a mixture consisting largely of branched octenes (codimer).　This, in turn, was hydrogenated to a composite of branched octanes (hydrocodimer), of considerable value as a component of military aviation gasoline of that time.　Codimer and hydrocodimer are no longer manufactured.　More recently mixtures of C_3 and C_4 olefins have been charged to the polymerization units.　The trend, however, is to utilize all the C_4 olefins for alkylation, leaving only the C_3 olefins available for polymerization and even these are also being used for alkylation in several refineries.　The polymerization of C_3 olefins gives a product rich in branched hexenes. An analysis of two hydrocodimers, possibly only of historic interest, is given in Table II-26.

Compared to the mild conditions employed in catalytic polymerization (from 300 to 450°F with solid phosphoric acid), thermal polymeri-

---

[1] Wagner, *Ind. Eng. Chem.*, **27**:933 (1935).

[2] McAllister, *Proc. API*, **18**(III):78 (1937).　The chemical reaction had been recognized by Butlerow long before.

TABLE II-26. COMPOSITION OF HYDROCODIMERS

	Volume per cent	
	Hot sulfuric acid process	Phosphoric acid process
C_6- and C_7-Hydrocarbons...........	1.2	3.6
2,2,4-Trimethylpentane.............	35.4	9.9
2,2,3-Trimethylpentane.............	26.0	9.2
2,3,4-Trimethylpentane.............	19.0	43.9
2,3,3-Trimethylpentane.............	7.0	8.6
Other hydrocarbons................	11.4	24.8

From Glasgow, Willingham, and Rossini, *J. Research Natl. Bur. Standards*, **38**:537 (1947).

zation requires temperatures from 1000 to 1200°F. The product contains paraffins, cycloparaffins, and aromatics (see Table II-27). An increase in temperature with a reduction in pressure causes a shift of the composition in the direction of higher aromatic content (compare gasoline 1 with 2 and 3).

TABLE II-27. COMPOSITION OF THERMAL POLYMER GASOLINES

Gasoline	Method of production	Volume per cent			
		Olefins	Aromatics	Cyclo-paraffins	Paraffins
1	From C_1 to C_4 feed, 47% unsaturates, at 1174°F and 61 psig	....	47		
2	From C_3 to C_4 feed, 35 to 45% unsaturates, at 1090°F and 625–500 psig	36.1	3.4	31.3	29.2
3	From C_3 to C_4 feed, 35% unsaturates, at 1040°F and 1225 psig	40	5	17	38

From Maschwitz and Henderson, *Advances in Chem. Ser.*, no. 5, p. 83, 1951.

II-11. Alkylates.   As used by the petroleum industry, the term alkylation usually refers to the alkylation of normally gaseous paraffins with gaseous olefins to produce liquid branched paraffins.   Frey and Hepp[1] were the first to observe and study thermal alkylation reactions.   In their work the olefin was dispersed at low concentrations in the paraffin, the

[1] *Ind. Eng. Chem.*, **28**:1439 (1936).

temperature and pressure were raised to the desired values, and the mixture was circulated through the reaction tube. As the olefin was consumed, additional quantities were injected. This procedure kept the olefin concentration low in all parts of the system, thus minimizing polymerization and permitting the alkylation reaction to proceed. At 950°F and 4,500 psig with propane and ethylene, the alkylate was found to consist largely of isopentane (55.5 per cent) and *n*-pentane (16.4 per cent); under similar conditions, the chief product of the alkylation of isobutane with ethylene was 2,2-dimethylbutane (44.3 per cent).

TABLE II-28. COMPOSITION OF BUTENE-ISOBUTANE ALKYLATES

	Volume per cent	
	Sulfuric acid process	Hydrogen fluoride process
2,2- and 2,3-Dimethylbutane.........	7.0 ⎫	2.1
2- and 3-Methylpentane.............	2.4 ⎭	
2,2- and 2,4-Dimethylpentane..	4.7	2.6
2,3-Dimethylpentane........... ...	2.5 ⎫	1.9
2- and 3-Methylhexane.............	0.5 ⎭	
2,2,4-Trimethylpentane.............	26.8	41.7
2,5- and 2,4-Dimethylhexane.........	8.3	13.4
2,2,3-Trimethylpentane.............	1.6	2.9
2,3,4-Trimethylpentane.............	19.2	9.4
2,3,3-Trimethylpentane.............	14.9	10.0
2,3-Dimethylhexane................	2.3	6.2
2,2,5-Trimethylhexane.............	6.3	3.4
Higher-boiling isoparaffins..........	3.5	6.4

From Glasgow, Streiff, Willingham, and Rossini, *J. Research Natl. Bur. Standards*, **38**:537 (1947).

The first experiments dealing with the action of ethylene on paraffin hydrocarbons, with aluminum chloride as the catalyst, are stated to have been performed in 1932.[1] In 1935, the alkylation of paraffins with olefins, using boron fluoride as the catalyst, was reported[2] together with the analogous reaction of cycloparaffins with olefins.[3] Subsequently, many studies have been made of catalytic alkylation reactions. Sulfuric acid, liquid hydrogen fluoride, boron fluoride, aluminum chloride, aluminum bromide, and zirconium chloride are effective as catalysts. In contrast to the thermal method, catalytic alkylation takes

[1] Ipatieff, "Catalytic Reactions," The Macmillan Company, New York, 1936.
[2] Ipatieff and Grosse, *J. ACS*, **57**:1616 (1935).
[3] *J. ACS*, **57**:1722 (1935).

TABLE II-29. HYDROCARBONS ISOLATED FROM PONCA, OKLAHOMA, PETROLEUM*

Formula	Hydrocarbon	Boiling point, °C at 1 atm	Estimated amount in the crude oil, volume per cent
	Paraffins		
CH_4	Methane	−161.49	
C_2H_6	Ethane	− 88.63	
C_3H_8	Propane	− 42.07	
C_4H_{10}	Isobutane	− 11.73	
C_4H_{10}	n-Butane	− 0.50	
C_5H_{12}	2-Methylbutane	27.85	
C_5H_{12}	n-Pentane	36.07	
C_6H_{14}	2,2-Dimethylbutane	49.74	0.04
C_6H_{14}	2,3-Dimethylbutane	57.99	0.08
C_6H_{14}	2-Methylpentane	60.27	0.37
C_6H_{14}	3-Methylpentane	63.28	0.35
C_6H_{14}	n-Hexane	68.74	1.80
C_7H_{16}	2,2-Dimethylpentane	79.20	0.02
C_7H_{16}	2,4-Dimethylpentane	80.50	0.08
C_7H_{16}	2,3-Dimethylpentane	89.78	0.15
C_7H_{16}	2-Methylhexane	90.05	0.73
C_7H_{16}	3-Methylhexane	91.85	0.51
C_7H_{16}	3-Ethylpentane	93.48	0.06
C_7H_{16}	n-Heptane	98.43	2.3
C_8H_{18}	2,2-Dimethylhexane	106.84	0.01
C_8H_{18}	2,5-Dimethylhexane	109.10	0.06
C_8H_{18}	2,4-Dimethylhexane	109.43	0.06
C_8H_{18}	2,2,3-Trimethylpentane	109.84	0.004
C_8H_{18}	3,3-Dimethylhexane	111.97	0.03
C_8H_{18}	2,3,4-Trimethylpentane	113.47	0.005
C_8H_{18}	2,3,3-Trimethylpentane	114.76	0.006
C_8H_{18}	2,3-Dimethylhexane	115.61	0.07
C_8H_{18}	2-Methyl-3-ethylpentane	115.65	0.06
C_8H_{18}	2-Methylheptane	117.65	0.90
C_8H_{18}	4-Methylheptane	117.71	0.20
C_8H_{18}	3,4-Dimethylhexane	117.72	0.13
C_8H_{18}	3-Methyl-3-ethylpentane	118.26	0.02
C_8H_{18}	3-Ethylhexane	118.53	0.09
C_8H_{18}	3-Methylheptane	118.92	0.30
C_9H_{20}	2,2,5-Trimethylhexane	124.08	0.002
C_8H_{18}	n-Octane	125.66	1.9
C_9H_{20}	2,3,5-Trimethylhexane	131.34	0.03
C_9H_{20}	2,6-Dimethylheptane	135.21	0.05
C_9H_{20}	2,3-Dimethylheptane	140.5	0.05
C_9H_{20}	4-Methyloctane	142.48	0.1
C_9H_{20}	2-Methyloctane	143.26	0.4
C_9H_{20}	3-Methyloctane	144.18	0.1

TABLE II-29. HYDROCARBONS ISOLATED FROM PONCA, OKLAHOMA, PETROLEUM*
(*Continued*)

Formula	Hydrocarbon	Boiling point, °C at 1 atm	Estimated amount in the crude oil, volume per cent
	Paraffins (*Continued*)		
C_9H_{20}	*n*-Nonane	150.80	1.8
$C_{10}H_{22}$	4-Methylnonane	165.7	0.1
$C_{10}H_{22}$	2-Methylnonane	166.8	0.3
$C_{10}H_{22}$	3-Methylnonane	167.8	0.1
$C_{10}H_{22}$	*n*-Decane	174.12	1.8
$C_{11}H_{24}$	*n*-Undecane	195.89	1.6
$C_{12}H_{26}$	*n*-Dodecane	216.28	1.4
$C_{13}H_{28}$	*n*-Tridecane	235.43	1.2
$C_{14}H_{30}$	*n*-Tetradecane	253.52	1.0
$C_{15}H_{32}$	*n*-Pentadecane	270.61	0.8
$C_{16}H_{34}$	*n*-Hexadecane	286.79	0.7
$C_{17}H_{36}$	*n*-Heptadecane	301.82	0.6
$C_{18}H_{38}$	*n*-Octadecane	316.12	0.5
$C_{19}H_{40}$	*n*-Nonadecane	329.7	0.43
$C_{20}H_{42}$	*n*-Eicosane	342.7	0.37
$C_{21}H_{44}$	*n*-Heneicosane	355.1	0.32
$C_{22}H_{46}$	*n*-Docosane	367.0	0.28
$C_{23}H_{48}$	*n*-Tricosane	378.3	0.24
$C_{24}H_{50}$	*n*-Tetracosane	389.2	0.21
	Cyclopentanes and cyclohexanes		
C_5H_{10}	Cyclopentane	49.26	0.05
C_6H_{12}	Methylcyclopentane	71.81	0.87
C_6H_{12}	Cyclohexane	80.74	0.71
C_7H_{14}	1,1-Dimethylcyclopentane	87.85	0.16
C_7H_{14}	1-*cis*-3-Dimethylcyclopentane	90.77	0.87
C_7H_{14}	1-*trans*-3-Dimethylcyclopentane	91.72	0.21
C_7H_{14}	1-*trans*-2-Dimethylcyclopentane	91.87	0.48
C_7H_{14}	Methylcyclohexane	100.93	1.6
C_7H_{14}	Ethylcyclopentane	103.47	0.16
C_8H_{16}	1,1,3-Trimethylcyclopentane	104.89	0.30
C_8H_{16}	1-*trans*-2-*cis*-4-Trimethylcyclopentane	109.29	0.22
C_8H_{16}	1-*trans*-2-*cis*-3-Trimethylcyclopentane	110.2	0.26
C_8H_{16}	1,1,2-Trimethylcyclopentane	113.73	0.06
C_8H_{16}	1-*cis*-2-*trans*-4-Trimethylcyclopentane	116.73	0.01
C_8H_{16}	1-*cis*-2-*trans*-3-Trimethylcyclopentane	117.5	0.07
C_8H_{16}	1-*trans*-4-Dimethylcyclohexane	119.35	0.25
C_8H_{16}	1,1-Dimethylcyclohexane	119.54	0.06
C_8H_{16}	1-*cis*-3-Dimethylcyclohexane	120.09	0.63
C_8H_{16}	1-Methyl-*trans*-3-ethylcyclopentane	120.8⎫	0.12
C_8H_{16}	1-Methyl-*cis*-3-ethylcyclopentane	121.4⎭	
C_8H_{16}	1-Methyl-*trans*-2-ethylcyclopentane	121.2	0.14

TABLE II-29. HYDROCARBONS ISOLATED FROM PONCA, OKLAHOMA, PETROLEUM*
(*Continued*)

Formula	Hydrocarbon	Boiling point, °C at 1 atm	Estimated amount in the crude oil, volume per cent
	Cyclopentanes and cyclohexanes (*Continued*)		
C_8H_{16}	1-Methyl-1-ethylcyclopentane	121.52	0.03
C_9H_{18}	1,1-*cis*-3-*trans*-4-Tetramethylcyclopentane	121.6	0.04
C_8H_{16}	1-*trans*-2-Dimethylcyclohexane	123.42	0.31
C_8H_{16}	1-*cis*-4-Dimethylcyclohexane	124.32	0.09
C_8H_{16}	1-*trans*-3-Dimethylcyclohexane	124.45	0.07
C_8H_{16}	Isopropylcyclopentane	126.42	0.01
C_9H_{18}	1-*trans*-2-*cis*-3-*trans*-4-Tetramethylcyclopentane	127.4	0.11
C_8H_{16}	1-Methyl,*cis*-2-ethylcyclopentane	128.05	0.04
C_8H_{16}	1-*cis*-2-Dimethylcyclohexane	129.73	0.06
C_8H_{16}	*n*-Propylcyclopentane	130.95	0.06
C_8H_{16}	Ethylcyclohexane	131.78	0.37
C_9H_{18}	1,1,3-Trimethylcyclohexane	136.63	0.2
C_8H_{18}	1,*trans*-2,*trans*-4-Trimethylcyclohexane	141.2	0.2
C_9H_{18}	1,*trans*-2,*cis*-3-Trimethylcyclohexane	145.6	
	Cycloheptanes		
C_7H_{14}	Cycloheptane	118.79	0.01
	Dicycloparaffins		
C_8H_{14}	*cis*-Bicyclo-[3.3.0.]-octane	136.5	0.06
C_8H_{14}	Bicyclo-[3.2.1]-octane	138.0	0.008
C_9H_{16}	Bicycloparaffin	146.7	
$C_{10}H_{18}$	*trans*-Decahydronaphthalene	187.25	
$C_{11}H_{20}$	Bicycloparaffin	202.5	
	Benzenes		
C_6H_6	Benzene	80.10	0.15
C_7H_8	Toluene	110.62	0.51
C_8H_{10}	Ethylbenzene	136.19	0.19
C_8H_{10}	*p*-Xylene	138.35	0.10
C_8H_{10}	*m*-Xylene	139.10	0.51
C_8H_{10}	*o*-Xylene	144.41	0.27
C_9H_{12}	Isopropylbenzene	152.39	0.07
C_9H_{12}	*n*-Propylbenzene	159.22	0.09
C_9H_{12}	1-Methyl-3-ethylbenzene	161.30	0.17
C_9H_{12}	1-Methyl-4-ethylbenzene	161.99	0.06
C_9H_{12}	1,3,5-Trimethylbenzene	164.72	0.12
C_9H_{12}	1-Methyl-2-ethylbenzene	165.15	0.09
$C_{10}H_{14}$	*tert*-Butylbenzene	169.12	0.01
C_9H_{12}	1,2,4-Trimethylbenzene	169.35	0.51
$C_{10}H_{14}$	Isobutylbenzene	172.76	0.008
$C_{10}H_{14}$	*sec*-Butylbenzene	173.30	0.017
$C_{10}H_{14}$	1-Methyl-3-isopropylbenzene	175.14	0.08

TABLE II-29. HYDROCARBONS ISOLATED FROM PONCA, OKLAHOMA, PETROLEUM*
(*Continued*)

Formula	Hydrocarbon	Boiling point, °C at 1 atm	Estimated amount in the crude oil, volume per cent
	Benzenes (*Continued*)		
C_9H_{12}	1,2,3-Trimethylbenzene	176.08	0.19
$C_{10}H_{14}$	1-Methyl-4-isopropylbenzene	177.10	0.04
$C_{10}H_{14}$	1-Methyl-2-isopropylbenzene	178.15	0.009
$C_{10}H_{14}$	1,3-Diethylbenzene	181.10	
$C_{10}H_{14}$	1-Methyl-3-propylbenzene	181.80	
$C_{10}H_{14}$	n-Butylbenzene	183.27	
$C_{10}H_{14}$	1-Methyl-4-propylbenzene	183.30	
$C_{10}H_{14}$	1,3-Dimethyl-5-ethylbenzene	183.58	
$C_{10}H_{14}$	1,4-Diethylbenzene	183.78	
$C_{10}H_{14}$	1-Methyl-2-propylbenzene	184.80	
$C_{10}H_{14}$	1,4-Dimethyl-2-ethylbenzene	186.83	
$C_{10}H_{14}$	1,3-Dimethyl-4-ethylbenzene	188.20	
$C_{10}H_{14}$	1,2-Dimethyl-4-ethylbenzene	189.48	
$C_{10}H_{14}$	1,3-Dimethyl-2-ethylbenzene	190.01	
$C_{10}H_{14}$	1,2-Dimethyl-3-ethylbenzene	193.91	
$C_{10}H_{14}$	1,2,4,5-Tetramethylbenzene	196.80	
$C_{10}H_{14}$	1,2,3,5-Tetramethylbenzene	198.00	
$C_{11}H_{16}$	1-Methyl-3-n-butylbenzene†	204.1	0.06
$C_{10}H_{14}$	1,2,3,4-Tetramethylbenzene	205.04	0.2
$C_{11}H_{16}$	1,3-Dimethyl-4-n-propylbenzene†	206.6	0.03
$C_{11}H_{16}$	1,2-Dimethyl-4-n-propylbenzene†	208.5	0.03
$C_{11}H_{16}$	Trimethylethylbenzene†	212.3	0.04
	Aromatic cycloparaffins		
C_9H_{10}	Indan	177.8	0.003
$C_{10}H_{12}$	4-Methylindan	204.5	
$C_{10}H_{12}$	1,2,3,4-Tetrahydronaphthalene	207.57	0.03
$C_{11}H_{14}$	2-Methyl-[1,2,3,4-tetrahydronaphthalene]†	220.7	0.04
$C_{11}H_{14}$	6-Methyl-[1,2,3,4-tetrahydronaphthalene]	229.03	0.09
$C_{11}H_{14}$	5-Methyl-[1,2,3,4-tetrahydronaphthalene]	234.35	0.08
	Dinuclear aromatics		
$C_{10}H_8$	Naphthalene	217.96	0.06
$C_{11}H_{10}$	2-Methylnaphthalene	241.05	0.2
$C_{11}H_{10}$	1-Methylnaphthalene	244.64	0.1
$C_{12}H_{10}$	Biphenyl	255.2	
$C_{12}H_{12}$	2,6-Dimethylnaphthalene	262	
$C_{12}H_{12}$	Dimethylnaphthalene	268	
$C_{13}H_{13}$	Trimethylnaphthalene	288	
$C_{14}H_{16}$	Dinuclear aromatic	312	

* From Rossini and Mair, *ACS, Div. Petrol. Chem.*, ACS Meeting, New York, September, 1957.

† Tentative, identification not complete.

place under very mild conditions, with temperatures in the range from −20 to 200°F; pressure is needed only to keep the reactants in the liquid phase.

The heavy demand for aviation-fuel components with high octane ratings, occasioned by war conditions, resulted in the rapid commercialization of the catalytic alkylation reaction. In the commercial process isobutane is alkylated with olefin feed stock. These are usually butenes, but propene and pentenes are being used increasingly. The composition of the finished alkylate depends on the charge, on the catalyst employed, and on the operating conditions. Results of analyses of two butene-isobutane alkylates, one produced with sulfuric acid, the other with hydrogen fluoride, are shown in Table II-28. The sulfuric acid alkylate contains a higher proportion of the 2,3,4- and 2,3,3-trimethylpentanes, the hydrogen fluoride alkylate, more of the 2,2,4-trimethylpentane.

Operation under high capacity conditions is reported to produce more of the less desirable dimethylhexanes and a smaller proportion of the valuable trimethylpentanes.[1] Compared with a butene-isobutane alkylate, a propylene-isobutane alkylate contains more heptanes and a pentene-isobutane alkylate, more nonanes; both contain less of the highly desirable trimethylpentanes and have lower octane ratings. A pentene stock containing a high proportion of branched pentenes yields a better alkylate than one composed largely of normal constituents.

[1] Gould and Field, *Proc. API*, **26**(III):170 (1946).

CHAPTER III

Chemical Reactions and Group Reactions

Customary processing of petroleum does not involve the separation and handling of pure hydrocarbons. Petroleum-derived fuels and lubricants are always mixtures, sometimes simple, usually quite complex. The chemical properties of such products are those of mixtures, and treatment may bring about results not to be anticipated from the properties of the main constituents. The group properties and group reactions of these products may be quite important.

OXIDATION OF HYDROCARBONS

The satisfactory use of gasoline and diesel motor fuels, of kerosene for lighting or for operating gas turbines, and of oil fuels generally depends on rapid and complete oxidation to gaseous products in a combustion reaction. At somewhat lower temperatures, the direct partial oxidation of hydrocarbons is of commercial importance in the manufacture of chemicals. On the other hand, for some applications, oxidation reactions are undesirable, and considerable effort is made to retard them. The satisfactory continued use of ordinary lubricating oils and greases, and particularly of special lubricants such as steam turbine oils and transformer oils, largely depends on resistance to oxidation at more normal temperatures. The sludges building up to stiff emulsions in turbine systems are largely the results of hydrocarbon oxidation; so also are the development of gum in cracked gasolines and to some extent the formation of insoluble deposits in automotive engines.

While petroleum oils are commonly regarded as resistant to oxidation, they are quite easily attacked by oxygen and even by air. Peroxides will form, for example, in cracked gasoline during storage at ordinary temperatures.[1] Distillation of kerosene in a stream of air will produce a

---

[1] The work of many investigators has definitely established that peroxides are early oxidation products. George, Rideal, and Robertson, *Nature*, **149**:601 (1942). Balsbaugh and Oncley, *Ind. Eng. Chem.*, **31**:318 (1939). Dornte, *Ind. Eng. Chem.*, **28**:26 (1936). Denison, *Ind. Eng. Chem.*, **36**:477 (1944). Larsen, Thorpe, and Arnfield, *Ind. Eng. Chem.*, **34**:183 (1942). Farmer and Sutton, *J. Chem. Soc.*, p. 119, 1943.

measurable acidity[1] and unrefined naphthenic lubricating cuts will develop color and resin content during a few days of standing exposed to air and daylight. It is generally believed that hydrocarbon oxidations take place by a chain mechanism, involving hydroperoxide radicals, somewhat in the following manner:[2]

Initiation. This step is difficult to explain, but presumably free radical chains are established by individual "energy-rich" molecules,[3]

$$RH \rightarrow R \cdot + H$$

Propagation. The reaction is believed to continue by steps such as:

$$R \cdot + O_2 \rightarrow ROO \cdot$$
$$ROO \cdot + RH \rightarrow ROOH + R \cdot$$
$$ROOH \rightarrow RO \cdot + HO \cdot$$
$$RH + RO \cdot \rightarrow ROH + R \cdot$$
$$RH + HO \cdot \rightarrow H_2O + R \cdot$$

Thus the alkyl hydroperoxides formed break up in such a manner as to form additional radicals[4] and these in turn react with fresh hydrocarbon molecules to set up a multiplicity of reaction chains (chain branching), forming additional supplies of hydrocarbon radicals ($R \cdot$).

Termination. The various radicals taking part in the over-all oxidation are subject to destruction, and when their rate of breaking up exceeds that of formation, the reaction slows down. Destruction of radicals may take place by the following paths (often wall reactions):

$$
\left.
\begin{array}{l}
R \cdot + R \cdot \rightarrow \\
R \cdot + ROO \cdot \rightarrow \\
ROO \cdot + ROO \cdot \rightarrow
\end{array}
\right\} \text{stable end products}
$$

Some of the hydroperoxides appearing as first products in hydrocarbon oxidation have been isolated; familiar ones are those of cumene, tetralin, 2-methyl-1-butene, 1-hexene, cyclopentene, cyclohexene, and monomethyl- and 1,2-dimethylcyclohexene. Those of saturated hydro-

---

[1] Zaloziecki, *Z. angew. Chem.*, **9**:416 (1896).

[2] For a comprehensive review of oxidation, see Zuidema, *Chem. Revs.*, **38**:197 (1946). Bondi, "Physical Chemistry of Lubricating Oils," p. 270, Reinhold Publishing Corporation, New York, 1951. Vaughan and Rust in "The Chemistry of Petroleum Hydrocarbons," Brooks, Boord, Kurtz, and Schmerling (eds.), vol. II, p. 309, New York, 1951. Robertson in "The Chemistry of Petroleum Hydrocarbons," vol. II, p. 365.

[3] George and Robertson, *Proc. Royal Soc. (London)*, **185**:288 (1946).

[4] The importance of RO· radicals as intermediates in the conversion of hydroperoxides to various end products is discussed by Bell, Raley, Rust, Seubold, and Vaughan, Hydrocarbons, *Discussions Faraday Soc.*, no. 10, p. 242, 1951. Raley, Porter, Rust, and Vaughan, *J. ACS*, **73**:15 (1951).

carbons are less stable and have been recognized only as type products during analyses. The hydroperoxides formed break down on the application of heat through a free radical mechanism, or by an ionic process in presence of an acid; specific carbonyl and hydroxy compounds are formed in each case. The decomposition of t-alkyl hydroperoxides takes place through the scission of the O-O bond, followed by that of the weakest C-C bond. Secondary alkyl hydroperoxides form ketones, and primary alkyl hydroperoxides yield aldehydes. At high temperatures, the primary and secondary peroxides decompose in the vapor phase in an explosive manner, in which chain propagating radicals are formed.[1]

A possible reaction sequence in the thermally catalyzed oxidation of paraffins may be written as follows:[2]

$$\underset{\text{H}}{\overset{\text{H}}{CH_3(CH_2)_nCCH_3}} + O_2 \rightarrow \underset{\substack{\text{Hydro-} \\ \text{peroxide}}}{\overset{\text{OOH}}{CH_3(CH_2)_n\underset{\text{H}}{C}CH_3}} \rightarrow \underset{\text{Ketone}}{CH_3(CH_2)_nCOCH_3} + H_2O$$

$$\rightarrow \underset{\text{Alcohol}}{CH_3(CH_2)_nCHOHCH_3} + O$$

$$\underset{\text{Ketone}}{CH_3(CH_2)_nCOCH_3} + O_2 \rightarrow \underset{\text{Acid}}{CH_3(CH_2)_nCOOH} + \underset{\text{Aldehyde}}{HCHO}$$

$$CH_3(CH_2)_nCOOH + O_2 \rightarrow \underset{\text{H}}{\overset{\text{OOH}}{CH_3(CH_2)_{n-1}C\ COOH}}$$

$$\rightarrow \underset{\text{Hydroxy acid}}{CH_3(CH_2)_{n-1}CHOHCOOH} + O_2$$

$$\rightarrow \underset{\text{Keto acid}}{CH_3(CH_2)_{n-1}COCOOH} + H_2O$$

$$\rightarrow CH_3(CH_2)_{n-1}CHO + CO_2 + H_2O$$

$$\rightarrow \text{Higher aldehyde condensation products}$$

The ketones are formed directly from the hydroperoxides. Other secondary effects include the dehydration of a hydroxy acid to form an unsaturated acid or of an alcohol to give an unsaturated hydrocarbon. Where the oxygen attaches to the gamma carbon atom, the ketone has its carbonyl group shifted one carbon atom toward the center of the molecule; the resulting acids contain one less carbon atom, and acetaldehyde

[1] George, *Trans. Faraday Soc.*, **42**:210 (1946). Walsh, *Trans. Faraday Soc.*, **42**:269 (1946).

[2] George and Robertson, *J. Inst. Petrol.*, **32**:382, 400 (1946). George and Walsh, *Trans. Faraday Soc.*, **42**:94, 210, 217 (1946). Polly, *ACS, Div. Petrol. Chem., Gen. Papers*, Preprint, p. 217, Atlantic City, April, 1946. Bondi, "Physical Chemistry of Lubricating Oils," p. 270, Reinhold Publishing Corporation, New York, 1951.

is formed instead of formaldehyde. The two aldehydes would be oxidized to acetic and formic acids, respectively. As expected, alcohols and acids form esters. In addition, condensation-polymerization leads to the formation of molecules of high molecular weight and of resinous nature. The chemistry involved in the formation of these compounds is not clear. Partially oxidized hydrocarbons, containing hydroxyl, carbonyl, and carboxylic acid groups, both saturated and unsaturated, are available for interreactions. The final reaction products are obviously complex.

III-1. Paraffinic Hydrocarbons. There is substantial agreement among investigators that in low-temperature reactions involving a paraffin, oxygen attacks carbon atoms all along the chain.[1] The ease of oxidation increases with the length of the chain, especially in the range of C_1 to C_{10} saturated hydrocarbons. Tertiary carbons are more susceptible to attack than secondary, and these in turn are less resistant than primary carbons.[2] The ratios of activities of primary to secondary to tertiary carbons have been calculated as $1.0:3.6:6.9$, somewhat analogous to those for hydrocarbon response to chlorination and nitration.[3] The readiness and extent of the oxidation will depend upon the number and type of each carbon atom present and also on steric factors. Thus, n-hexane has been found to oxidize 1,600 times as readily as 2,3-dimethylbutane, even though the latter contains one-half as many tertiary as it does primary carbon atoms.[4] Likewise, hexaethylethane, containing no hydrogen attached to secondary or tertiary carbons, is less reactive than 2,2,4-trimethylpentane.[5] In most cases, a long-chain paraffinic molecule, containing a large number of secondary carbon atoms, suffers attack mainly at a β-carbon, one adjacent to a terminal methyl group; progressively less action takes place at the γ- and δ-carbons, and so on toward the center of the molecule.[6] Thus, all the methylene groups in n-decane suffer a probability of attack.[7] In highly branched structures,

---

[1] For example, Wietzel observed the formation of a mixture of fatty acids of various chain lengths on the oxidation of single long-chain paraffin hydrocarbons at 80 to 170°C [*Angew. Chem.*, **51**:531 (1938)]. See also, Cullis, Hardy, and Turner, *Proc. Royal Soc. (London)*, **244A**:573 (1958).

[2] Walsh, *Trans. Faraday Soc.*, **42**:269 (1946). Badin, *J. ACS*, **70**:3965 (1948).

[3] Boord, *Third Symposium on Combustion, Flame and Explosion Phenomena*, Madison, Wis., p. 416, 1949.

[4] Cullins and Hinshelwood, *Discussions Faraday Soc.*, no. 2, p. 117, 1947.

[5] Day and Pease, *J. ACS*, **63**:912 (1941).

[6] Stephens, *J. ACS*, **48**:2920 (1926). Chavanne and Bode, *J. ACS*, **52**:1609 (1930). Chavanne and Tock, *Bull. soc. chim. Belges*, **41**:630 (1932). Dupont and Chavanne, *Bull. soc. chim. Belges*, **42**:537 (1933). Burwell, "Science of Petroleum," vol. II, p. 1028, Oxford University Press, New York and London, 1938. Pritzkow, *Angew. Chem.*, **67**(14):15, 399 (1955).

[7] Benton and Wirth, *Nature*, **171**:269 (1953).

such as 2,2-dimethylbutane and 2,2,3-trimethylpentane, some of the oxidation products can be explained only by assuming an initial attack on hydrogens attached to primary carbons.[1]

In the presence of hydrogen bromide, paraffin molecules containing a tertiary carbon atom react with oxygen to give alkyl hydroperoxides and dialkyl peroxides in good yield.[2]

Hinshelwood[3] has summarized the effects of substitution in paraffinic hydrocarbons on the rate of oxidation, as follows:

1. The rate is decreased by the introduction of side methyl groups. The initial attack by oxygen, leading to the peroxide most capable of chain branching, is made on a CH_2 group as remote as possible from the added methyl unit.

2. If there is no place for attack except at a methyl group, as in ethane, acetone, or methyl ether, the rate is much slower than that of the corresponding hydrocarbon containing a CH_2 group.

3. Substitution of chlorine or amino groups increases the rate of oxidation.

4. Carbonyl groups tend, subject to reservations, to increase oxidizability. While acetone oxidizes more slowly than propane (but faster than ethane), 3-pentanone oxidizes several times faster than pentane.

5. Ethers oxidize more readily than hydrocarbons of the same chain length, ethyl ether reacting 2,500 times as rapidly as pentane.

6. The effect of added chlorine, carbonyl, or amino groups increases with chain length of the parent hydrocarbon, but with ethers the increase from ethyl ether to higher homologs is small.

Again, it should be stressed that hydrocarbon oxidation is a complex phenomenon. The kinetics and even the actual course of the oxidation may be influenced by small changes in the degree of purity of the hydrocarbon, oxygen-hydrocarbon ratio, oxygen pressure, and temperature and such factors as phase condition, retention or removal of oxidation products, surface area, material of the reaction vessel, presence of catalysts, etc.

III-2. Naphthenic Hydrocarbons. The substituted naphthenic hydrocarbons, containing a tertiary carbon in the ring, are quite susceptible to low-temperature (100 to 175°C) oxidation, generally undergoing ring rupture. The thermal dimer of isobutylene, 1,1,3-trimethylcyclopentane, readily takes up oxygen at 100°C under pressure to form a liquid gum. A similar response was reported earlier for 1,2-dimethylcyclo-

[1] Rust and Collamar, *J. ACS*, **76**:1055 (1954).

[2] Raley, Rust, Vaughan, Nawrocki, Bell, and Dickey, *Ind. Eng. Chem.*, **41**:2597, 2604 (1949).

[3] Hydrocarbons, *Discussions Faraday Soc.*, no. 10, 266, 1951.

pentane and 1,2-dimethylcyclohexane.[1] The importance of reactions of this type in the formation of gums in gasoline and in fuel oils has not been established. At 100°C, 1,4-dimethylcyclohexane gives 1,4-dimethylcyclohexanol and ring-scission products such as β-methyl-γ-acetylvaleric acid, β-methylvaleric acid, acetic acid, dimethylhexanediol, and acetonylacetone.[2] Likewise ethyl-, butyl-, and phenylcyclopentanes give ethyl n-butyl ketone, a C_9 ketone, and phenyl n-butyl ketone, respectively; the ethyl- and butylcyclopentanes give ketoheptanoic and ketononanoic acids, while phenylcyclopentane yields phenylbutyric acid.[3]

III-3. Aromatic Hydrocarbons. The benzene ring itself is not susceptible to low-temperature oxidation, but its substitution into a paraffinic chain increases the response of the latter. Ethyl and n-propyl benzenes give acetophenone and propiophenone, respectively, with the point of attack at the carbon atom alpha to the ring.[4] Cymene and cumene, each containing an aliphatic tertiary carbon atom, oxidize in a like manner giving acetophenone and p-tolyl methyl ketone, respectively; t-butylbenzene is not oxidized at low temperatures.

III-4. Olefinic Hydrocarbons. In general, olefinic hydrocarbons oxidize more readily than the corresponding paraffins. Epoxides are formed by reaction with ozone, hydrogen peroxide, and per acids;[5] these products, however, are not common in the normal deterioration of unsaturated petroleum hydrocarbons or hydrocarbon mixtures. With oxygen, the attack is generally at a carbon atom adjacent to the double bond; the primary product is an unsaturated hydroperoxide. Conjugated diolefins yield polymeric dialkyl peroxides, a reaction which undoubtedly is of importance in gasoline gum formation.

GUM AND INSOLUBLE PRODUCTS IN LIQUID FUELS

When untreated cracked gasoline distillates, particularly of the older, thermal type are stored for long periods, especially in contact with air

---

[1] Chavanne, *API Bull.*, **10**(55):3 (1929); *Bull. soc. chim. Belges*, **36**:206 (1927). Chavanne and Bode, *J. ACS*, **52**:1609 (1930). Chavanne, Katsenstein, and Pahlavouni, *Bull. soc. chim. Belges*, **41**:209 (1932).

[2] Chavanne and Bode, *loc. cit.*

[3] Dupont and Chavanne, *Bull. soc. chim. Belges*, **42**:537 (1933).

[4] Stephens, *J. ACS*, **48**:2920 (1926). Stephens and Roduta, *J. ACS*, **57**:2380 (1935).

[5] For a review of the action of per acids on olefins, see Swern, *Chem. Revs.*, **45**:1 (1949). For hydroperoxides of olefins, see Tobolsky and Mesrobian, "Organic Peroxides," p. 4, Interscience Publishers, Inc., New York, 1954. Farmer, *Trans. Faraday Soc.*, **42**:228 (1946). Bolland and Gee, *Trans. Faraday Soc.*, **42**:244 (1946). Bolland, *Quart. Rev.*, **3**:1 (1949).

and metals, a slow oxidation takes place. In many cases, separation occurs, with the appearance of a phase which varies from an almost colorless mobile liquid to a brownish semifluid gum; this separation is favored by exposure to light. Even straight-run (uncracked) distillates will, when stored for several months in partially filled bottles exposed to daylight, become discolored and will form a thin deposit on the walls below the liquid level. This probably results from oxidation of substituted naphthenes in the mixture. The use in engines of gasoline containing an appreciable content of gum often results in the deposition of hard, dry resin on intake system surfaces, including valve stems and carburetor. The light-colored or fluid gums are easily converted to dark, hard resins on heating; it is thus possible that the deposits are converted to their harmful form by the temperature of the surfaces on which they are laid down. It is also true that cracked gasolines suffer a depreciation of octane number at the same time they are developing a gum content; this is probably related to the appearance of proknock peroxides during the oxidation.

The empirical compositions of a liquid gum, obtained by free air oxidation of a thermally cracked distillate stored in glass and exposed to sunlight, the hardened product collected on drying this liquid, and the characteristic dark resin produced on evaporation of the original distillate in a polished copper dish are shown in Table III-1. The analyses indicate the gums to be high in oxygen content; double bonds are not abundant. Acidity is high, but the saponifiable matter is

TABLE III-1

	Liquid gum	Dried liquid gum	Copper-dish gum
Carbon, per cent..............	64.97	71.95	70.73
Hydrogen, per cent............	8.56	7.99	6.95
Oxygen, per cent..............	26.08	19.48	19.51
Nitrogen, per cent.............	......	......	0.13
Sulfur, per cent...............	0.22	0.33	0.68
Ash, per cent.................	0.17	0.25	2.00*
Iodine number (Hanus).........	47	95	73
Saponification number..........	289	144	191
Neutralization number.........	625	651	732
Molecular weight..............	172	338	200
Melting point, °C.............	......	68–71	98–105
Consistency...................	Dark-brown viscous liquid, sp gr 1.0932	Brown resinous solid	Dark-brown resinous solid

* Mostly dust.
From Story, Provine, and Bennett, *Ind. Eng. Chem.*, **21**:1079 (1929).

relatively low. The molecular weights are only moderate, and this is consistent with the low melting points of the resinous material. The copper-dish gum was more than half water-insoluble acids and about one-third water-soluble acids; it contained only 13 per cent of unsaponifiable compounds, presumably mostly aldehydes and ketones. The liquid gum was similarly constituted. The oxidized gasoline, from which the gum had separated, showed the presence of acetic and acrylic acids, and higher unsaturated acids were indicated.

The over-all composition of gasoline gum is not unlike that of varnish found on pistons of engines operating under low-temperature, low-load conditions, and formed most readily from rather high-boiling cracked distillates.

	Liquid gum	Acetone-soluble varnish
Carbon, per cent..........	64.97	63.08
Hydrogen...............	8.56	5.65
Oxygen.................	26.08	26.06
Nitrogen...............	.....	3.16
Sulfur.................	0.22	1.34
Ash....................	0.17	0.71

Recent work on varnishes, however,[1] has recognized that oxides of nitrogen produced in the combustion, rather than oxygen alone, are involved in the varnish formation. This is evidenced by the high nitrogen content of the acetone-soluble varnish in the above analysis.

Considerable light has been thrown on the general composition of gasoline gum by studying the hydrocarbons obtained on reduction with lithium aluminum hydride, followed by dehydration of the alcohols produced.[2] As a result of analyzing the products by use of infrared, ultraviolet, and mass spectroscopy, nuclear magnetic resonance and gas-liquid chromatography, the predominance of aromatic structures is noteworthy. The following chemical types were recognized: alkyl benzenes, indanes, indenes, styrenes, naphthalenes, dihydronaphthalenes, acenaphthenes, olefins, diolefins, triolefins, cyclic mono- and diolefins, paraffins, and cycloparaffins. Among other items noted, the preformed gum in a cracked gasoline has about the same composition and compound distribution as the additional gum formed on oxygen-blowing the gasoline

[1] Spindt, Wolfe, and Stevens, *Quart. Trans. SAE*, **64**:797 (1956).

[2] Bassler and Smith, "Gum and Haze Formation in Motor Gasolines," Tech. Repts. 2–13, SRI Project No. S.U. 1243, Stanford Research Institute, Palo Alto, Calif., 1955–1959.

at 50°C for 36 hr.   The pentane-soluble portion of the gum has a molecular weight of about 200, while that of the pentane-insoluble gum ranges from about 200 to 500.

CHEMISTRY OF GUM FORMATION

In thermally cracked gasolines, gum content is higher and more troublesome as cracking temperature is increased and cracking becomes more drastic.   Catalytically cracked products are more resistant to gum formation, but usually require (particularly high-boiling cuts) a light alkali washing to remove thiophenols, which seem to accelerate the oxidation.

There are many facts which point to peroxide formation as the first step in the gum-forming oxidation sequence.   Peroxides can be recognized in a thermally cracked gasoline stock soon after it has been exposed to sunlight and air.   Peroxides and aldehydes presumably derived from them are observed during the evaporation of a cracked distillate; acidity develops and increases rapidly[1] during the last stages.   It is suspected that unsaturated aldehydes and acids resulting from peroxide decomposition are intermediate to gum formation.   The alkali solubility of typical gum is appreciable and increases with age; moreover, the removal of peroxides greatly reduces the gum left on evaporation in an oxygen-free atmosphere.   In addition, the gum-forming reaction is autocatalytic; an induction period occurs and it can be shortened by addition of peroxides or removal of natural inhibitors.[2]   Susceptible olefins and diolefins probably react with oxygen to form hydroperoxides,

$$RCH_2CH\!\!=\!\!CHCHR' \rightarrow \underset{\underset{OOH}{|}}{R}CHCH\!\!=\!\!CHR'$$

reaction occurring at a carbon atom adjacent to the olefinic group.   The peroxides are believed to decompose into aldehydes, ketones, and acids of unsaturated character, but the chemistry has not been cleared up satisfactorily.[3]   The importance of diolefins in gum formation has long been suspected.[4]   Conjugated aliphatic and cyclic diolefins and mono- and diolefins attached to aromatic rings are probably the most active.[5]   The

[1] Story, Provine, and Bennett, *Ind. Eng. Chem.*, **21**:1079 (1929).

[2] Yule and Wilson, *Ind. Eng. Chem.*, **23**:1254 (1931).

[3] See Brooks, *Ind. Eng. Chem.*, **18**:1198 (1926).   Vellinger and Radulesco, *World Petrol. Congr., Proc. 1st Congr., London*, **II**:103 (1933).   Walters, Minor, and Yabroff, *Ind. Eng. Chem.*, **41**:1723 (1949).   On the role of polymerization, see Schultze, *Oel u. Kohle ver. Erdoel u. Teer*, **14**:113 (1938).

[4] Brooks and Humphrey, *J. ACS*, **40**:822 (1915).   See Kawahara, *J. ACS*, **79**:1447 (1957), for a study of the autoxidation products of 2,3-dimethyl-1,3-butadiene.

[5] Flood, Hladky, and Edgar, *Ind. Eng. Chem.*, **25**:1234 (1933).   Berger and Bost, *Oil Gas J.*, **38**(46):81 (1940).

nonconjugated diolefins are relatively stable.[1] Simple olefins, however, are drawn into gum-forming reactions, the extent depending on their structure, by the fact that in mixtures, the oxidation of one responsive component often affects that of a second, which by itself would not be attacked appreciably under the conditions of the autoxidation.[2] Thus the amounts of gum formed from a cracked distillate may be considerably larger than can be accounted for by its diolefinic content. Several saturated cyclic hydrocarbons, such as 1,2-dimethylcyclopentane and 1,2-dimethylcyclohexane, are attacked slowly by gaseous oxygen.[3] A substantial amount of liquid gum readily forms and separates out when 1,1,3-trimethylcyclopentane (the thermal dimer of isobutylene) is heated with oxygen at 100°C and under 125 psi pressure.

That gum is caused by the oxidation of only certain types of hydrocarbons is further illustrated by a study of the oxidation of highly cracked gasolines at temperatures corresponding to those of storage.[4] Individual 10°F fractions of a "vapor-phase" cracked distillate were oxidized at 25 and 38°C, under an oxygen pressure of 20 lb, for one and two weeks, respectively, and the gum formed was determined by evaporation in a steam bath. By plotting the gum found in each oxidized fraction against the boiling point, a curve showing three peaks of high gum content was obtained, each corresponding roughly to the boiling point of a group of conjugated diolefins and cyclic olefins. Typical of each group would be 2,4-cyclohexadiene, boiling point 78.5°C, 1-methyl-1,3-cyclohexadiene, boiling point 110°C, and 1,3-dimethyl-1,5-cyclohexadiene, boiling point 130°C. Furthermore, different cracked gasolines showed the same peaks at the same places on the gum curves, the differences being only in the amount of gum formed, which increased with the temperature of the initial cracking. It was also noted that a cracked gasoline treated with maleic anhydride or sulfuric acid, to remove diolefins, might be made stable to oxidation at 38°C but that gum formation would proceed again at 50°C. It would seem from this that diolefins are the initiators of the gum-forming oxidation at ordinary temperatures; when these are removed and the temperature raised, another set of olefins, say the cyclic mono-olefins,[5] are attacked under the slightly more severe conditions, and gum formation is renewed.

[1] Kogerman, *Trans. World Power Conf., 2nd Conf. Berlin*, **8**:33 (1930).

[2] Engler and Weissberg, *Ber.*, **33**:1090 (1900).

[3] Chavanne, *API Bull.* **10**(55):3 (1929); *Bull. soc. chim. Belges*, **36**:206 (1927). Chavanne and Bode, *J. ACS*, **52**:1609 (1930). Chavanne, Katsenstein, and Pahlavouni, *Bull. soc. chim. Belges*, **41**:209, 630 (1932).

[4] Martin, Gruse, and Lowy, *Ind. Eng. Chem.*, **25**:381 (1933).

[5] The autoxidation of cyclohexene to give liquid and resinous peroxides and peroxides of polymers has been described by Stephens, *J. ACS*, **50**:568 (1928); *Ber.*, **64**:637 (1931); and by Zelinsky and Borrisov, *J. ACS*, **63**:2362 (1930).

III-5. Gum Content; Gum Tolerance. Gum may be classed as existing or preformed, and potential.[1] The former is that present in a gasoline at the moment and the latter is what may form during storage under oxidizing conditions. The gum existing at the time of use may cause induction system deposits in an engine. The potential gum is intimately related to the oxygen stability time, the length of the induction period before active oxidation sets in. This gives an indication of the storage stability of the fuel, while the insolubles present after the oxidation suggest the gum content after some selected period of oxidation. The gum content and oxygen stability time of a gasoline may be determined by several related tests. The deposit left by a 50-ml sample of the fuel when evaporated in an air stream preheated to 160 to 165°C is defined as the existent gum.[2] Oxygen stability is measured by exposing a sample to 100 lb oxygen pressure (measured cold) at boiling-water temperature and noting the time elapsed before rapid oxidation begins.[3] This period has sometimes been specified as at least 240 min. The amount of gum left on evaporation by the air-jet method after the sample has been oxidized in the oxygen stability apparatus for a given period (say 4 hr) can be defined as the potential gum.[4] The copper-dish test, evaporation of 100 ml of fuel from a hemispherical polished copper dish set on a steam bath, has been widely used, but is not standardized by official agencies.[5] A low result, say below 30 mg, is a good indication of a stable gasoline, but higher figures lose any direct relation to stability or quality.

The amount of gum which can be tolerated in a gasoline varies with the engines in which it is to be used. The specification of 5 mg per 100 ml of existent gum is not unreasonable for modern high-compression engines with complicated carburetors. Early results with fuels of varying gum contents in laboratory engines over a range of intake temperatures are shown in Fig. III-1.[6] At low temperatures, no gum deposits were obtained with any of the fuels; but, as the temperature rose, the deposits increased, except for the 3-mg fuel, which left a clean engine under all conditions. Changes in the air-fuel ratio made no difference at low temperatures; but, at the higher temperatures employed, the richer mixtures left more gum. Also, at higher temperatures, when the gum dropped out in the intake system, there was no change in carbon deposition in the combustion chamber; but at low intake temperatures, some of the gum was carried into the engine and increased the deposits there.

[1] Voorhees and Eisinger, *J. SAE*, **24**:584 (1929).

[2] ASTM D 381–54T.

[3] ASTM D 525–49.

[4] ASTM D 873–497.

[5] For an over-all review of methods, see Gruse, "Science of Petroleum," vol. II, p. 1016, Oxford University Press, New York and London, 1938.

[6] Marley and Gruse, *Ind. Eng. Chem.*, **24**:1298 (1932).

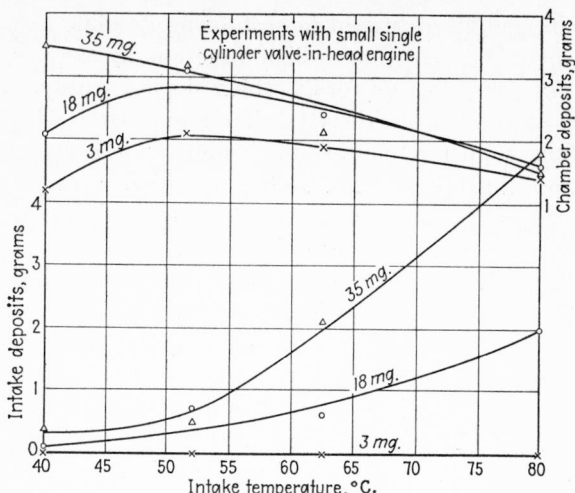

FIG. III-1. Influence of preformed gum content on engine deposits.

III-6. Oxidation Inhibitors. Unless desulfurization is necessary, cracked distillates are no longer treated chemically, except for sweetening (see Chap. VII). Instead, they are stabilized against gum formation by the addition of suitable inhibitors to control the autoxidation reaction. The antioxidants employed are generally alkylated phenols, substituted aminophenols, or substituted aromatic diamines. Useful representatives of these groups are 2,6-di-*t*-butyl-4-methylphenol, *N-n*-butyl-*p*-aminophenol, and *N-N'*-di-*sec*-butyl-*p*-phenylenediamine, respectively. Of these, the latter two are more efficient on a molar basis but suffer to some extent from lack of hydrocarbon solubility. It has also been reported that in some cases the amine-type inhibitors do not entirely prevent intake manifold deposits or separation of insoluble sludges in the crankcase.

The effectiveness of the usual inhibitors varies not only with their structure and composition[1] but also with the chemical nature of the material being protected. An attempt has been made to correlate effectiveness of antioxidants with oxidation-reduction potentials,[2] but it has not been very successful.

---

[1] Egloff, Morrell, Lowry, and Dryer, *Ind. Eng. Chem.*, **24**:1375 (1932). Morawetz, *Ind. Eng. Chem.*, **41**:1442 (1949). Pedersen, *Ind. Eng. Chem.*, **41**:924 (1949). Rosenwald, Hoatson, and Chenicek, *Ind. Eng. Chem.*, **42**:162 (1950). For the relation between inhibitor concentration and induction period, see Rosenwald and Hoatson, *Ind. Eng. Chem.*, **41**:914 (1949).

[2] Fieser, *J. ACS*, **52**:5204 (1930). Lowry, Egloff, Morrell, and Dryer, *Ind. Eng. Chem.*, **25**:805 (1933); **27**:15 (1935). Bolland and ten Have, *Trans. Faraday Soc.*, **43**:201 (1947); *Discussions, Faraday Soc.*, no. 2, p. 252, 1947. Pedersen, *Ind. Eng. Chem.*, **41**:924 (1949).

Other inhibitor additives useful in stabilizing gasoline against oxidation are the metal deactivators[1] which function by converting traces of metal present into inactive forms which do not catalyze oxidation. An example is N,N'-disalicylidene-1,2-diaminopropane, which chelates with any soluble copper remaining in gasoline from copper sweetening and thus renders it inactive.[2] The ability of inhibitors to prevent darkening in color of gasolines is closely related to the retardation of oxidation. Tributyl- and triamylamines are especially effective.[3]

III-7. Stability of Fuel Oils. Increasing use of catalytically cracked distillates in diesel fuels and particularly in domestic furnace oils has brought into notice the stability of these products. Both discoloration and precipitation of unsoluble resins occur[4] and the ordinary practice of mixing the cracked oils with straight-run distillates seems to make the trouble even worse.[5] The insoluble products are objectionable because they clog burner nozzles, screens, and any small orifices. The trouble has been attributed to oxidation of pyrroles and aromatic thiols in the cracked distillates,[6] but these seem to account for only part of the precipitates formed.[7] Antioxidants alone are not capable of remedying

---

[1] Downing, Clarkson, and Pedersen, *Oil Gas J.*, **38**(11):97 (1939).

[2] Pedersen, *Ind. Eng. Chem.*, **41**:924 (1949). Watson and Tom, *Ind. Eng. Chem.*, **41**:918 (1949).

[3] Sorg, *Ind. Eng. Chem.*, **27**:156 (1935). The development of haze in gasoline (a precipitation of fine filterable solids) is another phenomenon caused by oxidation. Morrell, Benedict, Egloff, and Wirth [*Ind. Eng. Chem.*, **27**:323 (1935); **28**:122, 448 (1936)] found the reaction to be photochemically induced and dependent upon the presence of elementary sulfur or alkyl disulfides. See also, Bassler and Smith, *loc. cit.* On the use of lecithin to retard haze formation, see Rees, Quimby, and Osterhout, *Refiner Nat. Gasoline Mfr.*, **19**:414 (1940).

[4] Martin and Bailey, *J. Inst. Petrol.*, **40**:138, 176 (1954).

[5] Thompson, Druge, and Chenicek, *Ind. Eng. Chem.*, **41**:2715 (1949); with Symon, *Ind. Eng. Chem.*, **43**:935 (1951). Batchelder and Wellman, *Refiner Nat. Gasoline Mfr.*, **17**(6):280 (1938). Separation of insolubles, measured by light scattering, has been employed as a test for stability. Johnson, Chiantella, and Carhart, *Ind. Eng. Chem.*, **47**:1226 (1955).

[6] Mapstone, *Petrol. Refiner*, **28**(10):111 (1949). Offenhauer, Brennan, and Miller, *ACS, Div. Petrol. Chem., Gen. Papers*, Preprints, p. 249, Atlantic City, September, 1956. Williams and Offenhauer, *ACS, Div. Petrol. Chem., Gen. Papers*, Preprints, p. 255, Atlantic City, September, 1956. Gel formation, sometimes taking place during fuel oil storage, has been attributed to reaction between mercaptans in the oil and copper parts of valves, etc., in the storage system. Kirshmer, Osterhout, and Schwindeman, *Oil Gas J.*, **54**(40):125 (1956).

[7] Ball, Whisman, and Wenger, *Ind. Eng. Chem.*, **43**:2577 (1951). Richter, Caeser, Meisel, and Offenhauer, *Ind. Eng. Chem.*, **44**:2601 (1952). Sauer, Malpolder, and Brown, *Ind. Eng. Chem.*, **44**:2606 (1952). Thompson, Symon, and Wankat, *Anal. Chem.*, **24**:1465 (1952). Ward, Moore, and Ball, *Anal. Chem.*, **25**:1070 (1953). Pozefsky and Kukin, *Anal. Chem.*, **27**:1466 (1955). Sauer, Weed, and Headington, *ACS, Div. Petrol. Chem., Gen. Papers*, Preprints, p. 95, Chicago, September, 1958.

this trouble. Some success has been achieved by use of dispersant type additives, alone or with antioxidants.

OXIDATION OF LUBRICATING OILS[1]

Oil deterioration in service, when not due to contamination, is presumably a result of intermediate-temperature oxidation. Oxidative changes, depending on the chemical composition and the degree and type of refining of the oils, may be observed at ordinary temperatures on long exposure to the atmosphere, and may become quite pronounced at 125 to 175°C. They are especially apparent in the presence of metal-containing contaminants, in which case both the rate and the course of the oxidation may be affected. Some of the identifying symptoms are lowering of the dielectric constant, increase of acidity, and sludge separation for insulating oils; development of acidity and appearance of emulsions in steam turbine oils; and engine varnish and crankcase sludge with automotive lubricating oils. These changes are observed by laboratory tests carried on at elevated temperatures and directed at the following:

1. Measuring oxygen absorption directly or by pressure drop.[2]
2. Determining changes in physical and chemical properties of the oil.[3]
3. Studying oxidation products.[4] It is obvious that combinations of these approaches will have many advantages. The oxidation of paraffinic lubricating oils in the ordinary service range—up to 150 or 200°C—is probably at first a chain reaction[5] and passes through three stages: an induction period, an autocatalytic phase, and an autoretardation. The curve of oxygen consumed against time is usually S-shaped, the

[1] For general reviews, see Zuidema, *Chem. Revs.*, **38**:197 (1946). Bondi, "Physical Chemistry of Lubricating Oils," p. 270, Reinhold Publishing Corporation, New York, 1951.

[2] This is useful chiefly in research. Dornte, *Ind. Eng. Chem.*, **28**:26, 863, 1342 (1936). von Fuchs and Diamond, *Ind. Eng. Chem.*, **34**:927 (1942). Davis, Lincoln, Byrkit, and Jones, *Ind. Eng. Chem.*, **33**:339 (1941). Fenske and others, *Ind. Eng. Chem.*, **33**:516 (1941). Larsen, Thorpe, and Arnfield, *Ind. Eng. Chem.*, **34**:183 (1942); **35**:581 (1943). Hicks-Bruun, *Ind. Eng. Chem.*, **36**:562 (1944). Denison, *Ind. Eng. Chem.*, **36**:477 (1944); **41**:934 (1949). George and Robertson, *Trans. Faraday Soc.*, **42**:217 (1946). *J. Inst. Petrol.*, **32**:382 (1946). Balsbaugh, Oncley, and Assaf, *Ind. Eng. Chem.*, **31**:318 (1939); **32**:1497 (1940); **33**:1321 (1941); **34**:92 (1942).

[3] Widely employed for commercial acceptance. Michie Test, *Proc. ASTM*, **28**(I):575 (1928). Sligh oxidation test, *Proc. ASTM*, **24**(II):964 (1924). Indiana Test, Rogers and Shoemaker, *Ind. Eng. Chem., Anal. Ed.*, **6**:419 (1934). Underwood Test, *J. SAE*, **43**:385T (1938).

[4] Michie, *J. Inst. Elec. Eng.*, **51**:213 (1913). Sligh, *Proc. ASTM*, **27**:461 (1927). Barnard, *J. SAE*, **35**:167, 181T (1934). Kroger and Kaller, *Oel u. Kohle*, **19**:669 (1943). Kapff, Bowman, and Lowy, *J. Inst. Petrol.*, **31**:453 (1945). Denison, *Ind. Eng. Chem.*, **36**:477 (1944).

[5] George and Robertson, *loc. cit.*

curvature depending on the oil, any catalyst present, and the temperature conditions. The S shape is most pronounced with paraffinic oils; these yield relatively more acids and less insolubles. With more naphthenic oils the induction period is less pronounced and the oxidation-time curve becomes concave downward over the remainder of its length; there is also a greater production of semisoluble or dispersed resins, which confer increased viscosity, and of insoluble asphaltene-like products.

During the induction period little oxygen is consumed and it is probable that the accumulation of hydroperoxides is limited at this time. Later, when conditions become more favorable, these propagate the reaction at a faster rate and the autocatalytic period sets in. As a result of chain growth, oxygen absorption becomes more rapid and this continues until chain termination allows the over-all rate to slacken off and autoretardation begins. This slowing down of the reaction rate may be a result of the consumption of the more easily oxidized molecules in the oil or it may be caused by autogenous inhibitors formed during the oxidation.[1]

The over-all reaction is very complex. As indicated earlier in this chapter, the primary oxidation products break down into many secondary ones, and some of these are probably more subject to oxidation than the parent hydrocarbons.

As might be expected, the oxidation is quite temperature-sensitive; the amount of oxygen absorbed more or less doubles for every 10°C rise. Table III-2 gives the results of oxidation of an acid-treated naphthenic oil over a 24-hr period at 160 to 180°C; oxygen was circulated through a 40-g sample of oil at atmospheric pressure.

A comparison of the products resulting from the noncatalytic oxidation of several types of hydrocarbon in a circulating-oxygen system at 110°C is given in Table III-3; values are expressed as percentage of total oxygen consumed. The paraffins and naphthenes yield the most acids, carbonyl compounds, and carbon dioxide; the paraffins yield the most water; naphthenes yield the most peroxides. Except for peroxides (bearing corrosion[2]), no relation seems to have been established between any of these products and engine performance.

The increase of viscosity by oxidation is caused by development of resins; their oxygen content increases as oxidation progresses.[3] A treat-

---

[1] Unless provision is made for the removal of carbon monoxide and hydrogen (generally by copper oxide), as well as carbon dioxide and water from the product gases, the dilution of the oxygen may be sufficient after extended oxidation to cause a decrease in reaction rate sufficiently great to be mistaken for autoretardation. Other gases formed in the oxidation include methane, ethane, ethylene, and propane.

[2] Denison, *Ind. Eng. Chem.*, **36**:477 (1944).

[3] Hans, *Oel u. Kohle*, **14**:299, 321 (1938).

TABLE III-2

	Original oil	160°C	165°C	170°C	175°C	180°C
Oxygen consumed, g.	....	0.2837	0.3661	0.4507	0.7648	1.2017
Volatile acids, milliequiv	....	0.457	0.275	0.470	....	2.410
Oxidized oil:						
Viscosity (SUS):						
100°F	774	1090	1107	1221	1704	2213
210°F	63.4	72.3	73.4	77.0	89.5	100.0
Viscosity index	33	30	33	35	35	29
Neutralization number	0.01	0.38	1.19	1.55	3.21	4.1
Saponification number	0.6	4.4	8.1	17.5	21.1	34.7
Pentane insoluble	0.01	0.48	0.60	1.07	2.24	4.01
Sp gr 60°/60°F	0.9291	0.9291	0.9291	0.9309	0.9346	0.9415

TABLE III-3

Hydrocarbon	Neutralization No.	Saponification No.	Peroxide	Alcohol	Carbonyl	Water	CO₂	Volatile acids
n-Decane	12.5	17.4	10.3	0	46	27.0	5.8	
Cetane	27.0	22.0	1.6	3.0	....	56.0	3.5	
Hydropolyisobutylene (C₅₀)	3.3	9.7	0.3	2.7	....	48.7	4.7	6.0
Polyisobutylene (C₅₀)	4.1	18.7	0.7	7.9	....	41.0	7.6	0.8
Decalin	12.8	11.4	14.9	8.9	....	13.3		
Octadecylcyclohexane	14.9	16.0	4.2	1.4	47.2	28.2	2.2	0.7
Perhydroanthracene	4.5	13.5	19.8	22.6	62.0	10.2	0.7	
Tetralin	7.9	21.5	5.6	3.0	....	7.8	2.8	
Octadecyltetralin	4.1	14.9	7.1	7.5	33.7	5.8	0.4	
Octahydroanthracene	2.9	14.4	4.5	19.4	30.6	5.1	0.3	0.1
Average paraffinic	14.3	16.3	4.1	1.9	46.0	43.9	4.7	
Average naphthenic	11.2	17.0	13.5	8.9	51.4	21.9	3.8*	0.6
Average aromatic-naphthenic	6.1	23.1	4.3	8.5	27.2	16.7	1.2	0.4

From Larsen, Thorpe, and Arnfield, *Ind. Eng. Chem.*, **34**:183 (1942).

ment with adsorptive clay will reduce the viscosity and acidity to their original values.

III-8. Inhibition of Oxidation. The oxidation of oils is further characterized by the manner (and often ease, especially with paraffinic materials) in which the rate can be slowed down by the use of inhibitors. Oxidation inhibitors can be divided into two classes, namely, antioxidants and oxidation retardants.

Antioxidants invariably lengthen the induction period; after this has passed, the oxidation usually proceeds along a normal course, although there are many recorded variations. They may function to some extent in retarding chain initiation by reacting with available oxygen,

$$AH + O_2 \rightarrow A\cdot$$
$$2A\cdot \rightarrow \text{stable products}$$

Their main effect, however, is probably the destruction of alkyl peroxy radicals,[1]

$$ROO\cdot + AH \rightarrow ROOH + \text{stable products}$$

although reactions of the antioxidant with $RO\cdot$ and $HO\cdot$ radicals can be important.[2] The destruction of $HOO\cdot$ radicals and $ROOH$ molecules[3] by the antioxidant has also been considered.

There is disagreement about the manner in which antioxidants react with chain-carrying radicals. The possibility of hydrogen abstraction from antioxidant has been proposed[4]

$$ROO\cdot + AH \rightarrow ROOH$$

as has electron abstraction[5]; neither has been proved.

$$ROO\cdot + :NH \rightarrow ROO: + (\cdot NH)^+$$

Kinetic measurements have suggested the initial formation of an intermediate complex between the antioxidant and alkyl peroxy radicals.[6]

Oxidation in the presence of oxidation retardants takes place without an extension of the induction period and without an autocatalytic phase. The oxygen consumed-time chart shows a low-slope line following the induction period.[7]

The range of chemicals having oxidation retardant powers has not

---

[1] Cole and Field, *Ind. Eng. Chem.*, **39**:174 (1947).   Bolland and ten Have, *Trans. Faraday Soc.*, **43**:201, 252 (1947); **45**:93 (1949).   Cooper and Melville, *J. Chem. Soc.*, p. 1995, 1951.   Boozer, Hammond, Hamilton, and Sen, *J. ACS*, **76**:3861 (1954); **77**:3233, 3238, 3380 (1955).

This is especially likely in accelerated oxidation tests, where a large excess of air or oxygen is always present, and where the reaction $R\cdot + O_2 \rightarrow ROO\cdot$ is so rapid that the reaction $R\cdot + AH \rightarrow RH + \text{stable products}$ may be neglected.

[2] Kennerly and Patterson, *Ind. Eng. Chem.*, **48**:1917 (1956).

[3] Ivanov and Vilanskaya, *Doklady Akad. Nauk.*, *U.S.S.R.*, pp. 102, 551, 1955; *CA*, **50**:2259 (1956).

[4] Boozer and Hammond, *J. ACS*, **76**:3861 (1954).

[5] Pedersen, *Ind. Eng. Chem.*, **48**:1881 (1956).

[6] Boozer and Hammond, *loc. cit.* See also Oberright, Leonardi, and Kozacik, *Additives and Lubricants*, *ACS*, *Div. Petrol. Chem.*, Preprints, p. 121, Atlantic City, September, 1956.

[7] von Fuchs and Diamond, *Ind. Eng. Chem.*, **34**:927 (1942).

been established; many sulfur compounds have this property[1] and compounds of this class make up the bulk of the so-called natural inhibitors contained in lubricating oil distillates.[2] Retardants are thought to function by decomposing hydroperoxide molecules, in contrast to antioxidants, which act on alkyl peroxy radicals. Some sulfur compounds (sulfides) apparently act directly to reduce hydroperoxides formed in the oil, while others are first oxidized to sulfonic acids, which in turn act to catalyze and direct the decomposition of the hydroperoxides to innocuous ions rather than to free radicals. A possible ionic mechanism[3] might be

$$
\begin{array}{c}
R \\
RCOOH + X \rightarrow RCO^+ + XOH^- \\
R
\end{array}
\qquad
\begin{array}{c}
R \\
\\
R
\end{array}
$$

$$
\begin{array}{c}
R \\
RCO^+ \rightarrow ROC^+ \\
R
\end{array}
\qquad
\begin{array}{c}
R \\
\\
R
\end{array}
$$

$$
\begin{array}{c}
R \\
ROC^+ + XOH^- \rightarrow ROH + C{=}O + X \\
R
\end{array}
\qquad
\begin{array}{c}
R \\
\\
R
\end{array}
$$

Some aromatic compounds, mainly those of the polynuclear type, such as methylnaphthalene, have been found to inhibit oxidation in hydrocarbon mixtures containing them. They appear to function as inhibitors through conversion to phenolic bodies, probably through hydroperoxides as intermediates. Mixtures of antioxidants and oxidation retardants exhibit a synergistic effect.

Certain phosphorus compounds, not acting as antioxidants or retardants, are thought to inhibit oil oxidation in engines by covering metal surfaces with a protective layer. The action of an antioxidant, bis(2-hydroxy-3-*t*-butyl-5-methylphenyl)methane, a retardant, dibenzyl disulfide, and a prooxidant, lead naphthenate, all present in a concentration of 0.0001 mol per 40 g oil, is illustrated in Fig. III-2 and Table III-4, showing the oxidation of a paraffinic oil at 170°C for 24 hr. The bisphenol lengthens the induction period, the prooxidant shortens it, and the retardant reduces the net consumption of oxygen.

[1] von Fuchs and Diamond, *ibid.* Larsen and Diamond, *Lubrication Eng.*, **7**(6):272 (1951). Kennerly and Patterson, *loc. cit.* For other types of compounds showing retardant properties, see Harle and Thomas, *ACS, Div. Petrol. Chem., Gen. Papers,* Preprints, pp. 43, 51, Miami, April, 1957.

[2] Denison, *Ind. Eng. Chem.*, **36**:477 (1944). Denison and Condit, *Ind. Eng. Chem.*, **37**:1102 (1945). Jezl, Stuart, and Schneider, *ACS, Div. Petrol. Chem., Gen. Papers,* Preprints, p. 27, Miami, April, 1957. Leonardi, Oberright, Orkin, and White, *ACS, Div. Petrol. Chem., Gen. Papers,* Preprints, p. 35, Miami, April, 1957.

[3] Kharasch, Fono, and Nudenburg, *J. Org. Chem.*, **15**:748 (1950); **16**:113 (1951).

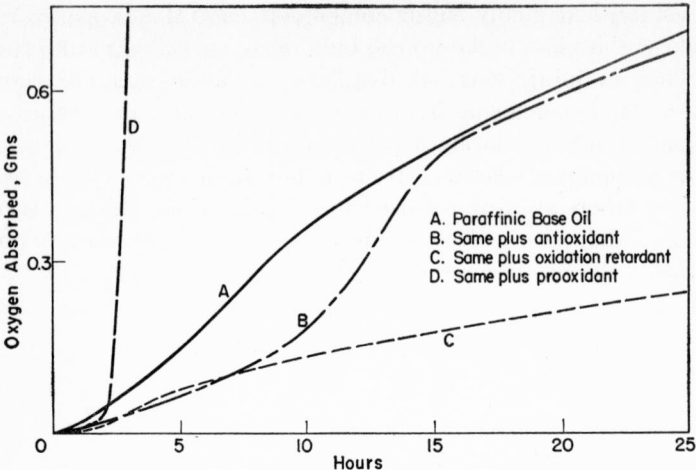

FIG. III-2. Oxidation of paraffinic base oil in oxygen at 170°C for 24 hr.

TABLE III-4

	Original oil	Base oil	Plus anti-oxidant	Plus oxidation retardant	Plus pro-oxidant
Temperature, °C............	....	170	172	170	170
Time, hr..................	....	24	24	24	24
Oxygen consumed, g.......	....	0.6613	0.6379	0.2638	1.8145
Volatile acids, milliequiv.....	....	0.951	1.0930	0.466	3.415
Oxidized oil:					
Viscosity (SUS):					
100°F................	179	232	226	205	352
210°F................	46	49.6	49.1	47.7	56.4
Viscosity index...........	112	111	111	109	104
Neutralization number....	0.001	2.6	2.63	0.99	6.41
Saponification number.....	0.2	12.4	11.0	7.9	30.4
Pentane insoluble, %......	....	0.15	0.21	0.07	0.15
sp gr 60°/60°F...........	0.8641	0.8772	0.8756	0.8718	0.8944

The development of autogenous inhibitors within the oil during the oxidation is also of interest. Their effect is easily demonstrated by adding an aliquot of an oxidized oil to a fresh oil prior to testing; oxidation is delayed in the manner characteristic of an antioxidant.[1]

[1] Autogenous inhibitor formation has been observed on oxidizing lubricating oils with ozone at room temperature. Pass, Pöll, and Zantl, *Petrol. Times*, **59**(1506):456 (1955). Leonardi, Oberright, Orkin, and White, *op. cit.* For evidence of antioxidant formation by oxidation of aromatic hydrocarbons, see Larsen, Thorpe, and Arnfeld, *Ind. Eng. Chem.*, **34**:183 (1942).

The presence and importance of naturally contained oxidation inhibitors became apparent with the development of the solvent extraction method of refining lubricating oil stocks; the raffinates are by no means as resistant to oxidation as the unrefined materials. The exact identity of the natural inhibitors has not been established; in the main, however, they can be classified as phenolic and sulfur compounds. The oxidation stability of an oil will increase during the early stages of a refining treatment (clay,[1] acid,[2,3] selective solvents[3]); presumably easily oxidized components are being removed from the oil. Further refining may, however, produce oils of decreased oxidation stability; for instance, white oils, which are products of drastic refining with sulfuric acid, are readily oxidized at rather low temperatures. This suggests removal of natural antioxidants; among these may be hydrocarbons, such as alkyl naphthalenes, which may exert a substantial protective power.

III-9. Oxidation Tests. In service, oil oxidation is accelerated by catalysts normally present in the lubrication system. These may be metal salts formed by the action of acidic products of oxidation on metals (iron, copper, chromium, nickel, lead, silver, cadmium, tin, aluminum), present in the system or introduced during operation. The salts of iron, copper, and lead are apparently the most harmful,[4] but oils and oil fractions differ in their response to these compounds.

The application of oxidation theory and oxidation tests to the estimation of oil quality and prediction of service is not well advanced. The chief difficulty is the fact that the conditions of use are ordinarily complicated by a variety of influences difficult to reproduce for test purposes; this is particularly true of engine crankcase oils. Tests for resistance to oxidation and resistance to thermal cracking should, in theory, predict how well an oil would stand up in service; these could be considered as abstract properties, just as oil viscosity is determined apart from the pumpability of the oil in an engine. However, oxidation stability and resistance to thermal cracking are so closely interrelated that it is difficult to treat them as separate properties. Cracked oils are more easily oxidized and oxidized oils are more easily cracked than the unchanged parent hydrocarbons. Because of these and similar difficulties, the practice has for many years been to rely on engine tests rather than on bench tests. While control of engine tests is not easy, the whole gamut of

---

[1] Fenske, Stevenson, Lawson, Herbolsheimer, and Koch, *Ind. Eng. Chem.*, **33**:516 (1941).

[2] von Fuchs and Diamond, *Ind. Eng. Chem.*, **34**:927 (1942).

[3] Davis, Lincoln, Byrkit, and Jones, *Ind. Eng. Chem.*, **33**:339 (1941).

[4] See Davis, Lincoln, Byrkit, and Jones, *loc. cit.*, and Booser and Fenske, *Ind. Eng. Chem.*, **44**:1850 (1952), for some curious effects reported for metal catalyst concentration.

influencing conditions can be brought to bear without too much trouble. It is significant that engine tests, and not bench tests, have been adopted by most public agencies in specifying engine oils.

Among the better known of the earlier oxidation tests are the Indiana,[1] the British Air Ministry,[2] and the Underwood[3] tests. The Indiana test will serve as an example. A controlled stream of air is bubbled through a measured volume of oil in a long, narrow container held at 341°F. Samples of oil are withdrawn at regular intervals and are examined for acidity, pentane-insoluble content, and viscosity, all of which increase with continued oxidation. The Underwood test was also employed for tendency to corrode alloy bearings.[4] Engine tests widely used for rating lubricating oils include the FL-2, L-4, and L-1.[5] They employ, respectively, a six-cylinder Chevrolet gasoline engine and a single-cylinder diesel test unit. Results are obtained in terms of engine cleanliness, ring sticking, effectiveness of lubrication, and bearing corrosion. A good deal of research on engine testing has been done with single-cylinder gasoline engines[6] and standardization of these is under way.[7]

HYDROGENATION

There is a rough correlation between the quality of petroleum products and their hydrogen content. It so happens that desirable aviation gasolines, kerosenes, diesel fuels, and steam turbine and most other good lubricating oils are made up of hydrocarbons containing high proportions of hydrogen. In addition, it is usually possible to convert olefins and polycyclics to paraffins and monocyclic hydrocarbons by hydrogen-adding processes. These facts have for many years encouraged attempts to employ hydrogenation for refining operations; in spite of considerable technical success, such processes were not economically possible until low-priced hydrogen became available as a result of the rise of hydro-

[1] Rogers and Shoemaker, *loc. cit.*

[2] Garner, Kelly, and Taylor, *World Petrol. Congr., Proc. 1st Congr., London,* **2**:448 (1933).

[3] Federal Specifications VV-L-791e, Method 3411·1.

[4] On the evaluation of some of these tests, see Gruse, *Petrol. Eng.,* **25**(13):C-23 (1953); **26**(1):C-9 (1954). For a tabulation of comparable tests, see Zuidema, "Performance of Lubricating Oils," p. 86, Reinhold Publishing Corporation, New York, 1952.

[5] Albright, Nelson, and Raymond, *Ind. Eng. Chem.,* **41**:897 (1949); "Coordinating Research Council Handbook," pp. 347, 365, 394, New York, 1946.

[6] Jacobson, *Petrol. Engr.,* **15**(8):196 (1944). Crowther, Pitkethly, and Stansfield, *Petrol. Engr.,* **21**(13):C-11 (1949). Penfold and Petry, *Lubrication Eng.,* **1**(1):7 (1945).

[7] Engine testing of petroleum lubricating oils is a complicated subject, beyond the scope of this work. See Zuidema, *loc. cit.,* and Georgi, "Motor Oils and Engine Lubrication," pp. 83–88, Reinhold Publishing Corporation, New York, 1950.

reforming, which converts naphthenes to aromatics with release of hydrogen.

Hydrogenation can be conducted without or with simultaneous cracking. In the first case, the reaction will be limited to saturating olefins or converting aromatics to naphthenes. The first may occur in altering a cracked or polymer gasoline or a cracked kerosene, and the latter in upgrading kerosene or lubricating oil stocks. Cracking and isomerization are involved to some extent in hydroforming of naphthas, but more extensively in the hydroconversion of high-boiling fractions and crude oil residua into lower-boiling stocks. Manipulation of temperature and pressure, together with choice of catalysts, renders hydrogen treating one of the most flexible processes available to petroleum refiners; much work has been done on the subject and an extensive literature has developed.

III-10. Saturating Hydrogenation. *Olefins.* Under atmospheric pressure, olefins can be hydrogenated up to about 500 to 550°C; beyond this range, dehydrogenation prevails. Application of pressure and the presence of catalysts make it possible to effect complete hydrogenation at room temperature or even lower; the same influences are helpful in minimizing dehydrogenation at higher temperatures. Increasing pressure emphasizes these effects.

A wide variety of metals are active hydrogenation catalysts; those of most interest are nickel, palladium, platinum, cobalt, iron, nickel-promoted copper, and copper chromite. Special preparations of the first three are active at room temperature and atmospheric pressure. The metallic catalysts are easily poisoned by sulfur-[1] and arsenic-containing compounds, and even by other metals.[2] To avoid such poisoning, less effective but more resistant metal oxides or sulfides are frequently employed, generally those of tungsten, cobalt, chromium, or molybdenum. The most efficient catalysts are those having high adsorptive capacity for hydrogen; this capacity may vary with temperature.[3]

Ethylene has been hydrogenated at −90°C in the presence of an iron catalyst,[4] and many other olefins can be saturated at room temperatures over Raney nickel.[5] Tertiary base olefins are, in general, more difficult

---

[1] Platinum on alumina is not affected appreciably by sulfur, unless present in amounts greater than 0.10 to 0.15 per cent in the stock treated. Hettinger et al., *Ind. Eng. Chem.*, **47**:719 (1955).

[2] Paal and Karl, *Ber.*, **46**:3069 (1913).

[3] Griffith and Marsh, "Contact Catalysis," pp. 97, 177, 186, Oxford University Press, London, 1957.

[4] Hansford and Emmett, *J. ACS*, **60**:1185 (1938).

[5] For a review of the catalytic hydrogenation of hydrocarbons, see Corson in "The Chemistry of Petroleum Hydrocarbons," Brooks et al. (eds.), vol. 3, p. 283, Reinhold Publishing Corporation, New York, 1955. See also, Sachanen, "Conversion of Petroleum," p. 374, Reinhold Publishing Corporation, New York, 1948.

to hydrogenate than the internally unsaturated straight-chain compounds, and these in turn are less responsive than terminal olefins.[1] Many opportunities for selective hydrogenation are afforded because the reaction is so flexible with respect to catalyst, temperature, pressure, and hydrocarbon structure. Examples are the removal of olefins from aromatic hydrocarbons at low temperature (20°C and 400 psi hydrogen pressure or 115 to 175°C at atmospheric pressure) over a nickel catalyst[2] and the saturation of thermally cracked naphthas.[3]

The heats of hydrogenation of some olefins have been measured,[4] and equilibrium data for destructive hydrogenations have been calculated.[5] The rate of hydrogenation of aromatic hydrocarbons depends largely on their structure. If the rate for benzene is regarded as unity, that for a series of substituted benzenes is approximately as follows:[6]

Toluene........................... 0.6
Ethylbenzene...................... 0.4
Isopropylbenzene.................. 0.3
n-Alkylbenzenes C_4 to C_9........... 0.25
1,3,5-Trimethylbenzene............ 0.2
1,2,4-Trimethylbenzene............ 0.2
1,2,3-Trimethylbenzene............ 0.1
p-Xylene.......................... 0.6
m-Xylene.......................... 0.3

On the same scale cyclohexene has a rating of 8. Catalytic hydrogenation of aromatics generally reduces the nucleus all the way to the cyclohexane derivative, but the reaction is completed at the cyclohexene stage in the presence of the ammonia complexes of calcium, strontium, barium, or lithium.[7]

III-11. Destructive Hydrogenation. *Paraffinic Hydrocarbons.* It is possible to hydrocrack paraffins without departing much from the kind of reactions which would proceed in the absence of hydrogen; the saturating of the olefins formed is the chief difference. The rate of cracking paraffin wax under hydrogen pressure of 400 to 1,500 psi and over the

[1] Lebedev, Kobliansky, and Yakubchik, *J. Chem. Soc.*, **127**:417 (1925).

[2] Ipatieff and Corson, *Ind. Eng. Chem.*, **30**:1039 (1938). For a discussion of selective hydrogenation, see Corson, *op. cit.*

[3] Hoffmann, Lewis, and Wadley, *Ind. Eng. Chem.*, **49**:656 (1957).

[4] Kistiakowsky, Ruhoff, Smith, and Vaughan, *J. ACS*, **58**:137 (1936). Crawford and Parks, *J. ACS*, **58**:373 (1936). Conant and Kistiakowsky, *Chem. Revs.*, **20**:181 (1937). See also Kassel, *Ind. Eng. Chem.*, **31**:275 (1939).

[5] Schultze, *Angew. Chem.*, **49**:284 (1936).

[6] Corson, *op. cit.*

[7] Kazansky and Glushnev, *J. Gen. Chem. (U.S.S.R.)*, **8**:642 (1938); *CA*, **33**:1279 (1939). *Bull. acad. sci. U.S.S.R. Classe sci. math. nat. ser. chim.*, p. 1061, 1938. *CA*, **33**:6256 (1939). Kazansky and Smirnova, *CA*, **32**:2090 (1938). Campbell and McDermott, *J. ACS*, **67**:282 (1945).

range 420 to 450°C with and without catalysts is about the same. Paraffins ranging down to pentane, but none higher than the charge stock, are produced; the reaction is one of cleavage at the alpha position. Branched chain paraffins, under the same conditions, undergo selective demethanation.[1] The methyl groups attached to secondary carbons are more easily removed than those attached to tertiary carbon atoms; those bound to quaternary carbons are the most resistant. Thus, over nickel or cobalt catalysts at 200 to 320°C and under about 600 psi hydrogen, isopentane gives methane and a C_4 mixture containing 92 per cent isobutane and 8 per cent n-butane; neohexane gives 94 per cent neopentane and 6 per cent isopentane, while 2,2,3-trimethylpentane forms 90 per cent 2,2,3-trimethylbutane and a few per cent each of 2,2- and 2,3-dimethylpentane. The same general sequence can be brought about at atmospheric pressure.

Naphthenic Hydrocarbons. The effect of hydrogen on naphthenic hydrocarbons is mainly that of ring scission followed by immediate saturation of each end of the fragment produced. The ring is preferentially broken at favored positions, although generally all the carbon-carbon bond positions are attacked to some extent. For example, methylcyclopentane is converted (40 per cent at 260°C and 90 per cent at 320°C) over platinized carbon into 2-methylpentane, 3-methylpentane, and n-hexane in the molar ratio of 7 to 2 to 1.[2] Under catalytic reforming (isomerizing) conditions (platinum-on-alumina, 250 to 275°C, 300 psi hydrogen), 2,2- and 2,3-dimethylbutane are also formed, along with aromatics and light paraffinic gases. The reactions may be pictured as shown at the top of page 116.[3]

Aromatic Hydrocarbons. The main reactions in the hydrogenation of aromatics are conversion of the aromatic to cyclohexane rings and carbon-bond scissions within the alkyl side chains. Polynuclear aromatics are more readily attacked than the single ring compounds, the reaction proceeding by a stepwise process in which one ring at a time is saturated and then opened. This is followed by cleavages which shorten the resulting alkyl side chains.[4] For example, naphthalene is hydrocracked in the

[1] Haensel and Ipatieff, *J. ACS*, **68**:345 (1946); *Ind. Eng. Chem.*, **39**:853 (1947).

[2] Kazansky and Rumgantseva, *Bull. acad. sci. U.S.S.R., Classe sci. chim.*, p. 473, 1947; *C.A.*, **42**:4535 (1948). Zelinsky, Kazansky, and Plate, *Ber.*, **68**:1869 (1935).

[3] Heinemann, Mills, Hattman, and Kirsch, *Ind. Eng. Chem.*, **45**:130 (1953).

[4] Orlow and Lickatschev, *Ber.*, **63**:2179–2185 (1930). Mailhe and Creusot, *Compt. rend.*, **193**:176 (1931). Kagehira, *Bull. Chem. Soc. Japan*, **6**:241 (1931). Kling and Florentin, *Compt. rend.*, **193**:1198 (1931). Zartman and Adkins, *J. ACS*, **54**:1668 (1932). Hall, *Fuel*, **12**:76 (1933). Hall, *J. Soc. Chem. Ind.*, **54**:208T (1935). Maillard, *Compt. rend.*, **200**:1856 (1935). Diakova, Lozovoy, and Stephantzeva, *J. Inst. Petrol. Technologists*, **23**:459 (1937). Smith, Rall, and Grandone, *U.S. Bur. Mines Tech. Paper* 587, 1938.

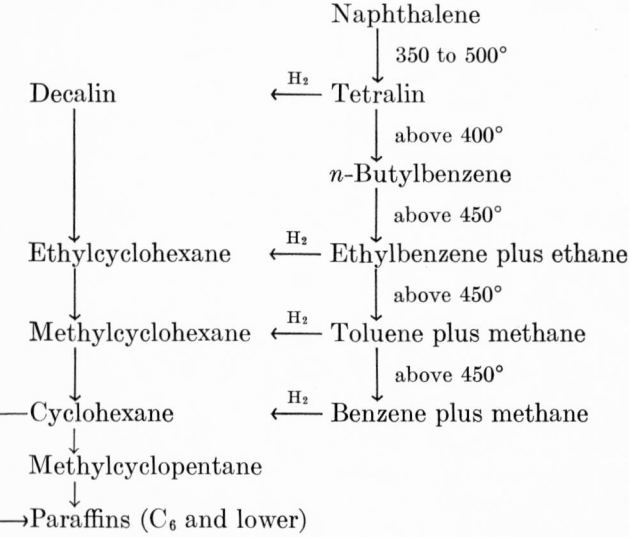

following manner over a molybdenum oxide-sulfide catalyst at 350 to 500°C under 1,500 psi hydrogen pressure.[1]

Naphthalene
  │ 350 to 500°
Decalin   ←H₂— Tetralin
  │   │ above 400°
  │   n-Butylbenzene
  │   │ above 450°
Ethylcyclohexane ←H₂— Ethylbenzene plus ethane
  │   │ above 450°
Methylcyclohexane ←H₂— Toluene plus methane
  │   │ above 450°
Cyclohexane ←H₂— Benzene plus methane
  │
Methylcyclopentane
  │
→Paraffins (C₆ and lower)

That destructive hydrogenation is favored by high partial pressures of hydrogen is shown by Fig. III-3, drawn from thermodynamic considera-

[1] Hall, *op. cit.*

tion of the reactions

Naphthalene plus hydrogen → benzene plus butane
Anthracene plus hydrogen → benzene plus *m*-xylene

Large equilibrium reaction constants are favored by high hydrogen pressures and low temperatures. Low-temperature hydrogenation, however, requires sensitive catalysts, such as Raney nickel, platinum, or palladium.

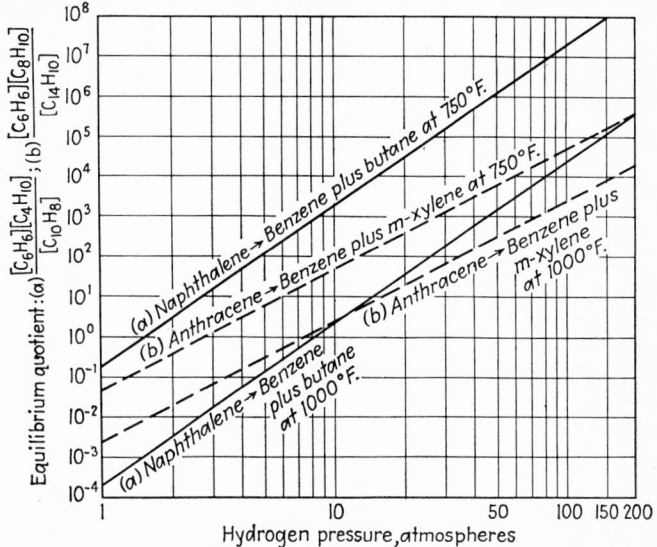

FIG. III-3. Effect of temperature and hydrogen pressure in destructive hydrogenation. [*From Sweeney and Voorhies, Ind. Eng. Chem.,* **26**:195 (1934).]

III-12. Processes. Applications of hydrogenation to petroleum refining may be divided into the nondestructive (200 to 400°C) used for double-bond saturation and the removal of contaminants and the destructive (400 to 550°C) in which hydrogenation accompanies cracking. The removal of sulfur, nitrogen, and oxygen compounds occurs also under the conditions of hydrocracking, and may be the object of the treatment. The nondestructive methods may again be divided into those employing low and high pressure, respectively; the catalysts for the latter need be less active.[1] An early application of the nondestructive process was the preparation of gum-stable high-octane aviation gasolines by hydrogenation of diisobutylene and the corresponding codimers derived from polymerization of butenes.[2] The polymerization was first

[1] For a review of destructive and nondestructive hydrogenation, see Sachanen, "Conversion of Petroleum," p. 374, Reinhold Publishing Corporation, New York, 1948.

[2] Murphree, Gohr, and Brown, *Ind. Eng. Chem.,* **31**:1083 (1939).

effected by cold or hot sulfuric acid and later by "solid" phosphoric acid —phosphoric acid baked on kieselguhr, etc. The hydrogenation was carried on under mild conditions with sulfur-sensitive nickel catalysts, or at higher temperatures and pressures with more sulfur-resistant agents. The products were the highly branched octanes closely related to iso-octane. Another application is the selective hydrogenation of the olefins in catalytically cracked gasolines; this involves also a refining action which removes sulfur, nitrogen, and oxygen from compounds containing them (as H_2S, NH_3 and H_2O).[1] An idea of the changes taking place on nondestructive hydrogenation of a catalytically cracked gasoline is given in Table III-5.[2]

TABLE III-5

Gasoline	Original	Hydrogenated	
		3,000 psi	150 psi
Gravity, °API	60.2	61.6	62.0
Aniline point, °F	66	99	96
Bromine number	63	1	3
Acid,heat, °F	135	5	7
Copper dish gum (mg per 100 ml)	17	4	4
Octane number:			
ASTM (motor)	80.5	79.9	79.4
ASTM (aviation) plus 4 ml per gal TEL	90.6	97.7	96.1
Toluene (volume per cent)	6	....	6
C_8 aromatics (volume per cent)	15	....	15

The success of the treatment depends on the preferential action of hydrogen on the nonhydrocarbons and the ease with which olefins can be hydrogenated selectively in presence of aromatics. Both low-pressure (60 to 150 psi) nickel catalyst and high pressure (3,000 psi) molybdenum sulfide catalyst processes have been employed during wartime. Partial hydrogenation of cracked gasolines to effect stabilization and more complete hydrogen pretreatment of similar naphthas to render them more suitable for catalytic reforming are now practiced to some extent. The adoption of such methods is often marginal because of economic considerations.

[1] Murphree, Brown, and Gohr, *Ind. Eng. Chem.*, **31**:1083 (1939); **32**:1203 (1940). Brown, Voorhies, and Smith, *Ind. Eng. Chem.*, **38**:136 (1946). Voorhies, Smith, and Hemminger, *Ind. Eng. Chem.*, **39**:1104 (1947). Abbott, Leidholm, and Sarno, *Petrol. Refiner*, **34**(6):118 (1955). The use of hydrogen as a refining agent is discussed in Chap. VII.

[2] Sachanen, "Conversion of Petroleum," p. 419, Reinhold Publishing Corporation, New York, 1948. Kirsch, Heinemann, and Stevenson, *Ind. Eng. Chem.*, **49**:646 (1957). Eberline, Wilson, and Larson, *Ind. Eng. Chem.*, **49**:661 (1957).

While paraffin wax decomposes at about equal rates in the presence and absence of hydrogen with and without catalyst, both gas oils and heavier tars high in polynuclear aromatics have been found to form gasoline faster in the presence of hydrogen and a suitable catalyst than when cracked thermally.[1] Coke formation is very low in such hydrocracking; secondary reactions such as polymerization and condensation, ordinary precursors to coke production, are suppressed, progressively so as hydrogen pressure is increased.[2] Petroleum fractions ranging from heavy naphthas to crude oils and even residua can be hydrocracked at temperatures from 400 to 560°C. A two-step operation, first at low temperature and then at high, is advantageous for residua.[3] The first stage gives over 100 volume per cent of a gasoline free of sulfur and gum-forming materials, but of relatively low aromatic content and octane number. The latter can be improved by selecting for the second stage a catalyst suitable for converting naphthenes to aromatics and paraffins to branched-chain isomers.

High-temperature hydrocracking of "middle oils" yields highly aromatic gasolines mainly by reaction of hydrogen on polycyclic aromatics; obviously cyclic charge stocks are to be preferred. Since loss to gas is high, the gasoline yield is apt to be low, but the product is of good quality. It is free of sulfur and gum formers and even the less volatile portion has a good octane number. The fraction boiling 100 to 325°F has at times been used as an aviation-gasoline base stock.

The high aromatic content of naphthas made by hydrogenating naphthenic charge stocks makes them suitable as solvents for the resins and gums used in paints and varnishes. For such use, an advantage is found in the general tendency of such fractions to be higher in aromatic content as boiling point rises. This can be deduced from the change in properties shown in Table III-6. The naphthas are rather like solvents derived from coal-tar materials.

The hydrogen treatment of catalytic cycle oils to make them less resistant to catalytic recracking is of some interest. The aromatics present are largely converted into naphthenes; this indicates the flexibility with which hydrogenation adapts itself to the requirements of the refiner. Table III-7 shows differences in results when virgin gas oil,

[1] Haslam and Russell, *Ind. Eng. Chem.*, **22**:1030 (1930). Byrne, Gohr, and Haslam, *Ind. Eng. Chem.*, **24**:1129 (1932). Tropsch, *Fuel*, **11**:61 (1932). Russell, "Science of Petroleum," vol. III, p. 1139, Oxford University Press, New York and London, 1939. Haslam and Russell, "Science of Petroleum," vol. III, p. 2139, Oxford University Press, New York and London, 1939.

[2] Sachanen and Tilicheyev, *Erdöl u. Teer*, **8**:317, 332, 349, 364 (1932).

[3] Russell, *loc. cit.* Pier, *World Petrol. Congr., Proc. 4th Congr., Rome*, **3**:517 (1955). Stevenson and Heinemann, *Ind. Eng. Chem.*, **49**:664 (1957). Gwin et al., *Ind. Eng.* **94**: 668, (1957).

TABLE III-6

Boiling range, °F	Specific gravity, 60°F	Aniline point, °F	Flash point, °F	Dimethyl sulfate value	Dilution ratio	Kauri butanol number	Evaporation rate (Hart balance) 100 per cent
200–275	0.777	52	<60	24	1.9	55.2	4.25
275–365	0.855	−1	61	62	2.8	75.6	21.25
365–419	0.897	−10	135	87	2.6	77.3	80.0
419–460	0.937	−33	190	100	2.4	85.7	

From Sweeney and Tilton, *Ind. Eng. Chem.*, **26**:693 (1934).

cycle stock, and hydrogenated cycle oils, respectively, are put through a catalytic cracking operation. It is generally more economical to carry out such a hydrogenation at lower pressures (750 psi) over a metal sulfide catalyst at 370°C; sulfur is reduced, some of the condensed polycyclic aromatics are converted to single-ring aromatics and naphthenes, and a satisfactory gasoline is then produced on cracking.[1]

TABLE III-7

	Virgin gas oil	Cracked cycle stock	Cycle stock hydrogenated at 3,000 psi	
			Partial	Almost complete
Volume per cent of virgin gas oil...	100	64	66	70
Sulfur, weight per cent............	1.1	0.78	0.21	0.06
Catalytic cracking results:				
Conversion, volume per cent.....	49.8	43.2	58.5	67.7
Gasoline, volume per cent.......	42.5	33.7	46.6	55.4
Octane number (motor).......	80.2	80.0	80.6	80.4
Octane number (motor) plus 3 ml TEL per gal...........	86.5	87.9–88.6	90.1	90.1

From Brown, Voorhies, and Smith, *Ind. Eng. Chem.*, **38**:136 (1946). See also, Smith in "The Chemistry of Petroleum Hydrocarbons," Brooks, Boord, Kurtz, and Schmerling (eds.), pp. 3, 327, Reinhold Publishing Corporation, New York, 1955.

The conversion of low-grade lubricating stocks, i.e., unrefined predominantly cyclic distillates, to refined oils of highly paraffinic character by hydrogenation is possible, but so far as known, at a considerable sacrifice in both yield and viscosity level. This loss is a result of the

[1] Voorhies and Smith, *Ind. Eng. Chem.*, **41**:2708 (1949).

mild hydrocracking cleavage of the low-viscosity-index polycyclic aromatic-naphthenic hydrocarbons. The products obtained on hydrogenating two lubricating oil distillates at 400°C are shown in Table III-8. The hydrogenated oils are low in sulfur and of improved color.[1]

TABLE III-8

	Winkler		Mid-Continent	
	Before	After*	Before	After
Gasoline, per cent..............	......	6	}	25
Gas oil, per cent................	......	26		
Lubricating oil, per cent.........	......	72	....	67.5
Gravity, °API.................	20.1	27.5	22.0	29.2
Viscosity:				
100°F (SUS)................	690	286	3100	580
210°F......................	62	50	144	68.7
Viscosity index................	32	83	72	101
Pour point, °F................	0	0		
Flash point, °F................	420	410		
Conradson carbon, per cent.......	0.41	0.015	3.31	0.13

* Steam distillate of hydrogenated product.

From Sachanen, "Conversion of Petroleum," p. 419, Reinhold Publishing Corporation, New York, 1948.

High-grade kerosene and high-cetane-number diesel fuels can also be prepared by hydrogenation of appropriate hydrocarbon fractions. As in other cases, sulfur, oxygen, and nitrogen compounds are decomposed under hydrogenating conditions, and both olefin bonds and aromatic rings become saturated; these reactions favor the production of stable smokeless kerosene. In the case of diesel fuels the increased paraffinicity raises the cetane number values appreciably.[2]

DEHYDROGENATION

The common primary reactions of pyrolysis are dehydrogenation and carbon-bond scission. The extent of the one or the other will vary with starting material and operating conditions, but because of its practical importance, methods have been found to increase the extent of

[1] Haslam, Russell, and Asbury, *World Petrol. Congr., Proc. 1st Congr., London*, **2**:302 (1933). See also, Schultz and Linden, *Ind. Eng. Chem.*, **48**:895 (1956). Davidson, *Petrol. Processing*, **11**(11):116 (1956).

[2] Brown, Voorhies, and Smith, *Ind. Eng. Chem.*, **38**:136 (1946). Tilton, Smith, and Hockberger, *Ind. Eng. Chem.*, **40**:1269 (1948). Vlugter, Waterman, and Van Westen, *J. Inst. Petrol.*, **25**:678 (1939).

dehydrogenation and, in some cases, to render it almost the only reaction. Dehydrogenation furnishes raw materials for the manufacture of petrochemicals, plastics, and synthetic rubber. Products of most importance are ethylene, propylene, and butadiene from the gaseous paraffins, styrene from ethylbenzene, and aromatic hydrocarbons from cyclohexane and its derivatives.

III-13. Paraffinic Hydrocarbons. Dehydrogenation is a first-order endothermic reaction; the extent at equilibrium conditions increases with rise of temperature and decreases with increase of pressure. Table III-9 gives the calculated temperatures required for various degrees of conversion of several low-boiling paraffins into their corresponding olefins, and the equilibrium constants of C_2, C_3, and C_4 olefin-paraffin-hydrogen mixtures are shown in Table III-10.

TABLE III-9

Conversion mole, per cent	C_2 Ethylene	C_3 Propylene	C_4 1-Butene	C_4 cis-2-Butene	C_4 trans-2-Butene	C_4 1-Butene	C_5 1-Pentene*
5	500°C	410	415	415	405	360	405
10	555	456	460	470	450	405	450
20	615	510	515	525	505	435	505
30	660	540	545	555	540	490	535
50	725	595	600	625	598	540	585
70	790	660	670	700	640	590	650
90	900	750	753	800	760	680	730

* Same values hold for C_6 and higher olefins.

From Kearby, "The Chemistry of Petroleum Hydrocarbons," Brooks, Boord, Kurtz, and Schmerling (eds.), vol. II, p. 221, Reinhold Publishing Corporation, New York, 1955.

TABLE III-10

	Equilibrium constants			
	350°C	400°C	450°C	500°C
C_2..................	....	0.00015	0.00076	0.0032
C_3..................	0.00038	0.0022	0.0074	
1-Butene............	0.00045	0.0022	0.0075	
trans-2-Butene.......	0.00083	0.0039	0.014	
cis-2-Butene.........	0.00052	0.0025	0.0087	
i-Butylene..........	0.0017	0.010	0.042	

From Frey and Huppke, *Ind. Eng. Chem.*, **25**:54 (1933).
See also, Pease and Durgin, *J. ACS*, **50**:2715 (1928).

Ethane-Propane. While ethylene can be prepared by the pyrolysis of any hydrocarbon material,[1] ethane, propane, or mixtures of the two are considered to be advantageous charge stocks. The treatment is strictly thermal, as no suitable catalyst has been found to increase the rate of dehydrogenation of ethane effectively or to affect differentially the two modes of propane decomposition—dehydrogenation and demethanation. The pyrolysis is carried out at about 730 to 815°C, under 20 to 30 psi pressure and at contact times of the order of 0.7 to 1.3 sec. A diluent, such as steam, is generally added to reduce condensation reactions and to supply heat. Typical conversion products are shown in Table III-11.

TABLE III-11

	Ethane	Propane
Coil outlet temperature, °C................	1523°F	1485°F
Coil outlet pressure, psi...................	31	32
Steam:hydrocarbon feed, molar ratio.......	0.78	1.15
Conversion, per cent.....................	62.6	82.0
Conversion products, mole per cent:		
H_2....................................	31.9	13.3
CH_4....................................	9.6	30.3
C_2H_4..................................	32.3	25.6
C_2H_6..................................	22.6	4.7
C_3H_6..................................	....	14.1
C_3H_8..................................	1.9	7.9

From Schutt and Zdonik, *Oil Gas J.*, **54**(41):98 (1956).

For additional discussion of ethane pyrolysis, see Hepp, Spessard, and Randall, *Ind. Eng. Chem.*, **41**:2531 (1949). Frey and Hepp, *Ind. Eng. Chem.*, **25**:441 (1933).

Butanes. Clean-cut dehydrogenation of the butanes is possible because selective catalysts have been developed. Chromic oxide is effective especially when supported on aluminum oxide and activated by alkali.[2] Operating at atmospheric pressure or lower, there is essentially no loss to polymers, and no structural isomerization is observed. The catalyst is not effective for pentanes, as cracking occurs.

n-Butane is dehydrogenated at 525 to 600°C, at about atmospheric pressure and advantageously at conversion levels of 20 to 32 per cent per pass. Butenes of 90 per cent purity are obtained with an over-all con-

[1] For production of ethylene from distillates and residua, see King and Warburton, *Oil Gas J.*, **51**(31):92 (1952); Schutt and Zdonik, *Oil Gas J.*, **54**(41):98 (1956).

[2] Frey and Huppke, *Ind. Eng. Chem.*, **25**:54 (1933). Burgin, Groll, and Roberts, *Petrol. Refiner*, **17**(10):495 (1938).

version, on recycling, of 90 to 95 per cent of the butane charged.[1]   The butene product consists of

	Per cent
1-Butene	33.5
cis-2-Butene	38.0
trans-2-Butene	28.5

Butadiene can be prepared from n-butane in one step[2] but the general practice is to start with available n-butenes or first to convert n-butane to n-butenes and then to complete the dehydrogenation in a second step.[3] Higher equilibrium yields of butadiene are obtained when one starts with the n-butenes.   In practice, the feed, at 540°C and containing about 70 per cent of n-butenes, is mixed with 20 to 30 times its volume of steam at 1300°C, and passed through a catalyst bed 4 to 6 ft long at a high space velocity;[4] the effluent is quenched with steam.   The yield of butadiene runs about 20 to 24 per cent per pass and the ultimate yield after recycling is of the order of 70 per cent.   The butadiene formed is separated by extraction with cuprous ammonium acetate or with furfural.[5]

The calculated equilibria between n-butane, n-butenes, and 1,3-butadiene at various temperatures and at 1.0 and 0.167 atmospheres pressure are shown in Table III-12.   Some carbon is formed in accompanying cracking reactions and this must be removed periodically from the catalyst by air burning.   Such carbon formation is reported to increase with the molecular weight of the olefin charged, but the data in Table III-13 suggest that contact time may also be of considerable importance. The figures were obtained in runs at 0.25 atmospheric pressure over a catalyst composed of 4 per cent chromia on alumina.

III-14. Naphthenic Hydrocarbons.   Cyclopentane and its derivatives will not undergo dehydrogenation reactions to form aromatics unless a preliminary isomerization to a C_6 ring structure can take place.[6] Although thermodynamic conditions are favorable at temperatures above

---

[1] Grosse and Ipatieff, *Oil Gas J.*, **38**(28):53 (1939); *Ind. Eng. Chem.*, **32**:268–309 (1940).   Haensel and Sterba, *Ind. Eng. Chem.*, **40**:1660 (1948).   Hanson and Hays, *Chem. Eng. Progr.*, **44**(6):431 (1948).   Ziegenhain, *Oil Gas J.*, **41**(15):30 (1942). Lassait and Parker, *Oil Gas J.*, **43**(28):229 (1944).   Reidal, *Oil Gas J.*, **55**(48):87; (49):114; (50):110; (51):74 (1957).

[2] Ziegenhain, *Oil Gas J.*, **41**(15):30 (1942).   Lassait and Parker, *Oil Gas J.*, **43**(28): 229 (1944).

[3] Russell, Murphree, and Asbury, *Trans. AIChE*, **42**:1 (1946).   Nicholson, Moise, Segura, and Kleiber, *Ind. Eng. Chem.*, **41**:646 (1949).

[4] Kearby in "The Chemistry of Petroleum Hydrocarbons," Brooks, Boord, Kurtz, and Schmerling (eds.), vol. 2, p. 221, Reinhold Publishing Corporation, New York, 1955.

[5] For review of the butadiene process, see van Antwerpen, *Chem. Eng. News*, **22**:316 (1944), and Reidal, *op. cit.*

[6] Zelinsky, Kasansky, and Plate, *Ber.*, **66**:1419 (1933); **68**:1869 (1935).

TABLE III-12. MOLAR PER CENT CONVERSION OF *n*-BUTANE

Conversion	Temperature, °C					
	550	600	650	700	750	800
At 1.0 atmospheric pressure						
To butadiene............	....	6.0	14	27.5	45	61.5
To total *n*-butenes........	....	62.5	69	64.5	54	37.5
1-Butene..............	....	22.5	27	26	22.5	17
cis-2-Butene...........	....	16	17	16	13	9
trans-2-Butene.........	....	24	25	23	18	12.5
At 0.167 atmospheric pressure						
To butadiene............	11.5	27.5	48.5	69	82	
To total *n*-butenes........	68.5	64.5	48.5	31.5	17.5	
1-Butene..............	23.5	23	19	13	7.5	
cis-2-Butene...........	18	16.5	12	7.5	4	
trans-2-Butene.........	27	25	17.5	11	6	

From Kearby in "The Chemistry of Petroleum Hydrocarbons," Brooks, Boord, Kurtz, and Schmerling (eds.), vol. II, Reinhold Publishing Corporation, New York, 1955.

TABLE III-13. FORMATION OF CONJUGATED DIOLEFINS

Compound dehydrogenated	Temperature, °C	Contact time, sec	Diolefin produced	Yield, weight per cent charge	Unreacted charge, weight per cent	Carbon, weight per cent charge
n-Butenes..........	600	0.75	1,3-Butadiene	18.0	50	11.2
n-Butenes..........	600	0.34	1,3-Butadiene	20.6	59	4.8
3-Methyl-1-butene..	600	0.5	Isoprene	21.4	34	12.8
2-Methyl-1- and 2-butenes.........	600	0.39	Isoprene	22.3	44	6.2
2-Pentene..........	600	0.40	Piperylene	30.3	44	7.6
Cyclopentane.......	500	1.85	Cyclopentadiene	8.9	62	8.8

From Grosse, Morrell, and Mavity, *Ind. Eng. Chem.*, **32**:309 (1940).

300°C,[1] cyclohexane is similarly resistant to aromatic formation by thermal treatment; very little benzene is formed at 550°C,[2] and at 620°C, only 0.4 mole per cent results, even though 24 per cent of the cyclohexane was decomposed by cracking.[3] Alkyl derivatives of cyclohexane dehy-

[1] Sachanen, "Conversion of Petroleum," p. 76, Reinhold Publishing Corporation, New York, 1948.
[2] Pease and Morton, *J. ACS*, **53**:3190 (1933).
[3] Frey, *Ind. Eng. Chem.*, **26**:198 (1934).

drogenate somewhat more easily; temperatures of the order of 480 to 500°C are sufficient.[1] Polycyclic naphthenes are also quite easy to dehydrogenate thermally.[2] In the presence of catalysts, however, cyclohexane and its derivatives are readily converted into aromatics; reactions of this type are prevalent in catalytic cracking and reforming (see Chap. IX). Benzene and toluene are prepared by the catalytic dehydrogenation of cyclohexane and methylcyclohexane, respectively;[3] the process has been applied commercially to appropriate naphthenic distillates. Polycyclic naphthenes can be converted into the corresponding aromatics by heating to 450°C in the presence of a chromia-alumina catalyst.[4] Diphenyl and some methylnaphthalenes are formed when solvent extracts of kerosene[5] are dehydrogenated, thus reflecting the presence of the corresponding naphthenes or their alkylated derivatives in the original stock.

Dehydrogenation of naphthenic hydrocarbons is aided by the presence of a hydrogen acceptor; benzene can be used with a nickel or platinum catalyst[6] and sulfur dioxide in the presence of activated carbon.[7]

III-15. Alkylaromatic Hydrocarbons. Styrene is prepared on a large scale by the catalytic dehydrogenation of ethylbenzene. The conditions favorable to the formation of butadiene from *n*-butane or *n*-butenes apply also to the production of styrene. The dehydrogenation will take place thermally to give ultimate yields of 50 to 55 per cent at temperatures above 600°C, but almost complete conversion can be obtained by the use of a catalyst at lower temperatures.[8] Higher yields and less cracking occur when the reaction is carried out under reduced pressure or in the presence of an inert diluent (steam, carbon dioxide, methane, or benzene).[9] The reaction temperature, 600°C at the start, is gradually increased to 660° as the catalyst ages. At a conversion per pass of the order of 35 to 40 per cent, the over-all yield of styrene is about 90 per cent.[10] Other alkylbenzenes can be dehydrogenated similarly; thus iso-

[1] Sachanen, *loc. cit.*

[2] Zelinsky, *Ber.*, **56**:1723 (1923); *Petrol. Refiner*, **20**(7):271 (1941). Linstead, Mulledge, Thomas, and Walpole, *J. Chem. Soc.*, **1937**, 1146.

[3] Oblad, Marschner, and Heard, *J. ACS*, **62**:2066 (1940). Weisz and Swegler, *J. Phys. Chem.*, **59**:823 (1955).

[4] Grosse, Mavity, and Mattox, *Ind. Eng. Chem.*, **38**:1041 (1946).

[5] Grosse and Mavity, *ACS, Div. Petrol. Chem.*, Preprints, p. 71, Boston, September, 1939.

[6] Adkins, Richards, and Davis, *J. ACS*, **63**:1320 (1941).

[7] Danforth and Bender, *Ind. Eng. Chem.*, **46**:1701 (1954).

[8] Kearby, *op. cit.*, p. 241.

[9] Mavity, Zetterholm, and Hervert, *Ind. Eng. Chem.*, **38**:829 (1946).

[10] Mitchell, *Trans. AIChE*, **42**:293 (1946).

propylbenzene gives α-methylstyrene;[1] under severe conditions, however, 15 to 30 per cent of the product is styrene.[2]

DEHYDROCYCLIZATION

Catalytic aromatization involving loss of one mole of hydrogen followed by ring formation and further loss of hydrogen has been demonstrated for a variety of paraffins (typically *n*-hexane and *n*-heptane) and for paraffinic gasolines.[3] Conversion takes place at atmospheric pressure and at temperatures above 300°C; the 450 to 550°C range is generally employed. The catalysts are metals and metal oxides of groups IV, V, and VI of the periodic table generally supported on alumina; chromic and vanadium oxides are most effective, cerium oxide less so, while thorium oxide produces dehydrogenation but little aromatization.[4] Other materials tried have been nickel on alumina,[5] platinized carbon,[6] oxides of zinc, titanium, and molybdenum, molybdenum sulfide, activated charcoal,[7] and aluminum chloride (metallic aluminum plus hydrogen chloride).[8] The addition of sulfur dioxide (a hydrogen acceptor) markedly reduces the operating temperature for chromia, and makes possible the use of alumina as a catalyst.[9] The yields per pass vary from 10 to 60 per cent, depending upon temperature and space velocity, and the total may reach 90 per cent on recycling. Thus, *n*-hexane, *n*-heptane, and *n*-octane at 460 to 470°C give about 50 to 60 per cent benzene, toluene, and *o*-xylene (plus some ethylbenzene), respectively, in a one-pass operation. Isooctane yields xylenes at 550°C over a molyb-

---

[1] Kearby, *op. cit.*, p. 242.

[2] Nickels, Webb, Heintzelman, and Corson, *Ind. Eng. Chem.*, **41**:563 (1949).

[3] Zelinsky and Shuykin, *Ind. Eng. Chem.*, **27**:1209 (1935). Karzhev, Severyanova, and Siova, *Oil Gas J.*, **37**(4):50 (1938). Komarewsky and Riesz, *J. ACS*, **61**:2524 (1939). Grosse, Morrell, and Mattox, *Ind. Eng. Chem.*, **32**:528 (1940). M ldavski, Kamusher, and Kobylskaya, *J. Gen. Chem. (U.S.S.R.)*, **7**:169, 1835 (1937). For English translation, see *Refiner Nat. Gasoline Mfr.*, **18**(3):118 (1939). Koch, *Brennstoff-Chem.*, **20**:1 (1939). For a general review of dehydrocyclization, see Hansch, *Chem. Revs.*, **53**:353 (1953).

[4] Grosse, Morrell, and Mattox, *Ind. Eng. Chem.*, **32**:528 (1940). Briggs and Taylor, *J. ACS*, **63**:2500 (1941).

[5] Zelinsky and Schuykin, *Ind. Eng. Chem.*, **27**:1209 (1935).

[6] Kazanski and Plate, *Ber.*, **69**:1862 (1936); *J. Gen. Chem. (U.S.S.R.)*, **7**:328 (1937). For English translation, see *Natl. Petrol. News*, **31**(14):R-134 (1939).

[7] Moldavski et al., *op. cit.*

[8] Otin and Dima, *Chimie & ind. (Paris)*, **40**:217 (1938).

[9] Teplitz, Maloney, and Reed, *ACS, Div. Petrol. Chem., Gen. Papers*, Preprints, p. 193, Kansas City, April, 1954. Murray, *ACS, Div. Petrol. Chem., Gen. Papers*, Preprints, p. 309, Miami, April, 1957.

dena-chromia catalyst,[1] but olefins over chromium oxide;[2] an intermediate isomerization is indicated.[3] Aromatics have been formed through the dehydrocyclization of diisobutyl and diisoamyl,[4] n-decane, pentacosane,[5] and kerosene.[6] Butylbenzene gives naphthalene;[7] a mixture of 1- and 2-octene is converted to o-xylene; compact olefin structures, such as 2-ethyl-1-butene and 3-methyl-2-pentene, also yield aromatics. In all the above conversions, no hydrocarbons boiling below the starting material are formed as long as mild conditions prevail.[7]

The catalytic dehydrocyclization of paraffins is more difficult than that of the olefins; both take place less readily than the conversion of naphthenes to aromatics by dehydrogenation discussed above.[8] Table III-14 gives a picture of the results obtainable over a chromic oxide

TABLE III-14

Hydrocarbon	Temperature, °C	Gas, per cent			Liquid, per cent		
		Hydrogen	Paraffins	Olefins	Aromatics	Paraffins	Olefins
n-Heptane............	468	94*	...	...	100*	0	0
	468	92	...	...	92.3	1.8	5.9
1-Heptene............	424	93	7	0	45	13	42
	474	89.5	4	6	90	2	8
3-Heptene............	420	....	...	...	48	12	40
3-Methylpentene-2.....	424	95	4	1	21	18	61
	474	55	38	7	32	5	72
1-Octene.............	474	94	3	3	84	1	15

* Hydrocarbon added at rate of 9 ml per hr per 15 g catalyst.
From Taylor and Turkevich, *Trans. Faraday Soc.*, **35**:921 (1939).

catalyst. The space velocity was 18 ml of hydrocarbon per hr per 15 g of catalyst.

The first step in the cyclization of paraffins is believed, as indicated

[1] Green and Nash, *Nature*, **148**:53 (1941).

[2] Oblad, Marschner, and Heard, *J. ACS*, **62**:2066 (1940).

[3] Herrington and Rideal, *Proc. Roy. Soc. (London)*, **184**:434 (1945).

[4] Kazansky and Plate, *Ber.*, **69**:1862 (1936). *J. Gen. Chem. (U.S.S.R.)*, **7**:328 (1937). For English translation, see *Natl. Petrol. News*, **31**(14):R-134 (1939). Moldavski et al., *op. cit.*

[5] Karzhev, Severyanova, and Siova, *Oil Gas J.*, **37**(4):50 (1938).

[6] Otin and Dima, *op. cit.*

[7] Moldavski et al., *op. cit.*

[8] Oblad, Marschner, and Heard, *ACS, Div. Petrol. Chem.*, Preprints, p. 131, Cincinnati, April, 1940.

above, to be that of dehydrogenation to an olefin, which in turn is cyclized and dehydrogenated to an aromatic hydrocarbon.[1] Evidence for an olefin intermediate in the conversion of n-heptane to toluene and data showing the progressive poisoning of the cyclization catalyst (Cr_2O_3 containing 10 per cent ZrO_2) are shown in Table III-15. The rate of

TABLE III-15

Reaction period, minimum	Mole per cent of liquid product			Heptene Heptane
	Heptane	Heptene	Toluene	
30	48	12	40	0.25
60	59	14	27	0.24
90	68.5	14.5	17	0.21
120	74	15	11	0.20

From Steiner, *J. ACS*, **67**:2052 (1945).

heptene formation remains fairly constant while that for toluene drops off rapidly.

The chief practical difficulties seem to lie in the lower conversion rates and in the short life of the catalysts. High adsorptive capacity is necessary, and this offers danger of structural breakdown. Furthermore, a thin coating of tar accumulates on the catalyst surface, possibly through hydrogen exchange reactions. In the presence of hydrogen under pressure, however, dehydrocyclization of paraffins is entirely feasible and (along with dehydrogenation of naphthenes) it plays an important part in aromatic formation when catalytic naphthas are produced under severe conditions.

POLYMERIZATION

Polymerization as defined by Staudinger[2] is a process in which a substance of low molecular weight is transformed into one of the same composition but of higher molecular weight while maintaining the atomic

[1] Herrington and Rideal, *op. cit.* Pitkethly and Steiner, *Trans. Faraday Soc.*, **35**:979 (1939). Mattox, *J. ACS*, **66**:2059 (1944). Steiner, *J. ACS*, **67**:2052 (1945). Salley, Fehrer, and Taylor, *J. ACS*, **63**:1131 (1941). Hoog, *Trans. Faraday Soc.*, **35**:1009 (1939). Taylor and Turkevich, *Trans. Faraday Soc.*, **35**:921 (1939). Turkevich, Taylor, and Fehrer, *J. ACS*, **63**:1129, 1387 (1941). See also Hoog, Verheus, and Zuiderweg, *Trans. Faraday Soc.*, **35**:993, 1009 (1939). Goldwasser and Taylor, *J. ACS*, **61**:1766 (1939). Green, *J. Inst. Petrol.*, **28**:179 (1942).

[2] *Trans. Faraday Soc.*, **32**:52, 97 (1936).

arrangement present in the basic molecule. Hansford[1] describes it as the successive addition of one molecule to another through a typical functional group which is characteristic of reactants and products alike; for hydrocarbons the functional group is an aliphatic-type olefin. This might be referred to as true or addition polymerization;[2] examples would be ethylene → 1-butene and isobutylene → diisobutylene.[3]

In true polymerization of hydrocarbons, it is not essential that only one monomer type be involved; isobutene may combine with propylene to form 2,2- and 2,3-dimethylpentenes, or with *n*-butene to form 2,3,4- and 3,4,4-trimethylpentenes.[4] Such a reaction is a copolymerization. Heat and pressure or an excess of catalyst may bring about conjunct or dehydropolymerization of an olefin.[5] The product is a complex mixture of hydrocarbons roughly equivalent in carbon and hydrogen content to that from true polymerization, but it includes olefins resulting from isomerization and some disproportioning, cyclization, and dehydrogenation to aromatics. When an acid catalyst is employed, the product recovered from the acid layer is cyclic and unsaturated.

In theory, true polymerization may yield a product of more or less unlimited molecular weight; sometimes, however, the size of the molecule may not exceed a definite limit because a change in structure may occur from that of the monomer. Thus, in polymerization of ethylene, some may end as cyclohexane; from propylene, the corresponding product is trimethylcyclohexane.[6] The thermal dimer of isobutene is 1,1,3-trimethylcyclopentane;[7] butadiene yields vinyl cyclohexene through a Diels-Alder type of addition[8] and isoprene gives dipentene;[9] allene forms 1,2-dimethylcyclobutane;[10] cyclopentadiene gives a terpene-like com-

[1] Farkas, "Physical Chemistry of Hydrocarbons," p. 292, Academic Press, Inc., New York, 1953.

[2] Ipatieff and Pines, *Ind. Eng. Chem.*, **28**:684 (1936).

[3] In the manufacture of plastics and other high-molecular-weight polymers, one often deals with molecules containing two or more functional groups, which increase in size through intermolecular condensations, splitting out water, ammonia, etc.; this process is referred to as condensation polymerization. Resins are formed from phenol and formaldehyde by condensations which split off water, and from amines with other reactants by the splitting off of ammonia.

[4] Brooks, *Ind. Eng. Chem.*, **41**:1694 (1949).

[5] Ipatieff and Pines, *J. Org. Chem.*, **1**:464 (1936–1937).

[6] Ipatieff, *Ber.*, **44**:2978 (1911). Ipatieff and Pines, *Ind. Eng. Chem.*, **28**:684 (1936). Waterman, Leendertse, and Klazinga, *Rec. trav. chim.*, **54**:79 (1935).

[7] McKinley, Stevens, and Baldwin, *J. ACS*, **67**:1455 (1945).

[8] Hofmann, *Angew. Chem.*, **25**:1465 (1912). Alder and Rickert, *Ber.*, **71**:373 (1938).

[9] Wagner-Juaregg, *Ann.*, **488**:176 (1931); **496**:52 (1932). Alder and Stein, *Ann.*, **496**:197, 204 (1932).

[10] Lebedev, *J. Russ. Phys.-Chem. Soc.*, **45**:1249 (1913).

pound, which is easily depolymerized on warming,

$$
2\ \
\begin{array}{c}
\ \ \ \ \mathrm{CH_2}\\
\diagup\ \ \ \diagdown\\
\mathrm{HC}\ \ \ \ \ \ \mathrm{CH}\\
\|\ \ \ \ \ \ \ \ \|\\
\mathrm{HC}\!-\!\!-\!\!-\!\mathrm{CH}
\end{array}
\ \longrightarrow\
\begin{array}{c}
\ \ \mathrm{CH}\ \ \ \ \ \ \ \ \ \ \ \ \mathrm{CH_2}\\
\diagup\ \ \ \diagdown\ \ \ \ \ \ \ \diagup\ \ \ \diagdown\\
\mathrm{HC}\ \ \ \ \ \mathrm{CH}\ \ \ \ \ \mathrm{CH}\\
\|\ \ \ \ \mathrm{CH_2}\ |\ \ \ \ \ \ \ \ \|\\
\mathrm{HC}\ \ \ \ \ \mathrm{CH}\!-\!\!-\!\!-\!\mathrm{CH}\\
\diagdown\ \ \ \diagup\\
\ \ \mathrm{CH}
\end{array}
$$

and cyclohexadiene forms[1]

$$
\begin{array}{c}
\ \ \ \ \mathrm{CH}\ \ \ \ \ \ \ \ \ \ \ \mathrm{CH}\\
\diagup\ |\ \ \diagdown\ \ \diagup\ \ \ \ \diagdown\\
\mathrm{H_1C}\ \ \mathrm{CH_2}\ \ \mathrm{CH}\ \ \ \ \ \ \ \ \mathrm{CH}\\
\|\ \ \ \ \ \ |\ \ \ \ \ \ |\ \ \ \ \ \ \ \ \ \ |\\
\mathrm{H_1C}\ \ \mathrm{CH_2}\ \ \mathrm{CH}\ \ \ \ \ \ \ \ \mathrm{CH_2}\\
\diagdown\ |\ \diagup\ \ \ \ \diagdown\ \ \ \diagup\\
\ \ \ \mathrm{CH}\ \ \ \ \ \ \ \ \ \mathrm{CH_2}
\end{array}
$$

The ease with which polymerization takes place is increased[2] by:

1. The presence of more negative substituents. Propylene (methylethylene) reacts less rapidly than styrene (phenylethylene).

2. Unsymmetrical location of the double bond. Phenylethylene and isobutylene react more rapidly than sym-diphenylethylene and 2-butene. Terminal double bonds are the most active.

3. Presence of substituent groups in nonterminal positions. 2-Methylbutadiene and 2,3-dimethylbutadiene polymerize more rapidly than 1-methylbutadiene and 1,4-dimethylbutadiene. It appears that 1,1,4,4-tetramethylbutadiene is resistant to polymerization.

A maximum in the tendency to polymerization with sulfuric acid has been reported at about C_5 or C_6 in the monoolefin series.[3] In diolefins, conjugation of the double bonds is favorable; as the double bonds become separated, the effect disappears.

III-16. Carbonium Ion. Apparently polymerization takes place through a chain mechanism. This may be a free radical chain when initiated thermally, by peroxides, or by radiations; or it may be an ionic chain when catalyzed by a carbonium ion or a carbanion. Catalysts

---

[1] Alder and Stein, *Ann.*, **496**:197, 204 (1932).

[2] Whitby, *Trans. Faraday Soc.*, **32**:315 (1936). Burk, *Ind. Eng. Chem.*, **30**:1054 (1938).

[3] Brooks and Humphrey, *J. ACS*, **40**:822 (1918).

furnishing carbonium ions[1] are acids (sulfuric, sulfonic, phosphoric, borophosphoric, hydrofluoric, dihydroxyfluoboric) and Friedel-Craft agents (aluminum chloride and bromide, boron trifluoride and trichloride, ferric chloride, zinc chloride, tin chloride, titanium chloride).[2] Examples of those forming carbanions are sodium,[3] alkyl sodium-sodium–alkoxide-sodium chloride,[4] and other organosodium compounds.[5]

In accordance with the carbonium ion theory a proton from the acid catalyst adds to an olefinic bond to form a positively charged fragment. In case of isobutylene, for example,

$$\begin{array}{ccc} CH_3 & & CH_3 \\ | & & | \\ C\!\!=\!\!CH_2 + H_2SO_4 \rightarrow CH_3\!\!-\!\!C^+ & + HSO_4^- \\ | & & | \\ CH_3 & & CH_3 \end{array}$$

The *t*-butyl carbonium ion then adds to another olefin molecule to form a C_8 carbonium ion. The latter can do one of the following:

1. Lose a proton to form a new C_8 olefin (termination).[6]
2. Add to another olefin monomer to form a still larger (C_{12}) carbonium ion (propagation), from which in turn a higher olefin (C_{12}) may be formed by loss of a proton.
3. The C_8 and C_{12} olefins thus formed can add to a *t*-butyl carbonium ion to form C_{12} and C_{16} carbonium ions, respectively. The exact nature of the termination reactions has not been definitely established. Apparently two carbonium ions do not react to terminate the chain; this is in contrast to free radical chains which are terminated by bi-radical reactions.

[1] For a comprehensive discussion of carbonium ion reactions in polymerization, isomerization, alkylation, and catalytic cracking, see Whitmore, *Ind. Eng. Chem.*, **26**:94 (1934); *Chem. Eng. News*, **26**:668 (1948). Schmerling, *Ind. Eng. Chem.*, **45**:1447 (1953).

[2] Thomas, *Ind. Eng. Chem.*, **37**:543 (1945).

[3] Juve, Goff, Schroeder, Meyer, and Brooks, *Ind. Eng. Chem.*, **39**:1490 (1947). Ziegler, Jakob, Wollthan, and Wenz, *Ann.*, **511**:13, 68 (1934). Whitmore and Cook, "Science of Petroleum," vol. V, part I, p. 114, Oxford University Press, New York and London, 1950.

[4] Morton, Magat, and Letsinger, *J. ACS*, **69**:172, 950 (1947); **71**:487 (1949); **72**:3785 (1950); *Ind. Eng. Chem.*, **42**:1488 (1950).

[5] Mark and Pines, *J. ACS*, **78**:5946 (1956).

[6] In this case a dimer, which consists of about four parts of 2,4,4-trimethyl-1-pentene and one part of 2,4,4-trimethyl-2-pentene. McCubbin and Adkins, *J. ACS*, **52**:2547 (1930).

Thus,

$$(CH_3)_3C^+ + \underset{\underset{CH_3}{|}}{\overset{\overset{CH_3}{|}}{C}}=CH_2 \rightarrow CH_3-\underset{\underset{CH_3}{|}}{\overset{\overset{CH_3}{|}}{C}}-CH_2-\underset{\underset{CH_3}{|}}{C^+}-CH_3$$

$$CH_3-\underset{\underset{CH_3}{|}}{\overset{\overset{CH_3}{|}}{C}}-CH_2-\underset{\underset{CH_3}{|}}{C^+}-CH_3 \rightarrow$$

$$\xrightarrow{82\%} CH_3-\underset{\underset{CH_3}{|}}{\overset{\overset{CH_3}{|}}{C}}-CH_2-\underset{\underset{CH_3}{|}}{C}=CH_2 + H^+$$

$$\xrightarrow{18\%} CH_3-\underset{\underset{CH_3}{|}}{\overset{\overset{CH_3}{|}}{C}}-CH=\underset{\underset{CH_3}{|}}{C}-CH_3 + H^+$$

The proportion of the 1-pentene derivative is the larger because it is easier to remove one of the six protons attached to the two primary carbons adjacent to the positive carbon atom than one of the two protons from the also adjacent secondary carbon atom. Trimers are formed by the addition of the *t*-butyl carbonium ion to the 1-pentene derivative; the reaction yields 55 per cent of 1,1-dineopentylethylene and 35 per cent of 2,2,4,6,6-pentamethyl-3-heptene. Alternatively trimers may form by the addition of the *t*-octyl carbonium ion to isobutylene, to form 5 per cent each of 2,4,4,6,6-pentamethyl-1 and 2-heptene.[1] Presumably the *t*-butyl carbonium ion does not add to the trimethyl-2-pentene dimeric isomer. A similar mechanism takes place in copolymerization where, for example, a *t*-butyl carbonium ion adds to a propylene molecule, producing in the end 4,4-dimethyl-1-pentene and 2,3-dimethyl-2-pentene. Carbonium ion intermediates can also be used in this manner to explain the products of conjunct or dehydropolymerization.[2]

With the Friedel-Craft type of catalysts, true carbonium ions are formed directly by the addition of a proton to the olefin, provided the catalyst has been activated.[3]

[1] Whitmore, Wilson, Capinjola, Tongberg, Fleming, McGrew, and Cosby, *J. ACS*, **63**:2035 (1941). McCubbin, *J. ACS*, **53**:356 (1931).

[2] For a comprehensive discussion of carbonium ions in olefin polymerization, see Schmerling and Ipatieff, "Advances in Catalysis," vol. II, p. 21, Academic Press, Inc., New York, 1950. Langlois, *Ind. Eng. Chem.*, **45**:1447, 1470 (1953). Schmerling in "The Chemistry of Petroleum Hydrocarbons," Boord, Kurtz, and Schmerling (eds.), vol. II, p. 247, Reinhold Publishing Corporation, New York, 1955.

[3] The free acid HAlCl$_4$ is nonexistent, but its esters are apparently stable. Fontana and Herold, *J. ACS*, **70**:2881 (1948). Brown and Pearsall, *J. ACS*, **72**:5347 (1950).

$$\underset{\underset{CH_3}{|}}{\overset{\overset{CH_3}{|}}{C}}{=}CH_2 + AlCl_3 + HCl \rightarrow (CH_3)_3C^+ + AlCl_4^-$$

With the unactivated catalyst (no free acid), a positively charged (electron deficient) complex forms by addition to an olefin molecule[1]

$$\underset{\underset{CH_3}{|}}{\overset{\overset{CH_3}{|}}{C}}{=}CH_2 \ + \ \overset{\overset{Cl}{\cdot\cdot}}{Cl:Al:Cl} \rightarrow \ +\overset{\overset{CH_3}{\,}\overset{H}{\,}\overset{Cl}{\cdot\cdot}}{C\ :\ \underset{\underset{CH_3}{\,}\underset{H}{\,}\underset{Cl}{\cdot\cdot}}{C}\ :\ Al\ :\ Cl}$$

which then can add to other olefin molecules in a manner similar to proton addition. This charged complex is more stable than a true carbonium ion and it has been postulated that the difference is responsible for the generally higher-molecular-weight polymers obtained with such catalysts.[2]

A number of other theories have been proposed to explain acid polymerization.[3] The objection to most of these is that a driving force is lacking in the reaction mechanism.

In radical-initiated polymerizations, a radical must be present before the reaction chain can be started. This is generally provided by the addition of oxygen, an easily decomposed alkyl hydroperoxide or acid peroxide in low-temperature polymerizations, or by heat in case of thermal polymerizations. The latter are generally carried out at temperatures sufficiently high to cause some cracking, which complicates the nature of the product. Free radical-initiated polymerizations do not conform to the definition of catalyzed reactions, for the initiator is consumed in the process; the final polymer (except in purely thermal treatments) generally contains a small percentage of oxygen.[4] This type of polymerization, but not that catalyzed by carbonium ion, can be

---

[1] Hunter and Yohe, *J. ACS*, **55**:1248 (1933). Houtman, *J. Soc. Chem. Ind.*, **66**:102 (1947). See Heiligman, *J. Polymer Sci.*, **4**:183 (1949) for a review of mechanisms proposed for Friedel-Craft metal catalyzed polymerizations.

[2] Whitmore and Meunier, *J. ACS*, **63**:2197 (1941).

[3] Ester intermediates: Ipatieff, *Ind. Eng. Chem.*, **27**:1067 (1935). Monroe and Gilliland, *Ind. Eng. Chem.*, **30**:58 (1938). Farkas and Farkas, *Ind. Eng. Chem.*, **34**:716 (1942). Turkevich and Smith, *J. Chem. Phys.*, **16**:466 (1948). Separation of carbon-carbon or carbon-hydrogen bonds: Kline and Drake, *J. Research Natl. Bur. Standards*, **13**:705 (1934). Drake, Kline, and Rose, *J. ACS*, **56**:2076 (1934). Wachter, *Ind. Eng. Chem.*, **30**:822 (1938).

[4] Walling, *J. ACS*, **66**:1602 (1944). Pfann, Williams, and Mark, *J. Polymer Sci.*, **1**:14 (1946).

inhibited by the addition of phenolic or aromatic amine antioxidants to the monomer.[1]

III-17. Ethylene. Ethylene can be converted to polymeric liquids by the application of heat and pressure. Under 70 to 135 atm, and at temperatures between 325 and 380°C, liquid products are obtained, of which about 50 per cent boils below 200°C.[2] The product contains appreciable amounts of naphthenic hydrocarbons. The thermal polymerization is accelerated by traces of oxygen[3] and modified by mercaptans.[4] Ethylene is not polymerized by concentrated sulfuric acid; instead, stable esters are formed. With 90 per cent phosphoric acid esters are formed below 250°C, but above that temperature (250 to 350°C), and under 750 to 1,000 psi pressure, polymers in the gasoline–light kerosene boiling range are formed; these are of the conjunct type, containing olefins, paraffins, naphthenes, and aromatics, with isobutane in the product gas.[5] Ethylene does not respond to pure aluminum chloride, even under pressure, but when the catalyst is activated by moisture or hydrogen chloride, and depending upon time, amount of catalyst, etc., liquid products varying from a gasoline to a lubricating oil are obtained.[6] They are of the conjunct type. The gasoline fraction up to 200°C is mostly saturated and has an octane number of about 77, suggesting the presence of branched structures; the higher-boiling portion of the distillate contains naphthenes.[7] This probably carries on into the lubricating oil fraction.[8] During World War II, rather high-viscosity-index oils (108 to 112) were produced in Germany by polymerizing ethylene with AlCl₃ over a temperature range of 100 to 140°C, under 500 to 800 psi.[9] A product more resembling a true polymer is obtained on using a mixture of aluminum and aluminum chloride or diethylaluminum chloride as the catalyst.[10] The dimer, trimer, and tetramer, etc., can be separated from

---

[1] For a listing of polymerization stopping agents, see Centflinger and Lufter, *Ind. Eng. Chem.*, **45**:182 (1953).

[2] Ipatieff and Haensel, *ACS, Div. Petrol. Chem.*, Preprints, *Symposium on Catalysts in Petroleum Industry*, p. 125, New York, September, 1944. Bhattacharyya and Schamaienger, *Petroleum (London)*, **19**:435 (1956).

[3] Storch, *J. ACS*, **56**:374 (1934).

[4] Storch, *J. ACS*, **57**:2598 (1935).

[5] Ipatieff and Pines, *Ind. Eng. Chem.*, **27**:1364 (1935). Schmerling, *Ind. Eng. Chem.*, **45**:1447 (1953).

[6] Ipatieff and Grosse, *J. ACS*, **58**:915 (1936).

[7] Bowen and Nash, *World Petrol. Congr., Proc. 1st Congr., London*, **2**:774 (1933).

[8] Nash, Stanley, and Bowen, *J. Inst. Petrol. Technologists*, **16**:830 (1930). Sullivan, Voohees, Neely, and Shankland, *Ind. Eng. Chem.*, **23**:604 (1931). See Sullivan, Ruthruff, and Kuentzel, *Ind. Eng. Chem.*, **27**:1072 (1935), for preparation of lubricating oils by the action of AlCl₃ on cetene and cracked wax.

[9] Spaght, *Petrol. Processing*, **1**:126 (1946). Horne, *Ind. Eng. Chem.*, **42**:2428 (1950).

[10] Hall and Nash, *J. Inst. Petrol. Technologists*, **23**:679 (1937); **24**:471 (1938).

the low-boiling products; the lubricating oil is also of higher viscosity index. True polymers of ethylene (1-butene, 1-hexene, 1-octene, 1-decene, etc.) can be obtained by heating to 100 to 200°C, under 750 to 1,500 psi pressure, in the presence of aluminum trialkyls, especially triethyl aluminum.[1]

Ethylene undergoes extensive polymerization when subjected to heat and pressure in the presence of peroxides as initiators. Olefin polymerizations of this type, following a free radical mechanism, generally lead to high-molecular-weight products such as polyethylene.

III-18. Propylene. Propylene is reported to dimerize to 4-methyl-1-pentene[2] over 90 to 92 per cent sulfuric acid at room temperature; stronger acid gives higher-boiling conjunct polymers. When mixed with isbutylene or isoamylene, propylene will copolymerize readily over sulfuric acid to give heptenes and octenes.[3] With phosphoric acid a true polymer is obtained below 300°C and conjunct polymers above that temperature; with hydrogen fluoride, conjunct polymers are obtained under all conditions.[4] A complex polymer is also formed by thermal polymerization, which will take place at a slightly higher temperature. A comparison of the high-temperature thermal and phosphoric acid[5] polymers, given in the tabulation,[6] shows the extent to which olefin polymers have been converted into paraffins, naphthenes, and aromatics,

	Thermal	Phosphoric acid
Temperature, °C	375	330
Pressure, lb	1,500–380	715–300
Time, hr	12	8
Olefins, per cent	48	69
Paraffins, per cent	8	15
Naphthenes, per cent	44	10
Aromatics, per cent	0	6
Percentage boiling below 225°C	61.6	85.3

Pressure as such will not bring about polymerization, but its application will lower the temperature needed, both in catalytic and thermal processes. This effect is employed in making clean-cut dimers, trimers,

[1] Ziegler, Gellert, Holzkamp, and Wilkie, *Brennstoff-Chem.*, **35**:321 (1954).

[2] Brooks, *J. ACS*, **56**:1998 (1934).

[3] Ipatieff, Pines, and Friedman, *J. ACS*, **61**:1825 (1939).

[4] Langlois, *Ind. Eng. Chem.*, **45**:1470 (1953).

[5] For a discussion of kinetics and variables affecting the polymerization over phosphoric acid, see Bethea and Karchmer, *Ind. Eng. Chem.*, **48**:370 (1956).

[6] Ipatieff and Pines, *Ind. Eng. Chem.*, **28**:684 (1936).

and tetramers of propylene. The diagram (Fig. III-4) shows the distribution of the various polymeric units in a typical product made at 150°C. Under 1,500 psi pressure over zinc chloride[1] the same relations

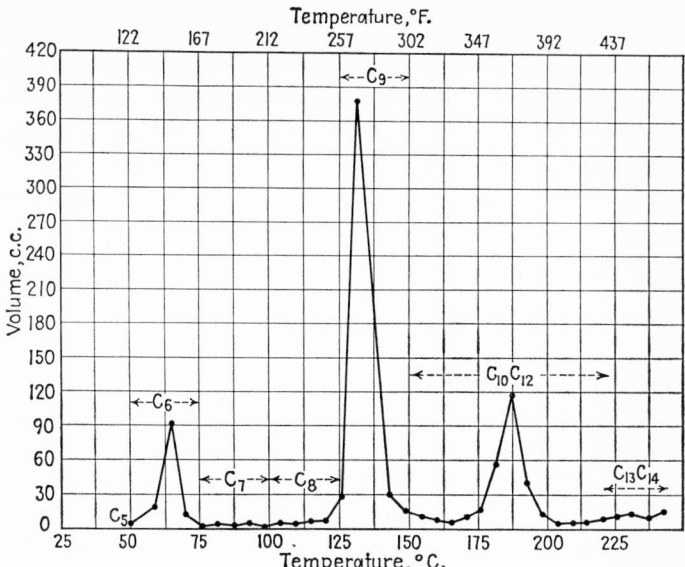

Fig. III-4. Distillation curve of polymer made at 150 to 160°C. [*Taken from Brandes, Gruse, and Lowy, Ind. Eng. Chem.,* **28**:554 (1936).]

prevail at 220°C; but at 300°C, the molecular weight distribution is more even. At the higher temperature aromatics were not found, although naphthenes were.

Silica-alumina catalysts are effective in the polymerization of propy-

[1] A propylene polymer having a very similar fractionation curve is obtained on using a silicotungstic acid catalyst at 150 to 160°C. Verstappen and Waterman, *J. Inst. Petrol.,* **41**:343 (1955). Petrow, *Fette u. Seifen,* **57**:798 (1955), found the zinc chloride-catalyzed propylene trimer to be composed mainly of 3-ethyl-4,4-dimethyl-2-pentene and 3,4,5-trimethyl-2-hexene along with a smaller amount of 3,4-dimethyl-3-heptene.

The composition of propylene trimers (nonenes) has not been established. One commercial product is said to contain:

Terminal olefins	Volume per cent
$RCH=CH_2$	5
$R_2C=CH_2$	12

Nonterminal olefins	Volume per cent
$R_1HC=CHR_2$ *trans*	16
cis	5
$R_1R_2C=CR_3H$	46
Tetra substituted	16

lene;[1] the reaction will occur at atmospheric pressure if a temperature of 350°C is employed; the polymer is a complex mixture of hydrocarbons boiling within the gasoline range. Presumably, a substantial amount of primary as well as secondary propyl carbonium ions is formed. A silica-alumina catalyst promoted by nickel oxide produced a polymer[2] containing a dimer fraction made up of:

Volume per cent

2-Methyl-2-pentene	10
4-Methyl-2-pentene	50
4-Methyl-1-pentene	5
2- and 3-Hexene	34
1-Hexene	1

Refinery Practice. Although practice varies, a high olefin C_3-C_4 gas fraction is often nonselectively polymerized over one of the above-mentioned phosphoric acid catalysts. The product is made up of the polymers and cross polymers of propylene and the butylenes, 90 per cent falling in the gasoline boiling range. The operating conditions are relatively mild; temperatures of 200 to 250°C and pressures between 150 and 200 psi are effective.[3,4] Results for several charging stocks are given in Table III-16. The product may contain up to 80 per cent of dimers and codimers in the aviation-gasoline boiling range, showing an

TABLE III-16

Operating conditions	C_3-C_4 cut	Liquid-vapor phase stabilizer gas	Gas from vapor-phase cracking
Pressure, lb per sq in	100	155	175
Temperature, °F	450	450	450
Inlet gas rate, cu ft per hr per lb of catalyst	0.10	4.4	3.9
Olefin content, per cent:			
Inlet gas	43.6	34.6	26.3
Exit gas	1.4	4.0	7.5
Olefin polymerization, per cent	98	92	77
Liquid, gal per 1,000 cu ft of gas	7.5	7.4	3.7

[1] Van Winkle, *J. Am. Pharm. Assoc.*, **17**:544 (1928). Gayer, *Ind. Eng. Chem.*, **25**:1112 (1933). Verstappen and Waterman, *J. Inst. Petrol.*, **41**:343, 347 (1955).

[2] Hogan, Banks, Lanning, and Clark, *Ind. Eng. Chem.*, **47**:752 (1955).

[3] Ipatieff and Egloff, *Petrol. Eng.*, **6**(10):29 (1935). Egloff, Morrell, and Nelson, *Proc. Am. Petrol. Inst.*, 18th Annual Meeting, sec. III, p. 64, 1937. deRousset, Riedl, and Czajkowski, *ACS, Div. Petrol. Chem., Gen. Papers*, Preprints, p. 137, Cincinnati, April, 1955. Sherwood, *Petroleum (London)*, **20**:183 (1957).

[4] Actually, a C_3 cut is usually polymerized and the C_4 material reserved for alkylation.

octane number of 82 (motor) and a blending value, in 60-octane base gasoline, of as much as 125. Hydrogenation will convert the branched olefins into an isoparaffinic mixture of about 96-octane number. Phosphoric acid has also been used to polymerize the isobutylene in a C_4 refinery cut selectively to di- and triisobutylene.[1]

III-19. Isobutylene. In addition to polymerizing some of the simple olefins, dilute sulfuric acid forms alcohols by catalytic hydration. The balance between the two reactions is particularly interesting in the case of isobutylene. The amount absorbed is a function of the water content of the acid, for most of the olefin is present in the solution as tertiary butyl alcohol.[2] The solution, however, yields free acid and a dimer-trimer mixture on standing several days or at once on warming to 80 to 100°C;[3] the shorter time at the higher temperature favors a more volatile polymer. The volatility of polymer formed can be controlled by adjusting the acidity of the solution before heating.[4] In an open system, not all the absorbed isobutylene is polymerized; some escapes as free gas, the amount again depending on the acidity. Low acidity favors a high release to gas; higher acidities give more polymer, but it contains less of the dimer. This relation is shown in Fig. III-5 which illustrates the effects produced in an isobutylene—63.5 per cent sulfuric acid system. For reference purposes, acid of this concentration fully charged with isobutylene at room temperature titrates to give 30 g H_2SO_4 per 100 ml solution.

Conjunct polymerization of isobutylene appears first with sulfuric acid as dilute as 70 per cent, and it increases with increasing acid strength. Over concentrated acid, little polymer is obtained; the action is mainly that of oxidation-reduction with liberal evolution of sulfur dioxide and tar formation. These latter effects can be prevented to a large extent by the addition to the acid of common ion salts such as metal sulfates, and also boric acid and glycerol; true polymerization is largely restored.[5] True polymers are also obtained on absorbing isobutylene in 85 per cent phosphoric acid and warming.

As indicated above, the catalyst plays an important part in the nature of the polymer obtained. While dilute sulfuric acid produces mainly a 3:1 mixture of dimers and trimers (having a wide boiling point spread), a 6:1 mixture of trimers and tetramers is obtained over etherates of boron trifluoride.[6] The trimer is very close boiling (174.1 to 175.2°C/760 mm); it

---

[1] Cotton, *Oil Gas J.*, **37**(48):25 (1939).
[2] Deanesly and Engs, U.S. Patent 2,012,785, 1935.
[3] Butlerow, *Ann.*, **189**:44 (1877).
[4] Stevens and Gruse, U.S. Patent 2,258,368, 1941.
[5] Stevens and Gruse, U.S. Patents 2,090,905, 1937; 2,205,159, 1940.
[6] Stevens and Bowman, U.S. Patents 2,588,426, 1952; 2,591,384, 1952.

is probably a mixture of 1,1-dineopentylethylene and 2,2,4,6,6-penta-methyl-3-heptene. This reaction would appear selective between the *t*-butyl carbonium ion and the two diisobutylene isomers, with little reaction between *t*-octyl carbonium ion and isobutylene. Diisobutylene, allowed to stand at room temperature for an hour over BF$_3$·diethyl etherate, is converted practically quantitatively into tetraisobutylene.[1]

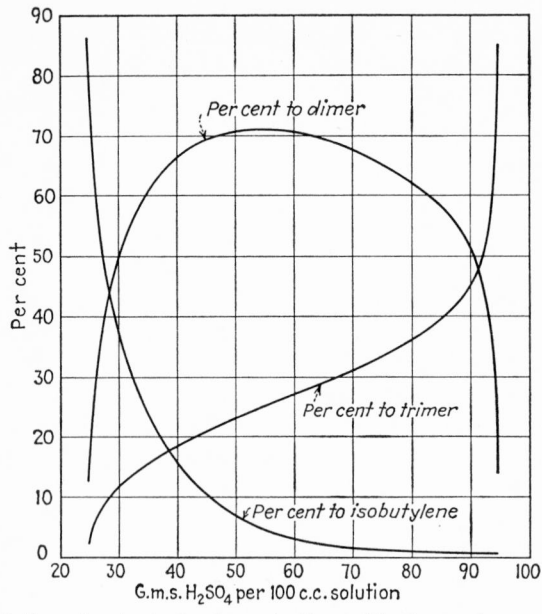

Fig. III-5. Variation of extent of polymerization with change in apparent acidity of the system.

Dilute sulfuric acid has been employed commercially in the so-called "cold" or "hot" acid processes for the polymerization of isobutylene; both are based on the principles outlined above. The cold acid process involves absorption of isobutylene, at normal temperature, from refinery gas cuts by contact with 60 to 65 per cent sulfuric acid, which will not absorb the normal butenes. The solution containing the isobutylene, largely in the form of *t*-butyl alcohols, is heated to about 100°C. A mixture of dimer and trimer, in the ratio of about 3:1, is obtained.[2] The above two-step process yields liquid hydrocarbons in amounts corresponding only to the isobutylene available.

In the hot acid process the same strength acid is employed but the absorption is carried on at a temperature corresponding roughly to that

[1] Stevens and Bowman, U.S. Patent 2,588,425, 1952.

[2] McAllister, *Proc. Am. Petrol. Inst.*, 18th Annual Meeting, sec. III, p. 78, 1937. Bauman and Smith, *Oil Gas J.*, **53**(21):71 (1954).

of the second stage in the cold acid procedure; absorption and polymerization are completed in one step. A simultaneous copolymerization between the normal butenes and isobutylene takes place; 3,4,4-, 2,3,3-, and 2,3,4-trimethylpentenes are found along with the two diisobutylene isomers.[1] The octane number is about 86 and becomes about 97 on hydrogenation.

Aluminum chloride, boron trifluoride, titanium tetrachloride, etc., polymerize isobutylene vigorously at ordinary temperatures, giving heavy complex liquids and tars. When the temperature is reduced to about −80°C, an energetic reaction takes place which can be controlled by choice of solvents. High-molecular-weight polybutenes are formed, which vary in character from viscous oils to elastic solids of the rubber class.[2]

ISOMERIZATION

While isobutane is now available in the gases from catalytic cracking, it was necessary during wartime to supplement the supply by isomerization of *n*-butane over aluminum chloride. Possibly the main advantage of catalytic over thermal cracking is the fact that the former causes isomerization reactions in which less desirable hydrocarbons are rearranged into those showing high octane numbers. There is a similar advantage in the isomerization of *n*-pentane and *n* hexane. The conversion of five-carbon naphthenes into structures suitable for dehydrogenation to aromatics is also of importance.

III-20. Paraffinic Hydrocarbons. These are readily isomerized at room temperature by aluminum chloride and bromide and by boron fluoride. The reaction proceeds to some extent in presence of concentrated (100 per cent) sulfuric acid, and very extensively at 300 to 450°C under hydrogen pressure over solid hydrogenation-dehydrogenation catalysts, including platinum or nickel, and tungsten and molybdenum oxides on alumina or silica-alumina.

The metal halide-catalyzed reaction is of first order and reversible. The composition of the reaction products is limited by thermodynamic equilibria; the percentages of isoparaffins decrease with rising temperatures. Anhydrous aluminum chloride has been employed most extensively for the isomerization of *n*-butane to isobutane. This catalyst, as well as aluminum bromide and boron trifluoride, must be activated with hydrogen halide or by substances capable of producing hydrogen halides

---

[1] Ciapetta, Macuga, and Leum, *ACS, Div. Petrol. Chem.*, Preprints, p. 205, Atlantic City, April, 1947.

[2] Thomas, Sparks, Frolich, Otto, and Muller-Conradi, *J. ACS*, **62**:276 (1940). Frolich and Sparks, "Science of Petroleum," vol. V, part II, p. 24, Oxford University Press, New York and London, 1953.

under reaction conditions before it will start to function.[1]　　Other activating agents include heat,[2] water,[3] oxygen,[4] olefins, and alkyl halides.

Paraffin isomerization is pictured as taking place through the formation and rearrangement of carbonium ions as follows:[5]

$$CH_3CH_2CH_2CH_3 + R^+ \rightarrow CH_3CH_2\overset{+}{C}HCH_3 + RH$$

The chain-initiating ion R^+ is formed by the addition of a proton from the acid catalyst to an olefin molecule which may be added, be present as an impurity, or be formed by dehydrogenation of the paraffin.

Ion isomerization:

$$CH_3CH_2\overset{+}{C}HCH_3 \rightleftharpoons CH_3-\underset{\underset{CH_3}{|}}{CH}-\overset{+}{C}H_2 \rightleftharpoons CH_3-\underset{\underset{CH_3}{|}}{\overset{+}{C}}-CH_3$$

Chain propagation:

$$CH_3-\underset{\underset{CH_3}{|}}{\overset{+}{C}}-CH_3 + CH_3CH_2CH_2CH_3 \rightleftharpoons CH_3\underset{\underset{CH_3}{|}}{CH}CH_3 + CH_3\overset{+}{C}HCH_2CH_3$$

Except for butane, the isomerization of paraffins is generally accompanied by side reactions involving carbon-carbon bond scissions when Friedel-Craft type catalysts are employed.　Compounds boiling both lower and higher than the starting hydrocarbon are synthesized.　The disproportionation reactions, taking place especially with the pentanes and higher paraffins, are caused apparently through the cracking of isoparaffin molecules by unactivated aluminum halide.[6]　The action, referred to as autodestructive alkylation, is thought to be a combination of dealkylation (cracking) and alkylation,[7] which results in the formation of isoparaffins of higher and lower molecular weight than the original alkane.　It is possible to minimize these side reactions for pentanes and hexanes, but not for heptanes and higher, by conducting the isomeriza-

[1] Glasebrook, Phillips, and Lovell, *J. ACS*, **58**:1944 (1936).　Leighton and Heldman, *J. ACS*, **65**:2276 (1943); **66**:1786, 1789 (1944).

[2] Pines and Wackher, *J. ACS*, **68**:595 (1946).

[3] Glasebrook, Phillips, and Lovell, *loc. cit.*

[4] Pines and Wackher, *J. ACS*, **68**:599 (1946).　Oblad and Gorin, *Ind. Eng. Chem.*, **38**:822 (1946).

[5] Bloch, Pines, and Schmerling, *J. ACS*, **68**:153 (1946).　Pines and Wackher, *J. ACS*, **68**:2518 (1946).　Burwell and Gordon, *J. ACS*, **70**:3128 (1948); **71**:2355 (1949).　Stevenson, Wagner, Beeck, and Otvos, *J. ACS*, **73**:5741 (1951); **74**:3269 (1952).　See Pines, "Advances in Catalysis," vol. I, p. 201, Academic Press, Inc., New York, 1948, for a discussion of other theories presented to explain paraffin isomerization.

[6] Grummitt, Case, and Mitchell, *Ind. Eng. Chem.*, **38**:141 (1946).

[7] Ipatieff and Schmerling, *Ind. Eng. Chem.*, **40**:2354 (1948).

tion either under hydrogen pressure,[1] in the presence of isobutane,[2] aromatic,[3] naphthenic,[4] hydrocarbons, or heterocyclics such as thiophene.[5] The suppression of the side reactions is generally accompanied by some inhibition of the isomerization. The addition of olefins, however, offsets the protective action of the above agents. The isomerization reaction passes through an induction period; very little disproportionation takes place during this time.[6]

Butane. *n*-Butane isomerizes 100 times faster than isobutane.[7] With 5 molar per cent of aluminum bromide as the catalyst at 27°C under 3 atm pressure in the liquid phase, the equilibrium mixture of *n*-butane and isobutane contains about 78 to 82 per cent of the latter. More than 1,000 hr are required to reach this condition; no other products are formed, and the catalyst remains unchanged.[8] The reaction rate is dependent upon temperature and the catalyst concentration. At higher temperatures disproportionation (cracking) becomes noticeable.

Commercial isomerization of *n*-butane to isobutane has been carried out over aluminum chloride in both the vapor (AlCl₃ on bauxite) and liquid (catalyst dissolved in AlCl₃-hydrocarbon complex or in antimony pentachloride) phases. In general, the temperatures employed ranged from 80 to 150°C, pressures from 200 to 365 psi, space velocities (vol per hr per vol of catalyst) 0.5 to 2.5, and in the presence of 2 to 14 per cent hydrogen chloride. The relatively low conversions obtained ranged from 35 to 45 per cent, giving 50 to 200 gal of isobutane per lb of catalyst.[9]

[1] Schuit, Hoog, and Verheus, *Rec. trav. chim.*, **59**:793 (1940). Evering, d'Ouville, Lien, and Waugh, *Ind. Eng. Chem.*, **45**:581 (1953). Ipatieff and Schmerling, *Ind. Eng. Chem.*, **40**:2354 (1948).

[2] Evering, d'Ouville, Lien, and Waugh, *op. cit.* Perry, *Trans. AIChE*, **42**:639 (1946).

[3] Evering, d'Ouville, Lien, and Waugh, *op. cit.*

[4] Evering, d'Ouville, Lien, and Waugh, *op. cit.* Mavity, Pines, Wackher, and Brooks, *Ind. Eng. Chem.*, **40**:2374 (1948). Schneider, *J. ACS*, **76**:4938 (1954). Condon, *J. ACS*, **73**:3938 (1951). Sensel and Goldsby, *Ind. Eng. Chem.*, **44**:2716 (1952).

[5] Myers, Hansford, and Sachanen, U.S. Patent 2,424,953, 1947.

[6] Grummitt, Sensel, Smith, Burk, and Lankelma, *J. ACS*, **67**:910 (1945). Mizushima, Ohno, and Sakuro, *J. ACS*, **72**:4820 (1950).

[7] Otvos, Stevenson, Wagner, and Beeck, *ACS, Div. Petrol. Chem., Joint Symposium on Mechanisms of Homogeneous and Heterogeneous Hydrocarbon Reactions*, Preprints, p. 85, Kansas City, March–April, 1954.

[8] Montgomery, McAteer, and Franke, *J. ACS*, **59**:1768 (1937). *ACS, Div. Petrol. Chem.*, Preprints, p. M1, Baltimore, April, 1939. See also Schuit, Hoog, and Verheus, *Rec. trav. chim.*, **59**:793 (1940).

[9] For a more detailed review of commercial isomerization processes, see Gunness, *Advances in Chem. Ser.*, no. 5, p. 109, 1951. Evering, "Advances in Catalysis," vol. VI, p. 197, Academic Press, Inc., New York, 1954. Sherwood, *Petroleum (London)*, **19**:393 (1956).

It is also feasible to isomerize *n*-butane to isobutane over a platinum catalyst under pressure of hydrogen at 600 to 850°F. A molar efficiency of about 95 per cent is obtained; some methane, ethane, propane, and pentane are formed in side reactions.[1]

Pentanes. The ease of paraffin isomerization increases with molecular weight, but the extent of disproportionation reactions also increases. Conditions can be established under which isomerization only will take place with the butanes, but this is difficult for the pentanes and higher hydrocarbons. At 27°C, over $AlBr_3$, the equilibrium mixture of *n*-pentane and isopentane contains 70 or more per cent of the branched-chain isomer; at 0°C, about 90 per cent.[2] Higher- and lower-boiling hydrocarbon products, hexanes, heptanes, and isobutane, are also formed in side reactions even at 0°C; in increased amounts when the temperature is raised.[3] Although the thermodynamic conditions are favorable, neopentane shows no signs of isomerization after thousands of hours at room temperature; neither has its presence been reported in the products of any pentane isomerization.

n-Pentane has been isomerized commercially under milder conditions than those employed for *n*-butane. The $AlCl_3$ isomerization of light naphthas containing *n*-pentane and hexanes of low octane number has also been practiced.[4]

More recently pentane isomerization has been practiced in a clean-cut manner over hydrogenation-dehydrogenation catalysts in the presence of hydrogen.[5]

Hexane and Heptane. *n*-Hexane and *n*-heptane, treated with aluminum chloride at reflux temperatures, give wide-boiling mixtures containing large proportions of products other than those caused by isomerization.[6] Of the hexane isomers, 2- and 3-methylpentanes, which are readily interchangeable, are formed first, and then 2,3-dimethylbutane; the latter isomerizes slowly into 2,2-dimethylbutane.[7] A complex product containing 65 per cent pentanes and lighter, 6 per cent isohexanes, 5 per cent isoheptanes, and 24 per cent higher-boiling hydrocarbons has been obtained from *n*-heptane.[8]

Sulfuric acid brings about selective paraffin isomerization. Normal

[1] Grote, *Oil Gas J.*, **56**(13):73 (1958).

[2] Montgomery, McAteer, and Franke, *loc. cit.*

[3] Montgomery, McAteer, and Franke, *loc. cit.* Glasebrook, Phillips, and Lovell, *J. ACS*, **58**:1944 (1936).

[4] Evering, Fragen, and Weems, *ACS, Div. Petrol. Chem., Symposium on Catalysts in Petroleum Industry*, Preprints, p. 155, New York, September, 1944.

[5] Belden, Haensel, Starnes, and Zabor, *Proc. API*, **37**(III):365 (1957).

[6] Nenitzescu and Dragen, *Ber.*, **66**:1892 (1933).

[7] Evering and Waugh, *Ind. Eng. Chem.*, **43**:1820 (1951).

[8] Calingaert, Beatty, and Flood, *J. ACS*, **57**:956 (1935); **58**:51 (1936).

paraffins and those containing quaternary carbon atoms are not isomerized;[1] only isoparaffins are affected and only isoparaffins are formed.[2] Methyl shifts along a paraffinic chain take place readily; other changes in branching less so.[3] The concentration of the sulfuric acid is critical; reaction rates show a sharp maximum at 99.8 per cent acid strength, and seem to be independent of the isohydrocarbon structure.[4] There is little loss of the hydrocarbon to the acid.[5]

Hydrogenation-dehydrogenation catalysts (nickel, platinum, MoO_3, WO_3), when supported on silica-alumina cracking catalysts, are strikingly effective in isomerizing paraffin hydrocarbons at 300 to 450°C under hydrogen pressures of about 350 to 500 psi. The isomerizations are clean-cut, being accompanied by very little cracking, and the liquid product recoveries are essentially quantitative.[6] Reactions of this type are commonplace in catalytic reforming operations. The side reaction is mainly hydrocracking of the isomerization products; only molecules smaller than the hydrocarbon charged are formed. As the carbon content of the n-paraffin increases, the temperature necessary to obtain the same percentage conversion decreases. For example, to obtain 50 per cent conversion, the temperature requirements are

Hydrocarbon	Temperature, °C
n-Pentane	384
n-Hexane	346
n-Heptane	323
n-Octane	302

The 2- and 3-methyl pentanes are the first products of isomerization of n-hexane. Dimethylbutanes appear only under conditions favorable for high conversion. The hexanes isomerize in the following decreasing order: 2-methlpentane, 3-methylpentane, n-hexane, 2,3-dimethylbutane, and 2,2-dimethylbutane.

[1] Gordon and Burwell, *J. ACS*, **70**:3128 (1948); **71**:2355 (1949).

[2] Stevenson, Wagner, Beeck, and Otvos, *J. ACS*, **74**:3269 (1952).

[3] Maury, Burwell, and Tuxworth, *J. ACS*, **76**:5831 (1954).

[4] Roebuck and Evering, *J. ACS*, **75**:1631 (1953).

[5] Komarewsky and Ruther, *J. ACS*, **72**:5501 (1950).

[6] Ciapetta and Hunter, *Ind. Eng. Chem.*, **45**:147, 155 (1953). See also McGrath, *Oil Gas J.*, **55**(23):119 (1957); Grave, Ozawa, and Worrell, *Oil Gas J.*, **55**(20):132 (1957); Belden, Haensel, Starnes, and Zabor, *Oil Gas J.*, **55**(20):142 (1957); *Proc. API*, **37**(III):365 (1957).

For data relating to paraffinic hydrocarbon equilibria, see Rossini, Prosen, and Pitzer, *J. Research Natl. Bur. Standards*, **27**:529 (1941); **34**:403 (1945). Evering, Fragen, and Weems, *Oil Gas J.*, **43**(25):77 (1944). Evering and d'Ouville, *J. ACS*, **71**:440 (1949). Ciapetta and Hunter, *loc. cit.* Weinberger and Montgomery, *Proc. Am. Petrol. Inst.*, **36**(III):220 (1956). Belden, Haensel, Starnes, and Zabor, *op. cit.*

The preferential formation of monomethyl derivatives also holds in the isomerization of n-heptane.   The 2- and 3-methylhexanes are the first to appear in low conversion treatments; 2,4-dimethylpentane is found in the 81 per cent conversion product, and other isomers are formed only at higher conversions.   The isomerization of 2,3-dimethylpentane gives all heptane isomers except n-heptane and 2-ethylpentane.   The heptanes isomerize with decreasing difficulty in the order: 2,2,3-trimethylbutane, n-heptane 2,3-dimethylpentane, and 2,4-dimethylpentane.

The hydroisomerization of n-octane is highly selective; even at 98 per cent conversion 71 per cent of the total reaction is isomerization.   At 63 per cent conversion, the isomers are 2,3-, and 4-methylheptanes and 2,3-dimethylhexane; 2,4-dimethylhexane does not form until a higher degree of conversion is reached.   Isooctane, 2,2,4-trimethylpentane, is reported to decompose largely into isobutane; a similar reaction is reported over sulfuric acid[1] and aluminum chloride.[2]

III-21. Olefinic Hydrocarbons. Olefin isomerization is easily catalyzed and plays an important part in the formation of the highly branched structures found in catalytically cracked distillates.   The extent of isomerization of such mixtures and the octane number improvement that can be attained are limited by the equilibrium concentrations of the several olefin isomers taking part in the reaction.[3]

The changes taking place during olefin isomerization involve either (1) shifting of the position of the double bond (hydrogen atom shift) or (2) structural changes caused by the shifting of the position of methyl groups, or changing the number and position of tertiary carbon atoms in the molecule (methyl group shift).

In thermal reactions, double-bond movement is observed,[4] and there may be some shifting of methyl groups in branched structures already present but new branched structures are not formed.   The same can be said of mild catalysts such as alumina at 400 to 450°C[5] and aluminum sulfate at 270 to 290°C.[6]   Catalysts, however, possessing acidic properties will cause chain branching or the shifting of methyl groups.   This is especially true when olefins are passed over acidified alumina at 300 to

[1] Dunstan, Fidler, Pim, and Tait, *J. Inst. Petrol. Technologists*, **24**:303 (1938).

[2] Ipatieff and Pines, *Ind. Eng. Chem.*, **28**:461 (1936).

[3] Berg, Sumner, and Montgomery, *Ind. Eng. Chem.*, **38**:734 (1946).   Kilpatrick, Prosen, Pitzer, and Rossini, *J. Research Natl. Bur. Standards*, **36**:559 (1946).

[4] Waterman, Leenderste, and Moklazingal, *Rec. trav. chim.*, **54**:79 (1935).   Hurd and Goldsby, *J. ACS*, **56**:1812 (1934).   Hurd, Goodyear, and Goldsby, *J. ACS*, **58**:235 (1936).   Norris and Reuter, *J. ACS*, **49**:2624 (1927).

[5] Ipatieff, *Ber.*, **36**:2003 (1903).   McCarthy and Turkevich, *J. Chem. Phys.*, **12**:405 (1944).   Oblad, Messenger, and Brown, *Ind. Eng. Chem.*, **39**:1462 (1947).

[6] Hay, Montgomery, and Coull, *Ind. Eng. Chem.*, **37**:335 (1945).   Gillett, *Bull. soc. chim. Belges*, **29**:192 (1920).   Cramer and Glasebrook, *J. ACS*, **61**:230 (1939).

$370°C$;[1] clays at $290°C$;[2] silica-alumina cracking catalysts at 400 to $600°C$;[3] and acids, such as phosphoric, at 200 to $350°C$.[4] Stronger acids, such as sulfuric acid and aluminum chloride, are effective isomerization agents at room temperature, but considerable cracking accompanies their use.[5]

Double-bond isomerizations are faster than those involving the transfer of methyl groups; the speed of the latter is influenced greatly by temperature and the proton concentration on the catalyst surface. Isomerizations over solid catalysts are also complicated to various degrees by side reactions involving polymerization and cracking; the latter appears to become appreciable at temperatures in the range of 335 to $350°C$ and above.

The carbonium ion mechanism, through which olefin isomerization is believed to take place, may be written as follows:

$$CH_3CH_2CH_2CH{=}CH_2 + H^+ \rightarrow CH_3CH_2CH_2\overset{+}{C}HCH_3$$

$$CH_3CH_2CH_2\overset{+}{C}HCH_3 \left\{ \begin{array}{l} \rightarrow CH_3CH_2CH{=}CHCH_3 + H^+ \quad \text{(Double bond or hydrogen atom shift)} \\[2mm] \rightarrow \overset{+}{C}H_2CHCH_2CH_3 \\ \qquad\quad | \\ \qquad\quad CH_3 \end{array} \right.$$

$$CH_3\overset{+}{C}CH_2CH_3 \rightleftharpoons CH_3C{=}CHCH_3 + H^+ \quad \text{(Methyl group}$$
$$\quad\ |\qquad\qquad\qquad |\qquad\qquad\qquad\qquad \text{shift)}$$
$$\quad\ CH_3\qquad\qquad\quad CH_3$$

The double-bond shift may also include a reorientation of the groups around the double bond to bring about a *cis-trans* isomerization. Thus, 1-butene is isomerized to a mixture of *cis*- and *trans*-2-butene.

$$CH_2{=}CHCH_2CH_3 \rightleftharpoons CH_3CH \rightleftharpoons CH_3CH$$
$$\qquad\qquad\qquad\qquad\quad \| \qquad\qquad\ \|$$
$$\qquad\qquad\qquad\quad CH_3CH \qquad\quad CHCH_3$$

Some generalizations can be made for olefin isomerization.[6]

[1] Hay, Montgomery, and Coull, *op. cit.* Oblad, Messenger, and Brown, *op. cit.* Goldwasser and Taylor, *J. ACS*, **61**:1766 (1939). Naragon, *Ind. Eng. Chem.*, **42**:2490 (1950). Berg, Sumner, and Montgomery, *op. cit.*

[2] Voge, Good, and Greensfelder, *Ind. Eng. Chem.*, **38**:1033 (1946).

[3] Egloff, Morrell, Thomas, and Bloch, *J. ACS*, **61**:3571 (1939). Greensfelder and Voge, *Ind. Eng. Chem.*, **37**:983 (1945).

[4] Ipatieff, Pines, and Schaad, *J. ACS*, **56**:2696 (1934).

[5] A comprehensive review of olefin isomerization is given by Dunning, *Ind. Eng. Chem.*, **45**:551 (1953).

[6] Wachter, *Ind. Eng. Chem.*, **30**:822 (1938). Ewell and Hardy, *J. ACS*, **63**:3460 (1941).

1. Olefins having a terminal double bond are the least stable.   They isomerize more rapidly than those in which the unsaturation is more centralized, and tend to revert to the latter.

$$CH_2=CHCH_2CH_3 \rightarrow CH_3CH=CHCH_3$$

2. A secondary base olefin (one hydrating to a secondary alcohol) will show a strong tendency to rearrange to a tertiary base olefin when a tertiary carbon atom is in the position alpha to a double-bonded carbon atom.

$$\underset{\displaystyle CH_3}{\overset{\displaystyle CH_3}{\underset{\displaystyle |}{CH_3\overset{|}{C}CH=CH_2}}} \rightarrow \underset{\displaystyle }{\overset{\displaystyle CH_3}{CH_3\overset{|}{C}=CHCH_3}}$$

3. When a quaternary carbon atom is in a position alpha to a secondary or tertiary double-bonded carbon atom, a pinacol type of rearrangement involving a carbon-to-carbon shift may take place.

$$CH_3\overset{\displaystyle CH_3}{\underset{\displaystyle CH_3}{\overset{|}{\underset{|}{C}}}}CH=CH_2 \rightarrow CH_3\overset{CH_3}{\overset{|}{C}H}=\overset{CH_3}{\overset{|}{C}}HCH_3$$

The calculated equilibrium concentrations at 400°C of the butenes is 20.8 per cent 1-butene, 31.6 per cent *cis*-2-butene, and 47.6 per cent *trans*-2-butene;[1] these have been closely approached experimentally over activated alumina.[2]   Isomerization of 1-pentene over alumina gel at 371°C gives a mixture containing 10.3 per cent 1-pentene, 40.9 per cent 2-pentene, and 41.7 per cent methylbutenes.[3]   Likewise, when 1-hexene is treated with an activated clay catalyst at 340°C, branched-chain hexene isomers are formed, 37.0 per cent of 2,3-dimethylbutenes, along with 15.4 per cent of normal hexenes.   Not much attention has been given to the isomerization of the heptenes.   When passed over phosphoric acid on pumice at 300°C, *n*-heptenes are converted to the extent of 5 per cent into 3-methyl-2-hexene;[4] the same isomer is obtained over alumina at 400°C.[5]

III-22. Naphthenic Hydrocarbons.   Aside from the fact that cyclopropane and cyclobutane, and their derivatives, can be converted into isomeric aliphatic olefins, and that some methylcyclopentane has been observed in thermally cracked cyclohexane,[6] the thermal isomerization of naphthenes is not common.

[1] Thacker, Folkins, and Miller, *Ind. Eng. Chem.*, **33**:584 (1941).
[2] McCarthy and Turkevich, *J. Chem. Phys.*, **12**:405 (1944).
[3] Oblad, Messenger, and Brown, *op. cit.*
[4] Petrov and Shchukin, *Oil Gas J.*, **43**(37):77 (1945).
[5] Goldwasser and Taylor, *J. ACS*, **61**:1762, 1766 (1939).
[6] Ipatieff and Dorgelevitch, *Ber.*, **44**:2987 (1911).   Haensel and Ipatieff, *Ind. Eng. Chem.*, **35**:632 (1943).

Over catalysts, generally aluminum chloride or aluminum bromide, the naphthenes may isomerize in several ways. The ring may open (in case of C_3 and C_4 rings) to form an olefin; carbon-carbon bond rupture in the side chains may result in the corresponding polymethyl derivatives, and the methyl groups may shift their positions around the ring; the C_5 and C_6 rings may expand and contract, respectively; *cis-trans* isomerization may occur; and the multiplanar isomerization (boat and chair form of cyclohexane) may take place.

The ring opening of C_3 and C_4 naphthenes to form isomeric olefins is generally followed by polymerization. Isopropylcyclobutane, however, is converted into *cis*- and *trans*-1,2 and 1,3-dimethylcyclopentanes and methylcyclohexane. Cyclopentane does not isomerize. Methyl and dimethylcyclohexanes are the isomerization products of cycloheptane[1] and cyclooctane, respectively.

In the case of petroleum products, the main interest is in the C_5 and C_6 ring naphthenes. The isomerization of methylcyclopentane to cyclohexane has been studied quite extensively.[2] The expansion of the C_5 to the C_6 ring isomer is favored by low temperatures. The methylcyclopentane content of the equilibrium mixture increases in the following manner:

Reaction temperature, °C	Average molar per cent of methylcyclopentane
25	12.5*
45	16.2*
77.4	25.6*
100	33.8†
160	50.8†
167	52.6†

* Glasebrook and Lovell, *J. ACS*, **61**:1717 (1939). Stevenson and Morgan *J. ACS*, **70**:2773 (1948).

† Lien, d'Ouville, Evering, and Grubb, *Ind. Eng. Chem.*, **44**:351 (1952).

Destructive alkylation side reactions become noticeable at temperatures above 150°C leading to the formation of 1,3-dimethylcyclohexane, dimethyldicyclopentyl, and dicyclohexyl.[3] The conversion of methylcyclopentane to cyclohexane over activated aluminum bromide at 25°C is inhibited by traces of benzene, and is completely stopped by 0.14 molar per cent of benzene.[4]

[1] Pines, Pavlik, and Ipatieff, *J. ACS*, **74**:5544 (1952). Willstätter and Kametaka, *Ber.*, **41**:1480 (1908). Zelinsky and Freimann, *Ber.*, **63**:1485 (1930).

[2] Glasebrook and Lovell, *J. ACS*, **61**:1717 (1939). Stevenson and Morgan, *J. ACS*, **70**:2773 (1948).

[3] Ipatieff and Komarewsky, *J. ACS*, **56**:1926 (1934); *Ber.*, **67**:1391 (1934).

[4] Pines, Aristoff, and Ipatieff, *J. ACS*, **71**:749 (1949).

Dimethylcyclopentanes[1] and ethylcyclopentanes[2] isomerize to methylcyclohexanes, and the propyl and butylcyclopentanes form di- and trimethylcyclohexanes, respectively.

The naphthenes are thought to isomerize through a carbonium ion intermediate according to the following illustration applied to methylcyclopentane:[3]

$$\begin{array}{ccc}
\text{CH}_2\ \text{CH}_3 & & \text{CH}_2\ \text{CH}_3 \\
\text{H}_2\text{C}\quad\text{CH} & + \text{R}^+\text{AlBr}_4^-\ \rightleftharpoons & \text{H}_2\text{C}\quad\overset{+}{\text{C}} \quad + \text{RH} \\
\text{H}_2\text{C}\text{——}\text{CH}_2 & & \text{H}_2\text{C}\text{——}\text{CH}_2
\end{array}$$

$$\begin{array}{ccc}
\text{CH}_2\ \text{CH}_3 & \text{CH}_2\ \overset{+}{\text{CH}}_2 & \text{CH}_2 \\
\text{H}_2\text{C}\quad\overset{+}{\text{C}} & \rightleftharpoons\quad \text{H}_2\text{C}\quad\text{CH} & \rightleftharpoons\quad \text{H}_2\text{C}\quad\overset{+}{\text{CH}} \\
\text{H}_2\text{C}\text{——}\text{CH}_2 & \text{H}_2\text{C}\text{——}\text{CH}_2 & \text{H}_2\text{C}\quad\text{CH}_2 \\
& & \text{CH}_2
\end{array}$$

$$\begin{array}{ccc}
\text{CH}_2 & \text{CH}_2\ \text{CH}_3 & \\
\text{H}_2\text{C}\quad\overset{+}{\text{CH}} & + \quad \text{H}_2\text{C}\quad\text{CH} & \rightleftharpoons \\
\text{H}_2\text{C}\quad\text{CH}_2 & \text{H}_2\text{C}\text{——}\text{CH}_2 & \\
\text{CH}_2 & &
\end{array}$$

$$\begin{array}{cc}
\text{CH}_2 & \text{CH}_2\ \text{CH}_3 \\
\text{H}_2\text{C}\quad\text{CH}_2 & + \quad \text{H}_2\text{C}\quad\overset{+}{\text{C}} \\
\text{H}_2\text{C}\quad\text{CH}_2 & \text{H}_2\text{C}\text{——}\text{CH}_2 \\
\text{CH}_2 &
\end{array}$$

Naphthenes are susceptible to isomerization by sulfuric acid, but only those having a tertiary carbon atom will enter the reaction, and only products containing a tertiary carbon atom are formed. Methylcyclopentane and methylcyclohexane do not undergo skeletal isomerizations, but ethylcyclopentane is converted to methylcyclohexane.[4] Sulfuric acid acts on dimethylcyclohexanes by causing shifts in the methyl groups around the ring.[5]

---

[1] Turova and Pollak, *J. Gen. Chem.* (*U.S.S.R.*), **11**:817, 824 (1941).

[2] Pines and Ipatieff, *J. ACS*, **61**:1076 (1939).

[3] Pines and Mavity, "The Chemistry of Petroleum Hydrocarbons," p. 44, Brooks, Boord, Kurtz, and Schmerling (eds.), Reinhold Publishing Corporation, New York, 1955.

[4] Stevenson, Wagner, Beeck, and Otvos, *J. ACS*, **74**:3269 (1952).

[5] Roebuck and Evering, *J. ACS*, **75**:1631 (1953).

Like the paraffins, the naphthene hydrocarbons are isomerized with good selectivity at 300 to 450°C in the presence of metals and metal sulfides and under high pressures of hydrogen; the resulting products may be nearly equilibrium mixtures.[1] Methylcyclopentane and cyclohexane are converted into each other; methylcyclohexane yields a mixture of 1,1-, 1,2-, and 1,3-dimethylcyclopentanes and ethylcyclopentanes; ethylcyclohexane gives 1,1- and 1,2-dimethylcyclohexane, 1,1,2- and 1,2,3-trimethylcyclopentane, and traces of isopropylcyclopentane.[2]

Cyclic olefins of naphthenic type may also be isomerized. Cyclohexene is converted into methylcyclopentene-1 and methylcyclopentene-2 on contact with alumina at 470 to 480°C.[3]

III-23. Alkylaromatic Hydrocarbons. The isomerization of alkylaromatics may involve changes in the side-chain configuration, disproportionation of the substituent groups, or their migration about the nucleus.

The conditions needed for isomerization within attached long side chains of alkylbenzenes and naphthalenes are also those for the scission of such groups from the ring. Such isomerizations, therefore, do not take place unless the side chains are relatively short. It has been noted that at elevated temperatures (475 to 530°C) and pressures (3,000 to 12,000 psi), purely thermal cracking-realkylation reactions convert isopropylbenzene to *n*-propylbenzene as the main product along with some benzene, toluene, and ethylbenzene; *p*-cymene into *n*-propyltoluenes; and to some extent, *sec*-butylbenzene into the *n*-butyl isomer.[4] The isomerization of ethylbenzene to xylenes, and the reverse reaction, have also been observed to take place under the conditions employed in the catalytic reforming of naphthas. An ethylbenzene-rich mixture responds as shown below at 427 to 510°C, 175 psi and under a hydrogen-hydrocarbon ratio of 10:1.[5]

	Charge, weight per cent	Temperature, °C				Equilibrium mixture at 454°C
		427	454	482	510	
Ethylbenzene........	97.0	57.3	69.3	73.6	76.5	8.5
o-Xylene............	1.0	11.5	9.2	7.5	4.5	23.0
m-Xylene............	1.2	14.9	11.3	8.8	5.8	46.5
p-Xylene............	0.7	7.5	5.9	5.2	4.0	22.0

[1] Ciapetta, *Ind. Eng. Chem.*, **45**:159, 162 (1953). Adkins and Roebuck, *J. ACS*, **70**:4041 (1948). Haensel and Donaldson, *Ind. Eng. Chem.*, **43**:2102 (1951).

[2] Ciapetta and Hunter, *op. cit.*

[3] Adkins and Roebuck, *op. cit.* Haensel and Donaldson, *op. cit.*

[4] Ipatieff, Kvetinskas, Meisinger, and Pines, *J. ACS*, **75**:3323 (1953). Kinney and Hamilton, *J. ACS*, **76**:786 (1954).

[5] Pitts, Connor, and Leum, *Ind. Eng. Chem.*, **47**:770 (1955).

At lower temperatures the isomerizations involve mainly the migration of alkyl groups along the aromatic ring.[1]   This is of some interest commercially in the preparation of stocks for oxidation to phthalic anhydride, isophthalic, and terephthalic acids.

In the preparation of propylbenzenes by alkylating benzene with propylene in the presence of mild catalysts, such as boron trifluoride and phosphoric acids, the disubstitution products are mainly the ortho and para isomers, as expected.[2]   Also, ortho and para isomers are favored on alkylation of toluene with methyl chloride in the presence of aluminum chloride, a strong catalyst, at 0 to 40°C, but at 50 to 100°C, more of the meta isomer is obtained,[3] actually in amounts far exceeding that in the equilibrium mixture at that temperature level.[4]   A study of xylene isomerization in the presence of boron trifluoride and hydrofluoric acid[5] has shown that a complex is formed by the meta isomer with the catalyst. This complex is considerably more stable than that formed from either the ortho or para isomer; the latter in turn are converted into the m-xylene complex.   If an excess of boron trifluoride is present, the catalyst and hydrocarbon are in a single phase, and the hydrolysis of the resulting complex leads to quantitative yields of m-xylene.   Similarly, a 100 per cent yield of mesitylene can be obtained in trimethylbenzene isomerization. Presumably, the stable hydrocarbon-catalyst adduct is of the type of the sigma complex referred to in the discussion of the alkylation of aromatic hydrocarbons.

Disproportionation of attached side chains is also a common occurrence; higher and lower alkyl substitution products are formed.   For example, xylenes will disproportionate in the presence of hydrogen fluoride-boron trifluoride or aluminum chloride,[6] to form benzene, toluene, and higher alkylated products.   Disproportionation may be

[1] For reviews of aromatic isomerization, see Calloway, *Chem. Revs.*, **17**:327 (1935). Nightingale, *Chem. Revs.*, **25**:329 (1939).   Price, *Chem. Revs.*, **29**:37 (1941).   Francis, *Chem. Revs.*, **43**:257 (1948).   Thomas, "Anhydrous Aluminum Chloride in Organic Chemistry," p. 94, Reinhold Publishing Corporation, New York, 1941.   See also Norris and Turner, *J. ACS*, **61**:2128 (1939).   Nightingale et al., *J. ACS*, **61**:101, 1411 (1939); **62**:280 (1940); **63**:258, 3514 (1941); **76**:5767 (1954).   Brown and Jungk, *J. ACS*, **77**:5579 (1955).

[2] Slanina, Sowa, and Nieuland, *J. ACS*, **57**:1547 (1935).   Melpolder, Woodbridge, and Headington, *J. ACS*, **70**:935 (1948).

[3] Norris and Rubenstein, *J. ACS*, **61**:1163, 2131 (1939).

[4] At 80°C, the equilibrium mixture contains ortho, meta, and para isomers in the amounts of 18, 58, and 24 per cent, respectively. Taylor, Wagman, Williams, Pitzer, and Rossini, *J. Research Natl. Bur. Standards*, **37**:95 (1946).

[5] McCaulay and Lien, *J. Research Natl. Bur. Standards*, **74**:6246 (1952); **75**:2407, 2411 (1953).

[6] Nightingale, *Chem. Revs.*, **25**:329 (1939).

made quantitative by proper choice of conditions. Thus, ethylbenzene, in presence of 90 molar per cent of boron trifluoride, forms a mixture of benzene and 1,3-diethylbenzene in 95 per cent yield. Here again, the relatively basic diethylbenzenes form sigma complexes with the catalyst, of which the meta isomer is the more stable.

ALKYLATION OF HYDROCARBONS

III-24. Isoparaffinic Hydrocarbons. Although the alkylation of low-molecular-weight isoparaffins by olefins to form higher isoparaffins is simply the reverse of cracking, the belief that paraffin hydrocarbons are chemically inert delayed its discovery until about 1935. Since then, the reaction has become a major factor in the production of isoparaffinic gasolines of high octane number.

Thermodynamic calculations show that the free energy of the reaction is negative at low temperatures.[1] In the absence of any catalyst, and at atmospheric pressure, the addition of isobutane to isobutylene is thermodynamically possible at temperatures up to 260°C.[2] The reaction proceeds readily with high yields at room temperature in the presence of Friedel-Craft type compounds and strong acids (chromium chloride, zirconium tetrachloride,[3] boron trifluoride,[4] sulfuric acid,[5] hydrofluoric acid[6]). As the reaction is accompanied by a decrease in volume, the application of moderate pressures permits higher temperatures. Milder catalysts such as aluminum chloride–sodium chloride[7] (150°C, 1,000 psi) and phosphoric acid[8] (230°C, 500 psi) are then effective, but the alkylation is not clean-cut. The reaction will take place at higher temperatures (510°C) and pressures (4,500 psi) without catalysts.[9] Lower temperatures and pressures than the above (300 to 400°C, and 2,500 to 3,000 psi) may be employed in thermal alkylations if a small amount (0.5 to 3.0 per

---

[1] Parks and Todd, *Ind. Eng. Chem.*, **28**:418 (1936).

[2] Ewell, *Ind. Eng. Chem.*, **32**:778 (1940).

[3] Ipatieff, Grosse, Komarewsky, and Pines, *J. ACS*, **58**:913 (1936).

[4] Ipatieff and Grosse, *J. ACS*, **57**:1616 (1935).

[5] Birch, Dunstan, Fidler, Pim, and Tait, *J. Inst. Petrol. Technologists*, **24**:303 (1938); *Ind. Eng. Chem.*, **31**: 884, 1079 (1939). Birch and Dunstan, *Trans. Faraday Soc.*, **35**:1013 (1939). Waterman, Leenderste, and Hesselink, *Rec. trav. chim.*, **58**:1040 (1939). MacKenzie, *Refiner Nat. Gasoline Mfr.*, **18**:494 (1939). Gorin, Kuhn, and Miles, *Ind. Eng. Chem.*, **38**:795 (1946).

[6] Linn and Grosse, *Ind. Eng. Chem.*, **37**:924 (1945).

[7] Blunck and Carmody, *Ind. Eng. Chem.*, **32**:328 (1940).

[8] Pinkerton and Mendina, U.S. Patent 2,177,579, 1939; U.S. Patent 2,212,951, 1940; U.S. Patent 2,212,952, 1940. Morrell, U.S. Patent 2,231,452, 1941.

[9] Frey and Hepp, *Ind. Eng. Chem.*, **28**:1439 (1936). Oberfell and Frey, *Refiner Nat. Gasoline Mfr.*, **18**:486 (1939).

cent) of a homogeneous promoter (chloroform, benzyl chloride, chlorinated naphtha, dichloropropane, nitromethane, acetyl chloride, etc.) is present.[1]

Of most commercial importance, however, is the low-temperature alkylation conducted in the presence of either sulfuric or hydrofluoric acid. The reaction product obtained with either catalyst does not consist entirely of the hydrocarbon expected by the direct addition of the olefin and isoparaffin. As a result of a rather complex and still not definitely established mechanism, a mixture of wide boiling point spread is obtained. By proper choice of operating conditions, the product can be made to fall mainly within the gasoline range. Since it is composed largely of branched-chain structures, octane numbers of 88 to 92 or higher are common.

In acid-catalyzed alkylation only paraffins with tertiary carbon atoms, such as isobutane and isopentane, will react with the olefin. However, isooctane, 2,2,4-trimethylpentane, a normal product of alkylation, will not act as the isoparaffinic reactant.[2] Neohexane, containing a quaternary carbon atom, is not alkylated. Commercially, only isobutane is used; the naturally high octane level and volatility of isopentane make it a sufficiently valuable blending stock for finished gasolines. Normal hydrocarbons, from butane up through dodecane, have been made to react when aluminum chloride or aluminum bromide is the catalyst, but here it is assumed that the catalyst brings about isomerization prior to the alkylation.

Ethylene is slower to react in catalyzed isoparaffin alkylation reactions than the higher olefins. It responds to an appreciable extent, however, when boron trifluoride or aluminum chloride[3] is the catalyst. Propylene will enter the alkylation reaction even with sulfuric acid if the acid concentration is raised to 100 per cent, or thereabouts. Olefins higher than the butenes are active but are not particularly satisfactory, especially the tertiary base compounds, because they enter hydrogen exchange reactions. Either normal or tertiary base olefin isomers may be used; the same compounds are obtained from both.[4] The same product is also obtained on reacting isobutane with isobutylene, diisobutylene, or triisobutylene, indicating preliminary depolymerizations.

The reaction with sulfuric acid is conducted at 10 to 20°C in order to

---

[1] O'Kelly and Sachanen, *Ind. Eng. Chem.*, **38**:462 (1946). Knap, Comings, and Drickamer, *Ind. Eng. Chem.*, **46**:708 (1954).

[2] Birch and Dunstan, *Trans. Faraday Soc.*, **35**:1013 (1939).

[3] Ipatieff and Grosse, *J. ACS*, **57**:1616 (1935). Axe and Schulze, *Ind. Eng. Chem.*, **39**:1273 (1947). Thompson and Chenicek, *Ind. Eng. Chem.*, **40**:1265 (1948).

[4] Birch, Dunstan, Fidler, Pim, and Tait, *J. Inst. Petrol. Technologists*, **24**:303 (1938); *Ind. Eng. Chem.*, **31**:884, 1079 (1939).

minimize oxidation-reduction reactions leading to sulfur dioxide evolution and charring.[1] With anhydrous hydrofluoric acid, temperature is not as critical; it is held at about 35°C. Sufficient pressure is maintained on the system to keep the olefin in the liquid state. With both sulfuric and hydrofluoric acids, the volume employed is about equal to that of the hydrocarbon liquid charge. Efficient agitation provides good phase contact, which is necessary for good yield and quality of the product. The reaction is rapid, but 10 to 40 min are generally allowed. To minimize polymerization, the isoparaffin-olefin ratios supplied are in the order of 4:1 or higher. The adjustment of this ratio, as well as the maintenance of the high acid-hydrocarbon ratio, offers a control of the yield, volatility, and octane number of the alkylate.

Sulfuric acid of about 98 per cent concentration is employed in practice. Its strength is allowed to decrease with use, to about 88 per cent before make-up acid is added. The acid becomes fouled to some extent through ester formation but more so through dehydrogenation of the olefin to give highly unsaturated acid-soluble hydrocarbons. On diluting the spent acid, a heavy unsaturated oil separates, which is probably similar in composition to the products obtained from the acid layer in conjunct polymerizations.[2]

The products obtained in thermal alkylation are essentially those expected by the addition of the scission products of the paraffin across the olefinic bond.[3] Some examples are given below, with the main product given first:

Ethylene plus			Propylene plus isobutane
Propane	*n*-Butane	Isobutane	
Isopentane	3-Methylpentane	2,2-Dimethylbutane	2,2-Dimethylpentane
n-Pentane	*n*-Hexane	2-Methylpentane	2-Methylhexane
			2,2,3-Trimethylbutane

The thermal alkylation may proceed through a free radical mechanism. Thus, for the reaction of isobutane with ethylene, tertiary butyl radicals form more readily than primary butyl radicals; as a result the preponderant product will be 2,2-dimethylbutane, and 2-methylpentane will be formed in minor amounts only.

[1] For a discussion of commercial alkylation of isobutane, see Mrstik, Smith, and Pinkerton, *Advances in Chem. Ser.*, no. 5, p. 97, 1951.

[2] Ipatieff and Pines, *J. Org. Chem.*, **1**:464 (1936–1937).

[3] Frey and Hepp, *loc. cit.* Oberfell and Frey, *loc. cit.*

$$R\cdot + CH_3\overset{\overset{\displaystyle CH_3}{|}}{\underset{\underset{\displaystyle CH_3}{|}}{C}}H \rightarrow CH_3\overset{\overset{\displaystyle CH_3}{|}}{\underset{\underset{\displaystyle CH_3}{|}}{C}}\cdot \quad \text{and} \quad CH_3\overset{\overset{\displaystyle \overset{\bullet}{C}H_2}{|}}{\underset{\underset{\displaystyle CH_3}{|}}{C}}H + RH$$

Major   Minor

$$CH_3\overset{\overset{\displaystyle CH_3}{|}}{\underset{\underset{\displaystyle CH_3}{|}}{C}}\cdot + CH_2{=}CH_2 \rightarrow CH_3\overset{\overset{\displaystyle CH_3}{|}}{\underset{\underset{\displaystyle CH_3}{|}}{C}}CH_2CH_2\cdot$$

$$CH_3\overset{\overset{\displaystyle CH_3}{|}}{\underset{\underset{\displaystyle CH_3}{|}}{C}}CH_2CH_2\cdot + CH_3{-}\overset{\overset{\displaystyle CH_3}{|}}{\underset{\underset{\displaystyle CH_3}{|}}{C}}H \rightarrow CH_3\overset{\overset{\displaystyle CH_3}{|}}{\underset{\underset{\displaystyle CH_3}{|}}{C}}CH_2CH_3 + CH_3\overset{\overset{\displaystyle CH_3}{|}}{\underset{\underset{\displaystyle \overset{\bullet}{C}H_3}{|}}{C}}\cdot$$

and as a minor reaction

$$CH_3\overset{\overset{\displaystyle \overset{\bullet}{C}H_2}{|}}{\underset{\underset{\displaystyle CH_3}{|}}{C}}H + CH_2{=}CH_2 \rightarrow CH_3\overset{\overset{\displaystyle CH_3}{|}}{\underset{\underset{\displaystyle CH_3}{|}}{}}CHCH_2CH_2CH_2\cdot$$

$$CH_3\overset{\overset{\displaystyle CH_3}{|}}{\underset{\underset{\displaystyle CH_3}{|}}{}}CHCH_2CH_2CH_2\cdot + CH_3{-}\overset{\overset{\displaystyle CH_3}{|}}{\underset{\underset{\displaystyle CH_3}{|}}{C}}H \rightarrow CH_3\overset{\overset{\displaystyle CH_3}{|}}{\underset{\underset{\displaystyle CH_3}{|}}{}}CHCH_2CH_2CH_3 + CH_3\overset{\overset{\displaystyle \overset{\bullet}{C}H_2}{|}}{\underset{\underset{\displaystyle CH_3}{|}}{C}}H$$

In acid-catalyzed alkylations, however, the expected products of such additions are not necessarily found in major amounts. For example, the thermal alkylation of isobutane with ethylene produces four times as much 2,2-dimethylbutane as 2-methylpentane. Alkylation in presence of aluminum chloride, however, yields 70 to 90 per cent of 2,3-dimethylbutane, along with 10 to 25 per cent of 2-methylpentane and only a small amount of 2,2-dimethylbutane. Similarly, the thermal alkylation product of propylene and isobutane is 2,2-dimethylpentane, while the acid-catalyzed product is a mixture composed largely of 2,3- and 2,4-dimethylpentanes. The composition of the alkylates made with sulfuric and hydrofluoric acids shows minor differences.[1] While both of the above acids produce quite similar compounds on alkylating isobutane with 1- and 2-butenes, aluminum chloride gives an alkylate of different composition with these two olefins. In each case, only about 20 per cent is in the octane boiling range; the C_8 isoparaffins are largely dimethylhexanes in the 1-butene alkylate and trimethylpentanes in the 2-butene

[1] Glasgow, Streiff, Willingham, and Rossini, *J. Research Natl. Bur. Standards*, **38**:537 (1947).

alkylate. Because of side reactions, aluminum chloride is not used in isoparaffin alkylations where olefins higher than ethylene are employed.

In all the above reactions, some isoparaffins of higher and lower molecular weight than that of the combined isoparaffin-olefin are obtained.[1] A typical analysis of a sulfuric acid catalyzed isobutane-C_4 olefin alkylate is given in Table III-17.

TABLE III-17*

Volume per cent

2,3-Dimethylbutane	5.2
2-Methylpentane	1.2
3-Methylpentane	0.4
2,2,3-Trimethylbutane	0.2
2,2-Dimethylpentane	0.2
2,4-Dimethylpentane	3.7
2,3-Dimethylpentane	2.6
2- and 3-Methylhexane	0.3
2,2,4-Trimethylpentane	26.7
2,2,3-Trimethylpentane	1.3
2,3,4-Trimethylpentane	14.3
2,3,3-Trimethylpentane	13.5
2,2-Dimethylhexane	0.3
2,3-Dimethylhexane	3.3
2,4-Dimethylhexane	7.2
2,5-Dimethylhexane	7.2
3,4-Dimethylhexane	0.4
2,2,5-Trimethylhexane	4.9
2,3,5-Trimethylhexane	1.0
Isononanes	0.5
Higher isoparaffins	12.8

* Glasgow, Streiff, Willingham, and Rossini, *J. Research Natl. Bur. Standards*, **38**:537 (1947).

The final alkylate is thus rather complex in composition. A number of mechanisms have been proposed to account for the various isomers found.[2]

[1] For a comprehensive review of isoparaffin-olefin alkylations, see Ipatieff and Schmerling, "Advances in Catalysis," vol. I, p. 27, Academic Press, Inc., New York, 1948. Schmerling in "The Chemistry of Petroleum Hydrocarbons," Brooks, Boord, Kurtz, and Schmerling (eds.), vol. III, p. 363, Reinhold Publishing Corporation, New York, 1955. Birch, "Science of Petroleum," vol. V, part II, p. 286, Oxford University Press, New York and London, 1953.

[2] These involve carbon-hydrogen bond scission of the isoparaffin followed by the addition of the hydrogen and tertiary alkyl groups [Ipatieff and Grosse, *J. ACS*, **57**:1616 (1935)] or of hydrogen and secondary alkyl groups [Birch and Dunstan, *Trans. Faraday Soc.*, **35**:1013 (1939)] across the olefinic double bond; the addition of methyl and isopropyl fragments from a polarized isobutane molecule across the olefinic double bond [Caesar and Francis, *Ind. Eng. Chem.*, **33**:1426 (1941); McAllister, Anderson, Ballard, and Ross, *J. Org. Chem.*, **6**:647 (1941); Gorin, Kuhn, and Miles, *Ind. Eng. Chem.*, **38**:795 (1946)] and the assumption of carbonium ions as intermediates [Bartlett, Condon, and Schneider, *J. ACS*, **66**:1531 (1944); Ciapetta, *Ind. Eng. Chem.*, **37**:1210 (1945); Schmerling, *J. ACS*, **66**:1422 (1944); **68**:275, 1778 (1946); **75**:4275 (1953)].

A possible role played by the formation and isomerization of carbonium ions in olefin-isoparaffin alkylation is outlined below, using the acid catalyzed reaction between isobutane and 2-butene as an example.

$$CH_3CH{=}CHCH_3 + H^+ \rightarrow CH_3\overset{+}{C}HCH_2CH_3$$

$$(CH_3)_3CH + CH_3\overset{+}{C}HCH_2CH_3 \rightarrow (CH_3)_3C^+ + CH_3CH_2CH_2CH_3$$

$$(CH_3)_3C^+ + CH_3CH{=}CHCH_3 \rightarrow CH_3\overset{+}{C}HCHCH_3$$
$$\underset{\underset{C(CH_3)_3}{|}}{}$$

Each of the above C_8 carbonium ions is capable of reacting with an isobutane molecule to form a C_8 isoparaffin and a tertiary-butyl ion, which would in turn react with another 2-butene molecule to continue the chain. While the application of this mechanism to 1-butene would indicate that different C_8 isoparaffins should result, it is found in practice that both 1- and 2-butenes give essentially the same products in the presence of sulfuric or hydrofluoric acids. The explanation for this appears to be that 1-butene is isomerized to 2-butene, and both of these olefins form the same carbonium ion. Aluminum chloride, on the other hand, presumably does not bring about the formation of a common carbonium ion from these olefins, which accounts for the different products in the reaction of isobutane with 1- and 2-butenes.[1]

The products from the alkylation of isobutane with C_4 olefins, however, contain hydrocarbons both higher and lower in molecular weight than the C_8 isoparaffins. These are the result of secondary reactions in which

[1] Schmerling, *J. ACS*, **68**:275 (1946).

either the expected hydrocarbon formed in the alkylation, or the carbonium ion from which it was formed, depolymerizes. The new olefins that result then add to a carbonium ion from isobutane (tertiary-butyl) to form new carbonium ions, and from these hydrocarbons of lower and higher molecular weight are formed.[1] Thus, the 2,3,4-trimethylpentyl-carbonium ion depolymerizes as follows:

$$CH_3CHCHCHCH_3 \rightarrow H^+ + C\text{—}C\text{=}C + CH_3C\text{=}CHCH_3$$

(with CH_3 substituents as drawn)

or $CH_3CH\text{—}CH\text{=}CH_2$ with CH_3

or $CH_2\text{=}CCH_2CH_3$ with CH_3

These olefins then react with tertiary-butyl carbonium ions to form isoheptanes and isononanes. The above pentenes also enter conjunct polymerizations (hydrogen transfers) to form isopentane and highly unsaturated olefins which end up in the acid layer.[2]

Alkylation of Naphthenes. Cycloparaffins, especially those containing tertiary carbon atoms, are alkylated with olefins in a manner similar to the isoparaffins; the reaction is not as clean-cut, and the yields are low because of the several side reactions that take place. Methylcyclopentane and propylene, in the presence of aluminum bromide, give 1-methyl-2-ethylcyclohexane;[3] with 1-butene (with H_2SO_4) 1,3-dimethyl-4- and 5-ethylcyclohexane are formed.[4] Cyclohexane, alkylated with ethylene $(AlCl_3)$, produces di- and tetramethylcyclohexane;[5] and 1,3,5-trimethylcyclohexane with propylene.[6] Methylcyclohexane reacts with propylene, $AlCl_3$, to yield 1-methyl-3- and 4-propylcyclohexanes. In general, the butenes and pentenes enter naphthene alkylation reluctantly. Boron trifluoride catalyzes the alkylation of methylcyclopentane and methylcyclohexane, both of which contain tertiary carbon atoms, but is not effective on unsubstituted naphthenes.

[1] Ciapetta, *Ind. Eng. Chem.*, **37**:1210 (1945).
[2] Ciapetta, *op. cit.* Hartig, Hughes, and Veatch, *ACS, Div. Petrol. Chem.*, Preprints, p. 423, Atlantic City, April, 1946.
[3] Pines and Ipatieff, *J. ACS*, **70**:531 (1948).
[4] *Ibid.*, **67**:1631 (1945).
[5] Ipatieff, Komarewsky, and Grosse, *J. ACS*, **57**:1722 (1935).
[6] Pines and Ipatieff, *J. Org. Chem.*, **6**:242 (1941).

When naphthenes are reacted with isoparaffins, a destructive alkylation reaction takes place similar to that between aromatics and isoparaffins.[1] Thus, cyclohexane or methylcyclohexane, reacted with 2,2,3- or 2,2,4-trimethylpentane, or 3,4-dimethylhexane, gives isobutane, polymethylcyclohexanes, methylethylcyclohexanes, and dicyclic compounds.

III-25. Aromatic Hydrocarbons. Aromatic hydrocarbons are more easily alkylated by olefins than are the isoparaffins. The thermal reaction between benzene and ethylene is thermodynamically favored by atmospheric pressure and temperatures up to 540°C,[2] as compared to about 300°C for the isoparaffins. Evidence of thermal alkylation of benzene with ethane, propane, and butanes, probably taking place through a free radical chain mechanism, has been obtained at 475 to 550°C, under 4,600 to 4,800 psi pressure; toluene, ethylbenzene, C_3 and C_4 alkylbenzenes, and xylenes are formed along with other products (biphenyl, fluorene, anthracene, diphenylbenzene, etc.).[3] Benzene alkylation proceeds readily in the presence of an acid catalyst. Alumina-silica complexes have been used at 240 to 260°C to alkylate benzene with ethylene, and at 190 to 240°C with propylene, under pressure, to form ethyl and isopropylbenzenes.[4] With stronger acids, the reaction proceeds still more easily. Cumene has been prepared by alkylating benzene with propylene over phosphoric acid–kieselguhr[5] or sulfuric acid.[6] Hydrofluoric acid is also an effective catalyst,[7] and alkane sulfonic acids[8] can be employed, as can metallic sodium plus a promoter.[9]

Several important aromatic alkylations are practiced commercially: the reaction of benzene with ethylene to form ethylbenzene, which is then dehydrogenated to styrene; the alkylation of mononuclear aromatics with propylene to give the corresponding isopropyl derivatives, which are in turn converted into phenol, cresols, etc., through a hydroperoxide intermediate (i.e., phenol and acetone from cumene hydroperoxide); the alkylation of benzene and naphthalene with long-chain alkyl chlorides for making the corresponding alkyl aromatics, which are sulfonated on the nucleus to sulfonic acids (sodium salts) for detergent use; and the alkylation of phenols with olefins or alkyl halides to prepare alkylated phenols

[1] Pines, Grosse, and Ipatieff, *J. ACS*, **61**:640 (1939).

[2] Brickwedde, Moscow, and Scott, *J. Chem. Phys.*, **13**:547 (1945).

[3] Nickels, Ph.D. Dissertation, "High Temperature Destructive Alkylation of Cyclic Hydrocarbons with Gaseous Paraffins under Pressure," University of Pittsburgh, 1942.

[4] O'Kelly, Kellett, and Plucker, *Ind. Eng. Chem.*, **39**:154 (1947).

[5] Ipatieff, Pines, and Komarewsky, *Trans. AIChE*, **28**:222 (1936); **41**:463 (1945).

[6] Ipatieff, Corson, and Pines, *Chem. Eng. Progr.*, **58**:919 (1936); **43**:189 (1947).

[7] Simon and Archer, *J. ACS*, **60**:986, 2952, 2953, 2955 (1938); **61**:1521 (1939).

[8] Proell, Adams, and Shoemaker, *Ind. Eng. Chem.*, **40**:1129 (1948).

[9] Pines, Vesely, and Ipatieff, *J. ACS*, **77**:554 (1955).

for use as additives (or as intermediates in the preparation of additives) in fuels and lubricants.[1]   The first and third of these processes are conducted in the presence of aluminum chloride, which, along with other metal halides, is the most important of the aromatic alkylation catalysts. The Friedel-Craft reagents have been classified according to their effectiveness in the following order:[2]

$$AlBr_3 > AlCl_3 > FeCl_3 > ZrCl_4 > BF_3 > TiCl_3 > ZnCl_2$$
$$> SnCl_4 > TiCl_4$$

As might be expected, there are overlappings and exceptions in the above order.   For example, boron trifluoride is an excellent catalyst for alkylation with alkyl fluorides, alcohols, and olefins but is not very good with alkyl chlorides and bromides.

The alkylation agent is generally an olefin,[3] although cyclopropane,[4] alkyl halides,[5] aliphatic alcohols,[6] ethers,[7] and esters[8] may also be used.[9] The alkylation with isobutylene can be carried out with about 80 to 85 per cent sulfuric acid, about 94 to 96 per cent acid with propylene, but with ethylene 98 to 100 per cent strength is required.   In the latter case, however, sulfonation also takes place.

Isoparaffins also may serve as alkylating agents in the presence of boron trifluoride,[10] aluminum chloride,[11] sulfuric acid,[12] or alumina-silica[13] as catalysts.   Toluene alkylated with isobutane, in the presence of boron trifluoride hydrate and with isohexene as a hydrogen acceptor, gives good

[1] For a review of commercial aromatic alkylations, see McAllister in "The Chemistry of Petroleum Hydrocarbons," Brooks, Boord, Kurtz, and Schmerling (eds.), vol. III, p. 579, Reinhold Publishing Corporation, New York, 1955.

[2] Burk, Twelfth Catalyst Report, National Research Council, p. 266, Washington, D.C., 1940.   A much more complete listing of metal chlorides is presented.

[3] Sanford, Kovach, and Friedman, *J. ACS*, **75**:6326 (1953).

[4] Grosse and Ipatieff, *J. Org. Chem.*, **2**:447 (1937).   Ipatieff, Pines, and Corson, *J. ACS*, **60**:577 (1938).   Simons, Archer, and Adams, *J. ACS*, **60**:2955 (1938).

[5] Simons and Archer, *J. ACS*, **60**:986, 2953 (1938).   Shoesmith and McGechen, *J. Chem. Soc.*, 2231 (1930).   Bartlett, Condon, and Schneider, *J. ACS*, **66**:1531 (1944).

[6] Huston and Hsich, *J. ACS*, **58**:439 (1936).   Sowa and McKenna, *J. ACS*, **59**:470 (1937).   Norris and Ingraham, *J. ACS*, **60**:1421 (1938).   Simons, Archer, and Passino, *J. ACS*, **60**:2956 (1938).   Norris and Sturgis, *J. ACS*, **61**:1413 (1939).

[7] O'Connor and Sowa, *J. ACS*, **60**:125 (1938).

[8] McKenna and Sowa, *J. ACS*, **59**:1204 (1937).   Bowden, *J. ACS*, **60**:645 (1938).

[9] For a discussion of directive effects in aromatic substitution, see Nelson and Brown, *ACS, Div. Petrol. Chem., Joint Symposium on Mechanics of Homogeneous and Heterogeneous Hydrocarbon Reactions*, Preprints, p. 49, Kansas City, March–April, 1954.

[10] Kelly and Lee, *Ind. Eng. Chem.*, **47**:757 (1955).

[11] Grosse, Mavity, and Ipatieff, *J. ACS*, **57**:2415 (1935); *J. Org. Chem.*, **3**:137 (1938).

[12] Komarewsky, U.S. Patent 2,333,866, 1933.

[13] Sachanen and Davis, U.S. Patent 2,234,984, 1941.

yields of *m*- and *p-tert*-butyltoluenes.[1] With higher isoparaffins, dealkylation apparently first takes place to form a smaller paraffin and an olefin, the latter acting as the alkylating agent. Thus, benzene alkylated with 2,2,4-trimethylpentane over aluminum chloride at 25 to 50°C forms nearly quantitative amounts of *t*-butylbenzene and isobutane. Benzene and other aromatics alkylated with isoamylene ($AlCl_3$, BF_3, catalyzed) yield substantial amounts of *t*-butyl derivatives, presumably through a series of processes including polymerization of the olefin, isomerization, and bond scission to form C_4 fragments.[2]

The alkylation of aromatic hydrocarbons with olefins, alcohols, ethers, esters, and tertiary alkyl halides is considered to take place in most cases through a carbonium ion mechanism with both acid and Friedel-Craft catalysts.

With acids:

$$CH_3CH{=}CH_2 + H^+ \rightarrow CH_3\overset{+}{C}HCH_3$$

$$C_6H_6 + CH_3\overset{+}{C}HCH_3 \rightleftharpoons \underset{H^+}{\bigcirc}\!CH(CH_3)_2 \rightleftharpoons \bigcirc\!CH(CH_3)_2 + H^+$$

With $AlCl_3$:

$$CH_3CH_2CH_2Cl + AlCl_3 \rightleftharpoons CH_3CH_2CH_2^+ + AlCl_4^-$$

$$\bigcirc + CH_3CH_2\overset{+}{C}H_2 \rightarrow \underset{\overset{+}{H}}{\bigcirc}\!\!\overset{CH_2CH_2CH_3}{\underset{H}{}} \rightarrow \bigcirc\!CH_2CH_2CH_3 + H^+$$

$$H^+ + AlCl_4^- \rightarrow HCl + AlCl_3$$

Recent evidence indicates that aromatic alkylations with primary alkyl halides (which can form carbonium ions only with difficulty) and $AlCl_3$ proceed through a bimolecular displacement reaction.[3] This involves the formation of a stabilized carbonium ion salt (sigma complex) through the action of the aromatic on the aluminum chloride–alkyl chloride

[1] Kelly and Lee, *op. cit.*

[2] Friedman and Morritz, *J. ACS*, **78**:3430 (1956).

[3] Brown, Pearsall, Eddy, Wallace, Grayson, and Nelson, *Ind. Eng. Chem.*, **45**:1462 (1953). Nelson and Brown in "The Chemistry of Petroleum Hydrocarbons," Brooks, Boord, Kurtz, and Schmerling (eds.), vol. III, p. 465, Reinhold Publishing Corporation, New York, 1955. Brown and Brady, *J. ACS*, **74**:3570 (1952).

complex

$$ArH + RCl:AlCl_3 \rightleftharpoons ArH\text{-}RCl:AlCl_3 \rightleftharpoons \left[Ar \begin{array}{c} H \\ R \end{array} \right]^{+} AlCl_4^{-}$$

Stable intermediate
sigma complex

$$\left[Ar \begin{array}{c} H \\ R \end{array} \right]^{+} AlCl_4^{-} \rightleftharpoons RAr + HCl + AlCl_3$$

The ease of forming the sigma complex depends upon the nucleophyllic nature of the aromatic hydrocarbons; their basic properties increase with degree of substitution, i.e., in the order of benzene < xylene < mesitylene.[1] Depending on reaction conditions and the aromatic being alkylated, the reaction with secondary alkyl halides may proceed through either the carbonium ion or the bimolecular displacement mechanism.

The difference in the stability of a carbonium ion intermediate and the sigma complex illustrated above is possibly the reason for the variation in products formed in alkylations catalyzed by sulfuric acid and aluminum chloride, respectively. With the former, isomerizations within the alkyl group (either prior to or during alkylation) are much more prevalent than when aluminum chloride is used. For example, 3-methyl-1-butene alkylates benzene to give tertiary-amylbenzene with sulfuric acid, and 2-methyl-3-phenylbutane with aluminum chloride;[2] alkylation of benzene with 2-butene over a phosphoric acid catalyst at 200°C gives a mixture of *sec*- and *tert*-butylbenzenes,[3] while benzene and *n*-butyl chloride over aluminum chloride give a mixture of *n*- and *sec*-butylbenzenes but no branched-chain alkyl benzene.[4] Cyclopropane alkylates benzene at all temperatures with aluminum chloride to give *n*-propylbenzene, while sulfuric acid gives the normal derivative at 65°C and the iso derivative at 0°C. Skeletal isomerizations are rare in aluminum chloride catalyzed alkylations. One case only has been reported, that of neopentylchloride and benzene forming 2-methyl-3-phenylbutane.[5]

ACTION OF ANHYDROUS ALUMINUM CHLORIDE

The action of anhydrous aluminum chloride on hydrocarbons can involve cleavage, destructive combination, rearrangement, and synthesis.

[1] McCaulay and Lien, *J. ACS*, **73**:2013 (1951); **74**:6246 (1952); **75**:2407, 2411 (1953); **76**:2354 (1954); **77**:1803 (1955). McCaulay, Shoemaker, and Lien, *Ind. Eng. Chem.*, **42**:2103 (1950).

[2] Ipatieff, Pines, and Schmerling, *J. Org. Chem.*, **5**:253 (1940).

[3] Pines, LaZerte, and Ipatieff, *J. ACS*, **72**:2850 (1950).

[4] Schmerling, *Ind. Eng. Chem.*, **45**:1447 (1953).

[5] Pines, Schmerling, and Ipatieff, *J. ACS*, **62**:2901 (1940).

Thus, the cracking of gas oils to gasoline by mild heating (225 to 300°C atmospheric pressure) over a few per cent of aluminum chloride was practiced commercially at one time.[1] The compound is still used for drastic refining of lubricating oil stocks to remove the more aromatic-type molecules and those containing oxygen, nitrogen, and sulfur. It has been employed in wartime for isomerization of normal to isobutane. Synthetic reactions are shown by its ability to polymerize lower olefins to lubricating oils and to alkylate both isoparaffins and aromatics with olefins. The versatile reactivity of aluminum chloride is sometimes embarrassing because of the ease with which side reactions proceed, particularly with higher-molecular-weight hydrocarbons.[2]

III-26. Paraffinic Hydrocarbons. Under sufficiently mild conditions, the action of aluminum chloride on normal and isobutanes can be confined pretty well to isomerization (see Sec. III-20). With higher hydrocarbons disproportionation occurs, leading to both higher- and lower-boiling products. The action, referred to also as destructive alkylation,[3] is believed to involve conversion of a normal to an isoparaffin; this latter is then decomposed to isobutane plus an olefin. Part of this olefin will alkylate the parent isoparaffin and part will combine with the catalyst reactant, where it undergoes conjunct polymerization. Products explained by such a sequence have been observed for *n*-pentane,[4] *n*-hexane, and *n*-heptane.[5] Isooctane, 2,2,4-trimethylpentane, also yields isobutane and higher-boiling saturated hydrocarbons.

In general, the disproportionation reactions increase with molecular size and branching of the paraffin molecule. Yields up to 76 per cent of isobutane have been obtained by the action of aluminum chloride on *n*-heptane at 95 to 100°C.[6] Destructive action and synthesis of higher compounds are reduced and isomerization is emphasized by adding metallic aluminum, magnesium, or sodium to the system. The same effects are obtained by maintaining a high pressure of hydrogen during the reaction; destructive hydrogenation products and a high yield of isobutane are observed.[7] The reactions between benzene and paraffins also throw light on aluminum chloride chemistry. Carbon-carbon bond

[1] McAfee, *Ind. Eng. Chem.*, **7**:737 (1915); *Chem. & Met. Eng.*, **13**:592 (1915).

[2] For a more complete discussion of aluminum chloride–hydrocarbon chemistry, see Thomas, "Anhydrous Aluminum Chloride in Organic Chemistry," Reinhold Publishing Corporation, New York, 1941; Egloff, Wilson, Halla, and van Arsdell, *Chem. Revs.*, **20**:345 (1937). For a review of Friedel-Craft reactions, see Nelson, *Ind. Eng. Chem.*, **48**:1670 (1956).

[3] Ipatieff and Grosse, *Ind. Eng. Chem.*, **28**:461 (1936).

[4] Glasebrook, Phillips, and Lovell, *J. ACS*, **58**:1944 (1936).

[5] Grummitt, Sensel, Smith, Burk, and Lankelma, *J. ACS*, **67**:910 (1945).

[6] Grummitt, Case, and Mitchell, *Ind. Eng. Chem.*, **38**:141 (1946).

[7] Ipatieff and Schmerling, *Ind. Eng. Chem.*, **40**:2354 (1948).

scission forms smaller paraffins and olefins; these latter alkylate the aromatic nucleus;[1] study of the products indicates that normal structures undergo scission at points all along the chain. With benzene, isooctane gives only isobutane and *t*-butylbenzenes, while the products from *n*-octane are propane, *n*- and isobutanes, pentanes, and hexanes, as well as ethyl, propyl, and other alkylated benzenes.

Cracking in Presence of Aluminum Chloride. Probably the first catalytic cracking practiced on a commercial scale was that in which heavy oils were distilled, with agitation, over anhydrous aluminum chloride.[2] The process was applied most successfully to naphthenic oils. With about 3 to 5 per cent of aluminum chloride, the mixture was heated slowly at atmospheric pressure until liquid temperatures in the range of 225°C were attained. Low-boiling hydrocarbon products of the reaction, largely in the gasoline and kerosene range, distilled over; they were saturated and highly refined. Table III-18 gives the results, in per-

TABLE III-18

	Naphthenic crude		Paraffinic crude	
	With AlCl$_3$	Without AlCl$_3$	With AlCl$_3$	Without AlCl$_3$
Gasoline.............	17.75	0	42.32	18.0
Naphtha.............	13.03	0.10	16.67	12.0
Kerosene............	8.66	4.3	3.93	35.0
Gas oil..............	17.15	52.0	8.11	21.0
Lubricating stock......	25.58	25.5		
Residual oil..........	.....	12.0	13.10	11.0
Loss................	17.83	6.1	15.87	3.0

centages, obtained on distilling a Texas naphthenic and a Caddo paraffinic crude oil alone and in the presence of aluminum chloride (no hydrogen chloride added). Continuous operation was also practiced; gas oil was pumped through a heating coil and a slurry of aluminum chloride was injected at some point in its travel. The reaction was completed in a soaking-chamber separator. The high loss with aluminum chloride treatment represents conversion to coke and gas. The results obtained on reacting several 400°C end-point gas oils and 221°C end-point naphthas at 400° and 225°C, respectively, over aluminum chloride activated with hydrogen chloride are given in Table III-19. On removing the small amounts of aromatics and olefins from the gasoline made by the aluminum chloride treatment of the Mid-Continent gas oil (last column of Table III-19) with sulfuric and nitric acids, the remaining paraffin and naph-

[1] Grosse, Mavity, and Ipatieff, *J. Org. Chem.*, **3**:137 (1938).
[2] McAfee, *op. cit.*

TABLE III-19

Stock cracked (1,500 ml)	California gas oil	Trinidad gas oil	Michigan naphtha	Trinidad naphtha	Paraffin* wax	Mid-Continent gas oil*
AlCl₃, weight per cent..............	10.0	10.5	5.0	3.0	3.0†	3.0†
Time, hr.......................	15	15	6	12		
Coke, weight per cent of charge.....	29.0	31.1	18.4	27.8		
Gas,‡ liters......................	99.0	132.0	180.0	120.0		
Liquid, volume per cent of charge:						
Propane......................	13.8	15.3	17.1	11.64		
Isobutane.....................	28.8	28.4	42.1	27.5		
Isopentane....................	19.6	18.2	15.9	13.8		
Aviation gasoline (end point						
<150°C).....................	47.9	44.9	33.9	43.9		
Octane number (motor method)...	80	80	71	80		
Analysis:						
Paraffins......................	87	83	.....	......	92.6§	71.8§
Olefins.......................	0	0	.....	......	4.7	1.2
Naphthenes....................	0	0	.....	......	2.7	18.0
Aromatics.....................	13	17	.....	......	0	9.0

* Data obtained in authors' laboratory.

† AlCl₃ not activated by HCl.

‡ Mostly hydrogen (40 to 50 per cent), methane, and ethane.

§ Garner method used for analysis.   Garner, *J. Inst. Petrol. Technologists*, **14**:695 (1928).

From Komarewsky and Warson, *Ind. Eng. Chem.*, **37**:323 (1945).

thenic hydrocarbons are distributed in a manner illustrated by the differential distillation curve of Fig. III-6.

The aluminum chloride cracked gasolines are characterized by moderately high octane numbers, absence of olefins, and high response to tetraethyllead.   The liquid and gaseous products from the two gas oils, as shown in Table III-19, are quite similar.   The products obtained on cracking *n*-heptane, *n*-nonane, and *n*-hexadecane over aluminum chloride are all about the same.[1]

III-27. Olefinic Hydrocarbons.   The primary reaction of the lower-molecular-weight olefins in the presence of aluminum chloride is one of polymerization, but the products are then subjected to isomerization; dehydrogenation-hydrogenation also takes place.   As a result, a complex mixture of hydrocarbons is usually obtained.

Ethylene is resistant to aluminum chloride unless the latter is activated

[1] Potolovsky and Spektor, *J. Gen. Chem. (U.S.S.R.)*, **24**:443 (1954).

by the presence of hydrogen chloride. Under pressure and at 25 to 125°C, a liquid product results which, depending on the time of reaction and the amount of catalyst, may vary from a gasoline to a lubricating oil. The gasoline boiling up to 200°C is mostly saturated and has a blending octane number of 77,[1] indicating the presence of branched structures; the higher-boiling portions contain naphthenic hydrocarbons. Apparently, the formation of cyclics takes place most easily in the polymerization of the lower olefins. None are reported from amylene and octene,[2] nor from

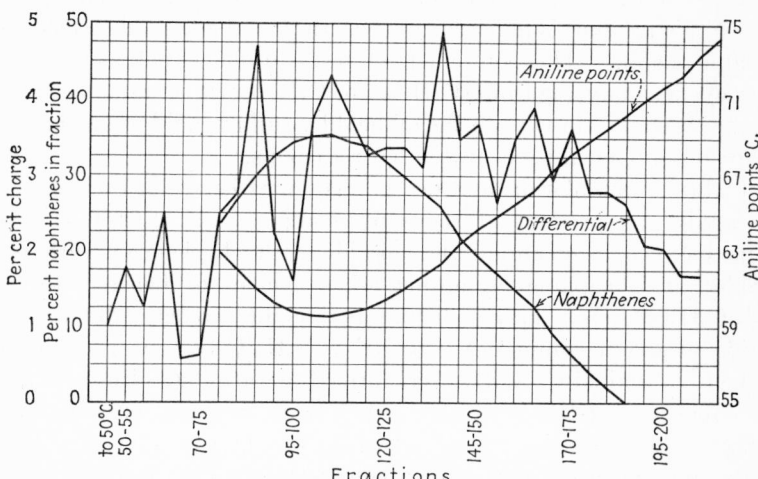

FIG. III-6. Differential distillation curve, aniline points, paraffin-naphthene distribution for an aluminum chloride gasoline.

propylene formed in the destructive alkylation on *n*-heptane,[3] or hexadecene.[4] The heavy oils from ethylene polymerization show a rather steep viscosity-temperature curve,[5] but the viscosity index improves as the molecular weight of the olefin reacted increases.[6] Oils of higher viscosity index are also obtained from ethylene if metallic aluminum is used along with aluminum chloride;[7] in this case the conditions are

[1] Bowen and Nash, *World Petrol. Congr., Proc. 1st Congr. (London)*, **2**:774 (1933).

[2] Nametkin, Abakumovskaya, and Rudenko, *J. Gen. Chem. (U.S.S.R.)*, **7**:759 (1937); *Oil Gas J.*, **37**(43):52 (1939).

[3] Grummitt, Sensel, Smith, Burk, and Lankelma, *J. ACS*, **67**:910 (1945).

[4] Waterman and Leendertse, *Trans. Faraday Soc.*, **32**:251 (1936); *J. Inst. Petrol. Technologists*, **24**:16 (1938).

[5] Nash, Stanley, and Bowen, *J. Inst. Petrol. Technologists*, **16**:830 (1930). Sullivan, Voorhees, Neeley, and Shankland, *Ind. Eng. Chem.*, **23**:604 (1931).

[6] For the polymerization of olefins to lubricating oils by aluminum chloride, see Spaght, *Petrol. Processing*, **1**:126 (1946).

[7] Hall and Nash, *J. Inst. Petrol. Technologists*, **23**:679 (1937); **24**:471 (1938).

favorable for the formation of true polymers (dimer, trimer, tetramer, etc.), and little hydrocarbon is lost to the catalyst.

In the polymerization of olefins with aluminum chloride, two layers separate. The upper is entirely hydrocarbon in nature and is referred to as "free oil." The lower layer, depending upon operating conditions, may vary from a thin, brown slurry to a thick, black mass. It is composed of the catalyst and the products of its reaction with the olefinic material. On addition of water, this "complex" decomposes to liberate a hydrocarbon layer referred to as the "combined oil." The viscosity index of this product is much lower than that of the free oil formed from the same olefin.[1] The combined oil from ethylene polymerization is highly cyclic, analyzing from $(C_8H_{12})_n$ to $(C_8H_{13})_n$;[2] it is soluble in sulfuric acid, and is similar in type to the oil held by sulfuric acid when the latter is used to polymerize unsaturated hydrocarbons.[3]

The aluminum chloride–hydrocarbon complex has been the subject of close study. A product of the same composition, $Al_2Cl_6 \cdot C_8H_{16}$, was obtained on treating aluminum chloride with ethylene or with ethyl chloride;[4] it is capable of adding six molecules of benzene to form $Al_2Cl_6 \cdot C_8H_{16} \cdot 6C_6H_6$. This, in turn, was thought to react with more ethyl chloride to give a complex $Al_2Cl_6 \cdot C_8H_{16} \cdot 6C_6H_3(C_2H_5)_3$, from which triethylbenzene and $Al_2Cl_6 \cdot C_8H_{16}$ were formed on warming. Unfortunately, the composition of the complexes is indefinite, varying with the olefin–aluminum chloride ratio. The work of Brown and coworkers has been of considerable aid in explaining such complex formation and its catalytic effect in Friedel-Craft reactions.[5]

Aluminum chloride is not soluble in aromatic hydrocarbons but aluminum bromide is; in solution it exists as the dimer, Al_2Br_6. When the solvent is evaporated, a solid separates from benzene and toluene solutions, the compositions corresponding to $Al_2Br_6 \cdot C_6H_6$ and $Al_2Br_6 \cdot C_6H_5CH_3$.[6] With *m*-xylene and mesitylene, solid complexes do not separate, but there is evidence for their existence in solution at room temperature. These complexes are thought to be the result of a weak interaction between the π electrons of the aromatic hydrocarbon and the Al_2Br_6 molecule.

As mentioned above, aluminum chloride is not soluble in toluene, but if

[1] Sullivan, Voorhees, Neeley, and Shankland, *op. cit.*

[2] Szayna, *Przemysl Chem.*, **12**:637 (1928).

[3] Ipatieff and Grosse, *J. ACS*, **58**:915 (1936).

[4] Gustavson, *J. prakt. chem.* (2), **34**:161 (1886); **68**:209 (1903); *Compt. rend.*, **136**:1065 (1903).

[5] Brown, Pearsall, Eddy, Wallace, Grayson, and Nelson, *Ind. Eng. Chem.*, **45**:1462 (1953).

[6] Brown, Pearsall, Eddy, Wallace, Grayson, and Nelson, *op. cit.* See also work of Eley and Kind, *Trans. Faraday Soc.*, **47**:1287 (1951), and of Van Dyke, *J. ACS*, **72**:3619 (1950).

hydrogen chloride is passed into the mixture, a liquid complex is formed.[1] Similar complexes are obtained from aluminum chloride or bromide and benzene, xylenes, triethylbenzenes, and mesitylene.

$$6C_6H_5CH_3 \cdot Al_2Br_6 \cdot HBr$$
$$2C_6H_3(C_2H_5)_3 \cdot Al_2Cl_6 \cdot HCl$$
$$3C_6H_3(CH_3)_3 \cdot Al_2Br_6 \cdot HBr$$

Each of these, under vacuum, loses hydrocarbon to give a final complex containing one molecule of hydrocarbon per molecule of aluminum halide dimer. Furthermore, these complexes are active chemically. The addition of ethyl chloride to the benzene complex, for example, gives a 90 per cent yield of 1,3,5-triethylbenzene. The corresponding toluene complex supplied an 82 per cent yield of diethyltoluene.

Further studies show the complexes of aromatic hydrocarbons with aluminum halides and halogen acids to have a composition[2] more or less as follows:

$$\text{Aromatic hydrocarbon} \cdot Al_2X_6 \cdot HX$$

and with an excess of the more basic aromatics (toluene, xylene, mesitylene)

$$2 \text{ Aromatic hydrocarbon} \cdot Al_2X_6 \cdot HX$$

These complexes, believed to be the active principles in Friedel-Craft catalysis, are assumed to be carbonium ion salts of the hypothetical acid, $HAlCl_4$.

The aluminum halide is assumed to dissolve in such salts to furnish a highly polar medium in which ionic intermediates may form and react.[2]

III-28. Naphthenic Hydrocarbons. The main reaction of aluminum halides on naphthenic hydrocarbons is that of isomerization, for example, that of cyclohexane to methylcyclopentane. Dehydrogenation and condensation also take place. Cyclohexane, reacted with aluminum

[1] Gustavson, *Compt. rend.*, **140**:940 (1905); *Bull. soc. chim. France* (2), **30**:435 (1878). Norris and Rubenstein, *J. ACS*, **61**:1163 (1939); Norris and Ingraham, *J. ACS*, **62**:1298 (1940); Norris and Wood, *J. ACS*, **62**:1428 (1940).
[2] Brown and Pearsall, *J. ACS*, **74**:191 (1952).

chloride at 150°C for 24 hr, produces dicyclohexyl and, as a result of destructive hydrogenation, isobutane and ethylene; the latter alkylates the cyclohexane to ethylcyclohexane, which in turn isomerizes to dimethyl-cyclohexane.[1] Another example of intermolecular dehydrogenation and condensation is the action of aluminum chloride on cyclohexane which is reported to give tetracyclohexylcyclohexene (a pentamer) and tetra-cyclohexylbenzene.[2] Naphthenes containing C_2 and C_3 side chains are only slightly susceptible to cracking, C_4 side chains slightly more so; in each case the alkyl group is broken off at the ring. In amylcyclohexane, however, the carbon-carbon bond scission takes place within the amyl group so as to give butane and methylcyclohexane.[3]

III-29. Aromatic Hydrocarbons. Besides isomerization of substituted benzenes, the action of aluminum chloride on aromatic compounds involves primarily dehydrogenation followed by condensation and destructive hydrogenation. Benzene containing dissolved aluminum bromide gives, on long standing at 18°C, biphenyl-, phenyl-, and diphenyl-cyclohexanes and phenylmethylcyclopentanes[4] and with aluminum chloride at 125°C, ethylbenzene and diphenyl.[1] The ethylene for the alkylation of the benzene is presumably formed by hydrogenation of benzene to cyclohexane followed by its decomposition.

Scission of attached alkyl groups may also take place. Toluene, for example, when distilled over aluminum chloride, gives ditolyl, benzene, ethylbenzene, xylenes, and methylcyclohexane;[5] xylene gives toluene in 25 per cent yield.[6]

Alkylated benzenes react with cyclohexane in the presence of aluminum chloride to release the alkyl groups as the corresponding paraffins; in addi-tion, a bicyclic condensation product is formed. For example, isopropyl-benzene and cyclohexane, treated with aluminum chloride at 80°C, form propane and phenylcyclohexane, along with disproportionation products such as benzene and diisopropylbenzene and side products such as cyclohexylisopropylbenzene and methylcyclopentane.[7]

III-30. AlCl₃ Solutions. Aluminum chloride is readily soluble in a number of organic solvents, and these solutions, in general, possess

[1] Ipatieff and Komarewsky, *J. ACS*, **56**:1926 (1934).

[2] Nametkin, Abakumorskaya, and Rudenko, *loc. cit.*

[3] Grignard and Stratford, *Compt. rend.*, **178**:2149 (1924).

[4] Wertzporock and Sagel, *Ber.*, **66**:1306 (1933).

[5] Moore and Egloff, *Chem. & Met. Eng.*, **17**:61 (1917). See also Brown and Smoot, *J. ACS*, **78**:2176 (1956). Brown and Jungk, *J. ACS*, **78**:2182, 2185 (1956). Nightin-gale and Shackelford, *J. ACS*, **78**:1225 (1956).

[6] Orlov and Solodar, *J. Appl. Chem.* (*U.S.S.R.*), **8**:117 (1935); *C.A.*, **29**:7296 (1935).

[7] Ipatieff and Pines, *J. ACS*, **59**:56 (1937). Nightingale and Shakelford, *J. ACS*, **61**:101 (1939); **76**:5767 (1954).

catalytic properties in varying degrees. Solutions of the salt in nitro-alkanes are effective in promoting the alkylation of isoparaffins and aromatics by olefins, but have little effect on the isomerization of par-affins. They show only moderate activity toward naphthenes.[1] Solutions of aluminum chloride, especially concentrated ones containing a molar excess of the solute, in ethers, esters, acetone, benzophenone, nitrobenzene, and sulfur dioxide, however, are vigorous catalysts for both alkylation and paraffin isomerization.[2]

III-31. Hydrocarbon Resins. Resins are formed by the action of aluminum chloride on cyclohexene[3] and diolefins.[4] Pure isoprene is inert in the presence of aluminum chloride over short time periods; after several days standing, it is gradually converted into a hydrocarbon-insoluble white resinous mass, analyzing $(C_5H_8)_x$. If a small amount of 2-pentene is added to the isoprene, however, a vigorous reaction takes place. The resulting product is a mixture of hydrocarbon-soluble and insoluble polymers, the amount of soluble product varying with the amount of 2-pentene present. The difference between the soluble and insoluble resins is apparently one of molecular weight.

Production of resins, for use in paints and varnishes, has been practiced to some extent by reacting highly cracked distillates with aluminum chloride.[5] The reaction involves, in all cases, the diolefins present. It is believed that such processes have never been employed on a large scale.

HALOGENATION

III-32. Paraffinic Hydrocarbons. With the exception of iodine, the halogens react readily with paraffin hydrocarbons. The attack with fluorine is vigorous; that with chlorine is somewhat less so, although here, too, lack of control may permit explosion; with bromine it proceeds in an orderly manner. The reaction is one of substitution and takes place by a free radical chain mechanism.[6]

Chlorination takes place in the dark in either the liquid or vapor phase, and may be accelerated by heat, light, and catalysts, such as iodine, metals, metal halides, or other agents that convert chlorine molecules into

---

[1] Schmerling, *Ind. Eng. Chem.*, **40**:2072 (1948).

[2] Francis, *Ind. Eng. Chem.*, **42**:342 (1950).

[3] Nametkin, Abakumovskaya, and Rudenko, *op. cit.*

[4] Thomas and Carmody, *J. ACS*, **54**:2480 (1932); **55**:3854 (1933); *Ind. Eng. Chem.*, **24**:1125 (1932).

[5] Thomas and Carmody, *op. cit.*

[6] Pease and Walz, *J. ACS*, **53**:3728 (1931). Vaughan and Rust, *J. Org. Chem.*, **5**:449 (1940).

chlorine atoms.[1] Substitution takes place at various positions and control is possible to a limited extent only.[2] Thus, methane chlorinates to give some of all the four possible chlorine derivatives; propane yields both primary and secondary chlorides. Liquid-phase chlorination gives higher percentages of primary substitution products.

Fully chlorinated (perchloro) ethane, propane, and butanes can be prepared by exhaustive chlorination of the paraffin or by the addition of chlorine to chloroolefins. The C_3 and C_4 perchloro derivatives break down on heating; the perchloro pentanes and higher are unstable at room temperature.[3] Thus, in the exhaustive high-temperature (460 to 480°F) chlorination of propane, butane, etc., the decomposition of the polychloro derivatives (chlorinolysis) takes place to form smaller chlorohydrocarbons.[4]

The action of bromine on paraffin hydrocarbons is definite but somewhat limited; the chain reaction is catalyzed by oxygen.[5] As with chlorination, hydrogen attached to a tertiary carbon atom is more easily substituted than that held by a primary carbon. The number of bromine atoms that can be added depends on the number of carbon atoms in the hydrocarbon treated; only by extreme means is it possible to add two bromine atoms to the same carbon atom.[6]

Fluorine and paraffin hydrocarbons react with explosive violence, but if care is taken, fluorocarbons can be obtained in good yield although they are of mixed composition. The reaction sequence is presumably substitution, fission of carbon-carbon atoms caused by the intense heat evolved in the exothermic reaction, and the formation of higher-molecular-weight products as a result of free radical reactions.

The vapor-phase fluorination[7] of methane[8] gives mainly carbon tetrafluoride together with some fluoroform, mono- and difluoromethane, hexafluoroethane, and octafluoropropane. Ethane gives carbon tetra-

---

[1] Kharasch and Berkman, *J. Org. Chem.*, **6**:810 (1941). Hirschkind, *Ind. Eng. Chem.*, **41**:2749 (1949). See also reviews of chlorination by Egloff, Schaad, and Lowry, *Chem. Revs.*, **8**:1 (1931). Ellis, "Chemistry of Petroleum Derivatives," vol. I, p. 686, Reinhold Publishing Corporation, New York, 1934; vol. II, p. 726, 1937.

[2] Hass and McBee, *Ind. Eng. Chem.*, **23**:352 (1931); **27**:1190 (1935); **28**:333, 1178 (1936); **29**:1335 (1937); **33**:185 (1941). Asinger, *Ber.*, **75**:668 (1942). For discussion of kinetics of chlorination, see Vaughan and Rust, *loc. cit.*, and Ewell, "Unit Processes in Organic Synthesis," Groggins (ed.), p. 191, McGraw-Hill Book Company, Inc., New York, 1952.

[3] Roldig, *Ann.*, **574**:122 (1951).

[4] McBee et al., *Ind. Eng. Chem.*, **33**:176, 185 (1941); **41**:803, 806, 809 (1949).

[5] Kharasch, Hered, and Mayo, *J. Org. Chem.*, **6**:818 (1941).

[6] Herzfelder, *Ber.*, **26**:2432 (1893).

[7] Bigelow, *Chem. Revs.*, **40**:68 (1947). Cady, von Grosse, Barber, Burger, and Sheldon, *Ind. Eng. Chem.*, **39**:290 (1947).

[8] Bigelow, *op. cit.* Hadley and Bigelow, *J. ACS*, **62**:3302 (1940).

fluoride and hexa-, penta-, tetra-, and trifluoroethanes. The extent of carbon-carbon bond scission increases as the molecular weight of the hydrocarbon increases. While the temperature control is better and higher yields are obtained in liquid phase, the process is seldom used because of explosion hazards. Much more clean-cut reactions are obtained if the hydrocarbons are fluorinated by metal fluorides.[1] Cobalt and silver fluorides are the most suitable.

The fluorination of chlorinated hydrocarbons by halogen exchange to produce mixed fluorochloro hydrocarbons is carried out mainly with the antimony fluorides.[2] The freons, chlorofluoromethanes, and ethanes are produced in this manner.[3] Substitution of fluorine in hydrocarbons is also accomplished by electrolysis in presence of liquid hydrofluoric acid.[4]

III-33. Olefinic Hydrocarbons. The action of chlorine on straight-chain olefins at temperatures below 150°C is predominantly one of addition, but substitution takes place to some extent; even more so with tertiary olefins. The reactions are exceedingly rapid when either of the reactants is in the liquid phase.[5] At high temperatures, substitution increases; propylene at 600°C chlorinates to form allyl chloride in 85 per cent yield. This reaction is used in the synthesis of glycerin (see Chap. XVI).

III-34. Naphthenic Hydrocarbons.[6] The liquid- and gas-phase chlorination of cyclopropane yields substitution products varying from mono- to pentachlorocyclopropane; at the higher levels of chlorination there is a tendency for the ring to open, yielding polychloropropanes.[7] Monochloro derivatives of cyclobutane, cyclopentane, and methylcyclopentane can be obtained in high yields by low-temperature (below 60°C) vapor-phase chlorination.[8] High-temperature (400 to 500°C) chlorination of cyclopentane is accompanied by dehydrohalogenation to give high yields of hexachlorocyclopentadiene.[9] Chlorine derivatives of cyclohexane vary-

[1] Swarts, *Rec. trav. chim.*, **27**:128 (1908). Fowler, Anderson, Hamilton, Burford, Spadetti, Bitterlich, and Litant, *Ind. Eng. Chem.*, **39**:343 (1947). McBee, *Ind. Eng. Chem.*, **39**:310 (1947).

[2] Henne, Organic Reactions, "The Preparation of Organic Fluorine Compounds," vol. II, p. 49, John Wiley & Sons, Inc., New York, 1944.

[3] Daudt and Youker, U.S. patent 2,005,705, 1935.

[4] Simons, *J. Electrochem. Soc.*, **95**:47 (1949).

[5] Groll, Hearne, Rust, and Vaughan, *Ind. Eng. Chem.*, **31**:1239 (1939).

[6] For a more complete discussion of the chlorination of naphthenic hydrocarbons, see McBee and Ungnade, "The Chemistry of Petroleum Hydrocarbons," p. 59, Brooks, Kurtz, Boord, and Schmerling (eds.), Reinhold Publishing Corporation, New York, 1955.

[7] Roberts and Dirstine, *J. ACS*, **67**:1281 (1945). Stevens, *J. ACS*, **68**:620 (1946).

[8] Bailey and McAllister, U.S. patent 2,342,072, 1942. Roberts and Mazur, *J. ACS*, **73**:2509 (1951).

[9] McBee and Devaney, *Ind. Eng. Chem.*, **41**:803 (1949).

ing from mono to nonachlorocyclohexane can be obtained.[1]   The latter dehydrohalogenates to a hexachlorobenzene, but not to the gamma isomer desired for insecticidal use.

III-35. Aromatic Hydrocarbons.   Aromatic hydrocarbons are chlorinated in substitution reactions either on the nucleus or on attached side chains.   Nuclear substitution occurs when the chlorination is carried out in presence of halogen carriers, such as iron, phosphorus, or iodine.   In strong light and in the absence of carriers, the chlorination takes place on the side chains, with the α-carbon atoms as the main point of attack. Sulfuryl chloride may be used as the chlorinating agent, in which case the presence of peroxides directs the substitution to side chains,[2] while the presence of aluminum chloride causes nuclear chlorination.[3]

There is little or no use of direct halogenation of petroleum fractions. Many attempts have been made to bring about chlorination followed by removal of one or more molecules of hydrogen chloride; the purpose is to leave one or more double bonds, which might confer drying or semidrying properties on the residual molecules.   The mixed character of the petroleum fractions themselves and the failure of such processes to remove chlorine cleanly have defeated such efforts.   The chlorinated products, even when largely dechlorinated, are unstable and continue to split off hydrogen chloride under storage conditions.

NITRATION

The action of nitric acid on hydrocarbons in the liquid phase is one of nitration and oxidation, the former favored by use of dilute acid and low treating temperatures.   The products are complex in nature, since the reaction is influenced by acid concentration, temperature, and time; it is often difficult to separate and identify the various nitro compounds formed.

The paraffin hydrocarbons are resistant to both concentrated and fuming nitric acid at room temperature.[4]   As the size of the molecule or the temperature is increased, the reaction becomes more extensive.   Both mono- and polynitro derivatives are formed in liquid-phase nitration; the reaction is thought not to follow a free radical mechanism.[5]   Nitration takes place at secondary carbon atoms more readily than at the primary, and still more easily at the tertiary; quaternary carbons are highly

[1] Kharasch and Brown, *J. ACS*, **61**:2142 (1939).   Kharasch and Berkman, *J. Org. Chem.*, **6**:810 (1941).   Riemschneider and Drescher, *Angew. Chem.*, **64**:30 (1952).

[2] Kharasch and Brown, *op. cit.*

[3] Cutter and Brown, *J. Chem. Educ.*, **21**:443 (1944).

[4] Kirschner, *J. prakt. chem.*, **56**:364 (1897).

[5] Stevens and Schiessler, *J. ACS*, **62**:2885 (1940).

resistant.[1] The order of decreasing activity with fuming acid is aromatics, tertiary paraffins, secondary paraffins, naphthenes, and normal paraffins.[2]

Straight-chain olefins are somewhat resistant to the action of nitric acid, but the tertiary-base olefins readily form the corresponding alkyl nitrates.[3] In all cases, oxidation is difficult to avoid.

Naphthenic hydrocarbons behave on nitration much like the paraffins. Those carrying side chains give isomeric ring-substituted mononitration products, consisting mainly of the tertiary, with lesser amounts of the secondary, compounds.[4] Oxidation also takes place.

Concentrated nitric acid readily nitrates aromatic hydrocarbons on the ring. By the use of dilute acid, alkylated aromatics can be nitrated on the side chains, the extent and positions depending on the structure of the aliphatic group.

While the action of nitric acid on paraffin hydrocarbons in the liquid phase is sluggish, nitration takes place readily in the vapor phase.[5] The normally gaseous hydrocarbons, together with normal and isopentane, have been found to react smoothly to give a mixture of mononitration products; dinitro compounds are not formed,[6] even when a nitroalkane is treated with nitric acid.[7] The nitration is carried out at atmospheric pressure, with either nitric acid or nitrogen dioxide, at temperatures varying over the range of 250 to 600°C, 400 to 500° giving optimum results. The ease of nitration increases in the following order: methane, ethane, propane, butanes, and pentanes; the latter are very responsive with little differentiation between them. The products obtained from each hydrocarbon correspond to those which might be expected if a primary scission of each carbon-carbon and carbon-hydrogen bond occurs followed by the addition of a nitro group. Ethane, for example, gives nitromethane and nitroethane; propane gives nitromethane, nitroethane, and 1- and 2-nitropropanes. Similarly, all the seven possible mononitro compounds are obtained from *n*-pentane, and nine from isopentane. The facts that tetraethyllead reacts vigorously with nitric acid to give nitroethane, that the presence of small amounts of oxygen and chlorine increases

---

[1] Konowalow, *Ber.*, **25**:1244 (1892); **28**:1850 (1895); **29**:2199 (1896); *J. Chem. Soc.*, **66**:265 (1894). Markownikoff, *Ber.*, **32**:1441 (1899).

[2] Francis and Young, *J. Chem. Soc.*, **73**:928 (1898).

[3] Michael and Carlson, *J. ACS*, **57**:1268 (1935).

[4] Nametkin, *J. Russ. Phys.-Chem. Soc.*, **42**:581, 691 (1910). *J. Chem. Soc.*, **98**(1):829, 830 (1910); **102**(1):175 (1912).

[5] For a comprehensive review of the nitration of paraffin hydrocarbons in the vapor phase, the products, and their physical and chemical properties, see Hass and Riley, *Chem. Revs.*, **32**:373 (1943).

[6] Dorsky, *Ind. Eng. Chem.*, **33**:1138 (1941).

[7] McCleary and Degering, *Ind. Eng. Chem.*, **30**:64 (1938).

the percentage of conversion,[1] and that nitrogen dioxide is a satisfactory nitrating agent suggest that the reaction is of the radical chain type.[2]

The main side reactions are those of oxidation, although less of this takes place than in liquid-phase nitration.[3]   Alcohols, aldehydes, ketones, and carboxylic acids are formed in various quantities.   Cyclohexane is readily nitrated in the vapor phase to mononitrocyclohexane.[4]   Toluene gives nitrobenzene and phenylnitromethane.[5]

The nitro derivatives of the lower paraffins are colorless, noncorrosive, and nonexplosive.   They have excellent solvent properties and are the starting materials for many interesting reactions.   For example, acid hydrolysis yields fatty acids and hydroxylamine salts;[6] condensations with aliphatic aldehydes give mono- and dihydric nitroalcohols.[7]

ACTION OF SULFUR

Petroleum products react readily with sulfur, as do practically all hydrocarbons.   In fact, elemental sulfur dissolved in crude oil will react at temperatures as low as about 100°C.   A convenient way to prepare hydrogen sulfide is to heat a mixture of sulfur and paraffin wax to about 150°C.   At 230°C carbon disulfide is also formed, and after long heating at this temperature a resinous material analyzing $(C_5S)_x$ is obtained.[8] Methane and sulfur are heated to 600°C in the manufacture of carbon disulfide; a silica gel catalyst is used.[9]   Thiophene is produced by heating butane and sulfur at 500 to 700°C;[10] butenes and butadiene are also formed; pentanes correspondingly give methylthiophene.   Similarly, octanes on reaction with sulfur at 270 to 280°C are reported to give dialkyl thiophenes.[11]   It seems probable that the primary reaction of paraffins with sulfur is one of dehydrogenation; then the hydrogen sulfide set free adds to the residual olefin also formed.   The mechanism has not

[1] Hass and Alexander, *Ind. Eng. Chem.*, **41**:2266 (1949).

[2] McCleary and Degering, *loc. cit.*   Bachman, Hass, Millikan, Pollack, Addison, Hewett, and Kohn, *J. Org. Chem.*, **17**:906, 914, 928, 935, 942 (1952); **19**:322 (1954); *Ind. Eng. Chem.*, **46**:713 (1954).

[3] Bender, Figueras, and Kilpatrick, *J. Org. Chem.*, **23**:410 (1958).

[4] Hass and Riley, *loc. cit.*

[5] Seigle, U.S. Patent 2,181,531, 1939.

[6] Lippincott and Hass, *Ind. Eng. Chem.*, **31**:118 (1939).

[7] Vanderbilt and Hass, *Ind. Eng. Chem.*, **32**:34 (1940).

[8] Siebeneck, *Petrol. Z.*, **18**:281 (1922).

[9] Thacker and Miller, *Ind. Eng. Chem.*, **36**:182 (1944).   Folkins, Miller, and Hennig, *Ind. Eng. Chem.*, **42**:2202 (1950).   Bacon and Boe, *Ind. Eng. Chem.*, **37**:469 (1945).

[10] Rasmussen, Hansford, and Sachanen, *Ind. Eng. Chem.*, **38**:376 (1946).   Caesar and Branton, *Ind. Eng. Chem.*, **44**:122 (1952).

[11] Friedman, *Ber.*, **49**:50, 1344, 1551 (1916); *Petrol. Z.*, **11**:693, 978 (1916); *Refiner Nat. Gasoline Mfr.*, **20**:395 (1941).

been proved. The rate of sulfurization increases with the molecular weight of the paraffin; branched paraffins and cycloparaffins sulfurize faster than the corresponding straight-chain hydrocarbons.[1]

Naphthenes sulfurize in much the same manner as do the paraffins. The C_6 naphthenes are converted through dehydrogenation into cyclohexenes, aromatic hydrocarbons,[2] and thiophenols. The latter are troublesome contaminants of raw catalytic cracked gasolines; they are removed by alkali washing, but there are difficulties in separating the alkali.

Unsaturated hydrocarbons are readily sulfurized.[3] The reaction is quite complex and its mechanism is not well understood. The isolation and identification of solid $C_nH_{2n-4}S_3$ derivatives obtained on sulfurizing isobutylene and diisobutylene at about 140 to 170°C have shed some light on the chemistry involved.[4] The $C_4H_4S_3$ compound from isobutylene has the structure

and the two $C_8H_{12}S_3$ isomers obtained from the trimethylpentenes making up diisobutylene were shown to be

mp = 86.5 to 87.3°C   mp = 80.5 to 81.3°C

Compounds bearing the same ring structure have apparently been pre-

---

[1] Bryce and Hinshelwood, *J. Chem. Soc.*, 1949, p. 3379.

[2] Friedman, *Petrol. Z.*, **11**:978 (1916); *Brennstoff-Chem.*, **8**:257 (1927).

[3] See Westlake, *Chem. Revs.*, **39**:219 (1946), for a review of the sulfurization of unsaturated compounds. Bateman and coworkers, *J. Chem. Soc.*, 1958, p. 2838.

[4] Spindt, Stevens, and Baldwin, *J. ACS*, **73**:3693 (1951).

pared by sulfurizing propylene[1] and aromatic-substituted olefins.[2]   There is some evidence that, as with olefin oxidation,[3] the sulfur first attaches at a carbon alpha to the double bond,[4] but the remainder of the mechanism is obscure.   A wide variety of products (sulfides, disulfides, polysulfides, etc.) have been reported from olefin-sulfur reactions, particularly in studies aimed at the vulcanization of rubber.[5,6]

Cracked naphthas,[7] isobutylene, and diisobutylene[8] are sulfurized with elemental sulfur in the preparation of high-sulfur cutting oil concentrates. Plastic cements have been prepared through the reaction of sulfur on solvent extracts from lubricating oil stocks.[9]

EFFECTS OF RADIATION

The effect of light on petroleum materials was observed in the early days of the industry.   It was noticed that unrefined fractions, particularly of the less stable crude oils, darkened more rapidly when exposed to light; this was even more true of cracked products.   A contrary effect was the sun bleaching of light neutral lubricating distillates from paraffinic oils, effected by exposing the oils in, say, 6-in.-thick layers on the surface of water in large shallow pans.[10]   There was some evaporation and sometimes enough oxidation to produce emulsifiable oils useful for wool scouring. The color developed by cracked oils is tied up with oxidation and is influenced by the content of sulfur compounds,[11] which may also be responsible for appearance of a haze of water particles carrying sulfur oxides and organic oxidation products resembling gasoline gum.   It will be recalled that gum formation is strongly accelerated by ultraviolet light—mercury vapor or iron arc.[12]   When so irradiated, even straight-

[1] Lüttringhaus, Konig, and Böttcher, *Ann.*, **557**:89 (1947); **560**:201 (1948).

[2] Voronkov, Broun, and Karpenko, *J. Gen. Chem. (U.S.S.R.)*, **19**:1927 (1947); *C.A.*, **44**:1955 (1950).   Schmitt and Lespagnol, *Compt. rend.*, **230**:551 (1950).

[3] Farmer, *Rubber Chem. and Technol.*, **15**:765 (1942).

[4] Armstrong, Little, and Doak, *Ind. Eng. Chem.*, **36**:628 (1944).

[5] Armstrong, Little, and Doak, *ibid.*

[6] Selker and Kemp, *Ind. Eng. Chem.*, **39**:895 (1947).

[7] Muskat, U.S. patent 2,112,677, 1938.

[8] Stevens and Whitaker, U.S. patent 2,535,706, 1950.   Stevens and Starnes, U.S. patent 2,535,705, 1950.

[9] McKinney, Mayberry, and Westlake, *Ind. Eng. Chem.*, **37**:177 (1945).

[10] Carpenter, *J. Inst. Petrol. Technologists*, **12**:518 (1926), has some account of the removal, by exposure to light, of color developed in kerosene distillates stored in darkness; continued exposure to light caused development of a more permanent color.

[11] Brooks, *Ind. Eng. Chem.*, **18**:1198 (1926); Egloff, Morrell, Benedict, and Wirth, *Ind. Eng. Chem.*, **27**:323 (1935).

[12] Morrell, Benedict, and Egloff, *Ind. Eng. Chem.*, **28**:122 (1936).   Freund, *World Petrol. Congr., Proc. 1st Congr. (London)*, **2**:108 (1933).   Story, Provine, and Bennett, *Ind. Eng. Chem.*, **21**:1079 (1929).

run gasolines will develop gum extensively. Minimal amounts of such light-induced oxidation may be recognized by change in the interfacial tension to water.[1] Qualitative evidence of the association of light-induced oxidation with color development is easy to find. Viscous oils and petrolatums exposed to light and air will often show darkening progressively from the top surface downward; this occurs more rapidly than when sheltered from light. Poorly refined paraffin wax will also develop color and rancidity more rapidly when exposed to light.

A considerable amount of qualitative work on effect of more intense radiation on hydrocarbons went on prior to 1930.[2] More quantitative study began with Lind and his assistants.[3] The silent electric discharge[4] and the available sources of high-energy radiations were employed.[5] It was found that the lower n-paraffins yield radicals which then combine to products of higher molecular weight. Olefins are similarly subject to scission of C-H and C-C bonds, with subsequent recombination, but can be polymerized directly; thus, ethylene yields 1-butene and 1-hexene, along with a little acetylene. Isobutene is converted to a wide-boiling (C_5 to C_6) paraffin-olefin mixture.

The availability in quantity of really high-energy radiation, with the building of cyclotrons, Van de Graaff generators, and nuclear reactors, and the use of nuclear-fission products have given a strong impetus to study of radiation chemistry. The same general effects are brought about by alpha, beta, and gamma rays, deuterons and neutrons, the extent of reaction depending on energy input and time of exposure. The basic action is, as stated above, the scission of C-H and C-C bonds, with recombination of fragments. A simple example is the electron bombardment of n-butane. The butyl radicals thus set free combine with butenes, with butane, or with themselves; liquid products, octanes and octenes, with lesser amounts

---

[1] Johansen, *Ind. Eng. Chem.*, **16**:132 (1924).

[2] For instance, Berthelot, *Compt. rend.*, **126**:561, 567, 609, 616 (1898). See second edition of this work, pp. 166–167. Mignonac and Vanier de Saint-Aunay, *Compt. rend.*, **188**:959 (1929).

[3] Lind, *J. ACS*, **48**:1556, 1575, 2335 (1926); **50**:1767 (1928); **51**:2811, 3655 (1929); **52**:4450 (1930); *Trans. Am. Electrochem. Soc.*, **52**:37, 83 (1927).

[4] An early application of silent electric discharge in Europe was the preparation of lubricants and lubricant additives by exposing mixtures of petroleum lubricating oils and fatty oils to discharge in an atmosphere of hydrogen; improvement in resistance to oxidation and in viscosity-temperature relations was claimed. The operation was known as the Elektrion or Voltöl process. See Isom, *Oil Gas J.*, **24**(13):156 (1925). Nash, Howard, and Hall, *J. Inst. Petrol. Eng.*, **20**:1027 (1934). Woods, *Petrol. Eng.*, **7**(13):158 (1936). Pritzker, *Petrol. Processing*, **2**:291 (1947). Panchenkov, *Petroleum (London)*, **10**:28 (1947).

[5] See also Prianischnikow, *Ber.*, **61**:1358 (1928). Harkins and Gans, *J. ACS*, **52**:2578 (1930). Heisig, *J. ACS*, **53**:3245, 4460 (1931); **54**:2328 (1932); **55**:2304 (1933).

of C_{12}, C_{16}, and C_{20} hydrocarbons, are recovered.[1] Isobutane yields more C_7 compounds—olefins as well as paraffins—indicating more breaking of C-C bonds. Exposure of *n*-hexane to 8.7×10^{21} electron volts (ev) gave a mixture containing 16 compounds, including *n*-pentane and 3-methyl-pentane; *n*-dodecane was the heaviest; cyclohexane yielded *n*-hexane and dicyclohexyl. It is interesting to note that electron irradiation of ethane and deuteroethane showed that hydrogen molecules can be broken out intramolecularly.[2] Polymer formation normally accompanies these paraffin irradiations; ethylene and butadiene are formed from ethane, together with a little acetylene, which ends up as a solid. The reactions are presumably radical-initiated addition polymerizations. Starting with ethylene, polyethylene resins can be formed by gamma-ray irradiation.[3]

The higher paraffins have been studied sufficiently[4] to indicate that the reactions are about as just described. Exposure in vacuum to 10^9 roentgens (r) of gamma rays (associated with slow neutrons in a pile) caused the melting point of paraffin wax to decrease until cross linking occurred; this resulted in sudden gelation with rise in melting point, so that the material is infusible at 160°C and essentially insoluble in the usual solvents. The energy required for each cross linking is about 32 electron volts. The higher olefins can be cross linked in the same way at an expenditure of 19 ev for double bonds near chain ends. Irradiation of polyethylene renders it harder and infusible; for every cross link established, about 0.35 C-C bond in the main chain is broken, involving some degradation. The polymerization of these unsaturated hydrocarbons goes stepwise, each link requiring a separate activation. Polyisobutene under electrons or X rays falls into the same pattern; random chain breaking occurs and vinyl groups are formed, while hydrogen, methane, and isobutene are released.

Aromatic hydrocarbons, because of their resonance characteristics, are

[1] Dewhurst, *J. Chem. Phys.*, **24**:1254 (1956). Keenan, Lincoln, and Rogers, *ACS, Div. Petrol. Chem.*, Preprints, *Gen. Papers*, p. 295, Atlantic City, September, 1956. See also Lampe, *ACS, Div. Petrol. Chem., Symposium on Nuclear Technology in the Petroleum and Chemical Industries*, Preprints, Miami, April, 1957. For the irradiation of methane with electrons, see Lampe, *J. ACS*, **79**:1055 (1957).

[2] Dorfman, *J. Phys. Chem.*, **60**:826 (1956).

[3] Anderson and Martin, *Proc. Intern. Conf. Peaceful Uses Atomic Energy, Geneva*, **15**:235 (1956). Weber, *Oil Gas J.*, **54**(82):54 (1956).

[4] Charlesby, *Proc. Roy. Soc. (London)*, **A222**:60 (1954); **A232**:31 (1955); *Chem. Eng. Progr.*, **51**:476 (1955); *Radiation Research*, **2**:96 (1955); *Nucleonics*, **14**(9):82 (1956); Okamotie and Isihara, *J. Polymer Sci.*, **20**(94):115 (1956). Snow, Uhle, and Lewis, *ACS, Div. Petrol. Chem., Symposium on Nuclear Technology in the Petroleum and Chemical Industries*, Preprints, p. 153, Miami, April, 1957.

more stable under irradiation,[1] but chemical reactions involving them can be induced.   Thus, X-ray treatment of neutral water solutions of benzene, also saturated with oxygen, formed phenol, catechol-quinol, *p*-benzoquinone, an aldehyde, and traces of diphenyl.   In this case molecular oxygen seemed to take part in the radical reactions.[2]   For comparison it may be noted that in water solutions containing oxygen and ethylene, gamma rays set up chain reactions which formed aldehydes, with smaller proportions of alcohols, acids, hydrogen peroxide, and other peroxides. For the aldehydes, the yield in molecules per 100 ev (G value) was about 200.[3]   In similar fashion the chlorination of lower aromatics, such as benzene, toluene, xylene, and mesitylene, is induced by gamma irradiation; ethylbenzene is, however, resistant.[4]   For both benzene and toluene the chlorination is proportional to the square root of the radiation intensity; this applies to both addition and substitution.[5]   Effect of radiation on asphalts has also been studied.[6]   The changes seem to differ from those induced by air blowing, are linear with time, and on the whole are rather slow.

Copolymerization can be induced by radiation; beta particles can initiate reaction between hexadecene and sulfur dioxide, much as occurs in presence of benzoyl peroxide.[7]   A variant is graft polymerization, by which a molecule or chain of one species can be tacked onto a different polymer.[8]

An interesting application of radiation is suggested by a report that energy recovery from jet fuels can be increased in presence of radioactive gold.[9]

[1] Colichman and Gercke, *Nucleonics*, **14**(7):50 (1956).   Beta radiation produced, per 100 ev:

From toluene	0.4 radical
Cyclohexane	1.0
CCl₄ ⎱	10 each
CHCl₃ ⎰	

Seitzer and Tobolsky, *ACS, Abstracts of Papers*, 4S-9, ACS Meeting, New York, September, 1954.

[2] Daniels, Scholes, and Weiss, *J. Chem. Soc.*, **1956**, 832.

[3] Henley, Schiffries, and Barr, *J. AIChE*, **2**:211 (1956).

[4] *Chem. Week*, **78**(4):54 (1956).

[5] Harmers, Martin, and Anderson, *J. Appl. Chem. (London)*, **6**:377 (1956).

[6] Hoiberg and Watson, *ACS, Abstracts of Papers*, 9J, ACS Meeting, Dallas, April, 1956.

[7] Dainton, Irvin, and Sheard, *Trans. Faraday Soc.*, **52**:414 (1956).

[8] Behn, *J. Polymer Sci.*, **19**(19):219 (1956).   On radiation as a tool in synthesis of organic compounds, see Bourne, Stacey, and Vaughan, *Chem. & Ind. (London)*, no. 46, p. 1372, 1956.

[9] Anonymous, *Ind. Eng. Chem.*, **46**(9):17A (1954).

CHAPTER **IV**

Physical Properties

by C. B. WILLINGHAM, M.S., and L. J. SULLIVAN, M.S.

The chemist or chemical engineer requires a set of basic characteristics of his materials which will define them chemically and correlate with their utility. These should be easy to determine and capable of broad use for both characterization and specification. The physical properties of petroleum oils and waxes serve this purpose to a good degree; they determine or control separation, purification, and composition of existing products and processes as well as the development of new products and processes.

MECHANICAL PROPERTIES

IV-1. Viscosity. Since practically all petroleum products are liquids, viscosity is a very important property. It was so recognized in the earliest days of the industry as the "body" of an oil, a significant number for lubricants or for any liquid pumped or handled in quantity. The changes of viscosity with temperature, pressure, and rate of shear are pertinent not only in lubrication but also for such engineering concepts as heat transfer. The viscosity and relative viscosities of different phases, such as gas, liquid oil, and water, are determining influences in producing the flow of reservoir fluids through porous oil-bearing formations. The rate and amount of oil production from a reservoir are often governed by these properties. Table IV-1 gives viscosity values for some common substances.

By way of definition, let us consider an infinite lamina of a fluid bounded by two parallel planes a unit distance apart, and let one of the boundaries be given a uniform unit velocity of translation in its own plane. Assume that the usual equations of continuity for an incompressible fluid apply and that there is no slippage at either boundary. The viscosity of the fluid is then defined as the tangential force per unit area on the moving boundary.

132

The definition in this form can, of course, be applied to any fluid. Modern usage, however, restricts the use of the term to fluids having the tangential drag proportional to the rate of shear, at least for small rates of shear. Most homogeneous liquids of low or moderate viscosity fall in

TABLE IV-1. ILLUSTRATIVE VISCOSITIES

Material	Viscosity	
	Poises	Stokes
Air.............	1.8×10^{-4}	1.5×10^{-1}
Ether...........	2×10^{-3}	2.8×10^{-3}
Water..........	1×10^{-2}	1×10^{-2}
Gasoline........	0.6×10^{-2}	0.9×10^{-2}
Mercury........	1.55×10^{-2}	1.2×10^{-3}
Kerosene	2.0×10^{-2}	2.3×10^{-2}
Lubricating oils..	8×10^{-2} to $1,200 \times 10^{-2}$	Same
Honey..........	10^3	Same
Asphalt and pitches......	10^3 to 10^7	Same
Glass...........	10^{14}	Same

this class and are termed "Newtonian." Thus more generally, we can write:

$$\text{Viscosity} = \frac{f}{(d/dt)(dy/dx)} \tag{IV-1}$$

where f is the tangential force, t the time, y the relative parallel displacement of one boundary, and x the distance between boundaries. Although several other equivalent forms of the definition may be given, nearly all problems concerning viscosity are more complicated than the resistance to flow between parallel planes, and the differential form is the most useful. The cgs unit of viscosity is the poise and it has the dimensions of $ml^{-1}t^{-1}$; it could be expressed as grams per centimeter per second. The centipoise, one-hundredth as great, is used more commonly.

Viscosity Measurement. Many types of instruments have been proposed for the determination of viscosity. These depend in principle on the definition given above. The simplest and most widely used types are capillaries, depending on Poiseuille's law[1] which may be stated as:

$$u = \frac{\pi r^4 P}{8 \eta l} \tag{IV-2}$$

where r is the tube radius, l the tube length, P the pressure difference between the ends of a capillary, η the "coefficient of viscosity," and u is

[1] *Compt. rend.*, **12**:1 (1841).

the quantity discharged in unit time. Not only are such capillary instruments the most simple, but when designed in accordance with the known principles and used with the known necessary correction factors,[1] they are probably the most accurate viscometers available. The constants of such devices are geometrical, and as these can be measured precisely, the principle lends itself to absolute measurements. It is more convenient, however, to use relative measurements. For this purpose the instrument is calibrated with an appropriate standard liquid of known viscosity. The primary standard for calibration is water; however, standard reference oils having certified viscosities are available from the U.S. National Bureau of Standards, Washington, D.C. These cover the viscosity range, at 20°C, of 2 to 30,000 centipoises (cp), and may be obtained with viscosity and density certified at various temperatures as required.

Batch flow times are generally used; i.e., the time required for a fixed amount of sample to flow from a reservoir through a capillary is the datum actually observed. Any features of technique which contribute to longer flow times are usually desirable. For any given instrument, a viscosity value exists below which functioning becomes erratic. Ordinarily, there is no upper limit to the useful range of a capillary viscometer, except as dictated by convenience. Most routine petroleum viscometry employs flow times between 100 and 1,000 sec.

Some of the principal capillary type viscometers[2] in use are those of Cannon-Fenske, Ubbelohde, Fitzsimmons, and Zeitfuchs. When appropriately calibrated they give the "coefficient of viscosity" in terms of "kinematic viscosity," the quotient of the absolute viscosity in poises, and the density in grams per milliliter. The unit of kinematic viscosity is the stoke, which has the dimensions of cm² per sec. The centistoke (stoke/ 100) is the more common unit.

A variety of instruments has been developed for measuring viscosity by some other means than the timing of flow through a capillary tube. The most useful of these are the rotating cylinder type and the rolling or falling ball variety. In the former a cylinder and a form within it—usually a

---

[1] For a discussion of the corrections, see the following: Merrington, "Viscometry," chap. II, p. 6, Edward Arnold & Co., London, 1949. Cannon, "Derivation of Viscosity Equation and Sources of Error in Viscometry," private report to ASTM Sub-committee on Viscosity, February, 1950. (Copy available on request to Dr. M. R. Cannon at Pennsylvania State University, School of Chemistry and Physics, University Park, Pennsylvania.)

[2] ASTM Handbook on Petroleum Products and Lubricants, Committee D-2, Standard D 445-53T, Appendixes A, C, D, and F. For a more detailed discussion of the advantages and limitations of capillary viscometry, see the second edition of this book, p. 176, 1942. For details of a useful microinstrument, see Bowman, *Ind. Eng. Chem., Anal. Ed.,* **11**:409 (1939).

concentric cylinder—are separated by a layer of the liquid to be examined, and one cylinder is rotated while the torque required to hold the other stationary is measured. Probably the most common of these are of the Couette[1] type based on the equation

$$F = c\eta\omega \tag{IV-3}$$

where η is the viscosity, ω the angular velocity of the rotating member, c an apparatus constant, and F the restraining torque. Such concentric cylinder instruments have been found useful in the examination of very viscous liquids and for materials in which the coefficient of viscosity changes with the rate of shear applied. Commercial variants are the MacMichael[2] and Stormer[3] instruments. The moving-sphere viscometers, Hoppler,[4] Exline and EnDean,[5] and a variant employing a falling cylinder[6] are useful for measurement under high pressure. They can be calibrated with liquids of known viscosity but, when employed at high pressure, corrections must be made for the compressibility of the liquid. The basic equation is

$$\eta = Kt(\rho_2 - \rho_1) \tag{IV-4}$$

where ρ_2 is the density of the ball and ρ_1 that of the liquid.

In the early years of the industry, viscosity-measuring instruments of the efflux type were developed empirically; these were employed almost exclusively until recent times. The results obtained were expressed as time in seconds required for a measured volume of liquid to flow from a reservoir through a capillary. This capillary was always too short to permit following Poiseuille's law. The most widely used[7] were and are the Redwood in Great Britain, the Engler in Germany, and the Saybolt in the United States. The Redwood and Saybolt instruments are available in two forms, one (Redwood No. 2 and Furol) affording an efflux time one-tenth that of the other.[8] By this means measurements on highly

[1] *Ann. chim. et phys.*, **21**:433 (1890). Detailed discussion of various ways of measuring viscosity are given by Merrington, "Viscometry," Edward Arnold & Co., London, 1949; Weissberger (ed.), "Technique of Organic Chemistry," vol. I, part I, chap. VIII, Interscience Publishers, Inc., New York, 1949; Reilly and Rae (eds.), "Physico-Chemical Methods," vol. I, section 7, Methuen & Co., Ltd., London, 1954.

[2] *Ind. Eng. Chem.*, **12**:817 (1920).

[3] *Ibid.*, p. 587, 1920. *Natl. Bur. Standards Tech. News Bull.* 151, November, 1929. Geddes and Dawson, *Ind. Eng. Chem.*, **34**:163 (1942).

[4] *World Petrol. Congr., Proc. 1st Congr., London*, **2**:503 (1933).

[5] "Drilling and Production Practice, 1939," p. 659, American Petroleum Institute, New York, 1940.

[6] Lawaczick, *Z. ver. deut. Ing.*, **63**:677 (1919). Bridgman, *Proc. Am. Acad. Sci.*, **61**:57 (1926).

[7] Merrington, *op. cit.*, chap. V.

[8] Standard Methods, Institute of Petroleum, p. 589, 1955. ASTM Standards, p. 17, 1954.

viscous materials can be made in short time periods. Engler results are expressed in seconds or degrees Engler. The latter are obtained by dividing efflux time in seconds by the corresponding efflux time for water. Such instruments have many scientific disadvantages and their actual use is disappearing, although the scales are still employed. For higher viscosities they give figures roughly proportional to kinematic values, but for less viscous products the relation is poor. Much effort has been spent on interconversion of the several scales,[1] and on converting Saybolt to kinematic viscosity;[2] the equations for this last take the form

$$\text{Kinematic viscosity} = A \text{ (Saybolt sec)} + \frac{b}{\text{Saybolt sec}}$$

where A and b are constants.

A few sample figures for equivalent values[3] are:

Kinematic viscosity, centistokes	Saybolt sec	
	100°F	210°F
2	32.6	32.9
10	58.9	59.3
20	97.8	98.5
30	140.3	142.3
40	186.3	187.6
50	232.1	233.8
60	278.3	280.2
70	324.4	326.7

Above 70 centistokes (cs) conversion is made by using the following factors:

$$\text{Saybolt sec at } 100°F = \text{cs} \times 4.635$$
$$\text{Saybolt sec at } 210°F = \text{cs} \times 4.667$$

The general relations of the several scales is shown in Fig. IV-1.

Viscosity-temperature Relations. The highly important effect of temperature on viscosity has not yet been dealt with on a sound theoretical basis, but satisfactory empirical correlations have been devised. Theo-

[1] MacCoull, "Lubrication," Texas Company, 1921. Herschel, *J. Soc. Automotive Engrs.*, **10**:32 (1922). Garner and Kelly, *Physics*, **4**:97 (1933). *Petroleum Z.*, **29**(28):1 (1933). Garner, Broom, and Taylor, *J. Inst. Petrol. Technologists*, **22**:11 (1936). Barr, *J. Petrol. Technologists*, **22**:1 (1936). Grosholtz, *Natl. Petrol. News*, **29**(2):151 (1937).

[2] McCluer and Fenske, *Ind. Eng. Chem.*, **27**:82, 978 (1935).

[3] Taken from ASTM D 446–53.

retical developments are due to Eyring,[1] Frenkel,[2] and Andrade.[3] A relation attributed to Arrhenius[4] lies at the bottom of much of the empirical work. It is

$$\eta = A e^{B/T} \qquad\qquad (IV\text{-}5)$$

where η is absolute viscosity, T is temperature, and A and B are constants.

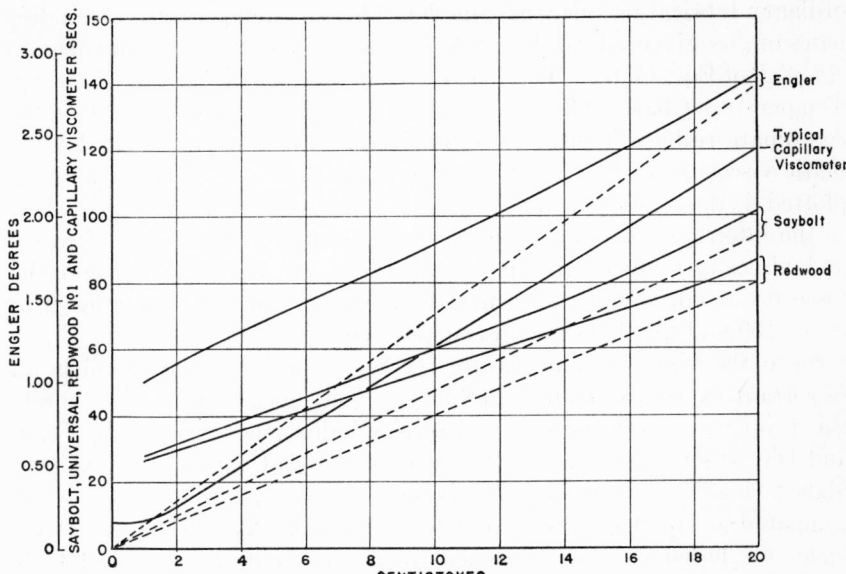

FIG. IV-1. Comparison of some viscometer scales. Dotted lines indicate extrapolation of high-viscosity portions of the curves.

Employed in logarithmic form over small temperature intervals, it yields satisfactory results. A great deal of effort has gone into another correlation.[5] The equation

$$\log \log (\eta + c) = A + B \log T \qquad\qquad (IV\text{-}6)$$

in which the symbols have the same meanings, has been found sufficiently

[1] Glasstone, Laidler, and Eyring, "Theory of Rate Processes," McGraw-Hill Book Company, Inc., New York, 1941. Moore, Gibbs, and Eyring, *J. Phys. Chem.*, **57**:172 (1953).

[2] "Kinematic Theory of Liquids," Oxford University Press, New York, 1946.

[3] "Viscosity and Plasticity," Reinhold Publishing Corporation, New York, 1951.

[4] *Medd. Vetenskapsakad. Nobelinst.*, **3**:20 (1916).

[5] Juge-Boirard, *Congr. mondial pétrole. 2me Congr.*, Paris, **2**, sec. 2, *Phys., Chim., Raffinage*, **5**:961 (1937). Baillie, *J. Inst. Petrol. Technologists*, **16**:643 (1930). Dibert, Dow, and Fenk, *J. Appl. Phys.*, **10**:113 (1939). MacCoull, "International Critical Tables," vol. II, p. 147, 1930. Walther, *Petroleum Z.*, **26**:755 (1930). Watson, Wien, and Murphy, *Ind. Eng. Chem.*, **28**:605 (1936).

good for most purposes and has come into very general use.[1] A chart based on an equation of this form was devised by MacCoull prior to 1926.[2] The constants A and B vary widely with different oils, but c remains fixed at 0.6 (the value 0.8 was formerly used) for all ordinary oils having viscosities over 1.5 cs; it increases only slightly at lower viscosities (0.75 at 0.5 cs).[3] Since the constant c remains fixed in the range of ordinary lubricating oils, the complete viscosity-temperature characteristics of any given oil can be expressed by two parameters equivalent to A and B of Eq. (IV-6). This is most easily done by the ASTM Viscosity-Temperature Charts D 341–43.[4] These nomographs have log and log log coordinate rulings, identified, respectively, with temperature and kinematic viscosity. The viscosity-temperature characteristic of any oil, so plotted, is thus a straight line and the parameters A and B are equivalent to the intercept and slope of the line. In order to express the viscosity and viscosity-temperature characteristics of an oil, the slope and the viscosity at one temperature must be known. The usual practice is to select 100 and 210°F as the observation temperatures.

Since the viscosity-temperature coefficient of a lubricating oil is an important expression of its suitability, a convenient number to express this property is very useful. A viscosity index was suggested by Dean and Davis[5] some years ago. It is well known that naphthenic oils have higher viscosity-temperature coefficients than do paraffinic ones, when compared at equal viscosities and temperatures. The Dean and Davis scale was based on the assignment of a zero value to a typical Gulf Coastal oil and that of 100 to a similarly typical Pennsylvania oil. Intermediate oils were rated by the formula

$$\text{Viscosity index} = \frac{L - U}{L - H} \times 100 \qquad \text{(IV-7)}$$

where L and H are the viscosities of the zero and 100 index reference oils (both having the same viscosity at 210°F) and U is that of the unknown, all at 100°F. Originally the viscosity index was calculated from Saybolt viscosity data, but subsequently figures were provided for kinematic viscosities. The resulting indices are the same in both cases.[6]

[1] Geniesse and Delbridge, *Proc. API*, **13**(III):56 (1932). Erdheim and Steiner, *Roczniki Chem.*, **14**:1526 (1934). *Proc. ASTM*, **37**(I):380 (1937). Grunberg and Nisson, "Science of Petroleum," vol. V, part III, p. 286, Oxford University Press, New York and London, 1955.

[2] "Lubrication," The Texas Co., New York, 1921.

[3] *Proc. ASTM*, **37**(I):380 (1937).

[4] Recently modified by extending the range to 700°F and from 0.4 to 20 million centistokes. Naval Research Laboratory, PB 131677.

[5] *Chem. & Met. Eng.*, **36**:618 (1929).

[6] Hersh, Fisher, and Fenske, *Ind. Eng. Chem.*, **27**:1441 (1935). Dean, Bauer, and Berglund, *Ind. Eng. Chem.*, **32**:102 (1940). ASTM Standard D 567–53; ASTM *Special Tech. Publ.* 43A.

For conventional products of the period, few problems arose in which viscosity indices showed anomalous behavior. With the advent of solvent extraction and other drastic refining methods, viscosity-index values above 100 and much below zero were encountered, offering some difficulties. This situation prompted the proposing of other index systems, none of which has gained general acceptance.[1]

Pressure, Shear, and Other Effects. The viscosity of petroleum fractions increases on the application of pressure and this increase may be very large.[2] It has been discussed extensively as a possible factor in lubrication.[3] The pressure coefficient of viscosity correlates rather well with the temperature coefficient, even when oils of widely different type are compared.[4] The plotting of log γ (kinematic viscosity) against pressure for several oils has given reasonably linear results up to about 20,000 psi. The slopes of the isotherms are such that extrapolated values for a given oil intersect.[5] At higher pressures the viscosity decreases with increasing temperature, as at atmospheric pressure. For a large class of oils, viscosity changes of small magnitude are proportional to density changes, whether these are caused by pressure or temperature.[6] Schiessler et al.[7] have shown that viscosity changes with pressure for several pure hydro-

[1] Umstatter, *Petroleum Z.*, **29**:1 (1933). Bell and Sharp, *Oil Gas J.*, **32**(13):13 (1933). Clayden, *Natl. Petrol. News*, **25**:27 (1933). Malschaert, *Congr. mondial pétrole, 2me Congr., Paris, sec. 2, Phys., Chim., Raffinage*, **2**:905 (1937). McCluer and Fenske, *Ind. Eng. Chem., Anal. Ed.*, **6**:389 (1934). Ramser, *Ind. Eng. Chem.*, **41**:2053 (1949). Sanderson, *Ind. Eng. Chem.*, **41**:368 (1949). Hardiman and Nisson, *J. Inst. Petrol.*, **35**:28 (1949). Fessler, *Erdöl u. Kohle*, **5**:718 (1952). Blott and Verver, *J. Inst. Petrol.*, **38**:193 (1952). Doolittle, *J. Appl. Phys.*, **24**:1067 (1953). Larson and Schwaderer, *World Petrol. Congr., Proc. 4th Congr., Rome, sec.* V/A, paper 12, 1955. Cornelissen and Waterman, *J. Inst. Petrol.*, **42**:62 (1956).

[2] Thomas, Dow, and Ham, *Phys. Rev.*, **53**:926 (1938); *Ind. Eng. Chem.*, **31**:1267 (1939). Suge, *Inst. Mech. Engrs.*, Group IV, p. 184, 1937; *Chem. Abstracts*, **32**:6848 (1938). Walther, *Erdöl u. Teer*, **4**:614 (1928). Dow, Fenske, and Morgan, *Ind. Eng. Chem.*, **29**:1078 (1937). Tammann and Pape, *Z. anorg. u. allgem. Chem.*, **197**:90 (1931). Hersey, *Natl. Advisory Comm. Aeronautics, Tech. Notes*, 315, 1929. Dow, *Phil. Mag.*, **28**:403 (1939). Beal, *Trans. AIMME*, **165**:94 (1946). Lundberg, *J. Inst. Petrol.*, **40**:104 (1954). Grundburg and Nisson, *Ind. Eng. Chem.*, **42**:885 (1950). Hersey and Hopkins, "Viscosity of Lubricants under Pressure," American Society of Mechanical Engineers, New York, 1954.

[3] Kochanoswky, *Kolloid-Z.*, **131**:74 (1953). Hersey, *loc. cit.* See also Chap. XIII of this book.

[4] Cragoe, *World Petrol. Congr., Proc. 1st Congr., London*, **2**:529 (1933). Dow, *Physics*, **6**:270 (1935); *J. Appl. Phys.*, **8**:267 (1937). Sanderson, *Mech. Eng.*, **71**:349 (1949).

[5] Lundberg, *J. Inst. Petrol.*, **40**:104 (1954).

[6] Ewell, *J. Chem. Phys.*, **5**:571 (1937). Murphy, Romans, and Zisman, *Trans. ASME*, **71**:561 (1949). Gomberg, *Intern. Congr. on Rheol., Proc. 2nd Congr.*, Oxford, p. 437, 1954.

[7] Webb, Spencer, and Schiessler, *Phys. Rev.*, **94**:753 (1954). *Proc. API*, **32**(I):139 (1952).

carbons are more sensitive to hydrocarbon type than to molecular weight. There are regular variations in the viscosity-pressure coefficients with molecular weight, but these vary according to chemical structure. This observation suggests that at high pressure, viscosity might be an additive function of structural units.

Viscosity of the liquid phase in a crude oil reservoir, at reservoir temperatures and pressures, decreases with amount of dissolved gases. Beal[1] shows that the logarithm of the viscosity at the bubble point for gas-free crudes having viscosities between 0.7 and 500 cp at reservoir temperatures and pressures decreases regularly with the amount of dissolved gases. The viscosities of undissolved natural gases decrease with molecular weight at low pressures, but as pressure increases at temperatures in the two-phase region, viscosity increases with molecular weight.[2]

It is now well recognized that high rates of shear may decrease liquid viscosities. This is particularly true for high-molecular-weight polymers or for mixtures of such polymers (as improving additives, raising viscosity index, or lowering pour point, see Chap. XIII, Lubrication) in lubricating oil stocks. Two possible phenomena are involved. The first is a temporary one in which viscosity decreases as rate of shear increases, returning in many cases to or nearly to its original value when shearing is stopped. This is well known for so called non-Newtonian liquids.[3] The other is a permanent decrease. A familiar example is the change in consistency of rubber on milling. Other polymers and elastomers are similarly changed.[4] Soap-thickened oils and greases as well as wax-containing oils will display anomalous viscosity changes on shearing. Capillary and rotary viscometers have given fairly consistent results in observing these phenomena.[5]

The ability to calculate the viscosity of a blended oil from the known viscosities of its components is a matter of practical importance. Several methods of doing this have been proposed, based on harmonic or logarithmic relations.[6] The errors are often large, particularly when the

---

[1] Beal, *Trans. AIMME*, **165**:94 (1946).

[2] Bicher and Katz, *Trans. AIMME*, **145**:246 (1944). See also Grunberg and Nisson, "Science of Petroleum," vol. V, part III, p. 285, Oxford University Press, New York and London, 1955.

[3] ASTM Designation E 24–42. Neale, *Chem. & Ind.* (*London*), 1937, p. 140. *Nature*, **149**:51 (1942). Fenske, Klaus, and Donnenbrink, *ASTM Special Tech. Publ.* 111, 3 (1941)

[4] Staudinger, *Ber.*, **67**:1159 (1934); **69**:1091 (1936). Zimmer and others, *Ind. Eng. Chem.*, **32**:299 (1940). A mathematical analysis of the phenomenon has been made by Pohl, *U.S. Naval Research Labs.*, *Rept.* P-2075. Ward, Neale, and Billen, *Brit. J. Appl. Phys.*, Suppl. 1, p. 12, 1951. Morres and Schwinan, *Nature*, **167**:317 (1951). Jones and Tyson, *J. Colloid Sci.*, **7**:272 (1952).

[5] *ASTM Special Publ.* 111, 1951.

[6] Herschel, *Chem. & Met. Eng.*, **22**:1109 (1920); Epperson and Dunlap, *Ind. Eng. Chem.*, **24**:1369 (1932); Erdheim, *Petroleum Z.*, **31**(15):(1935)

component viscosities differ widely, for example, a lubricating oil and gasoline.[1] Such extreme cases are rather uncommon and a good estimation is frequently made by employing the ASTM viscosity temperature charts; the 0 and 100°F lines are to be reported as percentage lines. A method has been suggested for dealing with gasoline as one component.[2]

Viscosity Classification. The classification of lubricating oils by viscosity is a matter of some importance. A useful system is that of the Society of Automotive Engineers (SAE). Each oil class carries an index designation given in Table IV-2. For those classes designated by letter and number, maximum and minimum viscosities are specified at 0°F. Those designated only by number are specified in viscosities at 210°F.[3] Viscosity is used in specifying several grades of fuel oils (Chap. XII, Kerosene and Fuel Oil) and in setting the rather severe requirements for kerosenes (Chap. XII) and insulating oils (Chap. XVI, Miscellaneous Products).

TABLE IV-2. VISCOSITY VALUES FOR CRANKCASE OILS

SAE designation	Viscosity range, SSU			
	At 0°F		At 210°F	
	Min	Max	Min	Max
5W	....	4,000		
10W	6,000*	Less than 12,000		
20W	12,000†	48,000		
20	....	....	45	Less than 58
30	....	....	58	Less than 70
40	....	....	70	Less than 85
50	....	....	85	110

* Minimum viscosity at 0°F can be waived, provided viscosity at 210°F is not below 40 SSU.

† Minimum viscosity at 0°F can be waived, provided viscosity at 210°F is not below 45 SSU.

"SAE Handbook," p. 357, Society of Automotive Engineers, Inc., New York, 1955.

IV-2. Density and Coefficient of Expansion. Density was, in the early years of the industry, the principal and often the only specification of crude oils and oil products. For crudes it was taken as an index of the proportion of gasoline and, particularly, kerosene present. As long as the industry was concerned with one kind of petroleum (the Pennsylvania crude), the relations were approximately true. As crude oils of other properties were discovered, the significance of density measurements dis-

[1] Herschel, *Natl. Bur. Standards Technol. Paper* 164.
[2] ASTM D 341–43. See also Rahmes and Nelson, *Anal. Chem.*, **20**:912 (1948).
[3] See Withers, *J. Inst. Petrol.*, **28**:250 (1952), on proposed changes in the system.

appeared. Crude oils of particular types are still rated by gravity, as are gasolines and naphthas within certain limits of other properties.

Density is defined as the mass of a unit volume of material at a specified temperature. In the centimeter-gram-second system, it has the dimensions of grams per cubic centimeter (closely approximates grams per milliliter). For no reason other than precedent, the arbitrary and general property of "specific gravity" is more widely used. This is the ratio of the mass of a volume of the substance to the mass of the same volume of water. It depends on two temperatures, those at which the masses of the sample and the water are measured. When the water temperature is 4°C, the specific gravity is equal to the density in the cgs system, since the volume of 1 g of water at that temperature is, by definition, 1 ml. Thus the density of water, for example, varies with temperature, while its specific gravity at equal temperatures is always unity. The standard temperatures for specific gravity in the petroleum industry in this country are 60°/60°F.

Density and specific gravity[1] are extensively used, but the industry generally prefers the "API gravity."[2] This property was derived from the Baumé scale, defined by the equation:

$$\text{Degrees Baumé} = \frac{140}{\text{sp gr } 60°/60°F} - 130 \qquad \text{(IV-8)}$$

A considerable number of hydrometers calibrated according to the Baumé scale were, at an early period, found to be in error by a consistent amount. This led to the adoption in 1921, at the instance of the American Petroleum Institute, of the following equation:

$$\text{Scale} = \frac{141.5}{\text{sp gr } 60°/60°F} - 131.5 \qquad \text{(IV-9)}$$

which was named the "API Gravity Scale" to avoid confusion with the Baumé scale. The API and Baumé systems are of value only for simplifying the construction of hydrometers. For a constant mass-variable displacement hydrometer of uniform stem section, they permit a linear calibration in distance along the stem.[3] The scales are, of course, of no fundamental scientific interest.

The specific gravities of petroleum products range from about 0.6 for casing-head gasolines to slightly over 1.0 for very heavy naphthenic oils. Petroleum gases liquefied under pressure are even lighter. Some typical figures are given in Table IV-3. Solid waxes at ordinary temperatures

---

[1] See ASTM Standard D 1298–55.
[2] See ASTM Standard D 287–55 for scope and measurement.
[3] Taber, *Ind. Eng. Chem.*, **12**:593 (1920).

have specific gravities of about 0.898 to 0.917. In the liquid state they have values about equal to or slightly less than those of the oil fractions from which they were isolated.

TABLE IV-3. SPECIFIC AND API GRAVITIES OF SOME PETROLEUM PRODUCTS

Material	Specific gravity 60°/60°F	API gravity, deg
Crude oils..........................	0.65–1.06	87– 2
Casing-head liquid..................	0.62–0.70	97–70
Gasoline...........................	0.70–0.77	70–52
Kerosene...........................	0.77–0.82	52–40
Lubricating oil, SAE 10.............	0.86–0.92	33–22
Lubricating oil, SAE 50.............	0.88–0.98	29–13
Residua and cracked residua.........	0.88–1.06	29– 2

The variation of density with temperature, effectively the coefficient of expansion, is a property of great technical importance, since most petroleum products are sold by volume and specific gravities are usually determined at the prevailing temperature rather than at the standard temperature, 60°F. Much work has been expended on the investigation of this function. The petroleum industry has generally accepted corrections recommended in ASTM Standard D 1250–55.[1] The tables of gravity corrections are based on an assumption, apparently well justified by the data, that the coefficient of expansion of all petroleum products is a function (at fixed temperatures) of density only.[2] This makes possible the calculation of gravity at any temperature from that at any other temperature within the ordinary range of experience.

A more accurate but more complicated method allowing for differences in molecular weight is that of Lipkin and Kurtz.[3] It will be obvious that such empirical corrections should not be applied to wax-containing oils at temperatures below the cloud point (where wax comes out of solutions). Densities may be determined by any one of several conventional methods.[4] Refineries and production laboratories generally employ special hydrom-

[1] ASTM-IP Petroleum Measurement Tables (available from ASTM and the Institute of Petroleum). The underlying work was that of the *U.S. Bur. Standards, Circ.* 410.

[2] The peculiarity of this empirical law may be indicated by mentioning that a heavy paraffinic lubricating oil and an aromatic gasoline can have the same density and hence the same coefficient of expansion.

[3] Lipkin and Kurtz, *Ind. Eng. Chem., Anal. Ed.*, **13**:291 (1941).

[4] Reilly and Rae, "Physico-Chemical Methods," vol. I, Methuen & Co., Ltd., London, 1954. Bauer, "Technique of Organic Chemistry," Weissberger (ed.), vol. I, part I, chap. VI, Interscience Publishers, Inc., New York, 1949.

eters graduated in degrees API[1] or specific gravity at 60°F.[2]   For accurate work with liquid samples, pycnometers are preferred.[3]

Volumetric contraction on blending of hydrocarbons is of considerable practical interest, as is also the special problem of densities for hydrocarbon gases and liquefied gases under high pressures.   A good deal of empirical work has been done on each subject.[4]

Molecular volume is defined as the molecular weight divided by the density; it is, therefore, proportional to the volume occupied by a single molecule of the material.   Assuming an additive nature for atomic increments, various investigators have proposed formulae for the calculation of molecular volume of pure hydrocarbons.   Such relations are very old (Kopp, 1842), but have been extended recently.[5]   Generally speaking, the normal paraffins have the largest molecular volumes; branching of the carbon chain decreases the value only slightly, double bonds distinctly, and ring closure to an amount about equivalent to three double bonds. Aromatic double bonds have nearly the same effect as aliphatic ones. Molecular volume is useful in the correlations of chemical constitution with physical properties.   The general idea is not new, but interest has revived within recent years.

IV-3. Surface and Interfacial Tensions.   Surface tension of petroleum products was studied many years ago,[6] but the low precision of the methods for measurement and the narrow range of values for widely diverse materials (about 24 to 38 dynes at most) have rendered the property of little value for characterization.   It is, however, of considerable technical importance.   Some typical values of surface tensions[7] are given in the table on page 195.

The increase of values with rise in molecular weight is evident; the correlation was noticed long ago.[8]   Rising temperature decreases surface tension and it, of course, becomes zero at the critical temperature.[9]

[1] ASTM Standard D 287–55.

[2] ASTM Standard D 1298–55.

[3] ASTM Standard D 941–55; ASTM Standard D 1217–54.

[4] On the former, see Reeves, *Petrol. Processing*, **7**:478 (1952); *Petrol. Refiner*, **31**(4):154 (1952).   On the latter, Katz, Matthews, and Roland, *Petrol. Eng.*, **13**(13):82; **14**(1):54; (3):58 (1942). Legatski and others, Technical Committee, National Gasoline Association, *Ind. Eng. Chem.*, **34**:1240 (1942).   *Petrol. Eng.*, **15**(2):161 (1943).   ASTM Committee D-2, Report, Appendix V, p. 28, Detroit, 1948.

[5] Kurtz and Sankin in "Physical Chemistry of Hydrocarbons," Farkas (ed.), vol. II, chap. I, Academic Press, Inc., New York, 1953.   Van Nes and Van Westen, "Aspects of the Constitution of Mineral Oils," chap. III, p. 73, Elsevier Press, Inc., Houston, 1951.

[6] Johansen, *Ind. Eng. Chem.*, **16**:132 (1924).

[7] Francis and Bennett, *Ind. Eng. Chem.*, **14**:622 (1922).

[8] Rittman and Egloff, *Ind. Eng. Chem.*, **7**:578 (1915).

[9] Bicker and Katz, *Petrol. Technol.*, **6**:1 (1943).

Dynes per centimeter

Light naphtha.............. 20*
Gasoline................... 26
Kerosene.................. 30
Lubricating oil:
    SAE 10................ 32
    SAE 50................ 34

* Probably contaminated.

Nonhydrocarbon materials dissolved in an oil will reduce the surface tension. Polar compounds such as soaps and fatty acids are particularly active. The effect is marked at low concentrations up to a critical value beyond which further additions cause little change; the critical value corresponds closely with that required for a monomolecular layer on the exposed surface, where it is adsorbed and accounts for the lowering. A high proportion of the complex phenomena shown by emulsions and foams can be traced to these induced surface tension effects. Dissolved gases, even hydrocarbon gases, will lower the surface tension of oils[1] but the effects are less dramatic and the changes are probably due to dilution. The matter is presumably of some importance in petroleum production engineering where the viscosity and surface tension of the reservoir fluid may govern the amount of oil recovered under certain conditions. Much of what has just been said applies even more emphatically to interfacial tension.[2] Where oil-water systems are involved, the pH of the aqueous phase will have an influence on the tension at the interface; the change is small for highly refined oils, but increasing pH will cause a rapid decrease for poorly refined, contaminated, or slightly oxidized oils.[3] Change of interfacial tension between oil and alkaline water has been proposed as an index for following refining or deterioration of certain products, e.g., turbine and insulating oils.[4] In cases where surface or interfacial tensions are lowered by the presence of solutes which tend to concentrate on the surface, some time is required to obtain the final concentration and hence the final value of the tension. In such systems, dynamic and static tension must be distinguished; the first concerns the freshly exposed sur-

[1] Swartz, *Physics*, **1**:245 (1931). Sumner, "Clayton's Theory of Emulsions and Their Technical Treatment," 5th ed., chap. I, The Blakiston Division, McGraw-Hill Book Company, Inc., New York, 1954.

[2] Becher, "Principles of Emulsion Technology," Reinhold Publishing Corporation, New York, 1955. Lawrence, "Science of Petroleum," vol. II, p. 1369, Oxford University Press, New York and London, 1938.

[3] Lawrence, *loc. cit.* Gay and Donnet, *J. chim. phys.*, **29**:385 (1932).

[4] Vellinger and Radulesco, *Ann. combustibles liquides*, **9**:279 (1934). von Fuchs, Wilson, and Edlund, *ACS, Div. Petrol. Chem.*, ACS Meeting, St. Louis, 1941, p. 213. Sommerman, "Science of Petroleum," vol. II, p. 1361, Oxford University Press, New York and London, 1938.

face having nearly the same composition as the body of the liquid; it usually has a value only slightly less than that of the pure solvent. The static tension is that existing after equilibrium concentrations have been reached at the surface.

Surface tensions are usually measured by the capillary rise, drop weight, or the duNuoy ring methods. The ring method is also adaptable to interfacial tensions.[1]

OPTICAL PROPERTIES

IV-4. Refractive Index. The refractive index, either alone or particularly when used in conjunction with other properties, is highly important in characterizing petroleum fractions. For close-cut fractions of the same molecular weight the values increase strongly in the order paraffin, naphthene, and aromatic; those for polycyclic naphthenes and polycyclic aromatics are, respectively, higher than for the corresponding monocyclics. For a series of hydrocarbons of essentially the same type, the refractive index increases with molecular weight, but not to a great extent, especially in the paraffin series. While crude oils vary widely in refractive index, this property alone is of little value in characterizing them. When liquid hydrocarbons are mixed, volumes of the resulting solutions are additive or nearly so; the refractive indices in such cases follow a volume mean compounding law.[2] The values for petroleum products vary widely; a few for close fractions are given in Table IV-4 with other properties for orientation.

TABLE IV-4. REFRACTIVE INDICES OF SOME CLOSELY CUT OILS

Oil	Refractive index n_D^{20}	Specific gravity 60°/60°F	Viscosity, cs		Molecular weight
			100°F	210°F	
1	1.5185	0.9250	26.35	3.87	300
2	1.4637	0.8406	14.55	3.28	353
3	1.5276	0.9367	1955.00	49.50	646
4	1.4799	0.8724	3597.00	27.35	822

The indices of light-colored liquid petroleum products are readily measured[3] with many of the standard forms of the Abbé refractometer. These instruments give sufficient accuracy, ± 1 or 2 numbers in the fourth decimal place, for most routine work. For precise determinations

[1] Reilly and Rae, "Physico-Chemical Methods," vol. I, sec. 5, Methuen & Co., Ltd., London, 1954. Harkins, "Technique of Organic Chemistry," Weissberger (ed.), vol. I, part I, chap. IX, Interscience Publishers, New York, 1949.

[2] MacFarlane and Wright, *J. Chem. Soc.*, 1933, p. 114.

[3] ASTM Standard D 1218–52T.

more elaborate types are available.[1] Refractive indices of nearly all materials decrease with increasing temperature, and several formulas have been given for expressing the change quantitatively. No tables similar to the extensive density correction tables (see above section on density) have been compiled for refractive indices of petroleum products, but a very simple rule has been pointed out; the temperature coefficient of refractive index is a constant times the temperature coefficient of density.[2] This rule may be applied over a narrow range of temperature, and an empirical equation of Eykman[3] can be used where the temperature range is wider.[4] For direct determinations at temperatures up to 100°C, an Abbé type[5] or an Eykman instrument[6] may be employed.

IV-5. Refractive and Specific Dispersion; Molecular and Specific Refraction. The refractive dispersion of a substance is defined as the difference between its refractive indices at two specified wavelengths of light. Two lines commonly used to calculate dispersions are the *C* (6,563 A, red) and *F* (4,861 A, blue) lines of the hydrogen spectrum. For best results precision instruments and monochromatic light are desirable,[7] but fair approximations can be obtained with some of the Abbé refractometers, using Amici prism compensation and white light. The dependence of refractive index on wavelength is closely approximated by the empirical formula of Cauchy,[8]

$$n_r = A + \frac{B}{\lambda^2} + \frac{C}{\lambda^4} \tag{IV-10}$$

where n_r is the refractive index, λ the wavelength, and A, B, and C are constants.

The specific dispersion is the refractive dispersion divided by the density at the same temperature. It is, as derived from the empirical equation for specific refraction of Gladstone and Dale,

$$\frac{N_F - N_C}{d} = C \tag{IV-11}$$

[1] General discussions of the instruments and methods of refractometry are given by Bauer and Fajans, "Technique of Organic Chemistry," Weissberger (ed.), vol. I, part II, chap. XX, Interscience Publishers, Inc., New York, 1949.

[2] Ward and Kurtz, *Ind. Eng. Chem., Anal. Ed.*, **10**:559 (1938). Kurtz and Ward, *J. Franklin Inst.*, **224**:583, 697 (1937). Kurtz, Amon, and Sankin, *Ind. Eng. Chem.*, **42**:174 (1950). Kurtz and Sankin in "Physical Chemistry of Hydrocarbons," Farkas (ed.), vol. II, chap. I, Academic Press, Inc., New York, 1953.

[3] Eykman, *Rec. trav. chim.*, **14**:185 (1895).

[4] Dreisbach, *Ind. Eng. Chem.*, **40**:2269 (1948).

[5] Black, Harvey, and Ferris, *Anal. Chem.*, **26**:1089 (1954).

[6] Lauer and King, *Anal. Chem.*, **28**:1697 (1956).

[7] ASTM D 1218–52T.

[8] Sankin, Martin, and Lipkin, *Anal. Chem.*, **22**:643 (1950).

This equation is of particular significance in petroleum chemistry, because all the saturated hydrocarbons, naphthene and paraffin, have nearly the same value, irrespective of molecular weight, while aromatics are much higher and unsaturated aliphatics are intermediate.[1]

Specific refraction is the term applied to the quantity defined by the expression of Lorentz-Lorenz:

$$\frac{n^2 - 1}{n^2 + 2}\frac{1}{d} = C \tag{IV-12}$$

where n is the refractive index, d the density, and C a constant independent of temperature. This expression was derived for gases and does not apply exactly to many hydrocarbon liquids. A much better fit of the experimental data is obtained with a modified formula, attributed to Eykman.[2]

$$\frac{N^2 - 1}{N + 0.4}\frac{1}{d} = C \tag{IV-12a}$$

Molecular refraction is taken to be specific refraction multiplied by molecular weight; its particular usefulness lies in the fact that it is very nearly additive for the components of a molecule; e.g., numerical values can be assigned to atoms and structural features such as double bonds, rings, etc.; the value for any pure compound is then approximately the sum of such component constants for the molecule.[3]

IV-6. Optical Activity. Nearly all crude oils show weak optical rotatory power. The rotation is usually to the right, but in a few cases, the direction is reversed and in still fewer, there is no rotation. The rotatory power is concentrated in certain fractions, the maximum lying at a molecular weight of about 350 to 400; this maximum is about the same for all crude oils examined.[4] The occurrence of optically active compounds in unaltered natural petroleum has been a strong argument in favor of a rather low temperature origin of petroleum from organic raw materials (see Chap. V). These compounds were in earlier years believed to be derivatives of sterols.[5] More recent study indicates that the

[1] Ward and Fulweiler, *Ind. Eng. Chem., Anal. Ed.*, **6**:396 (1934). Moutte, *Chim. & ind. (Paris)*, Special number 262, 1928. Mair, Willingham, and Streiff, *J. Research Natl. Bur. Standards*, **21**:581 (1938). A general discussion of dispersion theory has been given by Kurtz and Sankin in "Physical Chemistry of Hydrocarbons," Farkas (ed.), vol. II, chap. I, Academic Press, Inc., New York, 1953.

[2] Eisenlohr and Wolisch, *Ber.*, **53b**:1746, 2053 (1930). R. R. Dreisbach, *Ind. Eng. Chem.*, **40**:2269 (1948).

[3] Bauer in "Technique of Organic Chemistry," Weissberger (ed.), vol. I, part II, chap. 20, Interscience Publishers, Inc., New York, 1949.

[4] Zaloziecki and Klarfeld, *Chem. Z.*, **31**:1155 (1907). Fenske, Carnahan, Breston, Caser, and Rescorla, *Ind. Eng. Chem.*, **34**:638 (1942). Burwell in "Physical Chemistry of Hydrocarbons," Farkas (ed.), vol. II, chap. 5, Academic Press, Inc., 1953.

[5] Notably cholesterol; see first edition of this book, 1928, p. 89.

phenomenon can be attributed to hydrocarbons, particularly non-aromatic polycyclics.[1]

A magnetic field causes all liquids to exhibit optical rotation, usually in the same direction as that of the magnetizing current; this phenomenon is known as the "Faraday effect," and it may be expressed by the relation

$$\Theta = \rho t H \tag{IV-13}$$

where Θ is the total angle of rotation, t the thickness of substance through which the light passes, and H the magnetic field. The constant ρ is an intrinsic property of the substance, usually termed the "Verdet constant"; it has the dimensions

Minutes of arc per cm per gauss

It is found to appear in a number of simple relations resembling those applying to optical rotation.[2] Attempts have been made to use the constant in studying constitution of hydrocarbons by physical property correlations. An empirical constant has been found useful.

$$D = \frac{9 n \rho M}{(n^2 + 2)^2 d} \tag{IV-14}$$

where n = refractive index, M = molecular weight, d = density, and ρ = Verdet constant.

Verdet values have been measured for many hydrocarbons;[3] examples from the data of Foehr and Fenske are given in Table IV-5.

TABLE IV-5

Compound	Refractive index n_D^{20}	Verdet constant $\times 10^2$
n-Pentane	1.3578	1.150
n-Hexane	1.3750	1.197
n-Hexadecane	1.4340	1.346
Cyclopentane	1.4065	1.229
Cyclopentene	1.4224	1.525
Pentene-1	1.3714	1.391
1,3-Pentadiene	1.4309	2.080
Benzene	1.5011	2.999
cis-Decahydronaphthalene	1.4814	1.389
Methylnaphthalenes	1.6150	4.446

[1] Oakwood, Shriver, Fall, McAleer, and Wunz, *Ind. Eng. Chem.*, **44**:2568 (1952).

[2] Javelle, *Chim. & ind.*, Special number 264, 1928.

[3] Foehr and Fenske, *Ind. Eng. Chem.*, **41**:1956 (1949). Labbauf, Nutt, and Garner, *J. Inst. Petrol.*, **41**:336 (1955).

IV-7. X-ray Diffraction, Absorption, and Emission Spectra. (Approximate wavelength range 10^{-9} to 10^{-6} cm.) Diffraction studies with X rays give information concerning spatial periodicity within a substance. Quantitatively, they give interatomic distances in crystals and, rather roughly, in liquids. Furthermore, the regularity of the orientation is indicated by the sharpness of the lines and rings. Liquid X-ray diffraction spectra show only the distances at which the molecules are rather regularly spaced, with some indication of the principal molecular dimensions. Examination of a few simple hydrocarbons[1] has shown that both the extent and the nature of the orientation are strongly influenced by the type and position of substituents in cyclic compounds. Symmetrical molecules have sharper diffraction patterns than unsymmetrical ones, and double bonds tend to make the patterns more diffuse.[2] Petroleum fractions are so complex that the diffraction rings are very feeble.[3] Single crystals give more precise information than liquids or powders. While only a few studies have been made on olefinic and naphthenic compounds, the normal hydrocarbons, petroleum waxes, and aromatic compounds have been extensively investigated.[4] Listed below are the important dimensions obtained[5] for a single crystal of very pure *n*-nonocosane.

Unit cell....................................... Prism, 7.45 × 4.97 × 77.2 A
Distance between alternate CH_2 groups.............. 2.54 A
Distance between CH_2 groups, neighboring molecules.. 3.7 A
Cross-section area of chain........................ 18.5 sq A
Distance between axes of neighboring molecules...... 4.6 A

X-ray emission and absorption[6] have been used with petroleum fractions primarily to analyze for nonhydrocarbon components containing one or more heavy atoms in the molecule. Analyses for sulfur, bromine, and lead-containing molecules are the principal application.

IV-8. Ultraviolet Absorption Spectra. (Wavelength range 1×10^{-5} to 4×10^{-5} cm.) Electromagnetic radiation passing through matter is absorbed at definite energy levels in the molecules concerned.[7] There is

---

[1] Stewart, *Phys. Rev.*, **33**:889 (1929).

[2] Ishino, Tanaka, and Tsuji, *Mem. Coll. Sci., Kyoto Imp. Univ.*, **13**:1 (1930).

[3] Muller, *Proc. Roy. Soc. (London)*, **A120**:437 (1928).

[4] Robertson, "Science of Petroleum," vol. V, part III, p. 304, Oxford University Press, New York and London, 1955.

[5] Stewart, *Rev. Mod. Phys.*, **2**:116 (1930).

[6] Birks, Brooks, Friedman, and Rae, *Anal. Chem.*, **22**:1258 (1952). Lamb, Niebylski, and Kiefer, *Anal. Chem.*, **27**:129 (1955). Mottlau and Driesen, *Anal. Chem.*, **24**:1852 (1953). Liebhafsky, *Anal. Chem.*, **25**:689 (1953); **28**:583 (1956). Cranston, Mathews, and Evans, *J. Inst. Petrol.*, **40**:55 (1954).

[7] Discussions of the theory of electronic spectra based upon quantum-mechanical considerations have been presented by Duncan in "Technique of Organic Chemistry," Weissberger (ed.), vol. IX, chap. V, part 1, and Matsen, part 2, Interscience Publishers, Inc., New York, 1956.

good basic interpretation for the results obtained with light hydrocarbon gases and vapors in the vacuum ultraviolet (Schumann) region. *Cis* and *trans* isomers are readily distinguished and identified,[1] and ionization potentials,[2] appearance potentials, and dissociation energies[3] have been obtained which check well with data procured with the mass spectrometer. Many saturated hydrocarbons and nonconjugated olefins absorb in the vacuum ultraviolet but are transparent in the ordinary ultraviolet. Conjugated olefins and aromatics absorb in the longer wavelength region. As the number of conjugated double bonds increases, the absorption spectra are shifted toward the visible region of the spectrum. Petroleum fractions show complicated band patterns, but some conclusions can be drawn; for instance, a fraction containing C_4 and lighter hydrocarbons can be analyzed for 1,3-butadiene.[4] Benzene and toluene[5] can be found up to a maximum concentration of 25 per cent in petroleum products having a boiling range of 100 to 250°F, and methods have been established[6] for the determination of individual C_8 aromatics and for the total aromatics in gasoline and higher boiling fractions. Extensive catalogues of spectra of pure compounds are available and many specialized analyses are made on the basis of these standards of reference.[7]

IV-9. Infrared Absorption Spectra. (Wavelength range 7.5×10^{-5} to 1.5×10^{-3} cm.) No single physical property gives more information concerning the chemical constitution of hydrocarbons than the infrared absorption spectrum, especially for the simpler aliphatics. Most of the absorption bands arise from resonance vibrations of the valence bonds and hence are dependent on the effective inertia of atoms and atom groups in the molecule and the forces between them. Rotation and rotation-vibration spectra are also observed in the same region but are of less fundamental significance.[8] The bands arising from the aliphatic C-H bonds are of particular interest, since their frequencies depend on the atomic weights of the atoms to which the other three valences of the

[1] Carr and Stucklen, *J. ACS*, **59**:2138 (1937).

[2] Price and Tutte, *Proc. Roy. Soc. (London)*, **A174**:207 (1940); Price and Walsh, *Proc. Roy. Soc. (London)*, **A174**:230 (1940).

[3] Carr and Stucklen, *Helvetica Phys. Acta*, **6**:261 (1933).

[4] ASTM Standard D 1096–54.

[5] ASTM Standard D 1017–51.

[6] Jostes, *Oel Kohle ver. Erdoel u. Teer*, **14**:1012 (1938). Priestley and Dudenbostle, "The Chemistry of Petroleum Hydrocarbons," vol. I, chap. 12, p. 341, Reinhold Publishing Corporation, New York, 1954.

[7] American Petroleum Institute Research Project 44, "Ultraviolet Spectral Data," Carnegie Institute of Technology, Pittsburgh, Pa. Friedel and Orchin, "Ultraviolet Spectra of Aromatic Compounds," John Wiley & Sons, Inc., New York, 1951.

[8] For a detailed discussion of vibration and rotation in hydrocarbons, see Jones and Sandorfy, "Technique of Organic Chemistry," Weissberger (ed.), vol. IX, chap. IV, pp. 351–406, Interscience Publishers, Inc., New York, 1956.

carbon are linked.[1] Absorptivities vary for olefins, cycloparaffins, and aromatics. Very often qualitative information on specific structural elements can be obtained even though the spectra are too complex for individual compound analysis. Using characteristic frequencies, methods[2] have been established for group-type analysis of saturates and saturate-aromatic blends. When total olefin content is known, olefin types may be obtained from infrared data.[3] Analyses using separation techniques combined with infrared absorption have been made for individual compounds in the aromatic portion of a virgin naphtha[4] boiling to 380°F; and similar application to paraffin-naphthene mixtures[5] boiling up to 270°F has been devised. Extensive catalogues of spectra of pure compounds are available, and many specialized analyses are possible on the basis of these standards of reference.[6]

The spectroscopy of scattered light (Raman effect) yields information substantially equivalent to that obtained from direct spectroscopy in the infrared. This is a consequence of the fundamental Raman law

$$\gamma_0 = \gamma_i - \gamma_s \qquad\qquad\qquad \text{(IV-15)}$$

where γ_i is the frequency of the incident light, γ_s that of the scattered light, and γ_0 that of an absorption peak. High resolving power is required for this technique; however, light in the visible region can be used and experimentation is usually simpler than for the infrared.

Since Raman and infrared spectra both result from vibration and rotation-vibration within a molecule, they are complementary. For a systematic comparison of the two techniques, available comprehensive reviews[7] should be consulted.

IV-10. Fluorescence. Fluorescence is closely related to ultraviolet absorption. The fluorescent spectrum emitted is always of longer wavelength than the incident radiation. In the case of simple molecules which absorb in the ultraviolet region, simple fluorescent spectra are produced

[1] Liddel and Kasper, *J. Research Natl. Bur. Standards,* **11**:599 (1933). Rose, *J. Research Natl. Bur. Standards,* **19**:143 (1937). Fox and Martin, *Proc. Roy. Soc. (London),* **A175**:208 (1940). McMurray and Thornton, *Anal. Chem.,* **24**:318 (1952). Kaye, *Spectrochim. Acta,* **6**:257 (1954).

[2] Rose, *J. Research Natl. Bur. Standards,* **20**:129 (1938). Hibbard and Cleaves, *Anal. Chem.,* **21**:486 (1949). Lauer and Rosenbaum, *Appl. Spectroscopy,* **6**:29 (1952). Evans, Hibbard, and Powell, *Anal. Chem.,* **23**:1604 (1951). Hastings, Watson, Williams, and Anderson, *Anal. Chem.,* **24**:612 (1952).

[3] Anderson and Seyfried, *Anal. Chem.,* **20**:998 (1948).

[4] Williams, Hastings, and Anderson, *Anal. Chem.,* **24**:1911 (1952).

[5] Bell, *Anal. Chem.,* **22**:1005 (1950).

[6] Jones and Sandorfy, *loc. cit.*

[7] Tenney in "The Chemistry of Petroleum Hydrocarbons," Brooks, Boord, Kurtz, and Schmerling (eds.), vol. I, chap. 14, Reinhold Publishing Corporation, New York, 1954. Jones and Sandorfy, *loc. cit.*

when monochromatic light of the absorbed wavelength is used. However, molecules which absorb in the ultraviolet and visible regions give complex spectra even for monochromatic ultraviolet radiation, since the longer wavelengths of the fluorescent spectrum in the visible region may be reabsorbed and emitted as light of even longer wavelengths. In addition, trace impurities may quench fluorescence.[1] As may be expected from this and other considerations of ultraviolet absorption spectroscopy (see above), paraffins and naphthenes are at most only feebly fluorescent. Aromatics, starting with benzene, have only slight visible fluorescence (absorption bands are prominent in the short wavelengths of the ordinary ultraviolet), but develop strong visible fluorescence (absorption bands near or in the visible region)[2] as the ring structure becomes more complex.

The use of fluorescence spectra in analytical problems has been limited, although some of the aromatic compounds found in heavier petroleum fractions do show characteristic patterns.[3] However, since fluorescence is very sensitive to traces[4] of foreign compounds, another method, such as ultraviolet absorption spectroscopy, should be used to complement these analyses.

IV-11. Color. Colored hydrocarbons have long been known; red, green, and blue-to-black individual compounds[5] have been described. These are all condensed-ring aromatics. The absorption is probably analogous to that of the lighter aromatics in the ultraviolet, except that, since the molecular weights are higher, it is shifted toward the red end of the spectrum. It is probable that, in any case, most of the color of petroleum products does not arise from a content of such materials. For one thing, many low-boiling fractions are colored, and the known compounds, being of rather high molecular weight, could not be present. The yellow color of cracked gasolines has been attributed to fulvenes.[6] While much of the brownish-green to black color of unrefined distillates and residua is obviously caused by resinous and asphaltic substances dissolved or suspended, it is not certain that all the color of these heavier fractions is caused by such materials. However, the fact that adsorptive treatment with silica gel, active carbon, fuller's earth, or bauxite will remove a great deal of color seems quite suggestive.

[1] For a detailed discussion of fluorescence, see West, in "Technique of Organic Chemistry," Weissberger (ed.), vol. IX, chap. VI, Interscience Publishers, Inc., 1956. Dement, *Oil Weekly*, **101**(2):16 (1941).

[2] West, *loc. cit.*

[3] Berenblum and Schoental, *Brit. J. Expl. Pathol.*, **24**:232 (1943). Cahnmann, *Anal. Chem.*, **27**:1235 (1955).

[4] DeMent, *loc. cit.*

[5] Jones, *J. ACS*, **63**:313 (1941). Bergmann and Herlinger, *J. Chem. Phys.*, **4**:532 (1936). Clar, *Ber.*, **72B**:1817 (1939). Dufraisse and Girard, *Bull. soc. chim. France*, series 5, vol. 1, p. 1359 (1934). Badoche, *Ann. Chim.*, **20**:200 (1933).

[6] Brooks and Parker, *Ind. Eng. Chem.*, **11**:587 (1924).

Color is widely used in product specifications; it has been difficult to put color measurement on a sound physical basis because empirical methods and color scales were adopted very early and have continued in use. A good deal of effort has gone into standardizing and correlating these methods and scales.[1] Light-colored relatively volatile products are examined by use of the Saybolt chromometer.[2] For lubricating oils, the Union colorimeter is employed.[3] A respacing of the intervals on the scale of this instrument has been undertaken.[4]

IV-12. Mass Spectroscopy. Mass spectroscopy depends upon the resolution of charged particles of varying mass by means of electrical and magnetic fields. Thus while not an optical property in general nomenclature, it is considered here since it contains similar elements. The principal parts of a mass spectrometer are an ionization chamber (in which ions are formed by electron bombardment of gaseous materials), an electrical potential to accelerate the ions, and a magnetic field which induces an angular deflection. If either the electric or magnetic field strength is varied, the ions may be appropriately separated and collected on the basis of their mass-to-charge ratio.

Hydrocarbons ionize to produce specific fragments. These are characteristic of hydrocarbon type and for this reason, type analyses of narrow boiling fractions in gas oil, lubricating oil, and waxes are possible; however,[5] mixed structures may interfere.[6] It is necessary to use certified reference standards to calibrate the spectrometer.

Mass spectroscopy has been applied to hydrocarbon fractions for individual compound analysis. The fewer components present in the mixture, the better are the results; therefore, preliminary separations are usually carried out. Hydrocarbon analyses in the C_1 to C_5 range are readily accomplished.[7] In the liquid range,[8] individual components can

---

[1] For reviews of color measurement methods used for petroleum products, see Kalischevsky, *Petrol. Refiner*, **26**(1):93 (1947). Evans, McCue, and Woodrow, *J. Inst. Petrol.*, **35**:221 (1949).

[2] ASTM D 156–53 T. See *J. Inst. Petrol.*, **29**:357 (1943), for relation of these colors to those of the Lovibond instrument.

[3] ASTM D 155–45 T.

[4] Judd, Plaza, and Belknap, *J. Res. Natl. Bur. Standards*, **44**:559 (1950); *ASTM Bull.*, no. 167, p. 63, 1950.

[5] Robertson, "Mass Spectroscopy," John Wiley & Sons, Inc., New York, 1954. Powell and Ross, "Applied Mass Spectrometry," Institute of Petroleum, London, 1950. O'Neal, "Applied Mass Spectrometry," Institute of Petroleum, London, 1950.

[6] Young, "The Chemistry of Petroleum Hydrocarbons," Brooks, Boord, Kurtz, and Schmerling, vol. I, chap. 15, Reinhold Publishing Corporation, New York, 1934.

[7] Washburn, Wiley, Rock, and Berry, *Ind. Eng. Chem., Anal. Ed.*, **17**:74 (1945).

[8] Young, *loc. cit.* Starr, "Science of Petroleum," vol. V, part III, p. 355, Oxford University Press, New York and London, 1955.

be determined in virgin naphthas, olefin-free naphthas, and those in which olefins have been determined by an alternate technique. As indicated, group-type analyses have been made on narrow boiling fractions up into the lubricating oil and wax ranges.

THERMAL PROPERTIES

IV-13. Melting Points and Transition Points. Most petroleum products are liquids at temperatures ordinarily encountered, and solidification during use, which might be awkward or dangerous, is not a common occurrence. However, these phenomena may be quite important in the special cases involved in handling paraffin waxes, synthetic hydrocarbons as motor fuel constituents, and in hydrocarbon research.

No quantitative rule can be given for predicting the melting points of pure hydrocarbons; qualitatively, however the melting point tends to increase with the molecular weight and with symmetry of the molecule. The melting points of the normal paraffins are listed in Table IV-6. These values agree fairly well with the data for the lower crystalline paraffin waxes when the materials are compared on a molecular-weight basis, and this fact furnishes some of the best evidence for chemical constitution

TABLE IV-6. MELTING POINTS OF THE NORMAL PARAFFINS*

Number of C atoms	Melting point, °C	Number of C atoms	Melting point, °C
1	−182	20	36
2	−183	21	40
3	−188	22	44
4	−138	23	47
5	−130	24	51
6	− 95	25	54
7	− 91	26	56
8	− 57	27	59
9	− 54	28	61
10	− 30	29	64
11	− 26	30	66
12	− 10	31	68
13	− 5	32	70
14	6	33	71
15	10	34	73
16	18	35	75
17	22	40	82
18	28	50	92
19	32	60	99

* Selected Values of Properties of Hydrocarbons, *API RP* 44, Carnegie Institute of Technology, 1955.

of the macrocrystalline petroleum waxes. The effect of symmetry is far greater than that of molecular weight and often offsets it. When side chains are added to normal paraffins, the branched-chain hydrocarbon usually melts far below the normal compound of the same number of carbon atoms and often lower than the normal paraffin equivalent to the longest chain in the molecule. Striking exceptions occur, however, when the substitution is such as to lead to a compact, highly symmetrical molecule; for instance, 2,2-dimethylpropane melts at $-20°C$, while n-pentane melts at $-130°C$, and 2,2,3,3-tetramethylbutane melts at $104°C$, while n-octane melts at $-57°C$. Similar qualitative rules apply to cyclics, with even more extreme limits. Unsubstituted and symmetrically substituted compounds (e.g., benzene, cyclohexane, p-xylene, and naphthalene) melt at higher temperatures relative to the paraffin compounds of similar molecular weight, while the unsymmetrical isomers generally melt at lower temperatures than do the aliphatics of the same molecular weight.

Unsaturation affects the melting point principally by its alteration of symmetry; thus ethane ($-172°C$) and ethylene ($-169.5°C$) differ only slightly, but the melting points of cyclohexane ($6.2°C$) and cyclohexene ($-104°C$) contrast strongly. All types of highly unsymmetrical hydrocarbons are difficult to crystallize. Thus asymmetrically branched aliphatics as low as the octanes and most substituted cyclics, such as comprise the greater part of the lubricating fractions of petroleum, crystallize slowly, if at all. On cooling they merely increase in viscosity to glass-like solids.

Various methods are used for the determination of melting points.[1] For identification the capillary tube method is adequate.[2] For a pure compound, the melting point obtained in this way will be fairly sharp, but for impure materials, the melting may take place over a considerable temperature range. While mixed melting point tests are useful for identification, this does not apply to the higher normal paraffins, since they form solid solutions so readily that the melting point is nearly a linear function of composition. No eutectics are formed and even relatively wide mixtures behave as pure liquids.

In petrolatum technology, two arbitrary methods are used to determine the solidification temperature, usually designated the congealing point. The first[3] is a melting in which a film adhering to a thermometer is heated in an air bath; the temperature is noted at which the first drop leaves the

[1] Skau and Wakeham in "Technique of Organic Chemistry," Weissberger (ed.), vol. I, part I, Interscience Publishers, Inc., New York, 1949.

[2] Shriner and Fuson, "Identification of Organic Compounds," John Wiley & Sons, Inc., New York, 1948.

[3] ASTM Standard D 127–49.

bulb surface. The procedure is applied to petrolatums and to micro-crystalline waxes. The second method[1] involves measuring, under prescribed conditions, the temperature at which a melted substance (specifically petrolatum) ceases to flow. A thermometer bulb is coated with the liquid and the stem is then rotated, as temperature falls, until the liquid is seen to rotate with the bulb. Determination of the time-temperature curve through the melting point region is the best way of finding the precise melting or freezing point. The method is applied to refined paraffin waxes,[2] and to hydrocarbons for determinations of purity in the range above 95 per cent.[3] The sample is allowed to cool under controlled conditions and the temperature of the sample is read as a function of time. As predicted by the phase rule for a pure material, the temperature will be independent of time while two phases coexist. When the solid phase disappears (melts), a rise of temperature with time will result. The intersection of the plateau, or constant-temperature portion of the resulting curve, with the rapidly changing portion is the melting point. In practice, the change from one slope to the other is not instan-taneous and the point of intersection must be found by extrapolation. From the data obtained, the amount of impurity may be calculated, provided the melting point for zero impurity and the cryoscopic constant are known. The possibility of crystalline modifications must be kept in mind; they are likely to cause points of inflection in the cooling curve. For refined paraffin waxes, crystal transitions occur near the melting point and may influence measurements of density and coefficients of expansion.[4]

IV-14. Vapor Pressure and Boiling Points. Boiling points are much less affected by molecular symmetry than are melting points; they depend almost solely on molecular weight. This is strikingly exhibited by the fact that wax isolated from closely distilled oils has nearly the same molecular weight as the accompanying oil. In round numbers, the limiting molecular weight for distillation at atmospheric pressure is about 200; for conventional vacuum distillation about 500; and for molecular distillation about 1,200. The practical limit is reached when the tempera-ture required to vaporize sufficient material for distillation is above that at which substantial thermal cracking begins.

Boiling points alone are of little value in characterizing petroleum products, as most of these materials cover relatively wide molecular

---

[1] ASTM D 938–49.

[2] ASTM D 87–42.

[3] Taylor and Rossini, *J. Research Natl. Bur. Standards*, **32**(5):197 (1944). Glasgow, Streiff, and Rossini, *J. Research Natl. Bur. Standards*, **35**(6):355 (1945). ASTM Standards D 1015–55, D 1016–55.

[4] Bekkedahl, *J. Research Natl. Bur. Standards*, **43**:145 (1949). Templin, *Ind. Eng. Chem.*, **48**:154 (1956).

weight ranges.   Distillation curves, however, are very useful; the Engler distillation test[1] is one of the principal specifications of gasoline and other distillates; low-temperature distillation[2] is a convenient method for the analysis of hydrocarbon gases and liquefied petroleum gases.   A variation of analytical distillation useful for low-boiling petroleum products, especially liquefied petroleum gases, is gas chromatography.   This is essentially an isothermal distillation of materials in the presence of an extractive liquid phase.[3]   It can also be applied to plant streams as a control method.

The effect of pressure on the boiling point is a subject of great technical importance in petroleum refining.   Vapor-pressure–temperature data have been published for nearly all the lower hydrocarbons and for many petroleum fractions.   Graphic methods of generalization are the most useful and have been developed to a high degree of accuracy.   The simplest of these is based on the equation

$$\log p = A - \frac{B}{T} \tag{IV-16}$$

where p is the vapor pressure at $T°$ absolute and A and B are constants. A different arrangement of this equation

$$\log P = A - \frac{B}{t + C} \tag{IV-17}$$

where A, B, and C are constants and P is the vapor pressure at $t°C$ is known as the Antoine equation.[4]   It is sufficiently accurate for most hydrocarbons, for vapor-pressure calculations from the triple point to well above the atmospheric boiling point.   A complete discussion of the Antoine equation is given by Thomson.[5]   Cox[6] has presented a simple and satisfactory relationship extending from the triple to the critical point in the form:

$$\log P \text{ (in atm)} = A \left(1 - \frac{T_B}{T} \right) \tag{IV-18}$$

where $\log A = \log A_C + E(1 - T_R)/(F - T_R)$ and T_B equals the absolute boiling point. A_C is the value of A at the critical temperature, E is an empirical constant characteristic of the compound, T is the absolute temperature in question, T_R is the reduced temperature T/T_C,

[1] ASTM Standard D 86–54.

[2] Podbielniak, *Ind. Eng. Chem., Anal. Ed.*, **5**:172 (1933).

[3] Lichtenfels, Fleck, and Burrow, *Anal. Chem.*, **27**:1510 (1955).

[4] Antoine, *Compt. rend.*, **107**:681, 836, 1143 (1888).

[5] *Chem. Revs.*, **38**:1 (1946).

[6] Cox, *Ind. Eng. Chem.*, **28**:613 (1936).

and F is an empirical constant. Constants for the Antoine[1] equation and the Cox equation have been published for many compounds.[2] For the chemical engineer the collected data of Dreisbach[3] in the form of tables of Cox equation values are excellent. For small pressure intervals in the neighborhood of atmospheric pressure, as in correcting laboratory distillations for variations in barometric pressure, the data in Table IV-7 may be applied linearly.

The vapor pressure of liquefied petroleum gases (C_3-C_4) and gasoline motor fuel is important in considering storage losses and safety as well as tendency to vapor-lock systems which handle volatile liquids. Methods for determining arbitrary vapor pressures have been developed.[4] The Reid vapor pressure of a gasoline for summer use may be 7 lb, and of one for winter, 12 lb, depending on the design of the handling equipment.

IV-15. Latent Heat of Fusion. Latent heats of fusion have been measured for only a limited number of hydrocarbons, but some general rules can be given. In ascending the normal paraffin series, the values begin at about 15 cal per g for methane and increase rapidly to 40 for octane, after which the increase becomes less per step in such a way that a

TABLE IV-7. CORRECTION OF BOILING POINTS OF HYDROCARBON*

Mixtures to 760 mm Hg

Boiling point at 760 mm Hg °C	Correction factor °C per mm Hg
0	0.035
50	0.040
100	0.046
150	0.051
200	0.056
250	0.061
300	0.065
350	0.069

* This is much more convenient than other methods and is generally sufficiently accurate.

limit of about 55 is approached asymptotically. Isoparaffins have values considerably lower than their isomeric normal compounds, as do the

[1] American Petroleum Institute Research Project 44, "Selected Values for the Physical Properties of Hydrocarbons," Carnegie Institute of Technology, Pittsburgh, Pa.

[2] Stull, *Ind. Eng. Chem.*, **39**:517 (1947).

[3] "*PVT* Relationships of Organic Compounds, Handbook," Sandusky, Ohio, 1952. For a chart of vapor pressures for 36 hydrocarbons, extending from 1 mm to the critical pressures, see Myers, *Ind. Eng. Chem.*, **47**:1659 (1955). On the correlation with surface tension, see Bowden, *J. Chem. Phys.*, **23**:2454 (1955).

[4] For liquefied gases, ASTM D 1267; see also Hooper, *J. Inst. Petrol.*, **38**:394 (1952). For gasoline, ASTM D 323, Reid method. On conversion of Reid vapor pressure to true vapor pressure, see *Coordinating Research Council Rept.* 290, December, 1955.

naphthenes and aromatics of about the same molecular weight.   Paraffin wax has a heat of fusion of about 50 cal per g.

IV-16. Heat of Vaporization.   Unlike the preceding property, the latent heat of vaporization is of great importance in the petroleum industry because of its connection with the design of distillation equipment.   Consequently, much research has been expended on its investigation.[1]   The values in Btu per pound of the heats of vaporization at the normal boiling point decrease regularly with increasing molecular weight, as shown in Table IV-8.   Heats of vaporization of the normal paraffins,

TABLE IV-8. HEATS OF VAPORIZATION OF SOME *n*-PARAFFINS
AT THE NORMAL BOILING POINT*

Compound	Boiling point, °C	$H_{\text{vaporization}}$	
		Btu per lb	Kcal per mole
Methane...............	−161.5	219.2	1.96
Propane...............	− 42.1	183.1	4.49
Pentane...............	− 0.5	165.6	5.35
Heptane...............	98.4	135.9	7.58
Decane................	174.1	118.7	9.39
Tetradecane...........	253.6	103.4	11.4
Eicosane..............	345.1	87.8	13.8

* API Research Project 44 data.

in general, decrease with increasing temperature and pressure, the values decreasing rapidly to zero at the critical point.   Isoparaffins generally have heats of vaporization slightly less than the normal isomers, while the cyclics, especially the aromatics, are slightly higher.   The difference, however, is small.   Heats of vaporization of petroleum oils, sufficiently accurate for engineering calculations, are given by the formula[2]

$$L = \frac{1}{d} 110.9 - 0.09t \qquad\qquad (IV-19)$$

where L is the heat of vaporization in Btu per pound at $t°F$ and d is the specific gravity at 60°/60°F.

Hougen and Watson[3] have devised methods for the calculation of heat of vaporization as a function of the molal average boiling point and either molecular weight or API gravity.   For the case where specific gravity

[1] For a general review, see Beale, "Science of Petroleum," vol. II, p. 1256, Oxford University Press, New York and London, 1938.   Hobson and Weber, *Petrol. Processing*, **12**(8):43 (1957).   Weber and Imbody, *Petrol. Refiner*, **36**(3):221 (1957).

[2] Cragoe, *Natl. Bur. Standards Misc. Publ.* 97, 1929.

[3] "Chemical Process Principles," John Wiley & Sons, Inc., New York, 1947.

alone does not give sufficient accuracy, this method should be more precise. For the calculation of heats of vaporization at pressures other than atmospheric, Watson[1] gives a method based upon the following equation:

$$L = \gamma L_B \frac{T}{T_B} \qquad \text{(IV-20)}$$

where L and L_B are the latent heats at temperature T (degrees Rankine) and at the absolute normal boiling point, respectively, T and T_B are the corresponding temperatures, and γ is a correction factor based upon the relation between the ratio T_B/T and the critical temperature.

IV-17. Specific Heat. Specific heats are extremely important engineering quantities in refinery practice because they are used in all calculations on heating and cooling petroleum products. While many measurements have been made on various hydrocarbon materials, the data for most purposes may be summarized by the general equation[2]

$$C = \frac{1}{\sqrt{d}}(0.388 + 0.00045t) \qquad \text{(IV-21)}$$

where C is the specific heat at $t°F$ of an oil whose specific gravity 60°/60°F is d. From this equation it is seen that specific heat increases with temperature and decreases with specific gravity.[3] Solutions of this equation are plotted in Fig. IV-2.

The foregoing generalization is said to be accurate within 5 per cent.[4] It appears to hold very closely for straight-run distillates, especially paraffinic ones; highly aromatic materials may have lower values, and cracked ones still lower.[5]

IV-18. Enthalpy or Heat Content. Enthalpy is the heat energy necessary to bring a system from a reference state to a given state; it is a function only of the end states and is the integral of the specific heats with respect to temperature between the limit states, plus any latent heats of transition that occur within the interval. The usual reference temperature is 0°C. Enthalpy data are easily obtained from specific heat data by graphical integration[6] or, if the empirical equation given above for

[1] Watson, *Ind. Eng. Chem.*, **23**:360 (1931). Details are given on construction of graphs for these calculations.

[2] Cragoe, *loc. cit.*

[3] For tabulations of such data, see van Winkle, *Petrol. Refiner*, **27**:291 (1948). For the estimation of other engineering properties useful in distillation problems, see van Winkle, *Petrol. Processing*, **9**:1738 (1954); *Ind. Eng. Chem.*, **49**:232 (1957). Also Gambill, *Chem. Eng.*, **64**(2):235 (1957).

[4] Gould, "Science of Petroleum," vol. II, p. 1249, Oxford University Press, New York and London, 1938.

[5] Gary, Rubin, and Ward, *Ind. Eng. Chem.*, **25**:178 (1933).

[6] Weir and Eaton, *Ind. Eng. Chem.*, **24**:211 (1932). On relation to molecular structure, see Souders, Matthews, and Herd, *Ind. Eng. Chem.*, **41**:1037 (1949).

specific heat is sufficiently accurate, from the equation

$$H = \frac{1}{d}(0.388t + 0.000225t^2 - 12.65) \tag{IV-22}$$

Generally, only differences in enthalpy are required in engineering design, i.e., the quantity of heat necessary to heat (or cool) a unit amount of material from one temperature to another. Such calculations are very simple, since the quantities are arithmetically additive and the enthalpy for such a change of state is merely the difference between the enthalpies

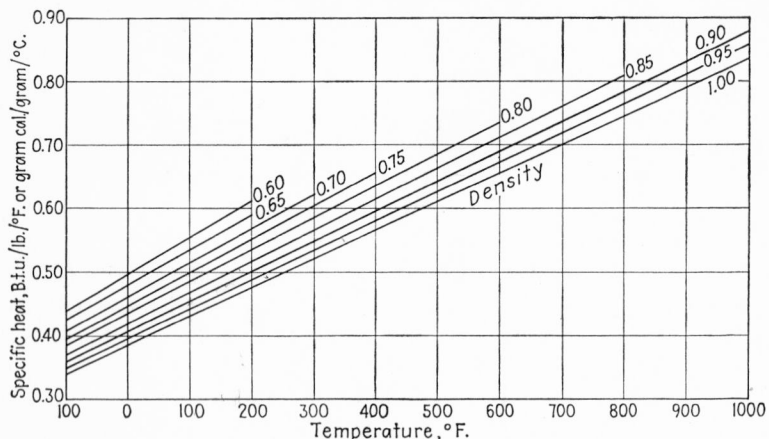

Fig. IV-2. Specific heat of hydrocarbon liquids.

of the end states. The reference state from which the latter are calculated is immaterial as long as it is the same for both.

IV-19. Thermal Conductivity. The thermal conductivity of hydrocarbon oils (in cgs units) is given by the equation[1]

$$K = \frac{0.28}{d}(1 - 0.00054t) \times 10^{-3} \tag{IV-23}$$

a rule which has been found to be very generally accurate.[2] The value for solid paraffin wax is about 0.00056,[3] nearly independent of temperature and wax type; the oil equation given above holds satisfactorily for waxes above the melting point.

IV-20. Pressure-Volume-Temperature Relationships. Hydrocarbon vapors, like other gases, follow the perfect-gas law

$$PV = RT \tag{IV-24}$$

[1] Cragoe, *loc. cit.*

[2] Smith, *Ind. Eng. Chem.*, **22**:1246 (1930).

[3] Beale, "Science of Petroleum," vol. II, p. 1261, Oxford University Press, New York and London, 1938.

only at relatively low pressures and high temperatures, i.e., far from the critical state. Several more empirical equations have been proposed to represent the gas laws more accurately, such as the well-known one of van der Waals, but they are either inconvenient for calculation or require the determination of several constants experimentally. A more useful device is to use the simple gas law and to introduce a correction, termed the "compressibility factor,"[1] so that the equation takes the form

$$PV = \mu RT \tag{IV-25}$$

For hydrocarbons, the compressibility factor is very nearly a function only of the reduced variables of state, i.e., of the pressure and temperature divided by the respective critical values.[2]

Much experimental information is at hand[3] in which the compressibility factor is plotted against reduced pressure, with reduced temperature as a parameter. Charts of this type for hydrocarbons were published by Brown, Souders, and Smith[4]; these have been extended by Dodge[5] to include some nonhydrocarbons.

The compressibility factor method functions excellently for pure compounds but may become ambiguous for mixtures, because the critical constants have a slightly different significance. However, the use of pseudocritical temperature and pressure values,[6] generally lower than the true ones, permits the compressibility factor to be employed in such cases.

IV-21. Critical Properties. The temperature, pressure, and volume at the critical state are of considerable interest in petroleum physics, particularly in connection with modern high-pressure–high-temperature refinery operations and in correlating pressure-temperature-volume relationships for other states. Critical data are known for most of the lower-molecular-weight pure hydrocarbons and standard methods are generally used for such determinations.

---

[1] Brown, Souders, and Smith, *Ind. Eng. Chem.*, **24**:513 (1932).

[2] Cope, Lewis, and Weber, *Ind. Eng. Chem.*, **23**:887 (1931). Lewis, *Ind. Eng. Chem.*, **28**:257 (1936).

[3] Storch, *U.S. Bur. Mines Circ.* 6549, 1932. Sage, Webster, and Lacey, *Ind. Eng. Chem.*, **29**:658 (1937). Cox, *Ind. Eng. Chem.*, **28**:613 (1936).

[4] Cox, *Ind. Eng. Chem.*, **24**:513 (1932). See also, for light hydrocarbons, Akers and Burns, *Petrol. Refiner*, **35**(3):154 (1956); for low-pressure ranges, Pfenning and McKetta, *Petrol. Refiner*, **36**(12):153 (1957); for higher hydrocarbons, Cutler, Webb, and Schiessler, *J. Chem. Phys.*, **23**:2466 (1955); Weir and Hoffman, *J. Research Natl. Bur. Standards*, **55**:307 (1955).

[5] *Ind. Eng. Chem.*, **24**:1353 (1932).

[6] Kay, *Ind. Eng. Chem.*, **28**:1014 (1936). For mixtures such as propane-propene, see Li and Canjar, *AIChE J.*, **2**(4):448 (1956). For natural gas mixtures over the range 0 to 3,000 psi, Zimmerman, Beitler, and Darrow, *Mech. Eng.*, **82**(2):103 (1958).

The critical point of a pure compound is the equilibrium state in which its gaseous and liquid phases are indistinguishable and coexistent; they have the same intensive properties. However, experimentally, localized variations in these phase properties may be evident. The definition for the critical point of a mixture is the same. However, mixtures generally have a maximum temperature or pressure at other than the true critical point. Maximum here denotes the greatest value at which two phases can coexist in equilibrium.[1]

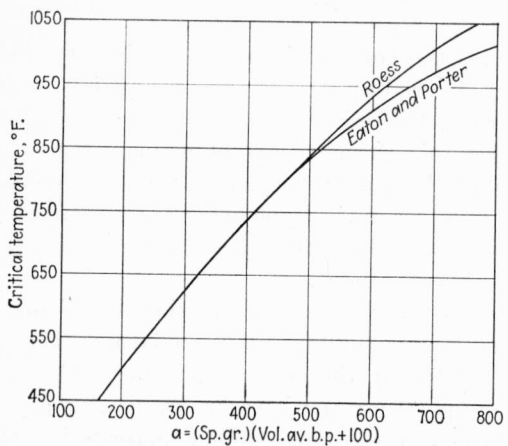

FIG. IV-3. Critical temperature of hydrocarbon mixtures.

Critical measurements have been made on a variety of petroleum fractions, both by static[2] and dynamic[3] methods. Two empirical correlations with volumetric average boiling point and density have been proposed;[4] these are depicted graphically in Fig. IV-3.

IV-22. Heat of Combustion. The gross heats of combustion of petroleum oils are given with fair accuracy by the equation[5]

$$Q = 12,400 - 2,100d^2 \qquad (IV\text{-}26)$$

where d is the 60°/60°F specific gravity. Deviation is generally less than

[1] For a general discussion of the critical point and critical properties of mixtures see Olds, "The Physical Chemistry of Hydrocarbon," vol. II, chap. IV, p. 139, Academic Press, Inc., New York, 1953.

[2] Zeitfuchs, *Ind. Eng. Chem.*, **18**:79 (1926). McKee and Parker, *Ind. Eng. Chem.*, **20**:1169 (1928). McKee and Szayna, *Ind. Eng. Chem.*, **22**:953 (1930). Eaton and Porter, *Ind. Eng. Chem.*, **24**:819 (1932). Weir and Eaton, *Ind. Eng. Chem.*, **24**:211 (1932). Bahlke and Kay, *Ind. Eng. Chem.*, **24**:291 (1932).

[3] Roess, *J. Inst. Petrol. Technologists*, **22**:665 (1936); "Science of Petroleum," vol. II, p. 1270, Oxford University Press, New York and London, 1938.

[4] Roess, *loc. cit.* Eaton and Porter, *loc. cit.*

[5] Cragoe, *Natl. Bur. Standards Misc. Publ.* 97, 1929.

1 per cent, although many Asiatic (highly aromatic) crudes show considerably higher values. These ranges for typical petroleum products are given in the following table.

TABLE IV-9. HEATS OF COMBUSTION

	Heat of combustion, cal per g
Crude oil	10,000 to 11,600
Gasoline	11,100 to 11,470
Kerosene and diesel fuels	10,450 to 11,200
Fuel oils	9,550 to 11,150

Heats of combustion of petroleum gases may be calculated from the analysis and data for the pure compounds; experimental values for gaseous fuels may be obtained by measurement in a water flow calorimeter,[1] while heats of combustion of liquids are usually measured in a bomb calorimeter.[2]

For thermodynamic calculation of equilibria useful in hydrocarbon research, combustion data of extreme accuracy are required, because the heats of formation of water and carbon dioxide are large in comparison with those of the hydrocarbons. Great accuracy is also required of the specific heat data for the calculation of free energy or entropy. Much care must be exercised in selecting values from the literature for these purposes, since many of those available were determined before the development of modern calorimetric techniques; the most reliable data on pure hydrocarbons are those compiled by Rossini under the auspices of the American Petroleum Institute.[3]

IV-23. Flash and Fire Points. These properties are measured by empirical tests, and although they are of little scientific interest, they are of considerable technical importance in specifications of ignitibility and fire hazard. Three test apparatus are in general use in this country, the Cleveland Open Cup,[4] the Tag Closed Cup,[5] and the Pensky-Martins Closed Tester.[6] The Cleveland Open Cup is intended for the determination of the flash and fire points of all petroleum products except fuel oils and products having an open cup flash below 175°F, but not for those classed as fuel oils. The flash point of fuel oils is determined in the Pensky-Martins Closed Tester. In making the tests, a small flame is periodically applied to the oil surface while the sample is being heated.

[1] ASTM D 900–55.
[2] ASTM D 240–50.
[3] "Selected Values of Physical and Thermodynamic Properties of Hydrocarbons and Related Compounds," Carnegie Press, Pittsburgh, Pa., 1953.
[4] ASTM D 92–52.
[5] ASTM D 56–52.
[6] ASTM D 93–52.

The flash point is recorded as the temperature at which the first flame passes over the surface, and the fire point is that at which the flame becomes self-maintaining. The flash point for light distillates corresponds to a vapor-pressure value of roughly 8 mm Hg, while for heavy materials, it coincides approximately with the incipient cracking temperature, about 300°C.

IV-24. Cloud and Pour Points.   These empirical indices are useful for specifying the behavior of oils at low temperatures.   The procedure for their determination[1] is to cool a sample of the oil by a standard method in a standardized apparatus; the temperature at the appearance of turbidity is noted as the cloud point, and that below which the oil will not flow in a definite manner as the pour point.   The cloud point is the temperature of initial precipitation of wax or other solid materials.   Control of the cooling rate is important here, especially with viscous oils, because rapid chilling will give low values.   Oils that are nearly or quite wax-free, such as some naphthenic types, show no cloud point.   The pour point for most oils also arises from the precipitation of wax, in this case to an extent sufficient to give a pasty, plastic mass of interlocking crystals.   Wax-free oils, however, having a pour point dependent on viscosity only, thicken to glassy materials.   For these, the pour point corresponds to a viscosity of about 5,000,000 cs.

Anomalous pour points[2] may be found for black oils, heavy lubricating oils such as cylinder stocks, and residual fuel oils, depending on their previous thermal history.   This must be considered in working with such oils, and special procedures for the determination and reporting of values are used.[3]

IV-25. Aniline Point.   The aniline point of a liquid was originally defined[4] as the consolute or critical solution temperature of the two liquids, i.e., the minimum temperature at which they are miscible in all proportions.   The term is now most generally applied to the temperature at which exactly equal parts of the two are miscible.[5]   This value is more conveniently measured than the original one and is only a few tenths of a degree lower for most substances.

The experimental determination is simple.   Equal volumes of the sample and aniline are mixed, heated, and stirred until homogeneous and then gradually cooled until the cloud point is noted.   Two procedures are

[1] ASTM Standard D 97–47.   On estimating pour points, Reid and Allen, *Petrol. Refiner*, **30**(M.5):93 (1951).

[2] Proc. ASTM, **31**, part I:468 (1931); **32**, part I:402 (1932).

[3] ASTM D 97–47, sec. 6.

[4] Chavanne and Simon, *Compt. rend.*, **169**:70, 185 (1949).

[5] Tizard and Marshall, *J. Soc. Chem. Ind.*, **40**:20T (1921).

given for the determination of the aniline point of petroleum products,[1] one for light-colored oils and a special thin film method for dark-colored oils. A special ASTM method is also provided for the determination of aniline points of hydrocarbon solvents.[2]

Although an arbitrary index, the aniline point is of considerable value in the characterization of petroleum products. For oils of a given type, it increases slightly with molecular weight, while for those of given molecular weight, it increases rapidly with paraffinicity. As a consequence, it was one of the first properties proposed for the group analysis of petroleum products with respect to aromatic and naphthene content.[3] It is used, alternately, even in one of the more recent methods.[4] The simplicity of the determination makes it attractive for the rough estimation of aromatic content where that value is important for functional requirements, as in the case of solvent power of naphthas and combustion characteristics of gasolines and diesel fuels.

ELECTRICAL PROPERTIES

IV-26. Conductivity.[5] The electrical conductivity of hydrocarbon oils is exceedingly small,[6] being of the order of 10^{-19} to 10^{-12} ohm-cm^{-1}. Data available indicate that the observed conductivity is frequently more dependent on the method of measurement and the presence of trace impurities than on the chemical type of the oil.[7]

Conduction through oils is not ohmic; that is, the current is not proportional to field strength; in some regions it is observed to increase exponentially[8] with the latter. Time effects are also observed, the current being at first relatively large and decreasing to a smaller steady value.[9] This is due partly to electrode polarization and partly to ions removed

---

[1] ASTM D 611–55T.

[2] ASTM D 1012–51.

[3] Carpenter, *J. Inst. Petrol. Technologists*, **14**:446–476 (1928). Garub, *J. Inst. Petrol. Technologists*, **14**:695 (1928). Aubert and Aubree, *Compt. rend.*, **182**:577 (1926). Schaarschmidt, Hotmeier, and Leist, *Angew. Chem.*, **43**:954 (1930). Vlugter, Waterman, and van Westen, *J. Inst. Petrol. Technologists*, **21**:661 (1935).

[4] Robert, *Rev. inst. franc. pétrole et Ann. Combustibles liquides*, **7**:55 (1952).

[5] For theory of conduction in dielectric media, see von Hippel, "Dielectrics and Waves," p. 228, John Wiley & Sons, Inc., New York, 1954. On dielectric materials and their uses, see von Hippel (ed.), "Dielectric Materials and Applications," John Wiley & Sons, Inc., New York, 1954.

[6] Welo, *Physics*, **1**:160 (1931).

[7] Hart and Simmons, *Can. J. Phys.*, **33**:54 (1955).

[8] Nikuradse, "Das flüssige Dielectrikum," Springer-Verlag, Berlin, Vienna, 1934. Baker and Boltz, *Phys. Rev.*, **51**:275 (1937). Dornte, *Ind. Eng. Chem.*, **32**:1529 (1940). Von Hippel, *op. cit.*

[9] Nikurdase, *op. cit.* Hart and Simmons, *Can. J. Phys.*, **33**:54 (1955).

from the solution.[1] Most oils increase in conductivity with rising temperatures.[2]

IV-27. Static Electrification. Dielectric liquids, particularly light naphthas, may acquire high static charges on flowing through or being sprayed from metal pipes.[3] The effect seems to be associated with colloidally dispersed contaminants such as oxidation products, which can be removed by drastic filtration or adsorption. Since a considerable fire hazard is involved, a variety of methods have been studied for minimizing the danger. For large-scale storage, avoidance of surface agitation and the use of floating metal roofs on tanks are beneficial. High humidity in the surrounding atmosphere is helpful in lowering the static charge, and radioactive materials have been tried to induce discharge to ground. A variety of additives have been found which increase the conductivity of petroleum liquids, thus lowering the degree of electrification; chromium salts of alkylated salicylic acids and other salts of alkylated sulfosuccinic acids are employed in low concentrations—say 0.005 per cent.[4]

IV-28. Dielectric Loss and Power Factor. A condenser insulated with an ideal dielectric shows no dissipation of energy when an alternating potential is applied. The charging current, technically termed the "circulating current," lags exactly 90° in phase angle behind the applied potential, and the energy stored in the condenser during each half cycle is completely recovered in the next. No real dielectric material exhibits this ideal behavior; i.e., some energy is dissipated under alternating stress and appears as heat. Such lack of efficiency is broadly termed "dielectric loss."

Ordinary conduction comprises one component of dielectric loss. Here the capacitance-held charge is partly lost by short circuit through the medium. Other effects in the presence of an alternating field occur, and a dielectric of zero conductivity may still exhibit losses. Suspended droplets of another phase will undergo spheroidal oscillation by electrostatic induction effects and will dissipate energy as heat, this as a consequence of the viscosity of the medium. Polar molecules will oscillate as electrets and dissipate energy on collision with others. All such losses are of practical importance where insulation is used in connection with alternating-current equipment.

---

[1] Hart and Simmons, *loc. cit.*

[2] Jackson, *Trans. Faraday Soc.*, **31**:827 (1935); *Naturwissenschaften*, **22**:238 (1934); *CA*, **28**:5644 (1934). Von Hippel (ed.), "Dielectric Materials and Applications," part III, A-2, John Wiley & Sons, Inc., New York, 1954.

[3] Klinkenberg, "Electrostatics in the Petroleum Industry," D. Van Nostrand Company, Inc., Princeton, N.J., 1957. Mackeon and Wouk, *Ind. Eng. Chem.*, **34**:659 (1942). Beach, *Sci. Monthly*, p. 339, 1943.

[4] On the several aspects of this problem, see Rogers and others, *Oil Gas J.*, **55**(46):166 (1957); Conradi and others, *Oil Gas J.*, **55**(46):197 (1957); Klinkenberg, *Oil Gas J.*, **55**(46):206 (1957); Bustin and others, *Proc. API*, **37**(III):24 (1957).

The measure of the dielectric loss is the power factor. This is defined as the factor k in the relation

$$k = \frac{W}{EI} \qquad \text{(IV-27)}$$

where W is the power in watts dissipated by a circuit portion under voltage E and passing current I. From a-c theory, the power factor is recognized as the cosine of the phase angle between the voltage and current when a pure sine waveform exists for both; it increases with rise in temperature. When an insulating material serves as the dielectric of a condenser, the power factor is an intrinsic property of the dielectric. For practical electrical equipment, low power factors for the insulation are, of course, always desirable; petroleum oils are generally excellent in this respect, having values of the order of 0.0005, comparable with fused quartz and polystyrene resins. The power factor of pure hydrocarbons is extremely small. Traces of polar impurities, however, cause a striking increase.[1] All electrical oils, therefore, are drastically refined and handled with care to avoid contamination. Insoluble oxidation products are particularly undesirable. Experimentally, the power factor for petroleum products such as cable, transformer, circuit breaker, and similar oils is measured by ASTM Standard method D 924–49.

IV-29. Dielectric Constant. The dielectric constant of a substance is theoretically equal to the square of its refractive index.[2] This law, a consequence of the electromagnetic theory of light, requires, however, that the two properties be compared at the same frequency. Therefore, since most substances exhibit some dispersion, the relationship cannot be tested exactly. Nonpolar molecules, however, show relatively small dispersion; and for them, the relationship holds rather well even when the refractive index for visible light (10^{18} cps) is compared with direct current potential dielectric constants (0 cps); agreement is always within a few hundredths of 1 per cent for refined petroleum oils.[3] Where polar molecules are present, the dielectric constant is always larger than that predicted from refractive index.[4] The standard method of testing insulating oils of petroleum origin is the same as for power factor.[5]

---

[1] Morgan, *Ind. Eng. Chem.*, **30**:273 (1938); von Hippel (ed.), "Dielectric Materials and Applications," part III, A-2, p. 163, John Wiley & Sons, Inc., New York, 1954.

[2] Smyth, "Dielectric Behavior and Structure," McGraw-Hill Book Company, Inc., New York, 1955.

[3] Ward, Kurtz, and Fulweiler, "Science of Petroleum," vol. II, p. 1176, Oxford University Press, New York and London, 1938.

[4] Balsbaugh, *Ind. Eng. Chem.*, **34**:92 (1942). Clark and Raab, *Ind. Eng. Chem.*, **34**:110 (1942). Sulfur and nitrogen compounds seem important. Piper and others, *Ind. Eng. Chem.*, **34**:1505 (1942). Irving and Thompson, *Chem. & Ind. (London)*, p. 978, 1952.

[5] ASTM D 924–49.

IV-30. Dielectric Strength. The dielectric strength, or breakdown voltage, is the greatest potential gradient or potential that an insulator will stand without permitting an electric discharge. The property is, in the case of oils as well as other dielectrics, dependent somewhat on the method of measurement, i.e., on the length of path through which the breakdown occurs, the composition, shape, and condition of the electrode surfaces,[1] and the duration of the applied potential difference.

The standard test[2] used in this country is applied to oils of petroleum origin for use in cables, transformers, oil circuit breakers, and similar apparatus. Oils of high purity and cleanliness show nearly the same value under standard conditions, generally ranging from 30 to 35 kv. For alkanes,[3] dielectric strength has been shown to increase linearly with liquid density and the value for a mineral oil fits the data well. For *n*-heptane a correlation was found between the dielectric strength and the density changes with temperature. There are many reasons why the dielectric strength of an insulator may fail; the most important appears to be the presence of some type of impurity,[4] produced by corrosion, oxidation, thermal or electrical cracking, or gaseous discharge; invasion by water is a common trouble.

MOLECULAR WEIGHT

Molecular weights of petroleum products are important in studies of chemical constitution; for instance, in the characterization of oil fractions discussed below in the section on indices and correlations. Some approximate molecular weights for petroleum products are listed in Table IV-10.

TABLE IV-10. ORDER OF MAGNITUDE OF MOLECULAR
WEIGHTS FOR SOME PETROLEUM PRODUCTS

Gasoline	100
Light naphthenic lubricating oil	150
Heavy naphthenic lubricating oil	300
Light paraffinic lubricating oil	300
Heavy paraffinic lubricating oil	600

Most of the early molecular-weight determinations on hydrocarbon oils employed simple forms of the cryoscopic (freezing point depression)

[1] Sorensen, *Elec. Eng.*, **59**:78 (1940). Bragg, Sharbaugh, and Crowe, *J. Appl. Phys.*, **25**:389 (1954).

[2] ASTM Standard D 877–49.

[3] Crowe, Bragg, and Sharbaugh, *J. Appl. Phys.*, **25**:392 (1954).

[4] von Hippel, "Dielectrics and Waves," p. 250, John Wiley & Sons, Inc., New York, 1954.

method.[1]   Many solvents have been tried, but with the best technique an accuracy of 1 to 2 per cent is to be considered good.   Ebullioscopic (boiling point elevation) methods are, in general use, more rapid and equally accurate.[2]   At least one survey has been made, comparing the methods in use at several different petroleum laboratories.   Molecular weights in the low range are readily determined by vapor-density methods.[3]   These methods all give number average molecular weights, defined by

$$\frac{\Sigma n_i M_i}{\Sigma n_i} = Mn \tag{IV-28}$$

where Mn is the number average molecular weight and n_i is the number of molecules having a molecular weight M_i.   Several indirect methods have been proposed for the estimation of molecular weight by correlation with other, more readily measured physical properties.[4]   They are satisfactory when dealing with average type oils and when approximate values are desired.

CORRELATION OF PHYSICAL PROPERTIES WITH CHEMICAL CONSTITUTION

Only the lowest-molecular-weight hydrocarbons, representing that portion of a crude oil boiling not far from room temperature, can be separated readily into individual compounds.   The possible and actual existence of many isomers for each distinct hydrocarbon formula makes such separation progressively more difficult as molecular weight rises, and soon renders it unprofitable.   The need for characterizing petroleum fractions in chemical terms remains, and ingenious methods have been

[1] Rall and Smith, *Ind. Eng. Chem., Anal. Ed.*, **8**:324, 436 (1936).   Quiggle, Tongberg, and Fry, *Ind. Eng. Chem., Anal. Ed.*, **9**:579 (1937).   Parks, Warren, and Green, *J. ACS*, **57**:616 (1935).   Gullick, *J. Inst. Petrol. Technologists*, **17**:541 (1931). Bernstein and Miller, *J. ACS*, **62**:948 (1940).   For a discussion of the theory of the cryoscopic method, see Skau and Wakeham in "Technique of Organic Chemistry," Weissberger (ed.), vol. I, part I, p. 90, Interscience Publishers, Inc., New York, 1949.

[2] Rall and Smith, *loc. cit.*   Hanson and Bowman, *Ind. Eng. Chem., Anal. Ed.*, **11**:440 (1939).   Mair, *J. Research Natl. Bur. Standards*, **14**:345 (1935).   Kitson, Oember, and Mitchell, *Anal. Chem.*, **21**:404 (1949).   Ray, *Trans. Faraday Soc.*, **48**:809 (1952).   Glover and Hill, *Anal. Chem.*, **25**:1379 (1953).   Polydoropoulas, *Chem. & Ind. (London)*, no. 33, p. 1000, 1954.

[3] Hicks-Brunn, *J. Research Natl. Bur. Standards*, **5**:575 (1930).   Washburn, *J. Research Natl. Bur. Standards*, **2**:703 (1929).

[4] Fenske, McCluer, and Cannon, *Ind. Eng. Chem.*, **26**:976 (1934).   Gilfoil, *Ind. Eng. Chem., Anal. Ed.*, **8**:228 (1936).   Keith and Roess, *Ind. Eng. Chem.*, **29**:456 (1937).   Lucy, *Ind. Eng. Chem.*, **30**:959 (1938).   Hirschler, *J. Inst. Petrol.*, **32**:133 (1946).   Mills, Hirschler, and Kurtz, *Ind. Eng. Chem.*, **38**:442 (1946).   Boelhouwer and Waterman, *Fuel (London)*, **33**:60 (1954); *J. Inst. Petrol.*, **40**:116 (1954).

devised for deducing chemical composition from the values of certain physical properties of the hydrocarbon mixtures. These methods first arose in dealing with the composition of naphthas, both cracked and virgin, as reflecting the antiknock value of these materials. The earliest attempts on higher-boiling fractions were more empirical; an index number was calculated, from physical measurements, which correlated well with certain desirable properties, but no great attempt was made to interpret these numbers in terms of chemical make-up. Two outstanding examples of such indices are:

1. Viscosity-gravity constant. This constant (usually abbreviated vgc) was the first index proposed to characterize oil types;[1] it is expressed by the formula

$$\text{vgc} = \frac{10d - 1.0752 \log (v - 38)}{10 - \log (v - 38)} \qquad \text{(IV-29)}$$

where d is the specific gravity 60°/60°F and v is the Saybolt viscosity at 100°F. For oils so heavy that the low-temperature viscosity is difficult to measure, an alternative formula

$$\text{vgc} = \frac{d - 0.24 - 0.022 \log (v - 35.5)}{0.755} \qquad \text{(IV-30)}$$

was proposed in the same paper, in which the 210°F Saybolt viscosity is used. The two do not agree well for low-viscosity oils. However, a formula has been devised[2] which covers the range, being additive for the heavier oils and agreeing well with that for the lighter ones. The vgc is of particular value in indicating a predominantly paraffinic or cyclic composition. The lower the index number, the more paraffinic the stock; examples are

	vgc
Naphthenic lubricating oil distillate	0.876
Raffinate by solvent extraction of lubricating oil distillate	0.840

2. The UOP characterization factor. This factor (Universal Oil Products Co.) is defined[3] by the formula

$$K = \frac{T^{1/3}}{d} \qquad \text{(IV-31)}$$

where T is the average boiling point in degrees Rankine (degrees Fahrenheit + 460) and d is the specific gravity 60°/60°F. This factor has been shown by Deanesly and Carleton[4] to be additive on a weight basis. It

[1] Hill and Coats, *Ind. Eng. Chem.*, **20**:641 (1928).

[2] Moore and Kaye, *Proc. API*, **15**(III):7 (1934).

[3] Watson and Nelson, *Ind. Eng. Chem.*, **25**:880 (1933).

[4] Deanesly and Carleton, *J. Phys. Chem.*, **46**:859 (1942).

has been correlated in some detail[1] with other characterization indices. It was originally devised to show the thermal cracking characteristics of heavy oils; examples of typical values are:

$$K$$

Highly paraffinic oils.	12.5–13.0
Cyclic oils. . . .ᵡ.	12.5–10.5

The methods for naphtha fractions were from the beginning interpreted more directly in terms of chemical composition. Some of the earliest were those of Egloff and Morrell,[2] Brame and Hunter,[3] and Garner;[4] this latter method is typical of the class. A cracked naphtha, say, was examined for iodine number, which after some empirical corrections yielded a figure for olefin content. Treatment with nitric acid removed both olefins and aromatics, and the volume loss permitted calculation of aromatic content. The aniline point value of the remainder gave a figure for proportions of paraffins and naphthenes. When olefins were absent, the aniline point value before and after acid treatment afforded an estimation of aromatic content.

It will be noticed that the two basic principles in both the above rather simple procedures and in some later more sophisticated ones, which depend on greater use of physical properties, are:

a. The determination of some property which responds in a sensitive way to differences in chemical composition; such a value, intermediate to those for the pure components, permits a more or less exact calculation of the percentages of pure components present.

b. The device of noting the change, in the significant property, caused by removing some constituent (possibly some embarrassing constituent) so that the residuum may be observed without this complication.

Methods aimed at expression of chemical composition and applicable to heavier oils began with Vlugter, Waterman, and van Westen, who introduced the concept of percentage of total carbon present, distributed into the various hydrocarbon structures present—typically paraffins, naphthenes, and aromatics in uncracked products.[5] The technique in the original form involved determination of aniline point of the sample before and after hydrogenation of the aromatics to naphthenes; this gave directly a figure for aromatic ring content. Naphthene rings were calculated from specific refractions of the hydrogenated sample, molecular weight being known; a correction for the aromatics hydrogenated to naphthenes gave

---

[1] Watson, Nelson, and Murphy, *Ind. Eng. Chem.*, **27**:1460 (1935).

[2] *Ind. Eng. Chem.*, **18**:354 (1926).

[3] *J. Inst. Petrol. Technologists*, **13**:794 (1927).

[4] *J. Inst. Petrol. Technologists*, **14**:695 (1928).

[5] *J. Inst. Petrol.*, **18**:735 (1932); **21**:661 (1935).

the original naphthenic content. The paraffins were obtained by difference. The improvements in simplicity which gave the procedure wide utility centered around the elimination of the difficult hydrogenation step.[1] The so called n-d-M method requires knowledge only of the refractive index and density (at 20°C unless wax content requires working at 70°) and molecular weight. It is based on linear relations between composition of hydrocarbon fractions and the above properties before and after a supposed hydrogenation. The relations are expressed by this type of equation

$$\text{Per cent } C = \frac{a}{m} + b\, \Delta d + c\, \Delta n \qquad (\text{IV-32})$$

where per cent C is the proportion of the carbon present distributed in aromatic, naphthenic, and paraffinic structures; a, b, and c are constants; m is molecular weight; Δd and Δn are the differences in density and refractive index between the values measured for the sample and those of a theoretical paraffin hydrocarbon of infinite molecular weight. The constants have been evaluated for fractions of known composition, and nomograms have been constructed which permit the convenient use of the equations on petroleum materials under prescribed conditions. The method is applicable to uncracked, olefin-free distillates boiling above the gasoline range; it is important that the materials examined be of the general type for which the correlations have been derived. The values obtained should be corrected where possible for any content of hydrocarbon-type compounds containing sulfur, nitrogen, or oxygen. Van Nes and Van Westen have provided an empirical correction which applies for sulfur content below 0.2 per cent. For higher amounts of sulfur, an improved method has been worked out by Karr, Wendland, and Hanson.[2] A variant of the n-d-M method, in which viscosity is substituted for molecular weight, also devised by Waterman[3] employs refractive index and density as in the earlier method. The structural make-up of the assumed composite molecule is calculated as before; molecular weight can also be calculated. This approach has been developed further by Cornelissen and Waterman[4] into a model in which log of kinematic viscosity, density, and refractive index are plotted on rectangular coordinates in space, permitting the construction of surfaces of equal percentages of

---

[1] For the evolution of the method, see Van Nes and Van Westen, "Constitution of Mineral Oils," p. 299, Elsevier Press, Inc., Houston, Tex., 1951.

[2] Mellon Institute, Pittsburgh, Pa. To be published.

[3] Boelhouwer and Waterman, *Fuel (London)*, **33**:60 (1954); *J. Inst. Petrol.*, **40**:116 (1954).

[4] *Brennstoff-Chem.*, **37**:404 (1956).

carbon in aromatic and naphthenic rings. The calculations have been simplified into nomograms.

A refinement in group analyses based on aniline point was introduced by Deanesly and Carleton.[1] They considered the relation of aniline point value to aromatic content too variable to be trustworthy, and extended the use of specific refraction to a wide variety of saturated oils. They also took account of olefin content by determining bromine number and elaborated a method pretty well applicable to what may be called group analysis of all the types of hydrocarbons present to any appreciable extent in petroleum oils. Though time-consuming, the method can be used for cracked products and even for widely different mixtures, such as those produced by solvent extraction or thermal diffusion.

TABLE IV-11. REFRACTIVITY INTERCEPT FOR SOME HOMOLOGOUS SERIES

Paraffins	1.0461
Saturated monocyclics	1.0400
Saturated polycyclics	1.0285
Olefins	1.0521
Diolefins	1.0592
Conjugated diolefins	1.0877
Cycloolefins	1.0461
Conjugated cyclodiolefins	1.0643
Aromatics	1.0627

Important research on calculating composition from known physical properties has been carried on by Kurtz and coworkers. Their most definitive method depends on recognition of what is known as the refractivity intercept.[2] If refractive indices of hydrocarbons are plotted against the respective densities, straight lines of constant slope are obtained, one for each homologous series; the intercepts of these lines with the ordinate of the plot are characteristic and can be used for calculation; they can be derived from the formula

$$\text{Refractivity intercept} = n - \frac{d}{2} \qquad \text{(IV-33)}$$

Table IV-11 shows that the intercept cannot differentiate accurately between all series, and this leads to a restriction on the number of different types of compounds which can be recognized in a sample. The technique has been applied to nonaromatic olefin-free materials in the gasoline range by assuming additivity of the constant on a volume basis. Kurtz and Headington[3] applied the method to gasolines, including cracked materials after distillation and chemical treatment. Plots of the intercept versus

[1] *Ind. Eng. Chem., Anal. Ed.*, **14**:220 (1942).

[2] Kurtz and Ward, *J. Franklin Inst.*, **222**:563 (1936).

[3] Kurtz and Headington, *Ind. Eng. Chem., Anal. Ed.*, **9**:21 (1937).

distillation cut or volume distilled can also be applied to cracked materials;[1] when the plotting is against densities averaged for hydrocarbon types, triangular plots are obtained, which can be used to obtain percentages of aromatics and naphthenes in straight-run gasoline fractions. A modified intercept and a nomogram for its use have been devised by Thomson.[2] Typical values of this intercept, calculated using the D line of sodium, are given in the table.

Leendertse[3] has devised an equation applicable to straight-run lubricating distillates containing between 25 and 75 per cent of the carbon present in naphthenic rings. The equation is

$$\text{Refractivity intercept} = 1.0502 - 0.00020 \text{ per cent } C_N \quad \text{(IV-34)}$$

Kurtz has also developed a method based on a relation between density and its change with temperature.[4] If the temperature coefficient of density is plotted against density, characteristic straight lines are obtained for different classes of hydrocarbons. If a paraffinic chain is attached to a naphthene ring, the properties of the resulting compound are changed proportionately in the paraffinic direction. In the limit the molecule will have the density of a paraffin of infinite molecular weight, 0.861.[5] From this the authors developed two equations for saturated fractions. For materials with a density lower than 0.861, the weight per cent rings in the molecule is given by

$$\text{Weight per cent rings} = \frac{A + 190.0d - 217.9}{0.593d - 0.249} \quad \text{(IV-35)}$$

and for samples above 0.861 by

$$\text{Weight per cent rings} = \frac{A + 102.8d - 142.8}{0.262} \quad \text{(IV-36)}$$

where d is the density at 20°C and $A = 10^5 \, dd/dt$; dd/dt is the change in density per degree change in temperature. The temperature coefficient of density can be derived from other physical property correlations.[6]

A similar correlation was found to exist between the density coefficient and refractive index; however, the density method is considered the more

[1] Farkas (ed.), "Physical Chemistry of Hydrocarbons," vol. II, chap. I, pp. 69–70, Academic Press, Inc., New York, 1953. For application to aromatic fractions, see *Anal. Chem.*, **30**:1224 (1958).

[2] *Anal. Chem.*, **21**:644 (1949).

[3] Van Nes and Van Westen, *op. cit.*, chap. IV, p. 368.

[4] Lipkin, Kurtz, and Martin, *Ind. Eng. Chem., Anal. Ed.*, **18**:376 (1946).

[5] Kurtz and Lipkin, *Ind. Eng. Chem.*, **33**:779 (1941). See above discussion of n-d-M method.

[6] Herschler, *J. Inst. Petrol.*, **32**:133 (1946). Mills, Herschler, and Kurtz, *Ind. Eng. Chem.*, **38**:442 (1946).

accurate. Van Nes and Van Westen[1] have found a relation between weight per cent rings, density, and molecular weight based on Lipkin and Martin's formula and a correlation of the temperature coefficient of density with the reciprocal of molecular weight. Lipkin and Martin have extended the correlations between the temperature coefficient of density and density to aromatic concentrates free of naphthene rings.[2] A discussion of these methods is also given by Van Nes and Van Westen.[3] Another procedure for the so-called ring analysis, percentage of carbon in the several kinds of rings and in chains, respectively, devised by Fenske, uses refractive index and molecular weight.[4] It resembles the density-density coefficient method and is applicable to pure hydrocarbons, but requires chemical separation when applied to petroleum fractions.

[1] Van Nes and Van Westen, *loc. cit.*

[2] Lipkin and Martin, *Ind. Eng. Chem., Anal. Ed.*, **19**:183 (1947).

[3] *Op. cit.*, p. 356.

[4] Hersch, Fenske, Booser, and Kock, *J. Inst. Petrol.*, **36**:624 (1950).

CHAPTER **V**

Origin of Petroleum

by W. E. HANSON, PH.D.

The problem of petroleum genesis has long been a topic of research interest.[1] Early investigators were generally narrow in their approaches and rarely took account of observations outside their own fields. Gradually, as the complexity of the problem became more evident, it was realized that the formation and accumulation of crude oil in the earth is a subject in which many sciences are involved and on which each has an important bearing.

It is now amply clear that the formation of petroleum is associated with the development of fine-grained sedimentary rocks, deposited in a marine or near-marine environment, and that petroleum is the product of the organic remains of plants and animals, incorporated in those sediments at the time of deposition.[2] The details of how this transformation takes place and the mechanism by which petroleum is expelled from the source sediment and accumulates in the reservoir rock are still uncertain or at least understood only in broad outline.

---

[1] One of the first discussions on the genesis of petroleum for the American reader appeared in "American Petroleum Industry," by Bacon and Hamor (vol. I, chap. 1, McGraw-Hill Book Company, Inc., New York, 1916) who proposed the terms petrologenesis and naphthogeny. The account contains numerous references of historical interest.

[2] In the early days, several hypotheses were current, based on an inorganic origin for petroleum. According to the original concept of Berthelot [*Compt. rend.*, **62**:949 (1866)], carbon dioxide in ground waters was supposedly reduced by alkali metals in the interior of the earth to yield acetylene and other hydrocarbons; alternatively, Mendelyeev [*J. Russ. Phys.-Chem. Soc.*, **9**:1 (1877); *Ber.*, **10**:229 (1877)] postulated a reaction between acidic waters and metal carbides to form petroleum-like hydrocarbons. These ideas were supported by Sabatier and Senderens [*Compt. rend.*, **134**:1185 (1902)], by Pyhälä [*Petroleum Z.*, **19**:495 (1923)], and more recently by Van Orstrand [*World Oil*, **128**(7):150 (1948)]. While such mechanisms may possibly be invoked to explain hydrocarbons, such as are occasionally observed in meteorites, they are no longer considered seriously for the formation of petroleum in the earth.

V-1. Limiting Conditions of Petroleum Formation. Practically all present-day thinking on oil origin has been guided by a framework of widely accepted limiting conditions, based on a wealth of field observations by geologists; these were first summarized by Cox,[1] and may be stated briefly as follows:

1. Petroleum and other types of bitumen are always associated with sedimentary rocks. Even when crude oil occurs in fractured metamorphic or igneous strata, close association with sedimentaries, from which the oil could have migrated, can be demonstrated.

2. Practically all petroleum appears to have originated in brackish to full marine sediments. This observation is complicated by the fluid and usually volatile nature of the crude, which permits it to move away from the point of origin. In fact, only rarely can a petroleum be identified unequivocally with its particular source bed. Instances have been cited[2] of oil[3] of possible nonmarine origin, and it is not unlikely that such may exist. It seems reasonable to assume that, somewhere between the truly marine sediments and those of clearly nonmarine character, a transition from the liquid to the essentially solid-type bitumen (peat-lignite-coal) must occur. Where this zone lies is uncertain, and no generalizations appear to be possible; it is perhaps a matter of how petroleum is defined.

3. High pressure is probably not necessary for the generation of petroleum. Some petroliferous basins, at least, could never have had a stratigraphic thickness of much more than 5,000 ft. The corresponding hydrostatic head at the deepest part of such a basin could not have exceeded 2,500 psi, although actual rock overburden pressure might have been twice this value; much higher figures could obtain at grain-to-grain contact points, but laboratory experiments in which high hydraulic or shear pressures have been applied to shales have given either indecisive or negative results.[4] The minimum depth value cited appears more likely to be related to the pressure required to expel oil from a fine-grained sediment.

4. Temperatures above 200°F are probably not required.[5] Under the

---

[1] *Bull. Am. Assoc. Petrol. Geologists*, **30**:645 (1946).

[2] Felts, *Bull. Am. Assoc. Petrol. Geologists*, **38**:1661 (1954); Kent, *Bull. Am. Assoc. Petrol. Geologists*, **38**:1699 (1954).

[3] By the term "oil" is meant fluid petroleum as distinguished from waxy bitumens (e.g., ozocerite) or the pyrobitumens (e.g., gilsonite), which probably had a nonmarine or brackish, lacustrine origin. See Hunt et al., *Bull. Am. Assoc. Petrol. Geologists*, **38**:1671 (1954).

[4] Hawley, *Bull. Am. Assoc. Petrol. Geologists*, **13**:303, 329 (1929); **14**:451 (1930); Rand, *Bull. Am. Assoc. Petrol. Geologists*, **17**:1229 (1933). Uwatoko, *Bull. Am. Assoc. Petrol. Geologists*, **16**:1029 (1932).

[5] As drilling has been carried to greater depths, correspondingly higher temperatures and pressures have been encountered. The temperature increase with depth (geo-

normal geothermal gradient and at the presumed minimum required depth of burial (5,000 ft), temperatures could hardly have exceeded 150°F.   The conclusion is that petroleum generation is a low-temperature process; chemical considerations have amply supported this view.

5. Petroleum has apparently been generated in strata laid down as early as Cambrian and certainly Ordovician time.[1]   There is no reason to believe that oil could not or did not form in earlier times.   Pre-Cambrian sediments have all been strongly metamorphosed, however, and any bitumen that did form must have been destroyed; carbon 13 to carbon 12 ratios determined on carbonaceous particles in pre-Cambrian rocks suggest that this carbon has passed through the life cycle and may, therefore, represent the indurated remains of crude oil or some other type of bitumen.[2]   One interesting conclusion can be drawn from the great antiquity of some petroleums: the relatively primitive marine forms which were the only living organisms of that day were evidently an adequate source material for crude oils; whatever mechanism of formation is proposed, it is unnecessary to postulate the need for higher-order marine organisms or land plants.

Beginning with the Ordovician or possibly the Cambrian, every geological age has produced oil; some were more prolific than others, but none was barren.   Until recently it was believed that Pliocene[3] oil was the youngest, and the apparent absence of petroleum in Pleistocene sediments was commonly credited to insufficient time for generation or perhaps to unfavorable climatic conditions imposed by extensive glaciation.   Owing to the accumulation of water in the polar ice caps during the Pleistocene, sea levels around the world were reduced by as much as 300 ft[4] and, as a result, marine sediments laid down during this epoch are now largely under water.   Only with the advent of offshore drilling have

thermal gradient) varies throughout the world but averages about 1.8°F per 100 ft. [Van Orstrand, "Problems of Petroleum Geology," p. 989, American Association of Petroleum Geologists, Tulsa, Okla., 1934]; bottom-hole pressures rise at a rate of about 44 psi per 100 ft [Kennedy, *Petrol. Engr.*, **11**:120 (1940)].   Abnormal temperatures commonly exist in the vicinity of salt intrusions from deeply buried evaporite deposits.   Owing to the high thermal conductivity of salt, heat is carried rapidly from the deeper zones to the upper strata, resulting in local thermal anomalies; a value of 460°F has been recorded recently [Keen, *Petrol. Engr.*, **29**(11):B21-29 (1957)].

[1] Radioactive methods of age determination place the Cambrian-to-Ordovician transition at about 430 million years ago [Zeuner, "Dating the Past," chap. X, Longmans, Green & Co., Inc., New York, 1951].

[2] Rankama, *Geochim. et Cosmochim. Acta*, **5**:142 (1954).

[3] Radioactive methods of age determination place the Pliocene-Pleistocene transition at about one million years ago (Zeuner, *op. cit.*, chap. X); it marked the beginning of a series of extensive glacial advances in the higher latitudes.

[4] Flint, "Glacial Geology and the Pleistocene Epoch," p. 437, John Wiley & Sons, Inc., New York, 1947.

these sediments been explored to any extent and, in particular, at depths sufficient to have resulted in the expulsion of fluids from the muds. Recent geological observations in certain Gulf of Mexico operations have indicated that, with respect to petroleum formation, the Pleistocene may not be essentially different from any of the earlier periods.[1]

V-2. Development of a Sedimentary Basin. Essential to the genesis of petroleum is the development of a basin or depression in the earth's crust in which the potential source sediments may accumulate. The formation of such a basin is an extremely complex and as yet only imperfectly understood phenomenon. The subject has been discussed in some detail by Weeks.[2]

In the normal transport of sediments into a basin, sands and coarser materials are dropped near the shore, the deposits grading to finer textures (muds) in the less shallow areas; in clearer waters there is ordinarily an accumulation of lime from the calcareous organisms which live there. During the basin-forming process, subsidence rarely progresses in a uniform manner and, under the existing mobile conditions of the crust, the sea may invade the land and recede many times, with the result that the coarser- and finer-grained sediments interfinger and overlap one another. This brings about, as mentioned again later, the highly important juxtaposition of potential source beds of fine-grained sediments with porous and more permeable deposits which can serve as reservoirs.

V-3. The Accumulation of Organic Material. With the exception of certain relatively minor sterile areas, the sea supports a tremendously complex floral and faunal population.[3] Free-floating (planktonic) forms greatly predominate over the swimming or bottom-frequenting forms. As these organisms die, their remains fall to the bottom to be incorporated into the sediments. If the area is one in which there are active bottom currents, the fines will be winnowed away, leaving a sandy or otherwise coarse-grained bottom, through which oxygen-bearing waters can circulate freely. Organic material deposited in such an environment will be destroyed quickly by aerobic bacteria to yield carbon dioxide and water. If the bottom waters are quiet, muddy sediments can accumulate, and the entrapped organic matter can be, at least, partially, preserved.

In general, the free oxygen content of the water drops as an organic-

---

[1] M. A. Hanna, chief paleontologist, Gulf Oil Corporation, Houston, Tex., personal communication; see also Kidwell and Hunt in "Habitat of Oil," *Symposium*, Weeks (ed.), p. 790, American Association of Petroleum Geologists, Tulsa, Okla., 1958. *World Oil*, **14**(1):79 (1958).

[2] *Bull. Am. Assoc. Petrol. Geologists*, **36**:2071 (1952); see also "Habitat of Oil," *Symposium*, Weeks (ed.), p. 1, American Association Petroleum Geologists, Tulsa, Okla., 1958.

[3] Sverdrup, Johnson, and Fleming, "The Oceans," Prentice-Hall, Inc., Englewood Cliffs, N.J., 1946.

rich bottom is approached and becomes practically zero in the uppermost mud layers. However, completely stagnant conditions are not at all essential to the accumulation of organic material. Organic-rich muds occur in quantity in relatively shallow depressions over many shelf areas of the world, as, for example, in the northern Gulf of Mexico.

With the disappearance of the aerobes in the uppermost portions of the bottom muds, a new and prolific flora takes over.[1] These organisms which can grow under anaerobic as well as aerobic conditions are represented by such genera as *Pseudomonas, Vibrio, Spirillum, Achromobacter,* and *Flavobacterium.* The populations will vary widely with sediment type, proximity to land, depth of water, and other factors. Typical bottom muds may have up to several hundred million organisms per gram for the first few centimeters of depth; with increasing depth of burial, the numbers fall off very rapidly, although bacteria have been reported in cores of ancient sediments and in fluids at depths up to several thousand feet.[2]

The enormous numbers of bacteria in the upper sediment zones imply some action on the entrapped organic detritus. Presumably a part of it is destroyed; possibly much of it is extensively altered.

Serious study of recent sediments as possible source beds of petroleum began with the work of Trask.[3] Organic contents of fresh, muddy sediments from many locations were found to vary from about 0.3 to 7 per cent; carbon to nitrogen dry weight percentage ratios averaged about 8.5, apparently with only slight variations from the richest to the leanest samples.

On the basis of a soil-type chemical examination,[4] Trask concluded that some 70 per cent of the total organic matter was complex nitrogen-containing material. Protein and other hydrolyzable nitrogenous compounds accounted for some 20 per cent, the remainder being presumably amino acids and other simple water-soluble organic substances. Oils and fatty materials were reported in trace amounts, but liquid hydrocarbons were not detected. This last observation led Trask to believe that petroleum was not formed in sediments at the time of deposition.[5]

[1] ZoBell, "Marine Microbiology," Chronica Botanica Co., Waltham, Mass., 1946. Stone and ZoBell, *Ind. Eng. Chem.*, **44**:2564 (1952). Beerstecher, "Petroleum Microbiology," Elsevier Press, Inc., Houston, Tex., 1954.

[2] ZoBell, *4th Quart. Rept.*, API Research Project 43-A, June 30, 1944; *Oil Weekly,* **120**:30 (1946); ZoBell and Johnson, *J. Bact.*, **57**:179 (1949); ZoBell, *Sci.*, **115**:507 (1952).

[3] "Origin and Environment of Source Sediments of Petroleum," Gulf Publ. Co., Houston, Tex., 1932.

[4] Waksman and Stevens, *Soil Sci.*, **30**:97 (1930).

[5] In earlier work, Trask and Wu [*Bull. Am. Assoc. Petrol. Geologists*, **14**:1451 (1930)]

More recent work on the carbon-nitrogen ratio of marine sediments has shown the picture to be much more complex than was apparent from the Trask studies, and wide variations in the observed ratio values are now believed to reflect the combined effects of differences in the types of organic matter being incorporated in the sediments and the depositional environment.[1]

In a study of sediments along the California coast, Emery and Rittenberg[2] have shown the carbon-to-nitrogen ratios of the topmost mud layers to be already considerably higher than those for plankton, indicating that decomposition of the organic material had begun even before reaching the bottom. At sediment depths of 4 to 8 ft, the ratio varies from 10.6 to 14.4, corresponding rather closely with the 12 to 15 range quoted by Trask and Patnode[3] for post-Miocene sediments of the Los Angeles Basin. Bader[4] has demonstrated, however, that this ratio may either rise or fall with depth of burial, depending upon local conditions.

Two of the most characteristic properties of recent sediments are the redox potential and the pH. ZoBell[5] has shown that E_H values for recent marine sediments may vary from approximately $+350$ mv for well-oxygenated bottoms to -500 mv for organic-rich muds; pH values range from 6.4 to 9.5. As a very general rule, E_H and redox capacity decrease with core depth, while pH increases.[6] The values measured are reasonably stable and, if appreciable amounts of organic matter are present, the systems appear to be well poised. There is no agreement, however, as to the reactions which determine the E_H value; considering the many organic and inorganic species present, it is doubtful that anything like true equilibrium exists.

---

reported the finding of "paraffins" ranging from 1 to 68 parts per thousand parts of dry sediment; while n-paraffins were unquestionably a part of this fraction, their presence was never proved and the authors realized that other waxy substances (e.g., high-molecular-weight alcohols) might also be present. Fatty acids from cerotic to melissic were detected, as were organic sulfur-containing compounds; free sulfur was noted to be a common minor component of all sediments. In view of later results, it is not clear why liquid hydrocarbons were missed in the early work. Possibly bacterial or chemical oxidative alteration occurred during storage or drying of the sediment samples prior to extraction.

[1] Grippenberg, *Fennia*, **60**:1 (1934). Mohamed, *Am. J. Sci.*, **247**:116 (1949). Arrhenius, *Geochim. et Cosmochim. Acta*, **1**:15 (1950).

[2] *Bull. Am. Assoc. Petrol. Geologists*, **36**:735 (1952).

[3] "Source Beds of Petroleum," p. 126, American Association of Petroleum Geologists, Tulsa, Okla., 1942.

[4] *Geochim. et Cosmochim. Acta*, **7**:205 (1955).

[5] *Bull. Am. Assoc. Petrol. Geologists*, **30**:477 (1946).

[6] As is common for redox systems involving organic substances, the E_H exhibits a pH effect; for the pH range 6 to 8, there is a decrease in E_H of approximately 80 to 120 mv per pH unit. Temperature has a complex and unpredictable effect on the E_H of marine sediments.

The drop in E_H that is noted on passing from the bottom water into an organic-rich mud is primarily the result of bacterial action. If the bottom is stagnant and the organic content high, E_H values of zero or less will be observed even in the upper layers; for less rich sediments, low positive values may persist to depths of several feet.[1] As soon as the redox potential nears zero, the *Desulfovibrio* become active. These bacteria, which are widely distributed in the sea, are strict anaerobes and utilize sulfate ion as a hydrogen acceptor in their energy-producing reactions, to yield hydrogen sulfide.[2] With the generation of sulfide, the E_H value drops steadily, usually becoming stabilized in the -200 to -500 mv range. Short of later exposure of the sediment to oxygen-bearing waters or to the atmosphere, this reduced condition persists throughout the processes of compaction and ultimate lithification of the sediment. The maintenance of a low E_H is believed to be of first importance, not only in preventing early oxidative destruction of the organic matter, but probably also in promoting the reductive conversion of the organic debris to hydrocarbons.

It appears likely that microorganisms are also an important agency in altering the hydrogen ion concentration in sediments, although their action will depend to a considerable extent on the type of organic matter present and the nature and disposition of the degradation products; reactions of clay minerals with ionic constituents of the occluded marine waters also affect the pH. Normal sea water in equilibrium with the carbon dioxide of the atmosphere has a pH value of 8.1 to 8.3, but in deeper waters where virtually all the oxygen has been consumed and where carbon dioxide is higher, the value may drop to 7.5.[3] In the work cited above, Emery and Rittenberg noted this minimum value immediately above the bottoms and attributed it to bacterially generated carbon dioxide and organic acids. Within the muddy sediment there is ordinarily a steady rise in pH with depth to approximately 8.5, and under special circumstances to as high as 9.5. The lower values are characteristic of the zones of most intense bacterial activity, highest organic content and greatest production of acid; the increase in pH is generally credited to the

---

[1] Emery and Rittenberg, *Bull. Am. Assoc. Petrol. Geologists*, **36**:735 (1952).

[2] ZoBell and Rittenberg, *J. Marine Research*, **7**:602 (1948). Apart from sulfate and such inorganic intermediates as may exist, no other hydrogen acceptors have been demonstrated for this group of bacteria. It is questionable whether elemental sulfur which is often found in sediments is the direct result of this reduction; more likely it is the product of a subsequent oxidation process. Zil'berman [*J. Gen. Chem.* (*U.S.S.R.*), **10**:1257 (1940)] has postulated a reaction between a sulfite intermediate and H_2S to yield sulfur and water. Earlier ideas of a purely chemical (abiogenetic) reaction for the reduction of sulfate in an organic-rich medium appear quite unlikely [Bastin, *Sci.*, **63**:21 (1926)].

[3] Sverdrup, Johnson, and Fleming, *op. cit.*

reduction of sulfate[1] and the gradual replacement of the sodium of the clays by calcium and magnesium.

V-4. Nature of the Source Material. Relatively few clues to the character of the source materials can be derived from the chemical composition of crude oils. There are two notable exceptions, however. The early work of Zalozieki and Klarfeld[2] and the later studies by Fenske et al.[3] have demonstrated the presence in petroleum of optically active material; these observations gave strong support to the idea that at least a part of the crude oil was derived from living systems. More recent work by Oakwood[4] has established the active principle to be a crystalline mixture of polynuclear naphthenes. While a steroid structure is suggested in view of the molecular-weight range (390 to 400), their polycyclic character, and optical activity ($[\alpha]_D = 27$ to $28°$), no evidence was educed to support that idea in this work.

Distinctive among nitrogen-containing constituents of crude oil is a class of compounds known as the porphyrins, which are recognized as the degradation products of the chlorophylls—the green photosynthetic pigments of plants and some bacteria, and of the hemes and hematins—the respiratory pigments of both plants and animals. They were detected originally by Treibs[5] not only in petroleum but in a wide variety of natural bitumens. Porphyrin precursors of the chlorophyll type have been demonstrated by Fox et al.[6] and by Orr, Emery, and Grady[7] to be present in sediments from the sea floor as well as from cores representing marine muds of several thousand years age. Apparently all of the porphyrin in crude oil is complexed with metal, of which vanadium[8] is the most important, followed by nickel; iron and copper may be present. These complexes possess highly characteristic ultraviolet-visible absorption spectra from which it is possible to estimate their concentrations in the oil. Vanadium is observed to range anywhere from a few parts per million for the nonasphaltic oils to a thousand or so parts per million for certain tarry crudes, with the nickel-to-vanadium ratio seldom exceeding one-tenth[9]; only a fraction of this metal is in the form of porphyrin complex,

---

[1] During sulfate reduction, the cation of a strong acid ($SO_4^=$) is converted to one of a weak acid (HS^-).

[2] *Chem. Z.*, **31**:1155 (1907).

[3] *Ind. Eng. Chem.*, **34**:638 (1942); **36**:383 (1944); *Anal. Chem.*, **20**:434 (1948).

[4] Oakwood, Schriver, Fall, McAleer, and Wunz, *Ind. Eng. Chem.*, **44**:2568 (1952).

[5] *Ann. Chem.*, **510**:42 (1934); **517**:172 (1935); **520**:144 (1935).

[6] *Proc. Natl. Acad. Sci. U.S.*, **23**:295 (1937); **27**:333 (1941); *Sci.*, **100**:111 (1944); *Arch. Biochem.*, **5**:1 (1944).

[7] *Bull. Amer. Assoc. Petrol. Geologists*, **42**:925 (1958).

[8] Erdman, Ramsey, Kalenda, and Hanson, *J. ACS*, **78**:5844 (1956).

[9] For certain crudes, nickel has been known to exceed vanadium, although the absolute amounts of both are generally low.

however.   The reason why vanadium should predominate in these complexes is not clear, although their inherent stability[1] is undoubtedly a factor.

A survey of the organic components of living plants and animals points up immediately the fact that one is dealing with substances of widely differing chemical character and stability.   For discussion, however, they can be broken down into the following gross classes: lipides, including the hydrocarbons and polyenes, the organic acids, alcohols, and esters; the proteins and their component amino acids; carbohydrates; the pyrrole pigments; and the lignins.   In the total organic debris that becomes incorporated into the sediments, it is likely that the relative proportions of the several compound classes vary widely, depending on the types of contributing organisms, which in turn depend on such environmental factors as proximity to land, light (water depth), salinity, availability of oxygen, temperature, etc.   While certain types of compounds appear more attractive as source material and, in fact, may be quantitatively more important than others, it does not seem possible to exclude any single class from consideration.

Of all possible source substances, hydrocarbons can be said almost certainly to have contributed to the formation of crude oil.   They are widely distributed in living plants, and work by Sirahama,[2] Whitmore and Oakwood,[3] Larsen and Haug,[4] and others has indicated concentrations up to several tenths per cent, dry weight basis.   Depending on the identity of the organism, the extracts contained not only paraffins and naphthenes but also other hydrocarbons of varying degrees of unsaturation.   The molecular weights covered a wide range.   The paraffinic and naphthenic hydrocarbon components undoubtedly survive after burial, ultimately to become incorporated in any crude oil that formed.   The polyenes, which comprise the terpene hydrocarbons and the carotenoid pigments (carotenes, xanthophylls, etc.), also survive for a time.   The carotenoids which are important constituents of aquatic flora and fauna of all types[5] have been shown by Fox et al.[6] to persist in marine sediments for at least several thousands of years; their importance as possible precursors of the more complex naphthenes and aromatics is discussed in a later section.

[1] Erdman, Walter, and Hanson, *ACS, Div. Petrol. Chem., Gen. Papers*, Preprints, p. 259, ACS Meeting, Miami, April, 1957.

[2] *J. Agr. Chem. Soc. Japan*, **14**:743 (1938).

[3] "Fundamental Research on Occurrence and Recovery of Petroleum," p. 99, American Petroleum Institute, New York, 1944–1945.

[4] *Acta Chem. Scand.*, **10**:470 (1956).

[5] Goodwin, "Carotenoids," Chemical Publishing Company, Inc., New York, 1954.

[6] Fox et al., *loc. cit.*

Calculations by Whitmore[1] indicate that the total hydrocarbon material derived from marine plant sources may be considerable, possibly as great as 60 million barrels per year. The estimate is highly approximate and accounts only for the observed heavier hydrocarbons. The source of the lighter liquid hydrocarbons and the hydrocarbon gases above methane is unknown, but would appear to be in the nonhydrocarbon source material.

The fatty acids have long been regarded favorably as source materials for petroleum because of their diversity in chemical structure and the fact that they might be converted to hydrocarbons by the simple elimination of a carboxyl group. It has been observed that the molecules of the natural fatty acids are largely of the straight-chain type and with rare exception contain an even number of carbon atoms; many are unsaturated, the polyethenoid type exhibiting wide variations in the arrangement of the double bonds. Hilditch[2] has noted the interesting fact that the fats of the simplest and most primitive organisms are usually composed of very complex mixtures of fatty acids, in contrast to the higher plants and animals for which the component acids are fewer in number.

The fats of aquatic organisms are largely of the unsaturated type. In terms of weight, they constitute an important part of the chemical make-up of both fresh-water and marine organisms and presumably must represent a significant contribution to the total organic fraction of sediments. Hilditch and Lovern[3] have noted distinct differences between the component fatty acids of fats from fresh-water and from marine organisms. Broadly viewed, the fats of all the green algae, the pond weed, and the diatoms are similar in many respects to those of the fresh-water animals; the fats of the brown algae are in a class by themselves, but retain similarities to the fresh-water types; the fat of the red algae approximates marine animal fat in composition.[4] Free fatty acids have been reported in appreciable amounts in the marine diatom *Nitzschia closterium*.[5] Associated with the natural triglycerides and the hydrocarbons is a variety of glycerophosphoric esters, higher alcohols in the free or esterified condition, and fatty acids combined with carbohydrates and containing nitrogen, but little is known of their natural degradation reactions. Sterols are present in a variety of fresh-water and marine diatoms; concentrations as high as 0.6 per cent have been reported for *Navicula pelliculosa*.[6]

[1] Whitmore, "Fundamental Research on Occurrence and Recovery of Petroleum," p. 124, American Petroleum Institute, New York, 1943.

[2] "Chemical Constitution of Natural Fats," p. 9, John Wiley & Sons, Inc., New York, 1956.

[3] *Nature*, **137**:478 (1936).

[4] Lovern, *Biochem. J.*, **30**:387 (1936).

[5] Clarke and Mazur, *J. Biol. Chem.*, **141**:283 (1941).

[6] Low, *J. Marine Research*, **14**:199 (1955).

Carbohydrates form an important part of all plants and, as such, presumably contribute materially to the total organic content of the sediments, particularly in the near-shore areas. As a class, carbohydrates are quite varied in character, ranging from the simple sugars through the polysaccharides, such as glycogen, the starches, and the celluloses, and including such substances as laminarin, agar, alginic acid of seaweed, and chitins which form the skeletal material of insects and crustacea.[1] The simpler members of the class are water-soluble[2] and form a highly acceptable substrate for bacteria. Thus, a part of the total carbohydrate is destroyed by oxidative organisms; a portion is consumed by animal forms and converted into animal tissue, and, finally, some of it is entrapped in the sediments. The fraction which escapes immediate destruction is presumably composed largely of the water-insoluble and biochemically more resistant compound types. However, very little is known of the possible fate of these materials following burial.

Proteins represent another important and highly complex component of all living matter. They are polymeric substances composed of one or more of some twenty-five amino acids linked to one another through the carboxyl carbon and the nitrogen; frequently molecules of other than protein type are associated with the protein structure as in the nucleoproteins. Chemically the proteins are very reactive; in the native state, they are hydrolyzed readily by either alkaline or acidic media to yield water-soluble products. As is also true for the carbohydrates, it is likely that they would disappear in the aquatic environment, for the most part by oxidative destruction or through consumption as food by animal life. Native protein is rare outside the living cell, however, owing to the ease with which it loses structural organization (denaturation). In many instances, solubility drops when this happens and incorporation in the sediment is favored. It is to be expected, therefore, that denatured protein would be preserved and possibly contribute to the formation of crude oil. Studies on the long-term thermal stability of amino acids by Abelson[3] have indicated that these substances should survive under the normal low temperature earth conditions for long periods of time. This was demonstrated by the detection of proteins or peptides in fossil clam

[1] Although highly resistant to chemical attack, chitin can be degraded through the action of microorganisms; several chitin-decomposing bacteria have been isolated from marine sediments. Hock, *J. Marine Research*, **4**:99 (1941).

[2] Collier [*Am. Wildlife Inst., Trans. 18th Conf.*, Washington, D.C., 1953] has reported concentrations of substances possessing carbohydrate properties as high as 50 mg per liter for Gulf of Mexico waters. While high values undoubtedly exist in inshore, shallow areas, the amount in the open sea is apparently much less. See Lewis and Rakestraw, *J. Marine Research*, **14**:253 (1955).

[3] *Sci.*, **119**:576 (1954); *Carnegie Institution Year Book*, no. 53, pp. 97–101, Washington, D.C., 1954.

shells from the Pleistocene and of amino acids in older invertebrate and vertebrate fossils, including an Ordovician trilobite. Erdman et al.[1] have shown recently that a variety of amino acids are present in the non-calcareous as well as the calcareous portions of recent marine sediments and in Oligocene shales, estimated to be some thirty million years old; a similar report on the Posidonia shales of northwestern Germany has been published.[2]

Lignin is a mixture of complex, high-molecular-weight amorphous substances; it forms the cell wall structure of plants, particularly those of woody type. Despite the extensive work on the lignin of the higher land plants, its structure is still not understood, except that it is probably built up of phenyl propane units containing methoxyl and hydroxyl groups;[3] in sediments, it is frequently found as a complex with protein or carbohydrate. Little is known about the lignin of marine plant forms or of its distribution, so that the ligneous substances in sediments cannot be typed as to source. In an investigation of recent marine sediments Bader[4] noted that the lignin-carbon to total-carbon ratio is extremely variable and confirmed the earlier observation that lignin is highly stable to both chemical and biological agents.[5]

In general, it may be said that the organic detritus of a sediment will vary with the environment in proportion as the aquatic organisms vary in their chemical make-up. In the sea the plants are restricted almost entirely to the algae, including the diatoms, the dinoflagellates, and other phytoplanktonic organisms, the marine fungi, and the bacteria; the few species of flowering plants (e.g., eel grass) are restricted to the littoral zones. The animal population is tremendously diverse in character. Except under very special conditions, animals can be only a very small contributor to the total organic detritus in near-shore, shallow-water sediments. In deeper waters, far removed from land, where competition for food is high, it is not unlikely that plant material is largely converted to animal tissue by the time it is incorporated in the sediments.

V-5. Hydrocarbons in Recent Sediments. Despite Trask's failure to detect liquid hydrocarbons in recent sediments,[6] it became evident from collateral studies by Heilbron et al.,[7] Whitmore and Oakwood,[8] Sisler and ZoBell,[9] and others that hydrocarbons were distributed widely in

[1] *Sci.*, **124**:1026 (1956).

[2] von Gaertner and Kroepelin, *Erdöl u. Kohle*, **9**:680 (1956).

[3] Brauns, "The Chemistry of Lignin," p. 15, Academic Press, Inc., New York, 1952.

[4] Bader, *Deep Sea Research*, **4**:15 (1956).

[5] Brauns, *op. cit.*, p. 604.

[6] *Bull. Am. Assoc. Petrol. Geologists*, **14**:1451 (1930).

[7] *J. Chem. Soc.*, 1934, p. 1572.

[8] Whitmore and Oakwood, *loc. cit.*

[9] *J. Bact.*, **62**:117 (1951).

living organisms. Specifically these authors had demonstrated that algae and bacteria of both marine and nonmarine types contained complex mixtures of paraffinic and naphthenic hydrocarbons, and there appeared no obvious reason why these substances should not accumulate as a part of the organic debris.

Smith[1] was the first to report the isolation of hydrocarbons from recent sediments. Extracts from a variety of saline, brackish, and fresh-water muds were shown to contain hydrocarbons in amounts varying from 9 to nearly 12,000 ppm of dried sample. The hydrocarbon fractions were demonstrated to be of recent origin by carbon 14 dating. Using chromatographic methods, paraffinic, naphthenic, and aromatic cuts were isolated. Average molecular weights fell in the 250 to 350 range. From these and other supporting data, Smith concluded that petroleum is being formed in present-day sediments, probably largely through the accumulation of the hydrocarbon remains of the many contributing types of aquatic organisms. Similar evidence for the generation of hydrocarbons in young sediments has been cited by Kidwell and Hunt[2] in their study of the grey clays and interbedded argillaceous sheet sands of the Orinoco River delta.

An interesting point which Smith makes is that, with respect to hydrocarbon content, no sharp distinction can be drawn between fresh-water and marine sediments; from the results, it might be inferred that the fresh-water samples were richer in hydrocarbons, although their proportion of the total organic content is usually smaller than was true for the marine sediments. Swain[3] has recently reported the isolation of hydrocarbon materials from the bottom sediments of five fresh-water lakes in Minnesota. Careful fractionation of the lipoid extracts revealed the presence of liquid and solid hydrocarbons of both saturated and aromatic type. A similar occurrence of hydrocarbons has been reported by Judson and Murray[4] for two Wisconsin lakes. In both instances, the recent character of the hydrocarbons was established by carbon 14 dating.

A critical study of the hydrocarbon content and character of a series of marine muds from the northern Gulf of Mexico has been presented by Stevens et al.[5] and by Evans et al.[6] Quantities comparable to those reported by earlier workers were isolated and their recent origin demonstrated by the radiocarbon method. Mass spectrometric measurements

[1] *Science*, **116**:437 (1952); *Bull. Am. Assoc. Petrol. Geologists*, **38**:377 (1954).

[2] Kidwell and Hunt, "Habitat of Oil," *Symposium*, Weeks (ed.), p. 790, American Association of Petroleum Geologists, Tulsa, Okla., 1958. *World Oil*, **14**(1):79 (1958).

[3] *Bull. Am. Assoc. Petrol. Geologists*, **40**:600 (1956).

[4] *Op. cit.*, **40**:747 (1956).

[5] *Bull. Am. Assoc. Petrol. Geologists*, **40**:975 (1956).

[6] *Anal. Chem.*, **29**:1856 (1958).

on the normal paraffinic fractions, however, showed clearly a strong predominance for molecules containing an odd number of carbon atoms; the same was true for hydrocarbons isolated from soil.[1] Hydrocarbons of comparable molecular-weight range isolated from crude oils and from the Woodford shale[2] exhibited no such preference. A sample of plankton, however, showed only slight odd carbon preference, the odd-to-even ratio being 1.1 as compared with 2.1 for the recent sediment hydrocarbons. Brenneman[3] has confirmed the high odd-to-even carbon ratio for Gulf Coast sediment extracts of Prairie and Montgomery age,[4] but has observed a more nearly equal distribution for hydrocarbons of some younger deposits.

A distinction has also been noted between the types of aromatic hydrocarbons derived from recent and from ancient sediments. Judging from spectral absorption characteristics, Stevens et al.[5] have concluded that the mixtures obtained from the fresh Gulf muds are substantially less complex than those derived from crude oil or from the Woodford shale. Recent work by Erdman et al.[6] has shown that benzene and naphthalene and their more volatile alkyl derivatives (up to about C_{16}) are absent in a variety of fresh aquatic sediments, ranging from acid fresh-water to marine in type.

The conclusion that hydrocarbons make up a normal component of recent sediments is now established beyond any doubt. It is further evident that this is true also for sediments which are not ordinarily considered by most geologists as potential source sediments of petroleum. It appears, however, that crude oil, as we know it, is not formed in recent sediments, at least in the uppermost zones, even for marine shelf deposits. The inference is that, if the sediment is of a type to yield petroleum, the missing components must be generated at some greater depth. This, in turn, argues for the idea that source material other than plant- and animal-generated hydrocarbon is required.

V-6. Transformation of the Organic Matter into Petroleum. Perhaps the least well understood phase of petroleum genesis is the chemistry of the transformation of the organic matter into petroleum. While several possible sources of hydrocarbons are recognized, it is impossible at the

---

[1] The observation is significant in view of the fact that, in contrast with molecules of the natural fatty acids and alcohols, many of the plant and animal hydrocarbon molecules have branched chains and contain an odd number of carbon atoms. [Deuel, "The Lipids," vol. I, p. 400, Interscience Publishers, Inc., New York, 1951.]

[2] A petroliferous shale of Mississippian age.

[3] *ACS Abst. Papers*, p. 16B, ACS Meeting, Miami, April, 1957.

[4] Late Pleistocene sediments.

[5] *Loc. cit.*

[6] ACS, *Div. Petrol. Chem., Symposium on Chemical Aspects of the Origin, Migration, and Accumulation of Oil*, ACS Meeting, Chicago, September, 1958.

present time to evaluate their relative contributions, except in qualitative fashion.

The discovery of prolific bacterial growths in at least the upper layers of recent sediments suggested immediately that, in addition to providing the protective reducing environment, biological activity might possibly be a generating agent for crude oil. It can be said that bacteria preferentially attack carbohydrates and proteins, leaving the more refractory substances such as certain of the lipides, insoluble proteins, lignins, and other complex materials, collectively known as aquatic humus. The result of this activity is the synthesis of simpler compounds such as carbon dioxide, hydrogen, hydrogen sulfide, ammonia, fatty acids, alcohols, and amines. An important inorganic bacterial reaction in recent sediments is the reduction of sulfate ion to sulfide.[1] Stone and ZoBell[2] noted that, except for the production of methane, bacteria tend to leave organic compounds bearing carboxyl, hydroxyl, amine, and sulfhydryl groups, rather than to accomplish the complete removal of oxygen, nitrogen, or sulfur atoms required to produce hydrocarbons. From the observation that tyrosine could be fermented to yield either phenol or *p*-cresol, Machamer and Stone[3] reasoned that phenylalanine might be made to yield benzene or toluene. Working with the same cultures, no trace of either hydrocarbon could be detected. The abundant production of methane[4] originally suggested that the higher paraffins might be so produced, but careful analysis of the products of a wide variety of microbial fermentations failed to show anything more than trace amounts of ethane or higher paraffins.[5]

A small amount of hydrocarbon is synthesized by bacteria as a part of their cell substance. Carbon tetrachloride extracts of cultures of autotrophic bacteria which used molecular hydrogen as the sole source of energy and carbon dioxide or carbonate as the sole source of carbon were demonstrated by ZoBell[6] to contain at least 25 per cent of paraffinic

---

[1] Stevenson and Stickland, *Biochem. J.*, **25**:205, 216 (1931). ZoBell and Rittenberg, *J. Marine Research*, **7**:602 (1948).

[2] *Ind. Eng. Chem.*, **44**:2564 (1952).

[3] *J. Bacteriol.*, **54**:39 (1947).

[4] Methane appears in large quantities and essentially free from higher hydrocarbons as the result of the anaerobic fermentation of cellulose in swamps (marsh gas). Such is thought to be the origin of the huge deposits of "dry" natural gas found throughout the world. A. J. Teplitz, Gulf Research & Development Co. (personal communication), has demonstrated the ethane-to-methane ratio for marsh gases to be between 8×10^{-6} and 5×10^{-6}.

[5] Buswell and Mueller, *Ind. Eng. Chem.*, **44**:550 (1952). Davis and Squires, *Sci.*, **119**:381 (1954).

[6] "Fundamental Research on Occurrence and Recovery of Petroleum," p. 174, American Petroleum Institute, 1952–1953.

and cycloparaffinic hydrocarbons. It appears likely that this is, at least, one of the sources of some of the heavier hydrocarbons in recent sediments.

The possibility that biocatalysts or enzymes are involved in the formation of hydrocarbons cannot be discounted at the present time. A wide variety of such organic catalysts are produced by bacteria, and it may be possible that, under the prevailing low-temperature anaerobic conditions, these substances may be preserved to function for a time after the organisms which produced them ceased to exist.[1]

Some years ago, Lind and Bardwell[2] suggested that the natural radioactivity of sediments might be involved in the generation of petroleum. While their proposed mechanism of methane polymerization has now been discounted, the work did point up an interesting source of energy for the possible transformation of organic material to hydrocarbon.

As the result of extensive investigations by Bell, Goodman, and Whitehead,[3] Russell,[4] Beers and Goodman,[5] and Beers,[6] it became evident that shales in general were considerably richer in radioactive elements than were other sedimentary rock types. It was further shown that thorium, uranium, and potassium are associated with the finer-grained constituents and more carbonaceous materials, suggesting that radioactive bombardment might alter this organic material and possibly produce appreciable amounts of hydrocarbon.

Since alpha particles account for more than three-quarters of the energy liberated by naturally occurring radioactive elements, first attention was devoted to them. The possible mechanisms by which these particles might induce chemical reaction were reviewed by Sheppard[7] who also carried out the first approximate calculation of the radiochemical conversion of organic material to petroleum under certain hypothetical, sedimentary conditions. Extensive work by Sheppard and Whitehead,[8] Honig,[9] Sheppard and Burton,[10] Whitehead, Goodman, and Breger,[11] Burton,[12] Breger and Burton,[13] and Breger[14] provided the data required to render these calculations quantitative. It was demonstrated that ali-

[1] ZoBell, *Oil Weekly*, **109**(8):15 (1943).

[2] *J. ACS*, **48**:2335 (1926).

[3] *Bull. Am. Assoc. Petrol. Geologists*, **24**:1529 (1940).

[4] *Geophysics*, **9**:180 (1944).

[5] *Bull. Geol. Soc. Am.*, **55**:1229 (1944).

[6] *Bull. Am. Assoc. Petrol. Geologists*, **29**:1 (1945).

[7] *Bull. Am. Assoc. Petrol. Geologists*, **28**:924 (1944).

[8] *Bull. Am. Assoc. Petrol. Geologists*, **30**:32 (1946).

[9] *Sci.*, **104**:27 (1946).

[10] *J. ACS*, **68**:1636 (1946).

[11] *J. chim. phys.*, **48**:184 (1951).

[12] *J. ACS*, **71**:4117 (1949).

[13] *J. ACS*, **68**:1639 (1946).

[14] *J. Phys. & Colloid Chem.*, **52**:551 (1948).

phatic fatty and naphthenic acids can be decarboxylated to the parent hydrocarbons by alpha or the equivalent deuteron radiation.   A variety of light saturated and olefinic hydrocarbons is also produced, along with carbon dioxide, carbon monoxide, water, and hydrogen; a portion of the hydrogen reacts with the olefins to yield saturated products.   In a summary of the work, Whitehead[1] concluded that some 3×10^{-7} g of hydrocarbon material might be expected to be produced per gram of typical, organic-rich marine shale per million years as a result of the radiation from the uranium and thorium series and from potassium.   It thus appears that radioactivity can account for only a very small fraction of the observed residual hydrocarbon contents of ancient marine sediments, and an even smaller portion of the total amount of petroleum which must have been generated in those sediments.

The thought that at least a part of the hydrocarbons of petroleum has been formed by some long-term thermal reaction was voiced at an early date.   By 1888, Engler[2] had demonstrated that the pressure distillation of fats would yield an oily material of high olefin content[3] and somewhat later outlined[4] in a rather broad way what was probably the first of the organic theories of petroleum genesis.   This highly unsaturated material, called protopetroleum by Engler, was believed possibly to have formed from the fatty components of the organic debris in sediments by mild thermal cracking and polymerization; paraffins were thought to form by decarboxylation of fatty acids, while the olefins isomerized to cyclic hydrocarbons.[5]

[1] "Fundamental Research on the Occurrence and Recovery of Petroleum," p. 205, American Petroleum Institute, 1952–1953.

[2] *Ber.*, **21**:1816 (1888); **22**:592 (1889).

[3] "Warren and Storer [*Am. Acad. Arts Sci.*, **9**:177 (1865)] first distilled petroleum from animal fats years before; i.e., by the distillation of menhaden oil soaps under pressure they made good kerosene and actually sold the product—an achievement remarkable for the time at which it was done—and far in advance of any similar work abroad" [Day, *Proc. Am. Phil. Soc.*, **36**:112–113 (1897)].

[4] *Z. angew. Chem.*, **21**:1585 (1908); *Petroleum Z.*, **7**:399 (1912).

[5] Two widely discussed suggestions for the genesis of bituminous materials and petroleum were those of Hackford [*J. Inst. Petrol. Technologists*, **18**:74 (1932)] and of Berl [*Z. angew. Chem.*, **43**:1018 (1930); *Naturwissenschaften*, **20**:652 (1932); *Ann.*, **504**:38 (1933); *AIMME, Tech. Publ.* 920, 1938; *Bull. Am. Assoc. Petrol. Geologists*, **24**:1865 (1940)].   The former advocated the acid hydrolysis of the fucosans of algae to yield a mixture of polyhydric alcohols (algarite) and, ultimately, hydrocarbons. The latter proposed an alkaline hydrolysis of cellulose to yield products resembling, first, noncoking coals, then coking or anthracite coals, and, finally, bitumens as the alkalinity increases; hydrogen, presumably derived from the reaction of ferrous iron with water, is required to convert the last into materials of the petroleum class. While both hypotheses were supported by detailed experimental work, the conditions were not compatible with those known to exist in nature, and neither is now considered seriously as an explanation for petroleum formation.

While these early ideas are no longer held—Engler, himself, recognized the difficulties these concepts implied—there appears no reason why low-temperature decarboxylations, deaminations, cyclizations, hydrogenations, isomerizations, or other type reactions might not proceed under the conditions known to exist in nature. Thus, at relatively low temperatures (200° to 250°C), polyene structures can be cyclicized to produce aromatic hydrocarbons. For example, *m*-xylene has been found in the pyrolysis products of bixin[1] and capsanthin,[2] while other carotenoids have yielded, in addition to *m*-xylene, toluene[1] and 2,6-dimethylnaphthalene.[3,4] Cyclization and polymerization reactions have been noted to occur in the same temperature range for several unsaturated fatty acids of marine organisms.[5] Considering the composition of the source material and the generally reducing conditions, such polyene-type reactions may well contribute substantially to the naphthene-aromatic fraction of crude oil.

Chemical reactions of the type suggested become particularly attractive when it is realized that the clays and other fine-grained minerals, which are always present in the sediment, may act as catalysts for both synthesis of hydrocarbons and for the degradation of the organic source material to hydrocarbons. In an early paper on the subject, Brooks[6] suggested that any of several naturally occurring minerals might be active in promoting polymerization; in later publications[7] the idea was further developed to include hydropolymerization, isomerization, and cyclization to explain the variety of hydrocarbon types present in petroleum. A carbonium ion mechanism was suggested, following Whitmore's[8] proposal to account for acid catalysis.

Because of the time factor involved, there have been very few attempts to demonstrate that the fine-grained mineral components of sediments might aid catalytically in the formation of petroleum. For the most part, the catalytic activity of minerals in the earth has been inferred from their properties under cracking or near-cracking temperatures. The extrapolation of kinetic data over wide ranges of conditions is, of

[1] Van Hasselt, *Rec. trav. chim.*, **30**:1 (1911).

[2] Zechmeister and Cholnoky, *Ann.*, **478**:95 (1930).

[3] Kuhn and Winterstein, *Ber.*, **65**:1873 (1932); **66**:429 (1933).

[4] Jones and Sharpe, *Can. J. Research*, **B26**:728 (1948).

[5] Farmer and van den Heuvel, *J. Soc. Chem. Ind. (London)*, **57**:24 (1938); *J. Chem. Soc.*, 1938, p. 427.

[6] *Bull. Am. Assoc. Petrol. Geologists*, **15**:611 (1931). Passing reference to the possibility of the catalytic effect of minerals had been made earlier. See Mrazek, *Petroleum Z.*, **22**:839 (1926); Haseman, *Bull. Am. Assoc. Petrol. Geologists*, **14**:1465 (1930).

[7] Brooks, *Bull. Am. Assoc. Petrol. Geologists*, **32**:2269 (1948); **33**:1600 (1949); *Sci.*, **111**:648 (1950); **114**:240 (1951); *Ind. Eng. Chem.*, **44**:2570 (1952).

[8] *J. ACS*, **54**:3274 (1932).

course, a highly questionable procedure. Also, as Van Nes and Van Westen[1] point out, there is no assurance that the structural changes known to occur in clays at high temperatures (about 300°C) do not fundamentally alter their catalytic nature; certainly the hydrocarbons obtained at the two temperature extremes cannot be the same by virtue of their difference in thermodynamic stability.[2] Recognizing these difficulties, Frost and coworkers[3] conducted their experiments with clays and other mineral types at temperatures ranging from 130°C up to a maximum of 275°C, using appropriately long periods of contact. Essentially, he showed that, at these temperatures, alcohols could be dehydrated, water split out of ketones, olefins polymerized, and hydrogen transfer induced. The apparent absence of hydrogen in natural gases and sediments is not inconsistent with low-temperature reactions of the type described, according to Van Nes and Van Westen, since it is known that, in low-temperature cracking, hydrogen production drops rapidly with temperature.[4]

Possibly the most serious objection that can be raised against the catalytic studies is the fact that all were carried out in the absence of water, although in sediments water is always present. The adsorption of water on the mineral components must reduce substantially any catalytic activity they may have and possibly alter seriously their catalytic nature. It is to be noted, however, that at least some components of crude oil and presumably the source materials are adsorbed by clays, even from an aqueous medium. Studies on simple organic-clay systems have shown that a wide variety of substances will enter the clay lattice to form highly stable complexes. For example, protein in combination with clay is substantially more resistant to bacterial destruction than is protein alone; possibly, in the adsorbed condition, time is available for slow chemical reaction which might otherwise not occur. Much remains to be known, however, before heterogeneous catalysis can be established definitely as having an important role in petroleum formation.

An interesting approach to the question of thermal reaction was suggested by Seyer.[5] On the observation that the pyrolysis of hydrocarbon

---

[1] "Aspects of the Constitution of Mineral Oils," p. 37, Elsevier Press, Inc., Houston, 1951.

[2] Francis, "Science of Petroleum," vol. III, p. 2097, Oxford University Press, New York and London, 1938.

[3] *Uspekhi Khim.*, **14**:501 (1945).

[4] Sachanan, "Conversion of Petroleum," p. 202, Reinhold Publishing Corporation, New York, 1948.

[5] *Bull. Am. Assoc. Petrol. Geologists*, **17**:1251 (1933); *J. Inst. Petrol. Technologists*, **19**:773 (1933). Seyer's assumption of a paraffinic protopetroleum is in direct opposition to Barton's hypothesis, based on the latter's work on Gulf Coast crudes. See Barton's discussion of the problem, *Bull. Am. Assoc. Petrol. Geologists*, **18**:143 (1934).

waxes yields oily products, he has postulated the formation of a waxy protoproduct which over long periods at moderate temperature and high pressure would crack to olefins, which would in turn rearrange and polymerize to give a wide variety of complex hydrocarbons containing branched chains and rings. Taking an average activation energy value of 65 kcal for the first-order cracking reaction, and an observed k value of 0.03456 min^{-1} at 470°C, he calculated the half life of a typical wax molecule such as hexadecane as a function of temperature, and concluded that it would take a temperature in excess of 150°C to effect any considerable amount of conversion within a geologically acceptable period. It has been pointed out,[1] however, that if one can assume a decrease in activation energy of 10 kcal as a result of catalysis, the half life at 100°C becomes 6.0×10^8 years; a decrease of 20 kcal brings the value down to 1.0×10^3 years; these are, at least, not unreasonable figures.

The occurrence in many crude oils of sulfur-containing compounds,[2] often in substantial quantities, suggests that a source of sulfur other than the minor amounts present in the source material is involved. The most reasonable mechanism for the formation of these sulfur-containing bodies appears to be a thermal reaction between elemental sulfur, and possibly also hydrogen sulfide, and the other organic components of the sediments, including the hydrocarbons. Presumably these reactions may continue even after the oil has accumulated in the reservoir, if elemental sulfur or hydrogen sulfide is still present, with resulting slow alteration in the character of the petroleum.

A consideration of the possibility of thermal or thermal-catalytic reactions immediately raises the question of thermodynamic equilibrium in crude oil systems. An inspection of typical total crude composition data[3] and equilibrium data for various isomers of the light paraffins, naphthenes, and aromatics[4] will indicate that, in so far as these components are concerned, crude oils cannot represent equilibrium mixtures. Equilibrium temperatures corresponding to the observed isomer ratios

---

[1] C. W. Montgomery, Gulf Research & Development Co., personal communication.

[2] As would be expected from the reducing character of the medium, all of the sulfur in petroleum is in the reduced (bivalent) state. The principal compound classes involved are aliphatic, cycloaliphatic, and aromatic thiols and sulfides; thiophenes; benzothiophenes; and higher condensed aromatic-thiophenic structures. Dissolved hydrogen sulfide is a common component of crude oil; occasionally elemental sulfur is also present.

[3] Reference is made to crude oil samples obtained under reservoir conditions by bottom-hole sampler or by reconstituting the gas and oil in their proper proportions at the well head.

[4] Rossini, "Science of Petroleum," vol. V, part I, p. 153, Oxford University Press, New York and London, 1950.

not only vary widely within a single crude but often assume impossibly low or high values. The subject has been discussed by Van Nes and Van Westen,[1] Rossini,[2] and Smith and Rall.[3]

V-7. Expulsion of Petroleum from the Source Rock and Accumulation. Geologists have recognized three necessary requirements for an oil deposit:

1. Source sediments.
2. A permeable rock of sufficient porosity to serve as a reservoir.
3. A trap of some type, associated with the reservoir, which will prevent the petroleum from migrating away and being lost, and which will facilitate accumulation.

From the discussion in the foregoing sections it is evident that sediment types and the geochemical environments favorable to the generation of crude oil are not uncommon in nature and, for this reason, widespread formation of petroleum must be assumed to be occurring even at the present day. However, the development of an available reservoir rock and trap, predating accumulation, is a much rarer event and is usually the controlling factor in the over-all process of formation of an oil deposit. Because of the importance of this aspect of the problem, it is considered briefly here, although not strictly a part of the origin question.

As the thickness of a sedimentary deposit increases, the weight of the overlying sediments becomes considerable. The result of this increase in overburden is that the muds begin to lose water and any other fluid materials contained in them to the more permeable, interfingering sand zones, mentioned earlier. The loss of fluids from the muds results in a substantial reduction in thickness and permeability. A typical mud section of 100 ft thickness containing about 75 per cent by volume of water and 25 per cent by volume of fine-grained minerals will have been reduced to some 40 ft of shale by the time it has been buried to a depth of 5,000 ft; the density will have risen from an initial 1.4 to 2.0 and the water content will have been reduced to about 42 volume per cent. Under 8,000 ft of overburden, the resulting shale will have a thickness of some 30 ft and a water content of approximately 20 volume per cent, or about 10 per cent of the original water content of the mud; the density will now be about 2.4.[4] The sand zones, being relatively incompressible, will retain their shape and permeability.

Exactly how and at what time the hydrocarbons are expelled from the mud and how they are segregated in the reservoir rock to form deposits

[1] *Op. cit.*, p. 33, 1951.

[2] ACS Southwest Regional Meeting, Houston, December, 1947.

[3] *Ind. Eng. Chem.*, **45**:1495 (1953).

[4] Cox, Hanna, Hanson, and Weaver, *ACS, Div. Petrol. Chem., Symposium on Origin of Petroleum*, ACS Meeting, New York, September, 1951.

of oil has been debated at length.[1] Presumably the oil is carried along as an extremely fine dispersion in the water, possibly as an emulsion. Actually the volumes of water expressed from muds during shale formation are so huge that one can hardly escape the conclusion that a considerable amount of hydrocarbon material must be removed in aqueous solution; it would seem likely that hydrocarbons so expelled would be swept out through the permeable zones and be irretrievably lost.

Once the oil has been transferred to the reservoir rock, it is free to move under any force which may be applied. At the now greatly reduced hydraulic gradient, gravitational forces are thought to become predominant, causing the oil, gas, and water to become segregated in the upper parts of the porous stratum, according to their relative densities. Favorable locations where the oil can accumulate may be anywhere along the path of fluid travel, and it is believed that, in some instances at least, the oil may migrate a considerable distance from its source before being trapped.

An attempt to find in young sediments a situation in which oil is currently migrating and accumulating has been reported recently by Kidwell and Hunt.[2] A study of the clays and interbedded argillaceous sheet sands on the Pedernales anticline of the Orinoco River delta in Venezuela has revealed hydrocarbon contents of 40 to 55 ppm. One lenticular sand at 110 ft depth showed the presence of free gas and some 160 ppm of liquid hydrocarbons, mostly aromatic in character. Carbon 14 data established that the sand body was deposited about five thousand years ago. Pressure measurements indicated a gradient in the muds upward toward the laterally continuous sands and downward toward the Pleistocene contact, from which it is inferred that both beds are acting as conduits for escape of the fluids to the outcrops.

While the porous zones adjacent to a compacting mud are commonly sand and while sands thus form important reservoir rocks, almost any porous and permeable stratum will suffice. A very common reservoir rock is a porous or fractured limestone, especially of the reef (bioherm) type; a less frequent occurrence is a fractured shale or even igneous or metamorphic rock. Many geologists are of the opinion that oil found in at least some reef structures is indigenous because of the large concen-

[1] Van Tuyl, Parker, and Skeeters, *Quart. Colo. School Mines*, **40**(1):1 (1945). Levorsen, "Geology of Petroleum," W. H. Freeman and Co., San Francisco, 1954. Roof and Rutherford, *Bull. Am. Assoc. Petrol. Geologists*, **42**:963 (1958). Baker, *ACS, Div. Petrol. Chem.*, Symposium on Chemical Aspects of the Origin, Migration, and Accumulation of Oil, ACS Meeting, Chicago, September, 1958. Dickey and Kidwell, *ACS, Div. Petrol. Chem.*, Symposium on Chemical Aspects of the Origin, Migration, and Accumulation of Oil, ACS Meeting, Chicago, September, 1958.
[2] *Loc. cit.*

tration of organisms in them, and because, in some instances, there is no other obvious source of the oil.[1]

Traps, in which oil may accumulate, are found in great variety. A trap may consist simply of a sand lens surrounded by relatively impermeable rock, such as shale. One of the earliest recognized forms is the anticline, produced by folding of a rock sequence. Oil may also accumulate against a slippage plane in the rocks (fault) where the displacement has been sufficient to bring the permeable zone up against an impermeable rock. Often sufficient oil escapes along such a fault to create a seep at the surface. A third type of trap, found frequently along the coastline of the Gulf of Mexico and elsewhere in the world, is the salt dome. A large plug of salt, rising under the sediment load by virtue of its relatively low density, from some deeply buried salt stratum, distorts the surrounding sediments to seal off permeable zones, into which oil may be moving. A gradual change in rock character (facies change) may also provide a trap for oil; thus, a permeable sand may become increasingly "dirty" in character, finally merging into an impermeable shale which may be quite indistinguishable from the shale zones above or below the sand. Because of the absence of any pronounced feature or rapid change in rock properties, this stratigraphic type of trap is one of the most difficult to locate.

V-8. Hydrocarbons in Ancient Sediments. An early effort to characterize rocks which have generated petroleum was that of Trask.[2] As the result of the examination of an enormous number of carbonaceous sediments of various types, he observed that the total organic content averaged about 1.5 per cent of the rock; of this approximately one-tenth was extractable with carbon tetrachloride or ether; the nitrogen content averaged about 0.06 per cent. Contrary to the then held notions, neither color nor organic content showed any particular correlation with proximity to oil. One derived property, the nitrogen-reduction ratio,[3] yielded consistently lower than average values for sediments in the vicinity of oil deposits.

Lacking at the time the necessary techniques for the analysis of the tarry extracts or for their proper protection against oxidation, no oily hydrocarbon fraction was ever isolated. Trask concluded, therefore, that ancient sediments, including those from oil fields, do not, in general, contain appreciable quantities of hydrocarbon material. In an earlier

[1] Link, *Bull. Am. Assoc. Petrol. Geologists*, **34**:263 (1950).

[2] "Source Beds of Petroleum," American Association of Petroleum Geologists, Tulsa, Okla., 1942.

[3] The reduction number, which is roughly proportional to the per cent of organic carbon, was defined arbitrarily in terms of the reaction of the sediment with chromic acid; nitrogen was determined by the conventional Kjeldahl procedure.

publication, however, he had noted[1] that all the oil in the Santa Fe Springs field could have represented no more than 1.8 per cent of the total quantity of organic matter in the prism of sediments from which this oil was presumably derived. This was probably the first clear recognition of the fact that the formation of a deposit of petroleum in nature is a very inefficient process.

Although it was generally agreed that ancient sediments associated with petroleum must contain some residual oil, albeit small in amount, some time elapsed before formal confirmation of the fact appeared in the literature. The first mention of hydrocarbons in ancient sediments was apparently that of Uspenskii[2] who reported the isolation of a hydrocarbon fraction from what evidently was a mixed sediment sample, representing deposits of different ages and from various areas of the Soviet Union. Somewhat later, Petrova and Karpova[3] carried out similar experiments on an oil-saturated sandstone and a sedimentary rock and fractionated the resulting extracts into a nonhydrocarbon and a hydrocarbon portion; the latter was further separated into solid hydrocarbons (largely *n*-paraffins), a paraffinic-naphthenic oily fraction, and an aromatic fraction. Failure in both instances to describe or document the samples under study detracts from the value of the findings.

Hunt, Stewart, and Dickey,[4] in a study of the Eocene sediments of the Uinta Basin, Utah, and the associated bitumen deposits, showed that each of the four distinct bitumen types—ozocerite, albertite, gilsonite, and wurtzelite—could be traced to a particular lithologic unit as a source. Extraction of each of these units yielded a hydrocarbon cut, which on fractionation proved to be highly distinctive in composition. By direct comparison of the fractions with comparable cuts from the individual bitumens, the source bed–bitumen relationships were confirmed.

In a recent and more extensive survey, Hunt and Jamisson[5] showed that almost all sedimentary rocks except certain red (oxidized) shales, sandstones, and metamorphosed materials contain hydrocarbons, soluble asphaltic substances, and a heavy, insoluble, pyrobituminous fraction; the hydrocarbons and soluble asphaltic materials were noted to be similar, respectively, to the heavy oily and asphaltic components of crude oil. A typical marine shale such as the Frontier formation of the Powder River Basin in Wyoming was shown still to contain some 6 bbl of oil, 20 bbl of soluble asphalt, and about 250 bbl of pyrobituminous material per acre-foot. A type distribution for the hydrocarbon mate-

[1] Trask, *Bull. Am. Assoc. Petrol. Geologists*, **20**:245 (1936).

[2] Uspenskii (1949) quoted by Petrova and Karpova, *op. cit.*

[3] *Doklady Akad. Nauk. S.S.S.R.*, **96**:331 (1954).

[4] *Bull. Am. Assoc. Petrol. Geologists*, **38**:1671 (1954).

[5] *Bull. Am. Assoc. Petrol. Geologists*, **40**:477 (1956).

rial boiling above 400°F for the Wall Creek crude oil and for the extract from the Frontier shale, from which the oil is believed to have been derived, exhibited a striking concordance. Similar comparisons between crude oils and source bed extracts have been reported by Smith and Brenneman.[1] That ancient sediments also retain appreciable amounts of the more volatile components of crude oil is demonstrated by the work of Erdman et al.[2] who have reported the presence of benzene and naphthalene and their lower alkyl derivatives (up to about C_{16}) in a variety of carbonaceous rocks, including several thought to be source beds of petroleum.

A broad study of the hydrocarbon and residual organic content of shales, silty shales, marls, and argillaceous limestones has been reported by Philippi.[3] Hydrocarbon contents ranging from 5 to 5,000 ppm by weight (0.12 to 120 bbl per acre-foot) are quite general for bitumen-containing sedimentary rock. In basins for which calculations could be made, it was observed that the indigenous hydrocarbons remaining in the source sediments exceed by many times the oil originally present in all of the known oil fields derived therefrom. Again, it is evident that the natural process of expulsion of the oil from the source bed and accumulation in the reservoir must be quite inefficient.

V-9. The In Situ Alteration of Petroleum. Geologists and field observers have repeatedly called attention to the variation in physical properties of crude oil produced in multiple-zone fields or in some instances from within a single reservoir; gravity is the variable usually observed to be changing. While this may simply reflect differences in gross composition, such as the content of gasoline or asphalt, a more careful analysis may show significant differences in sulfur content, or in the proportions of the various hydrocarbon types.

There are some obvious ways in which a petroleum can be gradually altered in composition. One of these involves simple exposure of the oil to the weathering action of the atmosphere, as might occur at an outcrop of a petroleum-bearing stratum. Heavy, oxidized, asphaltic oil at the exposure will give way to lighter and more volatile crude within the formation. A less evident case of oxidation might occur within the reservoir at the oil-water contact, as a result of a slow artesian movement of oxygen-bearing waters through the permeable stratum. Russell[4] has suggested the alteration of petroleum by oxygen-bearing ground

[1] "Habitat of Oil," *Symposium*, p. 818, Weeks (ed.), American Association Petroleum Geologists, Tulsa, Okla., 1958.

[2] Preprint, *ACS, Div. Petrol. Chem., Symposium on Chemical Aspects of the Origin, Migration, and Accumulation of Oil*, ACS Meeting, Chicago, September, 1958.

[3] *Intern. Geol. Conf.*, 20*th Conf.*, Mexico City, September, 1956 (to be published).

[4] *Econ. Geol.*, **28**:571 (1933).

waters as an explanation of the origin of the asphalt deposits of western Kentucky; the volatile components were thought to have been removed by solution in the percolating waters. Bacteria carried into the formation might cause considerable alteration of the crude under the prevailing oxidizing conditions.

Elemental sulfur is a common component of sediments, and, if present in the reservoir rock, will dissolve in the crude oil and react slowly with it to produce hydrogen sulfide and various sulfur compounds; hydrogen sulfide may react further with certain components of the oil. These reactions are probably much the same as those presumed to occur in the source bed, and it seems likely that they are to a large extent responsible for the sulfur content of a petroleum. As sulfur reacts with crude oil in a reservoir rock, there is a darkening of the oil and a substantial rise in density and viscosity.

The broader aspects of the question of petroleum evolution or maturation were considered by Barton,[1] who noted the variation in the character of the crude oils of the Gulf Coast and observed that for sands of the same age, there is an increase in the lighter constituents and a decrease in the density and in the amount of heavier constituents with increasing depth; in sands of the same depth, there is an increase in the lighter constituents and a decrease in density with age. Barton suggested, therefore, that the ancestral crudes of the Miocene, Oligocene, and Eocene oils of the Gulf Coast as well as the Cretaceous oils of the East Texas and Wyoming fields were of a common, heavy naphthenic type, which under the influences of pressure and temperature were slowly transformed into lighter more paraffinic oils. The various crudes of the area were thought to represent stages in the transformation.[2]

While Barton's idea elicited some support,[3] there were many exceptions cited against it. Bartram[4] has shown that, for the Rocky Mountain region, many of the Paleozoic oils were less paraffinic and of greater density than the overlying, younger Mesozoic crudes; differences in

---

[1] *Bull. Am. Assoc. Petrol. Geologists*, **18**:143 (1934); **21**:914 (1937); "Problems of Petroleum Geology," pp. 109–155, American Association of Petroleum Geologists, Tulsa, Okla., 1934.

[2] Filtering action, which, as a crude migrates upward from lower strata, has been suggested frequently as a possible mechanism for the selective removal of the heavier, darker components [Nenitzescu, *J. Inst. Petrol. Technologists*, **23**:469 (1937)]. While such a fractionation does undoubtedly occur for the total bitumen during expulsion of an oil from the source sediment, it seems unlikely that further refining action by water-wet clays or other fine-grained minerals during migration can produce more than second-order effects.

[3] Brooks, *Bull. Am. Assoc. Petrol. Geologists*, **33**:1600 (1949).

[4] "Problems of Petroleum Geology," pp. 157–176, American Association of Petroleum Geologists, Tulsa, Okla., 1934.

the source materials or later chemical alterations were cited as possible controlling factors. A reevaluation of the gravity relationships for oils of the Texas Gulf Coast has led Haeberle[1] to conclude that the basic factor is facies change; while it is recognized that the variation in crude character is a function of many variables, he notes that the observed gravities can be correlated with changes in depositional environment, the heavier oils being associated with shallow-water and continental sediments, the lighter ones with deeper water and marine facies.

Hunt,[2] in a study of the crude oils of Wyoming, observed a correlation between composition and environment of deposition, as reflected in the nature of the associated sediments; in the case of the Tensleep oils, which are believed to have come from a common source (Phosphoria shales and limestones), a correlation was observed with depth of burial. In contrast, no relationship with depth of burial was noted for all Wyoming oils combined, nor was there any evidence for a correlation with age or possible catalytic activity of their reservoir rocks. Similar conclusions were drawn[3] in a composition study of the hydrocarbon accumulations in the Eocene sediments of the Uinta Basin of Utah.

McNab et al.[4] have explored the possibility that young, heavy oils might be converted into lighter crudes over the course of geologic time by mild, thermal cracking. The heavy McMurray oil from the Athabaska tar sand in northern Alberta was heated in stainless-steel autoclaves with brine of approximately sea-water composition and mixtures of crushed limestone, shale, and sandstone, in an attempt to simulate natural conditions. Consistent cracking rate data were obtained for the 250 to 370°C range,[5] from which it was concluded that at 65°C (150°F) no reaction could be expected over a period of 400 million years (early Ordovician to the present). If such changes were to occur, catalysis of some sort would have to be assumed; however, thermal alteration appears definitely possible for those cases in which the crude has been subjected to substantially higher temperatures.

[1] *Bull. Am. Assoc. Petrol. Geologists,* **35**:2238 (1951).

[2] *Bull. Am. Assoc. Petrol. Geologists,* **37**:1837 (1953).

[3] Hunt, Stewart, and Dickey, *Bull. Am. Assoc. Petrol. Geologists,* **38**:1671 (1954).

[4] *Ind. Eng. Chem.,* **44**:2556 (1952).

[5] A ΔE value of 49,000 cal per mole was calculated; this compares with a value of 58,000 cal per mole for the average gas oil.

CHAPTER **VI**

Distillation

by w. d. weatherford, jr., ph.d.

Throughout the history of the industry, distillation has served as the pivotal process for resolving petroleum into useful substances. Improved distillation methods have resulted in higher-quality conventional products and in the deriving of many new and useful materials from crude oil.

The basis of all distillation processes is the partial separation of solution components by selective vaporization and condensation. The evaporation of part of a solution produces vapor enriched in the more volatile constituents, whereas the condensation of a portion of a vapor mixture yields liquid enriched in the less volatile substances. These enrichment operations may be conducted in processes and equipment of widely differing nature and appearances. Typical processes vary from simple batch distillation to complex multicolumn continuous processes. The type of apparatus employed ranges from laboratory flasks and relatively simple columns to massive industrial towers.

Column processes accomplish repetitive partial vaporization and partial condensation by achieving intimate contact between counter-current streams of liquid and nonequilibrium vapor. Condensing (or dissolving) vapor then provides the heat necessary for partial vaporization of liquid components. The resulting selective mass transfer causes the coexisting vapor and liquid phases to approach equilibrium conditions.

Vapor flow is induced in a column process by the introduction of reboil vapor at the base of the column or by the injection of heat by some other means, and a product enriched in the more volatile constituents of the feed is withdrawn from the top of the column. Liquid flow is maintained by introducing reflux or other liquid at the top of the column or by removing heat in some other way, and a product enriched in the less volatile components of the feed is withdrawn from the base of the column. The feed may be injected as vapor or liquid at one or more intermediate locations in the column. Vapor or liquid sidestream products of varying degrees of volatility may be withdrawn at appropriate locations along the length of the column.   In theory, each component of the feed is distributed throughout the length of the column; however, extreme purity may be approached at either end (not both) by the use of appropriate equipment and process conditions.

Distillation columns are provided with numerous internal devices which achieve varying degrees of contact between the countercurrent vapor and liquid streams.   The more simple columns are merely filled with a solid packing material which distributes the downflowing liquid as a film while providing channels for the upflowing vapor adjacent to the liquid film.   On the other hand, large industrial distillation towers may contain a multiplicity of trays, each of which is designed to approximate one equilibrium distillation stage.   The actual performance of a single tray, in terms of its approach to equilibrium, is expressed as the tray efficiency; this may vary from almost zero to greater than 100 per cent, depending on the tray design and process conditions.

FUNDAMENTALS

There are many factors influencing distillation procedures.   These include:

The nature of the liquids and their vapors
The degree of fractionation desired
The number of products required
The type of distillation process applied
The equipment employed
The operating conditions
The economics of the process

Each of these variables exerts considerable influence on the practice of distillation, but a detailed treatment of each is beyond the scope of this discussion.   On the other hand, the general theory is so important that a brief review of the fundamentals is essential to even a general understanding of the subject.

VI-1. Vapor-Liquid Equilibrium.   Although practical distillation processes are kinetic in nature, a knowledge of equilibrium properties of the vapor-liquid system is required for a rational analysis of distillation theory and practice.   The rigorous equilibrium requirement for vapor-liquid systems is that the activity of a component must be identical in all equilibrium phases.

$$(a_v)_i^* = (a_l)_i^* \qquad\qquad\qquad \text{(VI-1)}$$

Or, in terms of fugacities,

$$\left(\frac{f_v}{f^\circ}\right)_i^* = \left(\frac{f_l}{f^\circ}\right)_i^* \tag{VI-1a}$$

where f_i° is the fugacity of a pure component in either vapor or liquid equilibrium phase at the temperature and pressure of the solution. Hence, it follows that

$$(f_v)_i^* = (a_l)_i^* f_i^\circ \tag{VI-1b}$$

In practice, the thermodynamic properties utilized in the foregoing relation are expressed in terms of physical properties which may be measured experimentally, and as coefficients which may be evaluated empirically or derived from thermodynamic data.

The fugacity of a vapor may be expressed as

$$(f_v)_i = \left(\frac{f_v}{p_v}\right)_i p_i \tag{VI-2}$$

where $(f_v/p_v)_i$ signifies the vapor fugacity coefficient. This coefficient may be evaluated from compressibility data or estimated with appropriate generalized charts.[1] The partial pressure of a vapor component is defined by Dalton's law as

$$p_i = \pi y_i \tag{VI-3}$$

where π symbolizes the total system pressure and y_i designates the mole fraction concentration of a component in the vapor.

The activity of a component in the liquid phase may be expressed in terms of concentration as follows:

$$(a_l)_i = x_i \gamma_i \tag{VI-4}$$

where x_i denotes the mole fraction concentration of a component in the liquid phase and γ_i is referred to as an activity coefficient. This coefficient may be derived from thermodynamic principles, but its absolute value must be determined empirically.[2] The fundamental relation expressed by Eqs. (VI-1) may be extended with the aid of Eqs. (VI-2) to (VI-4) to yield the following general vapor-liquid equilibrium relationship:

$$y_i^* \pi \left(\frac{f_v}{p_v}\right)_i = x_i^* \gamma_i f_i^\circ = x_i^* \gamma_i P_i^\circ \left(\frac{f_v}{p_v}\right)_i^\circ \tag{VI-5}$$

where $(f_v/p_v)_i$ is evaluated at the component partial pressure and $(f_v/p_v)_i^\circ$ at the pure component vapor pressure. For convenience in recording, correlating, and utilizing equilibrium data, the vapor-liquid concentration

---

[1] Hougen and Watson, "Chemical Process Principles," John Wiley & Sons, Inc., New York, 1947.

[2] Carlson and Colburn, *Ind. Eng. Chem.*, **34**:581 (1942).

258 *Chemical Technology of Petroleum*

data are frequently expressed in terms of the so-called equilibrium constant (vapor-liquid equilibrium concentration ratio).

$$K_i = \frac{y_i^*}{x_i^*} \tag{VI-6}$$

or the relative volatility,

$$\alpha = \frac{K_i}{K_j} = \frac{y_i^*/x_i^*}{y_j^*/x_j^*} \tag{VI-7}$$

Ideal Solutions. Rigorous distillation calculations require precise heat and material balances as well as detailed knowledge of vapor-liquid equilibria throughout the process. Such calculation procedures are quite tedious and are seldom justified. Therefore, most distillation theories have been developed for ideal solutions and ideal vapors. The fundamental relationship for such systems, known as Raoult's law, requires that the vapor-phase partial pressure of an ideal gas component in equilibrium with an ideal solution must be identical to the partial vapor pressure of the liquid component at the temperature of the solution.

$$y_i^*\pi = x_i^* P_i^\circ \tag{VI-8}$$

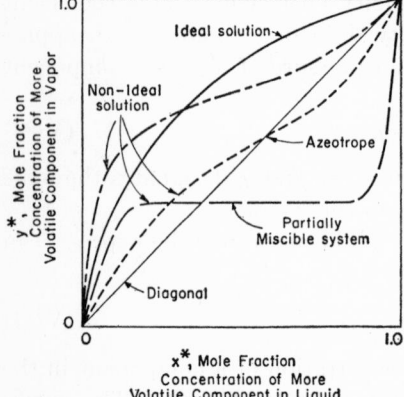

FIG. VI-1. Various types of vapor-liquid equilibrium behavior.

Comparison of Raoult's law with the foregoing general relationship [Eq. (VI-5)] demonstrates some of the criteria of ideal systems. At relatively low pressures or high temperatures most gases approach ideal gas behavior; hence, fugacities and pressures are nearly equal. When the components of a solution exhibit no heat of mixing and no volume change upon mixing, the liquid phase is ideal, and therefore the activity coefficient is unity. In addition, as a vapor-liquid system approaches ideal behavior, the relative volatility, expressed by Eq. (VI-7), becomes very nearly independent of concentration.

Many important vapor-liquid systems encountered in the petroleum and chemical industries approach the ideal behavior illustrated in Fig. VI-1. Chemically similar substances, such as members of an homologous series, are notable in this respect. For such systems vapor-liquid equilibrium data may be predicted from pure-component vapor-pressure data. In addition, the constant relative volatility provides for rapid solution of distillation problems by analytic methods, as discussed later in this chapter.

Real Solutions. The distillation properties of many solutions depart significantly from those described above for ideal systems. Since the behavior of such solutions may be nonideal in several different respects, it is important to distinguish the various phenomena which contribute to nonideality.

CRITICAL PHENOMENA. As the temperature and pressure of a vapor-liquid system are increased, physical interaction among the system molecules is altered, and limiting conditions are reached at the critical point, where the vapor and liquid phases become identical. As illustrated in Fig. VI-2, solutions containing more than one component exhibit a locus of critical temperatures which vary with solution composition. It is observed on inspection of Fig. VI-2 that the critical region includes points

for which the pure-component vapor pressure is hypothetical. Hence, it is obvious that Raoult's law breaks down in the critical region, even for ideal solutions. The fundamental relationship expressed by Eq. (VI-5) cannot be applied with precision to ideal solutions in the critical region because of the difficulty in evaluating pure-component fugacities. Many attempts have been made to estimate such fugacities by extrapolating the physical properties of pure components beyond their critical points.[1] Although such procedures

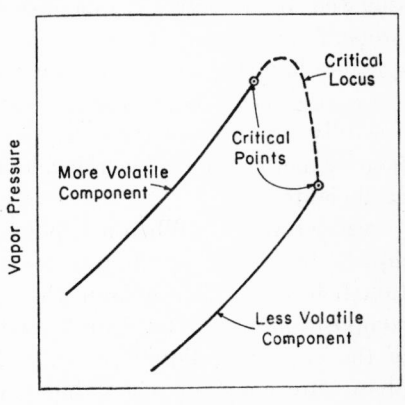

FIG. VI-2. Critical phenomena illustrated for a binary mixture.

involving the properties of hypothetical phases prove useful for correlating data, they are not generally satisfactory for predicting ideal vapor-liquid equilibrium data in the critical region.

The foregoing discussion points up the need for additional theoretical study of vapor-liquid equilibrium phenomena in the critical region. A new approach in the thermodynamic analysis of such phenomena may be required, possibly similar to that employed for predicting the ideal solubility of gases in molten hydrocarbon waxes.[2]

CHEMICAL DISSIMILARITY. When the components of a solution differ significantly in chemical type, physical interaction among the various molecules in the liquid phase may lead to appreciable departure from

[1] Edmister, *Petrol. Refiner,* **27**(6):104 (1948); **28**(2):137 (1949); **28**(5):149 (1949). Hildebrand and Scott, "Solubility of Nonelectrolytes," 3d ed., Reinhold Publishing Corporation, New York, 1950. Kay, *Ind. Eng. Chem.,* **30**:459 (1938).

[2] Ridenour, Weatherford, and Capell, *Ind. Eng. Chem.,* **46**:2376 (1954).

ideal solution behavior. Such interaction is evidenced by volume changes or heat effects on mixing the solution components, and the resulting composition deviations yield values other than unity for the activity coefficient of Eqs. (VI-4) and (VI-5). The relative volatility of a component in such a system varies with solution composition, as indicated by Fig. VI-1; however, the activity coefficient approaches unity as the composition approaches that of the pure component.

AZEOTROPISM. In extremely nonideal solutions, the relative volatilities of components may become reversed with changing composition as indicated by Fig. VI-1. In such systems, the solution of intermediate concentration in which the relative volatilities of the components are identical is referred to as an azeotrope. An azeotrope cannot be fractionated by selective vaporization; hence, it exhibits the distillation properties of a pure substance. The volatility of the azeotrope is always greater than that of any of its component substances.

These deviations from ideal solution behavior may be correlated successfully by use of thermodynamic principles.[1] However, no satisfactory methods have been developed for predicting liquid-phase activity coefficients.

IMMISCIBILITY. When a vapor-liquid mixture contains more than one liquid phase, the system appears to depart significantly from ideal solution behavior. Throughout the immiscible region, changes in system composition are obviously reflected as changes in the relative quantities of the coexisting liquid phases. The compositions of these coexisting phases are constant when the temperature is constant, and are represented by the terminal points of the constant-vapor-composition line in a vapor-liquid equilibrium diagram, such as that illustrated in Fig. VI-1.

In systems exhibiting appreciable partial miscibility, the coexisting liquid phases may display significant deviations from ideality with respect to all components. It has been mentioned earlier, however, that the activity coefficient of a system component approaches unity as the liquid-phase composition approaches that of the pure component. Hence, the individual liquid phases in a highly immiscible system should approach ideal solution behavior with respect to the major constituent of each phase.

Real liquids are never immiscible throughout all ranges of concentration. However, substances of greatly differing chemical type may display such extremely low mutual solubilities that, for all practical purposes, the liquid phases may be considered as completely immiscible. In the hypothetical case of extreme immiscibility where each phase is pure, the partial pressure of a vapor component is independent of the concentration

---

[1] Carlson and Colburn, *loc. cit.*

of other constituents, and it is identical to the vapor pressure of the pure substance. Under such conditions, the molar composition of the vapor is proportional to the vapor pressures of the pure liquid components.

A characteristic feature of immiscible systems is that the total pressure inherently exceeds the vapor pressure of any immiscible component and, hence, the saturation temperature is less than that of any immiscible component.

Molecular Distillation Equilibrium. Molecular distillation is basically different from all other types in that no liquid-vapor equilibria are established or desired.[1] Evaporation takes place from a large surface of the liquid, and a condensing surface is placed parallel to it at a distance of a few centimeters. The vapor space between the two surfaces is maintained at an exceedingly high vacuum, of the order of 0.001 mm Hg or less. At such pressures, the mean free path of the molecules of the vapor is large compared with the distance that they must travel from the liquid surface to the condenser; so most of them make the trip without experiencing deflecting collisions with other molecules.

Under these conditions, the distillation is performed essentially in a perfect vacuum, since there is no effect of back pressure tending to drive the molecules back into the liquid. Reduction of the pressure below that of the mean-free-path criterion does not affect the process in any way.

Obviously, the distillation rate is exactly the rate of escape from the liquid phase. It is meaningless to speak of boiling point in connection with molecular distillation. All substances distill at all temperatures, at a rate which is a function of the temperature alone and increases with it. Actually, however, the rate is so small for organic substances of molecular weight much over 2,000 that distillation is not feasible below their decomposition temperatures.

Langmuir[2] showed many years ago that for substances of the same vapor pressure, the rate of evaporation was inversely proportional to the square root of the molecular weight. Separation by molecular distillation, therefore, is not on the basis of vapor pressure but on the basis of the ratio of the vapor pressure to the square root of the molecular weight.[3]

---

[1] Bronsted and Hevesy, *Phil. Mag.*, **43**:31 (1922). Burch, *Proc. Roy. Soc. (London)*, **123A**:271 (1929). Washburn, *Natl. Bur. Standards J. Research*, **2**:476 (1929). Hickman, *J. Franklin Inst.*, **213**:119 (1932); *Ind. Eng. Chem.*, **29**:968 (1937). Hickman and Mees, *Ind. Eng. Chem.*, **38**:28 (1946). Carman, *Trans. Faraday Soc.*, **44**:529 (1948). Byron, Bowman, and Coull, *Ind. Eng. Chem.*, **43**:1002 (1951).

[2] *Phys. Rev.*, **2**:329 (1913).

[3] On construction and operation of molecular stills, see Burrows, *Process Eng.*, **35**(3):91 (1954); Nergaard, *Chem. Prodts.*, **17**:341 (1954); *Chem. Eng. News*, **34**(4):402 (1956); Melpolder, Washall, and Alexander, *ACS, Abstr. Papers*, 4P, ACS Meeting, Kansas City, March, 1954; Pignocco, API Research Project 6, Carnegie Institute of Technology, 1954.

VI-2. Process Principles. Although methods of operation and types of equipment employed in distillation may vary extensively, the basic principle of all such processes is the controlled selective vaporization and condensation of the components of a solution. In its simplest form, a distillation process may exploit favorable vapor-liquid equilibrium properties to achieve useful partial separations merely by vaporizing off a portion of a solution as indicated in Fig. VI-3, or by condensing out a fraction of a vapor mixture.

Most distillation applications require more than one equilibrium separation stage to achieve useful separations. In such processes, a solution is subjected to partial vaporization and partial condensation in a cascade[1] of stages, as illustrated schematically for a continuous process in Fig. VI-4. The distillate product from the original stage is progressively enriched in the more volatile components of the solution as it is produced in each successive enrichment stage. Likewise, the liquid distilland product from the original

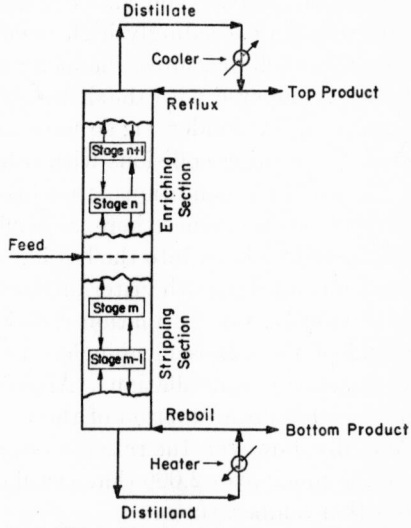

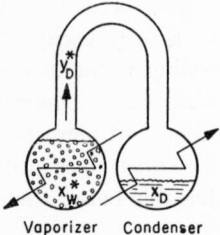

Fig. VI-3. Schematic representation of simple distillation process.

Fig. VI-4. Idealized representation of a multistage continuous distillation process.

stage is progressively depleted in the more volatile components as it is subjected to the sequence of stripping stages.

Successful functioning of the enriching stages in the cascade demands that a portion of the distillate product be condensed and returned as reflux to the final enriching stage. The liquid distilland from this stage is progressively enriched in the less volatile components of the solution as it is subjected to the sequence of enriching stages while returning to the original feed stage. In a like manner, the proper operation of the stripping stages in the cascade requires that a fraction of the distilland product must be vaporized and returned to the final stripping stage as reboil vapor. The vapor product from this stage is then progressively

[1] Benedict, *Chem. Eng. Progr.*, **43**:41 (1947).

depleted in the less volatile components of the mixture as it is produced in each successive stripping stage while returning to the original feed stage.

The operations involved in the cascade of single stages is usually referred to as a multistage column process. Each stage in such a cascade could be operated in a batchwise manner; however, this is rarely practiced because of its obviously tedious and impractical nature. In practical multistage distillations, the cascade consists of physically interconnected single stages which function in a continuous manner whether the feed solution is introduced continuously or as a single batch.

It should then be apparent that the extent of separation achieved in multistage distillation can be improved by increasing the number of stages in the cascade. In like manner, the degree of fractionation can be enhanced by increasing the proportion of the top and bottom products returned to the cascade as reflux liquid and reboil vapor, respectively. With a suitable number of stages and favorable reflux and reboil ratios, it is theoretically possible to approach extreme but not absolute purity for either the top or the bottom product. There may be a tendency for certain minor constituents of the charge to accumulate at intermediate locations within a distillation cascade. For extreme cases, such recycle accumulation may limit the capacity or performance of otherwise adequate equipment. It should be noted that no high-purity product can be withdrawn from an intermediate location in a continuous process, regardless of the number of stages or the magnitude of the reflux and reboil ratios. A direct sidestream product must of necessity contain at least some proportion of any component which passes the side stream withdrawal point on its way from the feed inlet to the end of the column at which it would be withdrawn as top or bottom product. Hence, additional fractionating equipment is necessary if a highly pure sidestream product is required.

VI-3. Process Variations. The vapor-liquid equilibrium phenomena described above have led to the development of several natural variations in distillation practices. However, no departure from fundamental operating principles or change in basic equipment is involved.

Ordinary Distillation. In many industries, particularly those which handle small volumes, batch operation is frequently advantageous; the entire charge is heated in a still pot, as illustrated for a single stage in Fig. VI-3. Batch distilling is practiced to a considerable extent in the chemical industry, where it may be desirable to isolate in high purity more than one constituent of a mixture available in only small quantities. In the petroleum industry, distillation practice is governed by the facts that the raw materials are nearly ideal solutions having volatility characteristics which make separations relatively easy. In addition, practically all distillations of petroleum are conducted on a large scale, and the products desired are rather well standardized. Under these conditions, steady-state compositions and flow rates are satisfactory, and there are great advantages for continuous operation. It should be obvious that single-stage (equivalent to flash) distillation will not yield highly purified products; these require many theoretical stages and relatively high reflux ratios. In general, a separate column is required for each high-purity product. The operating conditions may vary a great deal; for highly volatile hydrocarbons, low temperatures and high pressures may be advantageous, while high-molecular-weight materials will often require the lowest possible pressure and the highest temperatures possible without undesirable cracking. Equipment will of course vary with the operating conditions.

Steam Distillation. Water is highly immiscible with most petroleum fractions; hence, it is frequently employed to reduce the operating temperatures in ordinary distillation processes, according to the principles mentioned earlier. In practice, water is introduced as open steam at the bottom of the distillation column. By use of this technique, the equivalent of vacuum distillation may be performed at atmospheric pressure, and the effective pressure in vacuum distillation may be further reduced. Steam injection rates may vary from about 10 to 50 lb per bbl of charge.[1]

Although it is theoretically possible to employ such processes for distilling any water-immiscible substance, the practicality of such applications diminishes as the vapor pressure of the substance becomes quite low relative to that of water. Since, however, the molar composition of the distillate is proportional to the vapor pressures of the immiscible phases, the relatively low molecular weight of water is distinctly favorable in such cases.

Extractive Distillation. When a mixture of substances of differing chemical types is dissolved in a still different liquid, the volatility of the components of the mixture may be altered appreciably with respect to each other. Mixtures of close-boiling components which cannot be separated by ordinary distillation may easily be fractionated in the presence of an appropriate selective solvent. In fact, the relative order of effective boiling points may even be reversed by proper selection of the solvent. Extractive distillation is frequently employed industrially for separating paraffins from olefins and monoolefins from diolefins, as in making butadiene from butane or butene.

In practice, an extractive distillation solvent is selected, not only on the basis of its influence on the vapor-liquid equilibria of the system to be

[1] Nelson, "Petroleum Refinery Engineering," 4th ed., p. 231, McGraw-Hill Book Company, Inc., New York, 1958.

separated, but also for the ease with which it can be separated from the fractionated products. A solvent of low volatility, relative to that of the mixture to be separated, is appropriate. Other factors governing solvent selection include chemical stability, corrosiveness, effect on tray characteristics, and cost. Some typical solvents used industrially are acetone, phenol, furfural, and aniline. A solvent may contain an added substance which alters its selectivity. For example, controlled amounts of water may be added to furfural.

The fresh solvent is introduced near the top of the extractive distillation column, and the product-rich solution is withdrawn from the base of the column. Solvent-to-charge ratios of greater than 10:1 are not uncommon. A short section of the column is usually provided above the solvent entry point to prevent solvent carry-over in the overhead product. In a subsequent distillation the rich solvent is stripped of product and returned to the top of the column. In other respects, the operating principles of extractive distillation are analogous to those of ordinary distillation.

Azeotropic Distillation. Azeotropic distillation takes advantage of the phenomenon of azeotropism to achieve distillation separations which otherwise would be difficult or impossible. In such processes, the volatility characteristics of the system components are altered by the addition of an extraneous substance which forms an azeotrope selectively enriched in one of the components. Hence, the distillate is enriched in the lower-boiling azeotrope, and the bottoms are thereby depleted in the selective component of the azeotrope. For instance, aromatics may be separated from close-boiling paraffins by the addition of solvents such as methanol or nitromethane which form azeotropes enriched in paraffins.[1] The overhead and bottom products may be further fractionated and subsequently separated from the azeotropic solvent by other appropriate processes.[2]

Absorption. The fractionation (by ordinary distillation) of mixtures containing appreciable quantities of normally gaseous substances requires specialized low-temperature processing which is not practical in many instances. On the other hand, certain constituents of gaseous mixtures can be separated and recovered efficiently by absorption distillation processes. Absorption differs from ordinary distillation in that a low-volatility absorption solvent is introduced near the top of the distillation column, and the gaseous mixture is injected at the bottom. The solvent oil in effect extracts the lower-volatility components from the upflowing gases as it descends the column and is withdrawn from the bottom for subsequent stripping to recover absorbed product. In theory, the performance of an ordinary absorber is analogous to that of the enriching

[1] Benedict and Rubin, *Natl. Petrol. News*, **37**:R 729 (1945).
[2] Benedict, *loc. cit.*

section of an extractive distillation column employing superheated vapor feed. Reboil heat is not usually required since the upflowing vapor stream is largely noncondensable. In fact, intercoolers are frequently required to prevent overheating of the absorption oil by the latent heat of condensation and heat of solution of the absorbed substances. Reboiling may be practiced, however, if extreme selectivity is desired.

Absorption is commonly employed for recovering a highly volatile gasoline from natural gas; it is also utilized in conjunction with many refinery processes for recovering absorbable hydrocarbons.[1] Such gas absorption processes use gas oils or kerosenes as absorbents (see Chap. XII), whereas processes for removing nonhydrocarbon gases such as hydrogen sulfide (or mercaptans) and water utilize chemical absorption agents such as glycols and amines.[1]

VI-4. Calculation Principles. A detailed analysis of the theoretical aspects of the several types of distillation processes described is beyond the scope of this book. However, a brief review of the calculation principles involved in studying or predicting the effects of the major variables may be appropriate.

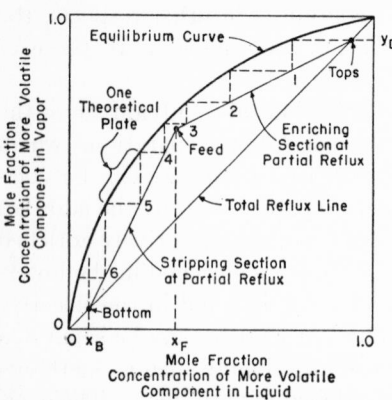

Process Variables. Several basic variables are important in almost all distillation processes. Although these variables may be treated analytically,[2] several graphical procedures have been developed in order to simplify distillation calculations.

FIG. VI-5. Graphical representation of multistage distillation process.

Notable among these are the Ponchon[3] enthalpy-concentration diagram method and the McCabe-Thiele[4] vapor-liquid equilibrium diagram method illustrated in Fig. VI-5.

STOICHIOMETRY. The basic principles involved in any distillation calculation are the mass and energy conservation laws. With the aid of appropriate vapor-liquid equilibrium concentration data, the behavior of distillation systems may be adequately described by employing heat balances and component material balances. For example, at steady

[1] Nelson, *loc. cit.*

[2] Acrivos and Amundson, *Chem. Eng. Sci.,* **4**:29 (1955). Bowman, *Ind. Eng. Chem.,* **41**:2004 (1949). Fenske, *Ind. Eng. Chem.,* **24**:482 (1932). Smoker, *Chem. Eng. Progr.,* **34**:165 (1938). Underwood, *Chem. Eng. Progr.,* **44**:603 (1948).

[3] White, *Petrol. Refiner,* **24**(8):101 (1945); **24**(9):127 (1945).

[4] *Ind. Eng. Chem.,* **17**:605 (1925).

state, the flow into and out of each tray in a continuous distillation column must be in balance with respect to heat content and the quantity of each component of the mixture being separated. The graphical method of Ponchon is rigorous in these respects, whereas the McCabe-Thiele method is less so since it assumes no heat of mixing and constant molal flow rates throughout the length of the column. This latter assumption is required in order to justify the use of linear material balance lines (operating lines) in the McCabe-Thiele diagram of Fig. VI-5. It is fortunate, however, that the simplifying assumptions of the method do not seriously limit its utility for most petroleum distillation calculations.

REFLUX AND REBOIL RATIOS. As stated earlier, a fraction of the distillate and distilland streams must be returned to the cascade as reflux liquid and reboil vapor, respectively, if a multistage distillation column is to function properly. In the extreme case of no reflux liquid or reboil vapor, the process is equivalent to a single-stage separation process, regardless of the number of physically distinct stages utilized.

The ratio

$$\frac{\text{Quantity of distillate returned to the top of the column as liquid reflux}}{\text{Quantity collected as overhead product}}$$

is referred to as the reflux ratio. Similarly, the ratio of the quantity of distilland returned to the bottom of the column as reboil vapor to the quantity collected as bottoms product is called the reboil ratio. The actual quantity of internal reflux liquid or reboil vapor may be different from that returned to the column. For example, internal reflux may be induced by the introduction of a solvent near the top of the column or by cooling the external reflux stream to temperatures below the saturation point. The maximum degree of fractionation is achieved when all the distillate and distilland are returned to the column as reflux and reboil, respectively. Although such total reflux operation is obviously impractical for an industrial process, it can be achieved approximately in laboratory distillations. For a specific separation, there is a minimum reflux ratio and a minimum reboil ratio below which the desired separation is impossible. Such a condition results when the coexisting vapor and liquid phases approach mutual equilibrium compositions at an intermediate location in the column, thereby requiring an infinite number of stages for the compositions to depart again from this equilibrium "pinch point" before the desired separation can be achieved. Graphically, this situation would correspond to the intersection of a material balance line (operating line) with the equilibrium curve in Fig. VI-5. Practical reflux ratios vary from less than 5:1 for most refinery distillations to greater than 20:1 for difficult separations of pure compounds.

NUMBER OF STAGES. By definition, one theoretical plate (stage) yields vapor at a composition which is in equilibrium with that of the liquid emerging from the same stage. Hence, when the process conditions for a distillation system are specified, and when the vapor-liquid equilibrium data are known, the required number of theoretical plates can be determined by plate-to-plate calculations or by other methods such as the analytical or graphical procedures referred to above. When ideal binary solutions are distilled at total reflux, the multistage calculations are performed easily with the aid of the following relation, originally derived by Fenske.[1]

$$\frac{y_D}{1 - y_D} = \frac{\alpha^{(N+1)} x_B}{1 - x_B} \qquad \text{(VI-9)}$$

where N signifies the number of theoretical plates (exclusive of the reboil vaporizer) and the subscripts D and B refer to the overhead and bottoms products, respectively. This simple relation may also be employed as an approximation for multicomponent systems by selecting a light and a heavy component as representative key components. In plate columns, the number of theoretical plates is practically always less than the number of actual plates. It is necessary, therefore, to employ plate efficiency factors to account for the discrepancies. In some instances, successful efficiency correlations have been established;[2] however, it remains difficult to predict such factors accurately for new solutions or for various types of fractionating trays.

For convenience in the theoretical analysis of packed column performance, a somewhat different concept[3] has been employed successfully. Instead of considering theoretical stages, this concept defines the number of diffusional transfer units as the ratio of the concentration differential to the diffusional driving force, integrated over the concentration change experienced by the particular phase under consideration. For absorption processes, which involve unidirectional diffusion, the number of "gas" transfer units is expressed as

$$\int_{\text{initial}}^{\text{final}} \frac{(1 - y)_f \, dy}{(1 - y)(y - y^*)} \qquad \text{(VI-10)}$$

where y represents the composition of the bulk vapor, y^* denotes the composition of the interfacial vapor which is assumed to be in equilibrium with the adjacent interfacial liquid, and $(1 - y)_f$ signifies the log mean of $(1 - y)$ and $(1 - y^*)$. For distillation, which involves equimolar

[1] Fenske, *loc. cit.*

[2] Bakowski, *Chem. Eng. Sci.*, **1**:266 (1952). Chu, *Petrol. Processing*, **6**:39, 48 (1951). Edmister, *Petrol. Engr.*, C45, January, 1949.

[3] Chilton and Colburn, *Ind. Eng. Chem.*, **27**:255, 904 (1935).

counterdiffusion, the $(1 - y)$ factors do not appear in the diffusion equations, and hence the number of "gas" transfer units may be expressed simply as

$$\int_{\text{initial}}^{\text{final}} \frac{dy}{y - y^*} \tag{VI-10a}$$

When the y^* term in these equations refers to the vapor composition which would be in equilibrium with the adjacent bulk liquid, the transfer units are called "over-all gas" transfer units. The number of "liquid" and "over-all liquid" transfer units may be expressed by analogous equations.

Operating Variables. As stated above, there are two contrasting methods of operation for distillation processes. Most large-scale industrial processes are conducted in a continuous manner, as illustrated for a multistage process in Fig. VI-4. However, certain specialized processes and most laboratory distillations are performed batchwise, as illustrated for a single-stage process in Fig. VI-3.

CONTINUOUS PROCESS. Continuous distillations are relatively simple in that steady-state conditions result in constant values for flow rates, temperatures, and compositions. Hence, the calculation principles discussed above apply directly to continuous, steady-state processes.

BATCH PROCESS. The unsteady-state nature of batch distillation leads to variations in the methods of operation and results in more complex calculation principles. There are two, more or less standard, methods for conducting batch distillations. In one, the reflux ratio is continually adjusted to maintain a constant overhead composition until the charge is depleted of the more volatile fraction. In the other, more common method, the reflux ratio is maintained constant, and the distillate is subdivided into cuts of varying composition as the charge components are distilled overhead.

The relation between the product composition and the quantity of charge remaining undistilled in batch distillation processes is conveniently expressed by the Rayleigh equation,[1] extended to include the effects of column holdup.

$$d[(W - H)x_W + Hx_H] = y_D dW \tag{VI-11}$$

or

$$\frac{dW}{W} = \frac{dx_W}{y_D - x_W + [d(x_W - x_H)/dW]H} \tag{VI-11a}$$

where W signifies the quantity of charge remaining undistilled, H represents the quantity of undistilled charge distributed throughout the length of the column as holdup, and the subscripts D, B, and H refer to the overhead product, bottom liquid, and average holdup, respectively.

[1] Rayleigh, *Phil. Mag.*, **4**:521 (1902).

This differential material balance, when used in conjunction with the calculation principles discussed above, provides a theoretical basis for analyzing batch distillation phenomena.

Several different methods are employed for expressing the fractionation efficiency or sharpness of separation in batch distillation. These have been studied extensively, and many of the various criteria have been correlated with process variables.[1]

VI-5. Process Equipment. A detailed description of distillation vessels and related equipment is beyond the scope of this book. It is of importance, however, that several basically different types of distillation apparatus should be distinguished.

Single Stage. The fundamental equipment required for continuous, single-stage distillation is a partial vaporizer or partial condenser and a suitable vapor-liquid disengaging vessel. Such a distillation is usually referred to as an equilibrium flash vaporization. In simple batch distillation, the heated still pot serves as the required vaporizing and disengaging unit.

Plate Columns. As mentioned above, a multistage process may be realized by arranging a cascade of discrete single stages within one vessel. In practice, the so-called plate distillation columns are equipped with internal trays, each of which approximates the performance of one single stage in a cascade. Basically each tray provides means for intimate contact between descending liquid and rising vapor, and this contact leads to simultaneous partial vaporization and condensation of the respective streams. Certain constituents of the countercurrent streams are thus exchanged selectively as the streams progress from tray to tray, disengaging in the vapor space between trays. In conventional refinery equipment between four and ten plates are provided between successive product streams.[2] In some instances, where efficient separation of close-boiling components, such as butene isomers, is required, one hundred or more plates may be provided, usually by operating two or more plate columns in series.

Many different types of tray designs have been developed, and notable among these is the bubble-cap tray, illustrated schematically in Fig. VI-6. The least elaborate tray style is the perforated (or sieve) plate which, although satisfactory for certain applications, is limited to rather narrow ranges of process variables. In other tray styles, the vapor-

[1] Bowman and Cichelli, *Ind. Eng. Chem.*, **41**:1985 (1949). Cichelli, Weatherford, Bowman, and Coull, *Ind. Eng. Chem.*, **42**:2502 (1950). Rose, *Ind. Eng. Chem.*, **41**:1985 (1949). Rose and Long, *Ind. Eng. Chem.*, **33**:684 (1941). Rose and Welshans, *Ind. Eng. Chem.*, **32**:668 (1940). Zuiderweg, *Chem. Eng. Sci.*, **1**:8 (1951); *Chem. Ing. Tech.*, **25**:297 (1953).

[2] Nelson, *op. cit.*, p. 513.

liquid contact is accomplished by modified perforated- or bubble-cap trays.[1] The modifications include perforations with floating valves, parallel vapor-liquid-flow trays, parallel slat trays, sinusoidally warped perforated plates,[2] and relatively complex trays with venturi-shaped vapor passages.

The selection of a tray for a specific duty is governed by considerations such as cost, durability, and maintenance and by the process requirements of the application.[3] For example, the anticipated range of vapor velocities, liquid flow rates, column pressure drop, and plate efficiencies should be considered when selecting the tray style and specific design. Depending on the process requirements, the diameter of refinery plate columns may vary from less than 2 to greater than 20 ft.

Differential Columns. When the rising vapor contacts the descending liquid intimately throughout the length of a distillation column, the process is referred to as a differential multistage column process. At no point in such a process is equilibrium approached; however, the fractionation efficiency may be expressed in terms of the column height equivalent to a theoretical plate (HETP) or transfer unit (HTU).[4]

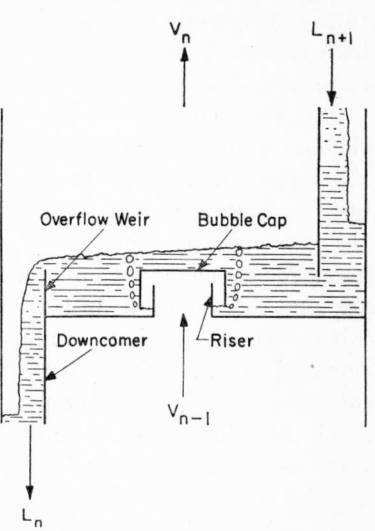

FIG. VI-6. Schematic representation bubble-cap distillation plate.

WETTED WALL. The simplest differential column is obtained when reflux liquid is distributed to the inside wall of a cylindrical tube in which reboil vapors are rising. Such columns are not very efficient because of the relatively large distance (from the axis to the wall) through which the vapor molecules must diffuse to contact the liquid film. However, when the vapors are confined in a narrow annulus formed by concentric tubes, and the reflux liquid is distributed to either or both confining walls, the resulting column may be extremely efficient.

ROTARY. The efficiency of open-tube wetted-wall columns can be

[1] Vener, *Chem. Eng.*, **63**(8):175 (1956).

[2] Hutchinson and Baddour, *Chem. Eng. Progr.*, **52**:503 (1956).

[3] Davies, *Petrol. Refiner*, **29**(8):93; (9):121 (1950). Huitt and Huntington, *Petrol. Refiner*, **30**(6):131; (8):111; (10):153 (1951). White, *Petrol. Processing*, **28**:(2)147 (1947).

[4] Chilton and Colburn, *loc. cit.*

increased enormously by adding a rotating mechanism which wipes the wetted wall.[1] The rotating member appears to increase diffusion rates by generating turbulence in the vapor phase while decreasing the effective thickness of the liquid film. Such columns are particularly advantageous for vacuum distillations because they may be designed for operation with minimum pressure drop.

In a similar manner, the efficiency of concentric-tube columns is significantly increased when the inner tube is caused to rotate at relatively high speeds.[2] In this case the improvement probably results primarily from increases in vapor-phase diffusion rates.

PACKED. Differential column performance is often approximated in the laboratory and in industry by use of columns filled with an appropriate packing material. The packing distributes the reflux liquid throughout the column in relatively thin films. Depending on the geometry of the particular packing, the liquid film may present very large surface areas for vapor-liquid contact. Almost any inert solid of appropriate size and shape may be utilized, as exemplified by early studies of various laboratory distillation column packings which included crimped wire, tacks, rivets, and bird shot.[3] Cobblestones were one of the first packing materials employed by the petroleum industry.

The packing materials most commonly utilized in the modern laboratory are metal or glass helices or rings, metal gauze, and perforated metal saddles. They are available in many different sizes and shapes. Packed industrial columns frequently employ ceramic materials in the shape of cylinders, rings, or saddles; however, many other high-efficiency packings of special size and shape have been developed and are commercially available. When the column diameter is large, there is a tendency for the reflux liquid to channel along the wall; hence packed columns larger than 2 or 3 ft in diameter are seldom employed.[4]

DISTILLATION IN THE PETROLEUM INDUSTRY

The applications of distillation in the petroleum industry are quite varied. Their primary importance is for manufacturing operations, where the greater part of all process equipment investment is for distillation. However, the extensive application which they find in analysis and control is almost indispensable. Thus the assaying of crude oils and the evaluation of many petroleum products depend on distillation.

[1] Murray, *J. Am. Oil Chemists' Soc.*, **2**(6): 235 (1951).
[2] Willingham, Sedlak, Rossini, and Westhaver, *Ind. Eng. Chem.*, **39**:706 (1947).
[3] Fenske, Tongberg, and Quiggle, *Ind. Eng. Chem.*, **26**:1169 (1934).
[4] Nelson, *op. cit.*, p. 477.

VI-6. Analytical Applications

Single-stage Processes. The simplest distillation analysis is the weathering (simple evaporation) of relatively light hydrocarbons at room temperature to detect the presence of heavy ends. Since this test can be conducted with a test tube or a graduated bottle, it is frequently performed "on the spot" by operating personnel.

A more quantitative estimate of the composition of a hydrocarbon mixture may be obtained by distilling the mixture batchwise in a single-stage apparatus and observing the variation of distillate yield with distillation temperature, as indicated in Fig. VI-7. When such distillations are conducted in a standardized manner, such as those prescribed by the ASTM,[1] the resulting figures may be utilized directly to estimate the quantity of certain petroleum products, such as gasoline, kerosene, naphtha, and light gas oil, present in the mixture. In addition, such results may be used in conjunction with physical property data to estimate the chemical composition of a hydrocarbon mixture.[2]

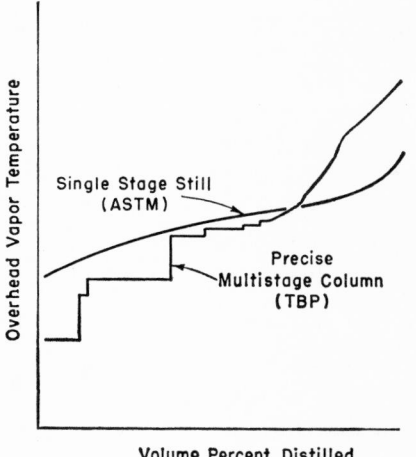

FIG. VI-7. Illustration of single-stage and multistage batch distillation of a hypothetical petroleum fraction.

Multistage Processes. Many analytical applications require the relatively accurate determination of hydrocarbon composition by distillation methods (true boiling point distillation).[3] Still others utilize precise distillation for the isolation of selected narrow distillate cuts for subsequent analysis by other means. These analytical batch distillations may be conducted in any of several different types of laboratory columns.[4]

In a precise analytical distillation, the instantaneous boiling point provides information as to which compounds are present, and the shape of the distillation curve reflects the relative concentration of the various

[1] ASTM Standards on Petroleum Products and Lubricants, Methods D 86, D 158, D 216, D 285, and D 447, 1956.

[2] Edmister, *Petrol. Refiner*, **28**(10):143 (1949); also, *Ind. Eng. Chem.*, **47**:1685 (1955); *AIChE Journal*, **3**:165 (1957). Van Nes and Van Westen, "Aspects of the Constitution of Mineral Oils," Elsevier Press, Inc., Houston, Tex., 1951.

[3] Nelson, *op. cit.*

[4] Podbielniak, *Petrol. Refiner*, **30**(4):85 (1951); **30**(5):145 (1951). Nelson, *op. cit.*

constituents of the feed mixture. For example, a precise distillation column should be efficient enough to yield a series of vapor-temperature plateaus as illustrated for a hypothetical case in Fig. VI-7. Under such conditions, the vapor temperature represents the true boiling point of the pure substance being distilled at the moment. It follows that the length of the constant-temperature step represents the volume of that component originally present in the charge. It should be noted that in the precise distillation curve of Fig. VI-7, the stair steps degenerate into a relatively smooth curve as the distillation proceeds. Such behavior is typical of petroleum fractions, partly because of the marked increase in the relative number of hydrocarbon isomers and, presumably, partly because of the formation of azeotropes among the different hydrocarbon classes.

VI-7. Manufacturing Applications. The system of operation employed in any refinery is governed by several basic considerations which may vary from time to time; it will depend on:

1. The nature and composition of the available crude oils
2. The quantity and quality of desired products
3. The availability of appropriate process equipment

Hence, figuratively speaking, there may be more different over-all distillation process schemes than there are refineries.[1] This inherent flexibility precludes a comprehensive discussion of specific start-to-finish distillation schemes in this book.

On the other hand, there are several building-block distillation processes, variations of which constitute the basic structure of most refinery distillation schemes. These fundamental processes comprise:

1. The primary separation of raw materials
2. The preparation of process feed
3. The fractionation of products

These various distillations may be integrated with other manufacturing operations by use of suitable storage facilities and appropriate networks of charge, product, and recycle streams.

Primary Distillation. Because of the complex nature of crude petroleum oils, described in other sections of this book, it is apparent that a preliminary separation should be performed before refining or chemical conversion of products is undertaken. Accordingly, modern refinery

---

[1] Since 1920, there have never been less than 300 refineries operating simultaneously in the United States. See Kirby, *U.S. Bur. Mines, Inform. Circ.* 7646, September, 1952.

practices almost always employ an atmospheric and vacuum distillation of the desalted or dehydrated crude[1] as the initial refining step.

In a typical atmospheric-vacuum distillation process, as illustrated in Fig. VI-8, the crude oil charge is preheated by exchange with emerging hot product streams in appropriate equipment. It is then pumped through a fired, tubular heater where its temperature is raised to 650 to

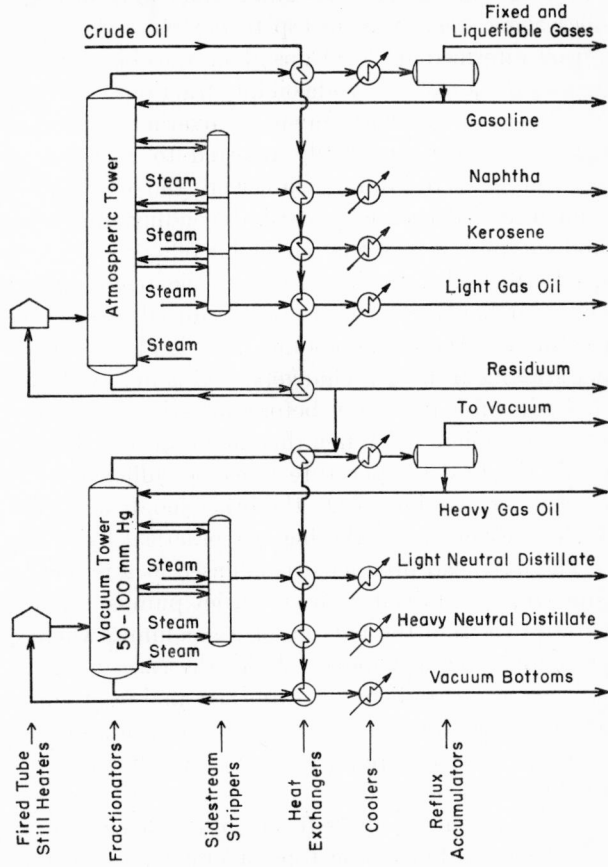

Fig. VI-8. Typical primary crude oil distillation process.

750°F, and the thus heated oil is discharged into a multiple-plate distillation column. The heat content of the feed results in partial vaporization of the more volatile constituents, and the over-all extent of vaporization is usually increased by the injection of open steam into a lower portion of the column.

The overhead vapor stream from this fractionator is condensed at a

[1] A discussion of desalting and dehydration processes is presented in Chap. I.

pressure of 1 to 2 atm. Any noncondensable portion of this stream is vented from the condensate accumulator to appropriate storage, and a portion of the condensate is returned to the top of the fractionator as reflux. The less volatile, undistilled portion of the crude oil is withdrawn from the base of the column, where reboil vapors are generated by the previously mentioned injection of open steam. A composition gradient is thereby established throughout the length of the column, the volatility decreasing steadily from top to bottom. Several streams are withdrawn from intermediate locations along the column, thereby giving a preliminary separation of the crude oil into fractions of differing physical properties. The products withdrawn as overhead, side stream, and bottom products are conventionally referred to as gasoline, naphtha, kerosene, gas oil, and residuum;[1] however, the exact range of their properties and intended uses may vary, depending upon the feed stock employed and the practices of the particular refiner.

The reduced crude oil from the bottom of the atmospheric distillation column may be further fractionated under reduced pressure in a vacuum distillation column. Again, the column feed is allowed to absorb heat from product streams in heat exchangers, and is finally heated to 700 to 800°F in a fired, tubular heater before injection into the multiplate vacuum distillation column. When the vacuum tower distillates include lubricating oils, the feed temperature must be sufficiently low to avoid undesirable cracking reactions. On the other hand, when the distillates are to serve as cracking stock, the highest practical feed temperature is employed. The overhead product is condensed at a reduced pressure of 50 to 100 mm Hg, maintained with steam jet pumps. The nonvolatile residue is withdrawn from the bottom of the column, where open steam is injected to supply reboil vapors. As in the case of the atmospheric column, a concentration gradient is established, and fractionated products may be withdrawn as side streams. The overhead, side stream, and residual products may be referred to as heavy gas oil, neutral (lubricating) distillates, and vacuum bottoms.

The liquid side stream products from both atmospheric and vacuum distillation columns are fed to the tops of multiplate stripping columns before they are withdrawn from the primary distillation system. Reboil vapors are generated in the bottom of each of these stripping columns by the injection of open steam, and the overhead vapors are fed back to the primary columns at the original liquid withdrawal location. This auxiliary stripping operation is necessary because of the inefficiency introduced by side stream withdrawal processes, discussed elsewhere in this chapter.

Typical yields from several crude oil assay distillations are given in

[1] If a relatively high proportion of the charge remains undistilled, the bottom product may be referred to as a long residuum.

Tables VI-1 and VI-2 for representative West Texas and Williston Basin crude oils.[1] It is readily apparent from examination of these data that no generalizations as to the type and quantity of primary products can be made without prior specification of the crude oil source.

TABLE VI-1. COMPOSITION OF TYPICAL WEST TEXAS CRUDE OILS

Geological age	Pennsyl-vanian	De-vonian	Ordo-vician	Permian	Silurian	Cre-taceous
Volume per cent of crude:						
Gasoline...............	16	14	11	11	10	1
Naphtha..............	23	25	21	21	21	9
Kerosene.............	10	10	20	4	8	0
Gas oil...............	14	14	12	18	13	19
Lube distillate........	14	14	12	18	16	28
Residuum.............	20	21	22	26	30	41
Loss.................	3	2	2	2	2	2

TABLE VI-2. COMPOSITION OF TYPICAL WILLISTON BASIN CRUDE OILS

Geological age	Silurian	Devonian	Mississippian	Cretaceous
Volume per cent of crude:				
Gasoline.................	21	15	12	8
Naphtha................	36	30	24	20
Kerosene ⎱ .... Gas oil ⎰	26	35	28	33
Lube distillate............	10	11	16	14
Residuum...............	6	8	19	24
Loss....................	1	1	1	1

The data of Table VI-3 provide an example of product yields from an atmospheric-vacuum primary distillation unit processing a Middle East crude. In Tables VI-4 and VI-5, vacuum distillation process data are presented for a reduced California crude[2] and a reduced Venezuelan crude.[3]

Process Feed Preparation. Various refining operations may require some degree of prefractionation of the charge stock. Such feed preparation may be practiced for economy or may be justified by requirements of the treating process. Prefractionation of feed streams is most common for operations involving chemical conversion of hydrocarbons. For example, narrow cuts of low-boiling olefins or other appropriate hydrocarbon reactants must be prepared for alkylation, isomerization, and

[1] Garton and McKinney, *U.S. Bur. Mines Rept. Invest.* 4959, March, 1953. Wenger and Lanum, *Petrol. Engr.,* C-43, July, 1954.

[2] Allinder, *Petrol. Refiner,* **34**(11):197 (1955).

[3] Kraft, *Ind. Eng. Chem.,* **40**:807 (1948).

TABLE VI-3. TYPICAL PRIMARY ATMOSPHERIC-VACUUM
DISTILLATION OF A MIDDLE EAST CRUDE

Product	Yield, volume per cent
Gas	0.1
Butanes	2
Gasoline	11
Naphtha	14
Furnace oil	17
Gas oil	39
Vacuum bottoms	17

TABLE VI-4. VACUUM DISTILLATION OF REDUCED CALIFORNIA CRUDE
AT 75 MM HG ABSOLUTE PRESSURE

Product	Column temperature, °F	Gravity, °API	Viscosity, SSU at 100°F	Yield, volume per cent
Feed	725	10		
Heavy gas oil	510	17	580	42
Residuum	764	5	...	58

TABLE VI-5. VACUUM DISTILLATION OF REDUCED VENEZUELAN CRUDE
AT 90 MM HG ABSOLUTE PRESSURE

Product	Column temperature, °F	Gravity, °API	Viscosity, SSU at 100°F	Yield, volume per cent
Feed	685	13		
Heavy gas oil	...	...	38	44
Light neutral distillate	...	...	100	7
250 neutral distillate	...	...	250	18
Heavy neutral distillate	...	...	70 (at 210°F)	4
Residuum	700	...	925 (at 210°F)	27

polymerization processes. In addition, the rapidly increasing emphasis on the synthetic chemical phases of petroleum processing places added importance on feed preparation.

Distillation directed toward producing narrow cuts, relatively rich in specific hydrocarbons, is usually carried out in multicolumn equipment such as that illustrated for C_4 hydrocarbons in Fig. VI-9. An appropriate charge stock is fed to a fractionating column where the more volatile constituents are removed as overhead product and those remaining are withdrawn in the bottoms stream. The portion enriched in the desired materials is charged to another fractionating column, and the desired components are recovered in one stream while the remaining materials are rejected as the other product. For example, in a two-column plant such as that shown in Fig. VI-9, a typical raw natural gasoline may be fractionated to yield debutanized gasoline while producing 6 per cent and 58 per cent yields, respectively, of 99 per cent purity propane and 97 per cent butanes.[1] If the desired substances cannot be separated easily from other constituents of a charge by ordinary distillation, special methods such as extractive or azeotropic distillation may be employed in one or more of the columns in the multicolumn process.

Product Fractionation. It is not unusual to find that the first distillation of a crude oil or a cracked product does not yield fractions satisfactory for use as they stand. Boiling range, composition, stability, or

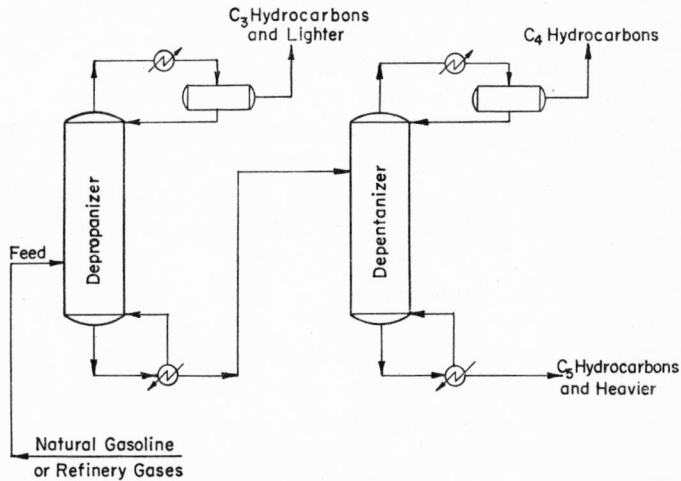

FIG. VI-9. Typical multicolumn distillation process for producing C_4 hydrocarbons.

performance in service may require subdivision of cuts or closer fractionation at particular points in the distillation curve.

For example, lubricating oil distillates may be redistilled into several fractions possessing appropriate viscosity and volatility for specified lubricant blending stocks. It is customary, particularly with wax-free naphthenic crudes, to blend a rather wide fraction of low-viscosity material with another of much higher viscosity. The redistillation process may be carried out after the lubricant stocks have been refined with appropriate chemical agents, solvents, asphalt precipitation, or dewaxing processes. The redistilled materials may of course be subjected to final purification by treatment with adsorbents such as fuller's earth or bauxite before blending into specification products.

Another common example of product fractionation is the redistillation of gasoline. The gasoline stock from a crude still or cracking unit

[1] Nelson, *op. cit.*, p. 244.

may contain appreciable proportions of normally gaseous hydrocarbons. Although controlled amounts of such components may be desirable for imparting adequate vapor pressure to finished motor fuel, presence of excessive amounts may lead to unnecessary losses in handling and storage. Hence, it is customary to stabilize gasolines by distilling most of the undesirably volatile components overhead in a fractionating column while recovering the stabilized end product from the bottom of the column. The vapor-pressure characteristics of the gasoline then may be adjusted by subsequent blending operations. A typical gasoline produced by fluid catalytic cracking[1] may be stabilized to 10 psi Reid vapor pressure by removal of butanes and lighter gases with an over-all volume decrease of about 16 per cent. Butanes usually constitute somewhat less than half of the gases removed.

The manufacture of butadiene from petroleum furnishes an excellent example of the use of multicolumn distillation for product fractionation. The C_4 fraction produced by the dehydrogenation of a butene-rich feed contains unreacted butenes and traces of butanes in addition to the butadiene. Since it is not possible to recover high-purity butadiene from this mixture by ordinary distillation, it is customary to employ extractive distillation as one of the purification steps. In a commercial operation, most of the butadiene, isobutene, butene-1, and a portion of the butene-2 hydrocarbons are taken overhead by ordinary distillation, yielding high-purity butene-2 as the bottom product. The overhead stream is then fed to a furfural extractive distillation column where all the butanes, iso-butene, butene-1, and a portion of the butene-2 are distilled over, and a butadiene-butene-2 concentrate is removed from the bottoms solvent by subsequent stripping. This concentrate is then fractionated by ordinary distillation to yield a butadiene distillate of about 98.5 per cent purity.

Combination Processing. It has for some years been customary to tie in distillation with other treating processes in self-contained combination units.[2] Such unified process schemes differ from straightforward refinery methods in that the various component operations are integrated directly without the use of conventional intermediate accumulation. This interlacing leads to significant economies through reduced storage and handling facilities and lower heat requirements which result from more efficient heat recovery.

Combination processing is typified by the joining of primary crude oil fractionation with conversions such as coking, viscosity breaking, reforming, and thermal or catalytic cracking. In such units, some of the conversion products may be blended with the crude oil charge or fed directly

[1] Nelson, *op. cit.*, p. 778.
[2] Beukers and Kelder, *Petrol. Refiner,* **34**(11):221 (1955). Sager, *Petrol. Refiner,* **35**(9):330 (1956). Swanson and Adams, *Ind. Eng. Chem.,* **45**:1429 (1953).

into the primary columns at various locations; the primary fractionation system may thus be utilized partly for product fractionation.

A typical combination unit,[1] processing Middle East crude, combines fluid catalytic cracking and reforming with primary fractionation. The crude oil is initially distilled in a conventional atmospheric column; from this point the reduced crude is fed to a fractionator in which several operations are combined. This column fulfills the function of vacuum still, reformer primary fractionator, catalytic fractionator, rerun still for by-products and off-specification product, and light ends absorber as well as fat oil stripper.

NOTATION

a	activity
f	fugacity
m (or n)	theoretical plate number
p	partial pressure
x	mole fraction concentration in liquid
y	mole fraction concentration in vapor
B	bottoms product flow rate
D	top product flow rate
F	feed rate
H	quantity of holdup in a batch distillation column
K	vapor–liquid equilibrium concentration ratio
L	liquid downflow rate
N	number of theoretical plates or transfer units
P	vapor pressure
V	vapor upflow rate
W	quantity of charge remaining undistilled in batch distillation
α	relative volatility
γ	liquid-phase activity coefficient
π	total pressure

Subscripts

i (or j)	component designation
l	liquid phase
v	vapor phase
B	bottom product
D	top product
F	feed
H	average holdup

Superscripts

$\circ$	refers to the properties of a pure component
$*$	refers to equilibrium conditions

SELECTED REFERENCES

Benedict and Rubin: Extractive and Azeotropic Distillation, *Natl. Petrol. News,* **37**:R729 (1945).

Bradley and Lake: *Advances in Chem. Ser.,* no. 5, p. 199, 1951.

[1] Beukers et al., *loc. cit.*

Carlson and Colburn: Vapor Liquid Equilibria of Nonideal Solutions, *Ind. Eng. Chem.*, **34**:581 (1942).

Edmister: Hydrocarbon Adsorption and Fractionation Process Design Methods, *Petrol. Engr.*, twenty monthly installments (May, 1947, through March, 1949, excluding May, October, and November, 1948).

Forbes: "Short History of the Art of Distillation," E. J. Brill, N. V., Leiden, Netherlands, 1948.

Liebmann: History of Distillation, *J. Chem. Educ.*, **33**:166 (1956).

Nelson: "Petroleum Refinery Engineering," 4th ed., McGraw-Hill Book Company, Inc., New York, 1958.

Nielsen (ed.): "Distillation in Practice," Reinhold Publishing Corporation, New York, 1956.

Perry (ed.): "Chemical Engineers' Handbook," 3d ed., McGraw-Hill Book Company, Inc., New York, 1950.

Weissberger (ed.): "Technique of Organic Chemistry," vol. IV, Distillation, Interscience Publishers, Inc., New York, 1951.

CHAPTER VII

Refining by Chemical Methods

Petroleum products obtained by physical processes such as distillation often need supplementary purification by chemical means, because they contain varying amounts of undesirable substances. The nature of the contaminant is likely to vary with the fraction; aromatic hydrocarbons are desirable in gasoline but unsuitable for kerosene. In general, easily oxidizable or otherwise unstable substances and resinous or asphaltic materials are deleterious in all refined petroleum products. Sulfur compounds are usually harmful, and it is customary to limit their content by specification. The removal of the undesired material, when not possible by convenient physical means, is accomplished by treatment with reagents which will react selectively with the contaminants.

A wide variety of reactive chemicals have been tried for refining, but few have stood the tests of time and changing practice. Sulfuric acid,[1] followed by aqueous alkali, and the sweetening reagents have been in use longest. Differential solvent extraction and precipitation have largely displaced sulfuric acid treatment in lubricating oil manufacture; anhydrous aluminum chloride has been applied for more drastic refining. Hydrogenation for sulfur removal, general refining, and upgrading of hydrocarbon types was developed as early as 1930. However, there was practically no application of the method until about 1955, when the cost of hydrogen had dropped enough to make such processes economical.

SULFURIC ACID TREATING

Until about 1930 acid treatment was almost universal for all types of refined petroleum products, and especially for cracked gasoline distillates, kerosenes, and lubricating stocks. Cracked products were acid-treated to stabilize against oxidation (which led to gum formation and color darkening) and, when necessary, to reduce sulfur content. The treating, however, produced appreciable losses to polymers and solution in the

---

[1] Recommended by Silliman in 1855, *Am. Chemist*, **2**:18 (1871–1872).

acid. It was found that acceptable oxidation stability could be attained without the losses inherent in acid treating. At the same time the advent of dyeing for finished gasolines made color stability less important. Sulfuric acid was also employed for refining kerosene distillates and lubricating oil stocks; the development of differential solvent processes has changed this practice for lubricating oils. It has also made possible the preparation of satisfactory kerosenes from highly aromatic distillates for which sulfuric acid was inadequate. Acid treating has continued for desulfurizing high-boiling fractions of cracked gasoline distillates, for refining paraffinic kerosenes, for manufacture of low-cost lubricating oils, and for making such specialties as insecticide naphthas, pharmaceutical white oils, and insulating oils. Also, its use for production of sulfonic acids from lubricating oil fractions is increasing. The rise of catalytic hydrogenation threatens to displace acid desulfurization.

VII-1. Reactions with Hydrocarbons. The reactions of sulfuric acid on hydrocarbon mixtures are rather complicated. The undesirable components to be removed are generally present in small percentages only, but many times their weight of acid is required for efficient removal; for this reason, marked changes may be caused in the remainder of the hydrocarbon mixture.

Paraffinic and Naphthenic Hydrocarbons. These, in their pure forms, are not attacked by concentrated sulfuric acid at low temperatures and during the short time of conventional refining treatment.[1] But the solution of light paraffins and naphthenes by the sludge has been observed, and concentrated acid will dissolve small amounts of isobutane. Fuming acid absorbs small amounts of the members of the paraffin series as far down as ethane when contact is induced by long agitation; the amount of absorption increases with time, temperature, concentration of the acid, and complexity of structure of the hydrocarbons. Vigorous agitation is of considerable influence in promoting reaction,[2] and possibly the comparative inertness of sulfuric acid toward saturated hydrocarbons may be influenced largely by the mutual insolubility of the two phases. No reactions have been established, but oxidation and sulfonation occur especially as the temperature is raised.[3] The preparation of mono- and disulfonic acids of normal hydrocarbons, hexane and higher, has been reported.[3] With naphthenes, the fuming acid acts to sulfonate and to split the ring and to cause oxidation and reduction. Burkhardt,[4] for

---

[1] Kincannon and Manning [*Ind. Eng. Chem.*, **47**:149 (1955)] purified *n*-hydrocarbons by treatment with fortified sulfuric acid (SO₃ or P₂O₅); Shepard, Henne, and Midgley [*J. ACS*, **53**:1948 (1931)] employed chlorosulfonic acid.

[2] McKee, *Chem. Ztg.*, **36**(2):872 (1912).

[3] Worstall, *Am. Chem. J.*, **20**:664 (1898).

[4] *J. Chem. Soc.*, 1930, p. 2387.

instance, found cyclohexane to give, among other things, the sulfonic acids of hexane and benzene. An original content of benzene in the cyclohexane might, however, be suspected.

Aromatics. These are not attacked by sulfuric acid to any great extent under ordinary refining conditions unless they are present in high concentrations; but if fuming acid is used, or if the temperature is allowed to rise far above normal, sulfonation may occur. The reaction is of importance in the case of oils containing aromatics or aromatic rings in more complex groups and in the preparation of white oils and kerosenes where drastic treatment is required. Where both aromatics and olefins are present, as in cracked distillates, the acid may also bring about alkylation; this was recognized quite early.[1] The alkylation of lower isoparaffins by olefins of similar molecular weight in the presence of excess acid and at a low temperature was developed industrially prior to 1940[2] and has become a standard operation of the industry (see Chap. III).

Olefins. The action of sulfuric acid on unsaturated hydrocarbons is not well understood. The main primary reactions are varying degrees of ester formation (the basis for alcohol manufacture) and polymerization; each of these has been studied extensively for the lower olefins.[3]

Ester formation takes place most readily with tertiary-base olefins (those which hydrate to tertiary alcohols). Isobutylene, for example, dissolves in 63 per cent sulfuric acid at room temperature and atmospheric pressure to from *t*-butyl acid sulfate (but not the diester), which is hydrolyzed *in situ* to the alcohol. The alcohol can be salted out by ammonium sulfate or distilled away after adding sufficient aniline to neutralize the sulfuric acid. Ester formation is reported to reach a maximum with the C_5–C_6 olefins.[4] The secondary olefins require stronger acid for absorption; propylene is taken up by 60 to 70 per cent acid under elevated temperature and pressure. The formation of neutral esters rather than mono esters is favored by acids of higher strength. In

[1] Kraemer and Spilker, *Ber.*, **23**:3169 (1890). Brochet, *Compt. rend.*, **117**:115 (1893).

[2] Birch, Dunstan, Fidler, Pim, and Tait, *J. Inst. Petrol. Technologists*, **24**:303 (1938); *Ind. Eng. Chem.*, **31**:884, 1079 (1939); *Trans. Faraday Soc.*, **35**:1013 (1939). See also Ormandy and Craven, *J. Inst. Petrol. Technologists*, **12**:68 (1926); **13**:311 (1927). Tarasov and Popova, *Neftyanoe Khoz.*, **18**:992 (1930); *C.A.*, **25**:406 (1931). McAllister, Anderson, Ballard, and Roos, *J. Org. Chem.*, **6**:647 (1941). Sinn and Grosse, *Ind. Eng. Chem.*, **37**:924 (1945). Mrstik, Smith, and Pinkerton, *Advances in Chem. Ser.*, no. 5, p. 97, 1951.

[3] Davis and Schuler, *J. ACS*, **52**:721 (1930). Davis and Crandall, *J. ACS*, **52**:3757, 3769 (1930). Davis and Quiggle, *Ind. Eng. Chem.*, *Anal. Ed.*, **2**:39 (1930). Marcovitch and Moore, *Natl. Petrol. News*, **23**(41):33; (42):27 (1931). Ellis, "The Chemistry of Petroleum Derivatives," vol. II, p. 319, Reinhold Publishing Corporation, New York, 1937.

[4] Brooks and Humphrey, *J. ACS*, **40**:822 (1918).

the manufacture of alcohols by ester hydrolysis, propylene and the normal butenes are absorbed in 85 to 90 per cent sulfuric acid, and the secondary amylenes in 80 to 85 per cent acid; under these conditions polymer formation is not extensive.   Ethylene is taken up in 94 to 98 per cent acid at 85°C; no polymer formation has been reported.

The neutral esters formed by reaction of sulfuric acid with olefins in cracked distillates are soluble in the acid phase but are also, to some extent, soluble in hydrocarbons; this becomes more evident as the molecular weight of the olefin increases.   These esters are rather difficult to hydrolyze for removal by alkali washing.   They are, however, unstable on standing for a long time; distillates containing them (acid-treated cracked gasolines) may evolve sulfur dioxide and deposit tarry condensates.   The esters are quite unstable on heating,[1] so that a redistilled, acid-treated cracked distillate usually requires alkali washing after the customary distillation.   In practice, vacuum is often employed to help keep down the temperature during the distillation process, in order to avoid the color instability and other consequences of ester decomposition.[2]

The rate of absorption by sulfuric acid is largely dependent upon the configuration of the hydrocarbon.   This is illustrated by the reactions of amylenes; a decreasing order of activity is shown by trimethylethylene, *unsym*-methylethylethylene, *sym*-methylethylethylene 1-pentene, and isopropylethylene.[3]   The latter olefin is absorbed only by acids of such strength that polymers, but no alcohols, are formed.

The tertiary base olefins will form polymers on warming their weak-acid solutions.   Thus, di- and triisobutylene are formed in a clean-cut manner by heating solutions of isobutylene in 63 per cent sulfuric acid.[4] In this system, as the strength of the acid is increased, the alcohol is converted more readily to polymer without heating, isomerizations take place, and the isobutylene dimer and trimer formation becomes less cleancut; finally, with concentrated acid, hydropolymerization (or conjunct polymerization, see Chap. III) takes place, and charring and sulfur dioxide evolution result from oxidation-reduction reactions between the polymer and the acid.   The latter can be reduced by saturation of the acid with a common ion salt.[5]   The secondary-base olefins enter polymerization reactions, even with concentrated sulfuric acid, with more difficulty. The formation of an alcohol derived from the dimer (4-methylpentene-1)

[1] Moser, *Petroleum Z.*, **28**(26):4 (1932).

[2] Treatment with phosphoric acid is stated to decompose these esters.   Ipatieff, "Catalytic Reactions at High Pressures and Temperatures," p. 555, The Macmillan Company, New York, 1936.

[3] Norris and Joubert, *J. ACS*, **49**:873 (1927).

[4] Butlerow, *Ann.*, **189**:44 (1877).

[5] Stevens and Gruse, U.S. Patent 2,303,769, 1942.

was noted when propylene was treated with 90 to 92 per cent acid.[1] The sulfuric acid polymerization of the normal butenes is not too advantageous and has not been developed. The amylenes are somewhat responsive.[2,3] The ease of polymerization increases with molecular weight (to an unestablished limit);[4] dodecene polymerizes rapidly to $C_{24}H_{48}$, a polymer in the kerosene boiling range which is as viscous as a light machine oil.

Reactions of olefins with sulfuric acid usually take place through carbonium ion intermediates; these have been suggested as a possible cause for the yellow color which often develops during such reactions.[5] Conventional olefin isomerization and polymerization are explained in terms of carbonium ions, but the latter reaction may be accompanied by hydrogen transfer leading to conjunct or hydropolymers (see Chap. III). Conjunct polymers are major products of treating propylene and higher olefins with 98 per cent sulfuric acid.[6] The disproportionation taking place is illustrated by the reaction of an amylene mixture; the product boiled from 90 to 350°C and was of low bromine number. Dilution of the acid layer with water separated out an oil having the properties of a mixed trimer. When isobutene and the lower polymers, the n-butenes, isopropylethylene, nonene, and dodecene were treated at 0°C with 96 per cent acid,[7] both conventional and conjunct polymers resulted. Sufficiently diluted acid, however, yields only conventional polymers, the amount of dilution varying with the olefin. Temperature is important in determining the nature of the polymer when phosphoric acid is the acid reactant; above 250 to 300°C conjunct polymers are formed.[8] True polymers never result from reaction of olefins with anhydrous aluminum chloride, unless a moderating agent is present.[9]

In true polymerization a carbonium ion is formed by the addition of a proton to an olefin

$$RCH{=}CH_2 + H^+ \rightarrow R\overset{+}{C}HCH_3$$

and this ion adds to another olefin molecule to form a new carbonium ion.

$$RCH{=}CH_2 + R\overset{+}{C}HCH_3 \rightarrow R\overset{+}{C}HCH_2CHRCH_3$$

[1] Brooks, *J. ACS*, **56**:1998 (1934).

[2] Ormandy and Craven, *J. Inst. Petrol. Technologists*, **13**:311, 844 (1927); *J. Soc., Chem. Ind.*, **47**:317T (1928).

[3] Norris, *loc. cit.*

[4] Brooks and Humphrey, *J. ACS*, **40**:822 (1918).

[5] Matsen, Gonzales-Vidal, Harwood, and Kohn, *ACS, Div. Petrol. Chem.*, Gen. Papers, Preprint, p. 21, Cincinnati, April, 1955; *J. Phys. Chem.*, **25**:181 (1956).

[6] Ormandy, *loc. cit.*

[7] Ipatieff and Pines, *J. Org. Chem.*, **1**:464 (1936).

[8] Ipatieff and Pines, *Ind. Eng. Chem.*, **27**:1364 (1935).

[9] Hall and Nash, *J. Inst. Petrol. Technologists*, **23**:679 (1937).

This resulting ion may:

1. Undergo isomerization
2. Add to another olefin molecule to build up a longer chain
3. Lose a proton to form a new olefin, a true polymer of the original olefin

In conjunct or dehydropolymerization, the second-stage carbonium ion abstracts a hydride ion from a neighboring olefin molecule to yield a paraffin and a new olefinic carbonium ion which, losing a proton, forms a diolefin. Repetition of this hydrogen transfer yields still more highly unsaturated compounds and these, in turn, may cyclicize. The ultimate product may thus range from paraffins to a variety of compounds quite low in hydrogen content.

VII-2. Manner and Effects of Treating

Light Distillates. As indicated above, acid treating of cracked gasoline distillates brings about a loss caused by chemical reaction and another due to polymerization of some of the olefins to constituents boiling above the gasoline range; this latter makes necessary a redistillation. Such losses may total 3 or 4 volume per cent even when refrigeration is employed to maintain low temperature.[1] The operation is thus not competitive with use of antioxidants or even with the combination of vapor-phase fuller's earth contact and antioxidants, and is applied only when no other will serve. Such a case is treatment of higher-boiling cracked gasoline cuts of high sulfur content.[2] Stabilization of such materials against oxidation

TABLE VII-1

	Gasoline	After hydrogenation	After H_2SO_4 treating	After catalytic retreating
Yield, volume on gasoline treated.....	100	100	85	76
Gravity, °API.....................	60.2	62.5	60.1	56.6
Aniline point, °F..................	66	100	86	64
Acid heat, °F......................	135	7	40	27
Olefins, volume per cent.............	37	3	11	7
Aromatics, volume per cent..........	26	26	28	35
Reid vapor pressure, psi.............	7.0	6.9	6.8	7.0
ASTM distillation:				
Per cent to 212°F................	62.0	60.5	55.5	51.0
90 per cent, °F...................	292	283	294	293
Octane number (motor).............	80.5	79.5	82.8	83.1

[1] Without cooling and under conditions required for substantial desulfurization, the losses may total 10 to 20 per cent.

[2] For sulfur compounds removed, see Thierry, *J. Chem. Soc.*, **127**:2756 (1925).

is difficult by other means and desulfurization is in any case not easy. Even hydrogenation, while effective in lowering sulfur content, is likely to cause undesirable changes in chemical make-up and loss of octane numbers. This is illustrated in Table VII-1 which lists changes resulting when a catalytically cracked gasoline was treated with hydrogen and with sulfuric acid, and also when retreated over the same cracking catalyst.[1]

Characteristically, the treating loss with sulfuric acid is high, but this is not as large as that suffered by repassing the gasoline over the cracking catalyst. Hydrogenation, as would be expected, gives a high recovery but the clear octane number suffers slightly.

Dilute acid, say 75 per cent concentration, will polymerize diolefins and remove colored constituents,[2] but is not active for desulfurization. Removal of olefins is likely to cause a reduction of octane number, while taking out sulfur compounds usually improves the susceptibility to increase of octane number by the addition of tetraethyllead; the two effects may cancel each other.[3] Cases have been recognized in which acid treating may lower the octane number of a cracked distillate derived from a paraffinic stock and improve that of a distillate made from an aromatic gas oil.

Sulfuric acid effects desulfurization by solvent extraction and also by chemical reaction;[4] change of acid concentration will influence both. Results of treating a California cracked distillate with the same amount of acid in different dilutions are as follows:[5]

Concentration of H_2SO_4, per cent	Lb per bbl	Sulfur in distillate, per cent
100	12.0	0.32
90	13.3	0.39
80	15.0	0.59
70	17.0	0.68
60	20.0	0.75
Original	....	0.88

[1] Murphree, Gohr, and Brown, "Science of Petroleum," vol. V, part II, p. 253, Oxford University Press, New York and London, 1953.

[2] Ormandy and Craven, *J. Inst. Petrol. Technologists*, **12**:68 (1926). Morrell, *Ind. Eng. Chem.*, **19**:794 (1927). Pierce, *Natl. Petrol. News*, **22**(46):121 (1930). Potthoff, *Oil Gas J.*, **29**(42):141 (1931). Sager, *J. Inst. Petrol. Technologists*, **20**:138 (1934). Morrell and Egloff, *Oil Gas J.*, **32**(45):51 (1934); **34**(44):105 (1936).

[3] Graves, *Ind. Eng. Chem.*, **31**:850 (1939).

[4] Wood, Lowry, and Faragher, *Ind. Eng. Chem.*, **16**:1116 (1924); **18**:169 (1926). Wilke and Wride, *Ind. Eng. Chem.*, **41**:395 (1949).

[5] Morrell and Egloff, *World Petrol. Congr., Proc. 1st Congr., London*, **2**:10 (1933).

As the amount of strong acid is increased, the rate of sulfur reduction decreases, the octane number loss becomes excessive, and prohibitive sludge and polymer losses occur.   The results obtained on treating a cracked California gasoline with various amounts of 93 per cent acid at room temperature[1] are shown in the following tabulation:

Acid:						
Lb per bbl................	Untreated	1.5	5.0	10.0	20.0	30.0
Sludge loss, per cent........	....	0.3	1.0	2.3	4.4	6.7
Polymer loss, per cent......	....	0.5	1.0	1.9	3.2	4.7
Distillate:						
Specific gravity............	0.778	0.769	0.769	0.769	0.770	0.771
Oxygen stability period, min	600	220	555	600+	600+	600+
Copper-dish gum, mg.......	472	232	38	13	6	7
Sulfur, per cent............	0.61	0.55	0.48	0.41	0.25	0.14
Octane number (motor).....	76	74	72.5	72.5	72	69.5

It is often advantageous to divide a distillate into fractions and to treat each separately, according to its sulfur content, before reblending. The lower-boiling fractions generally require only mild treatment.

The extent of parasitic oxidation and reduction reactions, which are responsible for loss of both acid and hydrocarbons, as well as the extent of polymerization, are controlled to a large extent by the temperature developed during the strongly exothermic reaction.   Curiously, however, the loss of hydrocarbon material to acid sludge is less at a treating temperature of 100°C than at 25°C.   Nevertheless, high temperatures are to be avoided, and for this reason the acid is best added incrementally to maintain a more even temperature during the treatment.   A useful device is to cool the acid and distillate[2] to such an extent that the heat of reaction does not carry the temperature to harmful levels, and to limit the time of contact; the treatment is by a continuous countercurrent system,[3] followed by centrifugal sludge separation.   Under these conditions, the acid acts predominantly as a differential solvent in removing sulfur compounds.   Polymerization and sulfation of the olefins are greatly reduced, as are side reactions, as a result of the lower temperatures and of the smaller amount of acid required by the treatment.   Most stocks can be treated advantageously at temperatures within the 20 to 60°F range,[4] as shown in Figs. VII-1 and VII-2.

The time of contact should be kept as short as possible in order to

[1] Morrell and Egloff, *op. cit.*

[2] Halloran, *Oil Gas J.*, **26**(29):36 (1927); *World Petroleum Congr., Proc. 1st Congr., London*, **2**:3 (1933).   Klemgard, *Refiner Nat. Gasoline Mfr.*, **6**(5):51 (1927).

[3] In all countercurrent systems, the dissolved reaction products in the last effluent acid serve to mitigate the vigor of the first reaction with entering oil.

[4] Stratford, Graves, and Brown, *Refiner Nat. Gasoline Mfr.*, **17**(3):109 (1938).

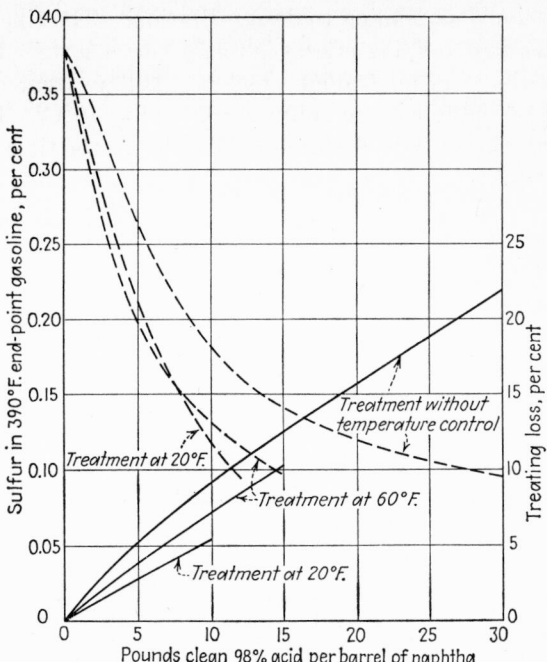

Fig. VII-1. Effect of treating temperature and amount of acid on sulfur removal and treating loss. [*From Stratford, Graves, and Brown, Refiner Nat. Gasoline Mfr.*, **17**:109 (1938).]

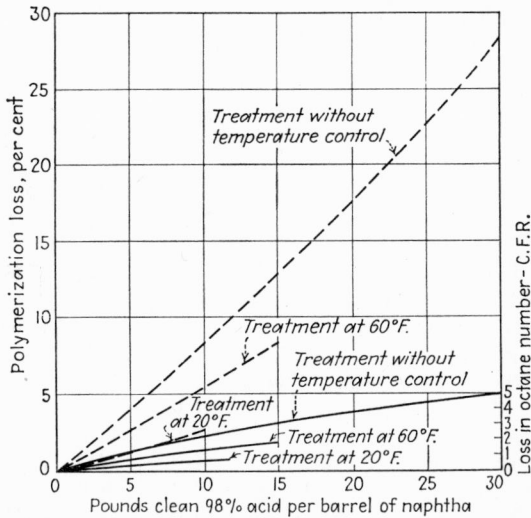

Fig. VII-2. Effect of treating temperature and amount of acid on polymerization loss and decrease in octane number. [*From Stratford, Graves, and Brown, Refiner Nat. Gasoline Mfr.*, **17**:109 (1938).]

minimize reactions not leading to desulfurization. The time required to produce the desired refining effects is really very short.[1] Figure VII-3 gives characteristics of an Iranian cracked distillate treated with 2 per cent (by weight) of 96 per cent sulfuric acid at 4 to 10°C. The chemical composition of the distillate changes considerably as the time of treatment

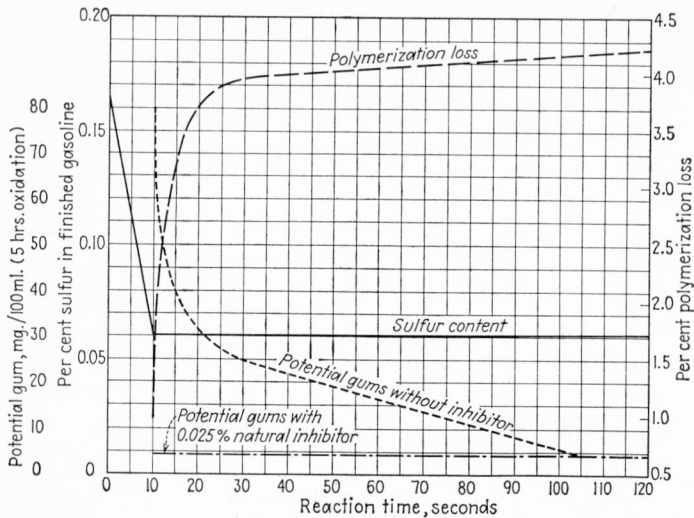

FIG. VII-3. Treatment of Iranian gasoline with 2 per cent by weight of 96 per cent H₂SO₄. [*From Sager, J. Inst. Petrol. Technologists,* **22**:609 (1936).]

is varied. The results of treating a highly cracked Rumanian distillate with 3 per cent of 98 per cent acid at 20°C are shown in Table VII-2. The advantages of a short contact time are evident.

TABLE VII-2

	0	6 sec	15 sec	80 min
Time of contact............................	0	6 sec	15 sec	80 min
Acidity (mg KOH)........................	0	0.2	0.2	0.56
End point (ASTM), °C....................	264	264	269	281
Dialkyl sulfates, g H₂SO₄ per 100 g..........	....	0.083	0.088	0.122
Gasoline to 200°C end point:				
Yield, per cent by weight................	60.5	60.0	58.0	55.0
Copper-dish gum, mg per 100 ml..........	220.0	21.0	13.0	37.7
Sulfur, per cent by weight................	0.048	0.035	0.035	0.032
Octane number (motor)...................	64	63	62	61
Chemical composition, per cent by volume:				
Diolefins.............................	1.0			
Olefins..............................	48.0	43.0	40.0	32.0
Aromatics...........................	2.0	2.0	2.0	2.6
Naphthenes..........................	30.0	33.0	35.0	38.4
Paraffins............................	20.0	22.0	23.0	27.0

[1] Sager, *J. Inst. Petrol. Technologists,* **22**:609 (1936). See also Pierce, *Natl. Petrol. News,* **22**(46):121 (1930).

It is difficult to correlate results of acid treating on a plant scale with laboratory experiments or with other steps in the refining operation. However, it seems clear that effective acid treating is dependent on the care exercised in distilling the stock to be treated, as well as the final acid-treated and alkali-washed stock. A closely cut and properly dephlegmated fraction will show a lower acid consumption and better refining than one containing entrained heavy ends. Furthermore, it is general experience that trouble in refining usually follows some trouble in distillation; anything tending to allow superheating and cracking or oxidation during distillation will increase acid treating difficulties, particularly by promoting formation of emulsions during the subsequent alkali washing. When redistilling the acid-treated stock it is important to keep the still temperatures low (below 375°F) in order to avoid decomposition of high-sulfur esters and polymers; vacuum and steam are employed for this purpose.

The amount of acid employed for the treatment of light cracked distillates for ordinary refining has usually been of the order of 0.5 to 1.0 per cent by volume (about 3 to 6 lb per bbl). For the heavier fractions of cracked gasolines for desulfurizing and stabilizing, 12 lb or more per bbl may be required. Double that amount might be necessary for a high-sulfur content kerosene distillate.

Heavy Oils. The acid treating of heavy distillates and residua presents different problems. Most of these contain at least a small proportion of asphaltic substances dissolved or suspended, and there has been a good deal of discussion about the chemical or possibly physical character of the treating reactions.[1] Practically all the acid comes out as a sludge (acid tar), and its separation is aided by addition of a little water or alkali solution; this suggests precipitation of a colloidal suspension. On the other hand, there are obvious chemical changes; sulfur dioxide is given off, and washed (thus acid-free) sludges from the treatment of practically sulfur-free oils may contain 8 or 9 per cent combined sulfur which could have been derived only from the treating acid. Furthermore, the usual recovery of sulfuric acid in refining operations is about 60 per cent of that employed. It seems that the refining action of the acid is primarily chemical and that the reaction products are colloidally dispersed in the treated oil until precipitated.[2]

Although largely displaced for bulk production of both gasoline and lubricating oils, acid treating still serves many special purposes. Paraf-

[1] Ubbelohde, *Petroleum Z.*, **4**:1394 (1908). Schulz, *Petroleum Z.*, **5**:205, 446 (1909). Condrea, *Z. angew Chem.*, **25**:1949 (1912). Gurwitsch, "Scientific Principles of Petroleum Technology," p. 402, D. Van Nostrand Company, Inc., Princeton, N.J., 1932.

[2] Weir, Houghton, and Majewski, *Ind. Eng. Chem.*, **22**:1293 (1930).

fin distillates, intended for dewaxing, may receive a treatment of up to 25 lb per bbl to facilitate wax crystallization and refining; insulating oils and refrigeration compressor oils may be heavily treated, up to 250 lb per bbl; and white oils may require even greater amounts. However, where acid is applied as a supplement to solvent refining, as for improvement of color of lubricating stocks, only 1 or 2 lb per bbl may be required.

Large amounts of acid, like those just mentioned, will consume high proportions of the charge stock and effect marked changes in the properties of the treated oil, as shown in the tabulation.[1]

	Distillate		Residuum	
	Original	Treated	Original	Treated
Gravity, °API....................	23.1	28.3	21.4	26.1
Viscosity at 100°F, Saybolt sec......	1590	796	4600	2107
Viscosity at 210°F, Saybolt sec......	98.7	79.5	197.1	142.1
Viscosity index....................	70	98	84	101
Carbon residue, weight per cent.....	1.45	0.51	5.6	1.58
Pour point, °F....................	5	10	10	20

The sludge produced on acid treating petroleum distillates, even gasolines and kerosenes, is necessarily complex in nature. Esters and alcohols are present from reactions with olefins; sulfonation products from the aromatics, naphthenes, and phenols; and salts from reactions with nitrogen bases. In addition, there are materials such as naphthenic acids, sulfur compounds, and asphaltic material, all retained by direct solution. To these constituents must be added the various products of oxidation-reduction reactions: coagulated resins, soluble hydrocarbons, water, and free acid. Gurwitsch[2] suggested that some of these substances represent unstable combinations of hydrocarbons with acid, broken up by long standing or by contact with water. The proportions of each will vary with the stock treated and the conditions under which the acid was applied.

The disposal of the sludge is quite troublesome, since it contains unused free acid which must be removed by dilution and settling. The disposal is a comparatively simple process for the sludges resulting from treating gasolines and kerosene—the so-called "light oils." The insoluble oil phase separates out as a mobile tar, which can be mixed and burned without too much difficulty. Sludges from heavier oils, however, separate out granular semisolids which offer considerable difficulty in handling.

[1] Woods, *Petrol. Eng.*, **7**(3):56 (1935). See also Thornton, Neighbors, and Keith, *Oil Gas J.*, **28**(42):184 (1930); Thornton, Wilson, and Hillis, *Oil Gas J.*, **29**(11):64 (1930).

[2] *Petroleum Z.*, **19**:1239 (1923).

The use of these materials in asphalt manufacture is mentioned in Chap. XV. Another process involves retorting the total sludge to set free sulfur dioxide, which is then oxidized catalytically to sulfur trioxide in a contact acid plant or reacted with hydrogen sulfide to form elemental sulfur. The general subject of sludge disposal is fully discussed by Kalichevsky and Stagner.[1]

In all cases careful separation of reaction products is important to the recovery of well-refined materials. This may not be easy if the temperature has risen as a consequence of chemical reaction, resulting in a persistent dark color traceable to colloidally distributed reaction products. Separation may also be difficult at too low a temperature because of high viscosity of the stock. This problem has been attacked by prediluting with light naphtha or with propane.[2]

When acid treatment cannot be applied continuously by mechanical agitation, followed by effective separation,[3] the old-fashioned batch agitators are employed. These devices are vertical reactors holding up to several thousand barrels, provided with conical bottoms for sludge drainage. Time of contact is difficult to control and may amount to several hours; agitation is provided by air blowing or by a circulating pump. The trend of evidence is that a short time of reaction is adequate; if proper contact can be induced, a few minutes may be sufficient. Prompt separation of acid tar is desirable to avoid discoloration by re-solution and to permit handling the sludge before it becomes undesirably viscous. Breaking out of the suspended acid tar, often referred to as pepper sludge, is helped by adding a little water and agitating as indicated above. The subsequent separation of tar resembles closely the precipitation of a colloidal suspension. The sludge is allowed to settle, and the "sour" oil is washed with water, usually after transfer to another container, to avoid retention of acid tar in the system during the alkali washing which follows. Care is taken to avoid emulsion difficulties. Sodium hydroxide solution of 10 to 25 per cent concentration may be used for nonviscous products, and no heat is applied; the alkali solution is in excess and is usually treated for recovery.[4] For viscous oils, more dilute

---

[1] "Chemical Refining of Petroleum," p. 120, Reinhold Publishing Corporation, New York, 1942. See also Sec. XVI-6 of the present work.

[2] Bray, Swift, and Carr, *Proc. API*, **14**(III):96 (1933).

[3] On centrifugal separation of acid and acid sludge, see *Oil Gas J.*, **28**(42):194 (1930); Petty, *Refiner Nat. Gasoline Mfr.*, **11**:13 (1932); Jones, *Natl. Petrol. News*, **26**(21):20K (1934); Walker, *Natl. Petrol. News*, **26**(22):29 (1934); *Proc. API*, **15M**(III):7 (1934).

[4] Where continuous acid and alkali treating are applied to gasoline distillates, the procedure is very simple and the various precautions described are not employed, because the danger of emulsification is almost nonexistent. Continuous treating of lubricating stocks, with vigorous agitation and subsequent electrostatic separation of the finely divided sludge, is described in *Petrol. Processing*, **11**(11):95 (1956).

solutions are employed, temperature is raised by direct steaming, only a very slight excess of alkali is used, and no attempt is made at its recovery. Emulsion-breaking chemicals are sometimes required in alkali washing; the use of aqueous alcohol is customary when fuming acid has been employed, as for sulfonates and white oils. Final water washing followed by air blowing to dry the oils is the customary procedure.

It must be remembered that for heavy oils and cylinder stocks modern practice has followed the line of using no water or alkali after acid treatment. Acid tar is not removed as such, but the sour oil is subject to contact clay adsorption at elevated temperatures, which neutralizes and decolorizes the oil at one time (see Chap. VIII).

MISCELLANEOUS CHEMICAL TREATMENTS. During the life of the petroleum industry a considerable number of chemical materials have been tried for refining purposes. These have usually been of the kind which react vigorously with the less stable hydrocarbons which are to be removed; most of those tried have lacked selectivity and have attacked also the stable, desirable constituents. The use of chlorine as hypochlorite is mentioned under sweetening, below. Careful adjustment of conditions was required to avoid direct chlorination. Since much of the deterioration of petroleum products starts with oxidation, a favorite approach to refining has been to attempt a selective oxidation of the unstable constituents, with the thought that only stable hydrocarbons would remain. Oxygen, ozone, and even nitric acid have been tried for this purpose. A resin-forming reaction of formaldehyde and sulfuric acid—the formolite reaction[1]—with cyclic unsaturated hydrocarbons at one time offered some promise. Treating with formaldehyde alone has been claimed for the degumming of cracked gasolines.[2] Friedel-Crafts type reagents such as zinc chloride,[3] boron trifluoride,[4] and anhydrous aluminum chloride have been of greater interest. The latter removes reactive olefins by polymerization and combined sulfur as addition complexes; the chemistry is very involved because of secondary reactions. Extent of removal of various types of sulfur compounds has been studied;[5] in general 1 g of aluminum chloride per 100 ml of rather dilute solution in naphtha removes one-third to one-half of the sulfur content, except for certain sulfides, where removal is much better. Redistillation lowers the sulfur content still more, so that in several cases conversion of sulfur

[1] Nastjukoff, *J. Soc. Chem. Ind.*, **23**:1082 (1904); Herr, *Petroleum Z.*, **4**:1284, 1397 (1908–1909); *Chem. Ztg.*, **34**:893 (1910); Marcusson, *Mitt. kgl. Materialprüfungsamt*, **31**:301 (1913); Richardson, *Ind. Eng. Chem.*, **8**:319 (1916). Nastjukoff and Maljarow, *J. Soc. Chem. Ind.*, **30**:201 (1911); Radcliffe, *J. Soc. Chem. Ind.*, **39**:259A (1920).

[2] Arundale and Haworth, U.S. Patent 2,567,174, 1951.

[3] Lachman, *Proc. API* (III):63 (1931).

[4] Beuther and Goldthwaite, *Ind. Eng. Chem.*, **47**:764 (1955).

[5] Youtz and Perkins, *Ind. Eng. Chem.*, **19**:1247 (1927).

compounds into higher-boiling complexes is indicated. Aluminum chloride is used for refining of high-grade lubricating oils.

VII-3. Sweetening Processes. Of the various types of sulfur compounds found in gasoline distillates, hydrogen sulfide and mercaptans are the most objectionable; both are malodorous and, under certain conditions, corrosive.[1] In addition, presence of mercaptans lowers the susceptibility to antioxidants and to tetraethyllead. Gasolines containing them are termed "sour," and the processes for their removal are called "sweetening."[2]

Chemical sweetening methods most commonly used are of two types: those which oxidize mercaptans to disulfides (doctor, copper chloride, lead sulfide, inhibitor sweetening, and sodium hypochlorite methods) and those that remove them by alkaline extraction (alkali solutizer and alkali methanol). Other methods employed which both desulfurize and sweeten include vapor-phase treatment over solid catalysts, with or without presence of hydrogen, to convert the sulfur compounds to hydrogen sulfide which is removed by alkali washing. Also, treatment with metallic sodium has been proposed.[3]

In case of the oxidative methods, each disulfide is higher boiling than the mercaptan from which it was derived but the lower-boiling disulfides are still within the distilling range of gasolines. Separation by fractionation is not possible[4] and, except in a few limited cases, the sweetened product is as high in sulfur content as was the untreated stock. While alkyl disulfides are less objectionable than mercaptans, they have been shown (especially *n*-propyl disulfide), along with elementary sulfur, to cause haze and color formation in gasolines exposed to light.[5] Lecithin is reported to be effective in retarding haze formation in gasolines containing tetraethyllead; these are sensitive in this respect to "oversweetening."

Doctor Method. The method of treating sour distillates first developed consists in agitating with alkaline sodium plumbite (doctor solution)[6] in

[1] Henderson, Agruss, and Ayres, *Ind. Eng. Chem., Anal. Ed.,* **12**:1 (1940). Free sulfur in gasoline is also corrosive.

[2] For a review of processes of sweetening and mercaptan removal, see Happel and Cauley, *Petrol. Refiner,* **21**(11):406 (1942). Kalichevsky, *Petrol. Refiner,* **29**(11):97 (1950); **29**(12):113 (1950); **30**(1):129 (1951); (2):95 (1951); (3):122 (1951); (4):111 (1951); (5):117 (1951); (6):135 (1951).

[3] Vanderbilt, *Ind. Eng. Chem.,* **49**:696 (1957).

[4] For a review of physical and chemical methods for the separation of sulfur compounds from petroleum, see Thompson, Coleman, Rall, and Smith, *ACS, Div. Petrol. Chem., Symposium on Advances in Separations of Hydrocarbons and Related Compounds,* Preprint, p. 35, ACS Meeting, New York, September, 1954.

[5] Morrell, Benedict, and Egloff, *Ind. Eng. Chem.,* **28**:448 (1936).

[6] The corresponding analytical reagent is prepared by saturating sodium hydroxide (12.5 g NaOH per 100 ml of solution) with litharge.

$$PbO + 2NaOH = Na_2PbO_2 + H_2O$$

the presence of a small amount of free sulfur. A black precipitate of lead sulfide is formed; the gasoline is of improved odor and has been rendered sweet.[1] While it had been known for a long time[2] that individual mercaptans are oxidized by sulfur in the presence of alkali at room temperature, many years passed before the essential equations of the doctor process were established.[3]

$$2RSH + Na_2PbO_2 \rightarrow Pb(SR)_2 + 2NaOH$$
$$Pb(SR)_2 + S \rightarrow PbS + R_2S_2$$

In practice, sour distillates are usually given an alkali wash before the doctor treatment to remove any trace of hydrogen sulfide and some of the lower-molecular-weight mercaptans; this is of material aid in reducing the plumbite requirement.

The gasoline first becomes sweet upon addition of the amount of sulfur indicated by the foregoing equation; actually, slightly more sulfur than the theoretical is required, owing to the formation of complex lead intermediates.[4] At this point, however, the precipitated lead sulfide is in the form of extremely fine particles and may require from several hours to a day to settle. Experience has shown that the formation of this stable lead sulfide–gasoline suspension can be avoided if a small amount of extra sulfur is used. In practice, the amount of extra sulfur added lies somewhere between that necessary to give a quick "break" of the suspension and that which will cause corrosion in the copper strip test. Generally, it increases with the degree of "sourness" (mercaptan

---

[1] A gasoline is sweet, or doctor negative, by definition when no dark discoloration occurs at the interface after shaking 10 ml of sample with 5 ml of sodium plumbite solution and a small amount of powdered sulfur (ASTM D 484–52). The test is very sensitive; the minimum amount of mercaptan sulfur needed to give a positive doctor test is quite small and varies with the compound.

Mercaptan	Wt per cent	Mercaptan	Wt per cent
Ethyl.............	0.0006	Isoamyl..........	0.0001
n-Propyl...........	0.0003	n-Heptyl..........	0.0001
n-Butyl.............	0.00015	Phenyl............	0.0010
n-Amyl.............	0.0002		

Backensto, U.S. Patent 2,543,953, 1951. Happel and Cauley, *Refiner Nat. Gasoline Mfr.*, **19**(6):207 (1940). Henderson, Agruss, and Ayres, *Ind. Eng. Chem., Anal. Ed.*, **12**:1 (1940).

[2] Holmberg, *Ann.*, **359**:81 (1908).

[3] Wendt and Diggs, *Ind. Eng. Chem.*, **16**:1113 (1924). Wood, Lowry, and Faragher, *Ind. Eng. Chem.*, **16**:1116 (1924).

[4] Ott and Reid, *Ind. Eng. Chem.*, **22**:878, 882 (1930). Duncan and Ott, *J. ACS*, **53**:3940 (1931).

content) of the stock being treated. It is significant that addition of free sulfur, after the stable suspension is formed, is ineffective in altering the settling rate. In the presence of lead mercaptides, however, the extra sulfur acts to form alkyl polysulfides, which are chemically analogous to peroxides.

$$Pb(SR)_2 + 2S \rightarrow PbS + R_2S_3$$
$$Pb(SR)_2 + 3S \rightarrow PbS + R_2S_4, \text{ etc.}$$

The precipitating effect is evidently a result of the presence of these polysulfides or possibly of sodium sulfide formed between mercaptans, sulfur, and the alkaline solution.

Besides affecting the susceptibility of gasolines toward tetraethyllead, the various sulfur compounds associated with sweetening also influence

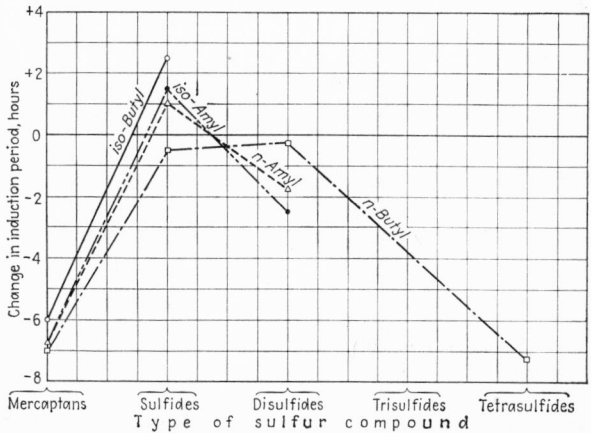

Fig. VII-4. Effect of sulfur compounds (0.025 per cent S) on induction period of peroxide-free diisobutylene.

the response of the fuel to antioxidants. The most detrimental in this respect are the mercaptans and the polysulfides, the latter being the more deleterious. The relative effect of various aliphatic sulfur compounds on inhibitor response is shown in Fig. VII-4. A typical inhibitor-response curve, showing the variation in oxygen stability period during the course of a doctor-sweetening operation, is given in Fig. VII-5. The induction period of the sour gasoline plus added inhibitor is shown by the ordinates. On washing with doctor solution, the oxygen stability is materially reduced (zone 1) owing to the removal of natural inhibitors by the alkali present or possibly to peroxides formed by the oxidation of neutral lead mercaptides.[1] Upon the incremental addition of sulfur, the induction period rises to a maximum (zone 2), the point at which the gasoline first becomes sweet and where the theoretical amount of sulfur

[1] Slagle and Reid, *Ind. Eng. Chem.*, **24**:448 (1932).

has been added; the mercaptans have been converted into disulfides. Further addition of sulfur causes a steady decrease in inhibitor susceptibility resulting from alkyl polysulfide formation. The amount of sulfur necessary to give the "break" (separation of lead sulfide) necessary in practice is somewhere in the neighborhood of zone 3, while the condition of commercially doctor-sweetened gasolines, where the amount of sulfur added is not carefully controlled, is probably best represented as being in zone 4. Zone 5 represents the very low inhibitor response obtained from badly oversweetened gasolines.

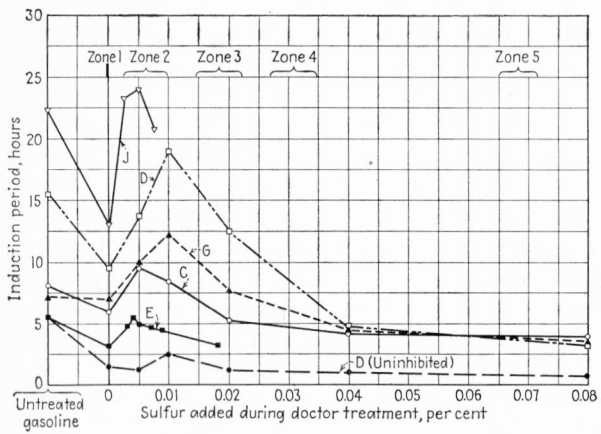

Fig. VII-5. Effect of quantity of sulfur added during doctor sweetening on inhibitor susceptibility of gasolines.

The doctor solution leaving the reactor consists essentially of a mixture of lead sulfide in free alkali, containing emulsified hydrocarbons. This spent solution is pumped to steam-heated vessels, where it is air blown for regeneration.[1] From the various compounds formed, it is evident that several reactions occur simultaneously. Morrell and Faragher[2] have shown experimentally that the lead sulfide is converted to plumbite according to the following equations:

$$PbS + 4NaOH + 2O_2 \rightarrow Na_2PbO_2 + Na_2SO_4 + 2H_2O$$

It is thought that the sulfide is first oxidized to the sulfite and that the latter reacts with the alkali to form the plumbite. Considerable amounts of sodium thiosulfate are also formed.

$$2PbS + 2O_2 + 6NaOH \rightarrow 2Na_2PbO_2 + Na_2S_2O_3 + 3H_2O$$

[1] Wilson has reported that a small addition of hydrogen peroxide increases the efficiency of the process [*Refiner Nat. Gasoline Mfr.*, **18**(3):96, (1939)].

[2] *Ind. Eng. Chem.*, **19**:1045 (1927).

The thiosulfate, in turn, may react with the alkali present to form Na_2SO_3 and Na_2S.[1] The loss of lead is very low; the main items of consumption are alkali and sulfur.

Where the doctor treatment is employed, it is now very likely to be combined with lead sulfide sweetening, discussed below.

Indirect Air Oxidation Methods

LEAD SULFIDE. It has long been known that lead sulfide itself may take a definite part in sweetening operations. Wendt and Diggs postulated that this was because mercaptans were adsorbed by the sulfide. Greer[2] showed this to be true, at least in part. It is interesting to note that the stable suspension settles to leave a sweet gasoline; but if it is treated with dilute aqueous $AlCl_3$, the gasoline is rendered sour again. Whether this result is caused by a release of adsorbed mercaptans, by the reaction of the aluminum chloride with the disulfides in the gasoline phase, or by the release of occluded mercaptides is not known. Lachman[3] suggested that the sulfide might supply a catalytic surface at which air could oxidize the mercaptans to disulfides. These ideas led to the development of a method in which the sulfur required to oxidize the mercaptides to disulfides is furnished by the air oxidation of lead sulfide.[4] The sour gasoline is brought into contact with a suspension of lead sulfide in strong alkali, and air is supplied. The equations for the reaction are similar to those given above.

$$PbS + \tfrac{1}{2}O_2 \rightarrow PbO + S$$
$$PbO + 2NaOH \rightarrow Na_2PbO_2 + H_2O$$
$$Na_2PbO_2 + 2RSH \rightarrow Pb(RS)_2 + 2NaOH$$
$$Pb(RS)_2 + S \rightarrow PbS + R_2S_2$$

When larger quantities of air must be supplied for treating gasoline of high mercaptan content, there is a tendency toward excessive plumbite and sulfur formation. In such cases, a controlled quantity of aqueous sodium sulfide is simultaneously added to reconvert the extra plumbite back to lead sulfide. The presence of the remaining extra sulfur is not desirable, and therefore it is advantageous to control the air oxidation carefully. The lead sulfide is essentially a catalyst, as only oxygen is consumed in the process; there is, however, a certain loss of alkali to sodium sulfate and thiosulfate.

[1] Birch, "Science of Petroleum," vol. III, p. 1708, Oxford University Press, New York and London, 1938.

[2] *Ind. Eng. Chem.*, **21**:1033 (1929).

[3] *Ind. Eng. Chem.*, **23**:354 (1931).

[4] Rowsey and Whitehurst, *Oil Gas J.*, **26**(32):250 (1927). Morrell and Faragher, *Ind. Eng. Chem.*, **19**:1045 (1927). Happel and Robertson, *Oil Gas J.*, **36**(46):125 (1938). See Waterman and Wiley, *Petrol. Refiner*, **34**(9):182 (1955), for lead sulfide sweetening in presence of added sulfur and alkali.

COPPER CHLORIDE. The oxidizing power of cupric salts has been utilized to convert mercaptans directly into disulfides. As free sulfur is not employed, polysulfides are not obtained. A commercial development is the use of cupric chloride in the presence of strong salt solutions, generally made up by dissolving copper sulfate in an aqueous solution of sodium chloride.[1]

$$4RSH + 2CuCl_2 \rightarrow R_2S_2 + 2CuSR + 4HCl$$
$$2CuSR + 2CuCl_2 \rightarrow R_2S_2 + 4CuCl$$
$$4CuCl + 4HCl + O_2 \rightarrow 4CuCl_2 + H_2O$$

The cuprous chloride is soluble in the salt solution, and there is no precipitation. Under operating conditions, a certain amount of copper is retained by the sweetened gasoline, probably as cuprous mercaptides or cuprous chloride–olefin addition products; it is removed by washing the gasoline with an aqueous solution of sodium sulfide. Sometimes addition to the finished gasoline of copper deactivators, normally chelating agents, is also required.[2] Air blowing the cuprous chloride solution, after or during the sweetening operation, regenerates the cupric chloride for further use.

The copper chloride solution may be employed as such, or the sour gasoline may be percolated through a porous mass saturated with the treating agent. Alternatively, the gasoline may be mixed with a solid carrier for the reagent, dispersed as a slurry.[3]

INHIBITOR SWEETENING. "Sour" distillates containing less than 0.02 weight per cent sulfur may also be "sweetened" by alkali washing, adding a small amount of di-*sec*-butylcatechol and allowing to stand for several days. It appears that some free alkali must be present for the mercaptan oxidation to take place. The additive is apparently first oxidized by air to a quinone, which in turn oxidizes the remaining mercaptans to disulfides, and itself is reconverted to the phenolic form.[4] Di-*sec*-butyl-p-phenylenediamine can also be used but it is a little less effective. The process is referred to as "inhibitor sweetening." It is employed mainly where low-mercaptan naphthas are treated only with aqueous alkali.[5]

[1] Staub, *Petrol. Eng.*, **2**(3):161 (1930). Schulze and Buell, *Oil Gas J.*, **34**(22):42 (1935); **36**(28):56 (1937). Conn, *Refiner Nat. Gasoline Mfr.*, **20**(3):53 (1941). Kalichevsky, *Petrol. Refiner*, **30**(3):122 (1951).

[2] Walters, Minor, and Yabroff, *Ind. Eng. Chem.*, **41**:1723 (1949). Downing, Clarkson, and Pedersen, *Oil Gas. J.*, **38**(11):97 (1939). Pedersen, *Ind. Eng. Chem.*, **41**:924 (1949). Watson and Tom, *Ind. Eng. Chem.*, **41**:918 (1949).

[3] Franklin, U.S. Patent 2,235,921, 1941; 2,284,273, 1942; with Weeks, 2,284,271, 1942; with Weeks and Harris, 2,284,272, 1942.

[4] Merguerian, *J. ACS*, **77**:5019 (1955).

[5] Campioni and Cordia, *World Petroleum Congr., Proc. 3rd Congr., Hague*, **4**:254 (1951). Rosenwald, *Petrol. Processing*, **6**:969 (1951); **11**:91 (1956); *Div. Petrol. Chem., Symposium on The Use of Additives in Petroleum Fuels, ACS*, Preprint, p. 83,

Other oxidation methods for sweetening are the hypochlorite process, employing sodium hypochlorite of controlled pH and concentration,[1] which was employed commercially at one time, and that based on sodium ferrocyanide.[2]

Extraction Methods. The alkali washing of sour distillates will remove hydrogen sulfide and to some extent a few of the lower alkyl mercaptans. As the molecular weight rises, there is an increased tendency for the sodium mercaptide to hydrolyze; the mercaptans set free are more soluble in the gasoline and go back into the hydrocarbon phase.[3] The effect of the molecular weight of the mercaptan on the extent of its extraction from gasoline by 5 per cent alkali is tabulated below:[4]

Mercaptan	Per cent removal
Ethyl	97.1
n-Propyl	88.8
Isopropyl	87.2
n-Butyl	63.2
Isobutyl	62.8
Isoamyl	33.0

Only 2 per cent of C_7 mercaptans are removed with 10 per cent aqueous alkali, and only 73 per cent with 40 per cent caustic.[5]

The solubility of the higher mercaptans in the aqueous alkali, however, can be increased materially by the addition of organic solvents (methyl alcohol) or other materials which act as "solutizers" (e.g., organic acids).[6] Several sweetening methods have been developed, based on the removal

---

ACS Meeting, Minneapolis, September, 1955. Barringer, *Ind. Eng. Chem.*, **47**:1022 (1955). Rampine and Gorham, *Petrol. Processing*, **10**:1146 (1955). For effects of olefin and mercaptan structure on inhibitor sweetening, see Minor and Nixon, *ACS, Div. Petrol. Chem. Gen. Papers*, Preprint, p. 53, ACS Meeting, Chicago, September, 1958.

[1] Wood, Greene, and Provine, *Ind. Eng. Chem.*, **18**:823 (1926). Birch and Norris, *J. Chem. Soc.*, **127**:1934 (1925). Dunstan and Brooks, *Ind. Eng. Chem.*, **14**:1112 (1922). Ardagh and Bowman, *J. Soc. Chem. Ind.*, **54**:267T (1935). Ardagh, Bowman, and Weatherburn, *J. Soc. Chem. Ind.*, **56**:249T (1939); **59**:27T (1940). Kalichevsky, *Petrol. Refiner*, **30**(2):95 (1951).

[2] Miller and Salmon, *Petroleum Refiner*, **34**(9):155 (1955).

[3] A laboratory method for essentially quantitative recovery of most mercaptans up through *t*-hexadecyl thiol from hydrocarbons by extraction with sodium amino-ethoxide dissolved in anhydrous ethylenediamine is described by Hopkins and Smith, *Anal. Chem.*, **26**:206 (1954).

[4] Birch and Norris, *J. Chem. Soc.*, **127**:898 (1925).

[5] Zandona and Rippie, *Petrol. Processing*, **6**:136 (1951).

[6] Yabroff, *Ind. Eng. Chem.*, **32**:257 (1940). Yabroff and White, *Ind. Eng. Chem.*, **32**:950 (1940). Happel and Robertson, *Ind. Eng. Chem.*, **27**:941 (1935).

of mercaptans, utilizing this principle.   In these processes desulfurization to the extent of the mercaptan content is accomplished.

In one of the methods the aqueous alkali-containing methanol is contacted with hydrogen sulfide–free "sour" gasoline at about 100°F and 75 to 100 psi in a counter current extraction column.[1]   After phase separation, the methanol and mercaptans are removed from the caustic solution by steam stripping; the mercaptans are recovered as such.   Phenols, pyrroles, and naphthenic acids are also removed from cracked gasolines which contain them.   In the process, the phenol and organic acid concentrations are allowed to build up to equilibrium values in the extractant, since they act as solutizers in aiding mercaptan removal.

In the second method, cresols, cresylic and other coal and wood tar acids, and naphthenic acids added to the aqueous alkali are effective solutizers for the mercaptans in the gasoline.   A one-phase[2] or a two-phase system may be employed;[3] isobutyric acid can also be used.   One process employs $6N$ potassium hydroxide and $3N$ potassium isobutyrate as the extracting solution.[4]   Potassium hydroxide is favored over sodium hydroxide because of the lower viscosity of its aqueous solutions.

Instead of recovering mercaptans in the caustic regeneration step by steam stripping, they may be oxidized directly to disulfides by air blowing. Most of the immiscible alkyl disulfides formed are recovered by phase separation.   The small amount remaining in the aqueous phase is removed by naphtha extraction.   Tannic acid or tannins, gallic acid, pyrogallol, and other polyhydroxybenzenes have been found to be catalysts for this oxidation reaction.[5]   The catalysts themselves are susceptible to oxidation but this is minimized by the antioxidant action of a small amount of mercaptan which is maintained in the aqueous solution. The mercaptans in the "fat" alkaline layer may also be converted to disulfides by electrolytic oxidation.[6]

VII-4.   Removal of Sulfur Compounds.   The sulfur compounds found in light petroleum distillates are probably, to some extent, degradation products formed from high-molecular-weight complexes during distillation or cracking of the heavier oils.   In addition to traces of elementary sulfur, hydrogen sulfide, mercaptans, sulfides, disulfides, and thiophenes have been recognized, as well as compounds of the nature of sulfates,

[1] Field, *Oil Gas J.*, **40**(20):40 (1941).   Happel, Cauley, and Kelly, *Petrol. Refiner*, **21**(11):406 (1942).

[2] MacKusick and Alves, *Oil Gas J.*, **42**(49):126 (1944).   Bond, *Oil Gas J.*, **44**(31):83 (1945).

[3] Duval and Kalichevsky, *Oil Gas J.*, **52**(49):122 (1954).

[4] Yabroff and Border, *Proc. API*, **20M**(III):95 (1939).

[5] Happel and Cauley, *Ind. Eng. Chem.*, **39**:1655 (1947).

[6] *Petrol. Refiner*, **33**(9):257 (1954).   Waterman and Wiley, *Petrol. Refiner*, **34**(9):182 (1955).

sulfonic acids, sulfuric acid, and carbon disulfide.[1] The removal of these various classes of sulfur compounds presents a series of individual problems. The elementary sulfur contained in light distillates may be a product of the oxidation, by air or treating chemicals, of hydrogen sulfide.[2] Sulfur is not generally affected by refining agents, except in doctor sweetening; and for this reason, it is best to prevent its formation by separating the hydrogen sulfide from the distillate before refining treatments are made. If the distillate is heated, most of the sulfur ends up as hydrogen sulfide,[3] which is taken off in the stabilizing tower of the fractionating system; remaining traces are easily removed by washing with aqueous alkali. This is essentially what happens to any free sulfur in an oil subjected to thermal cracking. For obvious reasons, hydrogen sulfide must be removed from refinery gases before the latter are cracked or polymerized to gasoline; hydrocarbon gases must also be essentially sulfur-free to make high-quality carbon blacks and certain chemical products. The sulfur compounds and elemental sulfur in petroleum oils as well as their thermal decomposition products are probably responsible for heavy corrosion losses in refinery equipment.

Chemical Treatment. A number of reagents have been found suitable for the efficient and inexpensive removal of hydrogen sulfide from gases, all working on the principle of absorbing the H_2S at a low temperature and expelling it by air blowing (Na_2CO_3 process),[4] by heating to a higher temperature (phenolates,[5] ethanolamines, and ethanolamine–ethylene glycol mixtures,[6] alkali salts of amino acids,[7] tripotassium phosphate),[8] or by oxidizing the absorbent solution to release elemental sulfur and to regenerate the absorbing agent (thioarsenates).[9]

Besides the methods discussed under sweetening, mercaptans may be

---

[1] Borgstrom and Reid, *Oil Gas J.*, **26**(4):352 (1927).

[2] Elemental sulfur has now, however, been identified and determined in certain crude oils, particularly from the West Texas Permian formations. Eccelston, Morrison, and Smith, *Anal. Chem.*, **24**:1745 (1952). The results have been confirmed in the authors' laboratory.

[3] The reaction of elementary sulfur with hydrocarbons, on heating, to liberate hydrogen sulfide is well known. See Rasmussen, Hansford, and Sachanen, *Ind. Eng. Chem.*, **38**:376 (1946). Bryce and Hinshelwood, *J. Chem. Soc.*, 1949, p. 3379.

[4] Sperr, *Proc. Am. Gas. Assoc., Tech. Section*, 1921, p. 282; 1923, p. 1200. Jacobson, *Oil Gas J.*, **27**(36):151; (46):115 (1929).

[5] Carlvin, *Proc. API*, **19M**(III):23 (1938). *Oil Gas J.*, **43**(47):188 (1945).

[6] Wood and Storrs, *Proc. API*, **19M**(III):34 (1938). Reed and Wood, *Trans. AIChE*, **37**:363 (1941). Culbertson and Connors, *Oil Gas J.*, **51**(14):114 (1952). Kohl and Blohm, *Petrol. Eng.*, **22**(6):C-37 (1950). Muhlbauer and Monaghan, *Oil Gas J.*, **55**(17):139 (1957).

[7] Baehr, *Proc. API*, **19M**(III):37 (1938).

[8] Rosebaugh, *Proc. API*, **19M**(III):47 (1938). Mullen, *Oil Gas J.*, **37**(48):37 (1939); **43**(46):195 (1945).

[9] Gollmar, *Ind. Eng. Chem.*, **26**:130 (1934).

converted to hydrogen sulfide and the corresponding olefin by heat alone,[1] but more easily in the presence of catalysts such as bauxite.[2] Thioethers may form if the catalyst contains some zinc and cadium sulfides.[3] The removal or conversion of mercaptans can be effected by drastic agents, such as sulfuric acid or anhydrous aluminum chloride. Sulfuric acid forms alkyl acid thiosulfates, alkyl dithiosulfates, and alkyl trisulfides;[4] the chemistry of the cold sulfuric acid desulfurization[5] is not fully understood. Sulfides and disulfides are removed by addition reactions with aluminum chloride[6] or by solution with sulfuric acid.[7] Cyclic sulfides, such as tetra- and pentamethylene sulfide, as well as sulfones and sulfoxides, are likewise removed by solution in the acid. Hypochlorites oxidize mercaptans to disulfides and alkyl sulfides to sulfones; those of low molecular weight are water soluble. Disulfides are oxidized slowly to sulfonic and sulfuric acid.

Catalytic Methods. The removal or conversion of sulfur in distillates by sweetening is limited to the mercaptan content. When this is more than about 0.02 to 0.05 per cent, it is often more economical to resort to other methods, generally those that also bring about a decrease in all types of sulfur compounds. Some of the sulfur compounds in petroleum break down readily in the mild thermal treatments to which they are exposed in distillation. For others, extensive decomposition does not take place until thermal conditions necessary for hydrocarbon cracking are reached. Some are very refractory, surviving even the severe conditions employed in processes leading to tar and coke formation. The sulfur in the lower-boiling straight-run distillates is mainly in the form of mercaptans, sulfides, and disulfides. Thermally cracked distillates contain the more refractory thiophene type; in addition, thiophenols are found in catalytically cracked distillates.

Desulfurization is still a serious problem, but considerable progress is being made in lowering the sulfur level of distillates and residual stocks handled by the refinery. It has been found that the stability of sulfur compounds is greatly reduced when they are heated in the presence of adsorptive-type catalysts, and this fact is employed in a number of desulfurization processes. The noncyclic sulfur compounds (mercaptans, sulfides, and disulfides) in straight-run distillates of the naphtha class

[1] Malisoff and Marks, *Ind. Eng. Chem.*, **23**:1114 (1931).

[2] Pew and Buell, *Natl. Petrol. News*, **32**:R-354 (1940). Brooner and Conn, *Oil Gas J.*, **45**(25):96 (1946).

[3] Wiezevich, Turner, and Frolich, *Ind. Eng. Chem.*, **25**:295 (1933).

[4] Wood, Lowy, and Faragher, *Ind. Eng. Chem.*, **16**:1116 (1924). Birch and Norris, *Ind. Eng. Chem.*, **21**:1087 (1929).

[5] Halloran, *Proc. 1st Congr., London, World Petrol. Congr.*, **2**:3 (1933); *Refiner Nat. Gasoline Mfr.*, **18**:267 (1939); **19**:97 (1940).

[6] Youtz and Perkins, *Ind. Eng. Chem.*, **19**:1247 (1927).

[7] Wood, Sheeley, and Trusty, *Ind. Eng. Chem.*, **18**:169 (1926).

are readily converted into hydrogen sulfide and olefins by contacting the vapors with clays,[1] with aluminum oxide,[2] or with alumina-silica cracking catalysts.[3] These processes generally operate at about 650 to 800°F and at about 50 psi pressure. When hydrogen is added and a dehydrogenation catalyst, such as cobalt and molybdenum sulfides on alumina, is employed, extensive desulfurization over a wider spectrum of compounds is brought about. The refractory cyclic sulfur compounds are than attacked: thiophene is converted into n- and isobutane, and the methylthiophenes into n- and isopentane.[4] Pyridines and quinolines are converted to alkyl aromatics; pyrroles to alkanes; phenols to aromatics; and alkyl peroxides to alkanes.[5]

The development of more efficient catalysts and the abundant supply of hydrogen available from catalytic reforming operations have encouraged the use of hydrogen as a refining agent. The hydrodesulfurization process developed can, depending on circumstances, operate under relatively mild conditions to bring about both stabilization (double-bond saturation) and desulfurization, with essentially quantitative volumetric yields. A minimum of carbon-carbon bond scission takes place.

Hydrodesulfurization has been reported as useful in a wide variety of refining and product upgrading operations. Through saturation or partial saturation, cracked gasolines (and sulfur dioxide extracts) have been converted to aviation fuels and at the same time stabilized with respect to odor, color, and gum formation; the burning characteristics and storage stability of kerosenes and fuel oils have been improved; the cetane numbers of diesel fuel stocks have been increased. Desulfurization also takes place, as it does in the treatment of straight-run naphthas, kerosenes, gas oils, and lubricating oil distillates. The process is useful for the preparation of low-sulfur, saturated charge stocks for both catalytic cracking and reforming,[6] and is also of considerable interest for the

[1] Martin and Carlson, *Oil Gas J.*, **40**(46):138 (1942). Ballard, *ACS, Div. Petrol. Chem., Symposium on Organic Sulfur Compounds as Related to Petroleum*, Preprint, p. 265, ACS Meeting, San Francisco, 1949.

[2] Schulze and Alden, *Oil Gas J.*, **38**(27):199 (1939). Padovani, Girelli, and Simaramed, *World Petrol. Congr., Proc. 3rd Congr., Hague*, **4**:263 (1951). Edwards, *Petroleum Engr.*, **26**(4):C-15 (1954).

[3] Norman, *Oil Gas J.*, **40**(46):138 (1942). Schwarzenbek, Slyngstad, and Knaus, *World Petrol. Congr., Proc. 3rd Congr., Hague*, **4**:274 (1951).

[4] Hendricks, Huffman, Parker, and Stirton, *ACS, Div. Petrol. Chem.*, Preprints, p. 1, ACS Meeting, Atlantic City, April, 1946.

[5] Grote, Watkins, Poll, and Hendricks, *Oil Gas J.*, **52**(50):211 (1954).

[6] Byrnes, Bradley, and Lee, *Ind. Eng. Chem.*, **35**:1160 (1943). Voorhies and Smith, *Ind. Eng. Chem.*, **39**:1104 (1947). Cole and Davidson, *Ind. Eng. Chem.*, **41**:2711 (1949). Hoog, Klinkert, and Schaafsma, *Proc. API*, **33**(III):71 (1953). Grote, Watkins, Poll, and Hendricks, *Oil Gas J.*, **52**(50):211 (1954). Patterson and Jones, *Oil Gas J.*, **53**(24):92 (1954). Baeder and Siegmond, *Oil Gas J.*, **53**(42):123 (1955). Guthrie, *Petrol. Processing*, **10**:1159 (1955). Davidson, *Petrol. Processing*, **11**(11):116 (1956).

upgrading of crude oils and residua.[1] Other changes that have been observed are improvements in inhibitor response, demulsibility and viscosity indexes, and reduction in acid values, carbon residues, Sligh oxidation numbers, and content of trace metals as well as of oxygen and nitrogen compounds. As might be expected, it is possible by proper adjustment of conditions to bring about more or less specific results. For instance, in the treatment of cracked distillates 60 to 70 per cent of the sulfur and about 90 per cent of the diolefins in a cracked gasoline can be removed without saturating more than 20 to 25 per cent of the monoolefins; this is effected by hydrogenating under mild temperature (600°F) and pressure (75 psi) conditions over a tungsten-nickel sulfide catalyst.[2]

The several processes developed for hydrodesulfurization seem to be basically similar, differing mainly in the nature of the catalysts employed and the amount of hydrogen present. In general, they involve passing a mixture of hydrogen and the hot oil vapors (or liquid) downward through the catalyst bed. About 70 cu ft of hydrogen per barrel of oil is consumed in the removal of 1 per cent sulfur in the feed stocks. Stabilization to remove hydrogen sulfide and dissolved gases or an alkali wash is about the only additional treatment needed. In one process, the operation is self-supporting with respect to the hydrogen consumed, since all of the latter is obtained through the dehydrogenation of the naphthenic hydrocarbons contained in the charge.[3] The amount of cracked distillate that can be blended into the charge is thus limited. In other processes extraneous hydrogen is added in quantities sufficient to maintain the desired hydrogen-oil ratio; this latter depends on the nature of the charge. The amount may be up to 3,500 cu ft per barrel of feed, from zero to 700 cu ft being consumed.[4] Pressures and temperatures also vary widely, again depending on the charge, the former from 50 to 800 psi and the latter from 400 to 850°F. Heavier stocks require higher treating temperatures, which in turn cause increased amounts of carbon lay-down on the catalyst. As in catalytic cracking, the catalyst is regenerated by burning in air-steam or air-nitrogen mixtures at about 1100°F.

The catalysts employed are physically rugged, are not readily poisoned by the sulfur compounds contained in the recycle gas or charge, and can be regenerated many times. Some are still active toward desulfurization

[1] McAfee, Montgomery, Summers, Hirsch, and Horne, *Oil Gas J.*, **54**(2):196 (1955). Gilmartin, Horne, and Walsh, *Oil Gas J.*, **54**(40):85 (1956). McAfee and Horne, *Petrol. Processing*, **11**(4):47 (1956). Davidson, *op. cit.*

[2] Casagrande, Meerbott, Sartor, and Trainer, *ACS, Div. Petrol. Chem.*, Preprints, no. 30, p. 63, ACS Meeting, New York, September, 1954. See also, Hammar, *World Petrol. Congr., Proc. 3rd Congr., Hague*, **4**:295 (1951).

[3] Porter, *J. Inst. Petrol.*, **40**:18 (1954).

[4] Patterson and Jones, *Oil Gas J.*, **53**(24):92 (1954); **53**(26):81 (1954).

even when holding up to 15 per cent their weight of deposited carbon. In general, those so far developed are modified forms of cobalt and molybdenum oxides on alumina,[1] tungsten and nickel sulfides,[2] nickel oxide,[3] nickel thiomolybdate,[4] and vanadium oxide.[5]

[1] Porter, *J. Inst. Petrol.*, **40**:18 (1954). Hendricks, Huffman, Parker, and Stirton, *ACS, Div. Petrol. Chem.*, Preprints, p. 1, ACS Meeting, Atlantic City, April, 1946.

[2] Casagrande, Meerbott, Sartor, and Trainer, *ACS, Div. Petrol. Chem.*, Preprints, no. 30, p. 63, ACS Meeting, New York, September, 1954.

[3] McAfee, Montgomery, Summers, Hirsch, and Horne, *op. cit.*

[4] Ipatieff, Monroe, and Schaad, *ACS, Div. Petrol. Chem., Gen. Papers*, Preprints, p. 47, ACS Meeting, San Francisco, March, 1949.

[5] Komarewsky, Kanggs, and Bragg, *Ind. Eng. Chem.*, **46**:1689 (1954).

CHAPTER **VIII**

Refining by Physical Methods

by BEVERIDGE J. MAIR, PH.D.

American Petroleum Institute Research Project 6
Carnegie Institute of Technology

Distillation is the most commonly used of the various physical processes involved in petroleum refining. Adsorption, selective solution, and selective precipitation, including crystallization, are important though practiced on a smaller scale. Distillation and crystallization of waxes are discussed in separate chapters. Thermal diffusion has proved quite useful for laboratory separations, but has apparently not been applied on a larger scale.[1]

The advantages of physical processes for refining are low costs, easier and more definite control of quality, and less serious treating losses. Residues from physical refining are of low grade, but are more useful than the sludges and cokes resulting from chemical treatment, as for example, sulfuric acid sludge. Furthermore, the use of oxidation inhibitors and similar additives has made drastic chemical refining less necessary and even less desirable.

REFINING BY ADSORPTION

The earliest application of adsorption refining was for the removal of undesirable, highly colored materials of an asphaltic or resinous nature from petroleum fractions. This application is almost as old as the petroleum industry itself. Bone char was used originally, first for the decolorizing of kerosene and finally for heavier oils, but was later displaced by fuller's earth which was found in 1893[2] to be effective for refining steam-cylinder stocks.

---

[1] Kramers and Broeder, *Anal. Chim. Acta*, **2**:687 (1948). Jones, *Petrol. Processing*, **6**:132 (1951). Broeder and Van Nes, *World Petrol. Congr., Proc. 3rd Congr., Hague*, **6**:25 (1951). Jones, *Ind. Eng. Chem.*, **47**:212 (1955).

[2] By George H. Taber in the Lubricating Works of the present Atlantic Refining Company at Philadelphia, Pa.

The removal of asphaltic or resinous materials from lubricating oil stocks using acid-activated bentonite, fuller's earth, and bauxite is still probably the most important commercial application of adsorption refining. However, it is now generally found more economical to remove the greater part of the undesirable constituents by newer processes involving solvent separations, such as propane deasphaltizing and solvent extraction. Adsorption refining is reserved primarily for the finishing of partially refined products such as waxes, petrolatums, and lubricating oils. Adsorption by use of clay has also been applied for nearly thirty years in the stabilization of gasoline stocks by the removal of gum-producing substances such as diolefins, which result from thermal cracking operations.

Within the last few years new applications of adsorption refining have been proposed which deal not merely with the removal of comparatively small amounts of undesirable components from broad petroleum fractions but with the actual separation of certain petroleum fractions into their constituent classes of hydrocarbons, for example, into paraffins plus cycloparaffins, olefins, and aromatics[1] or into paraffins plus cycloparaffins and aromatics.[2]

Another recent application of adsorption refining is for the recovery of natural or cracked hydrocarbon gases and their separation, in some instances, into individual constituents.[3] In this application, adsorption on carbon from the vapor phase is used in a continuous operation. It may also be noted that adsorption fractionating processes find extensive use on a laboratory scale in connection with the separation and analysis of petroleum products.[4]

VIII-1. Theory. When an adsorbent is placed in contact with a liquid (or gaseous) solution of two or more components, some of the molecules become attached to its surface. These molecules are not firmly bound[5] and a continual interchange takes place between those in the surface layer and those in the bulk of the solution. Different molecules differ in the strength of their attachment to the surface, and, when equilibrium is established, the composition of the material constituting the surface layer will differ from that of the surrounding solution. The material in the surface layer is referred to as the adsorbed phase as distinguished from the liquid phase. As with other two-phase fractionating processes, it is the difference in composition of the phases which makes possible the use

[1] Eagle and Scott, *Petrol. Processing*, **4**:881 (1949).

[2] Davis, Harper, and Weatherly, *Oil Gas J.*, **51**(2):112 (1953); see also Weatherford, Karr, and Capell, *Anal. Chem.*, **26**:252 (1954).

[3] Berg, *Trans. AIChE*, **42**:665 (1946).

[4] See, for example, Mair, *Ind. Eng. Chem.*, **42**:1355 (1950). Lipkin, Hoffecker, Martin, and Ledley, *Anal. Chem.*, **20**:130 (1948). Lillard, Jones, and Anderson, *Ind. Eng. Chem.*, **44**:2623 (1952). Furby, *Anal. Chem.*, **22**:876 (1950).

[5] This discussion refers only to physical adsorption.

of the process for the separation of the components of a mixture. Mair, Westhaver, and Rossini[1] have employed the concepts customary for other two-phase fractionating processes, for example, fractionation by distillation, in an analysis of the adsorption fractionating process.

As with distillation the concept of the single-stage process is applicable to adsorption fractionation. When a solid adsorbent is shaken with a solution until thermodynamic equilibrium is established between the adsorbed and liquid phases, the separation is equivalent to that for a single stage. For a binary solution of two components A, and B, the composition of the phases is described by the equation, $\alpha = (N_A/N_B)^a/(N_A/N_B)^l$, where N indicates mole fraction, α the separation factor, and the superscripts a and l refer, respectively, to the adsorbed and liquid phases.[2]

The effectiveness of distillation and extraction processes is greatly enhanced by the use of fractionating columns. Similarly, the effectiveness of the adsorption fractionating process is enhanced by the use of tall columns packed with finely divided adsorbent. Such columns may be considered as equivalent to a succession of equilibrium stages of fractionation. The investigators illustrated the analogy between adsorption and distillation fractionation by considering the simple case of the separation of two substances A and B. For the distillation process, the entire charge is present as liquid and vapor in the rectifying section of a vertical distilling column. Initially, the average composition of the gas and liquid phases is assumed to be the same throughout the length of the section. Before the molecules can be separated it is necessary to provide for the transport of the molecules A and B from one end of the system to the other and to provide for their interchange from one phase to another.

These requirements are met by providing a heater at the bottom end of the rectifying section and a condenser at the top end. By this means, molecules A and B in the liquid phase at the bottom are vaporized, and the vapors travel upward through the length of the column. On reaching the condenser at the top, the vapors are returned to the liquid phase and the liquid material flows by gravity down the rectifying section to the bottom end. As the vapors pass upward and the liquid phase flows down-

---

[1] *Ind. Eng. Chem.*, **42**:1279 (1950).

[2] Actually, it is not practical to determine the separation factor by contacting the solution and adsorbent, since there is no way of removing the excess liquid from the adsorbent without affecting the composition of the adsorbed material. However, the same results can be obtained without physical contact of the adsorbent and the liquid by letting the adsorbent come to equilibrium with the selected material in the gas phase, which is in turn in equilibrium with the same material in the liquid phase. The adsorbed material may then be desorbed and its composition determined from (for example) its refractive index. The composition of the material comprising the liquid phase may also be determined from refractive index measurements.

ward, a continual interchange of molecules between the two phases occurs. Finally, after a certain time, a state of equilibrium in the given system will be substantially attained with the concentration of the more volatile molecules, *A*, at the top of the column and the concentration of the less volatile molecules, *B*, at the bottom higher than the initial concentrations. For the adsorption process, the entire charge is present in two phases, liquid and adsorbed, in a section of a vertical column packed with a solid adsorbent. Initially, the average composition of the adsorbed and liquid phases is the same throughout the length of the section. Before the

molecules can be fractionated, it is necessary to provide for their transport through the system and for their interchange from one phase to another. This may be accomplished by introducing fresh adsorbent at the bottom of the column, letting it pass upward and placing a suitable desorbent at the top in order to keep the charge of material in the column. In this way, the molecules in the liquid phase at the bottom pass to the adsorbed state as fresh adsorbent is introduced and the molecules in the adsorbed phase at the top of the column are returned to the liquid phase as the desorbent meets the adsorbent on its way out of the column. As a result of the movement of the adsorbed phase upward and the liquid phase down-

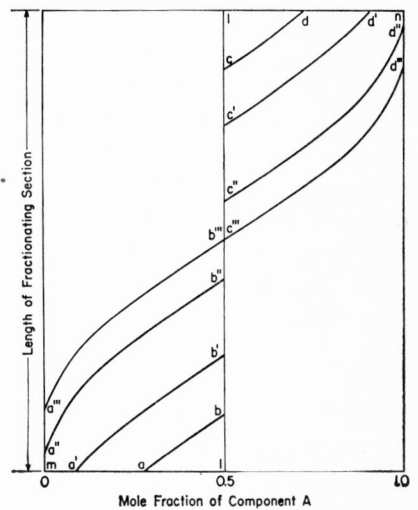

FIG. VIII-1. Schematic diagram of progressive changes in composition occurring in fractionation of equimolecular mixtures of *A* and *B*. [*From Mair, Westhaver, and Rossini, Ind. Eng. Chem.*, **42**: 1279 (1950).]

ward and the interchange of molecules between the phases, there is a net transport of the more strongly adsorbed constituent, *A*, upward and the less strongly adsorbed constituent, *B*, downward.

The manner in which the composition of an equimolecular mixture of two substances *A* and *B* (with equal molecular volumes) varies along the length of an adsorption column at various stages in the process is shown in Fig. VIII-1. Initially, the composition is represented by the line *ij*. As soon as the flow of material has started, component *A* begins to accumulate at the top of the section and component *B* at the bottom, while the middle portion remains, for some time, unchanged in composition. The net volumes of components *A* and *B* transported toward either end continue to increase as more adsorbent flows through the system until finally no material of the initial composition remains in the middle and a state of equilibrium has been established.   In Fig. VIII-1 progressive changes in composition are represented by the lines $abcd$, $a'b'c'd', a''b''c''d''$.   The final equilibrium state is represented by the line $a'''b'''c'''d'''$.

The investigators showed experimentally that the composition at various stages of the fractionating process does conform to this picture and have used these concepts to derive, from experiments in packed columns, equations for computing the separation factor and the height equivalent to unit theoretical stage of separation.   They found that the separation factor for the system benzene plus n-hexane, with silica gel as the adsorbent, decreased from about 8 at 10 per cent benzene to about 2.3 at 90 per cent benzene, whereas there was little change in the separation factor with change in composition for the systems benzene plus n-propylbenzene and benzene plus ethylbenzene.   Values for the separation factor for several equivolume mixtures were found to be as follows: benzene plus ethylbenzene, 1.2; benzene plus n-propylbenzene, 1.4; benzene plus n-hexane, 3.4; benzene plus cyclohexane, 3.0; ethanol plus n-heptane, 26.

For the height equivalent to unit theoretical stage of separation, values of about 1 cm were obtained with 200- to 300-mesh silica gel in columns 2 cm in diameter.

The theoretical principles outlined in the foregoing are useful in understanding commercial applications.   However, the quantitative aspects of these principles do not appear to have been applied extensively in commercial practice.   This condition is likely to prevail indefinitely in such cases as the refining of lubricating oils, petrolatums, and waxes, owing to the complex nature of these materials and the tendency for an adsorbent to change its characteristics during regeneration by burning.   However, in some of the newer processes, involving the separation of individual compounds or classes of compounds, it seems probable that the quantitative aspects will be of greater practical value.

VIII-2.   Adsorbents.   The particular property of an adsorbent which distinguishes it from other solid substances is its large surface area.   This area is attributable to the presence of numerous minute pores which permeate the individual particles and not to the fineness of the particles themselves, which, for all commercial adsorbents, contribute little to the surface area.   The surface area of an adsorbent does not depend on chemical composition but depends instead on the method of preparation or the origin of the product; it may vary considerably for commercial samples of the same adsorbent.

Methods are available for determining the surface area; the most common procedure involves the determination of the quantity of a gas (usually nitrogen) required to produce a monomolecular layer on the adsorbent.[1] Usually, the greater the surface area, the greater the amount of a substance absorbed. However, the surface area available to the nitrogen molecule may not necessarily be the same as that available to larger molecules, because some of the pores which are large enough to permit the entry of nitrogen molecules may be too small for some of the larger organic molecules found in petroleum.[2]

For commercial adsorbents, with the exception of some varieties of carbon,[3] the order of adsorbability from liquid solutions in going from weakly to strongly adsorbed substances is approximately as follows: paraffins plus cycloparaffins, olefins, mononuclear aromatics, polynuclear aromatics, and organic compounds containing oxygen, sulfur, or nitrogen. There are, however, significant differences between adsorbents, the reasons for which are not yet understood; they may be due, in part, at least, to the relative pore size distributions of the different adsorbents. A few of these may be mentioned. Silica gel is probably the most effective of all adsorbents for the separation of aromatics from paraffins and cycloparaffins but is much less useful than bauxite for the separation of colored substances from crude petroleum and petroleum fractions. Silica gel is also less suitable than florisil (synthetic magnesium silicate) for the separation of nitrogen compounds from shale oil distillates, whereas florisil is comparatively ineffective for separating aromatics from paraffins and cycloparaffins.[4] Bauxite is more effective than fuller's earth for the

[1] Brunauer, Emmett, and Teller, *J. ACS*, **60**:309 (1938).

[2] Chabazite is an example of an adsorbent with small pores which are very uniform in diameter. Adsorbents of this type have been termed "molecular sieves" and have been employed to effect a wide range of separations in which the shape of the organic molecule is the controlling factor. Barrer, *J. Soc. Chem. Ind.*, **64**:130–135 (1945); *Faraday Soc. Discussions*, **7**:135 (1949); *Trans. Faraday Soc.*, **49**:807, 929 (1953). Synthetic molecular sieves with pore diameters of 4 and 5 angstrom units (A), respectively, are available commercially. The adsorbent with pores 5 A in diameter can be used to separate normal paraffins from branched or cyclic hydrocarbons; the pores in this case are big enough to admit the straight chains but not the other structures. *Chem. Week*, **75**(21):64 (1954). On separation of carbon dioxide, acetylene, and acetone vapors from ethylene, see *Petrol. Refiner*, **36**(7):136 (1957). For fractionation of aromatics, see Mair and Shamaienger, *ACS, Div. Petrol. Chem.*, ACS Meeting, New York, September, 1957. For methods of determining pore size distribution and results for several adsorbents, see Barrett, Joyner, and Halenda, *J. ACS*, **73**:373 (1951); Wayne, *J. ACS*, **73**:5498 (1951); Drake, *Ind. Eng. Chem.*, **41**:780 (1949).

[3] For Columbia activated carbon, hydrocarbons are more strongly adsorbed than polar organic substances (alcohols, ketones, ethers, mercaptans, etc.). The order in which organic compounds are adsorbed on carbon depends on the method of preparation of the adsorbent, including the temperature and the atmosphere (oxidizing or inert) of activation. Bartell and Lloyd, *J. ACS*, **60**:2120 (1938).

[4] Smith, Smith, and Dinneen, *Anal. Chem.*, **22**:867 (1950).

removal of the last traces of colored material from petrolatums, waxes, and oils, whereas for the removal of the grosser part of the colored materials and the production of medium- or dark-colored oils these adsorbents are approximately on an equal footing.   With carbon an increase of the molecular weight of normal paraffins increases the adsorbability, whereas with silica gel the reverse is true.[1]

For gases, the adsorbability (strength of adsorption) in general increases with increase in boiling point (decrease in vapor pressure), although the effects of structure of the molecule may in some cases change the normal order.   Thus, for example, with silica gel as the adsorbent, toluene vapor is more strongly adsorbed than that of n-octane, although the boiling points of these compounds are 110.6 and 125.7°C, respectively.   For mixtures of paraffin and olefin gases, olefins are much more strongly adsorbed on silica gel than would be anticipated from their vapor pressures, whereas on carbon the type of molecule has less effect.[2]

Bauxite.   This adsorbent is composed principally of aluminum oxide with iron oxides as impurity.   It is prepared by thermal activation of naturally occurring bauxite, with grinding and screening to the desired particle size.   The principal applications include the refining of lubricating oil stocks, petrolatums, waxes, transformer oils, medicinal oils, kerosene, and the removal of sulfur compounds from gasoline (Perco process).   Bauxite is regenerated by burning off the colored adsorbed materials at 1000 to 1200°F with some loss of adsorption capacity during the first few regenerations.   It can then be regenerated almost indefinitely.   Handling losses are about 1.5 per cent per regeneration.   It is employed only for percolation.[3]   On a volume basis bauxite has three to four times the capacity of fuller's earth for the removal of colored substances from waxes and petrolatums, and even light-colored oils.   The surface area determined with nitrogen is in the range 180 to 350 sq m per g.

Fuller's Earth (*Attapulgite, Floridin, Florida Earth*).   This material is a hydrous magnesium aluminum silicate of the montmorillonite group. A typical analysis in weight per cent for the main factors is as follows (other elements in small proportions):[4]

SiO_2	53.42	TiO_2	0.52
Al_2O_3	10.06	CaO	1.29
Fe_2O_3	3.58	MgO	9.18
Ignition loss		9.42	
Uncombined water		11.83	

[1] Hirschler and Amon, *Ind. Eng. Chem.*, **39**:1585 (1947).
[2] Lewis, Gilliland, Chertov, and Cadogan, *Ind. Eng. Chem.*, **42**:1326 (1950).
[3] Hubbell and Ferguson, *Oil Gas J.*, **37**(27):1358 (1938).
[4] Bell and Funsten, "Industrial Rocks and Minerals," chap. VII, American Institute of Mining Engineers, New York, 1937.

It is usually prepared by working the natural earth (principally from Florida and Georgia) with water and extruding through multiple orifice dies. The resulting "spaghetti" is dried, ground, and screened to the desired particle size. Some material is still prepared by an older method in which the natural earth is dried, ground, and screened. With the extrusion method the final material has about a 30 per cent greater capacity for decolorization than that prepared directly.[1]

Applications include the stabilization of gasolines (Gray process) by the removal of gum-forming substances, and the refining of lubricating oil stocks to lighter colors. For the latter application it is competitive with bauxite. It is regenerated by burning at 1000 to 1200°F but is sensitive to overburning (sintering) and usually requires to be replaced after 5 to 15 regenerations. For percolation fuller's earth is used in granular form; the fines, however, are suitable only for contact treatment. The surface area determined with nitrogen is usually in the range from 130 to 170 sq m per g.

Acid-activated Bentonite. This adsorbent consists of hydrous magnesium aluminum silicates of the montmorillonite type. A typical analysis in weight per cent for the main constituents is as follows:[2]

SiO_2	55.70	TiO_2	0.33
Al_2O_3	13.13	CaO	0.31
Fe_2O_3	2.44	MgO	3.46
	Ignition loss	7.48	
	Uncombined water	15.77	

It is prepared by leaching specially selected bentonites which occur in Mississippi, Arizona, and California with sulfuric or hydrochloric acid at about 220°F and washing out the soluble material, drying, and powdering. The finely powdered material is suitable for only the contact process; it is not regenerated. It is employed to refine a wide variety of lubricating oil stocks and has the largest tonnage sale of all adsorbents to the petroleum industry. The capacity for clarification of petroleum oils is somewhat greater than that of fuller's earth. The surface area is usually in the range 150 to 270 sq m per g.

Magnesol. This is a synthetic hydrous magnesium silicate. It has been used commercially to refine lubricating oil stocks by the contact process.[3] Regeneration was accomplished by extracting the highly colored adsorbed constituents with acetone-naphtha mixtures at 90 to 100°F.

Florisil. This is a synthetic magnesium silicate. It has been found effective in analytical work to separate nitrogen compounds from shale

---

[1] Fitzsimmons, Amero, and Capell, *Natl. Petrol. News*, **33**(44):R-399 (1941).
[2] Bell and Funsten, *loc. cit.*
[3] Chenault and Miller, *Refiner Nat. Gasoline Mfr.*, **20**:449 (1941).

oil distillates.   It is apparently not effective for the separation of different types of hydrocarbons.[1]

Silica Gel.   This is silicon dioxide plus a small amount of combined water.   It is prepared by treating sodium silicate with mineral acids, sulfuric or hydrochloric.   The resulting gel is allowed to set, then leached with water to remove salts and excess acid, and the product dried, ground, and screened to size.   High selectivity and large capacity make it valuable for analytical separation of aromatics, olefins, and paraffins plus cycloparaffins.   The commercial separation of aromatics from paraffins plus cycloparaffins has been proposed and tested on a pilot-plant scale.[2] Adsorptive capacity is lost rapidly if the gel is heated to the temperatures required to burn off adsorbed materials.   It may be regenerated for use in a cyclic process by desorbing the more strongly adsorbed constituents, e.g., aromatics, by washing with comparatively large volumes of aromatic-free hydrocarbons, such as *n*-pentane.   The surface area is usually in the range from 500 to 800 sq m per g.

Carbon.   Adsorptive carbon is derived from a wide variety of sources; characteristics differ very appreciably, depending on the source and method of preparation.[3]   Carbon in the form of bone char was used in the early days of the petroleum industry for decolorizing lubricating oils.   It is now employed for the commercial vapor-phase separation and recovery of hydrocarbon gases.[4]   The adsorbed gases are removed by mild heating. On a laboratory scale it has been applied for the analysis of hydrocarbons of low molecular weight[5] and for the separation of normal from branched paraffins.[6]   Preparations made from coconut shells have very large surface areas (about 1,700 sq m per g) and show a high selectivity for aromatics.

Alumina.   This synthetic preparation of aluminum oxide has been investigated for small-scale separation of different types of hydrocarbons.[7] It is reported to be more effective than silica gel for the separation of polynuclear aromatic hydrocarbons according to the number of rings per molecule.[8]   The surface area is usually about 200 sq m per g.

[1] Smith, Smith, and Dinneen, *Anal. Chem.*, **22**:867 (1950).

[2] Eagle and Scott, *Petrol. Processing*, **4**:881 (1949).   Davis, Harper, and Weatherly, *Oil Gas J.*, **51**(2):112 (1953).   See also Hirschler and Mertes, *Ind. Eng. Chem.*, **47**:193 (1955).

[3] Bartell and Lloyd, *J. ACS*, **60**:2120 (1938).

[4] Berg, *Trans. AIChE*, **42**:665 (1946).

[5] Turner, *Petrol. Refiner*, **22**(5):140 (1943).

[6] Hirschler and Amon, *Ind. Eng. Chem.*, **39**:1585 (1947).   Hibshman, *Ind. Eng. Chem.*, **42**:1310 (1950).

[7] Hirschler and Amon, *Ind. Eng. Chem.*, **39**:1585 (1947).

[8] Launeau and Johnson, *ACS, Div. Petrol. Chem.*, ACS Meeting, Cleveland, April, 1951.

VIII-3. Commercial Applications

Recovery and Separation of Gaseous Hydrocarbons. The effectiveness of carbon as an adsorbent for the separation and analysis of petroleum gases was recognized by Turner,[1] who developed laboratory scale apparatus for this purpose. Within the past decade a continuous process which utilizes carbon has been developed for the recovery and separation of petroleum gases on a commercial scale.[2] The feed enters near the center of a vertical column to the top of which carbon is being fed at a relatively low temperature; at this point a portion of the gas becomes adsorbed and travels downward with the adsorbent; desorption takes place at the bottom of the column, which is maintained at a relatively high temperature. Here, a portion of the gas is withdrawn and a portion permitted to return as reflux in counterflow to the descending adsorbed phase. Throughout the length of the column there is an interchange between the phases, with a net transport of the weakly adsorbed components (usually those of lower boiling point) to the top, and a net transport of the more strongly adsorbed components to the bottom. The carbon, after regeneration at the bottom of the column, is returned to the top. If desired, side cuts may be withdrawn at intermediate points along the column. An example showing the separation of ethylene in pilot-plant operations is given in Table VIII-1. The process permits the recovery of hydrocarbons from streams that cannot be handled economically by more conventional methods.

TABLE VIII-1. SEPARATION OF ETHYLENE IN PILOT-PLANT OPERATIONS

	Composition in volume per cent		
	Feed	Make	Discharge
Methane...............	43.0	1.6	99.1
Ethylene...............	49.5	85.9	0.2
Ethane................	5.5	9.3	0.4
Propane...............	2.0	3.2	0.3

From Berg, *Trans. AIChE*, **42**:665 (1946).

Separation of Classes of Hydrocarbons. Silica gel is a very selective adsorbent for the separation of aromatic hydrocarbons from paraffins and cycloparaffins, and it is now widely used on a laboratory scale for the determination of the aromatic content of various petroleum fractions; it is also employed to some extent for the determination of their olefin content.[3] Two procedures for commercial operation which make use of this

[1] *Petrol. Refiner*, **22**(5):140 (1943).

[2] Berg, *loc. cit.*

[3] Mair, *Ind. Eng. Chem.*, **42**:1355 (1950). Lipkin, Hoffecker, Martin, and Ledley, *Anal. Chem.*, **20**:130 (1948). Criddle and LeTourneau, *Anal. Chem.*, **23**:1620 (1951).

high selectivity of silica gel have been developed. Eagle and Scott[1] have described a cyclic pilot unit suitable for the continuous separation of aromatics and olefins of high purity from a variety of light petroleum stocks. They found that the use of moving beds of adsorbent was impractical and instead achieved the counterflow of adsorbent and petroleum distillate by using a series of stationary columns and changing the position of the feed and desorbent injection points as well as the points where the products are withdrawn. Petroleum solvents, such as pentane, hexane, heptane, petroleum ether, or dearomatized kerosene, were used to desorb the aromatics from the columns as they were withdrawn successively from the aromatic (or olefin) enriching portion of the fractionating system. A portion of the aromatics (or olefins) thus obtained, together with some of the desorbent, was returned as reflux to the aromatic enriching zone. Columns from which the aromatics had been desorbed were cut into the cycle at the end of the saturate (paraffin-cycloparaffin) enriching zone. Thus, a complete cycle may be deemed to consist of the introduction of a column with freshly regenerated adsorbent at the end of the saturate enriching zone, the gradual change in position of the column past the feed injection point into the aromatic enriching zone, and, finally, the occurrence of desorption of aromatics and the regeneration of the adsorbent. The petroleum solvent used to desorb the aromatics is selected so that it may be separated from the aromatic (or olefin) and the saturated portions by distillation. Aromatic material with a purity of 99.8 per cent was obtained from a hydroformed naphtha by this method. Cracked naphtha was readily separated into saturated, olefin, and aromatic concentrates. The olefin concentrates could be separated by distillation to give high-purity olefin cuts useful as chemical intermediates. The preferred operating conditions were found to depend upon the character of the charge stock and adsorbent, but usually were within the following range:

Feed to adsorbent, gal per lb...............	0.05 to 0.10
Recycle to adsorbent, gal per lb.............	0.08 to 0.14
Desorbing solvent to adsorbent, gal per lb.....	0.2 to 0.5
Cycle time, hr............................	0.25 to 2.0
Liquid velocities, gal per hr per sq ft.........	100 to 1,000

Among advantages of the process were the following: wide flexibility with respect to type and boiling range of feed stock; higher-purity products than are obtainable by conventional solvent extraction, distillation, or acid treating; and control of product purity by simple adjustment of cycle time and flow rates of recycle and desorbent.

The other adsorption process[2] for the separation of aromatics from petroleum stocks also operates in a cyclic manner, but instead of cycling

[1] *Petrol. Processing,* **4**:881 (1949).

[2] Davis, Harper, and Weatherly, *Oil Gas J.,* **51**(2):112 (1953).

the columns, the feed stock and two desorbents are cycled to each individual column. In actual operation the flow through the column is continuous and there is a gradual increase and decrease of the various components in the effluent. This is pictured by the diagram in Fig. VIII-2 which gives the composition of the effluent at all points throughout the cycle. The desorbents *A* and *B* are present in both the aromatic and saturated streams and are recovered by distillation. For the separation of benzene and toluene from petroleum stocks, desorbent *A* may consist of mixed xylenes and desorbent *B* of butane. For the separation of other aromatic products such as DDT solvents, other desorbents having boiling points differing from that of the charge stock may be used. The silica gel is protected from moisture and other poisons by regenerative pretreatment driers on each of the streams feeding the columns, and life of one year is estimated.

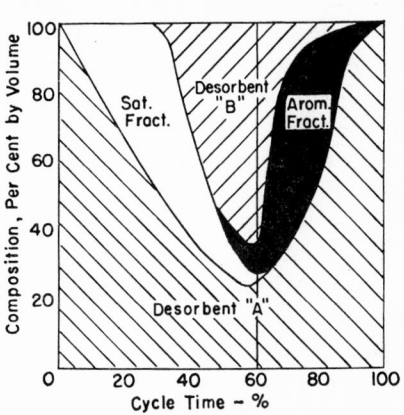

FIG. VIII-2. Composition of effluent from adsorption column as a function of time. [*From Guthrie, Petrol. Processing*, **6**: 833 (1951).]

The recovery of aromatics is high but depends to some extent on the purity required. Thus, for aromatic purities of 98, 96, 94, and 90 per cent the corresponding expected values for the recovery are 90, 94, 96, and 98 per cent.

Refining of Lubricating Oils, Petrolatums, and Waxes. Probably the most important commercial application of adsorption refining is still the time-honored use of adsorbents for the removal of highly colored materials and those of resinous nature from high-boiling petroleum products, principally from lubricating oils, petrolatums, and waxes. The fact that petroleum fractions on percolation through an adsorbent such as fuller's earth are separated into portions which differ not only in color but also in specific gravity, viscosity, and other properties was probably well known in the petroleum industry at an early date but was first published by Day.[1] Since then many others have observed this behavior. For example, Kaufmann[2] by percolating a steam-refined cylinder stock through fuller's earth found that the first portion of the effluent had a lower density, lower viscosity, and much lower ASTM carbon residue than succeeding

[1] *Proc. Am. Phil. Soc.*, **36**:112 (1897). See also Gilpin, *Am. Chem. J.*, **40**:495 (1908); **50**:59 (1913).

[2] *Chem. & Met. Eng.*, **30**:153 (1924).

fractions, which showed properties gradually approaching those of the original stock. It is now recognized that this change in properties is due to the preferential adsorption of sulfur-, oxygen-, and nitrogen-containing compounds as well as polynuclear aromatic hydrocarbons.

The two processes which are used commercially for these operations are known, respectively, as the contact process and the percolation process. As the name suggests, the contact process involves the thorough mixing of the oil with the adsorbent under controlled conditions of time and temperature and then separating the adsorbent carrying the adsorbed undesirable constituents. The operation thus corresponds to a single-stage fractionation. It is often applied after acid treating, serving to remove acid sludge, to neutralize, and to decolorize at the same time. Neutralization of highly viscous stocks containing the products of reaction with sulfuric acid, almost impossible with aqueous alkali because of ready emulsification, is easily accomplished by this means. Either acid-activated bentonite or the fines of fuller's earth are employed. These adsorbents are applied as powders of 100- to 200-mesh size in amounts ranging from 0.1 to 1.0 lb per gal; mixing may be with the dry clay or as a mud or pulp with excess water.[1] The latter is perhaps more convenient, and the subsequent conversion of the water to steam helps to protect the oil against oxidation by contact with air at high temperatures. Operation may be in batch or continuous, the latter being preferred for large-scale handling. The oil and mud are mixed in a closed vessel and pumped through a tubular heater; the temperature is from 250 to 600°F, the higher range for the more viscous cylinder stock residuals.[2]

The discharge stream is cooled and mixed with naphtha, which makes easier the removal of spent clay by filter pressing. Usually the diluted mixture is subjected to dewaxing after removal of clay, so that one dilution serves two purposes. On lighter lubricating distillates, SAE 20 and lower, the slurry is filter-pressed without naphtha at a temperature of 150 to 200°F.

The time required for treatment is generally about one-half to one hour, and no great advantage is recognized for longer treatments. Kalichevsky and Ramsay[3] have shown that most of the color removal occurs during the early stages of the treatment and is more rapid at the higher temperature. Adsorbents used in the contact process are not regenerated and are frequently discarded after the first operation.

---

[1] Five to twenty per cent moisture; the optimum water content depends on conditions. Fusten, *Refiner Nat. Gasoline Mfr.*, **16**:237 (1937).

[2] Troublesome foaming at this stage may be prevented by recycling some of the heated oil to the mixing tank so as to warm its contents and evaporate the excess water gradually.

[3] *Ind. Eng. Chem.*, **25**:941 (1933).

With the percolation process the oil to be refined is caused to flow through a column of granular fuller's earth or bauxite under sufficient pressure to provide the desired rate of flow. As oil is introduced to the column, the first portion comes in contact with successive layers of adsorbent and undergoes many stages of fractionation before issuing from the bottom of the column. In the meantime, the first or top layer of adsorbent comes in contact with successive portions of the original oil and comes to equilibrium with oil of this composition. As more oil is introduced, this equilibrium zone extends farther and farther down the column and finally reaches the bottom, at which point oil of the original composition issues. Thus, successive portions of oil which have issued from the column have undergone varying degrees of fractionation, from the first portions, which have been worked over extensively, to the latter portions, which have undergone comparatively little separation, and finally to the end portion which has undergone no fractionation and has the composition of the original oil. In practice, it is customary to discontinue the operation shortly before the charge oil issues from the column. It may be noted that the composition of the material adsorbed, when the column has been operated until the charge oil comes through, differs from that of the original oil by only a single stage of fractionation.

The percolation method has the advantage of separating different products in a single operation, the better grades being of higher quality than those obtainable with the contact process, which produces only a single product. The percolation process is, therefore, the only one suitable for the preparation of colorless or light-colored pharmaceutical oils, petrolatums, and waxes.

In commercial practice, the columns consist of vertical steel cylinders ranging from 15 to 30 ft in length and from 5 to 15 ft in diameter. The larger columns hold up to 50 tons of fuller's earth. Mechanical vibration is sometimes employed in packing the cylinders. This permits slightly greater amounts of adsorbent than would otherwise be possible and diminishes the tendency of the liquid to channel through the bed. Adsorbent of 30- to 60-mesh material is commonly employed, although 15- to 30-mesh and 60- to 90-mesh materials are used in some cases. A number of columns are usually assembled in one building and so arranged as to permit heating by steam coils. The oil to be filtered is pumped in at the top of the cylinder under a few pounds pressure until filtrate appears at the bottom. After danger of channeling through the earth has thus been partly removed, the pressure is often raised. The temperature of the system, varying between 100 and 200°F according to the stock being treated, may be maintained by supplying the charging oil at a regulated temperature; waxes and petrolatums are generally treated at about 25°F above their melting points.   Heavy stocks are frequently blended with naphtha to reduce their viscosity before filtration.

When the stream of filtrate has become too dark or otherwise undesirable for use, the pumping of the charging stock is interrupted and air pressure is applied to speed up the drainage of the adherent oil.   Petroleum naphtha is then pumped through the column to dissolve out as much oil as possible and this is continued[1] until the naphtha coming through shows no color.   A portion of the wash naphtha from one filter may be used for the next, and fresh naphtha is used only for the final washing; the naphtha is recovered by distillation.   This cyclic washing of columns substantially reduces the amount of fresh naphtha required, with a consequent saving in over-all distillation costs.[2]   Steam is then turned into the filter and continued for some hours to complete the removal of naphtha.   Finally, the adsorbent is removed from the bottom of the column and regenerated by burning off the strongly adsorbed asphaltic and resinous substances.

Stabilizing Gasolines.   In thermal cracking for the manufacture of gasoline, unstable substances are produced which, on standing, color the gasoline and deposit gums.   The chemical nature of these materials has been indicated[3] as involving cyclic unsaturated compounds (such as the fulvenes) for color and the same together with aliphatic diolefins and olefins attached to benzene rings for the oxidation which leads to gum formation.   These color- and gum-producing substances have for many years been removed commercially by the use of adsorbents.   While formerly it was customary to remove them rather completely, current practice is to remove only the more unstable constituents and to add antioxidants to stabilize the remainder.   In addition to being adsorbed, the unstable olefins are polymerized by the action of the clay.   The viscous polymer obtained has a high density and a low viscosity index; the iodine number is generally high.   When withdrawn from the contact chamber still, it may be orange in color but quickly darkens through oxidation, on exposure to air.

Of the various methods formerly in use, only one, the Gray process, still survives; distillate vapors are taken directly from the cracking unit bubble tower and sent downward through the clay.   ˙A portion of the heavy ends of the distillate is condensed and serves as a solvent to wash the polymers down the column.   The vapors leaving the clay towers are fractionated to desired end-point gasoline; the heavy ends are combined with the polymer collected at the base of the clay towers and are

[1] *Proc. API*, **19**(III):114 (1938).

[2] Reeves and Turkleson, *Petrol. Refiner*, **28**:135 (1949).

[3] Brooks, *Ind. Eng. Chem.*, **18**:1198 (1926).   Martin, Gruse, and Lowy, *Ind. Eng. Chem.*, **25**:381 (1933).   Flood, Hladky, and Edgar, *Ind. Eng. Chem.*, **25**:1234 (1933).

usually returned to the cracking unit. To ensure freedom from excessive coke formation, they are sometimes returned via the evaporator (or tar stripper) where the heavier polymers are removed with the tar. These heavier polymers are of interest as possible substitutes for paint resins, and attempts have been made to so use them.

The process generally operates at 50 to 400 psi pressure and at temperatures within the range of 280 to 500°F as established by the heat content of the naphtha and its final boiling point; the top temperature must not be high enough to vaporize any part of the polymer. Long times of contact within the tower, as induced by high-pressure operation, are evidently not harmful to octane number, cause but slight added loss to polymer formation, and improve the over-all efficiency.

One ton of fuller's earth may treat 1,000 to 30,000 bbl of distillate, depending upon the stock, cracking conditions, and gasoline specifications. Steam may be used at intervals to activate the clay.[1]

VIII-4. Regeneration of Adsorbents. The adsorbed material must be removed from an adsorbent before the latter can be used again; various methods are employed. Where the adsorbed constituents are normally gaseous or comparatively low-boiling,[2] heat is applied to desorb and vaporize them.   In those liquid-phase processes previously described for the separation of individual hydrocarbon types, special petroleum fractions which differ in boiling point from those to be separated are used to desorb and displace the adsorbed material. The desorbed material[3] is subsequently separated by distillation from the special fraction used as the desorbent. With bauxite or fuller's earth which has been used for percolation refining, the procedure, after naphtha washing, is to burn off the adsorbed organic materials at elevated temperatures (1000 to 1200°F). Multiple-hearth type furnaces and thermofor kilns are probably most commonly used for this purpose. The multiple-hearth furnace consists of a number, usually 7 to 12, of disk-shaped hearths mounted one above the other in a cylindrical steel housing. The adsorbent enters at the top and is rabbled across each hearth in succession as it passes from the top to the bottom of the furnace.

The Thermofor kiln[4] consists essentially of a stationary chamber containing vertical heat-transfer tubes, through which a heat-transfer medium (a molten metal or salt at 850 to 1150°F) flows. The tubes are

---

[1] Adsorption with fuller's earth is used to prepare feed stocks for catalytic reforming. Sulfur, nitrogen, and metal-containing compounds, poisonous to certain reforming catalysts, are removed.   See Ziegenhain, *Petrol. Eng.*, **24**(12):C-42 (1952).

[2] Berg, *Trans. AIChE*, **42**:665 (1946).

[3] Eagle and Scott, *Petrol. Processing,* **4**:881 (1949).   Davis, Harper, and Weatherly, *Oil Gas J.*, **51**(2):112 (1953).

[4] Simpson and Payne, *Refiner Nat. Gasoline Mfr.*, **18**:438 (1939).

surrounded by an interlaced structure of angle irons which are stacked in such a manner that the bundle resembles a huge honeycomb. The adsorbent enters at the top of the kiln and is discharged at the bottom while the heat-transfer medium is circulated through the vertical tubes. The kiln is stated to embody features of temperature control and heat transfer which prevent the adsorbents from reaching harmful temperatures, thus extending their period of usefulness.

The regeneration of adsorbents used in the percolation process by desorbing and displacing the adsorbed material with polar solvents has been the subject of patents and investigations. Among others, alcohol and glacial acetic acid mixtures,[1] water solutions of sulfonic acid soaps,[2] isopropyl alcohol containing less than 20 per cent of water,[3] and a mixture of 90 per cent of benzol and 10 per cent of acetone[4] have been proposed but none is applied commercially. Magnesol, which has been used in the contact process for refining lubricating oils, may be regenerated with acetone-naphtha mixtures at 90 to 100°F.[5]

DIFFERENTIAL SOLVENT REFINING

Solvent refining, with liquid sulfur dioxide as the solvent, was first used by the petroleum industry to improve the burning quality of highly aromatic Rumanian kerosene distillates which produced an objectionable smoky flame. The process was introduced by Edeleanu; a pilot plant was operated at Vega, Rumania, in 1909; commercial application began in 1911 at Rouen, France.[6] Originally, batch extraction was employed; a continuous process devised by Crawford was operated with California kerosene distillates in 1924.[7]

Previous attempts to employ amyl alcohol, ether-alcohol mixtures, and similar solvents for petroleum oils had not been successful beyond a laboratory scale.[8] Sulfur dioxide had been studied as a solvent for lubricating oils as early as 1917,[9] but the large development with other solvents occurred between 1930 and 1940. It should be remembered that conventional sulfuric acid refining has always suffered considerable

[1] Parson, U.S. Patent 1,112,650, 1914.

[2] Kennedy, U.S. Patent 1,356,631, 1920.

[3] Robinson, U.S. Patent 1,403,198, 1922.

[4] Hall, U.S. Patent 1,558,163, 1925.

[5] Chenault and Miller, *Refiner Nat. Gasoline Mfr.*, **20**:449 (1941).

[6] Edeleanu, *Petroleum Z.*, **9**:862 (1913–1914); *J. Inst. Petrol. Technologists*, **18**:898 (1932).

[7] *Advances in Chem. Ser.*, no. 5, p. 178, 1951.

[8] Engler-Höfer, "Das Erdöl," vol. I, p. 513, S. Hirzel, Leipzig, 1913.

[9] Lomax, *J. Inst. Petrol. Technologists*, **4**:221 (1917); see also Allibone and Wilson, *J. Inst. Petrol. Technologists*, **11**:180 (1925), for use of sulfur dioxide–acetone mixtures.

disadvantage. Resinous and asphaltic materials, certain reactive sulfur and nitrogen compounds, and hydrocarbons can be removed, but these cannot be separated or recovered unchanged. Furthermore, the disposal of the reaction products and the recovery of the spent acid are troublesome and expensive. By solvent extraction, however, products of highly paraffinic type resistant to oxidation and relatively free of coke-forming substances can be recovered, while the extracts are available for use as raw material for further conversion, say to asphalts, or for fuel oils. Special applications of the solvent process have been proposed, such as the treating of gas oils and kerosene distillates, to yield superior fuels for jet and diesel engines and to improve the quality of feed stocks for catalytic cracking.[1] The isolation of aromatic hydrocarbons of high purity by this method is in large-scale operation. It became important under the war conditions of 1940–1945 for the production of nitration-grade toluene and for other chemical applications.[2]

VIII-5. Theory. When a solution containing two hydrocarbon components A and B (for example, a paraffin and an aromatic hydrocarbon) is intimately mixed with a partially miscible solvent, an interchange of molecules takes place between the two liquid phases. When equilibrium is established, the solvent phase will contain some of the hydrocarbon molecules, and the hydrocarbon phase, some of the solvent molecules. The relative amounts of the hydrocarbon components, A and B, in the two liquid phases will usually differ, depending upon their distribution ratios. For the above one-stage process, the composition of the hydrocarbon material in the two phases may be described by the equation

$$\beta = \frac{(N_A/N_B)^{l_1}}{(N_A/N_B)^{l_2}}$$

where N indicates mole fraction, l_1 and l_2 refer, respectively, to the solvent-rich and hydrocarbon-rich phases, and β is the separation factor. The term β has the same significance for solvent extraction processes as the term α for distillation processes.[3]

It is customary to use ternary diagrams to describe the solubility rela-

[1] Halpern, *Oil Forum*, **4**:435 (1950).

[2] Love and Pfenning, *Advances in Chem. Ser.*, no. 5, p. 305, 1951. Read, *Petrol. Refiner*, **31**:5 (1952).

[3] The distribution of a single solute, A, at a given temperature, between two immiscible solvents is given by the equation, $K_A = N_A{}^{l_1}/N_A{}^{l_2}$, where K_A is the distribution coefficient for component A and is usually a constant for very low concentrations of this component. Similarly, for a second solute, B, the distribution is given by the equation, $K_B = N_B{}^{l_1}/N_B{}^{l_2}$. Thus the ratio of distribution coefficients is equal to the separation factor $K_A/K_B = (N_A{}^{l_1}/N_B{}^{l_2})/(N_A{}^{l_1}/N_B{}^{l_2}) = \beta$. Although some cases are known where the separation factor is substantially constant throughout the range of hydrocarbon concentrations, it is more usual for it to vary significantly.

tionships and the equilibrium concentrations for systems composed of two hydrocarbons and a solvent. Two types of diagram which may be used to describe hydrocarbon-solvent systems are given in Figs. VIII-3 and VIII-4. Figure VIII-3 shows the behavior[1] of a system in which neither of the hydrocarbon components is completely miscible with the solvent at the given temperature; it is typical of many systems involving a naphthene and a paraffin with a selective solvent.[2] The region in which the two phases coexist is bounded by the lines ab and cd, which give, respectively, the compositions at which the solvent-rich (extract) and hydrocarbon-rich (raffinate) phases separate. The compositions of the phases which are in equilibrium are joined by the tie lines eb, $e'b'$, and

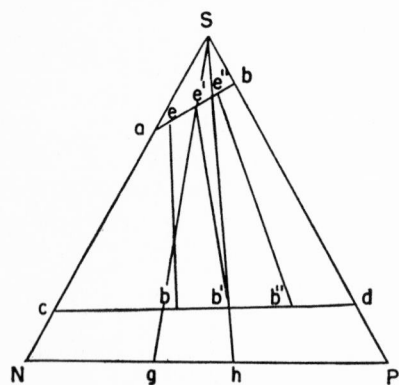

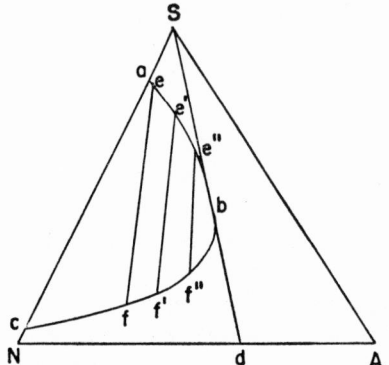

FIG. VIII-3. Triangular phase diagram for a system involving equilibrium between a paraffin, a naphthene, and a selective solvent. The letters N, P, and S refer, respectively, to naphthene, paraffin, and solvent.

FIG. VIII-4. Triangular phase diagram for a system involving equilibrium between a naphthene, an aromatic, and a selective solvent. The letters N, A, and S refer, respectively, to naphthene, aromatic, and solvent.

$e''b''$. The most direct method of determining the tie lines is, of course, by analysis of the conjugate phases throughout the concentration range desired. Various procedures which reduce the amount of analytical work have been proposed.[3] The compositions of the solvent-free extract and raffinate corresponding to points e' and b' are obtained by extrapolating the lines Se' and Sb' to zero solvent content at points g and h. Thus, the

[1] A discussion of a number of ternary diagrams involving hydrocarbon systems is given by Francis in "Physical Chemistry of Hydrocarbons," vol. I, p. 241, Academic Press, Inc., New York, 1950. Saunders, *Ind. Eng. Chem.*, **43**:121 (1951).

[2] See, for example, the system methylcyclohexane, *n*-heptane, and aniline: Varteressian and Fenske, *Ind. Eng. Chem.*, **29**:270 (1937).

[3] See, for example, Brancker, Hunter, and Nash, *Ind. Eng. Chem., Anal. Ed.*, **12**:35 (1940). Bachman, *Ind. Eng. Chem., Anal. Ed.*, **12**:38 (1940). Evans, *Ind. Eng. Chem., Anal. Ed.*, **6**:408 (1934).

line *gh* represents the change in composition resulting from this one-stage process.   It can be seen that with an adequate number of stages both of the hydrocarbon components can be separated in a substantially pure condition.   Figure VIII-4 shows the behavior of a system in which one of the hydrocarbon components is completely miscible with the solvent at the given temperature; it is typical of many systems involving a cyclo-paraffin (or paraffin), an aromatic, and a selective solvent.   In this case the region where the two phases coexist is bounded by the curved line *abc*, and the compositions which are in equilibrium, by the tie lines *ef*, *e′f′*, and *e″f″*.   The maximum content of aromatic hydrocarbon obtainable in the solvent-free extract, irrespective of the number of stages of fractionation available, is obtained by extrapolating the line *Sb* to zero solvent content at *d*.   The naphthenic component

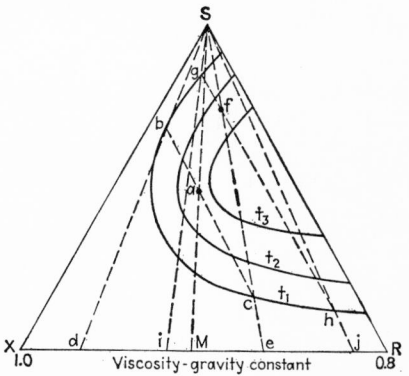

can be obtained in a pure condition by the use of a separating system with an adequate number of stages of fractionation.

For complex hydrocarbon mixtures such as exist in lubricating oils, it is not possible to regard the vertices of a triangular diagram as representing pure components or classes of components.   However, the physical properties of the extract and raffinate differ widely from those of the original mixture

Fig. VIII-5. Typical triangular phase equilibrium diagram.

and it is therefore possible to use the scale of their property differences as the base of the triangle, with the solvent as the apex.   The scale generally employed is that of change in specific gravity or viscosity-gravity constant.

From these diagrams, based on experimental data, the volume of each of the two phases in equilibrium, their composition, and the physical property of the oil present in each phase can be read.[1]   One may also determine the yield of refined oil and the number of ideal stages required to bring about the desired degree of refining.[2]

A typical equilibrium diagram representing the ternary system of solvent *S*, raffinate *R*, and extract *X* is shown in Fig. VIII-5.   The region confined within the curves and side *RS* represents compositions which

[1] Hunter and Nash, *J. Soc. Chem. Ind.*, **51**:285T (1932); *Ind. Eng. Chem.*, **27**:836 (1935).   Kurtz, *Ind. Eng. Chem.*, **27**:845 (1935).   Thompson, "Science of Petroleum," vol. III, p. 1829, Oxford University Press, New York and London, 1938.

[2] Hunter, "Science of Petroleum," vol. III, p. 1818, Oxford University Press, New York and London, 1938.

yield two layers at temperatures t_1, t_2, and t_3. If an oil having a viscosity-gravity constant (vgc) of M is treated with 100 per cent its volume of solvent at t_1, the resulting mixture will have the composition a; and as it lies within the equilibrium curve for t_1 it will separate into two layers. Points b and c, joined through a by a tie line, represent the composition of the extract layer and raffinate layer, respectively; and if the solvent is removed from each, the composition of the resulting extract and raffinate will have the vgc properties indicated by points d and e, obtained by extrapolating the lines Sb and Sc to zero solvent content. The tie line abc represents the volume of solvent plus extracted oil, and the ratio of ac/ab is the volume ratio of the extract layer to the raffinate layer. Knowing the volume of solvent in each layer, the amount of extract and raffinate can be calculated. If the raffinate e is further treated with the same amount of solvent used previously, a mixture of composition f results which again divides itself into two layers, g and h, representing the composition of the second extract and raffinate layers, respectively. If the two phases are separated and the solvent removed, the resulting extract and raffinate will have the viscosity-gravity constants i and j. In this manner the results obtained by any number of extraction stages may be determined, the values agreeing with those of actual operation in degree, depending upon the accuracy of the original equilibrium curve and the extent to which equilibrium was established at each step in the multiple-extraction process.

If the temperature of the extraction is raised, the curve obtained is that of t_2; the enclosed area for the two-phase system has become much smaller because of the increased mutual solubilities at the higher temperature. The difference in composition between the two phases has been reduced, which tends to decrease the selectivity because the points at the terminals of the tie lines are now closer together. The application of the solvent at temperature t_3 would cause no layer separation with this particular oil of viscosity-gravity constant M.

The analogy between distillation and solvent extraction has been developed by Saal and Van Dijck.[1] As with distillation, the effectiveness of the solvent extraction process may be enhanced by the use of equipment embodying a number of theoretical stages of separation and by the return of a portion of extract as reflux to the fractionating system. To illustrate this analogy, there may be considered the batch extraction of a mixture of two hydrocarbon components A and B in a vertical extraction column with a selective solvent lighter than the hydrocarbon portion. Solvent is continuously introduced at the bottom of the column, becomes saturated with the components A and B, and passes upward through the

[1] *World Petrol. Congr., Proc. 1st Congr., London*, **2**:352 (1933). For a discussion of the thermodynamic interrelation of distillation, vapor-liquid extraction, and liquid-liquid extraction, see Hibshman, *Ind. Eng. Chem.*, **41**:1366 (1950).

column.   Initially, the solution reaching the top of the column contains the two components A and B present in the same ratio as it did when it left the bottom.   Solvent is now removed by distillation from the extract at the top of the column and the hydrocarbon portion returned as reflux. As the hydrocarbon material works toward the bottom and the saturated solution moves upward, an interchange takes place throughout the length of the column between the molecules of A and B in the two phases.   As a result of this interchange and the movement of the phases, there is a net transport of the more soluble component, A, to the top and a net transport of the less soluble component, B, to the bottom.   Eventually, if component A is not completely miscible with the solvent at the temperature of operation and the column contains an adequate number of stages of fractionation, this component will be obtained in a substantially pure condition at the top of the column.   The foregoing operation corresponds to batch distillation with total reflux; the solvent-rich and hydrocarbon-rich phases correspond, respectively, to the vapor and liquid phases with distillation.   If now component A is withdrawn at the top and the column operated under partial reflux, the material remaining at the bottom of the column will be gradually enriched in component B until finally this component is obtained in a substantially pure condition.

In commercial practice a temperature gradient is sometimes employed to produce reflux, with the temperature of the raffinate end higher than that of the extract end of the fractionating system.   However, unless the temperature of the extract end is kept below the temperature of complete miscibility of the solvent with the most soluble component, the extract will contain the most soluble component together with some of the less soluble components, irrespective of the number of theoretical stages of separation involved.   In those cases where complete miscibility exists, as with low-boiling aromatics and many selective solvents, the second phase which is required to transport the less soluble components to the raffinate end of the fractionating system may be provided by the use of a second solvent.   For this purpose a paraffin-cycloparaffin fraction boiling in a different temperature range than the original stock may be employed.

VIII-6. Selective Solvents.   The list of compounds which have been suggested as selective solvents for the refining of petroleum materials is very large and includes organic esters, alcohols, aldehydes, acids, ketones, chloroethers, amines, amides, and nitro compounds.   Among those suggested is a series of mixed nitriles having the general formula $CN-(CH_2)n - X$, where $N = 1$ to 5 and $X = CN$, NR_1R_2, OR, or SR.[1] Oxy- and thiodipropionitriles have been proposed.[2]   The use of sulfur dioxide is well known.   Water and aqueous solutions have been investi-

[1] Saunders, *Ind. Eng. Chem.*, **43**:121 (1951).
[2] Skinner, *Ind. Eng. Chem.*, **47**:222 (1955).

gated recently for the separation of toluene from gasoline.[1] However, certain general rules can be deduced for the activity of all the solvents contemplated. It is known, for instance, that they will effect separations with respect to molecular weight as well as molecular structure. In the same structure class, the hydrocarbons of lower molecular weight will be the more soluble. For an approximately constant molecular weight, aromatic hydrocarbons and those containing sulfur, nitrogen, oxygen, and metallic atoms will be dissolved preferentially; it should be remembered that these latter classes may overlap. Among the conventional hydrocarbon types, the solubility order is polynuclear aromatics > mononuclear aromatics > cycloparaffins > paraffins. The solubility intervals are not necessarily the same. Thus, for a paraffin-aromatic system the separation factor is much greater than for a paraffin-cycloparaffin system.[2]

With fluorocarbon solvents the normal order of solubility is reversed. In this case, for compounds of nearly equal molecular weight, the solubility order is paraffins > cycloparaffins > aromatics.[3] Liquid carbon dioxide is also unusual; it mixes with paraffins and monocycloparaffins but is incompletely miscible with dicycloparaffins in the same boiling range.[4]

Of the large number of solvents proposed, the following have been used commercially:

Phenol	Dichloroethyl ether (chlorex)
Furfural	Sulfur dioxide
Nitrobenzene	Sulfur dioxide–benzene
Cresol-propane	Diethylene glycol–water
(Duosol)	(Udex)

Because of their special characteristics one solvent may be preferred to another for a particular application. Thus, because of its low solvent power and high vapor pressure, sulfur dioxide[5] is used to only a limited extent for the refining of lubricating oils. However, its solvent power is quite adequate for lower-boiling fractions and it may be used at $-20°F$ to $-30°F$ to separate aromatics from a gasoline fraction and is employed at 20°F to refine kerosene distillates. In its limited application to lubricating oil stocks, temperatures in the range 50 to 75°F are employed. The solvent power can be increased by the addition of ben-

---

[1] Arnold and Coghlan, *Ind. Eng. Chem.*, **42**:177, 1217 (1950).

[2] Varteressian and Fenske, *loc. cit.*

[3] Hildebrand, *Chem. Eng. Progr. Symposium*, ser. 48, no. 3, 1952.

[4] Francis, *Ind. Eng. Chem.*, **47**:230 (1955).

[5] Gester, *Advances in Chem. Ser.*, no. 5, p. 185, 1951.

zene, combinations of the two[1] giving a considerable variation in selectivity-solubility possibilities.[2]   Recent work has shown that practically all the advantages conferred by benzene can be obtained by operating with sulfur dioxide alone at higher temperatures.

Phenol, on the other hand, has broad solvent powers,[3] which can be modified by the addition of water, making it suitable for a wide variety of lubricating oil stocks.   Extraction temperatures are in the range from 100 to 200°F and are sufficiently high to effect a reduction in viscosity of the phases in the column, to permit the imposition of a temperature gradient, and to allow treatment of waxy stocks under conditions where all the wax will be in solution.   For lubricating oils, furfural extraction[4] temperatures are in the range of 175 to 250°F, thus providing the same benefits as with phenol.   Kerosenes and gas oils may also be refined with furfural near room temperature.   In such case, because of the small difference or even overlapping of the boiling point of furfural and the petroleum stock, azeotropic distillation may be necessary to recover the solvent.   The solubility of oils is relatively high in both nitrobenzene and chlorex (β,β'-dichlorodiethylether).   For this reason these solvents are best suited for use with comparatively insoluble paraffinic lubricating oils, such as the Pennsylvania type.[5]

In the refining of residual stocks with a single solvent, it is customary to remove asphalt by precipitation with propane before applying extraction.   In the Duosol[6] process both purposes are accomplished in a single operation.   The propane which is admitted at one end of the system precipitates the asphalt, preferentially dissolves the more paraffinic constituents, and transports them to the raffinate end of the system. The phenol-cresol mixture preferentially dissolves the asphaltic, resinous, and more aromatic constituents and transports them to the extract end of the system.   Operations are usually conducted in the range of 110 to 170°F.[7]

It will be evident that the choice of solvent depends on a number of

[1] Cottrell, *Petrol. Refiner*, **12**:11, 432 (1933).

[2] Sulfur dioxide promoted with boron trifluoride is reported to be effective for the simultaneous extraction of aromatics and sulfur compounds from petroleum stocks. Arnold and Lien, *Ind. Eng. Chem.*, **47**:234 (1955).

[3] Stratford, Moore, and Pokorny, *Natl. Petrol. News*, **25**(13):17 (1933).

[4] Manley, McCarty, and Gross, *Oil Gas J.*, **32**(23):78 (1933).   Kemp, Hamilton, and Gross, *Ind. Eng. Chem.*, **40**:220 (1948).

[5] Page, Buchler, and Diggs, *Ind. Eng. Chem.*, **25**:418 (1933).   Myers, *Oil Gas J.*, **34**(44):81 (1936).

[6] Tuttle and Miller, *Petrol. Refiner*, **12**:11, 453 (1933).

[7] Solvent refining processes are described in greater detail than is possible here by Kalichevsky, *Petrol. Processing*, **4**:415 (1949), and by Gester, *Advances in Chem. Ser.*, no. 5, p. 177, 1951.

factors, including adaptability to stock being treated, flexibility with respect to different stocks, cost, stability, toxicity, ease of recovery, solubility, selectivity, and ease of phase separation. The installed capacity for the refining of lubricating oil stocks in thousands of barrels per day (world-wide), as of 1950, was about as follows:[1]

Furfural	50	Sulfur dioxide	7
Phenol	37	Chlorex	5
Duosol	25	Nitrobenzene	3

VIII-7. Equipment for Solvent Refining. Solvent extraction is ordinarily carried on in towers packed with Raschig rings or the equivalent, in towers provided with spaced perforated plates, or in a series of mixer-settlers.[2] The first are customary when sulfur dioxide or furfural is employed. The second are preferred for phenol; and the last, for the nitrobenzene and the Duosol type of operation. The functions of these devices for promoting contact and separation will be obvious. The towers may be 20 to 80 ft high; depending on gravities, solvent is fed in near the top and oil near the bottom. The mixer-settlers may use four to seven stages of mixing and separation; solvent enters at one end, the propane precipitant at the other, and the oil at the middle. Depending on the conditions and the properties of oil and solvent, the height of an equivalent theoretical transfer unit in the towers employed may be 4 to 20 ft.

This rather low separating power has led to the development of towers in which the extraction process is aided by mechanical mixing of the phases. These include columns with stationary annular baffles in which agitation is produced in the baffled compartments by rotating disks, propellers, or paddles operated from a vertical shaft, and pulsed columns, in which, as the name implies, an intermittent pulse imposed on the column (often of the perforated-plate type) serves to produce intimate mixing of the phases in a finely divided state. Such columns are reported to have a high separating efficiency; some are in commercial operation in the petroleum industry.[3]

Centrifugal extractors, originally used by the pharmaceutical industry for the isolation of antibiotics, have been adapted for petroleum oils.[4] Commercial applications include refining of virgin gas oil cracking stocks with furfural[5] and lubricating oils with phenol.[6] The trend appears to

[1] Gester, *Advances in Chem. Ser.*, no. 5, p. 179, 1951.

[2] Morello and Poffenberger, *Ind. Eng. Chem.*, **42**:1021 (1950).

[3] Reman and van de Vusse, *Petrol. Refiner*, **54**(9):129 (1955). Oldshue and Rushton, *Chem. Eng. Progr.*, **48**:297 (1952).

[4] Doyle and Rauch, *Petrol. Engr.*, **27**(5):C-49 (1955).

[5] *Chem. Eng. News*, **34**:4028 (1956).

[6] *Chem. Eng.*, **63**(5):108 (1956).

favor the newer mechanically operated extractors over the older packed or perforated-plate columns. For operation on a small scale, in the laboratory or pilot plant, the pump mix extractor[1] and the Scheibel column should be mentioned.[2]

VIII-8. Solvent Refining Processes

Aromatics Recovery. The petroleum industry now supplies the greater part of the toluene and xylenes used in the United States and is also a major producer of benzene. Aromatic concentrates are produced by various catalytic cracking and reforming operations. Solvent extraction is one of a number of processes (azeotropic distillation, extractive distillation, and adsorption are others) which may be used to further concentrate the aromatics to the desired purity. In such an application, two extraction towers may be used. In the first, the stock is countercurrently extracted with cold liquid sulfur dioxide. The extract phase passes to a second tower where it is reextracted with a high-boiling "paraffinic" stock which replaces the remaining nonaromatic impurities with higher-boiling "paraffins"; these latter are later removed by distillation. Aromatics of a purity of 97 to 99 per cent may be obtained. After removal of sulfur dioxide and the high-boiling "paraffinic" components, the material from the raffinate end of the second tower has about the same composition as the original stock. It is returned to the first tower for reprocessing.[3]

The Udex process, which uses a mixture of ethylene glycol and water as the solvent, has been introduced commercially for the separation of high-purity aromatics (benzene, toluene, and the xylenes) from their concentrates. Selectivity and solubility can be adjusted to suit the charging stock by changing the ratio of ethylene glycol to water. The high boiling point of ethylene glycol makes it possible to distill the aromatics from the solvent rather than the reverse, thus reducing the utility requirements.[4]

In pilot-plant operations, with a wide boiling range feed containing 63 per cent aromatics, the aromatic content of the extract portion was raised to 99.8 per cent; recovery of benzene, toluene, and xylenes was 99, 98, and 91 per cent, respectively.[5]

[1] Coplan, Davidson, and Zebroski, *Chem. Eng. Progr.*, **50**:403 (1954).

[2] Scheibel and Karr, *Ind. Eng. Chem.*, **42**:1048 (1950).

[3] Love and Pfenning, *Advances in Chem. Ser.*, no. 5, p. 299, 1951. Wilkinson, Ghublikian, and Obergfell, *Chem. Engr. Progr.*, **49**(5):257 (1953). Ratliff and Strobel, *Petrol. Engr.*, **26**(12):C-26 (1954).

[4] Read, *Petrol. Refiner*, **31**:5, 97 (1952); *Oil Gas J.*, **51**(7):82 (1952). Fenske and Broughton, *Ind. Eng. Chem.*, **47**:714 (1955).

[5] Resen, *Oil Gas J.*, **50**(43):55 (1952). Application to unsaturated naphthas is discussed by Bloch and Wackher, *Petrol. Refiner*, **34**:145 (1955); for coal-tar distillates, see *Chem. Week*, **81**:64 (1957).

After clay treatment of the extract, benzene, toluene, and the xylenes are separated by distillation;[1] *p*-xylene is obtained from the xylene stream by fractional crystallization in a continuous operation.[2] The Udex process may also be used for the production of very high-quality fuels from catalytic reformates. In this case, the process is adjusted so that the high-octane components, comprising both the lower-boiling paraffins and the aromatics, are separated in the extract. The higher-boiling paraffins, of low octane value, are insoluble; these are recycled with fresh feed to the catalytic reformer. Milder reforming conditions may be employed with longer catalyst life; stocks low in naphthene content, formerly marginal, may be processed.[3]

Refining Lubricating Oil Stocks. The lubricant fraction of petroleum, as pointed out in Chap. II, contains a very complex mixture of hydrocarbons, some more valuable than others as lubricating oil constituents. Typical compounds consist of naphthenic and aromatic rings carrying paraffinic side chains of varying number, length, and structure.[4] Molecules with long side chains attached to one or two naphthenic or aromatic rings are characterized by their high viscosity indices, while poly-naphthenic and particularly polyaromatic structures with short side chains will show low viscosity index,[5] high viscosity-gravity constant, and poor stability against oxidation. The object of solvent refining is to extract these undesirable constituents and obtain as a refined oil a more "paraffinic" material. The separation usually obtained is not sharp.[6] Some of the undesirable constituents remain in the raffinate and some of the desirable constituents are lost to the extract. Other undesirable constituents, such as the asphaltic and resinous materials which include oxygen, sulfur, nitrogen, and metal-containing constituents, are removed in the extract more effectively. Lubricating oil extracts are used, in part, for the manufacture of sulfonates. They are also converted to asphalts, and, at worst, may be employed as fuel oil stocks.

Separation of Wax. There have been a number of investigations and patents concerning the separation of wax from lubricating oil stocks by solvent extraction at temperatures above the melting point of the wax but below the temperature of complete miscibility. Among the more

[1] Reidel, *Oil Gas J.*, **52**(35):72 (1954).

[2] *Oil Gas J.*, **52**(36):154 (1954).

[3] Grote, Haensel, and Sterba, *Oil Gas J.*, **53**(48):233 (1955).

[4] Rossini, *Proc. API*, **19**(III):99 (1938). Mair and Willingham, *Ind. Eng. Chem.*, **28**:1452 (1936). Mair, Willingham, and Streiff, *J. Research Natl. Bur. Standards*, **21**:581 (1938).

[5] Mikeska, *Ind. Eng. Chem.*, **28**:970 (1936). For a list and discussion of the physical properties of 121 hydrocarbons of high molecular weight, see Schiessler, *Proc. API*, **26**(III):254 (1946).

[6] Lillard, Jones, and Anderson, *Ind. Eng. Chem.*, **44**:2623 (1952).

recent is a study by Hunter and Brown,[1] who concluded that, with aniline as the solvent, a stock containing 15 per cent wax could not be treated economically but that the process held possibilities for stocks which were very rich in wax; no commercial application is known.

Propane Deasphalting. Compounds of an asphaltic nature have very high molecular weights and are concentrated in those residues which are too high boiling to be distilled. Materials of a resinous nature are of somewhat lower molecular weight and are found both in lubricating oil distillates and in residual stocks. Asphalts and resins are frequently separated commercially from the bulk of an oil by distilling off all the more volatile material, and this process is economic if the crude contains no significant amount of valuable high-molecular-weight hydrocarbons which do not distill over. In many cases, however, it is desirable to process these residua further to obtain viscous lubricating oil stocks or heavy catalytic cracking feed stocks. Conventional solvent refining with single solvents is not suitable, and propane deasphalting or the Duosol process, which also involves the use of propane, is employed.[2]

It has long been known that asphaltic materials could be precipitated by light petroleum naphthas which retained the accompanying hydrocarbons in solution. This separation is the basis of the current method of analysis for asphaltenes, originally devised by Holde.[3] Variations in the character of the naphtha have led to variations in the completeness of precipitation and also in the character of the material precipitated. A systematic following of these observations brought a recognition of the marked precipitating action of the lower paraffinic hydrocarbons in liquid phase as compared with those slightly higher in molecular weight. The extent of this effect is illustrated by the curves given in Figs. VIII-6 and VIII-7. It is evident that the action of methane and ethane is too drastic; the high pressures required to maintain them liquid is also against their use. Butane and particularly propane represent better reagents from both standpoints. No special pains are required to ensure the use of a pure propane, and a moderate content of ethane and butane may each balance the other and allow good results. The presence of propylene, however, is objectionable, particularly when the propane solution is acid-treated or subjected to solvent extraction. The effect of additions of ethane or butane to a propane medium is shown in Fig. VIII-7. As butane is added to propane, the viscosity of the residual

---

[1] *J. Inst. Petrol.*, **35**:73 (1949).

[2] For lubricating oil stocks, the asphaltic and resinous constituents may also be removed by adsorption, or by treatment with sulfuric acid with or without a diluent. After propane deasphalting, solvent refining with a single solvent may be employed to improve further the quality of the oil.

[3] ASTM Method, D 91–52.

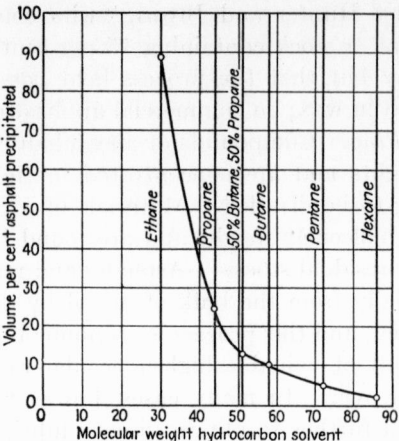

Fɪɢ. VIII-6. Effect of molecular weight of saturated hydrocarbon solvent on volume per cent asphalt precipitated from topped Poso Creek residuum, 10 volumes solvent at 80°F.   [*From Bray, Swift, and Carr, Proc. API*, **14** (III):96 (1933).]

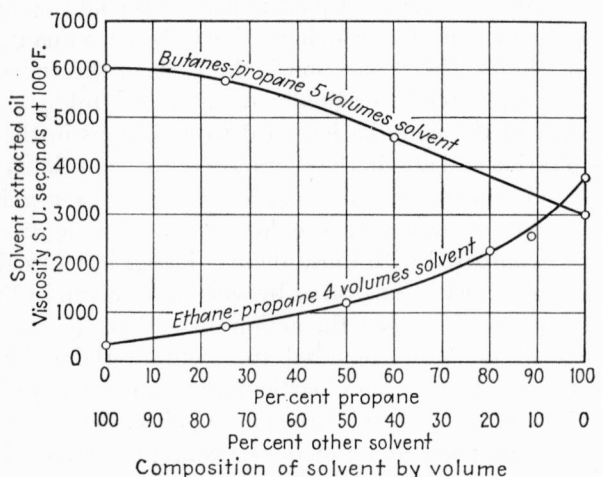

Composition of solvent by volume

Fɪɢ. VIII-7. Effect of proportion of butanes and ethane in propane on viscosity of oil extracted from Poso Creek residuum at 80°F.   [*From Bray, Swift, and Carr, Proc. API*, **14**(III):96 (1933).]

product rises; and as ethane is added to the same propane the viscosity of the residue decreases.   With the former, a less viscous and, with the latter, a more viscous precipitate has been thrown out of solution.   The same precipitating effect is shown by methane-propane mixtures[1] and by hydrogen-propane mixtures.[2]

[1] von Pilat, *Oil Gas J.*, **35**(10):54 (1936).
[2] Godlewics and von Pilat, *Oil Gas J.*, **34**(32):76 (1935).

The action of liquid propane as a precipitant of asphalts and resins is made more interesting by its unusual property of losing its solvent power as the temperature is raised above 100°F. Below this range, it behaves like a normal solvent in that larger amounts of solute are dissolved with rise in temperature. The abnormality is probably due to the proximity of the higher working temperatures to the critical point at 121°F. As this condition is approached, the characteristics of the liquid phase assume those of the gaseous, and the solubility of the various oil components is gradually decreased. The asphaltic and resinous compounds, being most incompatible, are precipitated first as the range 120 to 140°F is approached. A further increase in temperature is reflected in the

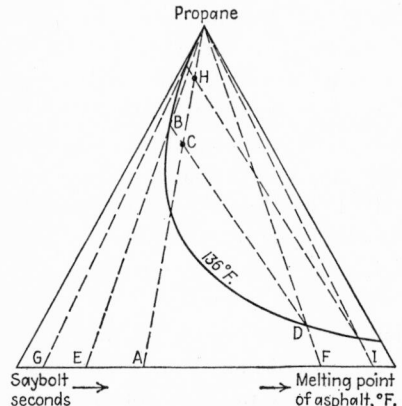

FIG. VIII-8. Propane deasphalting at 136°F. [*From Wilson, Keith, and Haylett, Ind. Eng. Chem.*, **28**:1065 (1936).]

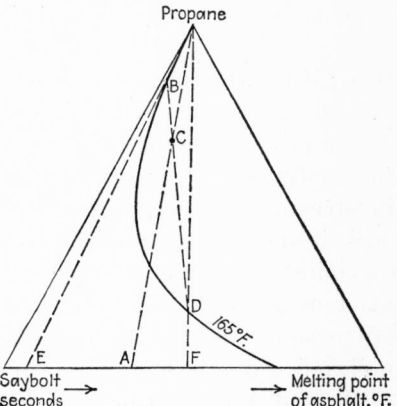

FIG. VIII-9. Propane deasphalting at 165°F. [*From Wilson, Keith, and Haylett, Ind. Eng. Chem.*, **28**:1065 (1936).]

separation of heavier cyclic compounds and the viscous lubricants in the order of their decreasing molecular weights. At just below the critical temperature, practically no heavy constituents remain in solution; an increase of pressure at this point materially aids solubility, presumably by causing a change in density of the propane system.

The negative temperature coefficient of solubility, exhibited by liquid propane at the higher temperatures, is illustrated by triangular diagrams, Figs. VIII-8 and VIII-9, showing graphically the conditions existing when a residuum of composition *A* is treated with propane at 136 and 165°F.

As drawn, point *C* represents a mixture made up of one part of oil, having property *A*, and two parts of propane. In each isotherm, the two layers separated are represented by *B* and *D* and the relative proportion of the propane and asphalt layers is given by the ratio of *CD* to *BC*.

The extension points E and F give the properties of the oil and asphalt, respectively, which are obtained on evaporation of the propane from their respective layers. It can be seen that if the propane-to-oil ratio is increased to give composition H the layers separated will contain oil and asphalt (G and I, respectively) of still wider variance in properties. As BC is relatively short in the 136°F isotherm, the oil contained (E) in the much larger propane layer is not greatly unlike that of the original oil A, although the small amount of asphalt precipitated (F) is widely different. If the temperature is raised to 165°F, however, the relative quantity of the asphalt layer BC is now much larger than at 136°F, giving an oil of lower viscosity and an asphalt of lower melting point due to its increased oil content.

From these considerations, it is evident that propane deasphalting is better carried on at higher temperatures with a large propane-to-oil ratio; if the treating temperature is too high (180°F), however, oil and propane become partly immiscible and a third phase separates.

The principles outlined above for batch deasphalting can be extended to continuous countercurrent operation. A possible modification[1] involves a primary precipitation at 110°F to throw out high-melting asphalt and then a warming of the propane layer to 150°F for a second precipitation of lower-melting material. The use of propane as outlined makes available for the manufacture of highly viscous oils a variety of stocks of large asphalt content which would be too costly to employ if chemical treatment were the only means of refining them. There is a further advantage to propane for dewaxing. A propane solution of a heavy oil may be deasphaltized at a high temperature and then cooled for removal of wax.[2]

In practice countercurrent towers are employed; the stock is introduced at the top and the propane at the bottom. Temperature ranges from 100 to 130°F at the bottom to 150 to 180°F at the top of the tower. About four to nine volumes of propane are used per unit volume of stock. Dewaxing frequently follows deasphalting, in which case the propane solution is cooled to the desired temperature by self-refrigeration. Sometimes, a two-stage operation is employed to separate resins from asphalts. After the separation of the asphalts in the first stage, the propane deasphalted oil is further diluted with propane (200 per cent of original residuum) and a resins fraction separated[3] in the second stage. In the deasphalting of residual stocks to produce catalytic cracker feed,

[1] Bray and Bahlke, "Science of Petroleum," vol. III, p. 1966, Oxford University Press, New York and London, 1938.

[2] For the application of propane to the refining of Pennsylvania crude oil, see *Chem. & Met. Eng.*, **46**:400 (1939).

[3] Graff and Forrest, *Ind. Eng. Chem.*, **32**:294 (1940).

a very marked reduction in salt content and in content of vanadium, iron, and nickel is effected.[1]

SOLID MOLECULAR COMPOUNDS WITH UREA

The formation of solid molecular compounds of the normal paraffins (or normal olefins) with urea[2] and the subsequent regeneration and recovery of the components provide the basis for a method, now widely used in the laboratories of the petroleum industry, for the separation of normal paraffins (or normal olefins) from petroleum fractions. With this method urea is added to a petroleum fraction in the presence of a solvent, such as acetone or methanol, while stirring the mixture vigorously. A crystalline precipitate of the solid compound of urea with the normal paraffins is formed. This compound is separated by filtration and decomposed by the addition of warm water to regenerate the normal paraffins. The other hydrocarbons may be recovered from the solution by removal of the methanol or acetone by water.

The process has been developed to the pilot-plant stage[3] and may be of importance for the production of normal paraffins. The improvement of jet fuels by this means has been discussed by Hepp, Box, and Ray.[4] In a similar way, dewaxing with urea is in use on a small commercial scale; the products are particularly useful for refrigerator oils, transformer oils, hydraulic fluids, and lubricants for arctic service.[5]

The solid molecular compounds which urea forms with the normal paraffins are not attributable to the operation of strongly attractive forces between the molecules. These compounds depend instead on the ability of urea to form a framework containing channels within which the molecules of the normal paraffins fit lengthwise. The framework which urea provides will accommodate molecules of different length but not those of widely different cross section.[6] Thus, the cross section of branched paraffins, cycloparaffins, and aromatics is too large to permit these hydrocarbons to form solid molecular compounds with urea. Hydrocarbons with long normal chains (18 carbon atoms or more)

---

[1] *Heat Eng.*, May, 1951, p. 78. Nitrogen compounds are also concentrated in the precipitate, Dunning and Moore, *Petrol. Refiner*, **36**(5):247 (1957). Pentane can be used similarly, *ACS, Div. Petrol. Chem.*, ACS Meeting, Atlantic City, September, 1956.

[2] Inclusion complexes are also formed by thiourea [*Ann. Chim.*, **4**(12):693 (1949)], by hydroquinone (*J. Chem. Soc.*, 1956, p. 61), and by a variety of other compounds.

[3] Bailey, Bannerot, Fetterly, and Smith, *Ind. Eng. Chem.*, **43**:2125 (1951).

[4] *Ind. Eng. Chem.*, **45**:112 (1953).

[5] *Oil Gas J.*, **55**(12):168 (1957).

[6] Powell, *Endeavour*, **9**:154 (1950). Bailey and others, *World Petrol. Congr., Proc. 3rd Congr., Hague*, **3**:161 (1951).

attached to cycloparaffin, aromatic, or side-chain groups may, however, form solid molecular compounds with urea.   In this case the long normal chain fits the channel in the urea framework with the ring or branched group extending outside.

The original observation that urea will form solid molecular compounds with a wide variety of linear molecules including hydrocarbons is attributable to Bergen.[1]   Conditions necessary for the effective use of the process have been investigated by Zimmerschied, Dinerstein, Weitkamp, and Marschner,[2] and by Redlich, Gable, Dunlop, and Millar.[3]   A discussion is also given by Kobe and Domask.[4]

[1] German Patent Application No. O. Z., 12,438, March 18, 1940.   U.S. Technical Oil Mission, Reel 6, Frames 263–270 (in German) and Reel 143, Frames 135–9 (in English).

[2] *Ind. Eng. Chem.*, **42**:1300 (1950).

[3] *J. ACS*, **72**:4153 (1950).

[4] *Petrol. Refiner*, **31**:106 (1953).

CHAPTER IX

Cracking of Petroleum Oils

The phenomena accompanying the thermal decomposition of hydrocarbons were recognized long before enough was learned of hydrocarbon structure and chemistry to permit the formulation of the present theories of this action. The manufacture of illuminating gas from oil is reported to have been discussed in England as early as 1792. Dalton, in 1809, studied the action of electric sparks on hydrocarbon gases, and Faraday, in 1825, discovered benzene and recognized unsaturated gases. The information on the subject was increased very largely by Berthelot, who, before 1870, published accounts of extensive experiments and offered a theory in explanation. In the meantime, Silliman had made oil gas from petroleum, and the cracking of heavier oil to kerosene is reported to have been observed in a New Jersey refinery. The growth of the petroleum industry and of the gas-making processes using petroleum prompted a number of interesting theoretical researches on low-temperature and particularly on high-temperature decomposition of hydrocarbons (pyrolysis). Interest in low-temperature reactions grew rapidly following the rise (about 1914) of processes for obtaining motor fuel by cracking.

A fairly homogeneous liquid hydrocarbon mixture, such as a petroleum or coal-tar oil, will yield, on pyrolysis, hydrocarbon gases and liquid hydrocarbons extending over the whole range of molecular weight. The heavy end product is usually pitch or coke containing 95 per cent or more of carbon. Hydrocarbon gas, containing compounds of very low molecular weight, may to an appreciable extent be converted by heating into liquid hydrocarbons and tars of relatively high molecular weight. At the same time, simpler hydrocarbons as well as coke and hydrogen are produced.

Thermal decomposition usually occurs in all petroleum distillation processes, even though inadvertently and in small amounts. It has been brought about deliberately in the so-called coking distillation of lubricating oils,[1] in the pyrolysis of higher-boiling oils to gasoline, a

---

[1] See the second edition of this work, p. 417.

process now disappearing, and in lowering the viscosity of heavy fuel oils and residua (vis-breaking). Petroleum oils are also decomposed into gaseous hydrocarbons in the making of oil gas; a similar operation occurs in carburetting water gas. The influence of temperature of decomposition on the products may be indicated broadly as follows: Between 400 and 500°C and under other suitable conditions, normally liquid products of lower-boiling range than the original oil will be obtained in excess of other products. Above 500°C gas production becomes important; and above 600°C, normally near 700°C, commercial production of oil gas is possible. Around 900°C, maximum yields of aromatic hydrocarbons may be obtained; and above 1000°C, methane, hydrogen, and carbon are the chief products. These temperatures are influenced by the time the charge material spends in the cracking coils; over a period of years changing design of furnaces has increased the permissible rate of heat transmission and thus allowed shorter residence time at higher temperatures. The result has been a marked throughput advantage.

THE CRACKING REACTION

IX-1. Low-molecular-weight Hydrocarbons. Individual gaseous hydrocarbons, whether recovered directly from crude oil and natural gas or produced by cracking of heavier oils, are in demand for manufacture of chemicals, plastics, and synthetic rubber (see Chap. XVI) or for conversion operations such as polymerization and alkylation to liquid hydrocarbon products (Chap. III). Most of such conversions depend on the reactivity of the olefinic and diolefinic constituents of the gases. It is often necessary to produce the unsaturated compounds by simple cracking—dehydrogenation or demethanation of the saturated hydrocarbons of the same molecular-weight range. Thus ethane may be dehydrogenated to ethylene, propane to propylene, or cracked to ethylene plus methane. These and similar reactions[1] can be performed effectively

---

[1] Lang and Morgan, *Ind. Eng. Chem.*, **27**:937 (1935). Egloff and Wilson, *Ind. Eng. Chem.*, **27**:917 (1935). Egloff, Thomas, and Linn, *Ind. Eng. Chem.*, **28**:1283 (1936). Egloff, "Reactions of Pure Hydrocarbons," Reinhold Publishing Corporation, New York, 1937. Frey and Hepp, "Science of Petroleum," vol. III, p. 1994, Oxford University Press, New York and London, 1938. Howes, "Science of Petroleum," pp. 2007, 2030, 2045. Steacie and Puddington, *Can. J. Research*, **16B**:411 (1938). Steacie and Shane, *Can. J. Research*, **18B**:203 (1940). Stubbs and Hinshelwood, *Discussions Faraday Soc.*, **10**:129 (1951). Kinney and Crowley, *Ind. Eng. Chem.*, **46**:258 (1954). A recent study of the cracking of ethane indicates that the primary reaction, to yield ethylene, hydrogen, and a little methane, can be inhibited by nitric oxide; secondary reactions, particularly those yielding higher hydrocarbons, cannot be so inhibited. Silcocks, *Proc. Roy. Soc. (London)*, **A233**:465 (1956).

by thermal treatment in the range 550 to 750°C.[1] Thermal decompositions of this kind are readily explained as proceeding by a free radical mechanism. The reactions are essentially the same as those invoked to make clear the similar decomposition of liquid hydrocarbons.[2]

Radical formation was postulated as far back as 1908, by Bone and Coward,[3] but it was not until 1929 that the existence of methyl and ethyl radicals was demonstrated.[4] Rice has since presented a workable mechanism[5] which assumes a primary decomposition of paraffins into free and active radicals which set up chain reactions.

It is postulated that paraffins other than methane break down on thermal treatment, by the scission of a C—C bond, to produce two free radicals. Propane, for example, would separate into free methyl and ethyl radicals. The methyl radical can act in one way only, namely, to form methane by removing a hydrogen atom from, say, a neighboring propane molecule, to form in turn a propyl or isopropyl radical. The ethyl radical, on the other hand, has two possible directions for reaction.

1. It may take a hydrogen atom from a nearby propane molecule, for example, to form ethane and a propyl (or isopropyl) radical. Being bimolecular this reaction would be retarded by dilution. The propyl radical would in turn dissociate as

$$CH_3CH_2CH_2 \cdot (\text{or } CH_3 \cdot CHCH_3) \rightarrow CH_3 \cdot + CH_2{=}CH_2$$
$$\rightarrow CH_3CH{=}CH_2 + H$$

Of these, the first requires the least activation energy and would be more probable.

2. It may lose a hydrogen atom to form ethylene. Any hydrogen atom so liberated would be capable of reacting with a fresh propane molecule to form molecular hydrogen and a propyl radical. Radicals larger than methyl and ethyl are not sufficiently stable to be recognized easily.

[1] However, the dehydrogenation of *n*-butane and the *n*-butenes to butadiene for rubber manufacture can be carried out to better advantage at lower temperatures by catalytic means.

[2] For detailed discussion of the thermal cracking of individual low-molecular-weight hydrocarbons, see the second edition of this work, chap. X, 1942.

[3] *J. Chem. Soc.*, **93**:1197 (1908).

[4] Paneth and Hofeditz, *Ber.*, **62**:1335 (1929). Paneth and Lautch, *Nature*, **125**:164 (1930).

[5] *J. ACS*, **53**:1959 (1931); **54**:3529 (1932); **55**:3035, 4245 (1933); **56**:214, 311, 2105, 2381, 2747 (1934). Rice and Herzfeld, *J. ACS*, **56**:284 (1934). Rice, *Ind. Eng. Chem.*, **27**:915 (1935). Rice and Rice, "The Aliphatic Free Radicals," Johns Hopkins Press, Baltimore, 1935. Rice and Teller, *J. Chem. Phys.*, **6**:489 (1938); **7**:199 (1939). Kossiakoff and Rice, *J. ACS*, **65**:590 (1943). Partington, *Discussions Faraday Soc.*, **2**:114 (1947). Szwarc, *J. Chem. Phys.*, **17**:284, 292 (1949). Rice, *ACS, Div. Petrol. Chem., Symposium on Catalysts in Hydrocarbon Chemistry*, Preprint, p. 5, Atlantic City, September, 1952.

The decomposition from this point on involves a series of chain-reaction cycles; if the chain is long enough, the composition of the end products is determined solely by the nature of the cycles and is practically independent of the primary decomposition of the molecule. The atoms or radicals which are regenerated act as the carriers responsible for continuing the chain.

According to Rice, the tendency for the reaction of hydrogen attached to primary, secondary, and tertiary carbon atoms, respectively, at 600°C, is in the ratio of 1:3.2:10.3.[1] For a given hydrocarbon, therefore, depending upon the relative number of the three types of attached hydrogen atoms present and knowing how the radicals decompose, the ultimate products can be predicted.[2] Kossiakoff and Rice have pointed out the possibility of isomerizations in the longer-chain alkyl radicals formed in the primary reaction.

The extent to which the thermal cracking of gas oils proceeds by a free radical mechanism is uncertain. It is well established that free radicals are formed under high-temperature low-pressure conditions. Their stability, however, decreases with increase of size and their concentration decreases with pressure.[3] The specific reaction rates of many such pyrolytic reactions are greater than those calculated by the Arrhenius equation

$$k = Ae^{-E/RT}$$

This is in agreement with the free-radical chain mechanism. However, when cracking is inhibited by nitric oxide[4] or propylene,[5] both of which are known to react readily with free radicals, the nonagreement in reaction rates still exists. The unexplained residual reaction has been attributed both to molecular reaction[6] and to a free-radical mechanism of short chain length.[7]

IX-2. High-molecular-weight Hydrocarbons. The application to high-molecular-weight hydrocarbons of the reactions observed for molecules of smaller size is not very helpful because of the extreme chemical complexity of the oil being cracked. A few principles, however, seem to be pretty well established. In general terms, the thermal stability decreases as the molecule increases in size; this generalization is supported by thermo-

[1] Kossiakoff and Rice, *J. ACS*, **65**:590 (1943).

[2] Rice, *J. ACS*, **55**:3035 (1933).

[3] Evering, *J. ACS*, **61**:1400 (1939).

[4] Staveley and Hinshelwood, *J. Chem. Soc.*, 1937, p. 1568.

[5] Rice and Polly, *J. Chem. Phys.*, **6**:273 (1938). Echols and Pease, *J. ACS*, **61**:1024 (1939).

[6] Stubbs and Hinshelwood, *Proc. Roy. Soc. (London)*, **A200**:458 (1950).

[7] Steacie and Folkins, *Can. J. Research*, **B18**:1 (1940). Klute and Walters, *J. ACS*, **67**:550 (1945).

dynamic considerations. It can also be said that cracking is endothermic and the rates of decomposition decrease in the following order: *n*-paraffins, isoparaffins, cycloparaffins, aromatics, aromatic-naphthenes, and polynuclear aromatics. Highly symmetrical molecules, such as neopentane, are more stable than their open-chain isomers. A double carbon-carbon bond also conveys stability; its heat of activation is higher than that of a single bond, and a single bond adjacent to a double bond shows a still higher resistance to scission. Thus the single C—C bond of propylene is more stable than those in propane, and 2-butene and 2-pentene are similarly more stable than the isomeric 1-butene and 1-pentene.[1] The observations agree with the general conclusion that a grouping

$$C\!=\!C^\alpha C^\beta C$$

will decompose preferentially at the β position.[2] It appears also that demethanation proceeds more easily when the available methyl groups are farthest from double bonds or foci of symmetry.

The shift from C—H scission to C—C scission with increase of molecular weight is also interesting. The heats of activation for the two in ethane are reported[3] as

	Calories
C—H	98,000
C—C	85,600

Nevertheless, with ethane and with isobutane (which contains a hydrogen atom weakly held by the tertiary carbon), the principal products are hydrogen and the corresponding olefin. As the carbon chain becomes longer, however, this reaction diminishes rapidly. The trend is shown by the following rough figures:

Percentage of reaction yielding hydrogen

Ethane	High
Propane	42
Isobutane	63
n-Butane	16
Isopentane	2
n-Pentane	Practically none

The average petroleum fraction suitable for cracking can be regarded[4]

[1] Hurd and Bollman, *J. ACS*, **55**:699 (1933).

[2] Diallyl, allylcyclohexane, 4-phenyl-1-butene, and 4-methyl-1-pentene all decomposed readily at 425 to 500°C to give considerably more propylene than ethylene.

[3] Kistiakowsky and Van Artsdalen, *J. Chem. Phys.*, **12**:469 (1944).

[4] Mabery, *Am. Chem. J.*, **28**:165 (1902); *Am. Chem. J.*, **33**:251 (1905). Smith, *U.S. Bur. Mines, Tech. Paper*, 428, 1928; 477, 1930. Mair and Rossini, *Ind. Eng. Chem.*, **47**:1062 (1955). Rossini and Mair, *Advances in Chem. Ser.*, no. 5, p. 334, 1951.

as a mixture containing (within the possible molecular-weight range) a minimal proportion of paraffins, condensed or otherwise polynuclear naphthenes and aromatics, and a predominating amount of mixed molecules; these probably include all the stable combinations of alkyl side chains with single or polynuclear naphthenes, single or polynuclear aromatics, or with naphthene-aromatic nuclei. Since long paraffinic chains break off easily, long olefinic groups may have a transitory existence. It is not easy to discuss intelligently the decomposition of such complex molecules, but it may be helpful to consider the reactions of the main classes of components which make them up.

Paraffinic Hydrocarbons. It is known that the pyrolysis of a simple paraffin yields smaller paraffin and olefinic hydrocarbons; these are assumed to be primary products. In the range of 600 to 800°C, the gas-making range, the paraffin will be small and the olefin relatively larger; at lower temperatures the two will be more nearly of equal size. This latter is what happens in cracking for gasoline.

The three possibilities in the thermal decomposition of large paraffin molecules are:

$$(1) \quad RCH_2CH_2CH_2CH_2R \rightarrow RCH_3 + CH_3CH_2R + C$$
$$(2) \quad RCH_2CH_2CH_2CH_2R \rightarrow 2\ RCH{=}CH_2 + H_2$$
$$(3) \quad RCH_2CH_2CH_2CH_2R \rightarrow RCH{=}CH_2 + RCH_2CH_3$$

Reaction 3 is generally accepted as describing the net result of the preliminary breakdown; little carbon or hydrogen appears. This general reaction was observed long ago by Thorpe and Young,[1] who distilled a Scotch shale paraffin wax to obtain mixtures of C_5 to C_8, etc., paraffins and olefins, present in approximately equal proportions in each fraction. Scission takes place at each carbon-carbon bond in isopentane, n-pentane, n-hexane, and[2] diisoamyl[3] at temperatures as low as 400 to 425°C.

The cracking of paraffin wax and paraffinic gas oils gives simple decomposition products.[4] There is no evidence of coke formation during the early stages, nor does the specific gravity of the cracked residue differ greatly from that of the original paraffinic charge. Coke formation can be attributed to secondary reactions involving the olefins produced in the primary cracking.

Olefinic Hydrocarbons. The decomposition of the large olefins arising from the primary cracking is an important factor in the over-all pyrolysis.

[1] *Proc. Roy. Soc.* (*London*), **19**:370 (1871); **20**:488 (1872); **21**:184 (1873).

[2] Frey and Hepp, *Ind. Eng. Chem.*, **25**:441 (1933).

[3] Sachanen and Tilicheyev, "Chemistry and Technology of Cracking," p. 116, Chemical Catalog Company, Inc., New York, 1932.

[4] *Ibid.*, p. 108.

The breakdown may be considered to take place in two ways:

(1) $RCH_2CH_2(CH_2)_nCH{=}CH_2 \rightarrow RH + CH_2{=}CH(CH_2)_nCH{=}CH_2$
$\qquad\qquad\qquad\qquad RCH_3 + CH_2{=}CH(CH_2)_{n-1}CH{=}CH_2$
etc.

(2) $RCH_2CH_2(CH_2)_nCH{=}CH_2 \rightarrow R(CH_2)_nCH{=}CH_2 + CH_2{=}CH_2$
$\qquad\qquad\qquad\qquad R(CH_2)_{n-1}CH{=}CH_2 + CH_3CH{=}CH_2$
etc.

In the pyrolysis of hexadecene[1] at the lower temperatures of decomposition, the gases produced are largely saturated, but as the temperature is increased gaseous olefins and hydrogen are formed. In view of the absence of sizable proportions of large diolefins the unsaturates might result from the decomposition of a large diolefin into a paraffin and a smaller diolefin, or into a smaller diolefin plus an olefin plus hydrogen. In this manner the butadiene generally found[2] in such reactions might be accounted for.

Under high pressure both olefins and diolefins are known to yield naphthenes by ring closure; the thermal polymers of ethylene, propylene, and isobutene contain naphthene hydrocarbons. Similarly, the product of cracking hexadecene shows a higher cyclic content as the temperature of cracking rises.[3] Aromatics may also be formed, perhaps through butadiene as intermediate[4]

Olefins and butadiene → cyclohexene derivative → aromatics
Aromatic and butadiene → polycyclic aromatic

or perhaps through biradical or acetylenic intermediates.[5]

Naphthenic Hydrocarbons. The thermal stability of naphthenic hydrocarbons is intermediate to that of paraffins and aromatics. Those most commonly present in petroleum are five- and six-carbon rings carrying alkyl side chains. Under cracking conditions these chains break off to yield longer olefins and smaller alkyl groups attached to the ring, i.e., a methyl or ethyl group. Condensed naphthene nuclei will presumably dissociate, with a good deal of destructive degradation.

[1] Gault and Altchidjian, *Ann. chim.*, **2**(10):209 (1924); *Compt. rend.*, **178**:2092 (1924).

[2] Lomax, Dunstan, and Thole, *J. Inst. Petrol. Technologists*, **3**:36 (1916–1917).

[3] Gault and Barmann, *Chimie & ind.* (*Paris*), **16**:242 (1926).

[4] Weizmann, *Ind. Eng. Chem.*, **43**:2312 (1951). Hague and Wheeler, *J. Chem. Soc.*, 1929, p. 378. Wheeler and Wood, *J. Chem. Soc.*, 1930, p. 1819. Schneider and Frolich, *Ind. Eng. Chem.*, **23**:1405 (1931).

[5] Lewes, *Proc. Roy. Soc.* (*London*), **55**:90 (1894); **57**:394 (1895). Bone and Coward, *J. Chem. Soc.*, **93**:1197 (1908). Zanetti, *J. ACS*, **44**:2036 (1922). Groll, *Ind. Eng. Chem.*, **25**:784 (1933).

Cyclopentane is relatively stable thermally; it does not dehydrogenate readily at normal cracking temperatures and under more severe conditions undergoes carbon-carbon bond scission to break the ring.[1] Cyclohexane begins to decompose at 490 to 510°C, releasing large amounts of hydrogen, ethylene, and butadiene,[2] and forming benzene;[3] there is also evidence of propylene formation.[4] Presumably cyclohexene is the intermediate which in turn forms benzene and hydrogen or butadiene and ethylene.[3] The latter reaction is almost quantitative at 800°C;[4] essentially no cyclo-hexadiene is present in the product.[5] There is no evidence for the iso-merization of cyclohexane into methylcyclopentane in thermal cracking.[4]

Aromatic Hydrocarbons.   The relatively low temperatures prevailing in ordinary thermal cracking for gasoline are not high enough to synthesize aromatic hydrocarbons.   It seems more likely that simple aromatics in such cracked products derive from mixed aromatic molecules in the charging stock.   These might be simple alkylated mononuclear compounds which suffer dealkylation or more complex mixed molecules containing naphthene rings and condensed aromatics.   Experimental support for this idea is found in early work of Brooks,[6] who cracked a reduced crude at 425°C; simple aromatics were present in the gasoline product.   Not enough hydrogen was produced to permit an explanation based on dehydrogenation of cyclohexane derivatives, so that release of preexisting aromatic rings is the most likely explanation.

While the simple aromatics are stable at low cracking temperatures, intermolecular condensation, with loss of hydrogen, begins somewhat above 500°C; benzene, for instance, is converted to diphenyl, and similar doubling occurs with toluene, xylene, and naphthalene.[7] As with most hydrocarbons, thermal stability decreases with increase of molecular size; naphthalene forms dinaphthyl at 475°C, anthracene decomposes at the same temperature to a hard coke-like mass, and indene does likewise at 290°C.

The long-chain alkyl-substituted aromatics crack in a manner similar to the paraffin hydrocarbons, leaving nuclei with smaller chains attached. These are quite stable, becoming more and more refractory as the chains

[1] Zelinsky, Titz, and Fatejew, *Ber.,* **59**:2580 (1926).   Zelinsky and Kasansky, *Ber.,* **64**:2265 (1931), and many earlier papers.   Moldavaski, Kamusher, and Livshits, *J. Gen. Chem. (USSR),* **7**:131 (1937); *C.A.,* **31**:4282 (1937).   Taylor and Yeddanapalli, *Bull. soc. chim. Belges,* **47**:163 (1938).

[2] Frolich, Simard, and White, *Ind. Eng. Chem.,* **22**:240 (1930).

[3] Jones, *J. Chem. Soc.,* **107**:1582 (1915).

[4] Kuchler, *Trans. Faraday Soc.,* **35**:874 (1939).

[5] Rice, Ruoff, and Rodowskas, *J. ACS,* **60**:955 (1938).

[6] With Bacon, Humphrey, and Padgett, *Ind. Eng. Chem.,* **7**:180 (1915).

[7] Dufton and Cobb, *Gas J.,* **150**:588 (1920).   Sachanen and Tilicheyev, *Ber.,* **62**:658 (1929).

are shortened; they are important components in recycle oils. At higher temperatures, they will condense as above and form progressively higher-molecular-weight compounds which end up as coke-like products.[1] The more unsaturated types of condensed ring systems polymerize readily and directly; examples are indene, fluorene,[2] and acenaphthene.[3] The simpler aliphatic derivatives carrying phenyl nuclei, such as diphenylmethane, *p*-di-*n*-butylbenzene, and dibenzyl, condense by intramolecular condensations forming fluorene, phenanthrene, and anthracene, respectively. Naphthalene and phenanthrene are formed by similar intramolecular condensations in *n*-butylbenzene and *o,o'*-bitolyl.[4]

Beyond these stages of polycyclic aromatic formation, the exact chemistry is not well known. Further removal of hydrogen by condensation leads to the heavy tars normally found in cracking-still residues and to petroleum coke. Polymerization and disproportionation may occur. For example, cyclic unsaturated substituted aromatics, such as indene, are readily polymerized, and these in turn may break down by disproportionation.

$$(\text{Indene})_6 \rightarrow (\text{indene})_3 + 3\text{-hydrindene}$$

When the temperature is high enough, the hydrogen set free in condensations may be consumed in hydrocracking other compounds present. Thus, hydrindene is believed to yield xylene and methylethylbenzene.[5] The course of further cracking seems to follow the lines indicated, the complex molecules becoming more so until they end up as resins and coke, while the lower-molecular-weight fragments form the simpler aromatics and simple paraffins or olefins found in the cracked products.[6]

THERMAL CRACKING PROCESSES

The early development of cracking as a dependable manufacturing operation included a number of somewhat different ways of accomplishing

[1] Sachanen and Tilicheyev, *loc. cit.*

[2] Tilicheyev and Shchitikov, *Foreign Petroleum Tech.*, **5**:481, 515 (1937); *C.A.*, **32**:2721, 3132 (1938).

[3] Dziewonski and Leyko, *Ber.*, **47**:1679 (1914).

[4] Meyer and Hofmann, *Monatsh.*, **37**:381 (1916). Kinney in "The Chemistry of Petroleum Hydrocarbons," Brooks, Boord, Kurtz, and Schmerling (eds.), vol. 2, p. 113, Reinhold Publishing Corporation, New York, 1955.

[5] Tilicheyev and Shchitikov, *Foreign Petroleum Technol.*, **5**:481, 515 (1937); *C.A.*, **32**:2721, 3132 (1938).

[6] With reference to the coke mentioned as a final product of aromatic decompositions, it should be kept in mind that it is by no means carbon; it usually has a high content (50 to 80 per cent) of material soluble in carbon disulfide [Frolich, *Chem. & Met. Eng.*, **38**:343 (1931)].

the same purpose.[1]   The large-scale production of cracked gasoline was first developed by Burton in 1912.[2]   He used batch distillation in horizontal shell stills, operating at about 750°F and under about 75 to 95 lb pressure.   The years immediately following were marked by the attempted setting up of vapor-phase procedures at low pressure and high temperature,[3] which had the basic advantage of permitting regulation of temperature and pressure independently.   Such processes were of interest during the war period 1915–1918 as possible sources for aromatics but did not survive in practice because of poor heat conduction, excessive coke formation, extreme sensitiveness to operating conditions, and the unstable gasoline produced.

The first departure in the direction of heating a stream of liquid oil instead of a bulk volume was Clark's modification of the Burton operation, employing a water-tube boiler type of still.[4]   The more efficient methods in which a stream of oil was pumped through a heating coil had their inception about 1920–1922 in the Cross and Dubbs processes.[5]   Modern development has more or less followed the latter direction.   There was a revival of interest in "vapor-phase" operation about 1927,[6] chiefly because these processes offered a source of gasolines of high antiknock value.   Operating difficulties brought about decrease in temperature and rise in pressure, while the current liquid-phase processes were shifting to increased temperature.   Thus, the two trends merged in the final mixed-phase process widely employed until well past 1940.

[1] The cracking of hydrocarbon oils dates back at least to 1865 when Young distilled shale oil under autogenous pressure to raise the boiling point and to cause partial pyrolysis during the distillation.   Benton, in 1887, pumped oil through a series of pipes in a heated furnace under a pressure of 285 lb and obtained lighter hydrocarbons than were charged.   A valve was placed at the end of the heating coil; but, in 1899, Dewar and Redwood made the improvement of having free communication between the still and condenser.   Wilson comments that Palmer (U.S. Patent 1,187,380, 1916) was the first to disclose a digestion step in a cracking operation that was entirely independent of distillation.   See Truesdell, *Natl. Petrol. News*, **18**(42):33 (1926). For the early history of cracking processes, see Rittman, *U.S. Bur. Mines Bull.* 114, 1916; Dunstan, Lomax, and Thole, *Ind. Eng. Chem.*, **9**:879 (1917).

[2] *Ind. Eng. Chem.*, **10**:484 (1918).   Other investigators were active at the time, Bacon, Brooks, and Clark, U.S. Patent 1,131,309, 1915; Fleming, U.S. Patent 1,324,766, 1919; Manley, U.S. Patent 1,428,338, 1922.

[3] Rittman, Dutton, and Dean, *U.S. Bur. Mines Bull.* 114, 1916.   Hall, *J. Inst. Petrol. Technologists*, **1**:147 (1914–1915).   Alexander, U.S. Patent 1,404,725, 1922; 1,407,619, 1922; 1,411,255, 1922.

[4] Described in *Oil Gas J.*, **23**(41):109 (1925).

[5] Bell, "American Petroleum Refining," p. 257, New York, 1930.   Brooks, "Science of Petroleum," vol. III, p. 2078, Oxford University Press, New York and London, 1938.   The development of pumps for hot oil was an important feature of the period.

[6] Leamon, *J. SAE*, **20**:67 (1927).   De Florez, *Oil Gas J.*, **26**(32):277 (1927).

IX-3. The Basic Process. Thermal cracking is now much less important than it was in, say, 1940. However, it is still practiced on a large scale for heavy residua. In any case, the development of successful thermal cracking processes represented a great technical achievement.

The evolution of the very considerable number of processes tried out between 1915 and 1930 culminated in a universal type of apparatus for effecting thermal decomposition. The basic elements were a heating coil and sometimes a reactor; the hydrocarbon mixture undergoing treatment was pumped through the coil so rapidly that the undesirable phases of the decomposition (e.g., coke deposition) occurred after the material had left the tube. The reactor retained the product long enough to provide the time factors required. Preheated oil (usually gas oil) was heated rapidly—e.g., during a total of about $\frac{1}{2}$ to 3 min, depending upon the composition of the charge and the extent of cracking desired—to a temperature of 850 to 1000°F, while in transit through pipe coils set in fireboxes. Actually the temperature was selected for the stock, somewhat as follows:

Degrees Fahrenheit

Reduced crudes..............	825 to 925
Gas oils................	900 to 975
Naphthas...................	950 to 1100

In some cases, the hot products were partially cooled at the entrance to the evaporator to avoid overcracking and deposition of coke (usually effected by quenching with some of the oil to be cracked).

The hot cracked material was sent, with release of pressure, to one or more separators, where cracked tar and heavy fuel oil were removed from the other reaction products. A fractionating tower, in which gas and gasoline were taken overhead, followed, and the higher-boiling gas oil fraction was collected for recycling. It was common practice to use the fresh gas oil charge as a reflux liquid in the fractionator, where it was warmed by contact with the cracked vapors and mixed with the cracked recycle oil; the mixture was then sent to the heating coils. The processes were very flexible, and much attention was devoted, in the later stages of the development, to modifications in which several basic operations could be conducted at once. Such an installation was known as a "combination unit"; the economies to be effected by assembling several reaction units in one set of fireboxes and fractionating towers were so real that this form of equipment was a permanent feature of refinery construction. During the latter part of the thermal cracking era, it was not unusual for a combination unit to handle the following subprocesses:

Topping. The primary distillation of gasoline, kerosene, and gas oil, or any of these, from the crude, leaving heavy fuel oil.

Reforming. The cracking of the heavy naphtha fraction of the straight-run or original gasoline, to raise its octane value.

Viscosity breaking. The mild cracking of heavy fuel oil to reduce its viscosity.

Cracking of the gas oil and recycle gas oil to gasoline.

Selective separate cracking of light and heavy fractions, respectively.

Stabilizing. The fractionating out from the gasoline of undesirably volatile constituents.[1] The advantage of combination units lies in the elimination of heat losses and of unnecessary handling of intermediate products. In general, only gas, gasoline, heavy fuel oil, and/or coke were removed from the system; a variation involved cracking the fuel oil to gasoline and coke if the demand for fuel oil was small.

Early in the development of the tube-and-reactor form of thermal cracking, it was found that adequate yields of gasoline could not be obtained by one passage of the stock through the heating coil; attempts to effect that much conversion in one pass brought about undesirably high formation of gas and coke. It was better to crack to a limited extent, remove the products, and recycle the rest of the oil (or a distilled fraction free of tar) for repeated partial conversion. The high-boiling constituents once exposed to cracking were so changed in composition as to be more refractory than originally, and further treatment made them even more so. As cracking proceeded, the gravity of the residual stock became heavier, the aniline point decreased, and the composition became more and more cyclic in nature. To what extent this was a result of polymerization and condensation reactions taking place during cracking or of the accumulation of naturally occurring refractory material is not definitely known; it is almost certain that both occurred. Table IX-1 shows the changes taking place on cracking a Mid-Continent gas oil at 450°C and 750 lb pressure, followed by a series of recracking operations on the gas oil recovered after fractionating out the gasoline and heavy fuel oil produced in the preceding operation. It will be noted that the yield of gas increased as recycling proceeded; its composition changed also. The proportion of hydrogen and methane increased.[2] The changes in the aniline point, gravity, etc., of the recycle oil and heavy tar after each recracking are significant. The gas and gasoline produced always contained more hydrogen than the charge stock, while the recycle stock and fuel oil contained less. The gasoline yield became smaller after each operation, while the conversion to fuel oil was increased. However, it is interesting

---

[1] Keith and Montgomery, *Ind. Eng. Chem.*, **26**:190 (1934). Smoley, Mekler, and Schutte, *Refiner Nat. Gasoline Mfr.*, **16**:288 (1937). Mase, *Oil Gas J.*, **36**(46):101 (1938). Armistead, "Science of Petroleum," vol. III, p. 2108, Oxford University Press, New York and London, 1938.

[2] Groll, *Ind. Eng. Chem.*, **25**:784 (1933).

to note that the physical properties and quality of the gasoline remained quite constant throughout the series of recycles.

While thermal cracking is no longer the mainstay process for motor fuel production from petroleum, it is still employed in specialized forms, particularly for (1) the further conversion of the heavier oils resulting from

TABLE IX-1

	Pass 1	Pass 2	Pass 3	Pass 4	Built-up yields	Continuous recycling operation
	Straight-run Mid-Continent gas oil	Recycle oil from 1	Recycle oil from 2	Recycle oil from 3		
Feed stock:						
API gravity............	33.7	30.4	28.9	26.5	.....	33.7
Aniline point, °F........	169	142	126	106	.....	169
Gasoline:						
Yield, per cent by volume	24.3	19.3	16.7	14.9	47.8	48.2
API gravity............	57.5	56.0	59.5	58.8	.....	58.8
Aniline point, °F........	41.5	41.5	42.0	42.0	.....	41.5
Octane number..........	67	65	66	64	.....	66
Recycle oil:						
Yield, per cent by volume	63.5	66.2	67.5	67.1	19.1	22.3
API gravity............	33.7	30.4	28.9	26.5		
Aniline point, °F........	142	126	106	84		
Heavy fuel oil:						
Yield, per cent by volume	4.4	7.3	8.6	11.0	15.7	19.1
API gravity............	10.0	12.0	9.0	8.5	.....	12.9
Flash point, °F..........	353	168	245	187		
Furol viscosity, 122°F ...	210	22	25	18		
To gas, per cent by weight..	5.5	4.2	4.5	5.5	11.7	12.7
To coke, per cent by weight	0.5	0.3	0.7	1.5	1.2	1.7
Ratio $\dfrac{\text{fuel oil yeild}}{\text{gasoline yield}}$.......	0.18	0.38	0.51	0.74	0.33	0.40
Conversion per pass, per cent..................	24.3	19.3	16.7	14.9	.....	21.3

Sydnor and Patterson, *Ind. Eng. Chem.*, **22**:1237 (1930).

catalytic cracking and for (2) what is known as vis-breaking, the mild cracking of very heavy tars and residua to lower their viscosity; this operation is ordinarily accompanied by the production of a small proportion of gasoline, say 5 or 10 per cent. The principles applied in controlling yield and quality of product remain valid and their study is instructive. The controlling factors are:

1. The nature of the oil being cracked, other conditions being constant.

2. Time and temperature of cracking, usually combined as a time-temperature function.

3. To a less extent, pressure at which cracking is carried on.

When the conditions of cracking are maintained constant and the temperature is not excessively high, the properties and nature of the gasoline produced will vary with the character of the high-boiling oil charged. This follows because thermal cracking is, as the name implies, an operation in which hydrocarbon fragments preexisting in the large molecules are broken off with little or no change in structure. Thus the cracking of paraffin wax can be expected to yield, in the ordinary cracking range of temperature, chiefly straight-chain paraffins and olefins; experiment shows that this is what happens. Similarly, a gas oil from a Gulf Coastal or California crude oil high in cyclic hydrocarbons will yield gasolines of predominantly naphthenic or aromatic nature. When, however, the operating temperature is very high—say, 700°C upward—aromatics and gaseous paraffins and olefins will be the major products from almost any charging stock.

Several procedures and indices have been used to characterize charge stocks for selection and for prediction of results. Since, in general, high-boiling hydrocarbons crack faster than lower-boiling ones, a true boiling point analysis such as first described by Peters and Baker[1] will supply useful information. It will be obvious that close fractionation of charge oil is desirable for uniform rate of cracking and maximum conversion per pass.

The influence of the chemical nature of the stock can be generalized to some extent. Paraffinic oils crack easily with small yields of coke; naphthenic stocks give, under the same conditions, somewhat lower yields of higher antiknock material; the gum-forming tendency of the product and the amount of coke will be greater in the latter case.[2] The paraffinic character of a stock may be indicated by a high aniline point, by a low viscosity-gravity constant,[3] or by a high viscosity index.[4] A more comprehensive index of the nature of the charge is the characterization factor,[5]

$$F = \sqrt[3]{\frac{\text{average molal boiling point, °R}}{\text{specific gravity at 60°F}}}$$

which ranges from 12.5 or 13.0 for purely paraffinic stocks to 10 or less

[1] *Ind. Eng. Chem.*, **18**:69 (1926).

[2] Trusty, *Refiner Nat. Gasoline Mfr.*, **11**:335, 519 (1932).

[3] Hill and Coats, *Ind. Eng. Chem.*, **20**:641 (1928).

[4] Dean and Davis, *Chem. & Met. Engr.*, **36**:618 (1929).

[5] Watson and Nelson, *Ind. Eng. Chem.*, **25**:880 (1933). See Chap. IV for all of these indices.

for the cyclic ones. By properly prepared charts,[1] the characterization factor can be expressed as a function of various properties which have themselves been used as indices, such as viscosity and gravity, viscosity index, aniline point, and carbon-hydrogen ratio.

The relationship between the paraffinicity of the charge, expressed by its characterization factor, and the octane number of the gasoline produced from it is shown below.[2]

Characterization factor of charge	Octane number	
	Motor	Research
11.0	75.4	88.4
11.4	71.3	85.0
11.8	67.1	76.6
12.2	62.5	66.0

The extent of cracking to which they have been subjected appreciably affects the characterization factor of cracked stocks,[3] ranging downward from 13.0 for low-boiling distillates to 9.5 for high-boiling residues. An attempt has been made to combine into one formula the influence of the cracking conditions and the nature of the charge.[4] Time and temperature of cracking have been employed with density and aniline point of stock to permit a prediction of the percentage conversion per pass.

The amount of coke formed will be governed not only by the chemical nature of the bulk of the charge oil but also by the presence of small proportions of asphaltic materials. This may be estimated from the tar number[5] or the carbon residue.[6] The latter indication is made more sensitive by determining the value on the highest-boiling 10 per cent fraction of the stock. A value higher than 0.12 per cent suggests excessive coke formation. The optimum procedure, which permits the commercial production of gasoline with a minimum of coke deposition in the apparatus, varies with each oil handled. This fact is to be attributed to variations in average stability of the fractions with changes in the proportions of different hydrocarbon classes present and to variations

[1] Watson, Nelson, and Murphy, *Ind. Eng. Chem.*, **27**:1460 (1935); *Oil Gas J.*, **47**(8):325 (1948).

[2] Nelson, *Oil Gas J.*, **50**(24):125 (1951).

[3] Nelson, *Oil Gas J.*, **47**(41):97 (1949); **55**(18):145 (1957) for catalytically cracked gasolines.

[4] Rude, Junkins, and Barnes, *Proc. API*, **19**(III):149 (1938).

[5] The amount of material removed by sulfuric acid; Trusty, *Oil Gas J.*, **30**(21):22 (1931).

[6] ASTM D 189–52.

within the classes, as of proportions of homologues. It may be understood, of course, that the changes in procedure required are often very slight. One fact, generally recognized, is the comparative resistance to pyrolysis offered by the hydrocarbons present in the so-called heavy naphtha fractions intermediate between gasoline and kerosene. This was noted quite early by Moore and Egloff,[1] who found the 200 to 250°C fraction of Pennsylvania crude oil to be less affected by passage through a furnace at 700°C than were the other fractions studied. Wagner[2] also reported the heavy recycle stock made at 1000°F to be especially resistant to further cracking.

Conditions of Cracking. For a given type of charge, thermal decomposition is directly influenced primarily by time, temperature, and pressure.[3] Of these, time and temperature, which are more or less equivalent in the cracking range, are the most important, as they affect the per cent conversion per pass. The over-all yield and product characterization are thus controlled by the nature of the charge stock, conversion per pass, and pressure.

Temperature is the most important of all the variables affecting the rate and extent of cracking. To interpret its effects, however, one must remember that oils undergoing cracking are made up of a variety of constituents, and some will decompose at a faster rate than others. Each stock, therefore, will show its own characteristic cracking features. In general, thermal decomposition begins at about 300 to 350°C but does not become appreciable until near 400°, and is quite rapid at 450° and higher. The rate of cracking is thus dependent on temperature and the nature of the charge at the time of cracking. At low conversions per pass, the decomposition follows that of a first-order reaction

$$K = \frac{1}{t} \ln \frac{a}{a - x}$$

where K is the reaction velocity constant, a is the amount of charge, and $a - x$ is the amount remaining after time t. The reaction velocity constant K is related to cracking temperature through the Arrhenius equation

$$\frac{d \ln K}{dT} = \frac{Q}{RT^2}$$

[1] *Chem. & Met. Eng.*, **16**:47 (1917).

[2] *Oil Gas J.*, **42**(19):53 (1943).

[3] A complete mathematical treatment of the cracking reaction, as influenced by these variables, is not available. However, the theoretical aspects of these factors in influencing the rate of cracking, the amount and composition of the gas, gasoline, and coke formed are discussed by Wilson, *Proc. Roy. Soc. (London)*, **A116**:501 (1927); **A120**:247 (1928); **A124**:16 (1929). See also Sung, Brown, and White, *Ind. Eng. Chem.*, **37**:1155 (1945).

where Q is the heat of activation; T is the absolute temperature; and R is the low gas constant, 1.986 cal per °C. This can be written

$$d \ln K = - \frac{Q}{RT^2} dT$$

which, on integration, becomes

$$\ln K = - \frac{Q}{RT} + C$$

From the straight-line functions obtained on plotting reaction velocity constants against the reciprocal of the absolute temperature, values of $Q = 53,400$ cal and $C = 28.8$ are obtained in the cracking of a gas oil.[1,2] In general, the activation energy (Q) decreases with rise in molecular weight and increases as the hydrocarbons in the recycle oils become more refractory. On an over-all basis, the velocity of cracking is doubled for each 12°C rise in temperature within the range of 370 to 425°C, 14°C at 450°C, and 17°C at 600°C.[3]

An increase in temperature at constant pressure and constant conversion increases the amount of lighter materials in the product and decreases the yield of heavy oils and coke; this is because the temperature coefficients for cracking reactions forming the lower-boiling hydrocarbons are larger than those of the secondary reactions forming the high-boiling products.[4] The practical importance of the increase in the velocity of cracking with temperature rise is limited by both the amounts and compositions of the three main products—gas, gasoline, and heavy oil—and by the length of time that the cracking still can be operated continuously.

The gas yield increases markedly with higher temperatures. For commercial thermal cracking operations the following are typical figures:

Gas oil charged	Temperature, °C	Pressure, psi	Weight per cent to gas
Mid-Continent*.........	460	200	10.2
Mid-Continent..........	480	200	16.9
Cabin Creek†..........	575	30	29.7

* Sydnor, *Ind. Eng. Chem.*, **26**:184 (1934).

† Osterstrom and Wagner, *Proc. API*, **11**(III):52 (1930). Very paraffinic crude.

[1] Geniesse and Reuter, *Ind. Eng. Chem.*, **22**:1274 (1930); **24**:219 (1932).

[2] The values of Q and C for number of pure hydrocarbons are given by Pease and Morton, *J. ACS*, **55**:3190 (1933). Paul and March, *Ind. Eng. Chem.*, **26**:454 (1934). Frey and Hepp, *Ind. Eng. Chem.*, **25**:441 (1933).

[3] Leslie and Potthoff, *Ind. Eng. Chem.*, **18**:776 (1926). Sachanen and Tilicheyev, *J. Inst. Petrol. Technologists*, **14**:761 (1928). Geniesse and Reuter, *Ind. Eng. Chem.*, **24**:219 (1932). Neppe, *J. Inst. Petrol. Technologists*, **28**:27 (1942).

[4] Sung, Brown, and White, *Ind. Eng. Chem.*, **37**:1153 (1945).

The composition of the gas also changes as the temperature is varied; the content of unsaturates reaches a maximum of near 50 per cent at about 600°C.[1]

The properties of the cracked gasoline also change with the cracking temperature, more slowly at the lower values. Thus, octane number and unsaturated content increase gradually in the range up to about 540°C, and more sharply above this point. There is an accompanying change in volatility, involving a shift to lower-boiling hydrocarbons, and an increase in easily oxidizable hydrocarbons. The latter are probably alkenyl aromatics, cyclic olefins, and conjugated diolefins, which lead to gum formation during storage (see Chap. III).

Cracked residua change with temperature of operation probably less than do the gasolines that are produced. The amount of aromatic content, indicated by specific gravity, increases gradually as the temperature rises. Viscosity, however, stays strikingly low unless large yields of gasoline have been removed, in which case the tar may become extremely thick, approaching a coke. Coke deposition on heating surfaces will occur more rapidly at the higher temperatures, so that, other things being the same, a cracking still may be operated much longer without cleaning if the operating temperature is not excessively high. In all these cases shorter time of exposure will permit somewhat higher temperature.

In general, lower-boiling stocks require more time for cracking, at a given temperature, than the heavier ones, and the same is true for oils that have had a prior thermal treatment (recycle stocks). The formation of both gas and heavy oils (and coke) increases with time. The yield of intermediate products (gasoline) increases to a maximum value and then decreases as the time of cracking conditions is extended. This is attributed to secondary reactions in which these products are themselves further cracked to form gas and, to a lesser extent, are polymerized and condensed to high-boiling residues and coke.[2] With longer times for cracking, the products become more saturated because the olefins have more opportunity for polymerization, possibly alkylation of aromatics, and cyclization. In the initial stages of cracking, however, an extension of the time during which decomposition takes place increases the yield of products in an approximately linear ratio. This linear effect has been observed for gas oil, residual fuel oil, and for a once-cracked recycle oil.[3] A qualitative indication of the magnitude of significant time changes is given in Table IX-2, showing the time periods required for maximum gasoline yield at various temperatures.[4]

[1] Cassar, *Ind. Eng. Chem.*, **24**:802 (1932).

[2] Sung, Brown, and White, *loc. cit.*

[3] Leslie and Potthoff, *Ind. Eng. Chem.*, **18**:776 (1926).

[4] Nelson, *Petrol. Engr.*, **4**(11):30 (1933); (12):27 (1933).

TABLE IX-2

Temperature, °C	Maximum yield (once through), per cent	Time at maximum yield, sec	Stock
430	40	14,000	Gas oil
450	48	7,500	Paraffin wax
500	31	1,000	Gas oil
580	26	30	Gas oil
640	23	3	Gas oil

The extent to which various stocks are cracked, when heated to 550°C for different time intervals, is given in Fig. IX-1.

The equivalence of time and temperature was demonstrated qualitatively in commerical practice where gasoline was produced with a time of reaction of about 2 to 10 sec in the vapor phase at 600°C, 1 to 2 min in a mixed-phase operation at 480°C, and possibly 15 to 20 min in liquid phase cracking at 440°C.

The mutual equivalence of time and temperature has been incorporated into a single function, described as the time-temperature index.[1] Assuming 480°C as a standard reference temperature, the index may be expressed as

$$\theta = 2^{\frac{(480 - T)t}{17}}$$

where $T = °C$ and $t =$ time in minutes. As the index value increases, the gasoline yield increases to a maximum and then decreases. The unsaturated content of the gasoline behaves similarly, while the gas-gasoline ratio and coke formation both increase directly.

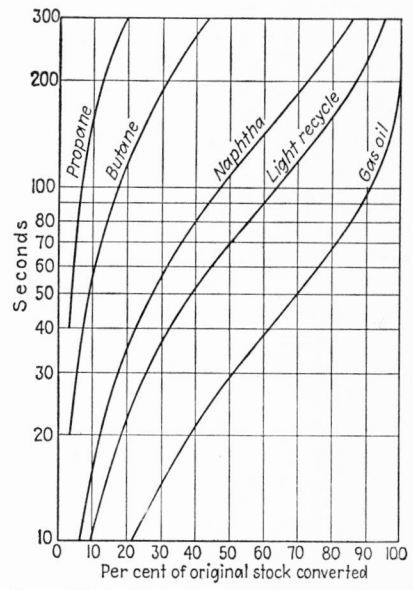

FIG. IX-1. Relative cracking rates of different stocks at 550°C. [*From Ostergaard and Smoley, Refiner Nat. Gasoline Mfr.*, **19**:301 (1940).]

The index has its limitations, however, and cannot be applied too broadly. The properties of the gasoline produced may be different for two sets of conditions having the same values of the index, because long times at low

[1] Geniesse and Reuter, *Ind. Eng. Chem.*, **22**:1274 (1930).

temperatures permit extensive secondary reactions and the resistance to cracking of high- and low-molecular-weight compounds of different hydrocarbon types (nature of charge) may not be the same at high and low temperatures.

Noncatalytic cracking processes for motor fuel production nearly all employed pressures in excess of 200 psi. Vapor-phase processes operated below this range, but in general, thermal cracking at pressures near atmospheric has been unsuccessful. Pressure itself has essentially no effect on the initial monomolecular hydrocarbon decomposition. As an indication of this, the reaction

$$\text{Neohexane} \rightleftharpoons \text{ethylene} + \text{isobutane}$$

could not be reversed at 500°C until a pressure of about 4,000 psi had been applied.[1]

Pressure, however, exerts considerable influence on the character of the product through changes in the rate and course of secondary reactions. In vapor-phase systems an increase in pressure accelerates the rate of olefin polymerization. In mixed-phase systems it increases the volume of the liquid (and also the time in the cracking zone for the hydrocarbon material that has been liquefied); the bimolecular secondary reactions are slowed down because of the resulting dilution. Thus, for the same time and temperature, the formation of heavy polymers from gasoline olefins is decreased; likewise, the yield of coke. This fact, and the decrease in gas yield[2] (as a result of increased polymerization), leads to a higher gasoline yield.[3] At constant conversion, higher pressure increases tar yield. At 600°C, ethylene and propylene yield highly aromatic liquids and gases rich in hydrogen at atmospheric pressure. As the pressure is raised, however, the aromatics and hydrogen both decrease because of polymer formation and probably hydrocracking of the polymer to give different products; at several thousand pounds pressure (same temperature), the liquid product was free of aromatics. A necessary consequence of the decrease in olefins and aromatics with rising pressure is a decrease in octane number.

An increase in pressure also has some effect on the heat content of the system since polymerization, along with some of the other secondary reactions, is exothermic; the net heat required to produce a pound of gasoline is thus reduced. Increases in time, temperature, and conversion per pass, which also favor exothermic secondary reactions, produce the same effect.[4]

[1] Frey and Hepp, *Ind. Eng. Chem.*, **28**:1439 (1936).

[2] Keith, Ward, and Rubin, *Proc. API*, **14M**(III):49 (1933).

[3] Sung, Brown, and White, *loc. cit.*

[4] Wagner, *Oil Gas J.*, **42**(18):66 (1943).

Still another function of pressure is the establishment of a preferred phase condition[1] for the material in the cracking zone. In general, a single phase system is considered desirable, since systems in which the liquid and vapor can stratify easily are difficult to crack because of differences in heat transfer. When operating under elevated pressures, the two phases approach some degree of homogeneity; the gas partially dissolves in the liquid to lower the density of the latter, and the gas phase itself becomes more dense. This change in phase condition, in turn, alters the time element to give a longer residence in the system, which is itself a factor in reducing losses to gas and lowering the unsaturated content of the gasoline as the pressure is increased. In the thermal reforming of naphthas conducted in the presence of added C_3 and C_4 gases, one of the benefits claimed was the reduction of the critical temperature of the mixture to below that of the heating coils. Any tendency for liquid oils to condense out on the surface of the coils, where it might have had a longer time of residence than desired, was thus reduced. This was stated to permit higher cracking temperature and conversion per pass with a minimum of coke formation.[2] It is thus apparent that the terms "liquid phase" and "vapor phase" as related to cracking operations are applied quite loosely. As a matter of fact processes working above 480°C, regardless of pressure, were probably in the vapor phase. This temperature lies above the critical value for most of the hydrocarbons in ordinary charging stocks.

The proportion of a charge which is cracked in a given time, usually for one passage through the heating zone (conversion per pass), is closely related to the recycle ratio (also known as throughput ratio).

$$\frac{\text{Volume of fresh oil charged} + \text{volume of previously cracked oil circulated}}{\text{Volume of fresh oil charged}}$$

This is because the conversion per pass is an intensity factor, influenced both by operating conditions and by the nature of the material charged. Under given conditions, a lower percentage conversion will be effected in one passage if the charge contains a high proportion of recycle material because the previously cracked stock has become more refractory.

[1] The distinction between liquid- and vapor-phase conditions in hydrocarbon systems held under elevated temperatures and pressures is indefinite. The possibility of the conversion of a liquid-phase into a vapor-phase system, or vice versa, even under so-called mixed-phase conditions, or the possibility of a hydrocarbon stream passing through the cracking zone without a change in phase is discussed by Hirsch and Fisher in "The Chemistry of Petroleum Hydrocarbons," Brooks, Boord, Kurtz, and Schmerling (eds.), vol. II, p. 27, Reinhold Publishing Corporation, New York, 1955. Also, see Brown, Lewis, and Weber, *Ind. Eng. Chem.*, **26**:325 (1934), for a discussion of phase equilibria in cracking operations.

[2] Ostergaard and Smoley, *Refiner Nat. Gasoline Mfr.*, **19**:301 (1940).

The choice of a high or a low reaction intensity, expressed as a high or a low conversion per pass, will bring about one or another set of results, either of which may be desirable.   Low conversion per pass gives:

High over-all gasoline yield
Small loss to coke and gas
Consequent long operating periods
Gasoline of low octane number, slightly lower volatility, and more saturated in character

These results are due in part to the absence of the secondary reactions accompanying more intense cracking.   High conversion per pass gives:

Lower gasoline yield
Higher gas and coke yields
Gasoline of higher volatility and octane number
Shorter operating periods[1]

The gasoline yield is less for high conversions per pass because some of the unsaturated hydrocarbons produced are polymerized to fuel oil, or to tar and coke if the pressure is high, or lost to gas if the pressure is low.   A direct relationship exists over a wide range of cracking temperatures[2] between the octane numbers of the gasolines produced and the conversions per pass; temperature, however, is less a factor in governing gasoline quality than commonly supposed.   Conversion per pass and operating pressures thus appear to be the most important factors controlling the yield and octane number of the gasoline produced in thermal cracking from a given charge.[3]

In conventional thermal cracking operations the recycle ratio was held between 2 and about 5, the exact value varying with the stock treated, somewhat as follows:

Reduced crudes . . . .   1:1 to 3:1
Gas oils . . . .   2:1 to 4:1
Naphthas 1:1

The ratio used was also dependent upon whether a coil-only or a coil-plus soaking chamber operation was employed.   The conversion per pass was of the order of 15 to 23 per cent; in vapor-phase cracking it was as low as 12 per cent of the total charge pumped.   Cracking stocks differ in the amount of conversion that can be tolerated for optimum results.   The figure for paraffinic oils is about 20 to 25 per cent, and about half that for naphthenic stocks.[4]

[1] Sydnor, *Ind. Eng. Chem.*, **26**:184 (1934).
[2] Keith, Ward, and Rubin, *Proc. API*, **14M**(III):49 (1933).
[3] Hirsch and Fisher, *op. cit.*
[4] Nelson, *Petrol. Eng.*, **7**(3):94 (1935).

Gas Formation. The gases formed in cracking are presumably the fragments released when a large molecule breaks at a variety of points, including those near the terminal positions. The large increase in yield of gas with rise in temperature is presumably the result of drastic recracking of the primary reaction products. The composition of the gas is affected primarily by the conditions of its production, and to a less extent by the nature of the charge. The gases are predominantly hydrocarbon in make-up, although carbon monoxide, carbon dioxide, hydrogen sulfide, oxygen, and hydrogen may be present. Even formic and acetic acids have been recognized.[1] All these latter are present in small amounts only and may be expected in higher proportions when oils high in sulfur compounds and asphaltic materials are charged. Typical figures for gas yield are:[2]

Charging stock	Gas, cu ft per bbl		
	Oil charged	Pressure distillate	Gasoline made
Mid-Continent gas oil..............	303	378	684
North Texas kerosene distillate.......	69	72	164
Panuco residuum..................	120	550	660

Some average figures, in percentages, for the composition of cracking still gases are:[3]

	510°C, 350 psi		565–620°C, 50 psi		
	East Texas gas oil	California gas oil	Pennsylvania gas oil	Coastal reduced crude	Polymerized olefins
Methane and hydrogen........	39.2	44.8	35.0	38.8	48.4
Ethane.....................	21.0	16.2	11.9	13.2	12.3
Ethylene...................	3.9	4.0	24.6	20.3	14.2
Propane...................	16.2	7.4	2.5	5.7	2.8
Propylene.................	7.4	14.2	18.0	13.1	12.6
C_4 fraction*...............	9.1	10.0	4.7	2.5	7.4
C_5 fraction...............	3.2	3.4	3.1	6.4	2.3

* Butadiene as high as 13 per cent of the C_4 fraction has been reported. Wagner, *Ind. Eng. Chem.*, **27**:933 (1935).

[1] These are presumably the result of cracking oxygen compounds in the oil. Hall and Taveau, *Proc. API*, **10**(III):122 (1929).

[2] Egloff and Morrell, *Ind. Eng. Chem.*, **17**:32 (1925).

[3] Wagner, *Ind. Eng. Chem.*, **26**:188 (1934). Egloff and Morrell, *Ind. Eng. Chem.*, **26**:940 (1934).

The predominance of methane and ethane in the gases is characteristic of those produced in thermal cracking, and reflects the prevalence of end-group scission in this type of operation.

Cracking-still Residues. The undistilled cracking-still residues, known as pressure still tar, consist essentially of high-boiling mixtures accumulated as a result of repeated cracking of the recycle oil and possibly of some refractory material remaining from the virgin charge. The residua are generally heavy in gravity but low in viscosity, a condition not natural for uncracked petroleum oils. In this regard they resemble coal-tar distillates, and while the evidence suggests that they are made up of highly condensed aromatic compounds, there are real chemical differences from coal tar. Likewise, the tar formed directly from high-temperature cracking of hydrocarbons contains large quantities of naphthalene, anthracene, and phenanthrene.[1] The tar usually carries appreciable percentages of coke-like material, probably colloidally dispersed, which has a tendency to precipitate out or to solidify in place during storage or handling. Mild warming (100°C) over an extended period of time causes an irreversible flocculation of the carbonaceous material,[2] while the addition of 1 per cent of rosin soap postpones its solidification.[3]

The composition of the residual oil varies to some extent with the nature of the charge and with type of treatment, but probably less so than is true for the gasoline and middle oils produced. This is because the residuum is the end product of a long series of decompositions which have an homogenizing effect. A wax-like material has been recovered from an Oklahoma cracked residue,[4] but since paraffin waxes are easily cracked, the question arises as to whether the material might have been solid naphthenes or aromatics. A waxy product melting at 52°C and analyzing for $(C_4H_5)n$, obviously not paraffinic, has been recovered from a cracked Gulf Coastal residuum.[5] On the other hand, paraffinic lubricating oil materials have been recovered by sulfur dioxide extraction of a cracked tar.[6]

IX-4. Coking Distillation. Coking distillation of reduced crude oils was practiced up until the 1930s for the making of lubricating oils of the class known as paraffin oils, simultaneously with the manufacture of paraffin wax. The process, discussed in Chap. XIV, has been discontinued, and coking distillation survives only for preparation of distillate charging stocks for cracking operations. The thermal decomposition of a

[1] Groll, *Ind. Eng. Chem.*, **25**:784 (1933).
[2] Voskuil and Rober, *J. Inst. Petrol.*, **24**:181 (1938).
[3] Sheppard and Eberlin, *Ind. Eng. Chem.*, **16**:832 (1934).
[4] Tropsch, Thomas, Morrell, and Egloff, *Ind. Eng. Chem.*, **31**:1112 (1939).
[5] C. R. Wagner, private communication.
[6] Baird, *Oil Gas J.*, **30**(46):56 (1932).

residual stock necessarily involves the cracking of heavy molecules of considerable size and high carbon content; this implies a large production of coke, which must be cared for in some way.[1] In general, the following methods have been practiced:

1. Conventional batch operation of horizontal cylindrical shell stills of about 1,000-bbl capacity, fired externally and operated at essentially atmospheric pressure. This procedure has practically disappeared.

2. Cracking of the reduced crude at about 480°C in conventional continuous cracking equipment—heating coil and soaking drum—suitably modified to provide mild temperature and pressure with short time in the heating coils.[2] Under these conditions the deposition of coke takes place as much as possible in the soaking drum, and for this reason the operation is referred to as delayed coking. Sometimes provision is made for heating of the zone in which coke deposition occurs. In any case, two or more coking chambers are provided, so that one may be cleaned of coke while another is in operation.

3. A continuous contact coking process consisting of a reactor (480 to 540°C, 35 psi) in which oil-wetted coke particles, or seed coke, flow downward as a dense bed; sufficient time is allowed for the cracking, coking, and drying reactions to take place.[3] A lift to a reheater is provided in which part of the circulating coke is raised in temperature (540 to 570°C) to supply heat for the reaction. In the reactor the lighter portions of the feed are vaporized and the heavier constituents are retained on the coke particles in a liquid film. As the coking reaction proceeds, the film is converted to gas, liquid hydrocarbons, and coke. The latter is retained on the seed particle where successive increments are deposited and a gradual increase in the particle size occurs.

4. A continuous process in which hot residuum is sprayed into a bed of finely divided previously formed fluidized coke (100 to 200 mesh) held at 480 to 570°C and at atmospheric pressure.[4] The unit consists of a reactor, a heater, and connecting transfer lines through which the particles circulate. Coke particles are allowed to grow to about the size of ordinary sand; some of the coke is employed as fuel for the process.

The products of all these operations include hydrocarbon gas, liquid oils, and coke. The gas differs little from ordinary cracking still gas, containing olefins up to 10 or 15 per cent and hydrogen sulfide in propor-

---

[1] On carbonizing of coal-oil mixtures see Brownlie, *Ind. Eng. Chem.*, **28**:629 (1936); Rainsburg and McGurl, American Gas Association, Technical Section (1940).

[2] Jones, *J. Inst. Petrol. Technologists*, **21**:895 (1935). *Refiner Nat. Gasoline Mfr.*, **17**:554 (1938). Watson, *Refiner Nat. Gasoline Mfr.*, **17**:652 (1938). Armistead, *Oil Gas J.*, **44**(45):103 (1946).

[3] Mekler, Schutte, and Whipple, *Petrol. Refiner*, **32**(12):131 (1953).

[4] Voorhies and Martin, *Oil Gas J.*, **52**(28):204 (1953). Martin, Barr, and Krebs, *Oil Gas J.*, **53**(1):166 (1954). Johnson and Wood, *Oil Gas J.*, **53**(30):61 (1954).

tion to the sulfur content of the charge. The liquids include a small proportion of gasoline, recovered chiefly from the gas; the rest of the liquids range through gas oil to hydrocarbons viscous enough to be classified as lubricating oils. Only that part of the gas oil boiling up to about 540°C is suitable as charge stock for catalytic cracking; that boiling above contains excessive amounts of volatile metal components (Ni, Fe, V); these are poisons for the catalyst. The obsolete batch coking operation supplied one product not obtained separately from the continuous processes. This is the so-called wax tailings, a sticky, viscous material, semisolid when cold, and suitable as a binder for briquets. Its composition is unknown, but it is believed to have consisted of compounds of condensed aromatic type such as chrysene and picene.[1] The wax tailings came off at the last stage in the distillation, accompanied by a sharp increase in gas production and an increased proportion of hydrogen sulfide, carbon monoxide, and carbon dioxide in the gas. These phenomena support the idea that this stage represented the decomposition of accumulated resinous and asphaltic materials along with the very high-molecular-weight hydrocarbons which had remained in the still until the last stage. It is uncertain how much cracking occurred during most of the distillation; it was probably limited to a small amount taking place in the highly heated layers adjacent to the heating surfaces. During the final period, however, the bulk of the coke was formed, and as indicated, most of the gas was released; the temperature during this period was observed to be about 450°C at a position within a few inches of the still bottom.

Typical yields from a heavy Mid-Continent residuum (25°API gravity) are of the order[2]

```
Gas, cu ft per bbl.........................  169
Gasoline, per cent volume, 400°F F.P........  22.4
Gas oil, per cent volume....................  69.1
Coke, lb per bbl............................  40.7
```

Cracked residua on coking give appreciably lower yields of gasoline, although coke production is about the same. The coke produced by the batch process was essentially ash free and of volatile content varying around 10 per cent (see Chap. XVI).

IX-5. Cracking for Gas Production. Petroleum oils have been used for many years as gasmaking materials, usually supplementary to coal except where the latter was scarce. However, the recent advent of long-distance pipelines carrying natural gas has decreased the importance

---

[1] Prunier, *Compt. rend.*, **86**:991 (1878); *Ann. chim. et phys.*, **17**(5):5 (1879).

[2] Sachanen, "Conversion of Petroleum," p. 246, Reinhold Publishing Corporation, New York, 1948.

of gasmaking processes.   Oil gas is now used primarily as a supplement to natural gas in taking care of peak-load demands, or for stand-by purposes in case of breakdown.[1]

The gasification may be by simple evaporation, as in the case of liquefied petroleum gases (which are generally mixed with other gases of lower Btu value or with air), or by the pyrolysis of oil under gasmaking conditions.   In the latter case the cracking may take place with the oil alone, in the presence of reactants such as air or steam, or in the presence of blue gas.[2]   In the reforming of natural gas or propane[3] catalysts (generally nickel) may[4] or may not[5] be employed.

The basic principles of the making of oil gas are quite simple and quite uniform.   The oil is sprayed along with superheated steam into a retort or chamber heated to a temperature near 800 to 850°C, where a pyrolytic decomposition takes place.   Usually about 40 to 60 per cent is recovered as gas; this depends on the type of oil used.[6]   The gas so made then passes through another retort or chamber in which it is subjected to a slightly higher temperature and for a somewhat longer time.   This is known as the "fixing" process and serves to complete the cracking, converting hydrocarbons of low molecular weight, but normally liquid, into hydrogen and permanently gaseous hydrocarbons.   The processes most employed in manufacturing oil gas have been those of Hall and Jones.   The former employs a so-called four-shell apparatus in which the regenerative principle is applied to both the air (for burning off carbon) and the steam.[7]

Nature of Products.   The chemical reactions involved in the formation of gaseous hydrocarbons from heavier oils, as employed in the oil-gas

---

[1] These stand-by plants can be used for manufacture of chemical raw materials. *Chem. Eng. News,* **34**:1434 (1956).

[2] For a general review of the various processes for making gas from oil, and the quality of the resulting gases, see Long, *Chem. & Process Eng.,* **35**(6):169 (1954); also *Petroleum,* **18**(5):180 (1955).   The early references are interesting: see Armstrong and Miller, *J. Chem. Soc.,* **49**:74 (1886).   Lewes, *J. Soc. Chem. Ind.,* **11**:584 (1892); Tocher, *J. Soc. Chem. Ind.,* **13**:231 (1894); Lewis-Dale, *J. Soc. Chem. Ind.,* **44**:189T (1925).

[3] C_4, C_5, and C_6 hydrocarbons can be used but they form excessive amounts of carbon.

[4] Smoker, *Am. Gas Assoc. Proc.,* **31**:854 (1949); **35**:852 (1953).

[5] Hasche and Fleming, *Am. Gas J.,* **181**(4):14 (1954).

[6] Linden and Peck, *Ind. Eng. Chem.,* **47**:2470 (1955).   Linden, Brooks, and Miller, *Ind. Eng. Chem.,* **47**:2475 (1955).   Schultz, Guyer, and Linden, *Ind. Eng. Chem.,* **47**:2479 (1955).   McKean, *Inst. Petrol. Rev.,* **11**(124):90 (1957).

[7] For detailed descriptions of various gasmaking processes, see Morgan, "Gasification of Hydrocarbons," Moore Pub. Co., New York, 1953.   Shnidman, "Gaseous Fuels," 2d ed., American Gas Association, New York, 1954.   "Gas Fundamentals," Koppers Co., Pittsburgh, 1950.   Garner and Long, *Inst. Petrol. Rev.,* **10**(109):5 (1956); *ibid.,* **10**(110):50 (1956).

processes discussed above, are of the same general nature as those taking place in the other cracking reactions already considered.   The temperature is higher than that employed for motor fuel production but about the same as that suitable for the making of aromatic hydrocarbons.   The reaction occurs in vapor phase and at low pressure.   Even the products are not different from those made by other cracking processes, since gases, volatile liquids, residual tar, and carbonaceous solids are obtained.   The increase in temperature and drop in pressure from the conditions of motor fuel production serve, however, to change the relative quantities of the different products.   In a motor fuel process, not over 10 to 15 per cent of the oil appears as gas; in a gasmaking process, upward of 50 per cent is so converted.

The liquid products of the various oil-gas processes, known as "drips" and "tar," respectively, have been studied to some extent.   The drips are highly unsaturated, gasoline-like products,[1] and the tar is an aromatic mixture of specific gravity slightly greater than 1.0.[2]   The composition of the volatile liquid constituents may be important in the effect of the gas on orifices, meter leathers, and other distributing apparatus.   Undercracked oil is likely to yield a gas containing indene and styrene, which may oxidize or polymerize or both, producing gum of a harmful nature.[3]   The remedy is more complete cracking.

Producer gas made from coke, coal, or oil has very limited use at the present time.   Except for a few gas plants in isolated communities, water gas manufacture has ceased to be important.   This is because both of the above types of manufactured gas are low in Btu content (about 130 to 180 and 300, respectively), and from the appliance standpoint are not suitable for blending with high (1040) Btu natural gas.   A higher Btu blending gas is needed.   By cracking hydrocarbon oils in the presence of water gas (or blue gas) a product can be obtained varying from 300 to 1000 Btu per cu ft.   Propane and butane (liquefied petroleum gas, LPG) are used in some communities; they are generally mixed with air to reduce Btu content from about 3000 to 500 Btu per cu ft for distribution.   Where burner installations are set for a lower Btu gas (650 or 810), natural gas may be mixed with reformed natural gas or reformed light hydrocarbons. The reforming is carried out thermally or catalytically in the presence of air or steam to give a product of proper Btu content for blending.[4]

[1] Armstrong and Miller, *op. cit.;* Lewes, *op. cit.;* Tocher, *op. cit.;* Lewis-Dale, *op. cit.*
[2] On the composition of water-gas tar, see Downs and Dean, *Ind. Eng. Chem.,* **6** :366 (1914).   Bateman, *U.S. Dept. Agr. Bull.* 1036, 73 (1922).
[3] Brown and Howard, *Ind. Eng. Chem.,* **15** :1147 (1923).   Brown and Berger, *Ind. Eng. Chem.,* **17** :168 (1925).   Fulweiler, *Proc. Am. Gas. Assoc.,* **14** :838 (1932); **15** :839 (1933); **16** :954 (1934); **17** :700 (1935).   Wenzel, *Gas Age-Record,* **71** :413 (1933).
[4] Schenk and Osterlok, *Gas u. Wasserfach,* **96**(1):1 (1955).

Evaluation of Gas Oils. The value of different oils for gasmaking has been the subject of much study on the part of the gas industry.[1] Actually, oils of widely different nature and properties can be used, so that economic considerations take first rank. A homogeneous, well-fractionated distillate is more desirable than one of wide boiling point or one blended of materials having widely different boiling points. This is because a closely cut product can be successfully cracked at one temperature while a blended oil presents danger of undercracking and overcracking the fractions of different boiling point. A Mid-Continent gas oil of 32 to 36°API gravity, as made by ordinary refinery distillation, is a satisfactory oil for most of these purposes. The competitive uses of such a product, however, have forced the employment of heavy oils[2] of lower price. For emergency, higher-priced distillates may be used. Under these circumstances, the evaluation of oils for gasmaking purposes is quite important. Two general approaches have been employed. One involves an examination of the oil for chemical constitution, and the other an actual gasmaking experiment with a laboratory apparatus.[3] The analytical examination is based on the recognition[4] that hydrocarbons of high hydrogen content, paraffins and olefins, are more desirable as to high gas yield and low tar yield than naphthenes and aromatics. The technique of analysis has been developed by Holmes[5] and by Griffith.[6] Laboratory cracking methods have been evaluated by Murphy[7] and by Schläpfer and Schaffhauser.[8] A relation between density, boiling point, and refractive dispersion of an oil as indicating constitution is reported by Holmes[9] as a good substitute for chemical examination or laboratory cracking.

[1] See Linden and Pettyjohn, "Selection of Oils for High Btu Oil Gas," *Bull.* 12, Institute of Gas Technology, 1952, for discussion of yields and products obtained from a series of oils, covering a range of carbon-hydrogen ratios and Conradson carbon numbers, cracked at various levels of severity; and useful nomographs showing the qualities of the gases produced.

[2] Wallers, *Gas J.*, **283**:629, 695 (1955). Garner and Long, *Inst. Petrol. Rev.*, **10**(109):5 (1956).

[3] Linden and Pettyjohn, *op. cit.*

[4] Ross and Leather, *Analyst*, **32**:241 (1907). Downing and Pohlman, *Proc. Am. Gas Inst.*, **11**(1):587 (1916).

[5] *Ind. Eng. Chem.*, **16**:258 (1924).

[6] *J. Soc. Chem. Ind.*, **48**:252T (1929). See also Mighill, *Proc. Am. Gas Assoc.*, 1927, p. 1454. Van Dijk, *Het Gas.*, **53**:449 (1933). *C.A.*, **28**:885 (1934). Merkius and White, *Proc. Am. Gas Assoc.*, 1934, p. 986.

[7] *Gas Age-Record*, **65**:389, 395 (1930).

[8] *Schweiz. Ver. Gas-u. Wasserfach Monatsbull.*, **13**:125, 159, 193 (1933). *C.A.*, **28**:1175 (1934).

[9] *Ind. Eng. Chem.*, **24**:325 (1932).

CATALYTIC CRACKING

Natural clays have long been known to exert a catalytic influence on the cracking of oils, but it was not until about 1936 that the process using silica-alumina catalysts was developed sufficiently for commercial use. Since then, catalytic cracking has progressively supplanted thermal cracking as the most advantageous means of converting distillate oils into gasoline. The general operation is not new; the patent literature supplies many references to methods of using the principle.

The advances which have made modern catalytic processes so successful are believed to be:

1. Employing a high catalyst-to-oil ratio
2. Allowing only a short time for the reaction
3. Applying frequent regeneration to the catalyst

Contributing from an operating standpoint are:

1. Efficient use of heat evolved in regeneration of catalyst
2. Good control of reaction temperature
3. Similar control of catalyst regeneration temperature

Catalysts now available are physically strong and retain a high activity. The reaction is uniform over long time periods and the products do not change with long use of catalyst.

The main reason for the wide adoption of catalytic cracking is the fact that a better yield of a higher-octane gasoline can be obtained than by any known thermal operation. At the same time the gas produced consists mostly of the preferred propane and butane hydrocarbons, with less methane and ethane; the production of heavy oils and tars, higher in molecular weight than the charge material, is minimized; both the gasoline and the uncracked "cycle oil" are more saturated than the thermal products. This is largely due to the high aromatic content.

While it is claimed that the methods now employed are effective for residual stocks and solvent extract tars[1] as well as for distillates, the charging of undistilled residues is not frequently practiced. They form excessive amounts of coke deposit on the catalyst, do not yield as good products, and contribute to rapid catalyst deterioration through poisoning by metallo organic compounds (mainly vanadium) which are often contained in asphaltic residua.

---

[1] Mateer and Haney, *Oil Gas J.*, **43**(9):87 (1944). Simpson, *Oil Gas J.*, **44**(1):88 (1945). Simpson, Eastwood, and Shimp, *Oil Gas J.*, **44**(29):119 (1945). Bland, *Petrol. Refiner*, **34**(9):166 (1955).

The operations are carried out in vapor phase at pressures of the order of 5 to 50 psi for times of contact varying with the process from 20 sec to 10 min, at temperatures between 425 and 540°C, but usually at the lower end of the range. On one pass through the apparatus, gasoline yield of the order of 40 to 55 per cent can be obtained; although recycling to extinction is not customary, a single recycle circuit will raise the total yield to as much as 75 per cent; if the gases are converted to polymer or to olefin-isoparaffin alkylate, the ultimate yield may be extended to 90 to 95 per cent.

While high-octane gasoline can also be obtained by thermal cracking, the temperatures required are high and the losses to gas and coke become excessive. As with thermal cracking, the cycle stock remaining from a catalytic treatment has been changed unfavorably for further cracking; that from the catalytic operations is, however, much more aromatic than the charge, and can best be further handled by a thermal process.[1] Hydrogenation will convert it into a naphthenic material quite suitable for recharging to the catalyst.[2] Such treatment is not often economical; the cycle stock is usually disposed of as a light fuel oil.

Differences in the products of catalytic and thermal cracking of a heavy paraffinic feed stock are shown in Table IX-3.

TABLE IX-3

	Thermal cracking, partial recycle	Catalytic cracking	
		Single pass	Recycle
Catalyst.........................	None	Silica-alumina	Silica-alumina
Yields:			
Gasoline plus polymer, volume per cent............................	38.9	57.2	75.3
Cycle oil, volume per cent..........	40.0	40.0	4.5
10°API tar, volume per cent........	20.1	nil	7.8
Coke, weight per cent.............	nil	3.5	10.6
Dry gas, weight per cent...........	4.3	5.6	7.6
Octane number, gasoline plus polymer:			
ASTM, clear.....................	72.6	81.1	83.1
CFR research, clear...............	82.5	95.7	95.7
CFR research, clear plus 1.5 ml tetraethyllead per gal................	89.0	99.3	98.5

From Russell, *Petroleum (London)*, **10**(7):151 (1947).

[1] McReynolds and Barron, *Petrol. Refiner*, **28**(4):111 (1949). Kimball and Scott, *Petrol. Refiner*, **27**(6):326 (1948).

[2] Brown, Voorhies, and Smith, *Ind. Eng. Chem.*, **38**:136 (1946). See also refining with hydrogen, Chap. III.

The differences in the molecular size of the gasoline components are illustrated in Table IX-4, which compares the carbon number distribution of the virgin naphtha and the thermal and catalytic gasolines obtained from a Mid-Continent petroleum.[1] Naphthenic gas oils produce highest yields of gasolines for a given coke deposit, and for this reason are preferred charge stocks for catalytic cracking.[2]

TABLE IX-4

	Virgin	Thermal	Catalytic
Specific gravity 60/60.........	0.724	0.683	0.668
ASTM distillation:			
Initial...................	55	35	40
10 per cent..............	75	40	45
50 per cent..............	105	55	60
90 per cent..............	140	110	95
End point...........	180	190	120
Carbon number distribution:			
C_4......................	2.3	4.7	2.8
C_5......................	10.2	45.4	38.5
C_6......................	19.9	25.9	35.2
C_7.....	26.7	12*	18.3
C_8......................	23.5	5*	4.5
C_9......................	14.4	3*	0.3
C_{10}, and heavier...........	3.0	4*	0.4

* Estimated from ASTM distillation. It should be noted that the end points of these gasolines were low and that of the catalytic product particularly so.

The process effects a rather complete desulfurization of the gasoline product. This is often, however, at the expense of rapid deterioration of the catalyst. The synthetic silica-aluminas are more resistant than activated natural clays to sulfur compounds, although the sulfur tolerance of the latter can be improved. Because of the extensive desulfurization, the gasolines are relatively easy to refine. Much of the sulfur ends up as thiophenols (compared to thiophenes in thermal cracking) which are removed by alkali washing. Catalytically cracked gasolines contain high proportions of branched-chain structures, both paraffinic and olefinic, especially in the more volatile portion; substantial amounts of aromatics are found in the higher-boiling fractions. The olefin content may be as high as 30 to 50 per cent, depending on the extent of saturation by hydrogen transfer; and the structures of both the gases and liquids will depend on the amount of isomerization that has taken place during their formation. Very few diolefins are present; more aromatics

[1] Cady, Marschner, and Cropper, *Ind. Eng. Chem.*, **44**:1859 (1952).
[2] Ardern, Dart, and Lassiat, *Advances in Chem. Ser.*, no. 5, p. 13, 1951.

are found than in thermal cracking,[1] the amount depending upon the stock treated.

Comparing thermal and catalytic cracking further, the latter takes place about 40 times faster for cetane and 60 times for paraffin wax at 500°C.[2] In thermal cracking the carbon-carbon bond scissions are more prone to take place near the end of the chain, producing large amounts of methane and ethane. The spread in boiling point of the products obtained in thermal cracking is considerably greater than when a catalyst is used. The thermal product ranges from gaseous hydrocarbons to heavy fuel oil and coke, while that from catalytic cracking contains very little material boiling above the charge and the gases are mainly C_3 and C_4 hydrocarbons. The thermal product is considerably more olefinic and contains less aromatic and branched-chain structures.

The cycle stock obtained in catalytic cracking is generally richer in aromatic hydrocarbons, has a lower hydrogen-carbon ratio, and is lower in end point than the original charge.[3] In catalytic cracking, however, there is always some coke formation, which makes repeated regeneration of the catalyst necessary. For this reason, the charge stock and cracking conditions are generally selected to give the lowest coke deposition consistent with economical operation; this coke meets a considerable part of the fuel requirement, but excessive production is of no advantage.

IX-6. Reactions of Hydrocarbon Classes. There are marked differences in the manner and extent of response shown, by different hydrocarbon types, to catalytic cracking. These differences are discussed in some detail as follows.

Paraffinic Hydrocarbons. The primary reactions taking place in the catalytic cracking of paraffin hydrocarbons are characterized by:

1. Greater velocity than thermal cracking
2. High production of C_3 and C_4 hydrocarbons in the cracked gases
3. Importance of the size and structure of the paraffin in determining the reaction rate and nature of the product
4. Boiling points of the heaviest products lower than those of the charge stock

The other effects observed, such as isomerization to branched structures, aromatic hydrocarbon formation, etc., are the result of secondary reactions involving the action of catalysts on olefins.[4] At 500°C, normal

---

[1] Starr, Tilton, and Hockberger, *Ind. Eng. Chem.*, **39**:195 (1947).

[2] Greensfelder and Voge, *Ind. Eng. Chem.*, **37**:514 (1945).

[3] Murphree, *Ind. Eng. Chem.*, **35**:768 (1943).

[4] Greensfelder and Voge, *Ind. Eng. Chem.*, **37**:514 (1945). Good, Voge, and Greensfelder, *Ind. Eng. Chem.*, **39**:1032 (1947); **41**:2573 (1949). Egloff, Morrell, Thomas, and Bloch, *J. ACS*, **61**:3571 (1939).

paraffins, ranging from C$_3$ to C$_{18}$, and also paraffin wax (about C$_{24}$) crack from 5 to 60 times faster in the presence of a silica-alumina-zirconia catalyst than in thermal cracking at the same temperature. While propane as well as *n*- and isobutane crack somewhat faster over a catalyst than thermally, the pronounced effect of the catalyst on cracking rates does not become appreciable until paraffins of C$_6$ or higher are charged. The relation between the rates of the two procedures is illustrated by Fig. IX-2 which shows the effect of molecular size on the catalytic cracking of *n*-paraffins at 500°C, and the ratio of catalytic-to-thermal cracking rates for these hydrocarbons.

The ease of cracking of the paraffin is influenced by its structure as well as its molecular weight.[1] At 550°C, over an alumina-silica catalyst and for the same time period, the five isomeric hexanes crack in the following percentages by weight:

C—C—C—C—C—C   14

C—C—C—C—C   25   C—C—C—C—C   25
     | |
     C   C

C

C—C—C—C   10   C—C—C—C   32
|
C   C   C

Hydrocarbons containing tertiary carbon atoms crack most readily, while quaternary carbon atoms are most resistant. In compounds containing both tertiary and quaternary carbon atoms, the accelerating influence of the former and retarding influence of the latter neutralize each other. Thus, the hydrocarbon 2,2,4-trimethylpentane, containing one of each, cracks only slightly faster than *n*-octane; 2,2,4,6,6-pentamethylheptane, containing two quaternary and one tertiary carbon atoms, cracks less readily than does *n*-dodecane.

The structure of the paraffin hydrocarbon undergoing cracking is also important with respect to the nature of products formed, but less so than in thermal cracking. For example, *n*-octane at 570°C gives predominantly C$_3$ and C$_5$ hydrocarbons and lesser amounts of C$_4$,[2] while 2,2,4-trimethylpentane at 500°C gives a gas rich in methane (because of the terminal methyl groups), butanes, and butenes but low in C$_3$ and C$_5$ hydrocarbons. The presence of 13 per cent of *n*-butenes in the cracked gases from the isooctane illustrates the extent of olefin isomerization in catalytic cracking. Gas rich in methane was also produced from the

---

[1] Good, Voge, and Greensfelder, *loc. cit.*

[2] Egloff, Morrell, Thomas, and Bloch, *J. ACS,* **61**:3571 (1939).

hexane, 2,2-dimethylbutane, again because of the large number of terminal methyl groups.

Isomerization of the paraffin molecule itself does not take place in catalytic cracking,[1] although, as mentioned above, the olefins produced are subjected to extensive rearrangements. In the above cracking of the hexane isomers, only negligible amounts of isomerization took place. For example, only small quantities of 2- and 3-methylpentane were obtained from 2,3-dimethylbutane.

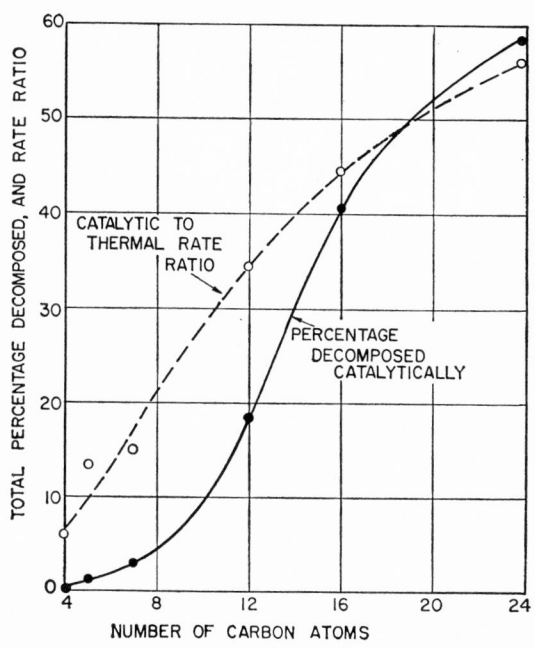

FIG. IX-2. Single-pass catalytic and thermal decomposition of paraffins; rates at 500°C. [*From Greensfelder, Ind. Eng. Chem.*, **37**:519 (1945).]

Going further up the molecular-weight scale, *n-* and isododecane (hydrogenated triisobutylene) crack about ten times faster over a catalyst than they do thermally.[2] Abundant gas formation takes place, especially with the branched-chain compound. The liquid products are high in olefins in the lower-boiling range but less so in the higher, where the aromatic content is substantial. The high hydrogen content of the

[1] Hinden, Oblad, and Mills, however, have shown that some isomerization of paraffin hydrocarbons (and also hydrogen exchange) will take place over a cracking catalyst, even at 100 to 150°C, if the catalyst is hydrated to a critical level and if the hydrocarbon contains at least one tertiary carbon atom. *J. ACS*, **77**:535, 538 (1955).

[2] Greensfelder and Voge, *Ind. Eng. Chem.*, **37**:514 (1945).

gases from both isomers is a result of hydrogen-transfer reactions which in turn produce considerable amounts of carbon.

Similar results are obtained in the catalytic cracking of cetane.[1,2] The C_4 gas is high in i-C_4H_{10}, indicating the extent of isomerization of n-butenes followed by saturation through hydrogen transfer. The liquid product contains more C_5 and C_6 hydrocarbons than C_7 and C_8, and sizable amounts of aromatics in the higher-boiling range.

Olefinic Hydrocarbons. The olefinic hydrocarbons respond to cracking catalysts much more readily and at lower temperatures than do the corresponding paraffins. The cracking takes place about a thousand to ten thousand times faster than thermal cracking. The main reactions are carbon-carbon bond scissions which, as with the paraffins, yield higher proportions of C_3, C_4, and larger fragments; isomerization, both by double bond and group shifting; polymerization; and saturation, aromatization, and carbon formation by inter- and intramolecular hydrogen transfer.

As with paraffinic hydrocarbons, catalytic cracking of olefins gives liquid products covering a narrower molecular-weight range than that from thermal cracking; there is more isomerization of the olefin charged and of the olefinic products; more saturation by hydrogen transfer takes place; the liquid-to-gas ratio is higher; and the amount of C_3 and C_4 hydrocarbons in the gas is greater.

At 400°C over an Al_2O_3-ZrO-SiO_2 catalyst, n-butenes undergo isomerization to isobutylene, cracking, polymerization, and hydrogen transfer to yield n- and isobutane, the saturation reactions becoming more pronounced as the temperature is raised. The n-pentenes crack extensively; substantial amounts of isopentane and much less n-pentane are formed, supporting other observations that isoolefins are saturated preferentially. The formation of some aromatics is indicated.

About equal quantities of gas and liquid products are formed from n-octene. The gas contains large amounts of propylene, isobutylene, n-butenes, and the two butanes. The lower-boiling liquid is mainly C_5, 72 per cent unsaturated, while the C_8 fraction is 40 per cent saturated and considerably isomerized. Some aromatics are present. Branched-chain olefins crack faster and more completely than their straight-chain isomers. The main product from the catalytic cracking of the two diisobutylenes is isobutylene, as a result of depolymerization; some n-butenes and butanes result from isomerization and saturation. As the molecular weight of the olefin increases, less of it remains as compounds of the same carbon number and this fraction is less unsaturated than the charge, reflecting the greater rates of cracking and the extensive

---

[1] Greensfelder and Voge, *Ind. Eng. Chem.*, **37**:514 (1945).

[2] Egloff, Morrell, Thomas, and Bloch, *loc. cit.*

saturation of the higher olefins. Cetene cracks more readily than cetane.[1] As would be expected, the gas contains predominant amounts of C_3 and C_4 hydrocarbons with considerable amounts of i-C_4H_8. Again, the olefin content of the liquid product decreases as the molecular weights of the components rise. The C_{16} cut, wider in boiling range than the cetene charged, is low in olefin content, indicating that the uncracked cetene becomes saturated and that extensive isomerization takes place prior to cracking.

A comparison of the reaction velocity constants of the thermal and catalytic cracking of cetene by the first-order equation

$$k = \frac{1}{t} \ln \frac{100}{100 - c}$$

where t = time, sec

c = per cent converted to material of different carbon number or to saturates

illustrates the tremendous accelerating effect of the catalyst.[2] Cyclic

	Type of cracking				
	Catalytic*		Thermal†		
Temperature, °C	400	450	450	500	550
Contact time, sec	7.3	6.4	75	61.5	50.5
Conversion, per cent	92	97	5	34.1	69.7
$k_1 \times 10^3$	ca. 340	ca. 550	0.67	6.8	23.6
Product:					
Gas, per cent	8.9	21.2	0.3	11.5	37.5
Liquid below C_{18}, per cent	51.8	62.3	4.7	22.8	32.2
Remainder	39.3	16.5	95.0	65.7	30.3
Gas analysis, per cent:					
H_2	2.2	2.8	0	3	5
Olefins	59.4	68.1	29	58	65
Saturates	38.4	29.1	71	39	30
Mol wt	49	48	......	28	31

* Greensfelder and Voge, *Ind. Eng. Chem.*, **37**:983 (1945).
† Gault and Altchidjian, *Ann. chim.* **2**(10):209 (1924).

olefins present some difficulty in cracking cleanly. Cyclopentene, for example, yields a liquid product rich in aromatics, some olefin polymers, a rather high proportion of coke, and only a little gas.[3] Diolefins, such

[1] Egloff, Morrell, Thomas, and Bloch, *J. ACS*, **61**:3571 (1939).
[2] For a discussion of reaction rates and rate of fall-off of activity of catalysts with use, see Blanding, *Ind. Eng. Chem.*, **45**:1186 (1953).
[3] Greensfelder and Voge, *Ind. Eng. Chem.*, **37**:983 (1945).

as butadiene and isoprene, readily enter reactions involving isomerization, hydrogen transfer, and formation of aromatic hydrocarbons and carbon.

The cracking effect of a silica-alumina catalyst involves certain primary reactions, the most important of which probably are isomerization and hydrogen transfer. The former may include:

1. Shifting the double bond
2. Change of the carbon skeleton
3. *cis-trans* rearrangements

The equilibria for the first and third are reached quickly and with ease.[1] This fits in well with the observation that the C_5 olefins produced in a cracking operation at 550°C are distributed about as follows:[2]

	Per cent
1-Pentene	8
2-Pentene	27
2-Methyl-1-butene	26
2-Methyl-2-butene	32
3-Methyl-1-butene	7

The proportions are very close to the equilibrium values calculated from the free energy equation of Ewell and Hardy.[3]

The pentenes undergo chain-branching isomerization more readily than do the butenes. The reaction does not generally take place as rapidly as those involving double-bond shifts. For the pentenes it is fast enough to produce equilibrium mixtures at 500°C. At lower temperatures, however, the normal cracking reaction will outstrip the isomerization. Cyclic olefins are affected more drastically and at lower temperatures. Cyclohexene is rearranged at 250°C and more rapidly at 300°C; methylcyclopentenes-1 and -2 have been identified, as well as methylcyclopentane. At 400°C hydrogen transfer is involved, and high-boiling naphthenic and aromatic liquids are produced.[4]

Olefin isomerizations, followed by the saturation of a sizable proportion by inter- and intramolecular hydrogen-transfer reactions, are responsible to a large extent for the presence, in catalytically cracked gasolines, of hydrocarbons of high octane number and lead susceptibility. The hydrogen transfer reaction was recognized when the passage of *n*-octene over a cracking catalyst at 375°C resulted in substantial isomerization into branched-chain olefins followed by self-saturation to isooctanes,

[1] Voge and May, *J. ACS*, **68**:550 (1946). Voge, Good, and Greensfelder, *Ind. Eng. Chem.*, **38**:1033 (1946). Frost and Khimmi, *Refiner Nat. Gasoline Mfr.*, **20**(1):30 (1941). Ewell and Hardy, *J. ACS*, **63**:3460 (1941).

[2] Voge, Good, and Greensfelder, *op. cit.*

[3] *Op. cit.*

[4] Bloch and Thomas, *J. ACS*, **66**:1589 (1944).

accompanied by coke formation.[1] Saturation takes place more readily as temperature increases and as space velocity decreases.[2] In practice, however, a more highly saturated gasoline can be obtained by operating at relatively low temperatures because the rate of hydrogen transfer is higher than that of cracking in the lower part of the cracking temperature zone. A high catalyst-to-oil ratio is also favorable to the transfer.

Because of the higher velocity of the transfer reactions for branched olefins, the ratio of isoparaffins to normal paraffins is generally higher than the equilibrium ratio of the parent olefins. For example, the ratio of iso to n-butane found in gases from catalytic cracking at 525°C usually ranges from 2:6, while the equilibrium ratio of iso- to n-butenes at that temperature is only about 0.65.[3] The higher rate of saturation of branched olefins is further illustrated by the passage of an equilibrium mixture composed of 42 per cent isobutylene and 58 per cent n-butenes over a cracking catalyst at 400°C; the resulting C_4 fraction contained 46 per cent butanes, in which the ratio of iso- to n-butane was 7:1. Of the 54 per cent unreacted olefins, the ratio isobutylene: n-butene was considerably less than at the start; at this temperature isomerization was slower than saturation. On the other hand, at 500°C, isomerization is the faster; a gas containing 98.7 per cent n-butenes gives a C_4 fraction in which the ratio of iso- to n-butane is 3.5:1.

The importance of hydrogen transfer has been illustrated further by diluting mixtures of iso and n-butenes with molecular hydrogen and passing over a conventional hydrogenation-dehydrogenation catalyst; equal rates of hydrogenation are shown by both butenes.[4] Molecular hydrogen apparently does not enter the transfer reaction; this has been confirmed by exchange studies using deuterium. The hydrogen transfer presumably takes place through a carbonium ion intermediate.[5]

Tertiary-base olefins are saturated most readily, and doubly branched olefins several times as fast as the singly branched. Naphthenic hydrocarbons (cyclohexane, decalin, and tetralin) can act as hydrogen donors in transfer reactions with olefins, yielding isoparaffins and aromatic hydrocarbons.[6]

The polymerizing activity of silica-alumina complexes is well-estab-

[1] Thomas, *J. ACS*, **66**:1586 (1944).

[2] Voge, Good, and Greensfelder, *Ind. Eng. Chem.*, **38**:1033 (1946).

[3] Bloch and Thomas, *op. cit.*

[4] Voge, Good, and Greensfelder, *op. cit.*

[5] Hansford, *Ind. Eng. Chem.*, **39**:849 (1947). Parravano, Hammel, and Taylor, *J. ACS*, **70**:2269 (1948). Holm and Blue, *Ind. Eng. Chem.*, **43**:501 (1951). Hansford, Waldo, Drake, and Honig, *Ind. Eng. Chem.*, **44**:1108 (1952).

[6] Blue and Engle, *Ind. Eng. Chem.*, **43**:494 (1951). Hansford, Waldo, Drake, and Honig, *Ind. Eng. Chem.*, **44**:1108 (1952). Voge, Good, and Greensfelder, *Ind. Eng. Chem.*, **38**:1033 (1946).

lished for temperatures in the range 150 to 350°C. Prior to the development of catalytic cracking, Gayer obtained propylene polymers with an alumina-on-silica catalyst at 340° at atmospheric pressure.[1] Butenes can be polymerized at upward of 210°, but under 100 lb pressure the reaction proceeds at 175°.[2] At the temperatures of catalytic cracking, the thermodynamic relations are not favorable to polymerization; the polymers found are likely to be changed by isomerization and saturation.

The aromatics found in catalytically cracked gasoline may be attributed either to dehydrogenation of cyclohexane derivatives, or more simply to the breaking off of alkyl groups from substituted aromatics present in the charge stock. The slight dehydrogenating activity of silica-alumina and the observation that toluene is not found in the products from catalytic cracking of heptane under rather severe conditions have raised some doubt about the possibility of forming aromatics extensively in catalytic cracking by dehydrocyclization. It seems probable that aromatic synthesis occurs by reaction of lower olefins, which are always present when paraffinic chains are cracked; for instance, the common mononuclear aromatics have been identified in the products formed from propylene, n-butenes, pentenes, and hexenes.

Naphthenic Hydrocarbons. In the presence of silica-alumina, naphthenic hydrocarbons undergo dehydrogenation and C—C bond scission in both ring and attached side chains; at temperatures above 550°C, ring scission becomes the more important.[3] The simpler naphthenic hydrocarbons (cyclopentane, cyclohexane, and decalin) are resistant, responding appreciably only at relatively high temperatures. Alkyl groups attached to the C_5 and C_6 rings, particularly as their size increases, react more easily; in fact, the rate of cracking of naphthenes appears to depend more on their molecular weights than on their structure; all types (C_5 and C_6 rings, mono- and bicyclic, fused and linked rings) display similar rates of decomposition for the same molecular-weight level.

A wider variety of products is formed than in the cracking of individual paraffin, olefin, or aromatic hydrocarbons. Like the paraffins, naphthenes do not appear to isomerize prior to cracking. The isomerization products found may result from the isomerization of cyclic olefin intermediates, followed by saturation through hydrogen transfer.[4] For instance, only a small amount of methylcyclopentane is obtained from cyclohexane, while cyclohexene is converted at 400°C to the extent of 30 per cent into methylcyclopentenes and methylcyclopentane.

The naphthenic hydrocarbons, starting with C_9 or C_{10}, produce con-

[1] *Ind. Eng. Chem.*, **25**:1122 (1933).

[2] Voge, Good, and Greensfelder, *op. cit.* Thomas, *Ind. Eng. Chem.*, **37**:543 (1945).

[3] Greensfelder and Voge, *Ind. Eng. Chem.*, **37**:1038 (1945).

[4] Bloch and Thomas, *loc. cit.*

siderable amounts of aromatic hydrocarbons and hence yield a high-octane gasoline. Dehydrogenation is extensive in this range and it is likely that some of the aromatics found are produced through this channel; biphenyl (but no benzene) was found in the products from bicyclohexyl, and naphthalene was obtained from decalin. On the other hand, cyclohexane and methylcyclohexane gave very little benzene and toluene. In general, only small amounts of benzene were formed in the catalytic cracking of the various individual naphthenes.

The reaction gases from the catalytic cracking of naphthenes are high in hydrogen, and the liquid products are more saturated than those obtained from paraffins and olefins. As is true for the paraffins, the gases are rich in propylene and the butanes. The length of side chains on the ring does not affect appreciably the distribution of the products.

The catalytic cracking of naphthenes takes place 500 to 4,000 times as fast as the corresponding thermal cracking; more saturated gaseous and liquid products are obtained, the liquid-to-gas ratio is higher, less condensation product is formed, and the boiling range of the liquid is more evenly distributed.

Aromatic Hydrocarbons. Catalytic cracking of aromatics is much faster than the corresponding thermal process; it is marked also by clean splitting out of side chains without breaking the ring. For instance, ethyl-, isopropyl-, *n*-butyl-, and amylbenzenes can be cracked at 500°C with nearly quantitative recovery of benzene.[1] Actually, the simple rings are quite resistant to cleavage, while large alkyl or cycloalkyl substituents convey increased reactivity. Thus at 500°C toluene cracked to the extent of about 1 per cent.[2]

> Ethylbenzene.............. 11
> *n*-Propylbenzene........... 43
> Isopropylbenzene........... 83.5

A similar comparison of the butylbenzenes at 400° showed:

> *n*-Butylbenzene............ 13.9
> *sec*-Butylbenzene........... 49.2
> *tert*-Butylbenzene........... 80.4

These reactions are reversible; over the same catalyst and at the same temperature propylene and benzene will yield mono- and diisopropylbenzene.[3]

The polymethylbenzenes increase in activity as the number of methyl groups increases. Scission of methyl groups is accompanied by isomerization and disproportionation reactions; *p*-xylene at 500°C, for example,

[1] Thomas, Hoekstra, and Pinkston, *J. ACS*, **66**:1694 (1944).
[2] Greensfelder, Voge, and Good, *Ind. Eng. Chem.*, **37**:1168 (1945).
[3] Haensel, "Advances in Catalysis," vol. III, p. 193, Academic Press, Inc., New York, 1951.

forms an equilibrium mixture of the three isomeric xylenes; some of the charge disproportionates to toluene and trimethylbenzenes. Mesitylene and pseudocumene give xylenes and toluene but no benzene. There is also some tendency for the CH_3 fragments to combine, as C_2, C_3, and C_4 gases are formed in small amounts. Styrene at 500°C gives mainly ethylbenzene and coke, along with a small amount of benzene.[1] Alkyl naphthalenes react in much the same way as the benzene homologues. Methylnaphthalenes are fairly resistant, *t*-butyl and amylnaphthalenes, considerably less so; naphthalene is formed in all cases. Commercial catalytically cracked distillates are generally rich in methylnaphthalenes. The fused-ring cycloalkylaryl compounds such as hydrindene and tetrahydronaphthalene also crack readily to give benzene and substituted benzenes.

IX-7. Theory of the Reaction. There is general acceptance of the theory that catalytic cracking reactions take place through the formation of carbonium ions,[2] as was early postulated.[3] Since the response of paraffin hydrocarbons to cracking catalysts is relatively slow, Thomas[4] has pictured the primary reaction, and rate-forming step, as that of a thermal action on the saturated compounds. The olefin formed combines with an available proton on the surface of the catalyst (Brönsted acid) to form a carbonium ion.[5] This can react chainwise with a fresh paraffin molecule to give a new paraffin and a new carbonium ion by way of hydride ion (H^-) exchange according to the following mechanism,[6]

$$t—C_4H_9^+ + i—C_5H_{12} \rightarrow i—C_4H_{10} + t—C_5H_{11}^+$$

It has been suggested, however,[7] as a result of experiments on deuterium exchange between silica-alumina catalysts and the two butanes, that the

---

[1] Greensfelder and Voge, *Ind. Eng. Chem.*, **37**:983 (1945).

[2] For discussions of the structure of carbonium ions, see Brown and Brady, *J. ACS*, **74**:3570 (1952); Winstein and Morse, *J. ACS*, **74**:1133 (1952).

[3] Hansford, *Ind. Eng. Chem.*, **39**:849 (1947).

[4] *Ind. Eng. Chem.*, **41**:2564 (1949).

[5] Whitmore, *Ind. Eng. Chem.*, **26**:94 (1934); *Chem. Eng. News*, **26**:668 (1948). It has been demonstrated that carbonium ions can form on the adsorption of paraffins on cracking catalysts, and their formation is through hydride ion extraction by the catalyst itself. Private communication, W. K. Hall and H. P. Leftin, Petroleum Fellowship, Mellon Institute.

[6] Bartlett, Condon, and Schneider, *J. ACS*, **66**:1531 (1944). See also Schmerling, *J. ACS*, **68**:275 (1946); Bloch, Pines, and Schmerling, *J. ACS*, **68**:153 (1946); Hansford, *Ind. Eng. Chem.*, **39**:849 (1947); Greensfelder, Voge, and Good, *Ind. Eng. Chem.*, **41**:2573 (1949); Ciapetta, Macuga, and Leum, *Ind. Eng. Chem.*, **40**:2091 (1948); Hansford, "Physical Chemistry of Hydrocarbons," vol. II, p. 187, Academic Press, Inc., New York, 1953.

[7] Oblad, Milliken, and Mills, "Advances in Catalysis," vol. III, p. 199, Academic Press, Inc., New York, 1951.

acid responsible for the catalytic activity is of the Lewis type.[1] For this, one must assume the creation of electron-deficient aluminum atoms by structural changes made possible by the presence of the silica atoms, in which the coordination of the aluminum is changed from six to four. Stable carbonium ion complexes are pictured as follows:

Proton shift:

$$R(\text{olefin}) + H_2O + \left[\begin{array}{c} O \\ | \\ Al—O—Si \\ | \\ O \end{array}\right] \longrightarrow R^+ \left[\begin{array}{c} O \\ | \\ —O—Al—O—Si \\ | \\ O \end{array}\right]^-$$

and by

Hydride ion transfer:

$$RH + \left[\begin{array}{c} | \\ O \\ | \\ Al—O—Si \\ | \\ O \\ | \end{array}\right] \longrightarrow R^+ \left[\begin{array}{c} | \\ O \\ | \\ \overset{..}{H}\ Al—O—Si \\ | \\ O \\ | \end{array}\right]^-$$

The necessary hydrocarbon skeletal isomerizations and hydrogen transfers take place in the secondary reactions. Thus, the nature of the over-all products depends largely on the dissociation of the carbonium ions formed during the several phases of the cracking. This dissociation may go in several ways,[2] and Thomas[3] suggested the following sequence for the cracking of *n*-octane, a typical *n*-paraffin hydrocarbon.

Step 1. The reaction is initiated by a mild thermal cracking

$$n\text{-}C_8H_{18} \rightarrow CH_4 + C_7H_{14}$$

Step 2. The heptene formed attached itself to an active point on the catalyst surface which furnishes a proton to form a secondary carbonium ion; this remains adsorbed on the surface.

Step 3. The carbonium ion formed is converted according to the beta rule (carbon-carbon bond scission takes place at the carbon in the position beta to the carbonium carbon atom).

$$CH_3\overset{+}{C}HCH_2CH_2CH_2CH_2CH_3 \rightarrow CH_3CH_2{=}CH_2 + \overset{+}{C}H_2CH_2CH_2CH_3$$

[1] A catalyst having a structure possessing the dual properties of both Lewis and Brönsted acids has been proposed by Danforth, *ACS, Div. Petrol. Chem., Gen. Papers,* Preprint, p. 41, ACS Meeting, Cincinnati, April, 1955.

[2] Whitmore and Cook, "Science of Petroleum," vol. I, p. 114, Oxford University Press, New York and London, 1950.

[3] *Ind. Eng. Chem.,* **41**:2564 (1949).

The smallest olefin that can split off from a secondary carbonium ion would be C_3 (propylene) and from a tertiary carbonium ion, C_4 (isobutylene). This explains the preponderance of C_3 and C_4 in the gases from catalytic cracking operations.

Step 4. Primary carbonium ions are less stable than secondary ions, which in turn are less stable than the tertiary. Rearrangements toward more stable structures, therefore, take place.

$$\underset{+}{CH_2}CH_2CH_2CH_3 \rightleftharpoons CH_3\underset{+}{CH}CH_2CH_3 \rightleftharpoons$$

$$CH_3-\underset{\underset{CH_3}{|}}{CH}-CH_2 \rightleftharpoons CH_3-\underset{+}{\overset{\overset{CH_3}{|}}{C}}-CH_3$$

Step 5. The C_4 carbonium ion, either before or after rearrangement, may exchange with a fresh octane molecule to form an octyl carbonium ion and a butane molecule, thus acting as a chain propagator.

$$CH_3\underset{+}{\overset{\overset{CH_3}{|}}{C}}-CH_3 + C_8H_{18} \rightarrow i-C_4H_{10} + CH_3\underset{+}{CH}(CH_2)_5CH_3$$

Step 6

$$CH_3\underset{+}{CH}(CH_2)_5CH_3 \rightleftharpoons CH_3\overset{\overset{\overset{+}{C}H_2}{|}}{CH}(CH_2)_4CH_3 \rightleftharpoons CH_3\underset{+}{\overset{\overset{CH_3}{|}}{C}}(CH_2)_4CH_3$$

$$CH_3CH_2\underset{+}{CH}(CH_2)_4CH_3 \rightleftharpoons CH_3CH_2\overset{\overset{\overset{+}{C}H_2}{|}}{CH}(CH_2)_3CH_3 \rightleftharpoons$$

$$CH_3CH_2\underset{+}{\overset{\overset{CH_3}{|}}{C}}(CH_2)_3CH_3$$

$$CH_3(CH_2)_2\underset{+}{CH}(CH_2)_2CH_3 \rightleftharpoons CH_3(CH_2)_2\overset{\overset{\overset{+}{C}H_2}{|}}{CH}(CH_2)_2CH_3 \rightleftharpoons$$

$$CH_3(CH_2)_2\underset{+}{\overset{\overset{CH_3}{|}}{C}}(CH_2)_2CH_3$$

Any of the above carbonium ions may react with a fresh *n*-octane molecule to form a new carbonium ion and a branched octane, or dissociate according to the beta rule:

$$CH_3CH(CH_2)_5CH_3 \rightarrow CH_3CH{=}CH_2 + CH_2(CH_2)_3CH_3$$
$$\overset{+}{} \qquad\qquad\qquad \overset{\phantom{CH_3CH{=}CH_2 + }}{+}$$

$$CH_3CH_2CH(CH_2)_4CH_3 \rightarrow CH_3CH_2CH{=}CH_2 + CH_2(CH_2)_2CH_3$$

$$CH_3(CH_2)_2CH(CH_2)_3CH_3 \rightarrow CH_3(CH_2)_2CH{=}CH_2 + CH_2CH_2CH_3$$
$$\searrow CH_3(CH_2)_3CH{=}CH_3 + CH_2CH_3$$

$$\overset{\displaystyle CH_3}{\underset{|}{CH_3C}}(CH_2)_4CH_3 \rightarrow \overset{\displaystyle CH_3}{\underset{|}{CH_3C}}{=}CH_2 + CH_2(CH_2)_2CH_3$$

$$\overset{\displaystyle CH_3}{\underset{|}{CH_3CH_2C}}(CH_2)_3CH_3 \rightarrow \overset{\displaystyle CH_3}{\underset{|}{CH_3CH_2C}}{=}CH_2 + CH_2CH_2CH_3$$

$$\overset{\displaystyle CH_3}{\underset{|}{CH_3(CH_2)_2C}}(CH_2)_2CH_3 \rightarrow \overset{\displaystyle CH_3}{\underset{|}{CH_3(CH_2)_2C}}{=}CH_2 + CH_2CH_3$$

A mechanism of this type would explain the lack of formation of any compound of higher molecular weight than the starting n-octane or lower than propylene, and the smaller dependence of the composition of the final product on the structure of the parent molecule than in thermal cracking. Thomas points out that 70 per cent of the catalytic cracking of n-octane can be expressed as $C_8 \rightarrow C_5 + C_3$, but that in thermal cracking only 15 per cent proceeds in this manner.

Other carbonium ion mechanisms account for secondary reactions such as polymerization and depolymerization, hydrogen transfer, aromatic formation, etc. There may be some stray thermal changes. Hydrogen possibly results from some naphthene dehydrogenation. Methane and ethane formation may be ascribed to "less favored types of cracking," not necessarily thermal.[1] The formation of naphthenic hydrocarbons is not explained. Aromatics are thought to be formed through reactions in which a carbonium ion reacts with an olefin to give a paraffin and an olefinic carbonium ion; this can react with an olefin to form a carbonium ion and a diolefin, which in turn may be converted into a triolefin and on to an aromatic hydrocarbon.[2]

IX-8. Catalysts. The cracking of hydrocarbon oils occurs over many types of catalytic materials but high yields of desirable products are obtained with hydrated aluminum silicates. These may be either activated (acid-treated) natural clays of the bentonite type or synthe-

[1] Greensfelder, Voge, and Good, *Ind. Eng. Chem.*, **41**:2573 (1949).
[2] Thomas, *Ind. Eng. Chem.*, **41**:2564 (1949).

sized silica-alumina or silica-magnesia preparations.[1]   Their activity to yield essentially the same products may be enhanced to some extent by the incorporation of small amounts of other materials such as the oxides of zirconium, boron (which has a tendency to volatilize away on use), and thorium.   Both the natural and the synthetic catalysts can be used as pellets or beads, and also in the form of powder; in either case replacements are necessary because of attrition and gradual loss of efficiency. It is essential that they be stable to physical impact loading and thermal shock, and that they withstand the action of carbon dioxide, air, nitrogen compounds, and steam.   They should also be resistant to sulfur compounds; the synthetic catalysts and certain selected clays appear to be better in this regard than average untreated natural catalysts.   The silica-alumina catalysts are reported to give the highest-octane gasolines and silica-magnesia the largest yields, with the natural clays falling in between.

Neither silica nor alumina alone is effective in promoting catalytic cracking reactions.   In fact, they (and also activated carbon) promote hydrocarbon decompositions of the thermal type.[2]   A mixture of anhydrous silica and alumina, or anhydrous silica with hydrated alumina, is also essentially noneffective.   A catalyst having appreciable cracking activity is obtained only when prepared from hydrous oxides, followed by partial dehydration (calcining).   The small amount of water remaining is necessary for proper functioning.   Studies made with deuterium oxide have shown that this water is involved in hydrogen-transfer reactions between the catalyst and hydrocarbon molecules; these begin considerably below cracking temperatures.[3]

The catalysts are porous and highly adsorptive.[4]   Their performance depends largely on the method of preparation.   Two catalysts chemically identical, but having pores of different size and distribution, may have different activities, selectivities, temperature coefficients of reaction rates, and responses to poisons.[5]   While the intrinsic chemistry and catalytic action of a surface may be independent of pore size, small pores appear to

[1] Oblad, "Advances in Catalysts," vol. III, p. 199, Academic Press, Inc., New York, 1951.   Voorhees, *Petrol. Engr.*, **28**(3):C-11 (1956).

[2] Greensfelder, Voge, and Good, *loc. cit.*

[3] Hansford, *Ind. Eng. Chem.*, **39**:849 (1947); Hansford, Waldo, Drake, and Honig, *Ind. Eng. Chem.*, **44**:1108 (1952).

[4] The importance of the physical structure of catalysts has been stressed in a mathematical treatment of the subject by Wheeler, "Advances in Chemistry," vol. III, p. 250, Academic Press, Inc., New York, 1951.   *ACS, Div. Petrol. Chem., Symposium on Catalysis in Hydrocarbon Chemistry*, Preprints, p. 55, ACS Meeting, Atlantic City, September, 1952.

[5] Wheeler, "Advances in Catalysis," vol. III, p. 250, Academic Press, Inc., New York, 1951.   Oblad, *Oil Gas J.*, **53**(46):184 (1955).

produce different effects because of the manner and time in which hydrocarbon vapors are transported into and out of the interstices. The adsorption of individual hydrocarbons (*n*-butane, isobutane, *n*-heptane, and *n*-octane) on the acid sites on alumina-silica catalyst has been studied.[1] Definite adsorption was observed at low temperatures but at the temperatures of incipient cracking the amount of hydrocarbon adsorbed was very small. Presumably the amount held by the catalyst for the time necessary to bring about cracking need not be very large. The rate controlling factor would appear to be the formation of the carbonium ion.

The active sites on the surface impart definite acidic properties to the silica-alumina complex.[2] This acidity can be demonstrated by pH measurements in water and by titration with ammonia or quinoline. Titration or the neutralization with other alkaline agents will suppress the cracking activity but it is restored by reversing the treatment.[3]

The chemical changes taking place in the hydrocarbons during the cracking reaction are quite similar to those occurring at lower temperatures in polymerization, isomerization, and alkylation over other acid catalysts, such as H_2SO_4, H_3PO_4, $ZnCl_2$, $AlCl_3$, BF_3, etc. The maximum acidity of a silica-alumina complex is obtained when the ratio of aluminum to silicon is 1, while the ratio for maximum catalytic activity is 2.[4] This has been attributed to a certain degree of catalytic effectiveness of the free Al_2O_3 present, presumably not dependent upon an acidic condition. The active catalyst is assumed to be a polymer of a hypothetical aluminosilicic acid $(HAlSiO_4)_n$. This acid is presumably very stable and is distributed in such a manner as to provide active centers on the surface,[5] their number and intrinsic activity determining the effectiveness. Com-

[1] Emmett and Zabor, *J. ACS*, **73**:5639 (1951). MacIver, Emmett, and Frank, *ACS, Div. Petrol. Chem., Symposium on Nuclear Technology in the Petroleum and Chemical Industries*, Preprints, p. 61, ACS Meeting, Miami, April, 1957.

[2] For a study of the acid strength of solid surfaces, see Walling, *J. ACS*, **72**:1164 (1950). See also, Holm, Bailey, and Clark, *ACS, Div. Petrol. Chem., Gen. Papers*, Preprints, p. 333, ACS Meeting, Miami, April, 1957. Johnson, *J. Phys. Chem.*, **59**:827 (1955), observed the acid strength of a silica-alumina catalyst to be between that of perchloric and silico-tungstic acids.

[3] Oblad, Milliken, and Mills, *Discussions Faraday Soc.*, **8**:279 (1950); "Advances in Catalysis," vol. III, p. 199, Academic Press, Inc., New York, 1951. Mills, Boedeker, and Oblad, *J. ACS*, **72**:1554 (1950).

[4] Thomas, *Ind. Eng. Chem.*, **41**:2564 (1949).

[5] For a discussion of the structural characteristics of cracking catalysts which lead to development of an acidic state, see Oblad, Milliken, and Mills, "Advances in Catalysis," vol. III, p. 199, Academic Press, Inc., New York, 1951. Mills, Boedeker, and Oblad, *J. ACS*, **72**:1554 (1950). Mills and Hindin, *J. ACS*, **72**:5549 (1950). Oblad, Hinden, and Mills, *J. ACS*, **75**:4096 (1953). Thomas, *Ind. Eng. Chem.*, **41**:2564 (1949). Thomas, Hickey, and Stecker, *Ind. Eng. Chem.*, **42**:866 (1950). Cook and Oblad, *Ind. Eng. Chem.*, **45**:1456 (1953).

mercial synthetic catalysts are amorphous and contain more silica than is called for by the above formula; they are generally composed of 10 to 15 per cent Al_2O_3 and 85 to 90 per cent SiO_2. The corresponding natural materials, montmorillonite, a nonswelling bentonite, and halloysite, are hydrosilicates of aluminum, with a well-defined crystal structure and approximate composition of $Al_2O_3 \cdot 4SiO_2 \cdot XH_2O$. Some of the newer catalysts contain up to 25 per cent of alumina; longer active life is reported.

IX-9. Processes. The several processes presently employed in catalytic cracking[1] differ mainly in the method of handling the catalyst. Each uses a solid of the type discussed and the characteristics of the products are about the same.[2]

In the fixed-bed process[3,4] oil vapors are passed through a bed of pelleted catalyst at 830 to 880°F for a set period of time (9 to 15 min, before carbon deposition becomes excessive) at the end of which the charge flow is stopped. Residual vapors are purged by the combined effect of sweeping the system with steam and the vacuum produced by the steam injectors. In another short cycle the carbon deposited on the catalyst is burned away with air and after further purging the catalyst is ready for reuse. An essentially continuous process is achieved by the use of three manifolded reactor cases, each serving in turn as a reactor and catalyst regenerator.

The moving-bed process[5,6] involves a reaction vessel and a separate kiln in which the catalyst is regenerated. The reactor operates continuously at 800 to 950°F under 6 to 12 psi pressure. Hot regenerated catalyst is fed to the top of the reactor. In the earlier designs the spent catalyst was transferred from the bottom of the reactor to the top of the regenerator by bucket elevators; a pneumatic lift was later adopted. The catalyst is in the form of $\frac{1}{8}$-in. beads and the catalyst-to-oil ratio is in the neighborhood of 4 to 7:1.

In the fluid catalytic cracking process[7,8] the catalyst is in powder form,

[1] For review, see Haensel and Sterba, *Ind. Eng. Chem.*, **40**:1660 (1948); **41**:1914 (1949); **42**:1739 (1950); **43**:2017 (1951); **44**:2073 (1952).

[2] For a general review of catalytic cracking, see Sittig, *Petrol. Refiner*, **29**(6):91 (1950); **29**(8):99 (1950); **29**(10):130 (1950); **29**(11):125 (1950); **31**(9):263 (1952). Shankland, "Advances in Catalysts," vol. VI, p. 272, Academic Press, Inc., New York, 1954.

[3] Ardern, Dart, and Lassiat, *Advances in Chem. Ser.*, No. 5, p. 13, 1951.

[4] Faragher, Noll, and Bland, *World Petrol. Congr., Proc. 3rd Congr., Hague*, **4**:138 (1951).

[5] Ardern, Dart, and Lassiat, *op. cit.*

[6] Thornton, *Petrol. Processing*, **6**:146 (1951).

[7] Murphree, Brown, Fischer, Gohr, and Sweeney, *Ind. Eng. Chem.*, **35**:768 (1943).

[8] Murphree, *Advances in Chem. Ser.*, No. 5, p. 30, 1951.

5 to 100 mesh. Use is made of the principle that solids of proper particle size, when intimately mixed with a flowing gas, will form a homogeneous solid-gas system having the properties of a liquid. The process is continuous: preheated oil vapors enter the reactor carrying the catalyst as a dispersed powder; the fluidized mixture on passing into the reactor suffers a decrease in velocity which permits some of the powder to settle out, forming a dense but still fluidized bed which moves downward toward the exit. It is within this bed that cracking takes place at temperatures between 875 and 975°F. The pressure in the reactor is about 8 psi. Catalyst-oil ratios may vary from 5 to 30:1. The depth of the catalytic bed and consequently the contact time are controlled. Catalyst is separated from the cracked vapors and is withdrawn from the bottom of the reactor for transmission, by means of an air stream to the regenerator, from which it is returned to the stream of hot oil vapors entering the reactor.

Frequent regeneration of the catalyst is necessary because of carbon deposition,[1] which is greater than in thermal cracking. As coke accumulates on the catalyst, the gasoline yield falls off steadily. The cracking becomes less selective and increased amounts of gas are formed. The carbon is removed from the catalyst by burning in the presence of air supplied at atmospheric or slightly higher pressure. The temperature of regeneration is higher than that of cracking (about 1000 to 1200°F), and is limited by the thermal stability of the catalyst. Depending on the material, surface changes take place at temperatures above 1200 to 1300°F. The regeneration is, of course, exothermic and care must be taken to prevent sintering of the catalyst surface; for this reason careful control is required; the regenerated hot catalyst helps to heat the charge oil.

IX-10. Operating Variables. The important process characteristics of catalytic cracking, the extent of conversion and product distribution, are influenced by all the ordinary operating conditions, type of catalyst, catalyst-oil ratio, space velocity, temperature, pressure, and presence of steam, as well as by the nature of the charge stock.[2] In general, the most economical level for extent of cracking seems to be at about 50 per cent for a single pass. It will obviously increase with greater amount of a more active catalyst, higher temperature, and longer time of contact. Product distribution is affected to some extent by the depth of cracking; at the 50 per cent conversion just mentioned hydrogen formation will be about 0.1, C_1 and C_2 1 to 2, and coke deposit about 3 to 5 weight per cent

[1] For a discussion of carbon formation in catalytic cracking, see Voorhies, *Ind. Eng. Chem.*, **37**:318 (1945). McMahon, *Ind. Eng. Chem.*, **47**:844 (1955). Crawford and Cunningham, *Petrol. Refiner*, **35**(1):169 (1956).

[2] Ardern, Dart, and Lassiat, *Advances in Chem. Ser.*, No. 5, p. 13, 1951.

of the charge. Increase of temperature will increase all these figures, as well as the C_3-C_4 yield and the octane number of the gasoline, but will decrease gasoline yield.[1] Increase of pressure increases coke yield and also the degree of saturation of the gasoline; this is accompanied by a decrease of octane number.

The ratio of catalyst to oil varies with the process; it is ordinarily set at about 10:1 for fluid operation. A higher-boiling charge stock requires less catalyst; it cracks more easily and forms a greater yield of a more olefinic gasoline and a smaller amount of gas. This would indicate the advantage of charging reduced crudes; however, they form undesirable amounts of coke. Reduced crudes can be handled more economically by converting them to distillates by way of coking or viscosity breaking. Catalyst-to-oil ratio is often used to help control the operating temperature.

Some steam is always present in order to maintain the hydrated condition of the catalyst. Steam reduces the partial pressure of the oil, and this in turn suppresses overcracking and carbon formation. The resistance of some natural catalysts to sulfur poisoning is also increased.[2]

REFORMING

Reforming is a treatment given a low-octane, usually straight-run naphtha or gasoline to improve its octane number. This upgrading may be accomplished in part by an increase in the volatility (reduction of molecular size) or chiefly by the conversion of n-paraffins to isoparaffins, olefins, and aromatics, and naphthenes to aromatics. The nature of the final product is, of course, influenced by the source (and composition) of the straight-run naphtha charge. In thermal reforming the reactions resemble those taking place in the cracking of gas oils; molecular size is reduced, while olefins and some aromatics are synthesized. Catalytic reforming is conducted in the presence of hydrogen over hydrogenation-dehydrogenation catalysts which may be supported on alumina or silica-alumina. Depending on the catalyst, a definite sequence of reactions takes place, involving structural changes in the charge stock.[3] The principal reactions over nickel or cobalt are those of isomerization and hydrocracking; with molybdena and chromia, dehydrogenation and

[1] The kinetics involved are discussed by Wheeler, *ACS, Div. Petrol. Chem., Symposium on Catalysts*, Preprints, p. 55, ACS Meeting, Atlantic City, September, 1952.

[2] Davidson, *Petrol. Refiner*, **26**(9):663 (1947).

[3] Haensel and Donaldson, *Ind. Eng. Chem.*, **43**:2102 (1951). McGrath and Hill, *Advances in Chem. Ser.*, No. 5, p. 39, 1951. Kirkbride, *Petrol. Refiner*, **30**(6):95 (1951). Ciapetta, Pitts, and Leum, *ACS, Div. Petrol. Chem.*, Preprints, p. 113, ACS Meeting, Atlantic City, September, 1952. Ciapetta and Hunter, *Ind. Eng. Chem.*, **45**:147, 155, 159 (1953). Hettinger, Keith, Gring, and Teter, *Ind. Eng. Chem.*, **47**:719 (1955).

dehydrocyclization; while platinum, palladium, iridium, and rhodium promote dehydrogenation, isomerization, dehydrocyclization, and hydrocracking.

In reforming operations the naphtha charged is generally in the 120 to 200°C boiling range; it is stripped of butanes and pentanes because these undergo no increase in useful volatility and only a mild octane improvement as a result of structural changes; in addition, cracking losses are avoided.

IX-11. Thermal Reforming. Thermal reforming is in general less effective and less economical than catalytic processes. It has been largely supplanted. As practiced, a single-pass operation was employed at temperatures in the order of 1000 to 1140°F and pressures of about 500 to 1,000 psi. The degree of octane number improvement depended on the extent of conversion but was not directly proportional to the extent of crack per pass. For example, reforming a 250 to 400°F Illinois naphtha at a series of conversion levels produced reformates having the octane values given below.[1] Not only is the octane level changed

Reformate yield, per cent volume	Octane number	
	ASTM	Research
100	34.0	33.7
90	47.7	51.5
80	59.3	65.3
70	65.5	73.7
65	67.6	76.6

by the depth of cracking but the gasolines produced increase in volatility; the distillation curves approach limiting values for volume over at given temperatures.[2] At very deep conversions the production of coke and gas became prohibitively high. The gases produced, though high in methane, were quite olefinic and the process was generally accompanied by either a separate gas polymerization operation or one in which C_3-C_4 gases, autogenous as well as extraneous, were added back to the reforming system (polyforming),[3] where they were converted by polymerization. In addition Nickels[4] demonstrated the possibility of olefin consumption through reactions with aromatic hydrocarbons. Propane and benzene,

[1] Wagner, *Oil Gas J.*, **42**(25):62 (1943).
[2] Ferris, *Ind. Eng. Chem.*, **33**:752 (1941).
[3] Ostergaard and Smoley, *Refiner Nat. Gasoline Mfr.*, **19**:301 (1940). Offutt, Ostergaard, Fogle, and Beuther, *Oil Gas J.*, **45**(28):180 (1946).
[4] Ph.D. dissertation, "High Temperature Destructive Alkylation of Cyclic Hydrocarbons with Gaseous Paraffins under Pressure," University of Pittsburgh, 1942.

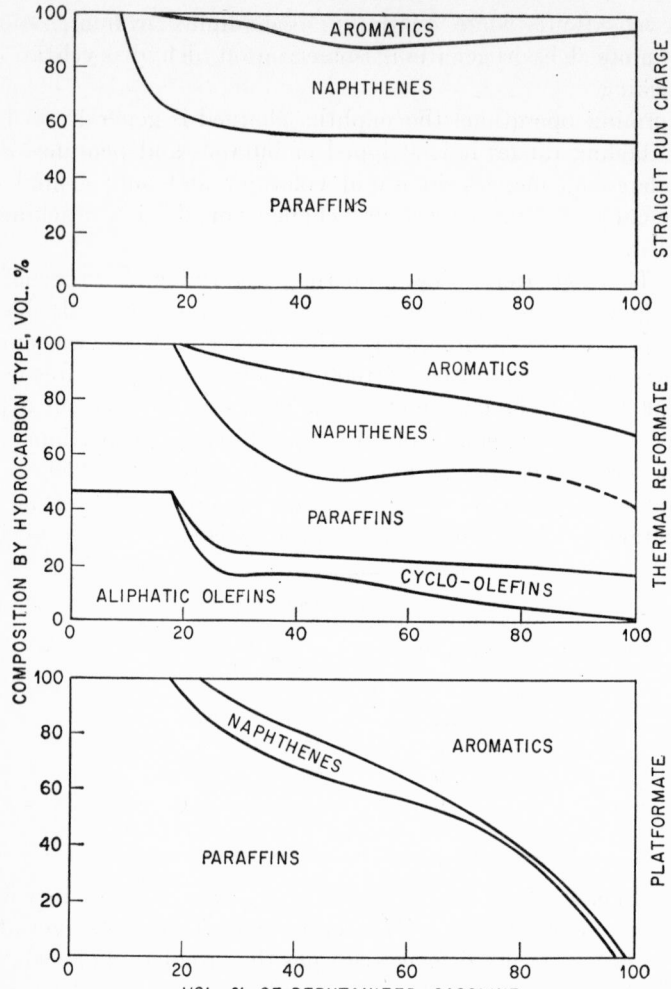

Hydrocarbon–Type Content of Debutanized Pennsylvania Straight-
Run Gasoline, Platformate, and Thermal Reformate

FIG. IX-3. Hydrocarbon-type content of debutanized Pennsylvania straight-run gasoline, platformate, and thermal reformate. [*From Haensel and Sterba, Advances in Chem. Ser.,* No. 5, p. 72, 1951.)

for example, at 525°C and 1,125 psi form toluene, xylenes, ethylbenzene, p-ethyltoluene, propylbenzenes, diethylbenzenes, naphthalene, and other polynuclear aromatics.

The composition of a straight-run Pennsylvania gasoline before and after thermal and catalytic reforming is illustrated in Fig. IX-3.

Thermal reforming increases the aromatic content slightly at the expense of naphthenes, while considerable amounts of paraffins are removed by conversion to olefins. The catalytically reformed (hydroformed) product, however, is saturated and highly aromatic. Table IX-5 gives a comparision of the yields and octane numbers obtained on reforming by several methods a Mid-Continent naphtha of 35 clear octane number.[1]

TABLE IX-5

	Thermal	Thermal plus polymer- ization	Thermal plus gas recycle	Hydro- forming over MoO_3	Hydro- forming over Pt
Yield (reported as 10 lb vapor pressure), volume per cent....	66	80	80	84	95
Outside butane required for 10 lb vapor-pressure product, volume per cent...............	0	2	0	6	4
Total yield, volume per cent....	66	82	80	90	99
Octane rating:					
Motor:					
Clear....................	75	75	75	75	75
Plus 3 ml tetraethyllead....	84	84	85	86	87
Research:					
Clear....................	85	85	86	81	80
Plus 3 ml tetraethyllead....	93	93	93	93	93

IX-12. Catalytic Reforming. It is seen that the reforming of naphthas over catalysts and in the presence of hydrogen gives considerably higher yield-octane values and gasolines of higher lead susceptibility than are obtained in the various modifications of thermal reforming. Characteristically, the octane level of catalytic reformates is relatively high throughout its boiling range, although there is some variation because of the differences in chemical make-up of its various fractions. The high-boiling portions of a paraffinic naphtha can be converted very rapidly to aromatics and, even at moderate reforming severity, are high in octane number. On the other hand, the lower-boiling portions of the naphtha are limited in isoparaffin content by the equilibria involved; they cyclize slowly and only under severe conditions. A typical catalytic reformate has the following octane number distribution:[2]

[1] M. L. Kastens and R. Sutherland, *Ind. Eng. Chem.*, **42**:582 (1950). See also R. E. Maples, *Petrol. Refiner*, **33**(9):284 (1954), for a more detailed discussion of the influence of cracking, polymerization, and reforming on octane numbers, lead susceptibilities, etc.

[2] Private communication, M. C. Fogle, Gulf Research & Development Co. See also, Haensel and Sterba, *Advances in Chem. Ser.*, No. 5, p. 60, 1951.

Octane number, clear,
research method

Total reformate...............	86 to 88
Pentane fraction..............	80
110 to 270°F.......	60 to 65
270 to 320°F...	75 to 80
320 to E.P..................	100

Molecular hydrogen is essentially inert in the cracking of hydrocarbons over a silica-alumina catalyst; the latter in turn has very little power to isomerize paraffinic groups. When a hydrogenation-dehydrogenation catalyst, however, is incorporated in or deposited on the silica-alumina and hydrogen is added to the system, the catalyst complex becomes bifunctional, and deep-seated reactions take place. Straight chains are isomerized to branched structures, dehydrocyclized to aromatics, and hydrocracked to olefins; these in turn are isomerized and hydrogenated to lower-molecular-weight saturates. The substituted C_5 ring naphthenes are isomerized to C_6 rings which are then dehydrogenated to aromatics. Desulfurization also takes place. These effects are predominant, but a number of side reactions take place to a lesser degree.[1]

Isomerization. Paraffin hydrocarbons are isomerized readily. For example, *n*-heptane gives a C_7 fraction that approximates an equilibrium mixture of isomers.[2] Methylcyclopentane undergoes a similar reaction.[3] Such isomerization is favored by high space velocities; the rate is greater than that of dehydrocyclization or hydrocracking, and is, up to about 65 per cent heptane conversion, more or less insensitive to temperature and pressure variations.[4] The temperatures employed in commercial practice (850 to 950°F) are not excessively destructive to the isoparaffins formed, possibly because the aromatics present act as cracking inhibitors.[5]

Usually about 60 to 80 per cent of the naphthenic constituents in petroleum naphthas are of the C_5 ring type. These, except for cyclopentane, are of relatively low octane value. In processing, the alkyl cyclopentanes are isomerized readily to cyclohexanes. The isomerization is favored by high temperatures and low space velocities.[6] Even though

---

[1] For a general review of catalytic reforming, see Sittig and Warren, *Petrol. Refiner*, **34**(9):230 (1955). Guthrie and Davidson, *Petrol. Processing*, **10**:1157 (1955). Davidson, *Petrol. Processing*, **11**(11):116 (1956).

[2] Haensel and Donaldson, *loc. cit.*

[3] Fowle, Bent, Ciapetta, Pitts, and Leum, *Advances in Chem. Ser.*, No. 5, p. 76, 1951.

[4] Hettinger, Keith, Gring, and Teter, *Ind. Eng. Chem.*, **47**:719 (1955).

[5] Haensel and Donaldson, *loc. cit.*

[6] Heinemann, Mills, Hattman, Kirsch, Millikan, and Oblad, *Ind. Eng. Chem.*, **45**:130, 134 (1953).

the equilibrium is in favor of the C_5 ring compounds, it is disturbed by the rapid dehydrogenation of the C_6 naphthenes to aromatics.

Optimum yields of benzene and toluene are obtained at pressures in the range of 250 to 400 psi with molar hydrogen-to-oil ratios of 4:1 and a space velocity of about 3. Some isomerization to cyclopentanes takes place, as well as ring scission to give a nearly equilibrium mixture of paraffin hydrocarbons.[1] Excessively high hydrogen partial pressures favor C_6 to C_5 ring isomerization, illustrating the versatility of hydroforming reactions.

As would be expected, naphthenic distillates produce reformates of the highest octane value; the aromatic content may run as high as 60 per cent. Toluene has been prepared in large amounts for military uses by hydroforming, over a molybdena-alumina catalyst, selected naphtha containing large proportions of methylcyclohexane and ethylcyclopentane. Present-day operations for the production of aromatic hydrocarbons favor the use of platinum-containing catalysts;[2] cobalt and molybdenum compounds on alumina are also employed. Alkyl aromatics undergo both isomerization and disproportionation; cumene gives isomeric C_9 alkyl aromatics, toluene, xylenes, and hydrogenation products.[3]

Dehydrocyclization. That dehydrocyclization takes place[4] is evidenced by the fact that the amount of aromatics formed is larger than can be accounted for by the naphthene content of the charge. The importance of this reaction is illustrated by the fact that *n*-octane, with an octane number of -20, on conversion to xylenes and ethylbenzene will have an octane value of over 100, while an equilibrium mixture of octane isomers has an octane number of 38.[5] Dehydrocyclization is favored by high temperatures, low pressures, and low space velocities; conversion of *n*-heptane to aromatics to the extent of 58 molar per cent has been observed.[6] It has been postulated that in conversion of paraffins[7] benzene rings containing large alkyl groups are formed first; these are rehydrogenated to the corresponding naphthenes. These are then isomerized to polyalkyl naphthenes with small side chains; dehydrogenation to the final alkyl aromatics then occurs.

Hydrocracking. Hydrogenolysis of paraffin and naphthene hydrocarbons is less rapid than dehydrogenation and isomerization; it does not

[1] Heinemann, Mills, Hatmann, and Kirsch, *Ind. Eng. Chem.*, **45**:130 (1953).

[2] Beyler, Shuman, and Stevenson, *ACS, Div. Petrol. Chem.*, Preprints, Symposium on Catalytic Processing, p. 53, ACS Meeting, New York, September, 1954.

[3] Haensel and Donaldson, *loc. cit.*

[4] Donaldson, Pasik, and Haensel, *Ind. Eng. Chem.*, **47**:731 (1955). Grote, Haensel, and Sterba, *Petrol. Refiner*, **34**(4):116 (1955).

[5] Hettinger, Keith, Gring, and Teter, *loc. cit.*

[6] *Ibid.*, Mitchell, *J. ACS*, **80**:5848 (1958).

[7] Donaldson, Pasik, and Haensel, *loc. cit.*

occur extensively in hydroforming, except at low space velocities. In general, hydrocracking reactions are more characteristic of catalytic than of thermal treatment. Thus, in the hydrocracking of n-heptane, the products are mainly C_3 and C_4 hydrocarbons. A thermal treatment would have yielded much higher proportions of the fragment pairs C_1-C_7 and C_2-C_5.[1] The main contribution of hydrocracking to octane improvement is the reduction in molecular size. An equilibrium mixture of C_n paraffins will show an improvement of about 14 to 15 octane numbers in going to C_{n-1}; this is accompanied, however, by a volume loss of 8 to 10 per cent of the charge.[2]

Fuels having octane values in the neighborhood of 100 (clear, lead-free) can be obtained by an accessory treatment. This involves a solvent extraction for the separation and subsequent catalytic reforming of the nonaromatic high-boiling components.[3] The 100 octane number (clear) fuel can also be made by following the catalytic reforming operation with a thermal reforming treatment; the low-octane paraffins present are cracked to smaller paraffins and olefins.[4]

Desulfurization is quite complete in hydroforming, to the extent of 97 per cent as compared to about 15 per cent in thermal reforming.[5] Mercaptans, sulfides, disulfides, and thiophenes are readily attacked.[6]

Operating Variables. Even though hydrogen is one of the net products in hydroforming, the amount of hydrogen or hydrogen-rich (75 to 90 per cent) gases employed is generally in the ratio of about eight moles per mole of naphtha. Pressures are in the range of 250 to 600 psi, and temperatures of the order of 850 to 950°F. The added hydrogen is necessary for efficient action of the catalyst, which presumably functions through both active acidic (carbonium ion) and dehydrogenation sites.[2] The hydrogen release is of considerable economic importance because in large-scale operations the amount produced is sufficiently greater than recycle needs to warrant its utilization either in the manufacture of ammonia or in various refining operations (see Chap. VII, "Refining by Chemical Methods").

Hydroforming is an essentially nondestructive process. A considerable variation in the product with respect to both volatility and chemical

[1] Haensel and Donaldson, *Ind. Eng. Chem.*, **43**:2102 (1951).

[2] Hettinger, Keith, Gring, and Teter, *op. cit.*

[3] Grote, Haensel, and Sterba, *loc. cit.*

[4] Heinemann, Maerker, Welser, and Kirsch, *Petrol. Processing*, **10**:1571 (1955). Noll, Schall, Craig, and Stevenson, *Oil Gas J.*, **53**(47):102 (1955).

[5] Haensel and Sterba, *Advances in Chem. Ser.*, no. 5, p. 60, 1951.

[6] McGrath, *J. Appl. Chem.*, **4**(1):26 (1954). For a more thorough discussion of hydrodesulfurization, see McKinley in "Catalysis," Emmett (ed.), vol. V, p. 405, Reinhold Publishing Corporation, New York, 1957.

composition is obtainable by varying the operating temperature, pressure, hydrogen-oil ratio, and space velocity. Low pressures give most aromatics and least hydrocracking. The upper limit of pressure is set by the yield-octane curve (showing thermal effects) and the lower limit by the amount of hydrocracking desired and by the progressive carbonization of the catalyst. By varying the pressure it is possible to recover a highly aromatic reformate of low volatility with high hydrogen production or a more volatile product of low aromaticity accompanied by low hydrogen production.[1]

Cracked stocks produce relatively little hydrogen on hydroforming. They are either blended with a straight-run distillate to maintain the required hydrogen level or are given a preliminary hydrogenation to bring about saturation. The hydrogen produced by subsequent hydroforming is equal to or greater in amount than that consumed during the presaturation. The use of a platinum catalyst for hydroforming generally requires a fairly well-saturated stock. [2]

Carbon lay-down on the catalyst (either platinum, molybdena, chromia-alumina, or nickel-alumina-silica base) is not as serious in hydroforming as it is in catalytic cracking. Long periods of operation are possible before catalyst regeneration or renewal is required. Platinum-containing catalysts are usually renewed when spent. They may, however, be regenerated at temperatures of 950 to 975°F in gases containing only one or two per cent of oxygen.

When platinum-on-alumina is the catalyst, small amounts of water promote hydrocracking and inhibit dehydrocyclization, but have no effect on dehydrogenation; sulfur (H_2S) increases hydrocracking and decreases dehydrogenation; ammonia inhibits both hydrocracking and dehydrocyclization. Both arsenic and lead may be considered as poisons. The effects of water can often be counteracted by adding to the charge minimal amounts of alkyl chlorides.[3]

---

[1] Kastens and Sutherland, *Ind. Eng. Chem.*, **42**:582 (1950).

[2] Sittig and Warren, *Petrol. Refiner*, **34**(9):230 (1955).

[3] For pretreatment of charge stocks to remove impurities, see Ziegenhain, *Petrol. Eng.*, **24**(12):C-42 (1952). See also, "Preparation of Petroleum Feeds for Platinum Catalysts," Attapulgus Division, Minerals and Chemicals Corp., 1955, and Hettinger, Keith, Gring, and Teter, *op. cit.*

CHAPTER X

Chemical Thermodynamics of Petroleum Hydrocarbons

by J. R. TOMLINSON, PH.D.

Gulf Research and Development Co.

The work of Francis and of Parks and his collaborators[1] may be said to have been the first organized efforts to apply thermodynamics to the hydrocarbon systems encountered in the petroleum industry. Although practically all this early work requires revision and amplification in the light of more recent accurate results and newly developed techniques, it should be recognized that the contributions of these early workers gave the impetus for a considerable part of the newer developments.

The research projects of the American Petroleum Institute are revising and extending the results of these early investigators. This carefully planned program includes the preparation of pure hydrocarbons and related compounds and the determination of their physical, spectral, and thermodynamic properties. API Research Project 44[2] serves as the central agency for the collection, correlation, selection, and compilation of such data. Statistical calculations of the thermodynamic properties of gaseous hydrocarbons are being used to great advantage in these studies. This continuation of the work of Pitzer and others[3] permits the calculation of thermodynamic properties at high temperatures, where experimental data are difficult to obtain and consequently very meager.

Thermodynamic properties data are determined by a variety of methods. They may be measured experimentally or calculated theoretically. The thermodynamic properties of a single pure hydrocarbon

[1] Francis, *Ind. Eng. Chem.*, **20**:277 (1928). Parks and Huffman, "Free Energies of Some Organic Compounds," Reinhold Publishing Corporation, New York, 1932.

[2] Under the direction of Prof. F. D. Rossini, Carnegie Institute of Technology, Pittsburgh, Pa.

[3] Pitzer, *Chem. Revs.*, **27**:39 (1940). Aston, *Chem. Revs.*, **27**:59 (1940). Wilson, *Chem. Revs.*, **27**:17 (1940).

system are usually obtained by a combination or correlation of the results of several determinational methods. These properties vary with temperature and pressure and are related to the equation of state or compressibility data applicable to the substance. The initial aim of this chapter is to review fundamental principles which permit the correlation of data to obtain the desired property at the required conditions. In view of the growing importance of statistical calculations to the determination of the thermodynamic properties of gases, the method will be outlined briefly.

The final aim of this chapter will be to illustrate the practical application of thermodynamic principles to problems arising in the petroleum industry.

X-1. Fundamental Relationships. The thermodynamic properties of a chemical reaction which are of primary interest to the petroleum chemist or engineer are the standard free energy change ΔF° and the standard heat of reaction ΔH°. From values of these properties at the temperature under consideration, equilibrium concentrations and heat effects can be calculated. This section will be devoted to methods of determining values of these properties. The relationship between free energy change and equilibrium and the application to practical problems will be discussed in later sections.

Experimental measurements of the equilibrium constants of hydrocarbon reactions are quite meager. Experimental heats of reaction are generally limited to heats of combustion usually determined at room temperature. However, the combination of these limited reaction data with the thermodynamic properties of the individual components of the reaction permits the calculation of ΔF° and ΔH° at the particular temperature of interest. In view of this and the fact that ΔF and ΔH are defined in terms of properties of the reaction components, it is therefore necessary to consider the properties of pure substances.

The free energy F, heat content H, and entropy S of a pure substance depend upon the quantity, the pressure, the physical state, and the temperature of the substance. By defining the standard state of a solid or liquid as that of the real solid or liquid at 1 atm pressure and for a gas as that of an ideal gas at 1 atm pressure, these properties for one mole of the substance in a particular standard state are functions only of the temperature. The properties of more or less than a mole are obtained proportionally. The properties for pressures other than atmospheric may be obtained from those in the standard state with the use of fundamental thermodynamic relationships which involve only the equation of state or compressibility of the substance. The effect of pressure on these properties of a pure solid or liquid is quite small and is usually neglected for moderate pressure changes. The equation of state of an ideal gas is quite simple; hence, its choice for the gaseous standard state. The free energy and entropy of an ideal gas vary linearly with the logarithm of the pressure. The heat content and, thus, heat capacity of an ideal gas are independent of the pressure. For practical purposes a real gas may be considered ideal for pressures up to several atmospheres.

The property for a substance in its standard state is identified by a superscribed small zero. It is conventional to identify the temperature of the property as a subscript. The free energy, heat content, and entropy of a pure substance in its standard state at 298°K (25°C) would be symbolized as $F_{298}°$, $H_{298}°$, and $S_{298}°$, respectively.

The thermodynamic properties of a reaction are defined as the change in the properties of the reaction components, assuming complete conversion of reactants to products. The standard free energy change $\Delta F°$ for the reaction

$$A + 2B \rightarrow 3C + D$$

is, then,

$$\Delta F° = 3F°(C) + F°(D) - F°(A) - 2F°(B) = \Sigma F° \text{ (products)}$$
$$- \Sigma F° \text{ (reactants)} \quad \text{(X-1)}$$

where the free energies of the products are taken with positive signs because of their creation and the free energies of the reactants are subtracted because of their disappearance. This type of summation with sign convention and the use of equation coefficients is always employed in determining reaction properties from those of the reaction components. Equations similar to (X-1) may be written for the heat of reaction $\Delta H°$, involving the individual heat contents, and the entropy change $\Delta S°$, involving the individual entropies. These reaction properties are interrelated by

$$\Delta F° = \Delta H° - T \Delta S° \quad \text{(X-2)}$$

which has been derived from the expression relating the properties of a pure substance

$$F° = H° - TS° \quad \text{(X-3)}$$

Values of the thermodynamic properties, $\Delta F°$, $\Delta H°$, or $\Delta S°$, for several reactions may be combined to yield the thermodynamic property for the resultant reaction. For example, the heat of hydrogenation of 1, 3-butadiene to n-butane may be determined by summing values of the heats of combustion of 1,3-butadiene, n-butane, and hydrogen in the following manner.

$$
\begin{array}{lll}
C_4H_6 + 11\frac{1}{2}O_2 \rightarrow 4CO_2 + 3H_2O & \Delta H_{298}° = -575.93 \text{ kcal} & \\
4CO_2 + 5H_2O \rightarrow C_4H_{10} + 13\frac{1}{2}O_2 & \Delta H_{298}° = +635.05 \text{ kcal} & \text{(X-4)} \\
2H_2 + O_2 \quad\quad \rightarrow 2H_2O & \Delta H_{298}° = -115.60 \text{ kcal} & \\
\hline
C_4H_6 + 2H_2 \quad \rightarrow C_4H_{10} & \Delta H_{298}° = \quad -56.48 \text{ kcal} &
\end{array}
$$

The heats of the various combustion reactions are summed just as the equations for the reactions are summed. The heat of combustion of hydrogen has been doubled in that two moles of hydrogen are reacted. A change of sign of the heat of combustion of n-butane is required by the writing of the reaction in reverse. A negative heat of reaction denotes exothermicity. In this and following reactions the physical state of all components is that of the gas unless otherwise noted.

The desired thermodynamic properties $\Delta F°$ and $\Delta H°$ for a reaction are obtainable either by a summation of the properties for the individual components of the reaction as in Eq. (X-1) or by a summation of the property for several reactions as in Eq. (X-4). It would appear that the first method would be preferred. However, as will subsequently be shown, values of $F°$ and $H°$ are not determinable in themselves, but only in the forms $(F° - H_0°)$ and $(H° - H_0°)$, where $H_0°$ is the heat content of the substance at absolute zero. A summation of these properties involves a consideration of $\Delta H_0°$, the heat of reaction at absolute zero. The second method will be considered first.

Reactions involving the formation of compounds from their elements are most convenient for use in these summation processes. The standard free energy of formation of a substance, $\Delta F f°$, refers to the free energy change involved in the formation of that substance in its standard state (solid, liquid, or gas) from its constituent elements in their standard reference states. The standard state of an element is usually taken as its most stable form at room temperature. The standard state for carbon is graphite, for hydrogen or oxygen the diatomic gases. By summing the individual standard free energies of formation of the components of a reaction, the standard free energy change may be calculated simply. For example, $\Delta F°$ for the combustion of butadiene [first reaction Eq. (X-4)] is calculated by

$$\Delta F° = 4 \, \Delta F f°(CO_2) + 3 \, \Delta F f°(H_2O) - \Delta F f°(C_4H_6) - 1\frac{1}{2} \, \Delta F f°(O_2)$$

$$(X-5)$$

where the free energy of formation of O_2 is zero by definition. A similar equation can be written for the heat of the reaction involving the summation of the standard heats of formation $\Delta H f°$.

Standard free energies and heats of formation for many of the gaseous hydrocarbons and their derivatives and for many inorganic gases are available in tabular form over a wide range of temperature. The method by which these data have been obtained is of interest from several aspects. The principles involved are fundamental to the relationship between the thermodynamic properties of a reaction and those of the reaction components. Thus, these principles are applicable to reactions other than the formation reaction. In addition, in a few cases complete thermodynamic data for a substance will be available but will need assembling by these principles into useful form.

Thermodynamic properties for the hydrocarbons in the standard gaseous state are obtained almost exclusively from statistical calculations; the method of calculation will be described in a later section. These calculations yield

$$\frac{F° - H_0°}{T}$$ the free energy function

$$\frac{H° - H_0°}{T}$$ the heat content function

$$H° - H_0°$$ the heat content (enthalpy)

$$S_T°$$ the entropy

$$C_P°$$ the heat capacity

where $H_0°$ is the heat content of the ideal gas at absolute zero. These data are usually found tabulated for 100° intervals from 298°K (25°C) to 1500°K. Values for intermediate temperatures are determined by interpolation.

The above thermodynamic quantities are interrelated in the following manner:

$$S° = \frac{H° - H_0°}{T} - \frac{F° - H_0°}{T} = \int_0^T \frac{C_P}{T}\, dT \qquad \text{(X-6)}$$

$$H° - H_0° = T\,\frac{H° - H_0°}{T} = \int_0^T C_P\, dT \qquad \text{(X-7)}$$

$$H_{T_2}° - H_{T_1}° = H_{T_2}° - H_0° - H_{T_1}° - H_0° = \int_{T_1}^{T_2} C_P\, dT \qquad \text{(X-8)}$$

$$S_{T_2}° - S_{T_1}° = \int_{T_1}^{T_2} \frac{C_P}{T}\, dT \qquad \text{(X-9)}$$

The availability of free energy and heat content functions eliminates the need for heat capacity data in tabular or equation form. This will explain the lack of emphasis on heat capacity in this chapter.

The summation of the free energy and heat content functions for the components of a reaction yields the desired reaction properties $\Delta F°$ and $\Delta H°$, apart from the constant $\Delta H_0°$.

$$\frac{\Delta F° - \Delta H_0°}{T} = \sum \frac{F° - H_0°}{T} \qquad \text{(X-10)}$$

$$\frac{\Delta H° - \Delta H_0°}{T} = \sum \frac{H° - H_0°}{T} \qquad \text{(X-11)}$$

The summations are made in the usual fashion, the functions of the products less the functions of the reactants, with the functions multiplied by the coefficient of each component in the balanced reaction equation.

The evaluation of $\Delta H_0°$, the heat of the reaction at absolute zero, permits the calculations of $\Delta F°$ and $\Delta H°$ over the temperature range of the summations. An experimental value of either $\Delta H°$ or $\Delta F°$ at a single temperature is required for the evaluation.

Heat of combustion measurements furnish the most accurate values for the heats of reaction of hydrocarbons and thus are used to evaluate $\Delta H_0°$. For example, the standard heat of formation of n-hexane can be obtained from heats of combustion of liquid hexane, hydrogen, and graphite and the heat of vaporization of hexane by the following summation:

$6CO_2 + 7H_2O\ (l)$	$\rightarrow C_6H_{14}\ (l) + 19\!\!\frac{1}{2}O_2$	$\Delta H_{298}° = +995.01 \text{ kcal}$
$7H_2 + \frac{7}{2}O_2$	$\rightarrow 7H_2O\ (l)$	$\Delta H_{298}° = -478.24 \text{ kcal}$
$6C \text{ (graphite)} + 6O_2$	$\rightarrow 6CO_2$	$\Delta H_{298}° = -564.30 \text{ kcal}$
$C_6H_{14}\ (l)$	$\rightarrow C_6H_{14}\ (g)$	$\Delta H_{298}° = +\ \ 7.56 \text{ kcal}$
$6C \text{ (graphite)} + 7H_2 \rightarrow C_6H_{14}$		$\Delta H_{298}° = -\ \ 39.97 \text{ kcal}$

The substitution of this value along with the heat content function summation for 298°K into (X-11) yields $\Delta H f_0°$, the heat of formation of gaseous n-hexane at absolute zero. The properties of graphite, being a solid, are obtained by the integration of experimental heat capacities.

Experimental thermodynamic data are required to determine the thermodynamic properties of solids and liquids. The heat content of a substance can be determined experimentally from an integration of the heat capacity of each phase over its appropriate temperature range and the addition of any heat effects involved in the transition between phases. Thus

$$H° - H_0°\ (s) = \int_0^{T_m} C_P°\ (s)\ dT + \Delta H_m° + \int_{T_m}^{T_v} C_P°\ (l)\ dT$$
$$+ \Delta H_v° + \int_{T_v}^{T} C_P°\ (g)\ dT \quad \text{(X-12)}$$

where $H_0°\ (s)$ is the heat content of the solid at absolute zero; T_m, the melting point; $\Delta H_m°$, the heat of fusion; T_v, the boiling point; and $\Delta H_v°$, the heat of vaporization. The entropy is determined by the integration

$$S° = \int_0^{T_m} \frac{C_P°\ (s)}{T}\ dT + \frac{\Delta H_m°}{T_m} + \int_{T_m}^{T_v} \frac{C_P°\ (l)}{T}\ dT + \frac{\Delta H_v°}{T_v}$$
$$+ \int_{T_v}^{T} \frac{C_P°\ (g)}{T}\ dT \quad \text{(X-13)}$$

the term $S_0°\ (s)$ being omitted in that at absolute zero, by the third law of thermodynamics, the entropy of a perfect crystal is zero.

For completeness Eqs. (X-12) and (X-13) indicate integration to a temperature above the boiling point, thus determining the properties of the gas. For the properties of the liquid and solid phases, the integrations would be carried out to temperatures equal to, or below, the boiling and melting points, respectively. Any terms involving higher temperatures would be eliminated.

Heats of fusion and vaporization are determined calorimetrically by measuring the quantity of heat necessary to effect the phase transition.

These properties may be determined, alternatively, from a combination of vapor pressure and compressibility data. Measurements of the heats of combustion of solids and liquids are made in a bomb calorimeter usually at room temperature. Values are corrected to standard heats of combustion and are reported for 298°K. Flow calorimeters are used for combustion measurements on gases.

As in the case of gases, the properties of liquids and solids at pressures other than atmospheric are determined from those in the standard state with the use of fundamental thermodynamic relationships which involve the compressibility of the substance. Vapor-pressure measurements are used to advantage in these studies. For a discussion of such determinations and the more complicated cases of solid and liquid solutions, the reader is referred to standard texts on thermodynamics.

X-2. The Standard Free Energy and Equilibrium. The standard free energy change ΔF° of a reaction is a measure of the "driving force" tending to bring about its completion. A negative ΔF° indicates the reaction will tend to approach completion; the more negative, the greater the degree of completion. This does not, however, indicate that reaction will proceed spontaneously or even at a measurable rate. While the tendency is for the reaction to take place, a catalyst may be required actually to bring it about. If the ΔF° is large and positive, the reaction cannot take place to any appreciable extent even in the presence of a catalyst. Catalysts may influence the rate of approach to equilibrium but never the position of equilibrium. Reactions with apparent positive ΔF°'s may be forced to take place by the application of an external force, such as electrical energy in electrolytic and light in photochemical reactions. In these cases the external force must be included in the free energy summation and in effect makes the free energy change negative.

The criterion for equilibrium at constant temperature and pressure is that the actual free energy change ΔF is zero. For the reaction

$$2A + B \rightarrow C + 3D \qquad \text{(X-14)}$$

this would mean that

$$\Delta F = 0 = F(C) + 3F(D) - 2F(A) - F(B) \qquad \text{(X-15)}$$

In other words, at equilibrium the sum of the actual free energies of products must equal the sum of the actual free energies of the reactants. Before reaction, the sum of the free energies of the reactants is a positive value, whereas the free energy of the products, by virtue of their absence, is zero. As the reaction progresses, the concentrations or partial pressures of the reactants decrease, thus decreasing their free energies. Simultaneously, the concentrations of the products increase, increasing their free energies. The composition of the reactant mixture at which the sums of the free energies of the products and of the reactants are equal is the equilibrium composition.

The relationship between the standard free energy change ΔF° and the equilibrium composition can be expressed quantitatively by the use of the equation relating the change of free energy of each single component with concentration. Expressing concentrations in terms of the activity a, the difference in free energies of a single component between two activity states, at constant temperature, is

$$F_1 - F_2 = RT \ln \frac{a_1}{a_2} = RT \ln a_1 - RT \ln a_2 \qquad (\text{X-16})$$

If one of these states is the standard or reference state for which the activity is unity, then Eq. (X-16) reduces to

$$F = F^\circ + RT \ln a \qquad (\text{X-17})$$

Upon substitution of Eq. (X-17) for each component in Eq. (X-15) and separation of the energy and concentration terms, one obtains

$$F^\circ(C) + 3F^\circ(D) - 2F^\circ(A) - F^\circ(B) = -RT \ln \frac{a_C a_D^3}{a_A^2 a_B} \qquad (\text{X-18})$$

The quantity to the left in Eq. (X-18) is the standard free energy change for the reaction. The fraction to the right is the equilibrium constant K. Thus Eq. (X-18) reduces to

$$\Delta F^\circ = -RT \ln K \qquad (\text{X-19})$$

where R is the gas constant in calories per degree and K is dimensionless.

Concentrations of gases are more practically expressed as partial pressures. For gases, the activity a is equal to the fugacity f. The activity coefficient γ is the proportionality constant relating the fugacity to the partial pressure, P. Hence

$$a = f = \gamma P \qquad (\text{X-20})$$

Substituting Eq. (X-20) in the equilibrium constant expression, one obtains

$$K = \frac{a_C a_D^3}{a_A^2 a_B} = \frac{\gamma_C \gamma_D^3}{\gamma_A^2 \gamma_B} \cdot \frac{P_C P_D^3}{P_A^2 P_B} \qquad (\text{X-21})$$

By defining K_γ as the quotient of activity coefficients and K_P as the quotient of partial pressures, Eq. (X-21) simplifies to

$$K = K_\gamma K_P \qquad (\text{X-22})$$

The activity coefficient of an ideal gas is unity and for real gases, at moderate pressures, may be considered unity; hence $K \cong K_P$. For gases at moderate pressures, Eq. (X-19) becomes

$$\Delta F^\circ = -RT \ln K \cong -RT \ln K_P \qquad (\text{X-23})$$

For gases at high pressures,

$$\Delta F° = -RT \ln K = -RT \ln K_\gamma K_P \qquad (X\text{-}24)$$

For gaseous mixtures it is customary to assume that the activity coefficient of a constituent of the mixture is equal to the activity coefficient of the pure gas at a pressure equal to that of the gas mixture. Thus, K_γ is independent of the composition of the gas mixture and may be calculated separately from tables or graphs of activity coefficients.

Although $\Delta F°$, $\Delta H°$, and $\Delta S°$ for a reaction are usually obtained from the thermodynamic properties of the reaction components, as discussed in the preceding section, values of these properties may be determined from experimental equilibrium constants. $\Delta F°$ is obtained by the use of Eq. (X-23). A plot of $\Delta F°$ against the absolute temperature is usually linear if the temperature range is not large. From values of the constants in the linear equation

$$\Delta F° = A - BT$$

"average" values of $\Delta H°$ and $\Delta S°$ for the experimental temperature range may be obtained by analogy to the well-known relation

$$\Delta F° = \Delta H° - T\,\Delta S°$$

These average values may also be obtained from a plot of the natural logarithm of the equilibrium constant versus the reciprocal of the absolute temperature by the combination of Eq. (X-19) with the above equation to yield

$$\ln K = -\frac{\Delta H°}{R}\frac{1}{T} + \frac{\Delta S°}{R}$$

It is beyond the scope of this chapter to discuss equilibria in the solid or liquid states. The reader is referred to standard texts.[1] However, for the limited case, in which the components of the liquid solution are also present in a gaseous phase, a calculation of the liquid equilibria can be easily made.

Consider an isomerization reaction

$$A_{(l)} \rightleftharpoons B_{(l)}$$

and assume the liquid phase is an ideal solution. By Raoult's law the partial pressures of A and B in the gaseous phase are related to the composition of the liquid phase by

$$P_A = N_A P_A°$$
$$P_B = N_B P_B°$$

[1] Lewis and Randall, "Thermodynamics and the Free Energy of Chemical Substances," McGraw-Hill Book Company, Inc., New York, 1923. Rossini, "Chemical Thermodynamics," John Wiley & Sons, Inc., New York, 1950.

where P_A and P_B are the partial pressures of A and B in the gas phase, N_A and N_B are their mole fractions in the liquid phase, and $P_A°$ and $P_B°$ are the vapor pressures of pure A and B at the temperature of the reaction. The gas-phase equilibrium constant K_P can be expressed in terms of the partial pressures which in turn can be expressed in terms of the mole fractions and vapor pressures.

Hence

$$K_P\,(g) = \frac{P_B}{P_A} = \frac{N_A P_A°}{N_B P_B°}$$

The ratio of B to A in the equilibrated liquid phase is, then,

$$\frac{N_A}{N_B} = \frac{P_B°}{P_A°} K_P\,(g)$$

and the total pressure of the system, which is the vapor pressure of the liquid solution, is

$$P = P_A + P_B = N_A P_A° + N_B P_B°$$

X-3. Statistical Calculations of Thermodynamic Properties. The statistical calculation of the thermodynamic properties of an ideal gas is based upon the assumption of a Boltzmann distribution of the molecules among their various possible energy states. According to the Boltzmann distribution law the fraction of molecules, χ_i, in a given energy state, ϵ_i, is related to the energies of all the possible states and the temperature by the expression

$$\chi_i = \frac{e^{-\epsilon_i/kT}}{e^{-\epsilon_1/kT} + e^{-\epsilon_2/kT} + e^{-\epsilon_3/kT} + \cdots} \qquad \text{(X-25)}$$

where k is the Boltzmann constant, e is the base of natural logarithms, and ϵ_1, ϵ_2, ϵ_3, etc., are the possible energy states of the molecules. The denominator of Eq. (X-25) is defined as the partition function Q. That is,

$$Q = \Sigma e^{-\epsilon_i/kT} = e^{-\epsilon_1/kT} + e^{-\epsilon_2/kT} + e^{-\epsilon_3/kT} + \cdots \qquad \text{(X-26)}$$

The natural logarithm of the partition function Q and its first and second derivatives with respect to temperature completely define the thermodynamic properties of the molecule. These relationships are

$$
\begin{aligned}
F° - H_0° &= -RT \ln \frac{Q}{N} \\
H° - H_0° &= RT^2 \frac{d \ln Q}{dT} \\
S° &= RT \frac{d \ln Q}{dT} + R \ln \frac{Q}{N} \\
C_P° &= 2RT \frac{d \ln Q}{dT} + RT^2 \frac{d^2 \ln Q}{dT^2}
\end{aligned}
\qquad \text{(X-27)}
$$

where N is Avagadro's number and R is the gas constant.

In order to evaluate the possible energy states of a molecule, the concept of degrees of freedom is used. The motion of a single atom in space can be described in terms of three coordinates. Thus, the atom has three degrees of freedom of translational motion. The motions of the atoms in a molecule made up of n atoms must have $3n$ degrees of freedom to describe completely the motions of the n atoms. However, instead of describing the motions of the n atoms individually, certain combinations of motion are considered. Three translational degrees of freedom are ascribed to the motion of the molecule as a whole just as in the case of the single atom. Three more degrees of freedom are ascribed to the rotation of the molecule about its three principal axes. The remaining $3n - 6$ degrees of freedom are ascribed to the displacement of atoms within the molecule and are the vibrational degrees of freedom. In the case of a linear molecule which has a zero moment of inertia about one axis, there is one less rotational degree of freedom and, in order to maintain a total of $3n$ degrees of freedom, one more vibrational degree of freedom. Each vibrational degree of freedom is associated with a specific mode of vibration within the molecule. In chain-like molecules, as certain hydrocarbons, segments of the molecule can rotate about single bonds. For each such internal rotation there is ascribed a degree of freedom and consequently there is one less vibrational degree of freedom.

Just as the motions of the atoms in a molecule can be separated into several types, the energy states associated with these motions can also be separated. The total energy of a molecule can then be written

$$\epsilon_i = \epsilon_{\text{trans}} + \epsilon_{\text{rot}} + \epsilon_{\text{vib}} + \epsilon_{\text{int-rot}} \qquad \text{(X-28)}$$

Since the partition function involves energy as an exponent only, upon substitution of Eq. (X-28) in Eq. (X-26) the summation of energies in a single exponential can be factored to yield a product of exponentials each containing a single energy. Thus, the total partition function becomes

$$Q_{\text{total}} = \Sigma e^{-\epsilon_{\text{trans}}/kT} \, \Sigma e^{-\epsilon_{\text{rot}}/kT} \, \Sigma e^{-\epsilon_{\text{vib}}/kT} \, \Sigma e^{-\epsilon_{\text{int-rot}}/kT} \qquad \text{(X-29)}$$

The summations on the right-hand side of Eq. (X-29) are the partition functions for the various types of motion, each involving only the energy associated with its particular type. Expressing these partition functions as small q's the total partition function becomes

$$Q_{\text{total}} = q_{\text{trans}} \, q_{\text{rot}} \, q_{\text{vib}} \, q_{\text{int-rot}}$$

which expressed logarithmically is

$$\ln Q_{\text{total}} = \ln q_{\text{trans}} + \ln q_{\text{rot}} + \ln q_{\text{vib}} + \ln q_{\text{int-rot}}$$

This separation of partition functions results in a separation of their contributions to thermodynamic properties as determined by Eqs. (X-27).

Hence, each partition function can be evaluated separately. The energy states peculiar to each type of motion have been derived quantum mechanically. Certain simplifying assumptions may be made, principally that the vibrations are harmonic and that the rotations are those of a rigid rotator. With the use of these energy states the partition functions have been calculated. These functions will not be given here but some of their features will be described. A detailed discussion of these partition functions and the statistical method can be found in several texts.[1]

The partition function for translation involves the temperature, the molecular weight, and the molar volume of the gas, along with fundamental physical constants.

The rotational partition function depends upon temperature, the principal moments of inertia, and the symmetry of the molecule. The moments of inertia can be calculated either from bond angles and bond distances or from far infrared or microwave spectra of the molecule.

The internal rotational partition function involves the temperature, moment of inertia of the rotating group, and, if the rotation is restricted by steric effects, the potential barrier hindering such rotation. The magnitudes of these potential barriers have been determined for the lighter hydrocarbons by comparing the experimental entropy with that calculated statistically. A barrier height is then assigned to make up the discrepancy. If an experimental entropy is not available, the barrier height may be estimated by comparison with molecules having similar rotating groups.

The partition function for vibration involves the temperature and the fundamental vibrational frequencies of the molecule. These fundamental frequencies along with their linear combinations are observed in infrared and Raman spectra of both the liquid and gaseous hydrocarbon. Because of these combinations and the fact that many of these fundamental frequencies are degenerate, a careful correlation of the observed spectra with a theoretical analysis of the vibrational modes of the molecule is necessary. These fundamental frequencies can also be estimated by a comparison with similar molecules.

For room temperature and above, the contributions of several of these partition functions to heat capacity reduce to simple fractions of the gas constant R. The contribution to heat capacity for rotation of a non-linear molecule is $\frac{3}{2}R$, for rotation of a linear molecule is R, for free internal rotation is $\frac{1}{2}R$, and for translation either $\frac{3}{2}R$ or $\frac{5}{2}R$, depending

---

[1] Taylor and Glasstone, "A Treatise on Physical Chemistry," Vol. I, "Atomistics and Thermodynamics," 3d ed., D. Van Nostrand Company, Inc., Princeton, N.J., 1942. Herzberg, "Infrared and Raman Spectra," D. Van Nostrand Company, Inc., Princeton, N.J., 1945. Rossini, *op. cit.*

upon whether the gas is considered at constant volume or at constant pressure. These values are consistent with the classical interpretation that each degree of freedom should contribute $\frac{1}{2}R$ to the heat capacity.

X-4. Status of Thermodynamic Data. Prior to the application of statistical methods, accurate thermodynamic data for hydrocarbons were mostly available only at room temperature. Heats of formation were obtained from a combination of heats of combustion and entropies by the integration of experimental heat capacities. Free energies of formation were then calculated from the heats of formation and entropy changes. These data were generally tabulated for 298°K.

The statistical method has permitted the general extension of many of these data to the higher temperatures which are necessary for petroleum processing. By this method the thermodynamic properties of ideal gases may be calculated. Experimental heats of combustion then permit the determination of $\Delta H_0°$. the link between the thermodynamic properties for a reaction and those for pure substances. A combination of the calculated and experimental data yields the free energies and heats of formation over a wide temperature range.

The most convenient sources of these data are the publications of the American Petroleum Institute Project 44, which since 1942 has been engaged in collecting, analyzing, calculating, and correlating both physical and thermodynamic properties of hydrocarbons and related compounds. Thermodynamic data in various stages of completeness are available in reports of the Institute and in the current literature. Complete thermodynamic data for most hydrocarbons through C_8, including isomeric species, have been tabulated in a recent publication.[1] Also included are data for higher members of several homologous series. At the time of this writing properties of approximately twenty sulfur-containing hydrocarbons were to be found in the various publications of American Petroleum Institute Project 48A. Included in the future program of the Institute are the collection and subsequent publication of the properties of oxygen- and nitrogen-containing hydrocarbons.

Correlation methods offer a means of extending these data to higher-molecular-weight hydrocarbons. As a saturated hydrocarbon side chain, in a homologous series, is increased in length, the change in thermodynamic properties effected by the addition of a CH_2 group becomes essentially constant. This is evidenced in Table X-1, which gives thermodynamic properties of several homologous series. Several investigators[2] have correlated the properties on a broader scale by dividing

---

[1] Rossini and others, "Selected Values of Physical and Thermodynamic Properties of Hydrocarbons and Related Compounds," Carnegie Press, Pittsburgh, Pa., 1953.

[2] Franklin, *Ind. Eng. Chem.*, **41**:1070 (1949). Souders, Matthews, and Hurd, *Ind. Eng. Chem.*, **41**:1048 (1948). van Kreveler and Chermin, *Chem. Eng. Sci.*, **1**:66 (1951).

TABLE X-1. THERMODYNAMIC DATA* FOR VARIOUS HYDROCARBONS IN THE IDEAL
GASEOUS STATE. INCREMENTAL CHANGES OF PROPERTIES
WITHIN HOMOLOGOUS SERIES ARE INCLUDED

Gas	$\Delta Hf_0°$, kcal/mole	$\Delta Hf_{298}°$, kcal/mole	$\Delta Ff_{298}°$, kcal/mole	$S_{298}°$, cal/(deg)(mole)
Methane	−15.99	−17.89	−12.14	44.50
	0.53	2.35	4.28	10.35
Ethane	−16.52	−20.24	−7.86	54.85
	2.96	4.58	2.25	9.66
Propane	−19.48	−24.82	−5.61	64.51
	4.19	5.33	1.51	9.61
n-Butane	−23.67	−30.15	−4.10	74.12
	3.56	4.85	2.10	9.28
n-Pentane	−27.23	−35.00	−2.00	83.40
	3.68	4.96	1.93	9.43
n-Hexane	−30.91	−39.96	−0.07	92.83
	3.64	4.93	2.01	9.41
n-Heptane	−34.55	−44.89	1.94	102.24
	3.65	4.93	2.01	9.31
n-Octane	−38.20	−49.82	3.95	111.55
Ethylene	14.52	12.50	16.28	52.45
	6.05	7.62	....	11.35
Propylene	8.47	4.88	14.99	63.80
	3.51	4.91	2.10	9.24
1-Butene	4.96	−0.03	17.09	73.04
	3.83	4.97	1.87	9.61
1-Pentene	1.13	−5.00	18.96	82.65
	3.69	4.96	1.98	9.28
1-Hexene	−2.54	−9.96	20.94	91.93
	3.66	4.93	2.01	9.31
1-Heptene	−6.18	−14.89	22.95	101.24
	3.65	4.93	2.01	9.31
1-Octene	−9.83	−19.82	24.96	110.55
Benzene	24.00	19.82	30.99	64.34
	6.50	7.87	....	12.08
Toluene	17.50	11.95	29.23	76.42
	3.58	4.83	1.98	9.73
Ethylbenzene	13.92	7.12	31.21	86.15
	4.11	5.25	1.60	9.61
n-Propylbenzene	9.81	1.87	32.81	95.76
	3.88	5.17	1.77	9.28
n-Butylbenzene	5.93	−3.30	34.58	105.04
	3.65	4.93	1.96	9.43
n-Pentylbenzene	2.28	−8.23	36.54	114.47
	3.64	4.92	2.01	9.31
n-Hexylbenzene	−1.36	−13.15	38.55	123.78
n-Heptane	−34.55	−44.89	1.94	102.24
2-Methylhexane	−35.77	−46.60	0.77	100.35
3-Methylhexane	−34.96	−45.96	1.10	101.37
3-Ethylpentane	−34.10	−45.34	2.57	98.30
2,2-Dimethylpentane	−38.00	−49.29	0.02	93.85
2,3-Dimethylpentane	−36.29	−47.62	0.16	98.96
2,4-Dimethylpentane	−36.98	−48.30	0.72	94.80
3,3-Dimethylpentane	−36.92	−48.17	0.63	95.53
2,2,3-Trimethylbutane	−37.71	−48.96	1.02	91.60

* Rossini et al., "Selected Values of Physical and Thermodymic Properties of Hydrocarbons and Related Properties," Carnegie Press, Pittsburgh, Pa., 1953.

the molecules into characteristic groups, each containing a single carbon atom.   Values of thermodynamic properties were then assigned to each group, depending upon the number of hydrogen atoms attached, the types of bonds formed, and the position of the group relative to other groups.   A summation of these group properties along with additional effects of symmetry and internal rotation yields the desired property of the compound.

This second method of correlation is of limited use because of the low accuracy (1 kcal per mole) of the free energies of formation it predicts. Included in Table X-1 are the properties of the isomers of *n*-heptane. These values indicate the small variation between properties of isomeric species and thus emphasize the need for accurate data in equilibrium calculations.

X-5. Applications to Petroleum Processing

General Considerations.   Reactions involved in petroleum processing include isomerization, hydrogenation, dehydrogenation, polymerization, cracking, cyclization, aromatization, desulfurization, etc.   In hydrocarbon systems all these reactions are thermodynamically possible to a greater or less extent.   Fortunately, catalyst selectivity and the choice of operating conditions, such as temperature and pressure, eliminate many of these reactions by virtue of a negligible reaction rate even though their thermodynamics may be quite favorable.   For example, the hydrocracking of paraffins takes place only at high temperatures, although at room temperature these reactions have large negative standard free energies.

The initial step in any equilibrium calculation is the selection of the reactions to consider.   It must be assumed that true equilibrium is established in these selected reactions, and that other reactions, although thermodynamically favorable, can be disregarded because of a negligible rate.   Hence, a supposition or prior knowledge of the reaction system is necessary.

With the selection of these reactions and the availability of the thermodynamic data, a complete equilibrium calculation can be made for a given system.   A minimum number of chemical equations are written to include all the reaction products.   For gas-phase reactions it is convenient to express equilibrium concentrations as partial pressures.   The equilibrium conditions then include the equilibrium equations for these reactions, the sum of the partial pressures of all components to equal the total pressure, and the stoichiometric considerations which depend upon the composition of the feed.   The number of equilibrium conditions must equal the number of species present.

Stoichiometric requirements demand that the atomic ratio of elements in the feed be maintained in the equilibrated species.   By multiplying the partial pressure of a component by the number of atoms of a given element in its formula and summing these quantities for all the components of a mixture, a measure of the number of atoms of the given element is obtained. The ratio of these summations for several elements is the atomic ratio of these elements in the mixture. For example, the C/H ratio in a gaseous mixture of ethylene, ethane, and hydrogen would be

$$\text{C/H ratio} = \frac{2P_{C_2H_4} + 2P_{C_2H_6}}{4P_{C_2H_4} + 6P_{C_2H_6} + 2P_{H_2}}$$

If the feed for a reaction were two moles of hydrogen to one mole of ethylene, the above quantity would equal $\frac{1}{4}$, the C/H ratio in this feed. The presence of a third element, i.e., sulfur, imposes an additional stoichiometric condition involving the C/S or H/S ratio.

In the present section, four examples are given of the application of thermodynamic methods and data to petroleum processes. These examples have been selected primarily to illustrate methods of solution and secondarily to deal with problems of current interest.

Alkylation of Isobutane with Ethylene. The alkylation of isobutane with ethylene to produce neohexane is important as a process of manufacturing a high-octane aviation motor fuel blending agent intermediate in volatility between isopentane and isooctane.

For simplicity, we shall consider the reaction system with all constituents as gases.

$$i\text{-}C_4H_{10} + C_2H_4 \rightarrow \text{neo-}C_6H_{14}$$

The equilibrium conditions for an equal molar mixture, or feed, of isobutane and ethylene are

$$\frac{P_{C_6H_{14}}}{P_{C_4H_{10}}P_{C_2H_4}} = K_P$$

$$P_{C_4H_{10}} + P_{C_2H_4} + P_{C_6H_{14}} = P$$

$$\frac{4P_{C_4H_{10}} + 2P_{C_2H_4} + 6P_{C_6H_{14}}}{10P_{C_4H_{10}} + 4P_{C_2H_4} + 14P_{C_6H_{14}}} = \text{C/H ratio} = \frac{6}{14}$$

the latter equation reducing to

$$P_{C_4H_{10}} = P_{C_2H_4}$$

These equilibrium conditions can be reduced to the single equation

$$K_P P_{C_6H_{14}}^2 - (2PK_P + 4)P_{C_6H_{14}} + K_P P^2 = 0$$

which may be solved by the quadratic formula. The mole fraction of neohexane in the equilibrated mixture is obtained by dividing the partial pressure of neohexane by the total pressure P.

In this example we shall calculate the equilibrium for total pressures of 1, 10, and 100 atm and include effects of gas imperfection. From Rossini's tabulated data, we may obtain values for log Kf, the equilibrium constant of formation, for each component of the reaction. These may be combined in the manner required for thermodynamic quantities [see Eqs. (X-1) and (X-5)] and the antilogarithm taken to yield the equilibrium constant for the reaction. With the use of Eq. (X-22)

$$K_P = \frac{K}{K_\gamma}$$

K_P can be calculated. Values of K_γ were obtained from Newton's[1] graphs, using recent critical data from the literature (data for diisopropyl being used in the absence of data for neohexane). Table X-2 gives values of K, K_γ, and K_P for the temperature range considered.

TABLE X-2

Temperature, °K	K	K_γ			K_P		
		1 atm	10 atm	100 atm	1 atm	10 atm	100 atm
300	7.87×10^9	0.96	0.41	....	8.20×10^9	1.92×10^{10}	
400	2.43×10^5	0.98	0.88	....	2.48×10^5	2.76×10^5	
500	5.00×10^3	1.00	0.95	0.50	5.00×10^3	5.26×10^3	1.00×10^4
600	8.39	1.00	0.96	0.72	8.39	8.74	11.50
700	4.49×10^{-1}	1.00	0.98	0.84	4.49×10^{-1}	4.68×10^{-1}	5.35×10^{-1}
800	5.40×10^{-2}	1.00	0.99	0.90	5.40×10^{-2}	5.45×10^{-2}	6.00×10^{-2}
900	1.06×10^{-2}	1.00	1.00	0.90	1.06×10^{-2}	1.06×10^{-2}	1.18×10^{-2}
1000	2.77×10^{-3}	1.00	1.00	0.91	2.77×10^{-3}	2.77×10^{-2}	3.04×10^{-2}

The results of the equilibrium calculation obtained by substituting values of total pressure P and K_P in the quadratic equation are shown graphically in Fig. X-1. They indicate a marked effect of temperature and pressure upon the equilibrium conversion. The large effect of temperature upon the equilibrium necessitated calculations at several intermediate temperatures. Values of K_γ for these intermediate temperatures were obtained by graphical interpolation. A log K versus $1/T$ plot was used to interpolate values of K.

Aromatization of Paraffins and Naphthenes. The catalytic dehydrogenation of naphthenes and cyclization-dehydrogenation of paraffins to form aromatics are important reactions involved in reforming. Typical operating conditions are a 4:1 mole ratio of hydrogen to hydrocarbon, 500 psig (35.0 atm) and 500°C.

Considering the aromatization of cyclohexane to benzene

$$C_6H_{12} \rightleftharpoons C_6H_6 + 3H_2$$

[1] Newton, *Ind. Eng. Chem.*, **27**:302 (1935).

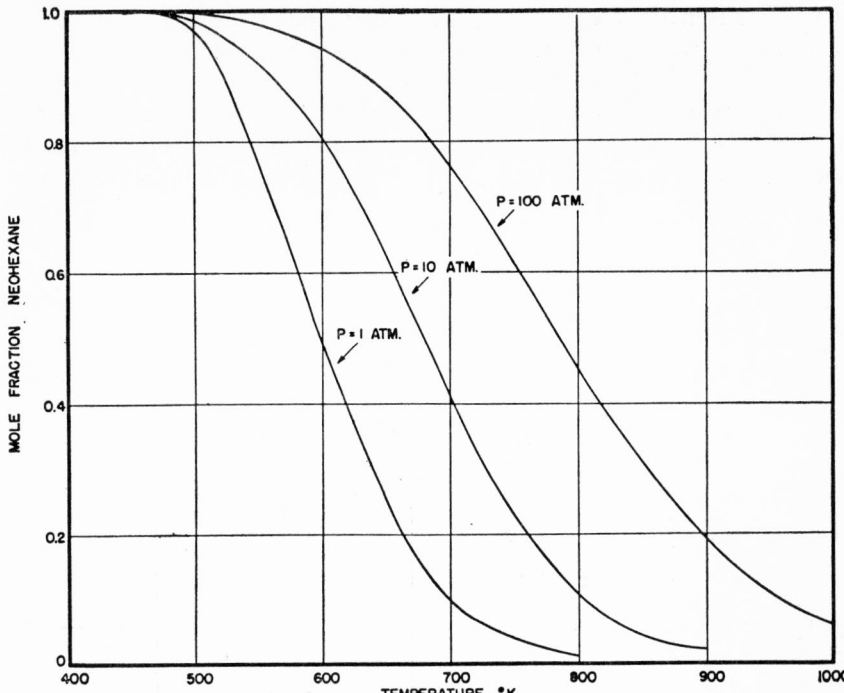

FIG. X-1. Equilibrium mole fraction of neohexane from an equimolar feed of isobutane and ethylene.

the C/H ratio is $\frac{3}{10}$ for a feed ratio of four moles of hydrogen to one mole of cyclohexane. The equilibrium conditions are

$$\frac{P_{C_6H_6}P_{H_2}^{3}}{P_{C_6H_{12}}} = K_P$$

$$P_{C_6H_{12}} + P_{C_6H_6} + P_{H_2} = P = 35.0$$

$$\frac{6P_{C_6H_{12}} + 6P_{C_6H_6}}{12P_{C_6H_{12}} + 6P_{C_6H_6} + 2P_{H_2}} = \frac{3}{10}$$

the latter equation reducing to

$$4P_{C_6H_{12}} + 7P_{C_6H_6} = P_{H_2}$$

These equilibrium conditions can be further reduced to

$$3P_{C_6H_{12}} = 7P - 8P_{H_2}$$
$$3P_{C_6H_6} = 5P_{H_2} - 4P$$
$$\frac{(5P_{H_2} - 4P)P_{H_2}^{3}}{7P - 8P_{H_2}} = K_P$$

A convenient method of solution is to assume a value for P_{H_2} and solve for K_P.   From a plot of log K against $1/T$ the temperature is determined. Values of P_{H_2} to be considered range from 28 atm ($\frac{4}{5}P$) for zero conversion to 30.625 ($\frac{7}{8}P$) for complete conversion.

Values of K were obtained from Rossini's tabulation and, since the gases were considered ideal, K_p was taken equal to K.   Figure X-2 shows the results of such calculation in terms of the equilibrium yield of benzene

$$\text{Equilibrium yield} = \frac{P_{C_6H_6}}{P_{C_6H_{12}} + P_{C_6H_6}}$$

The figure also gives the equilibrium yield of benzene from *n*-hexane for the same operating conditions (4:1 mole ratio of hydrogen to hydrocarbon and 500 psig).   For comparison there are included equilibrium yields of benzene expected from these hydrocarbons at one atmosphere pressure and no hydrogen in the feed.

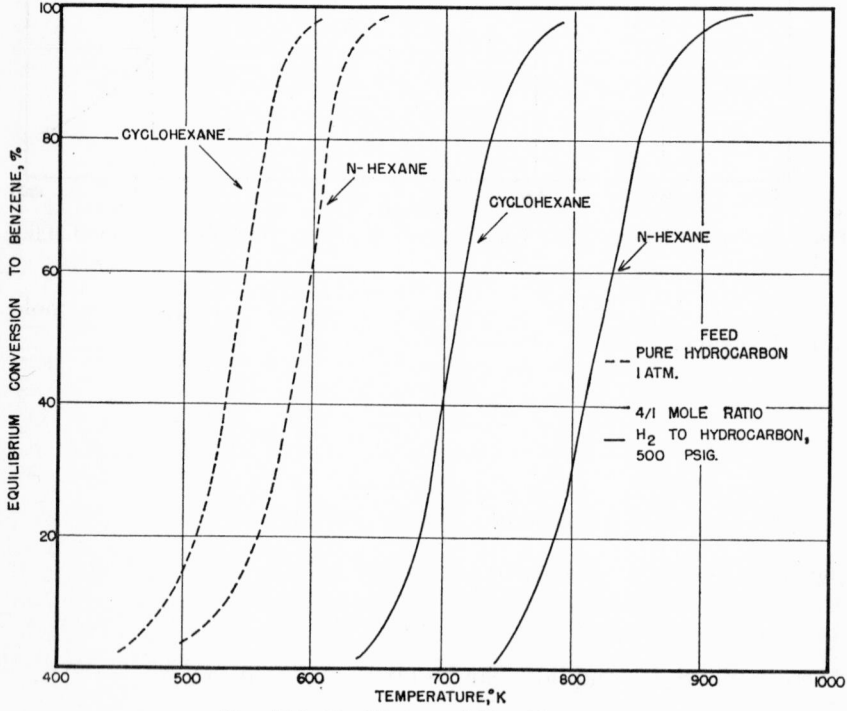

Fig. X-2. Equilibrium yields of benzene.

Reforming reactions are carried out with high hydrogen partial pressures to suppress cracking and coke formation.   Figure X-2 indicates the necessity of a high operating temperature to counteract the equilibrium suppression effected by the high hydrogen pressure.

Isomerization of n-Butane.   The third example deals with the experimental method of determining $\Delta F°$ and $\Delta H°$ directly from measured equilibrium concentrations.   Cases of true equilibrium among the hydrocarbons are rather rare, but in the field of isomerization a number of examples have been found, among which may be mentioned n-butane $\rightleftharpoons$ isobutane and cyclohexane $\rightleftharpoons$ methylcyclopentane.   The former reaction is considered in view of its importance in supplying charge stock for the process of alkylation.

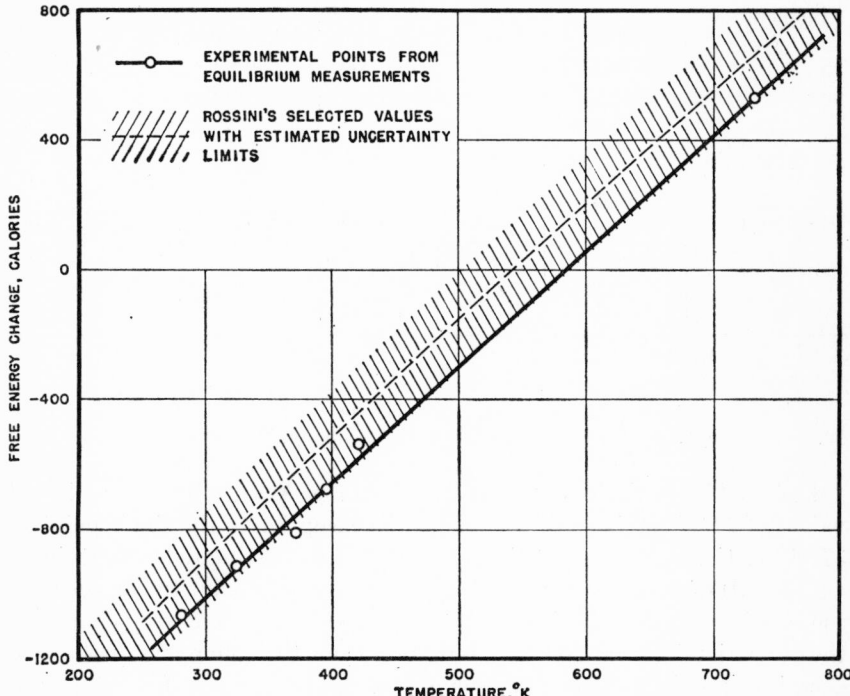

FIG. X-3. Free energy change for butane isomerization.

Unpublished results[1] give values (Table X-3) for the equilibrium concentration of isobutane, obtained at various temperatures in the aluminum halide-catalyzed butane isomerization at atmospheric pressure

$$n\text{-Butane }(g) \rightleftharpoons \text{isobutane }(g)$$

In the third and fourth columns of Table X-3 are given the equilibrium constants and free energy changes calculated from the experimental results.   Figure X-3 shows a plot of $\Delta F°$ vs. T.

The linear curve through the data was calculated by the method of

[1] Obtained by W. A. Horne, Gulf Research & Development Company.

least squares and is defined by

$$\Delta F°(\text{cal}) = -2088 + 3.57T$$

The average values of $\Delta H°$ and $\Delta S°$ over the experimental temperature range are the constants in the above equation, -2088 cal and -3.57 cal per deg, respectively.

TABLE X-3

Temperature, °K	Experimental equilibrium data			Rossini's selected values*	
	Per cent isobutane equilibrium	K	$\Delta F°$, cal	Per cent isobutane† equilibrium	$\Delta F°$, cal
283.1	87.0	6.692	−1069	84.4	−951 ± 150
303.4	84.0	5.250	−1000	81.1	−877 ± 150
325.1	80.5	4.128	− 916	77.4	−795 ± 150
372.1	75.0	3.000	− 812	69.8	−620 ± 150
396.1	70.3	2.367	− 678	66.3	−534 ± 150
423.1	65.5	1.899	− 539	62.8	−441 ± 150
733‡	41‡	0.695	+ 530	38.9	+670 ± 150

* Interpolated from tabulated data.
† Calculated, assuming gas ideality.
‡ Obtained with a platinum catalyst at 500 psig, private communication from W. C. Starnes, Gulf Research & Development Company.

Included in Table X-3 (column 5) and in Fig. X-3 are Rossini's selected values of $\Delta F°$ for this reaction. With the exception of the single point at 372.1°K, the experimental data are within the estimated uncertainty[1] (± 150 cal) of these values. It is of interest at this point to consider the source of uncertainty in these selected values. The free energy change of the isomerization reaction is determined from the difference in the free energies of formation of the isomers. Free energies of formation are obtained, as outlined in the first section, from a combination of heats of combustion with free energy and heat content functions. However, for the purpose of this illustration the free energy change will be determined by the relationship

$$\Delta F° = \Delta H° - T \Delta S°$$

where $\Delta H°$ is the difference in the heats of combustion and $\Delta S°$ is the difference in the entropies of the isomers. This alternative method is

[1] On a temperature rather than free energy basis, this uncertainty is equivalent to about 35°C. By way of contrast the same uncertainty in $\Delta F°$ for the aromatization of cyclohexane (previous example) is equivalent to only 2°C. Thus, calculations of isomerization equilibria, by virtue of the low-temperature dependence of the reaction, are quite sensitive to small variations in $\Delta F°$.

identical with the method outlined because of the interrelationship of the thermodynamic quantities [see Eq. (X-6)]. From Rossini's selected values, the difference in the heats of combustion, at 298°K, is

$$\Delta H_{298}{}^\circ = 685,650 - 687,650 = -2000 \text{ cal}$$

and the entropy change

$$\Delta S_{298}{}^\circ = 70.42 - 74.12 = -3.70 \text{ cal per deg}$$

The discrepancies between these values and those obtained from equilibrium measurements are 88 cal in ΔH° and 0.13 cal per deg in ΔS°. However, the discrepancy in ΔH° is only 0.01 per cent of either heat of combustion and in ΔS° only 0.2 per cent of either entropy. The subtraction of large numbers to yield small numbers, which is especially true in isomerization calculations, emphasizes the need of accurate thermodynamic data.

Dehydrogenation of n-Butane. A final example deals with the equilibria involved in the catalytic dehydrogenation of *n*-butane to produce 1-butene and 1,3-butadiene. These reactions have become important as providing a method of augmenting the supply of olefins for polymerization and alkylation as well as of securing the raw material for synthetic rubber manufacture.

The reactions to be considered are

$$\underset{n\text{-Butane}}{C_4H_{10}} \rightleftharpoons \underset{1\text{-Butene}}{C_4H_8} + H_2$$

$$\underset{1\text{-Butene}}{C_4H_8} \rightleftharpoons \underset{1,3\text{-Butadiene}}{C_4H_6} + H_2$$

For a feed of pure *n*-butane the C/H ratio is $4/10$. The equilibrium conditions are

$$\frac{P_{C_4H_8} P_{H_2}}{P_{C_4H_{10}}} = K_1$$

$$\frac{P_{C_4H_6} P_{H_2}}{P_{C_4H_8}} = K_2$$

$$P_{C_4H_{10}} + P_{C_4H_8} + P_{C_4H_6} + P_{H_2} = P$$

$$\frac{4P_{C_4H_{10}} + 4P_{C_4H_8} + 4P_{C_4H_6}}{10P_{C_4H_{10}} + 8P_{C_4H_8} + 6P_{C_4H_6} + 2P_{H_2}} = \frac{4}{10}$$

the latter equation reducing to

$$P_{C_4H_8} + 2P_{C_4H_6} = P_{H_2}$$

By algebraic manipulation these equilibrium conditions can be simplified to yield

$$P_{C_4H_6} = \frac{K_2 x}{x + 2K_2} \qquad P_{C_4H_8} = \frac{x^2}{x + 2K_2}$$

$$P_{C_4H_{10}} = \frac{x^3}{K_1(x + 2K_2)}$$

$$x^3 + 2K_1x^2 + x(3K_1K_2 - K_1P) - 2PK_1K_2 = 0$$

where x is P_{H_2}. The cubic equation is most conveniently solved by assuming values of x and solving for the total pressure P. By trial and error, or interpolation, values of P_{H_2} are determined to yield the desired total pressure. The equilibrium partial pressures of the hydrocarbons are then obtained by substitution in the other equations.

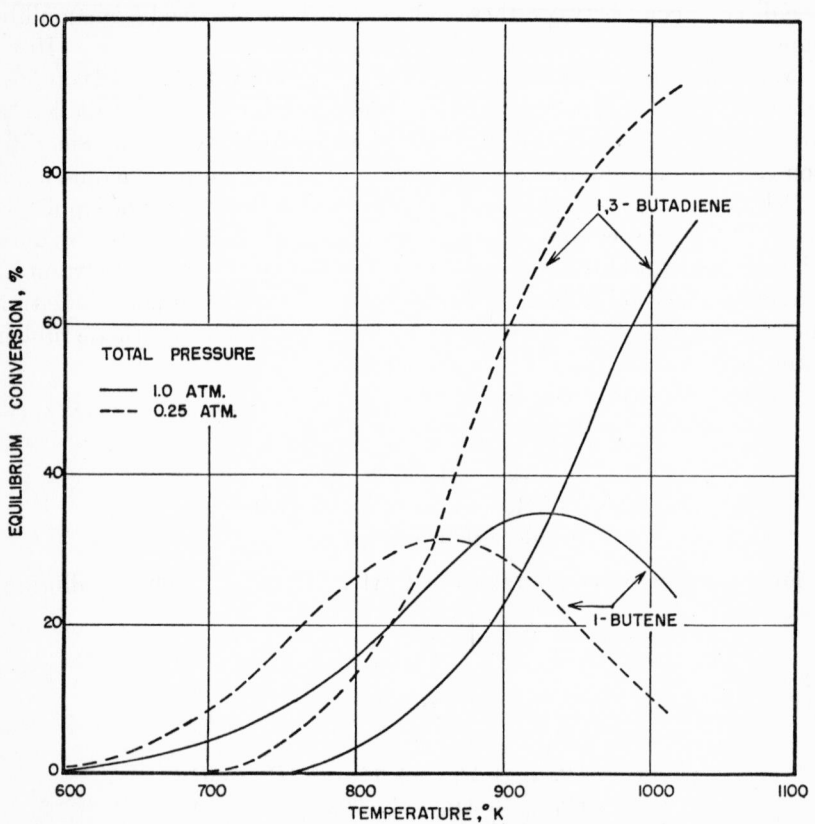

FIG. X-4. Equilibrium conversions of n-butane to 1-butene and 1,3-butadiene.

The results of such a calculation for a total pressure of 1 atm are given in Table X-4. Rossini's values of the equilibrium constants were taken, assuming gas ideality.

The equilibrium conversion of butane to the olefin and diolefin can be obtained by normalizing these results on a hydrogen-free basis. These conversions are shown graphically in Fig. X-4 along with results of a similar calculation for a total pressure of 0.25 atm.

TABLE X-4

Temperature, °K	P_{H_2}, atm	$P_{C_4H_{10}}$, atm	$P_{C_4H_8}$, atm	$P_{C_4H_6}$, atm
600	0.0064₆	0.9871	0.0062	0.0001
700	0.0474	0.9083	0.0413	0.0030
800	0.1874	0.6536	0.1292	0.0291
900	0.4428	0.2420	0.1878	0.1275
1000	0.6097	0.0318	0.1072	0.2513

It is apparent that operation at reduced pressure, achieved with the use of an inert diluent gas, has the effect of lowering the reaction temperature requirements. Selective production of 1-butene can be only achieved under equilibrium conditions at a sacrifice of yield.

CHAPTER XI

Gasoline and Other Motor Fuels

Low-boiling petroleum fractions constitute the great bulk of the world's motor fuel and they will probably do so as long as an adequate supply is available. The demands of the early gasoline engines were not exacting; design was such as to utilize distillates boiling up to 200 to 220°C, and the most difficult problems were those of starting and steady operation. With the improvement of the engine, other qualities, such as antiknock value, chemical stability, and controlled volatility, have become important. The development of fuels and engines has been mutually interdependent, but it appears that fuels have been shaped to meet the demands of engine builders. If a long-extended fuel scarcity should occur, the situation would presumably change.

Petroleum fractions used as motor fuels vary from liquefied petroleum gases (usually propane and butane) through conventional gasoline to kerosene and the light gas oil suitable for turbojet units and automotive-type diesels. One variety of jet fuel covers the entire range of gasoline and kerosene together.

COMPOSITION, MANUFACTURE, AND USE OF GASOLINE

As indicated, gasoline is usually a blend of the hydrocarbons boiling within the range 40 to 200°C (100 to 400°F) which occur naturally in petroleum and natural gas, together with the similar hydrocarbons made by cracking heavy oils thermally or catalytically. For the uncracked (straight-run) and lightly cracked materials, the composition is influenced by the nature of the crude oil from which the gasoline is obtained. Thus gasoline from Pennsylvania, Michigan, and Mexican crudes is somewhat paraffinic in make-up; that from Gulf Coastal and some Russian crudes is high in naphthenes; and that from selected crudes of California or Borneo is quite aromatic. Only when cracking temperature is made relatively high or when catalytic cracking and reforming are employed does the composition of the product become somewhat independent of the high-

424

boiling stock subjected to cracking. Because of the large number of possible hydrocarbons occurring in the several classes and within the range C_4 to C_{12}, gasoline is potentially a very complex mixture. Thus there are 661 possible paraffins and 3,839 olefins within these limits.[1] To these must be added the possible aromatic and naphthenic hydrocarbons; the former are few, say 10 to 15, but the latter are potentially numerous, say 800 or more. Just how many of these are really present in any one gasoline is impossible to say, but considerations of stability indicate that the number present in quantity is probably quite small in comparison.

The most comprehensive and reliable determination of the hydrocarbons actually present in a straight-run gasoline is that by American Petroleum Institute Project 6. The results are summarized earlier in this volume.[2] A few predominant type hydrocarbons are present in large amount and most of the possible ones in very small proportions. This concept should not, however, minimize the possible complexity of commercial gasolines, which are mixtures derived from various crudes and from cracking operations. In addition, gasolines in the raw state contain small proportions of organic sulfur compounds, along with, in many cases, traces of oxygen and nitrogen compounds. The latter pretty well disappear in refining but removal of the sulfur compounds is usually not complete.

The hydrocarbon types found in gasolines from various manufacturing processes are illustrated in Fig. XI-1.

The making of gasoline depends basically on separating the usable fractions by careful fractional distillation.[3] The problems of isolating a suitable gasoline fraction are essentially the same for cracked oils and virgin crudes (straight-run products). Modern fractionating equipment will deliver a gasoline "cut" to specifications at both the low-boiling and high-boiling ends. Blending with more or less volatile products to control the volatility at intermediate points on the distillation curve is customary.

Chemical treating of gasoline fractions is applied when required, but is by no means universal. Properties requiring adjustment are:

Total sulfur	Gum content
Corrosive sulfur	Color and color stability

Straight-run gasolines are usually only alkali-washed or sweetened to control odor and sulfur content (see Chap. VII); run-of-plant cracked gasolines are in addition protected against gum formation by use of oxidation inhibitors; this is advantageously done at a very early stage, before oxidation can occur. The amount of chemical treating or chemical

---

[1] Henze and Blair, Paraffins, *J. ACS*, **53**:3077 (1931). *Ibid.*, Olefins, **55**:680 (1933).
[2] See Chap. II.
[3] See Chap. VI.

protection required has been minimized by clay contact polymerization of unstable diolefins or cyclic olefins present in thermally cracked stocks (Chap. VIII). The method has been used extensively, but is disappearing with thermal cracking. Catalytically cracked gasolines are alkali-washed to remove thiophenols.

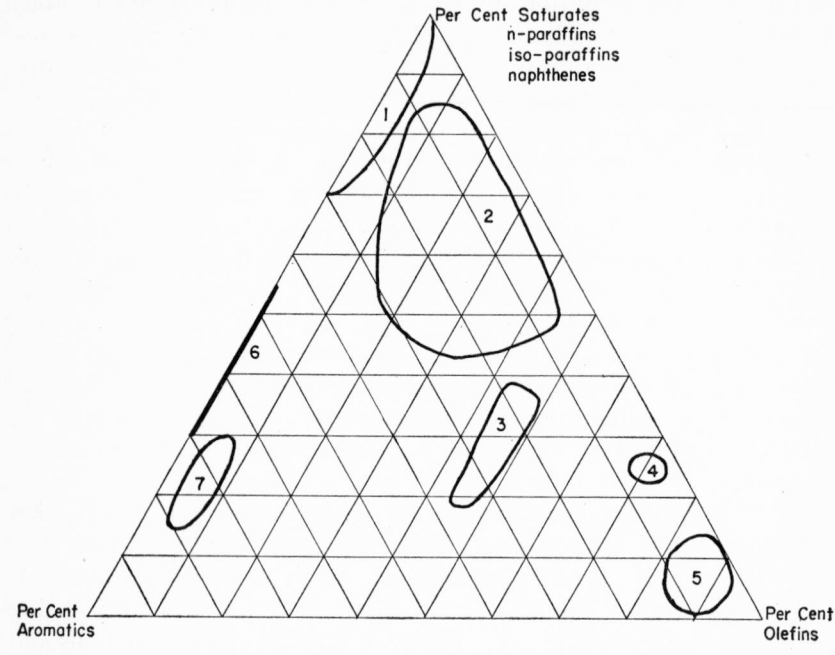

FIG. XI-1. Approximate compositions of gasolines (weight per cent) of various types. (1) Straight-run gasoline. (2) Thermally and catalytically cracked gasolines. (3) Vapor-phase, high-temperature cracked gasoline. (4) Catalytic polymers. (5) Fischer-Tropsch gasoline. (6) Catalytic reformate. (7) Thermal reformate of catalytic reformate. Modification of chart originally devised by Nelson, *Oil Gas J.*, **47**(34):78 (1948); **54**(37):127 (1956). Additional data from Heinemann, Maerker, Walser, and Kirsch, *Petrol. Processing*, **10**:1571 (1955). Noll, Schall, Craig, and Stevenson, *Oil Gas J.*, **53**(47):102 (1955).

Sulfuric acid treating of cracked gasolines was at one time universal. This method of refining, properly applied, exerts a favorable effect on all the above properties; however, it also causes a loss to acid sludge and to high-boiling polymer, necessitating redistillation. There is also some reduction in octane number. Acid treating is now employed, if at all, only for higher-boiling naphthas of undesirably high sulfur content or otherwise unstable. A fairly heavy treatment—10 to 15 lb per bbl—was customary, or alternatively the so-called "cold process" was employed.[1]

---

[1] Halloran, *World Petrol. Congr., Proc. 1st Congr. (London)*, **2**:3 (1933). Stratford, Graves, and Brown, *Refiner Nat. Gasoline Mfr.*, **17**(3):109 (1938).

Here the treating occurs at about 50°F and the acid functions chiefly as a differential solvent; desulfurization and necessary refining are effected with only moderate loss of yield to side reactions.

Use of dyed gasolines has rendered color improvement of little importance. Color stability of a gross kind is usually difficult to attain only when trouble in sweetening has been encountered; this instability seems to be associated with presence of polysulfides.

VOLATILITY OF GASOLINE

Although it is usually taken for granted, the property of most importance for a gasoline is its volatility under the conditions of use; an explosive and completely combustible mixture of fuel and air must be produced in the combustion chamber. The carburetor aspirates gasoline in the form of a spray into the stream of air drawn into the motor by action of the pistons; in principle, the spray vaporizes to give a dry mixture of air and fuel vapor. In practice, the process is incomplete and a substantial proportion of liquid is carried through the intake manifold and into the cylinder as droplets or as a moving film along the manifold wall. The degree of vaporization can be improved (assuming the atomizing to be constant) by increasing time of contact with the air, by raising the temperature of the mixture,[1] or by using a more volatile fuel. The first is limited by the engine design and operations, the second by an increasing loss in volumetric efficiency, and the third by economic considerations. Nevertheless, the trend has for some years been toward more volatile gasolines.

XI-1. Air-Fuel Mixtures and Combustion. A simple carburetor functions to supply a gasoline vapor-air mixture falling within explosive limits. These are, roughly, by weight

Rich		Lean	
Air	Gasoline	Air	Gasoline
6	1	20	1

Assuming a gasoline to have an average molecular weight corresponding to that of octane, 114, a theoretical air-fuel ratio, for complete burning, of 15.1:1 can be calculated. Most engines, however, give greater power and more flexible performance on a slightly rich mixture; in general, about

[1] See Mock and Chandler, *J. SAE*, **11**:474 (1922), and Mock, *Trans. SAE*, **39**:257 (1936), on various ways of raising the temperature of fuel-air mixtures and the effects noted.

14.5:1 gives greatest economy (maximum carbon dioxide), while 12.5:1, an excess of, say, 20 per cent of fuel over the theoretical, is best for power. As power output has been improved, however, good performance with lean mixtures has become more possible.[1] This shift to lean mixture operation is limited by the fact that such compositions burn slowly and may injure exhaust valves.

Figure XI-2 shows the general relations, air-fuel ratio against power and thermal efficiency and air-fuel ratio against exhaust gas composition,

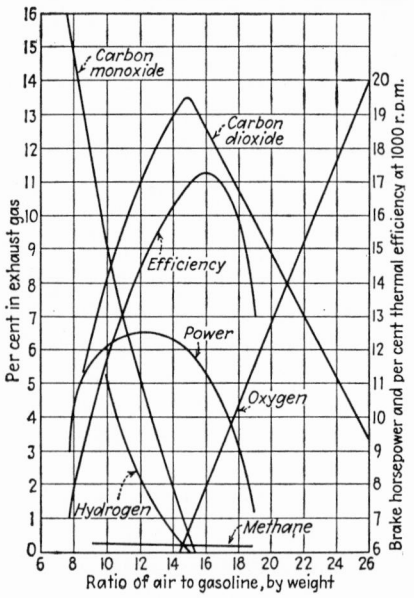

Fig. XI-2. Variation of power, efficiency, and exhaust-gas analysis with air-fuel ratio. Graf and Gleeson, *Ore. State Agr. Coll. Eng. Expt. Sta. Circ. Ser.* 2, 1930. D'Alleva and Lovell, *J.A.S.E.*, **38**:90 (1936).

which includes oxygen, carbon monoxide, and carbon dioxide, as well as the unburned hydrogen and methane; the last probably represents all unburned hydrocarbons. The carbon dioxide concentration reaches a maximum of approximately 13.8 per cent for best economy, although theory requires 14.7 per cent.[2] This is because, in practice, only 94 to 94.5 per cent conversion of the fuel to water and carbon dioxide occurs. Remaining unburned hydrocarbon material appears in the exhaust gases.[3] Nitrogen oxide, formed by nitrogen fixation during combustion, is also

[1] Lovell, Campbell, D'Alleva, and Winter, *Trans. SAE*, **48**:160 (1941).

[2] D'Alleva and Lovell, *J. SAE*, **38**:90 (1936).

[3] Wentworth and Daniel, Preprint, SAE Annual Meeting, Detroit, January, 1955. Rounds, Bennett, and Nebel, Preprint, SAE Annual Meeting, Detroit, January, 1955.

present in small amounts in the exhaust gas.[1] The rest of the combustible material may be accounted for by a reaction of carbon monoxide with water, probably taking place in accordance with the following equilibrium

$$CO + H_2O \rightleftharpoons CO_2 + H_2$$

While reliable information is not available, it is believed that a modern carburetor will deliver a mixture which is more than half vapor. The residue moves as a spray, or as a liquid film on the manifold walls, where exhaust heat is applied to help vaporize it. Information is not available on the extent to which the mixture under compression in the cylinder is vapor or fog. The nonhomogeneous character of the air-fuel charge in the manifold is responsible for uneven distribution to the engine cylinders. This is especially important in fuels containing tetraethyllead which is relatively high boiling (200°C). As a result, some cylinders may receive more of the antiknock agent than intended and others less; this effect is not larger, however. It has been shown that better distribution prevails at part throttle than with wide-open operation.[2]

XI-2. Distillation and Dew-point Relations. Other conditions being constant, the performance of a motor fuel depends on its "effective" volatility. This can be deduced from its gross volatility,[3] which may be determined from the assay distillation curve.[4] Because a spread in volatility is desired, the boiling range is quite wide, generally in the range from 90 to 420°F (32 to 210°C). The ASTM distillation curve of a typical motor gasoline distributed in the United States is shown in Fig. XI-3. Such curves give the relation between the distillation temperature and the percentage of the gasoline distilled.[5] The figure also gives approximate location of the sections of the curve which control the properties of the gasoline involved in its performance, and the dependence of these properties on the shape of the curve.[6] For the prevention of

---

[1] Hanson and Egerton, *Proc. Roy. Soc. (London)*, **A163**:90 (1937). Spindt, Wolfe, and Stevens, *Trans. SAE*, **64**:797 (1956).

[2] Campbell, Lovell, and Boyd, *Trans. SAE*, **40**:144 (1937). Bartholomew, Chalk, and Brewster, *Trans. SAE*, **42**:141 (1938). Sabina, *Trans. SAE*, **43**:416 (1938). Lovell, Campbell, D'Alleva, and Winter, *loc. cit.*

[3] For effect of fuel volatility on octane number, see Nelson, *Oil Gas J.*, **50**(35):86 (1952). Fleming, Hakala, Moody, Scott, and Tongberg, *Oil Gas J.*, **53**(43):100 (1955).

[4] ASTM Methods D 86 and D 216.

[5] Which may be the percentage evaporated or percentage condensed. The difference is sometimes significant.

[6] J. E. Taylor, Gulf Research & Development Co., private communication. For other charts interpreting the significance of the ASTM distillation curve see Wilson, *J. SAE*, **27**:33 (1930), and Blair and Alden, *Ind. Eng. Chem.*, **25**:559 (1933).

carburetor icing, for example, the midrange section of the curve should be high, but on the other hand quick engine warm-up and acceleration are favored by a low midrange. The need for compromises to secure over-all performance is evident.

The use of the distillation curve as a means of measuring the effective volatility of a gasoline has its limitations because the conditions of vaporization in a distilling flask are widely different from those in the carburetor. In the former, the fractional character of the vaporization is emphasized, each portion of the vapor being in approximate equilibrium

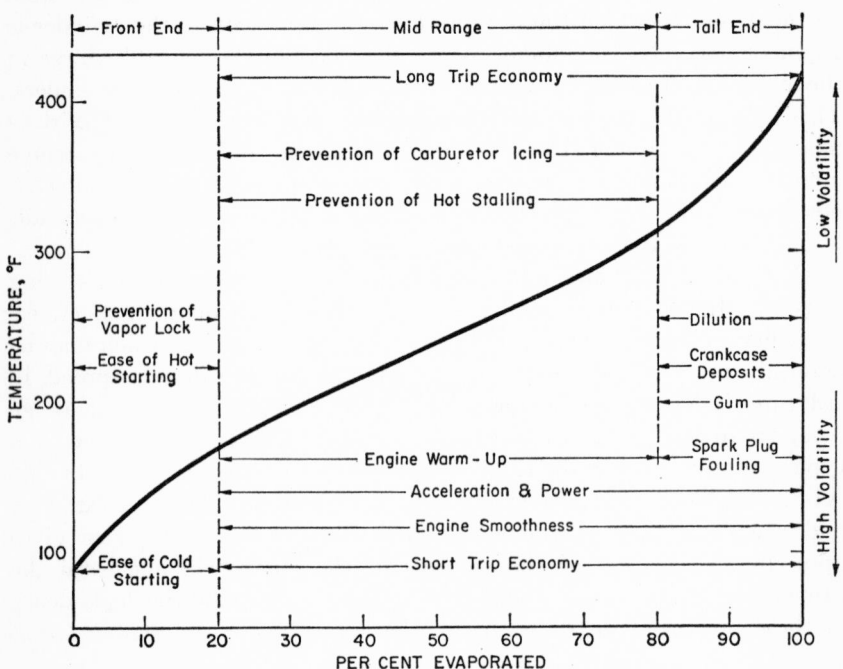

Fig. XI-3. Typical ASTM gasoline distillation curve and significances attached to various portions of the curve.

with the liquid remaining at that point in the distillation. With an ideally made air-fuel mixture, however, the last portion to vaporize or the first to condense is more or less in equilibrium with the whole fuel. Although the mixtures supplied by many carburetors are wet, owing to incomplete vaporization, it is probable that, because of the speed with which fresh gasoline is supplied, the liquid consists of droplets of practically complete gasoline, so that even a wet mixture is in equilibrium with the complete fuel rather than with a partially vaporized one. From this it follows that the best measure of the total effective volatility of a gasoline in the presence of an appropriate amount of air is the dew point,[1] the temperature of initial condensation observed on cooling a completely dry air-fuel mixture.[2] The dew points of conventional gasolines, in air-fuel mixtures in the order of 15:1, lie in the range of 50 to 140°F. Although the dew point is of fundamental significance, it does not vary enough for the ordinary grades of motor fuel to make its determination of daily importance.

The use of superchargers would increase the importance of dew points as a factor in carburetion. No data on the precipitation of liquid from gasoline-air mixtures under superatmospheric pressure have been reported. By utilizing the vapor-pressure data for *n*-octane (an average motor-gasoline hydrocarbon) and making the broad assumption that the difference between the dew point of an air-gasoline mixture and a corresponding air-octane mixture is independent of pressure, some estimation of probable dew-point temperatures can be made. The following figures are to be considered only as approximations, applying to a gasoline having a 90 per cent ASTM temperature of 336°F and an end point of 394°F.

Absolute pressure, lb	Dew point, °F, air-gasoline mixture		
	11.0:1.0	13.0:1.0	15.0:1.0
14.7	111	106	101
22.7	126	120	116
29.7	136	129	125
34.7	142	136	131

XI-3. Equilibrium Distillation. Another means of measuring effective volatility is that of equilibrium distillation.[3] Gasoline is slowly fed through a miniature pipe still, held at a constant temperature. The unvaporized residue obtained at each of a series of temperatures is collected and the volume plotted against the temperature of the operation. The curves obtained are much narrower than that of an ASTM distillation; they are practically linear, and for a number of gasolines tried, the range from zero volatility to complete evaporation was 160 to 320°F.

A profitable modification of the procedure is that adopted by Sligh,[4]

---

[1] Wilson and Barnard, *Ind. Eng. Chem.*, **13**:906 (1921); **17**:428 (1925).

[2] For methods of determining dew points, see Gruse, *Ind. Eng. Chem.*, **15**:796 (1923). Stevenson and Babor, *Ind. Eng. Chem.*, **19**:1361 (1927). Stevenson and Stark, *Ind. Eng. Chem.*, **17**:679 (1925). Hixon and White, *Ind. Eng. Chem., Anal. Ed.*, **10**:235 (1938). Kennedy, *Natl. Bur. Standards Sci. Papers*, **20**:500 (1925).

[3] James, *J. SAE*, **18**:501 (1926).

[4] *J. SAE*, **19**:151 (1926).

who performed the equilibrium distillation in the presence of an amount of air corresponding to some definite air-to-fuel ratio. Such an operation more closely represents conditions existing in the intake manifold. Air-fuel mixtures varying from 3:1 to 20:1 parts by weight were studied; the data collected by examining a representative commercial gasoline are shown graphically in Fig. XI-4.

Each curve shows the proportion of fuel evaporated at different temperatures from some one designated air-fuel mixture. The temperature at 100 per cent vaporization is the dew point for that particular mixture; if one were dealing with a pure compound, this would be its boiling point at its partial pressure in the mixture. The two dashed lines represent the loci of points showing where 8:1 and 20:1 air-vapor mixtures,

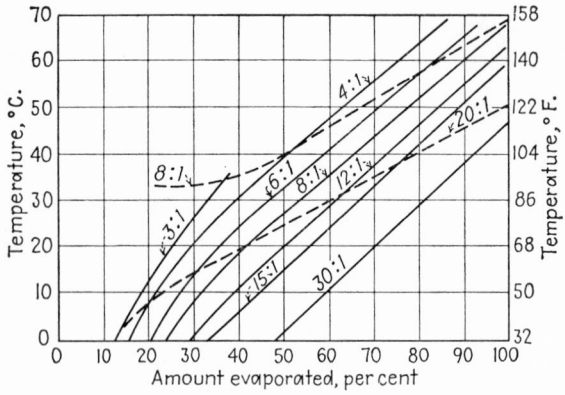

FIG. XI-4. Evaporation data for various air-fuel ratios. [*From Sligh, J. SAE,* **19**:151 (1926)].

respectively, are furnished on partial evaporation of the fuel from the various air-liquid mixtures supplied. These represent the practical limits of explosibility in the engine; thus an air-liquid mixture of 30:1 could not be used in the engine, for under no condition does it furnish an air-vapor mixture of 20:1 or less.

When an engine is cold, the proportion of fuel evaporated from the mixture drawn in during the first few revolutions is small. Excess liquid fuel must be supplied by the use of the choke valve, so that the actual vapor-air mixture formed will be rich enough to explode. Because the manifold operates under a variable vacuum, it is necessary to know the extent of vaporization of the fuel in these mixtures under the various reduced pressures which may prevail. The volume of a given weight of air, at constant temperature, is inversely proportional to the pressure, and an air-fuel mixture of 3:1 supplied at ½ atm vaporizes into a volume of air equivalent to that which would be occupied at 1 atm by the air in a 6:1 mixture. Thus, at ½ atm, the 3:1 curve shifts to the right and may be superimposed on the 6:1 curve.   From these relations, the proper air-fuel supply for "choking" and acceleration may be more logically defined.[1]

XI-4. Empirical Relationships between Assay Distillation Curve and Fundamental Properties.   The conventional ASTM distillation[2] of a gasoline is well standardized, universally employed, and easy to perform. Valuable contributions have been made[3] in setting up empirical relations between fundamental vapor-pressure properties of the fuel and the ASTM curve; these are often surprisingly close.   Comparisons of the dew points of a large number of gasolines (both those determined directly and those deduced from air distillation measurements) showed them to bear a direct relation to the 90 per cent evaporated temperature (corrected for uncondensed vapors) on the ASTM curves.   This relationship is expressed by the following factors:[4]

Ratio of the 90 *per cent ASTM temperature to dew-point temperatures, degrees absolute*

Whole fuel......................	1.084
8:1 mixture....................	1.375
12:1 mixture...................	1.400
16:1 mixture...................	1.422
20:1 mixture...................	1.446

It has also been reported that the temperature of initial boiling of the fuel in the ASTM distillation corresponds approximately to that of the vapor at the 10 per cent distillation point, and that this in turn is equal to the bubble point as determined by direct measurement.[5]   The normal bubble point is the temperature at which bubbles will start to form in a gas-free gasoline at atmospheric pressure.   Here, a small portion of the vapor is in equilibrium with the liquid fuel, while in case of the dew point, a small portion of the liquid is in equilibrium with the vaporized fuel. The bubble point is important in evaluating evaporation losses and vapor-locking tendency of gasolines.

---

[1] The value of air distillation has been emphasized by Bartholomew, Chalk, and Brewster, *Trans. SAE*, **42**:141 (1938), who utilized this procedure to study the distribution of tetraethyllead in the manifold mixture under various conditions.

[2] Originated by C. Engler; Holde-Mueller, "Examination of Hydrocarbon Oils," p. 27, John Wiley & Sons, Inc., New York, 1915.

[3] Wilson and Barnard, *Ind. Eng. Chem.*, **13**:906 (1921); **17**:428 (1925).   Bridgeman, *J. Research Natl. Bur. Standards*, **13**:53 (1934); *Oil Gas J.*, **54**(7):93 (1955).   Blair and Alden, *Ind. Eng. Chem.*, **25**:559 (1933).   See also Scheumann, *Oil Gas J.*, **34**(52):238 (1936).

[4] See Bridgeman, *J. SAE*, **23**:478 (1928).   A useful nomograph for obtaining true volatility data from ASTM distillation curves is also given.

[5] For correlation of the temperature–vapor-liquid characteristics of motor gasolines, see Aldrich, Barber, and Robertson, *Trans. SAE*, **52**:364 (1944).

The slope of the ASTM curve at the 10 per cent distillation point has also been found to be related to the vapor pressure; it has been employed as a characterization factor in predicting changes in vapor pressure with temperature, vapor-liquid ratios, and evaporation losses in storage and in high-altitude flying, vapor locking, and cold starting behavior.[1]

A general relationship has also been found between the ASTM distillation curve and air-equilibrium volatility data from 0 to 100 per cent evaporation.[2] It is expressed by the equation

$$\frac{T_{\text{ASTM}}}{T_{16}} = 1.5 - \frac{C}{T_{16}}$$

where T_{16} is the air-equilibrium distillation temperature at a 16:1 air-fuel ratio and C is a function of the percentage evaporated and the slope of the ASTM curve at the point under consideration; the temperatures are in degrees centigrade absolute. Since the equation is based on a 16:1 air-vapor ratio, the values for other mixtures are calculated from this by use of known factors.

XI-5. Operating Characteristics

Vapor Locking. Vapor lock is the self-explanatory name given to a set of engine operating difficulties attributable to an excess of extremely volatile constituents in the motor fuel or to high temperatures in the gasoline systems of engines. It operates as partial or complete interruption of fuel supply by the formation of bubbles of vapor in supply lines, pump, or carburetor passages. In current engines, it shows up as uneven running or stalling during idling after a hot run, as irregular acceleration, as failure of the engine to start after a brief stop, or as momentary failure during steady operation. The incoming gasoline becomes heated to a temperature above its bubble point. The difficulty has been corrected by changes in engine design which reduce the temperature of the fuel, adoption of fuel pumps of greater vapor-handling capacity, by better adjustment of the summer and winter volatility of the fuel, and by more careful fractionation of the low-boiling constituents to eliminate propane and to control the butane content.[3] The incidence of hot stalling, hot

---

[1] Bridgeman, *Oil Gas J.*, **54**(7):93 (1955). Legatski and Bridgeman, *Oil Gas J.*, **54**(16):136 (1955). See also Wilson, *J. SAE*, **27**:33 (1930), and Blair and Alden, *Ind. Eng. Chem.*, **25**:559 (1933), for charts for interpreting the significance of ASTM curves.

[2] Bridgeman, Aldrich, and White, *Proc. API*, **11**(III):4 (1930).

[3] Aldrich, Barber, and Robertson, *Trans. SAE*, **53**:392 (1945). Bridgeman and Aldrich, *J. SAE*, **27**:93 (1930). Barnum, Clarke, and Hamer, Preprint, SAE Fuels and Lubricants Meeting, Atlantic City, June, 1954. Bridgeman, *Oil Gas J.*, **51**(30):127 (1952). Bridgeman, Aldrich, and Rohde, *Fuels and Fuel Systems, Special Publ.*, pp. 14–108, Natural Gasoline Association of America, 1955.

starting, and vapor-lock troubles has also been found to vary with ambient temperature, type of motor operation, soaking period involved, altitude, and other factors.[1]

As indicated, vapor locking is related to the bubble point, which, in turn, is a function of the temperature of the 10 per cent point on the ASTM distillation curve. It has been suggested[2] that this figure be kept below a value corresponding to

$$100 + \frac{\text{prevailing air temperature, } °F}{2}$$

In refinery control, vapor-locking tendency is judged by the Reid vapor pressure[3] of the fuel. A number of empirical relations are observed. The following equation, for instance, has been set up for determining the permissible Reid vapor pressure (that at which vapor locking will not occur) of a fuel.[4]

$$t_a + t = 259 - 140 \log p^R$$

where t_a is the atmospheric temperature, °F, t is the temperature difference between ambient air and the point of vapor lock, and p^R is the Reid vapor pressure. Another relationship has been set up in which the slope at the 10 per cent point of the ASTM curve is used to determine the permissible Reid vapor pressure.[5]

$$\text{Reid vapor pressure} = R + \text{slope}$$

R being a factor dependent upon ambient temperature and altitude.

It should be pointed out that the Reid vapor pressure is not an accurate measure of the initial volatility of a gasoline. Two products of the same vapor pressure at 100°F may exert quite different pressures at higher temperatures. The test is of value for refinery control chiefly because of

---

[1] Heath, Moxey, and Way, *Proc. API*, **35**(III):374 (1955). See also, Stone and Bier, *Proc. API*, **33**:101 (1953). Domke, Tracy, and Taliaferro, *Proc. API*, **33**:112 (1953). Dugan, Finnegan, Moxey, and Way, Preprint 643, SAE National Fuels and Lubricant Meeting, Philadelphia, November, 1955.

[2] Clarke, Coats, and Brown, *Ind. Eng. Chem.*, **22**:672 (1930).

[3] The Reid vapor-pressure apparatus (ASTM D 323–52) consists of an air chamber (400 ml) connected at the top with an accurate pressure gage and at the bottom to the gasoline reservoir (100 ml), which is removable. The reservoir is charged with gasoline at 32°F and is then connected to the air chamber, containing air saturated with moisture at room temperature. The whole is then thoroughly shaken and placed in a bath held at 100°F. Intermittent shaking is employed until the pressure gage shows a constant value. Corrections are then made for the expansion of air and moisture, and the corrected reading is taken as the Reid vapor pressure of the gasoline.

[4] Bridgeman, White, and Gary, *Trans. SAE*, **32**:157 (1933).

[5] Legatski and Bridgeman, *Oil Gas J.*, **54**(16):136 (1955).

its simplicity.   A more significant factor would be the ratio of vapor to liquid volume over a series of operating conditions; this can be estimated from Reid vapor-pressure and ASTM distillation data.[1]   It should probably lie between 5 and 15.

Starting.   Ease of engine starting[2] is a matter of delivering the proper air-vapor mixture to the cylinders.   With a cold engine and manifold, evaporation of the fuel is limited and the normal air-fuel mixture does not furnish a resulting air-vapor mixture that falls within the 4:1 to 20:1 range required for explosion.   To increase the amount of fuel vapors sufficiently, an overrich mixture must be supplied; this is done by use of the choke valve.   If an air-vapor mixture of 20:1 is taken as the limit for possible starting or of 12:1 for satisfactory starting, the obtaining of these mixtures at definite temperatures will be possible only if the gasoline furnishing them has definite volatility characteristics.   The reading of these characteristics from the assay distillation curve is possible from existing relationships.[3]   A 1:1 air-fuel mixture supplied by "choking" requires 5 per cent evaporation of the fuel to furnish the necessary 20:1 air-vapor mixture or 8.3 per cent for the desirable 12:1 mixture; a 2:1 air-fuel mixture requires 10 and 16.7 per cent evaporation, respectively. The necessary ASTM distillation temperatures for these evaporation percentages can be obtained from the air distillation–ASTM distillation relationships and are shown in Table XI-1.[4]

The 5 and 16.7 per cent distillation temperatures are seemingly the most important; the closely associated figure for 10 per cent distilled temperature is generally taken as the point of reference for evaluating the starting qualities of a gasoline; this temperature is usually set at below 158°F.   There is a disadvantage in allowing this point to be too low, since, then, the lowest-boiling fractions may evaporate too easily and bring about vapor locking.

Acceleration.   Acceleration and flexibility in power output are influenced by the volatility of that part of the fuel distilling over the middle part of the distillation curve, say, between the 20 and 80 per cent points.[5] No definite relationships have been established, because performance also depends upon the operating temperature of the air-fuel mixture, which is

[1] Barber and Kulason, *Trans. SAE*, **39**:351 (1936).   Campbell, Lovell, and Mulligan, *Trans. SAE*, **39**:356 (1936).   Bridgeman, *Oil Gas J.*, **54**(7):93 (1955).

[2] For discussion of relationships between ASTM distillation curve and engine warm-up time, see Moore, Young, and Tomlinson, Preprint, SAE National Fuels and Lubricants Meeting, Tulsa, Okla., November, 1956.

[3] Bridgeman and Cragoe, *Proc. API*, **9**(7):54 (1927).

[4] Engine starting in cold weather is influenced also by the viscosity of the crankcase oil, the rate at which the starting system will crank the engine, and the condition of the ignition system.   The discussion assumes these to be the same in all cases.

[5] Bridgeman and Aldrich, *Oil Gas J.*, **56**(22):90 (1958).

not constant. Thus, if the mixture is warmed appreciably above its dew point, power output will suffer because the actual amount of combustible mixture drawn into the engine per cycle will have decreased. More volatile fuels have made lower manifold temperatures desirable on this account. The reduction in mixture temperature also results in a decrease in the knocking tendency of a fuel; the effect may be as much as one octane number per each 15 to 20°F lowering.[1]

TABLE XI-1

Engine temperature, °F	Possible starting assay temperature for 5 per cent evaporation, °F	Satisfactory starting assay temperature for 8.3 per cent evaporation, °F
1:1 Air-fuel mixture		
86	250	235
68	226	212
50	203	189
32	180	165
14	156	144
−4	133	120
2:1 Air-fuel mixture		
86	261	250
68	237	226
50	214	203
32	190	180
14	167	156
−4	142	133

The volatility of gasoline is of significance in another respect. The heat energy absorbed in evaporation of quite volatile fuels may cause the formation of ice in the carburetor by the freezing of moisture in the intake air. This factor is of extreme importance in aircraft but is less troublesome in automobiles. It has been reported to occur, within the ordinary range of humidities, at a carburetor temperature of 9°F below the atmospheric dew point.[2] Experience indicates, however, that icing occurs readily when humidities are high and atmospheric temperatures near 40 to 45°F. Ice formation can be avoided by addition to the gasoline of water-soluble compounds, such as alcohols, or of substances which otherwise influence the crystal habit of the frozen water.

[1] Eisinger and Barnard, *Trans. SAE,* **37**:293 (1935).
[2] Allen, Rodgers, and Brooks, *Trans. SAE,* **35**:390, 417 (1934). Madden and Droegemueller, *J. SAE,* **63**(4):29 (1955).

Still another manner in which volatility is reflected in service is the amount of crankcase-oil dilution which occurs.[1]   Under winter conditions or in stop-and-go driving, the amount of heavy fractions of motor fuel accumulating in the crankcase oil may be appreciable.   Other conditions being the same, the dilution will become greater as the volatility of the gasoline, or of its heavy fractions, becomes less; the 90 per cent point on the assay distillation curve is a rough indication of the diluting tendency. Dilution was a more serious matter when gasolines were made to include higher proportions of heavy ends; the demand for higher octane numbers some years ago put a premium on lower end points, and dilution will not be a problem in temperate climates as long as this condition prevails.   This remains true in spite of the high content of good antiknock aromatics in the high-boiling portion of catalytically cracked gasoline.

COMMERCIAL GASOLINES

An idea of the significant properties of gasolines sold over a period of years may be obtained from Tables XI-2 and XI-3.   A rough picture of the composition of various manufactured gasoline constituents is given by Fig. XI-1.

TABLE XI-2. MOTOR GASOLINES

	1905	1920	1930 Regular	1930 Premium	1936 Regular	1936 Premium	1945 Regular	1945 Premium	1955 Regular	1955 Premium
Distillation, °F:										
Initial..........	...	130	98	99	103	107	102	103	100	100
10 per cent......	165	182	142	141	148	149	145	142	130	128
50 per cent......	205	268	265	250	250	231	251	243	222	218
90 per cent......	260	388	377	352	355	325	351	346	338	335
End............	295	446	406	392	401	354	405	401	405	404
Octane number:*										
Motor..........	...	...	59.2†	73.7†	69.6	77.2	69.7	74.9	81.6	85.4
Research........	...	...	......	......	......	......	73.3	79.7	87.4	95.0

* It should be remembered that both octane number and volatility are ordinarily adjusted to suit season, climate, and the character of the country in which they are distributed.   Thus, a more volatile gasoline is required in winter and a higher octane number in hilly country.   At high altitudes the octane requirement is lower.

† The Motor Method was just being formulated at that date.   There is some uncertainty about the test procedures employed.

From Smith, *U.S. Bur. Mines Tech. Paper* 328, 1920.   Hopkins, *U.S. Bur. Mines Bull.* 367, 1930.   Lane, *U.S. Bur. Mines Inform. Circ.* 3335, 1936.   Blade, *U.S. Bur. Mines Inform. Circ.* 3883, 1945; 7746, 1955.

[1] *Coordinating Research Council Rept.* 283, February, 1954.

TABLE XI-3. COMMERCIAL AVIATION GASOLINES

	1947		1950		1955	
	91/98	100/130	91/96	100/130	91/96	100/130
Distillation °F:						
Initial................	114	112	112	108	115	110
10 per cent...........	150	150	148	147	148	148
50 per cent...........	198	207	192	206	193	206
90 per cent......	240	246	235	244	237	245
End................	306	318	294	305	297	309
Octane number:*						
ASTM D 614..........	93.0	.....	92.6	...	94.2	
ASTM D 909..........	98.9	.....	99.0	...	98.7	
Performance number:						
ASTM D 614..........	.....	106.1	.....	106	.....	108
ASTM D 909..........	.....	131.2	.....	131	.....	131

* By way of indicating early practice, it has been stated by Heron (SAE Preprint, Atlantic City Meeting, June, 1953) that British military aviation gasoline of 1917 had an octane number of about 55.

From Blade, *U.S. Bur. Mines Inform. Circ.* 4353, 1947; 4789, 1950; 7747, 1955.

PHENOMENA OF KNOCKING

Knocking is most commonly perceived in gasoline engines as a metallic sound of varying pitch, accompanied by overheating and loss of power. It occurs during slow running at high temperatures under heavy load, during rapid acceleration, or when the spark is too far advanced.[1] Continued severe knocking is detrimental to an engine, expecially to the pistons and bearings; its occurrence has in the past been attributed to preignition, to carbon deposits, and to the fuel, as the influence of each of these factors has been observed.[2]

[1] In high-compression automotive engines a knock may be heard at the time of restarting a hot engine; this is referred to as starting knock. It is thought to be caused by the autoignition of an air-fuel charge originating from carburetor percolation of light gases just after the engine has been shut off, and which has been drawn into one of the cylinders. As a measure of its severity, the starting knock of a gasoline is referred to a blend of toluene and *n*-heptane having the same starting knock intensity. The index is the toluene number or volume percentage of toluene in the blend. Toluene, giving no knock of this type, is assigned a value of 100 and *n*-heptane, which knocks readily, is assigned a zero value. Potter, *ACS, Div. Petrol. Chem.*, Preprints, Chemistry and Technology of Petroleum Fuels of the Future, C-5, San Francisco, April, 1958. Bender, Meyer, and Palinke, *ACS, Div. Petrol. Chem.*, Preprints, Chemistry and Technology of Petroleum Fuels of the Future, C-33, San Francisco, April, 1958.

[2] For reference to early work, see Ricardo, *J. SAE*, **10**:305 (1922). Midgley, *J. SAE*, **7**:489 (1920).

It can be shown from thermodynamic considerations that the efficiency of an internal-combustion engine is a function of the compression ratio

$$\frac{\text{Clearance volume of cylinder with piston at bottom of stroke}}{\text{Clearance volume of cylinder with piston at top of stroke}}$$

When attempts are made to raise the output by increasing this ratio, limitations are set by the occurrence of knocking. Present-day automobile engines (Otto cycle) have compression ratios as high as 10.5:1. Commercial development of nonknocking fuels has allowed this ratio to rise from about 4.25:1 in 1920 to the present value. The most striking fact about knocking is the spectacular effect of chemical additives to the gasoline in suppressing the knocking phenomenon. Less striking but equally important is the similar action of larger additions (20 to 40 per cent) of blending materials such as benzene, ethyl alcohol, or diisopropyl ether. Iodine and aniline as antiknock materials were first recognized by Midgley and Boyd;[1] additions of the order of 0.1 to 3.0 per cent are effective. The metal alkyls, specifically tetraethyllead, are still more effective.[2] Other metallo-organic compounds, such as iron and nickel carbonyls, iron dicyclopentadienyl, and many amines have good antiknock value, but only the lead derivative has survived in commercial use.[3] The methyl derivative of cyclopentadienyl manganese tricarbonyl, a recently developed antiknock agent, is proposed as a supplement to tetraethyllead in high-octane gasolines.[4]

A number of antiknock agents are listed in Table XI-4, their effective values expressed in terms of the value of aniline as unity. The relative

[1] *Ind. Eng. Chem.*, **14**:894 (1922).

[2] The use of a less effective but more volatile antiknock agent, such as tetramethyllead, may result in higher octane values because of better distribution in the manifold of a multicylinder engine. Campbell, Lovell, and Boyd, *Trans. SAE*, **40**:144 (1937).

[3] Tetraethyllead is sold as Ethyl fluid, reported to have the following composition. The halogen compounds are added to assist removal of lead as volatile halides from engines during combustion.

	Motor plus		Motor mixture		Aviation mixture	
	Per cent volume	Per cent weight	Per cent volume	Per cent weight	Per cent volume	Per cent weight
Tetraethyllead............	...	59.79	61.48	59.17	61.41	64.83
Ethylene dichloride.......	...	18.30	18.81	23.8		
Ethylene dibromide.......	...	20.84	17.86	13.0	35.68	28.6
Dye and impurities.......	...	1.07	1.85	4.03	2.91	6.57

[4] Brown and Lovell, *Ind. Eng. Chem.*, **50**:1547 (1958).

effectiveness of several of these compounds is further illustrated in Fig. XI-5, which gives their values in 60:40 isooctane-*n*-heptane blends.

The amount of the lead compound required is surprisingly small. It was estimated by Midgley and Boyd that the quantity of tetraethyllead needed to suppress knocking in an engine burning a kerosene fuel is only

TABLE XI-4

Compound	Reciprocal of number of moles to give same antiknock effect as 1 mole aniline
Metallic:	
Lead tetraethyl	118
Lead diphenyldimethyl	115
Lead tetraphenyl	70
Iron carbonyl	50
Nickel carbonyl	35
Bismuth triethyl	23.8
Tellurium diethyl	26.6
Selenium diethyl	6.9
Tin tetraethyl	4.0
Cadmium diethyl	1.24
Nitrogen compounds:	
Aniline	1.0
Toluidine	1.2
Xylidine	1.4
n-Propylaminobenzene	1.10
Monomethylaniline	1.4
Monoethylaniline	1.02
Mono-*n*-propylaniline	0.75
Dimethylaniline	0.21
Di-*n*-propylaniline	0.27
Miscellaneous:	
Ethyl iodide	1.09
Titanium tetrachloride	3.2
Stannic iodide	15.1

Midgley and Boyd, *Ind. Eng. Chem.*, **14**:589, 894 (1922). Boyd, *Ind. Eng. Chem.*, **16**:893 (1924). Charch, Mack, and Boord, *Ind. Eng. Chem.*, **18**:334 (1926). Calingaert, "Science of Petroleum," vol. IV, p. 3024, Oxford University Press, New York and London, 1938.

1 mole in 215,000 moles of the theoretical air-fuel mixture. It is remarkable to find the vapors of thallium eleven times more effective than tetraethyllead (on a weight basis) and those of potassium, four times as effective, while sodium vapors are practically inert.[1] These results may involve contradictions, to be resolved.

[1] Egerton, "Science of Petroleum," vol. IV, p. 2911, Oxford University Press, New York and London, 1938.

The knocking tendency of a fuel can be increased by the addition of diethyl ether, small amounts of organic nitrites and nitrates,[1] peroxides,[2] and ozone.[3]

XI-6. Theory of Knocking. Studies of the kinetics of hydrocarbon oxidation show the process to have the characteristics of a chain reaction.[4] When such a chain is once established, it will continue until broken, generally by wall contact of the carriers. As long as termination proceeds as fast as propagation, normal combustion will take place. If, however,

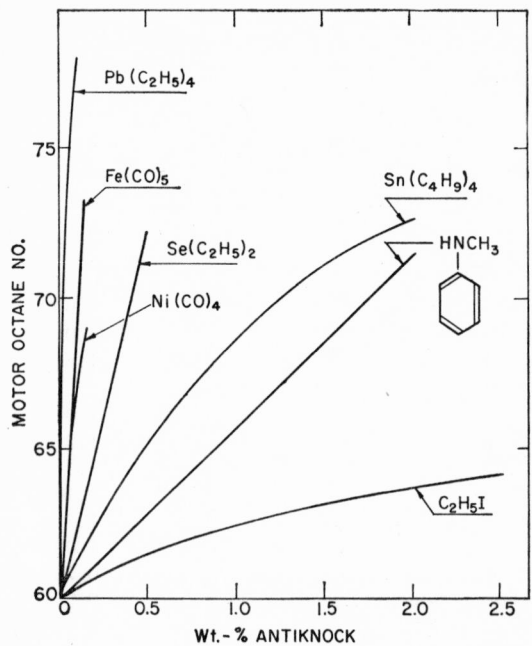

Fig. XI-5. Relative effects of several metallo-organic and organic compounds as antiknock agents. [*From Fig. 4, Livingston, Ind. Eng. Chem.,* **43**:663 (1951).]

deactivation is not as fast as chain propagation, a time will come when the number of chains and chain carriers will reach a concentration sufficient to raise the reaction velocity materially; the unburned gases may then oxidize to complete the reaction with sudden violence.

[1] Midgley and Boyd, *Ind. Eng. Chem.,* **14**:894 (1922).

[2] Dumanois, Mondain-Monval, and Quanquin, *Compt. rend.,* **192**:1158 (1931). Egerton and Ubbelohde, *Nature,* **133**:179 (1934); **135**:67 (1935); *Phil. Trans. Roy. Soc. London,* **A234**:433 (1935); *Proc. Roy. Soc. (London),* **A153**:103 (1935). Downs, Walsh, and Wheeler, *Phil. Trans. Roy. Soc. London,* **A243**:299 (1951).

[3] Brooks, *J. Inst. Petrol. Technologists,* **19**:835 (1933).

[4] Norrish, *Proc. Roy. Soc. (London),* **A150**:36 (1935). George and Robertson, *Proc. Roy. Soc. (London),* **A185**:288, 309 (1946); *J. Inst. Petrol.,* **32**:382 (1946). von Elbe and Lewis, *Ind. Eng. Chem.,* **29**:551 (1937).

What actually occurs in knocking is not known. It has been found, however, from photographic and spectroscopic studies, that, during normal explosion in a gasoline engine, a narrow, ideally convex combustion wave travels from the spark plug across the combustion chamber at a fairly constant rate (up to 250 ft per sec, depending on various factors). Under knocking conditions the flame front is altered only during the burning of the last part of the charge. The flame then travels much faster—at about 1,000 ft per sec. It appears then that knocking occurs only after most of the combustion has been completed.

The most commonly accepted theory assumes that the advancing flame front compresses the unburned charge in an essentially adiabatic way, thus raising the charge density and temperature; the unburned gases also receive some heat by radiation from the flame. When critical temperature and pressure conditions are exceeded, the autocatalyzed precombustion taking place in the unburned charge ahead of the flame front becomes so rapid that a manyfold increase in its rate leads to self-ignition before the combustion can be completed in an orderly manner. This is accompanied by a sudden rise in pressure as shock waves are set up; these have a much higher velocity than the normal flame and the same frequency as the sound associated with knock.[1] Photographic evidence shows[2] that knock is a sudden explosion in the end zone, completed in less than 50 microseconds (μsec), but preceded by exothermic reactions in the same area. It is commonly said that knocking differs from detonation in being slower and less brisant; however, the peak pressure in the detonation of TNT is reached in about the same time—50 to 300 μsec.[3]

It seems almost certain that the spontaneous oxidation occurring before spark ignition makes up an important part of what goes on in an internal-combustion engine, and that a preoxidized material is more likely to ignite spontaneously. The kinetic probabilities are all in favor of a stepwise reaction with a series of intermediate products. A substantial part of the over-all process may occur during the compression stroke and until the spark-induced flame takes over. Variations in the extent of these preflame reactions obviously will not alter the total energy released in the combustion but they do influence the timing of its distribution throughout the cycle, and can affect engine performance in this manner. It has been observed that in a fired engine with delayed spark, and with a *n*-heptane-isooctane fuel, from 10 to 27 per cent of the Btu value was

---

[1] Grimstead, *J. Aeronaut. Sci.*, **6**:412 (1939).

[2] Rothrock, Spencer, and Miller, *Natl. Advisory Comm. Aeronaut. Rept.* 704, 1941.

[3] Cook and Keyes, *J. Chem. Phys.*, **24**:191 (1956). See also Jost, "Explosions and Combustion Processes in Gases," p. 519, McGraw-Hill Book Company, Inc., New York, 1946.

lost through precombustion reaction.[1] In a motored engine of about
10:1 compression ratio, approximately 52 per cent of a 75 isooctane-25
n-heptane mixture was converted to other products in precombustion
reactions.[2] The amount of these preflame reaction products increases
with the time available and the initial temperature of the charge in the
cylinder; these may in turn be influenced by such factors as the nature
of the fuel, compression ratio, engine speed, air-fuel ratio, valve
timing, etc.

Precombustion reactions are complex in nature and in spite of the
excellent work that has been done in studies with open tubes and bombs,[3]
motored engines and rapid compression devices,[4] the sampling of gases
from fired engines,[5] and flame photography[6] the subject is not well understood. As just stated, they are accompanied by the release of a considerable proportion of the heat of combustion of the fuel. The rate of
release of this heat can be lowered by increasing the octane level of the
fuel through blending with selected hydrocarbons, but not by adding
tetraethyllead. Within each fuel class, increasing the octane number
lowers the total heat of precombustion reactions, but the magnitude of
the change is not specifically related to octane number.

[1] Walcutt and Rifkin, *Ind. Eng. Chem.*, **43**:2844 (1951); *Quart. Trans. SAE*, **6**:472 (1952).

[2] Retailliau, Ricards, and Jones, *Quart. Trans. SAE*, **4**:438 (1950); *Am. Scientist*, **39**:656 (1951).

[3] Woodbury, Lewis, and Canby, *J. SAE*, **8**:209 (1921). Maxwell and Wheeler, *J. Inst. Petrol. Technologists*, **14**:175 (1928); **15**:408 (1929). Walsh, *Trans. Faraday Soc.*, **42**:269 (1946); **43**:297 (1947). Egerton and Powling, *Proc. Roy. Soc. (London)*, **A193**:172 (1948). Williams, Johnson, and Carhart, *Ind. Eng. Chem.*, **47**:2528 (1955). Johnson, Crellin, and Carhart, *Ind. Eng. Chem.*, **46**:1512 (1954).

[4] Retailliau, Ricards, and Jones, *SAE Quart. Trans.*, **4**:438 (1950); *Am. Scientist*, **39**:656 (1951). Pastell, *SAE Quart. Trans.*, **4**:571 (1950). Corzilius, Diggs, and Pastell, Preprint, SAE Fuels and Lubricants Meeting, Tulsa, Okla., November, 1952. Rifkin, Walcutt, and Betker, *Quart. Trans. SAE*, **6**:472 (1952). Walcutt, Mason, and Rifkin, *Ind. Eng. Chem.*, **46**:1029 (1954). Walcutt and Rifkin, *Ind. Eng. Chem.*, **43**:2844 (1951). Mason and Hesselburg, Preprint, SAE Fuels and Lubricants Meeting, Chicago, November, 1953. Davis, Smith, Malmberg, and Bobbitt, *J. SAE*, **62**(11):103 (1954). Cornelius and Caplan, *Quart. Trans. SAE*, **6**:488 (1952). Taylor, Taylor, Livengood, Russell, and Leary, *Quart. Trans. SAE*, **4**:232 (1950). Livengood and Leary, *Ind. Eng. Chem.*, **43**:2797 (1951). Levedahl and Howard, *Ind. Eng. Chem.*, **43**:2805 (1951).

[5] Withrow, Lovell, and Boyd, *Ind. Eng. Chem.*, **22**:945 (1930). Downs, Walsh, and Wheeler, *Phil. Trans. Roy. Soc. London*, **A243**:463 (1951). Pahnke, Cohen, and Sturgis, *Ind. Eng. Chem.*, **46**:1024 (1954).

[6] Withrow and Rassweiler, *Ind. Eng. Chem.*, **23**:769 (1931); **25**:923 (1933); **28**:672 (1936); *Trans. SAE*, **42**(4):185 (1938). Withrow and Boyd, *Ind. Eng. Chem.*, **23**:539 (1921). Review by Boyd, *Trans. SAE*, **45**:421 (1939). Marvin and Steele, *Natl. Advisory Comm. Aeronaut. Rept.* 486, 1934. Ball, Preprint, SAE Fuels and Lubri-cants Meeting, Tulsa, Okla. November, 1954. Erhard and Norrish, *Proc. Roy. Soc. (London)*, **A234**:178 (1956).

Two types of reaction prior to combustion have been observed;[1] one is thermoneutral and is directly related to the production of relatively stable knock-inducing materials. This reaction, sensitive to the temperature and pressure of the unburned charge, was found to take place with n-heptane in glass tubes at about 225°C and in motored engines at compression temperatures above 450°C. The other type occurs at a somewhat higher temperature, is exothermic, and is accompanied by cool flame phenomena.[2] Tetraethyllead has little effect on the start of either type, but appears to act on the products of the thermoneutral reaction at some intermediate point between the formation of knock inducers and the ensuing knock. Autoignition is thus retarded by the presence of this additive, permitting a greater proportion of normal combustion to take place. It appears that tetraethyllead causes the decomposition of free radicals resulting from the breakdown of peroxides. It has been shown that the additive deactivates those free radicals acting as chain carriers in carbonyl decomposition reactions in the blue flame region, thereby slowing down the further reactions of carbonyl compounds.[3]

Thus, there is much evidence that the preflame period is one of intense chemical activity. Cracking and dehydrogenation, polymerization of oxidation products, and formation of various acids, alcohols, aldehydes, ketones, and peroxides have been noted.[4] The degradation of the latter is presumably associated with the subsequent knock.[5] Peroxides and

[1] Mason and Hesselburg, Preprint, SAE National Fuels and Lubricants Meeting, Chicago, November, 1953. Walcutt, Mason, and Rifkin, *Ind. Eng. Chem.*, **46**:1029 (1954).

[2] Cool flames accompany some kinds of low-temperature precombustion; they are characterized by relatively low sensitivity and heat release and have long been known in the slow oxidation of hydrocarbons under laboratory conditions [Perkins, *J. Chem. Soc.*, **41**:363 (1882)]. Their occurrence in engines was observed later. Peletier, Van Hoogstraten, Smittenberg, and Kooyman [*Chaleur & ind.*, **20**:120 (1939)], Ubbelohde [*Proc. Royal Soc. (London)*, **A152**:354 (1935)], Emeleus [*J. Chem. Soc.*, **48**:2948 (1926); **51**:1733 (1929)] and others have proved fairly well that this luminescence can be traced, at least in part, to excited formaldehyde molecules. A separate phenomenon, blue flame, may occur just prior to autoignition [Downs, Walsh, and Wheeler, *Proc. Royal Soc. (London)*, **A243**:463 (1951); Sturgis, *J. SAE*, **62**(12):36 (1954); *Trans. SAE*, **63**:253 (1955)]. It is associated with degradation reactions of carbonyl compounds.

[3] Pipenberg and Pahnke, *Ind. Eng. Chem.*, **49**:2067 (1957).

[4] Egerton, Smith, and Ubbelohde, *Phil. Trans. Royal Soc. London*, **A234**:433 (1935). Wheeler and Downs, *Nature*, **162**:893 (1948); *Fuel*, **32**(3):279 (1953). Rassweiler and Withrow, *Ind. Eng. Chem.*, **24**:528 (1932); **25**:1359 (1933); **26**:1256 (1934); **27**:872 (1935). Beatty and Edgar, *J. ACS*, **56**:102, 107, 112 (1934); "Science of Petroleum," vol. IV, p. 2927, Oxford University Press, New York and London, 1938. Egerton, "Science of Petroleum," vol. IV, p. 2911. Although formaldehyde is found under knocking conditions, knocking cannot be induced by introducing it into a normally operating engine. Downs, Walsh, and Wheeler, *Phil. Trans. Roy. Soc. London*, **A243**:299 (1951).

[5] Downs, Walsh, and Wheeler, *Phil. Trans. Roy. Soc. London*, **A243**:463 (1951).

aldehydes, including formaldehyde, have been found by sampling engine cylinder gases; ketones and diketones have also been recognized.[1] These compounds are presumably all derived from peroxides or hydroperoxides.

When precombustion was measured by pressure rise prior to ignition, higher initial temperature increased and higher knock resistance of the fuel decreased this pressure rise; however, the effects brought about by equivalent tetraethyllead and isooctane were different.[2] Direct observation through a quartz window showed luminous cool flames during the period of pressure rise. Isooctane afforded a cool flame before top center, but blending in of *n*-heptane gave rise to a second one after top center. This second flame was made more intense by knock-increasing influences, and was extinguished by tetraethyllead; the first cool flame was not so affected.

Something analogous to preflame oxidation has been studied by examining the products exhausted by a motored non-ignited engine.[3] When severity was altered by increasing compression ratio, peroxides, aldehydes, and ketones were present at peak cycle temperatures of about 340°C, hydrogen peroxide and formaldehyde at a few degrees higher, and cool flames at slightly above this point. It is surmised that hydrogen peroxide may play a part in knocking because engines operated on hydrogen as a fuel will knock.[4] Comparison of isooctane and *n*-heptane under preflame conditions indicated that the former was more oxidation resistant, and more susceptible to the inhibiting influence of tetraethyllead. Diisobutylene underwent precombustion oxidation very slowly; essentially no products accumulated until just prior to autoignition. Benzene did not oxidize under the preoxidizing conditions; apparently its mode of ignition is unlike that of the paraffins.[5]

It may be deduced from these scattered observations that if the fuel is composed largely of straight-chain paraffins, the preoxidation will start at a low temperature and proceed rapidly, accumulating proknock intermediates. A branched-chain fuel, however, starts to preoxidize only at a higher temperature and does so more slowly.[6] Relatively little preoxidized material will have accumulated by the time the normal flame

---

[1] Thomas and Crandall, *Ind. Eng. Chem.*, **43**:2761 (1951). Barusch, Crandall, Payne, and Thomas, *Ind. Eng. Chem.*, **43**:2764, 2766 (1951). See also Kahler, Bearse, and Stoner, *Ind. Eng. Chem.*, **43**:2777 (1951), for a study of the products from the preflame oxidation of hexanes.

[2] Cornelius and Caplan, *Quart. Trans. SAE*, **6**:488 (1952).

[3] Pahnke, Cohen, and Sturgis, *Ind. Eng. Chem.*, **46**:1024 (1954). Sturgis, *J. SAE*, **62**(12):36 (1954); *Trans. SAE*, **63**:253 (1955).

[4] Downs, Walsh, and Wheeler, *Phil. Trans. Roy. Soc. London*, **A243**:463 (1951). Anzilotti, Rogers, Scott, and Tomsic, *Ind. Eng. Chem.*, **46**:1314 (1954).

[5] See work of Downs, Walsh, and Wheeler, *loc. cit.*

[6] Pahnke, Cohen, and Sturgis, *loc. cit.*

has consumed the bulk of the charge; any knock which occurs from branched structures is likely to be feeble on this account.

The temperatures and pressures required for trace knock in a fired engine are approximately the same as those needed for autoignition in a motored engine adjusted to produce precombustion reactions; this would indicate that the reactions which lead to spontaneous ignition are probably the same as those leading to knock.[1] Also, the carbonyl products formed in motored engines are of the same type as found in the end gases of fired engines,[2] and essentially the same types of intermediates are formed from propane, *n*-pentane, *n*-heptane, isooctane, cyclohexane, and propylene, although the engine operating conditions required differed markedly for the several fuels.

Study of pure hydrocarbons, *n*-heptane-isooctane blends, and oxygen-containing compounds has shown that as octane number and resistance to self-ignition increase, the temperature at which peroxides and cool flames are first detected also rises,[3] while the amount of heat liberated during the cool flame decreases.[4] Over a wide range of air-fuel ratios, however, the temperatures at which hot flames appear lie in the same range, about 1100°F for all the aliphatic compounds studied. Because the octane numbers of hydrocarbons and their resistances to self-ignition vary widely, the latter property is thought to be dependent on the extent of the heat release in the early stages of the precombustion reactions. According to this view of the over-all process, a very high-octane fuel must be heated by compression alone to nearly 1100°F before hot flames begin, whereas a low-octane fuel may contribute several hundred degrees of the required temperature by its own early reactions; it thus self-ignites with greater ease.

The possibility that knock was caused by a secondary explosion resulting from the spontaneous ignition of some part of the unburned charge was first postulated by Ricardo.[5] Apparently, the part played by preflame oxidation was not recognized until much later. The increase in density of the unburned charge as well as its rise in temperature, resulting from the heat of adiabatic compression produced by the advancing flame front, favors spontaneous ignition. Hydrocarbons and fuels of low ignition temperature have a tendency to knock most easily;[6] furthermore,

---

[1] Pastell, *Quart. Trans. SAE*, **4**:571 (1950).

[2] Davis, Smith, Malmberg, and Bobbitt, *J. SAE*, **62**(11):103 (1954).

[3] Barusch and Payne, *Ind. Eng. Chem.*, **43**:2329, 2761 (1951). Oberdorfer and Boord, *ACS, Div. Petrol. Chem.*, Preprints, p. 183, ACS Meeting, Minneapolis, September, 1955.

[4] Levedahl and Yokely, *Natl. Bur. Standards, Summary Tech. Rept.* 1802, 1953.

[5] *J. SAE*, **10**:305 (1922). See also, however, Woodbury, Canby, and Lewis, *J. SAE*, **8**:209 (1921).

[6] Brown and Watkins, *Ind. Eng. Chem.*, **19**:366 (1927).

antiknock agents raise the ignition temperatures in air, while knock inducers have the opposite effect.[1]   The following table lists some auto-ignition temperatures in air and the effect of the presence of tetraethyl-lead.[2]

	Ignition temperature, °C	Rise after addition of 0.25 per cent $Pb(C_2H_5)_4$, °C
Benzene...............	690	18
Cyclohexane............	535	27
Methylcyclohexane......	470	92
Pentane...............	515	75
Isohexane.............	525	46
Heptane..............	430	83
Gasoline.............	460	82

It must be remembered that the spontaneous ignition temperature is an entirely empirical constant.   Its values depend upon the experimental method and its details, such as rate of heating, oxygen concentration, gas pressure, and even the material of which the ignition cup is made.[3]

Autoignition itself has been shown to take place in two stages;[4] the first is characterized by emission of light of low intensity and the generation of moderate pressures; the second by light of high intensity, a sharp

[1] Berl, Heise, and Winnacker, *Z. physik. Chem.*, **A139**:453 (1928).   Layng and Youker, *Ind. Eng. Chem.*, **20**:1048 (1928).   Butkov, *Erdöl u. Teer*, **4**:162 (1928). Masson and Hamilton, *Ind. Eng. Chem.*, **21**:544 (1929).   Townend, *Chem. Revs.*, **21**:259 (1937).   Helmore, "Science of Petroleum," vol. IV, p. 2970, Oxford University Press, New York and London, 1938.   Maccormac and Townend, *J. Chem. Soc.*, 1938, p. 238.   Townend and Maccormac, *J. Inst. Petrol.*, **25**:459 (1939). Sortman, Beatty, and Heron, *Ind. Eng. Chem.*, **33**:357 (1941).

[2] Egerton and Gates, *J. Inst. Petrol. Technologists*, **13**:244 (1927).   See Jackson, *Ind. Eng. Chem.*, **43**:2869 (1951), for the spontaneous ignition temperatures of a longer list of individual hydrocarbons; also compilations by Scott, Jones, and Scott, *Anal. Chem.*, **20**:238 (1948), and Associated Factory Mutual Fire Insurance Cos., *Ind. Eng. Chem.*, **32**:880 (1940); see also correlations of autoignition temperature with structure, octane number, cetane number, cool flame, etc., Zabetakis, Furno, and Jones, *Ind. Eng. Chem.*, **46**:2173 (1954).   Crellin, Johnson, and Carhart, *ACS, Div. Petrol. Chem., Gen. Papers ACS Meeting*, Preprint, p. 47, Atlantic City, September, 1952; p. 29, Kansas City, April, 1954.   Frank, Blackham, and Swarts, *Ind. Eng. Chem.*, **45**:1753 (1953); and dependence upon surface-volume ratio, Swarts and Orchin, *Ind. Eng. Chem.*, **49**:432 (1957).

[3] The significance of an empirical constant of this type will depend pretty much on the conditions under which it is operative.   Thus, ignition delay, which presumably bears a direct relation to spontaneous ignition temperature, varies with the prevailing temperature and pressure [Rifkin and Walcutt, *J. SAE* **65**(7):30 (1957)].

[4] Taylor, Taylor, Livengood, Russell, and Leary, *Quart. Trans. SAE*, **4**:232 (1950). Levedahl and Howard, *Ind. Eng. Chem.*, **43**:2805 (1951).

rise in pressure, and the ionization of the gases. The resistance of a fuel to knock (by this theory) varies directly with the compression pressure required to initiate the first stage and inversely with the heat liberated during this stage. The addition of a peroxide reduces the pressure and temperature required for initiation. In any case, the knock occurs during the second phase of the autoignition.

The burning taking place within the knocking zone is thus self-ignited and early evidence showed that the knock may occur in different manners: by (1) the ignition of the unburned charge, originating at a point well in advance of the flame front; (2) the whole of the unburned charge bursting in flame simultaneously with the knock, or (3) a sudden increase in the velocity of the normal combustion wave as it enters the knocking zone. The intensity of the knock is governed by the amount and composition of the charge unburned, including the extent of preoxidation, the prevailing temperature, the shape of the combustion chamber, and similar circumstances.

Knocking can be suppressed or at least minimized by various mechanical adjustments, some of them quite undesirable from the standpoint of engine operation. These include:

> Increasing engine speed
> Decreasing manifold pressure
> Retarding spark
> Changing air-fuel ratio
> Changing valve timing

Alteration of engine design may also be effective as, for example, by:

> Decreasing compression ratio
> Increasing charge turbulence
> Altering shape of combustion chamber
> Relocating spark plugs

Most of these affect the time-temperature history of the unburned charge.[1] Knocking is sometimes controlled by injecting water or water and alcohol, the latter containing tetraethyllead.[2]

As stated above, the luminosity of the existing flame is greatly increased at the time of knocking. Withrow and Rassweiler were able to show by

---

[1] Young and Holloway, *J. SAE*, **14**:315 (1924).

[2] Wiebe, Schultz, and Porter, *Ind. Eng. Chem.*, **34**:575 (1942); **36**:672 (1944). Colwell, Cummings, and Anderson, *Trans. SAE*, **53**:358 (1945). Rowe and Ladd, *Trans. SAE*, **54**:26 (1946). Van Hartesveldt, *Quart. Trans. SAE*, **3**:277 (1949). Porter and Wiebe, *Ind. Eng. Chem.*, **44**:1098 (1952). Cramer, *Oil Gas J.*, **54**(13):92 (1955).

spectrographic methods[1] that the characteristic C—C and C—H spectral bands of burning hydrocarbons are present with much less intensity during knocking and that the spectra of the unburned gases in the knocking zone, just prior to the knock, indicate a much greater absorption than for the same gases at the same point in a nonknocking combustion. Furthermore, the absorption during knocking is still greater when the fuel-air mixture is preheated; this suggests that materials of high absorptive power are formed in the heated charge while it is being compressed by the piston and by the movement of the flame front. The addition of tetraethyllead to the gasoline, in quantities sufficient to eliminate knock, suppresses the absorption bands of the unburned charge and restores the intensity of the C—C and C—H lines in the burning gases. The (unidentified) materials of high absorbing capacity seem to be the precursors of the autoignition which causes the knock.

In its simplest form the autoignition theory of knocking says that the phenomenon rests on chemical reactions in the unburned portion of the charge ahead of the flame front; if these can be made to take place slowly enough and in an orderly progression, or if the normal advance of the flame can consume the charge before these preflame oxidations pass beyond control, then knocking can be prevented.[2] However, some research indicates that this mechanism is oversimplified. It is maintained[3] that a light knock may occur before completion of combustion and that the combustion may then proceed to completion normally; also, that the knock need not originate in the unburned portion of the charge. It may arise in a portion previously ignited by autoignition or passage of flame, but which has not burned to completion. While a heavy knock implies completion of combustion, it is not an entirely sudden phenomenon, but involves a gradual build-up of reflected pressure waves just before the knock occurs.

It is quite possible that some of the confusion and contradiction encountered in theorizing about knocking arise from the assumption that all hydrocarbons oxidize, burn, and knock by the same mechanism; this is not necessarily true.[4] The hydrocarbons making up a gasoline offer considerable differences in structure, and can oxidize by different paths. The existence of at least two kinds of knock-inducing reactions

[1] *Ind. Eng. Chem.*, **25**:923 (1933). Ball, Preprint, SAE Fuels and Lubricants Meeting, Tulsa, Okla., 1954.

[2] Diggs, *Trans. SAE*, **61**:402 (1953). Rounds and Caplan, *Ind. Eng. Chem.*, **46**:1677 (1954).

[3] Miller, *Natl. Advisory Comm. Aeronaut. Rept.* 727, 1942; 761, 1943.

[4] For an interesting correlation of the manner of oxidation of hydrocarbons with their structure and their knock resistance, see Boord, Ohio State University Research Foundation, Serial No. 51, January, 1948, reprinted from *9th Ann. Rept.*, API Research Project 45.

has been recognized.[1] For ordinary gasoline hydrocarbons, say, iso-octane and *n*-heptane, one reaction proceeds under low-temperature, preflame conditions through two stages, involving peroxides and developing knock-inducing materials. However, compounds like methane and benzene do not undergo low-temperature oxidation of this variety. There is some difference of opinion about whether and how tetraethyllead affects the low-temperature oxidation,[2] but, of course, no doubt that it inhibits the onset of the final autoignition.

A somewhat different theory of knocking is that presented by King,[3] in which knocking combustion is believed to take place flamelessly at the surface of fine carbon particles set free by pyrolysis of fuel hydrocarbons or lubricating oil, or by sudden cooling of rich-mixture flames. The introduction of fine graphite powder into a manufactured gas fuel was shown to induce knocking. Some support for this may be found in observations of Miller,[4] who noted in high-speed photographs of engine flames that free carbon could be observed when knocking was set up. Tetraethyllead, in this theory, is visualized as exerting an antiknock effect by depositing metal on the carbon surfaces. The metal is presumed to catalyze reactions differently than those leading to knocking.

An understanding of the mechanism of knocking is hardly complete without some idea of how antiknock agents, and particularly tetraethyllead, bring about their effects. No adequate theory is yet available in spite of much study. It has been shown that tetraethyllead may act as a prooxidant in the liquid phase, and as an antioxidant in the vapor-phase oxidation of fuels.[5] Tetraethyllead and tetratolyllead are prooxidants in the oxidation of lubricating oils at 170°C, under atmospheric pressure. There is considerable support, however, for the supposition that in an engine the antiknock agent functions through an inhibitor action, i.e., by its effect on the elevation of spontaneous ignition temperatures and by its retardation of oxidation rates.[6]

---

[1] Retailliau, Richards, and Jones, *Am. Scientist*, **39**:656 (1951). Downs, Walsh, and Wheeler, *Phil. Trans. Roy Soc. London*, **A243**:299 (1951). Downs and Wheeler, *Proc. IME*, part 3, p. 88, 1951–1952. Walcutt, Mason, and Rifkin, *Ind. Eng. Chem.*, **46**:1029 (1954).

[2] There is some agreement that the active agent is a colloidal fog of PbO, which by surface contact destroys chains that would otherwise lead to secondary oxidation of aldehydes; tetraethyllead may thus be pictured as affecting only the second stage of oxidation. See Chamberlain, Hoare, and Walsh, *Discussions Faraday Soc.*, no. 14, p. 89, 1953; Erhard and Norrish, *Proc. Roy. Soc. (London)*, **A234**:178 (1956).

[3] *Can. J. Research*, **26F**:125, 228, 366 (1948), and later papers in the same journal.

[4] *Quart. Trans. SAE*, **1**:98 (1947).

[5] Layng and Youker, *Ind. Eng. Chem.*, **20**:1048 (1928).

[6] Chamberlain and Walsh, *Proc. Roy. Soc. (London)*, **A215**:175 (1952).

It is known that the tetraethyllead must be dissociated to be effective;[1] the ethyl radicals so formed seem to be inactive. Colloidal suspensions of metallic lead, made up in a heavy oil and diluted with gasoline, have no antiknock properties,[2] although particles of the same size in a smoke produced by an electric arc showed a distinct suppressing action;[3] the same was true of a lead oxide smoke. In fact, lead oxide has been proposed as the active agent in all cases.[4] It is noticeable that only those metals are active as antiknocks which can form higher and lower oxides. An oxidation-reduction cycle involving a chain carrier may represent part of the mechanism. It has been shown that t-butyl hydroperoxide is readily decomposed by PbO_2 but not by PbO.[5] At 170°C monomethylaniline does not decompose t-butyl hydroperoxide but it does affect precombustion reactions in much the same way as tetraethyllead.[6] Until recently aniline and its derivatives were considered to suppress knocking by a different mechanism than the metallo-organic compounds, but it is now thought that they also function by destroying chain-propagating free radicals; this may be either by the weakly bound π electrons in the benzene ring[7] or more probably by release of hydrogen attached to the nitrogen atom.[8]

A practically very important feature of the knocking problem is the fact that, with continued operation, an engine will require a higher and higher octane number fuel to avoid knocking. This increase is particularly noticeable as the engine severity increases and the margin of unused octane numbers becomes less. A fuel may be quite satisfactorily knock-resistant when an engine is new, but inadequate after five or ten

---

[1] Olin, Read, and Goss, *Ind. Eng. Chem.*, **18**:1316 (1926). Olin and Jebens, *Ind. Eng. Chem.*, **21**:43 (1929). Rifkin and Walcutt, *J. SAE*, **65**(7):34 (1957). The nature of the thermal dissociation of tetraethyllead has been studied by Rifkin and Walcutt, *ACS, Div. Petrol. Chem., Gen. Papers*, Preprint, p. 159, ACS Meeting, Minneapolis, September, 1955.

[2] Ross and Rifkin, *ACS, Div. Petrol. Chem., Gen. Papers*, Preprint, p. 151, ACS Meeting, Minneapolis, September, 1955.

[3] Egerton and Gates, *J. Inst. Petrol. Technologists*, **13**:250 (1927).

[4] Withrow and Rassweiler, *Ind. Eng. Chem.*, **27**:872 (1935). Chamberlain and Walsh, *Proc. Roy. Soc. (London)*, **A215**:175, 454 (1952). Downs, Walsh, and Wheeler, *Phil. Trans. Roy. Soc. London*, **243**:463 (1951). Anzilotti, Rogers, Scott, and Tomsic, *Ind. Eng. Chem.*, **46**:1314 (1954). Retailliau, Ricards, and Jones, *Am. Scientist*, **39**:656 (1951). Chamberlain, Hoare, and Walsh, *Discussions Faraday Soc.*, no. 14, p. 89, 1953. Erhard and Norrish, *Proc. Roy. Soc. (London)*, **A234**:178 (1956).

[5] Egerton, *Fuel*, **33**(3):274 (1954).

[6] Pastell, *Quart. Trans. SAE*, **4**:571 (1950).

[7] Walsh, *Trans. Faraday Soc.*, **45**:1043 (1949).

[8] Brown, Markley, and Shapiro, *Ind. Eng. Chem.*, **47**:2141 (1955). Brennan, Giammaria, and Oberright, *ACS, Div. Petrol. Chem., Gen. Papers*, Preprint, p. 211, ACS Meeting, Miami, April, 1957.

thousand miles of operation. The octane demand of the thus used engine may be as much as 10 or more octane numbers above what it was when the engine was clean. The result is apparently attributable to the heat-insulating properties of the combustion chamber deposits (causing higher prespark air-fuel mixture temperatures), to changes of air-fuel flow, and, to a minor extent, to an increase in the compression ratio.[1] Cornelius and Caplan[2] found the deposits to have little effect on the pressure development caused by precombustion reactions in the engine, but possible catalytic effects on fuel oxidation cannot be ignored.

Preignition, a form of ignition not a direct result of the spark, may be caused either before or after the incidence of spark by incandescent combustion chamber deposits or by highly heated spark plug porcelains and exhaust valves. It may often be recognized by noises differing from that associated with knock, by engine roughness, and by the continuance of engine operation ("after running") when the ignition circuit has been broken. It is generally (but not always) of prespark origin, while knocking is definitely the result of a postspark event. Knocking can cause preignition and preignition can bring on knocking. High temperature and pressure development, a characteristic of ignition at advanced spark timing, accompanies preignition. Beside power losses which occur, the high temperatures are deleterious to the metal parts of an engine, especially to piston crowns.

Preignition seems to be a complex phenomenon for which no complete explanation is available. Several types have been proposed;[3] these include:

Silent	Autoignition
Steady with noise	Wild ping

Silent preignition, identified as flame by gas ionization measurements, has been known to induce essentially complete combustion before the normal spark ignition begins. This requires a much retarded spark; an engine under these conditions may run normally and without noise after the ignition circuit has been broken. Steady preignition with noise (thudding) has essentially the same characteristics as silent preignition.

[1] Raviolo, *J. SAE*, **59**(2):27 (1951). Dumont, *Quart. Trans. SAE*, **5**:565 (1951). Carr, McReynolds, Britton, and Linnard, *J. SAE*, **60**(8):32 (1952). Gibson, Hall, and Huffman, *J. SAE*, **60**(11):20 (1952). Newby and Dumont, *Ind. Eng. Chem.*, **45**:1336 (1953).

[2] *Quart. Trans. SAE*, **6**:489 (1952).

[3] Melby, Diggs, and Sturgis, *J. SAE*, **62**(1):42 (1954). See also Hirschler, McCullough, and Hall, *J. SAE*, **62**(1):45 (1954). Winch, *J. SAE*, **62**(1):51 (1954). Williams and Landis, *J. SAE*, **62**(1):47 (1954). Bender, Meyer, and Palinke, *ACS, Div. Petrol. Chem.*, Preprints, Chemistry and Technology of Petroleum Fuels of the Future, C-33, ACS Meeting, San Francisco, April, 1958.

The source of the noise has not been established. Autoignition is associated with heated deposit surfaces, generally anchored to the wall of the combustion chamber. It is accompanied by loud noise, will often persist after the ignition is turned off, and usually takes place at about the same time for each engine cycle. Wild ping is also associated with heated combustion chamber deposits. It occurs at irregular intervals and is believed to be caused by floating heated particles broken off from the anchored deposits. This is the type of preignition most commonly observed in cars on the road. It is not the same as knock; yet it does respond to some extent to antiknock agents.

The trouble-making deposits may attain the required temperature through heat supplied by oxidation of their own carbonaceous material. Preignition has been found to be considerably more prevalent from deposits built up of fuels containing tetraethyllead than from unleaded fuels.[1] Oxides and salts of lead and other metals lower the ignition temperature of carbon and promote its combustion. Thus, conditions which favor the combustion of the deposits (increased time at high temperatures) will encourage preignition. Some of the recognized factors are lean air-fuel ratios (plentiful oxygen supply), high inlet air temperatures and pressures (supercharging), retarded spark timing, increase in compression ratio, type of oil (higher volatility decreases deposit formation), and the nature of the fuel. For instance, reduction in fuel distillation end point reduces the tendency toward preignition and, in general, preignition decreases with the hydrocarbon types in the following order: aromatics, olefins, paraffins.[2]

Preignition is one of the limiting factors in the development of high compression engines. At present the corrective measures employed for its reduction are use of relatively more volatile high-octane fuels, and gasoline additives.[3]

XI-7. Knocking Characteristics of Individual Hydrocarbons. Differences in the knocking behavior of the various types of hydrocarbons were recognized quite early both by Midgely[4] and by Ricardo.[5] Data on the value of branched-chain paraffins was first published by Edgar.[6] Since

---

[1] Withrow and Bowditch, *Quart. Trans. SAE,* **6**:724 (1952). Nebel and Cramer, *Ind. Eng. Chem.,* **47**:2393 (1955).

[2] Sabina, Mikita, and Campbell, *Proc. API,* **33**(III):137 (1953). Hirschler, McCullough, and Hall, *loc. cit.*

[3] Nebel and Cramer, *loc. cit.* Burnham, *ACS, Div. Petrol. Chem.,* Use of Additives in Motor Fuels, Preprint, p. 39, ACS Meeting, Minneapolis, September, 1955. Hinkamp and Warren, *ACS, Div. Petrol. Chem., Gen. Papers,* Preprint, p. 195, ACS Meeting, Miami, April, 1957.

[4] *J. SAE,* **7**:489 (1920).

[5] *Engineering,* **121**:147, 182, 475, 509, 605 (1926).

[6] *Ind. Eng. Chem.,* **19**:145 (1927).

then, the examination of individual hydrocarbons of various structures, although troublesome and expensive, has continued steadily. Some of the earliest determinations were made by Lovell, Campbell, and Boyd,[1] who prepared and carried out engine tests on some one hundred and eighty separate paraffinic, olefinic, naphthenic, and aromatic hydrocarbons as molar blends in a reference gasoline; about one hundred were evaluated in pure form. The published work in this field has been summarized by Lovell.[2] Notable contributions have been made by

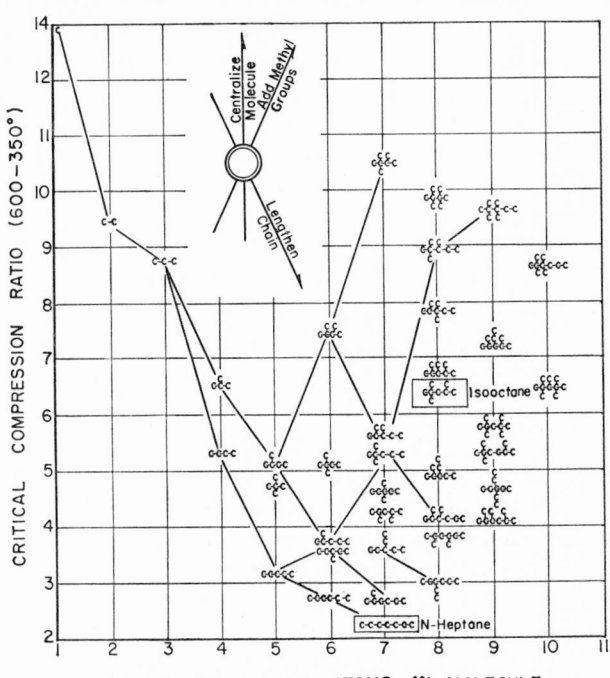

FIG. XI-6. The influence of hydrocarbon structure on critical compression ratios of paraffinic hydrocarbons. [*Lovell, Ind. Eng. Chem.,* **40**:2388 (1948).]

American Petroleum Institute Project 45,[3] by the U.S. National Advisory Committee for Aeronautics, and by many individuals.

The influence of hydrocarbon structure on antiknock properties is illustrated by Fig. XI-6, showing the consistent relationships between the size and structural features of a number of paraffins and their critical

[1] *Ind. Eng. Chem.,* **23**:26, 555 (1931); **25**:1107 (1933); **26**:475, 1105 (1934). Lovell, *Ind. Eng. Chem.,* **40**:2388 (1948).

[2] "Science of Petroleum," vol. II, part 3, p. 43, Oxford University Press, New York and London, 1953.

[3] *Proc. API,* **32**(I):131 (1952). See also 18*th Ann. Rept.,* API Project 45, 1955–1956.

compression ratios. Similar relations are found among the other hydrocarbon types. The following summary covers most of the results:

Paraffin Hydrocarbons

1. For similar structures, an increase in the length of an unbranched
carbon chain produces a regular increase in the tendency to knock.

2. An increase in the number of methyl groups attached to a carbon
chain regularly decreases the tendency to knock.

3. For a given molecular size, the centralization of the groups to make
a more compact molecule reduces the tendency to knock.

4. The larger the molecule, the greater the possible spread in knocking
tendency of its isomers. The spread may be very wide, as for *n*-heptane
and 2,2,4-trimethylbutane, known as triptane.[1]

Olefin Hydrocarbons. The knocking tendency of the olefins, in general,
lies between that of the normal and branched-chain paraffins.[2]

1. Lengthening of the carbon chain, unbroken by a double bond, causes
a steady increase in the tendency to knock.

2. Olefins of the same carbon chain length knock less as the double
bond is moved toward the center of the molecule.

3. Branched olefins knock less than the isomeric straight-chain olefins.

4. Irrespective of the position of the double bond or of the molecular
size, olefins containing saturated carbon chains of the same length have
the same knocking properties.

Diolefins, with the exception of 1,3-butadiene, knock less than the
normal paraffins. Both centralization and conjugation of the double
bonds reduce the knocking tendency.

Acetylene compounds may be either higher or lower knocking than
corresponding paraffins; centralization of the triple bond reduces knock.

Cyclic Olefins

1. These compounds knock less than the corresponding naphthenes;
indeed they show very high knock resistance.

2. Straight-chain alkyl substituents are undesirable; increasing the
chain length increases this effect.

Naphthenic Hydrocarbons. In most cases, the saturated naphthenic
hydrocarbons are slightly higher in knocking tendency than the straight-
chain olefins of the same number of carbon atoms. Only cyclopetane is
much better than its α-olefin isomer.

1. The tendency to knock increases as the size of the ring increases.

2. Straight-chain alkyl substituents are undesirable; increasing the
lengths of the chains makes them even more so.

3. Several small chains are better than one long one containing the

---

[1] Triptane has the highest known critical compression ratio, octane number, and
octane blending value of the paraffinic hydrocarbons.

[2] See also Meeks and Randall, 16*th Ann. Rept.*, API Project 45, pp. 1, 17–33, 1953–
1954.

same number of carbon atoms. Otherwise, position of substituent groups makes no great difference among the alkylated naphthenes.

4. Branching of side chains is favorable.

Aromatic Hydrocarbons. The aromatic hydrocarbons, in general, knock less than any other hydrocarbon type.

1. As the length of a side chain is increased up to three carbon atoms, i.e., n-propylbenzene, the tendency toward knock decreases, but further chain lengthening is unfavorable.

2. Successive additions of methyl groups to the ring are favorable as one proceeds from benzene to toluene, xylene, and mesitylene. The effect of methyl group addition to n-propyl, butyl, or amylbenzene is small; but with isopropyl or isoamylbenzene, the added group reduces the knocking tendency appreciably.

3. The further the ring distance between the side chains, the less is the tendency to knock.

4. As with other types of hydrocarbons, branching of the side chains is desirable.

5. Aromatics with olefinic side chains are consistently better than the corresponding compounds with saturated side groups. A triple bond in the side chain, however, is unfavorable; the isomeric aryl diolefin is nevertheless high in antiknock quality.

From the foregoing, it would appear that the general order of increasing knocking tendency for the more common types would be aromatics, branched-chain olefins, branched-chain paraffins, unsaturated side-chain naphthenes, straight-chain olefins, naphthenes, and straight-chain paraffins. Double bonds and branched aliphatic chains are always desirable; this is especially true when they can be centralized within the molecule.

XI-8. Blending Value. While the octane numbers of diisobutylene are 82 and 95 by the motor and research methods, respectively, it is known that addition of a gram mole (112) of this hydrocarbon to a liter of a reference gasoline is more effective in increasing the knock resistance of the blend than is the addition of a corresponding gram mole (114) of isooctane to the same gasoline, although the latter has by definition an octane number of 100 by either test method. Diisobutylene is said to have a higher octane blending value than isooctane.

The blending value is a characteristic number but never an exact figure, since it varies with the amount and chemical nature of the hydrocarbon and the stock to which it is added, and with the severity of the engine conditions. There are good arguments for supposing that the blending value of a hydrocarbon is a function of the antiknock quality of the products resulting from its precombustion reactions.[1]

[1] Blanding, *ACS, Div. Petrol. Chem., Gen. Papers*, Preprints, p. 277, ACS Meeting, Cincinnati, April, 1955.

Work by American Petroleum Institute Project 45, based on binary blends of pure hydrocarbons, has indicated that paraffins in paraffins, paraffins in naphthenes, and naphthenes in naphthenes blend almost linearly in terms of octane numbers.[1]   In general, however, linear relationships are exceptional.[2]   Increases in antiknock value over the calculated average are referred to as positive, and decreases, as negative blending values.   Interreactions of unknown nature between fuels or their precombustion products are thought to be responsible for the nonlinear effects.   If critical compression ratios or performance numbers are plotted against composition, curved lines are obtained, even for paraffin-isoparaffin mixtures.

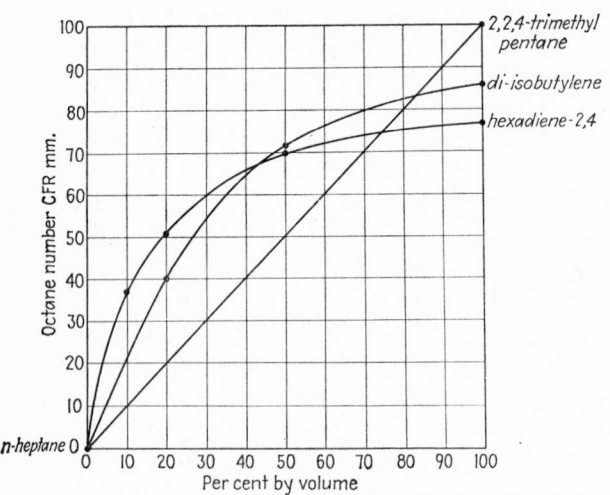

FIG. XI-7. Octane-number curves of mixtures of *n*-heptane with olefins. [*From Smittenberg, Hoog, Moerbeek, and Zijden, J. Inst. Petrol.*, **26**:294 (1940).]

Figure XI-7, based on composition-octane numbers, shows the results obtained on blending *n*-heptane with isooctane, diisobutylene, and hexadiene-2,4.   In contrast to the straight-line value shown by addition of isooctane to *n*-heptane, the olefin and diolefin are positive blending agents (higher values), most effect being shown at their lower concentrations.   This is in accordance with the observation that blends of paraffins

[1] *Proc. API*, **32**(I):137 (1952); 18*th Ann. Rept.*, API Project 45, 1955–1956.   See also, Lovell, *Ind. Eng. Chem.*, **40**:2388 (1948).   Blanding, *op. cit.*   For conversion of measurements of blending values in terms of aniline additions, see Lovell, Campbell, and Boyd, *Ind. Eng. Chem.*, **23**:26 (1931).   Garner, Evans, Sprake, and Broom, *World Petrol. Cong., Proc. 1st Congr., London*, **2**:170 (1933).

[2] Heath and Hicks, *ACS, Div. Petrol. Chem. Symposium on Motor Fuels*, Preprint, p. 23, ACS Meeting, Chicago, April, 1948.   Frey, Kerley, and Lovell, *Oil Gas J.*, **47**(18):61 (1948).   Bogen and Nichols, *Ind. Eng. Chem.*, **41**:2629 (1949).   Scott, *Petrol. Refiner*, **37**(5):191 (1958).

and olefins are generally higher in octane number than their calculated linear values; the same holds for olefins in naphthenes. Aromatic hydrocarbons are usually high in blending value.

The lower the octane number of the reference gasoline, the higher is the blending octane value of the hydrocarbon added, for it is easier to raise the octane number of a poor gasoline than of one already high in antiknock quality. The blending value of a hydrocarbon is obtained by determining the octane value of several blends at different concentrations in a reference gasoline. It is calculated by the following equation:

$$O_B = \frac{VO_H + (100 - V)O_R}{100}$$

where O_B is the octane number of the blend, V is the volume per cent of hydrocarbon in the mixture, O_R is the octane number of the reference gasoline, and O_H is the blending octane number of the hydrocarbon.

The following values are typical of 20 per cent blends in a 60:40 mixture of isooctane and n-heptane.[1]

	Blending octane number	
	Research method	Motor method
Paraffins:		
2,2-Dimethylpropane	100	90
2,3-Dimethylbutane	96	107
2-Methylpentane	83	79
2,2,3-Trimethylbutane	113	113
Olefins:		
2-Pentene (*cis*)	154	137
2-Methyl-2-butene	176	141
1-Heptene	68	46
3-Heptene (*trans*)	124	119
Diisobutylene	168	151
Naphthenes:		
Cyclopentane	141	141
Ethylcyclopentane	75	67
Cyclohexane	110	97
Butylcyclohexane	116	101
Aromatics:		
Benzene	99	91
Ethylbenzene	167	142
n-Propylbenzene	127	129
o-Xylene	120	103
p-Xylene	146	127
Mesitylene	171	137

[1] API Research Project 45, 18*th Ann. Rept.*, p. 165, 1955–1956.

The high values for the olefins and the aromatics are noticeable; they show, as might be expected, marked deterioration with rise in the temperature of the test engine in which the values are determined.

Cyclopentadiene, dicyclopentadiene, dimethylfulvene, and cyclohexadiene, surprisingly, have the highest blending octane numbers reported (above 200, research method). They would be undesirable gasoline constituents, however, from the standpoint of instability and gum formation.

XI-9. Lead Susceptibility. Both gasolines and individual hydrocarbons are characterized not only by their octane-number values but also by the magnitude of their response in octane number to the addition of tetraethyllead; similar differences probably exist in response to other antiknock agents. The extent to which hydrocarbons differ among themselves in this regard is much greater than is true of gasoline mixtures. When tetraethyllead is added to a pure hydrocarbon, the resulting change may be from 1.0 to 3.0 units of compression ratio per cubic centimeter per gallon, while a similar addition to commercial gasolines causes increases of the order of only one-tenth that amount.[1]

Tetraethyllead may actually cause a decrease in critical compression ratio when added to certain types of hydrocarbons; in such cases, the lead component acts as a knock inducer. This applies only to cyclic diolefins, aromatic acetylene derivatives, certain aromatic compounds with unsaturated side chains, and hydrocarbons of the nature of indane and the fulvenes, generally those having conjugated double bonds.[2] Such compounds are extremely sensitive to engine conditions.

Lovell,[3] and Zang and Lovell[4] have exhaustively reviewed the effect of tetraethyllead on individual hydrocarbons. Paraffins respond favorably; when measured by increases in critical compression ratio, the addition of 3.0 ml per gal under a variety of operating conditions consistently shows a 10 per cent increase in power output for all except some very highly branched paraffins, irrespective of their octane-number level. The gains effected by the use of tetraethyllead appear constant, whether the engine conditions are mild or severe. The same conclusions can be drawn from engines operating under supercharge conditions; here the addition of 1.0 ml per gal results in a 30 per cent increase in knock-limited power. Measurements by the research and motor methods also indicate

---

[1] Campbell, Signaigo, Lovell, and Boyd, *Ind. Eng. Chem.*, **27**:593 (1935).

[2] An example is cyclopentadiene; in general, hydrocarbons which themselves exert an oxidation-inhibiting action, presumably because they oxidize by means of a large number of very short chains. Walsh, Ethyl Corporation Lectures on Combustion, p. 112, 1954.

[3] *Ind. Eng. Chem.*, **40**:2388 (1948).

[4] *Ind. Eng. Chem.*, **43**:2826 (1951).

the effectiveness to be independent of operating conditions, but in those test methods the effect of the tetraethyllead varies greatly with the octane number of the compound, most response being given by the lower-octane hydrocarbons.[1] The few highly branched paraffin hydrocarbons that do not fit into the above patterns are compounds such as 2,2,3,3-tetramethylpentane and 2,2,3,3-tetramethylhexane; these in turn are highly sensitive to changes in air-fuel mixture and engine operating conditions.

The effect of tetraethyllead on the mono- and bicyclic naphthenes is much the same as that on the paraffins; in general, the same gain in efficiency results. The response to the antiknock agent is slightly less and a few more deviations occur, especially with methyl and *t*-butylcyclopentane. Cyclopentane has a higher lead susceptibility than cyclohexane.

The olefins are less responsive to lead addition than are the paraffins. The effect on some of the low-octane olefins, notably the straight-chains alpha compounds, approaches that on the paraffins, but in high-octane olefins (chiefly those highly branched) the response may be only a small fraction of that obtained in paraffins or naphthenes of equivalent octane level. A possible reason for this has been proposed.[2] It is possible that tetraethyllead acts by its effect on certain intermediates of precombustion reactions; the essential absence of such reactions and products with diisobutylene may explain the poor lead response of that hydrocarbon.

The effectiveness of lead in aromatics has not been studied in the same detail as for other hydrocarbon types. A large variation exists even between isomers, ranging from a negative effect to a positive one as high as that in paraffins. Tetraethyllead appears to be a slight knock inducer in benzene; toluene, ethyl, *n*-propyl, and *n*-butylbenzenes lie on a line of constant relative lead effectiveness (as do the paraffins). Branching of the alkyl group is accompanied by a considerably lower lead response. In polysubstituted alkyl aromatics the effect of the position held is important; thus, *o*-xylene is practically inert to tetraethyllead while *p*-xylene is nearly as responsive as the paraffins; *m*-xylene is intermediate.

The response of gasolines is empirically dependent on a number of factors, such as source, degree of cracking, volatility, type and amount of refining, and the presence of dissolved sulfur compounds. The actual difference may be quite considerable, and serious attention is given by refiners to obtaining the highest possible octane value with the least amount of added tetraethyllead.

[1] For a discussion of the relation between lead susceptibility and preflame reactions, see Walcutt and Rifkin, *Ind. Eng. Chem.*, **43**:2844 (1951).

[2] *Ibid.*

From what has been said about hydrocarbons, it is evident that two gasolines of the same octane rating may respond unequally to a given amount of lead.   The shape of the curves showing the increase in highest useful compression ratios or octane numbers with various additions of tetraethyllead suggests that the improvement is an exponential function of the concentration present,[1]

$$I = SN^k$$

where I is the improvement in highest useful compression ratio noted, S is the slope of the line and represents lead susceptibility, and N is the concentration of the tetraethyllead present.

The equation may also be expressed as

$$K = \frac{\log I - \log S}{\log N}$$

and in applying experimental data obtained from a large number of gasolines of various types, the value of this constant turns out to be about 0.75 when highest useful compression ratios are measured and when N is expressed as cubic centimeters per gallon.   Useful charts have been developed which show the effect of the addition of various amounts of tetraethyllead to gasolines of different octane levels.[2]

The good response of straight-run gasolines is useful in making high antiknock fuels.   While the gasoline itself may be low in octane value, the small addition required to bring it up to a certain standard often renders it a more suitable premium gasoline stock than a less susceptible cracked gasoline.   The more volatile straight-run gasolines have higher octane numbers, as well as higher lead susceptibility values, than the less volatile; stabilized natural gasolines are thus excellent blending stocks, the octane value varying more or less directly with the Reid vapor pressure.[3]

XI-10. Antiknock Antagonists.   The adverse effect of sulfur compounds on the antiknock efficiency of tetraethyllead has long been known.[4]

[1] Hebl and Rendel, *J. Inst. Petrol. Technologists*, **18**:187 (1932).

[2] Cattaneo and Stanly, *Ind. Eng. Chem.*, **33**:1370 (1941).   Eastman, *Ind. Eng. Chem.*, **33**:1555 (1941).

[3] Alden, *Natl. Petrol. News*, **24**(3):32 (1932).   See also Trusty, *Refiner Nat. Gasoline Mfr.*, **19**(4):93 (1940).   Nonhydrocarbon compounds present may influence the lead response of a gasoline to a marked extent.   It is reported that tertiary butyl alcohol (Schneider, U.S. Patent 2,087,582, 1937) and diisopropyl ether [Buc and Aldrin, *Trans. SAE*, **39**:333 (1936)] have a favorable effect.

[4] Hebl and Rendel, *J. Inst. Petrol.*, **18**:187 (1932).   Schulze and Buell, *Natl. Petrol. News*, **27**(41):25 (1935); **29**(23):54 (1937).   Birch and Stansfield, *Ind. Eng. Chem.*, **28**:668 (1936).   Eastman, *Ind. Eng. Chem.*, **33**:1555 (1941).   Mapstone and Durham, *J. Inst. Petrol.*, **37**:737 (1951).   Fooksom and Bell, *Petrol. Refiner*, **27**(9):459 (1948).

A less familiar fact is that at least a portion of the antagonistic effect on the ability of tetraethyllead to suppress end gas reactions occurs in motored engines, and thus at temperatures considerably lower than those of the unburned gases prevailing in normal combustion.[1] In general, the detrimental effect increases in the following order: thiophenes, sulfides, mercaptans, disulfides, and polysulfides. The magnitude of the drop in octane values[2] is shown in Table XI-5; the various sulfur

TABLE XI-5

Sulfur compound	Octane number	Decrease
None...........................	83	
Sulfur..........................	76	7
Hydrogen sulfide................	72	11
Sulfur dioxide...................	72	11
Carbon disulfide.................	76	7
Thiophenes......................	79	4
Alkyl sulfides...................	75	8
Aryl sulfides....................	77	6
Alkyl disulfides.................	73	10
Aryl disulfides..................	77	6
Aliphatic dithiols...............	72	11
Alkyl and aryl mercaptans........	72	11
Tetrasulfides....................	70	13
Thiophene thiol.................	69	14

compounds were added to give 0.1 per cent sulfur in a blend of 60 per cent isooctane and 40 per cent n-heptane containing 3.0 ml $Pb(C_2H_5)_4$ per gal. Study has indicated[3] that:

1. All sulfur compounds of the same type show equal suppressing effect at the same sulfur level.

2. The decrease in octane number is a function of the concentration of the antagonist, but is independent of fuel composition and tetraethyllead concentration. For a given sulfur compound and concentration, the suppression of antiknock activity is the same fractional part of the total tetraethyllead effect regardless of the total concentration of the latter. The same result is found, whether the engine is operating under motor or research test conditions. These regularities are somewhat tempered by the observation[4] that the antagonistic effect of sulfur compounds is noticeably less in automobile engines than in test equipment.

[1] Pastell, *Quart. Trans. SAE*, **4**:57 (1950).

[2] Livingston, *Oil Gas J.*, **46**(45):81 (1948); **47**(38):67 (1949).

[3] Ryan, *Ind. Eng. Chem.*, **34**:824 (1942). Livingston, *Ind. Eng. Chem.*, **41**:888 (1949). Livingston, Hyde, and Campbell, *Ind. Eng. Chem.*, **41**:2722 (1949).

[4] Pulleyblank and Lovell, *Proc. API*, **30M**(III):280 (1950).

The phenomenon of antagonism is not limited to sulfur compounds.[1] Tetraethyllead, iron and nickel carbonyls, and tin compounds are affected also by compounds of other elements. The order of antagonism is halogen < sulfur < arsenic < silicon < phosphorus; organic peroxides have no effect. On the other hand, aniline and its derivatives are not influenced by the above, but are affected by peroxides. Diethylselenide seems to have no antagonists.

XI-11. Measurement of Knocking Tendency. The devising of satisfactory methods for rating fuels as to knocking tendency presents a good deal of difficulty because of the steady improvement of fuels in knock resistance. Determination of highest useful compression ratio[2] offers a good absolute scale, but it is dependent on the test engine used. A reference scale has been found more convenient, since standard fuels can be reproduced and their purity controlled. The adoption of 2,2,4-trimethylpentane (isooctane) and *n*-heptane, first recommended by Edgar[3] as primary standards, provided a scale which has been satisfactory as long as the antiknock values of the fuels to be rated have stayed below this nominal top value. By definition pure isooctane has a value of 100 and *n*-heptane of 0 on a scale in which heptane is the hard-knocking constituent; mixtures of the two are employed for matching particular fuels in knocking intensity, and the percentage of isooctane present in any mixture defines the octane number of that mixture. It need hardly be pointed out that this scale is in no sense absolute. Some hydrocarbons are more knock-resistant than isooctane, and the upper end of the scale really lies (with present knowledge) at about 128.[4]

Testing of knocking tendency of a fuel is accomplished by comparing it in a standardized test engine, under carefully defined knocking conditions, with mixtures of the primary standards (or of secondary standards already compared with the primary) until satisfactory matching is obtained. A gasoline which, under the defined conditions, matches a mixture of 20 per cent *n*-heptane and 80 per cent isooctane has by definition an octane number of 80.

The determining of octane numbers is properly made only in the Cooperative Fuel Research (CFR) engine and by the standardized methods adopted.[5] Changes in engines have at various times required alteration of the test conditions. The first[6] in order of time was what

[1] Livingston, *Ind. Eng. Chem.*, **43**:633 (1951).

[2] King and Moss, *Engineering*, **128**:219, 272 (1929). Stansfield and Thole, *Engineering*, **130**:468, 512 (1930).

[3] *Ind. Eng. Chem.*, **19**:145 (1927).

[4] Brooks, *Trans. SAE*, **54**:394 (1946).

[5] ASTM Manual of Engine Test Methods, pp. 5, 29, 1956.

[6] ASTM D 908; also known as CRC F-1.

later became known as the research method. Certain important varibles were set as follows:

Engine speed	600 rpm
Intake air temperature	125°F
Jacket temperature	212°F
Spark advance	For maximum power (later at 13°)
Mixture ratio	For maximum knock

Comparisons by this method rated fuels in about the order found in automobile engines manufactured prior to 1932. Increases in engine speed, compression ratio, and temperature made it unsatisfactory, and in that year the "motor" method[1] was adopted. In addition to minor changes in the test engine, certain significant conditions were altered to

Engine speed	900 rpm
Jacket temperature	212°F
Intake air temperature	100°F
Mixture temperature	300°F
Spark advance	Automatic
Mixture ratio	For maximum knock

Correlation of laboratory results with those obtained in automobiles on the road has involved a good deal of experimentation. It has been found that some gasolines will register on the road higher-octane and others lower-octane values than their ASTM ratings, and these deviations are not always the same when different automobiles are used for the test.[2] Various road rating methods have been employed,[3] the most satisfactory of which involves measuring the spark advance required to produce incipient knock at various speeds;[4] it is referred to as the border-line method. A given gasoline is thus characterized by a curve relating spark advance at incipient knock to engine speed; a comparison with the patterns of known reference fuels gives an octane equivalence. This

---

[1] ASTM D 357–48; also CRC F-2. Barometric pressure may also be a factor. See Siegel, "Methods for Reducing the Effect of Barometric Pressure in Measurement of Octane Number" (STP 186), ASTM, 1956.

[2] Boyd, *Proc. API, Second Midyear Meeting, Refining Div.*, 98, June, 1932. Veal, Best, Campbell, and Holaday, *Trans. SAE*, **32**:105 (1933). Veal, *Trans. SAE*, **36**:165 (1935). Campbell, Lovell, and Boyd, *Trans. SAE*, **40**:144 (1937). Boyd, *Trans. SAE*, **42**:244 (1938). Sabina, *Trans. SAE*, **43**:416 (1938). Blackwood, Kass, and Davis, *Trans. SAE*, **43**:427 (1938).

[3] Campbell, Lovell, and Boyd, *Trans. SAE*, **40**:144 (1937). Greenshields and Hebl, *Trans. SAE*, **40**:148 (1937). Bartholomew, Chalk, and Brewster, *Trans. SAE*, **42**:141 (1938). Blackwood, Kass, and Davis, *Trans. SAE*, **43**:427 (1938). Drinkard and Macauley, *Trans. SAE*, **43**:436 (1938). Hebl and Rendel, *Trans. SAE*, **44**:210 (1939).

[4] Campbell, Greenshields, and Holaday, *Trans. SAE*, **48**:193 (1941). Wagner, Ross, Henderson, and Risk, *Refiner Nat. Gasoline Mfr.*, **20**(11):436 (1941).

relation has the advantage that it appears to be fairly constant for given set of fuels in different engines. The shape of the curve varies considerably with the chemical composition of the gasoline and its volatility.[1]

The road rating of a fuel will, of course, change with changes in road vehicle engines. It also varies in a somewhat uncertain way with the sensitivity of the fuel to changes in test methods; this is formalized as the difference between octane values determined by the research and motor methods, respectively. The sensitivity is dependent largely on chemical composition, and it has been observed that fuels containing considerable proportions of olefins and aromatics rate higher by the research method than those made up largely of paraffins and naphthenes. This is shown in Table XI-6.[2]

TABLE XI-6

	Thermally cracked	Catalytically cracked	Catalytically reformed		Catalytic C_3-C_4 polymers
Composition, per cent volume:					
Aromatics....................	14	22	50	65	1
Olefins.......................	29	45	...	...	94
Saturates....................	57	33	50	35	5
Octane number:					
Research:					
Clear......................	75	92	86	100	97
Plus 3 cc $Pb(C_2H_5)_4$ per gal....	86	96	...	...	100
Motor:					
Clear......................	68	80	77	88	82
Plus 3 cc $Pb(C_2H_5)_4$ per gal....	78	85	...	...	85
Sensitivity:					
Clear......................	7	12	9	12	15
Plus 3 cc $Pb(C_2H_5)_4$ per gal.......	8	11	...	...	15

This sensitivity has been related by Rifkin and Walcutt to the change of ignition delay of the hydrocarbons with the peak temperatures and pressures prevailing in a given engine.[3]

Two methods are in use for testing aviation fuels, one each for evaluating cruising and take-off qualities. The former (the more severe) is a lean mixture test and the temperature developed in a thermal plug in

[1] Risk and Jordan, *Refiner Nat. Gasoline Mfr.*, **26**:389 (1947). Offutt, Taylor, and Swartz, *Ind. Eng. Chem.*, **41**:2359 (1949). Prickett, Campbell, Johnson, and Knee, *Proc. API*, **30M**(III):291 (1950).

[2] Boyd, Domke, and White, Preprint, SAE Fuels and Lubricants Manufacturing, November, 1955. See also Nelson, *Oil Gas J.*, **50**(35):86 (1952). Fleming, Hakala, Moody, Scott, and Tongberg, *Oil Gas J.*, **53**(43):100 (1955).

[3] *J. SAE*, **65**(7):32 (1957).

the combustion chamber is employed as an index of knock.[1]   The technique of bracketing with reference fuels is followed.   The method for take-off ability (rich mixture) depends upon the amount of supercharging that the test fuel will tolerate before audible knock appears, as compared with results from bracketing by reference fuels.[2]   Pertinent test conditions are

	CRC F-3	CRC F-4
Engine speed...................	1,200	1,800
Compression ratio..............	Variable	7.0
Spark advance.................	35	45
Coolant temperature...........	374	375
Mixture temperature...........	220	

The octane scale has been satisfactory for automobile fuels, but is not so for those used in aviation, where octane numbers higher than 100 have been current for some years; the unit, in this case, has been the performance number.   The measurement and rating of such octane values above 100 have presented a good deal of difficulty.   It is true that various hydrocarbons such as triptane are more knock-resistant than isooctane, but this is not the whole answer.   An obvious, though perhaps not a permanent, solution has been the use of reference fuels made by adding tetraethyllead to isooctane.   Something more basic, which can be related to values above and below that of isooctane, is desirable.   The problem was, until recently, most acute for aviation gasolines as used in reciprocating engines.   However, the development of turbines and jets for airplanes has relieved this situation, since jet fuels are usually not gasolines and have no octane number requirements.

Various other reference fuels have been suggested, including blends made of leaded (4.6 ml per gal) isooctane[3] and similarly leaded normal heptane, and another set composed of leaded triptane and leaded heptane.[4]   In order to relate fuel quality to power generated, the performance number was developed.[5]   It is the ratio

$$\frac{\text{Knock limited performance of test fuel}}{\text{Knock limited performance of reference fuel}}$$

[1] ASTM D 614–49T; CRC F-3.

[2] ASTM D 909–47T; CRC F-4.

[3] For table giving octane numbers above 100 for isooctane containing tetraethyllead, see *Oil Gas J.*, **54**(82):96 (1956).

[4] Brooks, *Trans. SAE*, **54**:394 (1946).

[5] Robert V. Kerley of Ethyl Corporation advises (private communication) that development of the performance number concept and scale should be attributed to the personnel of the Military Air Services, including the U.S. Air Force at Wright Field,

In the A-N (Army-Navy) performance number, the performance is measured as indicated mean effective pressure and the reference fuel is isooctane. The performance number of isooctane is then, by definition, 100. The relation to octane number is expressed by an S-shaped curve in which 21.9 on the PN scale = zero octane number, and PN of 161 = the value of isooctane + 6 ml of tetraethyllead per gallon.[1] It has been recognized that under certain conditions of testing, the reciprocal of the indicated mean effective pressure can be related in a linear fashion to one or more of the suggested reference fuel scales, and that an index system can be based on such a relation.[2] As a practical matter, aviation gasolines have been specified by two performance numbers, since they must be rated for cruising under lean-mixture and for take-off under rich-mixture conditions. An example is a military fuel described as 100/130, which has a performance number (an octane number) of 100 by the F-3 method (cruising) and a performance number of 130 by the F-4 method, to indicate its quality at rich mixture and wide-open throttle.

No proved satisfactory rating for motor gasolines of octane number above 100 has yet been developed. Empirical equations showing relation between "octane number" and tetraethyllead in isooctane and between performance number and projected octane number have been proposed. One based on the relation

$$\text{Octane number} = 100 + \frac{\text{performance number} - 100}{3}$$

has recently been adopted for use.[3] A mathematical conversion of this equation indicates that

$$\text{Isooctane} + 6 \text{ ml TEL per gal} = 120.3 \text{ O.N.}$$

An interconversion table has been constructed.[4]

Attempts have been made to develop methods for calculating the octane value of individual hydrocarbons through their structural charac-

---

the Bureau of Aeronautics of the U.S. Navy Department, and the British Air Commission, during the period 1939–1942. The authors believe, however, that Robert V. Kerley himself and S. D. Heron of Ethyl Corporation were intimately concerned in the development. See also Kerley, "Origin of A-N Performance Number System," Ethyl Corporation Report, Detroit, 1956. The proportionality of knock-limited power to performance number is limited to such conditions that only throttle opening is varied to obtain knock and that other major engine variables such as engine speed and air-fuel ratio are kept constant.

[1] Brooks, *op. cit.* Edgar, *Advances in Chem. Ser.*, No. 5, p. 231, 1951.

[2] On these scales, see also *Coordinating Research Council Rept.* 249, 1949. Hesselberg and Lovell, *J. SAE*, **59**(4):32 (1951).

[3] Wiese, National Petroleum Association Meeting, Cleveland, April, 1956; *Petrol. Processing*, **11**:90 (1956).

[4] *Oil Gas J.*, **54**(82):96 (1956).

teristics. It has been observed that the relative susceptibilities of paraffin hydrocarbons to knock are directly proportional to the number of hydrogen atoms attached to secondary and tertiary carbon atoms; the agreement is similar but less definite for the olefins.[1] A moderately close relationship has been found between the research octane values of various hydrocarbons and their "structural retardation factors," which are based on a consideration of their specific vulnerability to oxidation.[2] A variety of attempts have been made to calculate performance characteristics of multicomponent motor fuel blends.[3] While some of these have been useful as rough guides in making estimates, engine testing is still necessary.

SPECIAL MOTOR FUELS

Demand and economic conditions have caused the study and, at one time or another, the use of special fuel constituents. Most commonly, this has occurred to meet the requirements for high-octane aviation fuels, ordinarily by segregating selected petroleum distillates and adding synthetic or otherwise nonpetroleum materials.

Base stocks for aviation gasoline have been made by distilling suitable fractions, usually rather low boiling, from naphthenic or aromatic crudes of naturally high octane number; examples are those from California, the Gulf Coast, Eastern Venezuela, or the East Indies. These yield "clear" (unleaded) gasolines of 70 to 76 octane number, motor method. It is also possible to supply similar, more knock-resistant base stocks by catalytically re-treating gasolines made by catalytic cracking.[4] This has the effect of increasing the aromatic and reducing the unsaturated content to a very low value. Alternately, catalytically reformed stocks of high aromatic and isoparaffin content may be employed. The wartime practice involved blending such a base stock with isopentane, olefin- isoparaffin alkylates (see Chap. III), or equivalent isooctane materials and tetraethyllead. By suitable combinations, performance numbers 80/87, 100/130, and 115/145, for example, could be obtained. Variants on the above blending constituents, considered at various times, have been

[1] Cramer and Campbell, *Ind. Eng. Chem.*, **41**:893 (1949).

[2] Livingston, *Ind. Eng. Chem.*, **43**:2834 (1951). See also Kobayaski, *J. Soc. Chem. Ind. Japan*, vol. 40, Suppl. bindings, 153, 219, 317, 1937. Mibashan, *Petrol. Refiner*, **22**:195 (1943).

[3] Kerley and Thurston, Preprint, SAE Fuels and Lubricants Meeting, Philadelphia, November, 1955. Nelson, *Oil Gas J.*, **54**(20):135 (1955). Kobayaski, *loc. cit.* Mibashan, *loc. cit.* Eastman, *Ind. Eng. Chem.*, **33**:1155 (1941). Heath and Hicks, *ACS, Div. Petrol. Chem., Symposium on Modern Motor Fuels*, Preprint, p. 23, ACS Meeting, Chicago, April, 1948. Bogen and Nichols, *Ind. Eng. Chem.*, **41**:2629 (1949). Schoen and Mrstik, *Ind. Eng. Chem.*, **47**:1740 (1955).

[4] Murphree, Gohr, and Brown, "Science of Petroleum," vol. V, part II, p. 253, Oxford University Press, New York and London, 1953.

neohexane or 2,2-dimethylbutane,[1] 2,3-dimethylbutane, triptane or 2,2,3-trimethylbutane, isopropyl ether,[2] synthetic branched decanes,[3] and nitromethane-methanol.[4] So far as known, none of these except 2,3-dimethylbutane (diisopropyl) has found permanent use. Isopropylbenzene, monomethylaniline, and mixed xylidines have, during wartime, been added to aviation gasolines in considerable proportions to improve rich-mixture take-off performance.

Benzene has always been a valuable constituent of motor gasolines; concentrations up to 40 per cent have conferred excellent knock resistance; the material has usually been rather scarce and costly for such use. In aviation gasoline it has suffered the disadvantage of high freezing point—undesirable at high altitudes—and the deterioration of performance at high engine temperatures.

The lower alcohols have always been intriguing as motor fuels. Most have octane numbers ranging from 92 to above 100.[5] Ethyl alcohol has sometimes been used as a blending agent where petroleum is scarce; attempts to force acceptance by legislation have not been successful. Its use has not been adopted to any large extent because of cost and certain technical reasons. Probably the most serious of these is the tendency toward layer separation after small amounts of water are absorbed from the air or accumulated through condensation following fuel tank breathing. Gasoline and anhydrous ethyl alcohol are miscible in all proportions within the temperature range encountered in service. The easily produced, constant-boiling mixture containing 95 per cent alcohol is immiscible with gasoline below 120°F in 10 per cent blends and below 100°F in 20 per cent blends; the necessity of dehydration of the alcohol is apparent.[6] At 68°F (20°C), layer separation occurs when the following percentages of water are added:[7]

Per cent alcohol	Per cent water
3	0.02
10	0.30
25	1.12
50	1.42

[1] Oberfell and Frey, *Proc. API*, **20**(III):78 (1939).

[2] Buc and Aldrin, *Trans. SAE*, **39**:333 (1936).

[3] Cramer and Campbell, *Ind. Eng. Chem.*, **29**:234 (1937).

[4] Starkman, Preprint, SAE Fuels and Lubricants Meeting, Tulsa, Okla., November, 1954. Starkman, Moulic, and Dunn, *Automotive Inds.*, **114**(8):57 (1956). Moulic and Dunn, *Chem. & ind.*, **77**(3):557 (1957). Starkman, *ACS, Div. Petrol. Chem.*, Preprints, Chemistry and Technology of Petroleum Fuels of the Future, C-83, San Francisco Meeting, April, 1958.

[5] Pickett, *J. Research Natl. Bur. Standards*, **35**(4):276 (1945); Egloff and Van Arsdell, *J. Inst. Petrol.*, **27**:121 (1941).

[6] Bridgeman, *Ind. Eng. Chem., News Ed.*, **11**:139 (1933).

[7] Killifer, *Ind. Eng. Chem.*, **25**:117 (1933).

The water tolerance increases with the concentration of the alcohol and is materially raised by the addition of aromatic hydrocarbons and higher alcohols.[1] The addition of 10 per cent of benzene or toluene to a 10 per cent alcohol blend will lower the critical solution temperature 15 to 20°F. Cracked gasolines have been reported to offer a greater tolerance than straight-run fuels.[2]

The heat of combustion of ethyl alcohol is considerably lower than that of gasoline, and alcohol-gasoline blends are somewhat lower in Btu content per unit volume for this reason. This is reflected in the decreased power output or higher fuel consumption. The air-fuel ratio for complete combustion of alcohol is about 9.0:1 as compared to about 15.0:1 for gasoline. Consequently, a carburetor set for maximum power with gasoline will, with a blend, produce a mixture somewhat leaner than that for maximum power. Although mileage, with this particular setting, may increase, the power and performance are noticeably decreased. If the carburetor is set richer to restore power and performance, fuel consumption is increased, about 3 to 4 per cent[3] for a 10 per cent blend.

From an antiknock standpoint, ethyl alcohol is valuable, being about twice as effective as benzene; a comparison[4] is shown in the tabulation below.

Alcohol, per cent	Octane number	Benzene, per cent	Octane number
0	65	0	65
5	68	5	66.5
10	72.5	10	68
15	77	15	69.5
		20	71.5
		30	76
		35	79

When compared with tetraethyllead, however, alcohol as an antiknock agent is not so attractive. It has been shown that 10 and 20 per cent of alcohol are equivalent to about 1 and 2 ml of tetraethyllead per gallon of gasoline.[5]

Owing to the high heat of vaporization, intake manifold temperatures run about 11°F lower with gasolines containing 10 per cent of alcohol.[6]

[1] Bridgeman, *Ind. Eng. Chem.*, **28**:1102 (1936).

[2] Killifer, *loc. cit.*

[3] Bridgeman, *loc. cit.* Ross and Ormandy, *Trans. Inst. Chem. Engrs. (London)*, **4**:104 (1926).

[4] Dumanois, *Rev. pétrolifère*, **444**:1323 (1931).

[5] Lichty and Phelps, *Ind. Eng. Chem.*, **30**:222 (1938).

[6] Brown and Christiansen, *Ind. Eng. Chem.*, **28**:650 (1936).

This effect may be considered desirable, since it reduces knock and increases the volumetric efficiency of the engine. However, the latter amounts to not more than 1 or 2 per cent for 10 and 20 per cent blends, respectively.[1]

As larger amounts of alcohol are used, the problem of fuel evaporation at the carburetor or in the manifold presents itself and changes in engine design become necessary. A voluminous literature has grown up on the use of alcohol for motor fuel purposes.[2]

DIESEL FUELS

XI-12. Diesel Combustion. The diesel (compression ignition) engine depends upon the heat developed by compressing a charge of air to ignite the fuel injected into it. An idea of the temperature attainable is given by the fact that dry air at 60°F, compressed adiabatically to one-tenth its volume, is raised in temperature to 825°F; or to 1050°F if compressed to one-fifteenth its volume. The Diesel cycle is ideally a constant pressure one; i.e., the fuel is injected and burned through a definite crankshaft angle, the pressure presumably remaining constant while the piston travels down on the power stroke; but in practice, this ideal is not attained, and pressures rise during combustion. The Otto cycle gasoline engine, on the other hand, conforms to a constant-volume cycle. In this case, the burning is supposedly instantaneous at the time of the spark ignition, the power being developed by the expansion of the heated gases. Practically, however, instantaneous burning is not obtained; a flame front develops and travels through the unburned portion of the charge. The limiting factor of the gasoline engine is the compression pressure; for as this is made higher, the temperature of the compressed gases at ignition increases and the tendency to knock, likewise, becomes greater. For present-day gasoline fuels, the maximum compression ratio permissible is around 10 to 11:1. On the other hand, with a diesel engine using average available fuels, the compression ratio must not fall much below 12:1 or 13:1; otherwise, not enough heat is developed during compression of the air to ignite the fuel. Diesel engines, in general, show about 14:1 to 17:1 in compression ratio; and as engine efficiency varies directly with the compression ratio used, they develop more useful work than car-

---

[1] Lichty and Phelps, *loc. cit.*

[2] Egloff and Morrell, *Ind. Eng. Chem.*, **28**:1080 (1936). Ogston, *J. Inst. Petrol. Technologists*, **23**:506 (1937). Jacobs and Newton, *U.S. Dept. Agr., Misc. Pub.* 327, 1938. Phelps and Lichty, *Proc. API*, **20M**(III):53 (1939). Pleath, *J. Inst. Petrol.*, **28**:240 (1942). Porter and Wiebe, *Ind. Eng. Chem.*, **44**:1098 (1952). Also see Mapstone, *S. African Ind. Chemist*, **8**:187 (1954.) Pleath, *loc. cit.*, for fuel qualities and physical properties of alcohol-benzene blends.

buretor engines for the same quantity of fuel consumed. The general relation between the theoretical efficiency and compression ratio for an Otto cycle and a diesel engine is shown by Fig. XI-8.[1]

It will be noted that for a given compression ratio, the theoretical Otto cycle develops more useful work than the Diesel. Neither engine, however, runs true to its cycle, and actual efficiencies are much below those indicated. The marked advantage of the Diesel cycle lies in the fact that at part load its efficiency is much better than that of the Otto cycle.

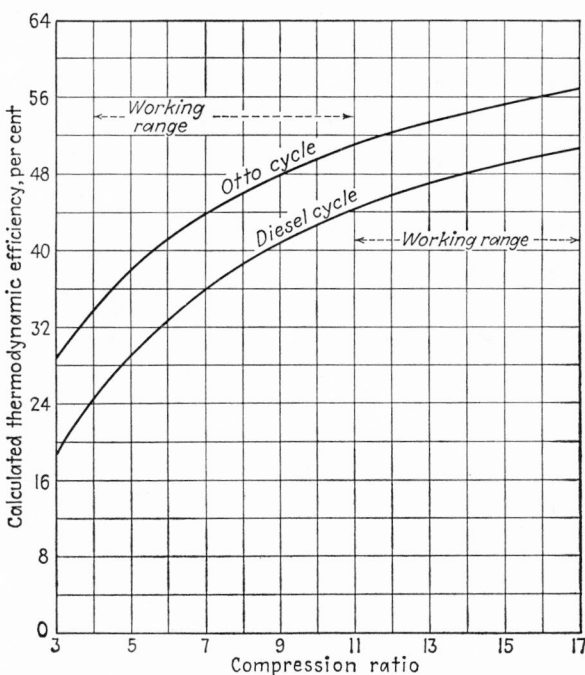

FIG. XI-8. Comparison of the thermodynamic efficiency of Diesel and Otto cycles. [*From Liston, Petrol. Eng.,* **7**(8):42 (1936).]

The success of diesel operation depends upon the atomization and distribution of the fuel before explosion. The problem is complicated by the fact that so much homogenizing has to be done in so short a time. The gasoline engine has 360° of crank angle to condition a highly volatile mixture, but the diesel must prepare a relatively nonvolatile charge in about 30°. Furthermore, it is essential that a diesel make best use of the air charged, for excess air increases the power required for its compression and cuts down output: complete distribution is thus essential.

[1] See also Taylor and Taylor, "Internal Combustion Engines," p. 7, International Textbook Company, Scranton, Pa., 1942.

Assuming this, the tendency of the fuel to prompt ignition, the so-called "ignition-delay characteristic," is of dominant importance. It is measured as the period of time or crank angle between the beginning of fuel injection and the beginning of explosion, and is made up of the following:

1. Physical factors, including the time necessary to heat and vaporize the liquid; these are influenced by atomization, viscosity, volatility, turbulence, temperature, and pressure. Since it has been shown that completely vaporized fuels do not burn instantaneously, even at high temperatures and pressures,[1] the presence of chemical factors becomes apparent.

2. Chemical factors, involving reactions which take place during the time necessary for the heat of reaction (developing at local points of ignition) to raise the mixture to autoignition temperatures.[2]

The start of ignition is influenced largely by fuel composition. Physical delay has been studied mathematically by Wentzel;[3] it is evaluated as of the order of one-tenth of the total delay observed.[4]   The chemical nature of the fuel is thus definitely more significant but it must be remembered that slight changes in engine design are often more effective than gross changes in fuel.

If ignition is long delayed, fuel will accumulate in the combustion chamber until it becomes hot enough to burn rapidly, causing a sudden rise of pressure which results in engine roughness or knock.[5]   Attendant phenomena are decrease of efficiency, smoking exhaust, crankcase oil dilution, and carbonaceous deposits in piston ring grooves.   Any influence which encourages oxidation, such as preheating, improved distribution, or increased compression ratio, will reduce ignition delay and mini-

---

[1] Rothrock and Waldron, *Natl. Advisory Comm. Aeronaut. Tech. Mem.* 435, 1932. Miller, *Trans. SAE*, **53**:719 (1945).   See Taylor, Taylor, Livengood, Russell, and Leary, *Quart. Trans. SAE*, **4**:232 (1950).

[2] See Taylor, Taylor, Livengood, Russell, and Leary, *loc. cit.*   Mullins, *Fuel*, **32**:211 (1953).   Scott, Jones, and Scott, *Anal. Chem.*, **20**:238 (1948).   Livengood and Leary, *Ind. Eng. Chem.*, **43**:2805 (1951).   Frank and Blackham, *Ind. Eng. Chem.*, **44**:862 (1952); *Natl. Advisory Comm. Aeronaut. Tech. Note* 2958, 1953.   Johnson, Crellin, and Carhart, *Natl. Advisory Comm. Aeronaut.*, **44**:1612 (1952).   Frank, Blackham, and Swarts, *Natl. Advisory Comm. Aeronaut.*, **45**:2586 (1953).   Zabetakis, Furno, and Jones, *Natl. Advisory Comm. Aeronaut.*, **46**:2173 (1954).

[3] *Natl. Advisory Comm. Aeronaut. Tech. Mem.* 797, 1936.

[4] El Wakil, Mayers, and Uyehara (Preprint, Fuel Vaporization and Ignition Lag in Diesel Combustion, SAE Diesel Engine Meeting, St. Louis, November, 1955), working with both bombs and engines, attribute considerably more importance to physical delay.

[5] For a comparison of gasoline engine and diesel engine combustion and knock, see Boerlage and van Dyck, *J. Roy. Aeronaut. Sci.*, **38**:953 (1934); *J. Inst. Petrol. Technologists*, **21**:40 (1935).

mize knocking. Operation[1] under high load will have a similar result, because of the effect of higher engine temperatures.[2] As may be expected, the intensity of the knock becomes greater as the ignition lag of the fuel increases.[3]

XI-13. Fuel Characteristics. The differences in diesel and gasoline engine operation call for very distinct types of fuel. The latter requires low boiling, smooth-burning hydrocarbons of relatively high spontaneous ignition temperature.[4] For the former, low spontaneous ignition temperatures are desired and low-boiling compounds are not suitable. The entire fuel charge is not present at the time of ignition as in the gasoline engine; the addition is timed over an extended crank angle period, generally starting about 15 to 20° before top dead center, with the mixture burning independently of any moving flame front. Fuel decomposition (cracking) probably precedes burning, and for this reason, thermally unstable fuels such as those of high paraffinicity are found particularly suitable. In a given hydrocarbon series, the ignition temperature decreases as the molecular weight increases, for less energy of activation is needed for cracking of the large molecules. Hydrocarbons showing low spontaneous ignition temperatures have, in general, a short ignition lag. Relative ease of ignition can be indicated approximately by the figures for critical compression ratio; this is the lowest compression ratio in a given test engine which will permit development of enough heat by compression to fire the charge supplied. Figure XI-9 gives the range of ignition tendency shown in this way by various fuels.

Contrary to popular opinion, diesel engines (and particularly those of the small high-speed type) cannot be operated successfully on miscellaneous or waste oils of every sort. The requirements as to cleanliness are severe; viscosity is significant, while pour point, ash content, carbon-residue value, and flash point also serve as indications of suitability. Boiling range is, in general, between 350 and 700°F except in the case of residual oils.[5] Starting difficulties in cold weather can be eased by the injection of diethyl ether into the intake air;[6] warming of the intake air or the cooling water is also practiced.

---

[1] Davies and Griffin, *J. Inst. Fuel*, **5**:78 (1931). Boerlage and Broeze, *Ind. Eng. Chem.*, **28**:1229 (1936).

[2] The opposite condition may lead to incomplete combustion and engine lacquering. Bouman, *World Petrol. Congr., Proc. 1st Congr., London*, **2**:248 (1933).

[3] Withers, *J. Inst. Petrol. Technologists*, **19**:713 (1933).

[4] Hurn and Smith, *Ind. Eng. Chem.*, **43**:2788 (1951). Shoemaker and Gadebusch, *Oil Gas J.*, **44**(36):74 (1946).

[5] For properties of commercial diesel fuels, see Blade, *National Annual Diesel Fuel Survey*, 1954; *U.S. Bur. Mines Rept. Invest.* 5084, 1954.

[6] For a discussion of the function of starting fluids, see Ainsley and Young, Preprint, SAE Diesel Engine Meeting, Cleveland, October, 1954.

The degree of volatility of a fuel is limited not only by the tendency to preignition but also because the sprays of volatile oil produced are "soft" and have a poor penetrating power, i.e., they do not travel far enough into the air space, and uneven distribution results. Heavy oils are not used, except in large, slow-speed installations; under other conditions, they tend to slow combustion and cause soot formation.

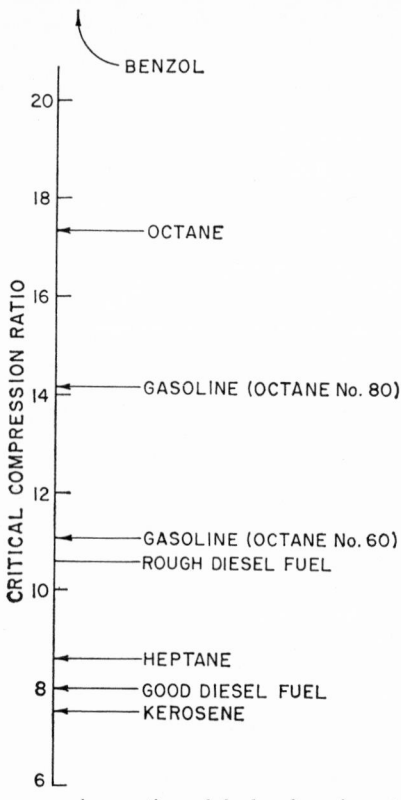

Fig. XI-9. Critical compression ratios of fuels of various types. [*From Pope, J. SAE*, **35**:385 (1934).]

The viscosity of the fuel must be high enough to satisfy the lubrication requirements of injector parts but must not be so high as to impede the ease of pumping. Highly viscous oils are generally warmed to overcome any pumping troubles. Viscosity is an important factor in controlling the spray produced by the atomizing jets; for if the spray cone is too penetrating, some of the fuel droplets will reach the relatively cool cylinder wall, where they will not burn easily.

While the sulfur tolerance for diesel fuels is greater than that for gasolines, the sulfur content should be kept low. Increasing it from

0.2 to 1.0 per cent results in substantial engine fouling and increased piston ring and cylinder wear.[1]

XI-14. Ignition Quality. The ignition quality of diesel fuels is expressed in terms of cetane numbers, which are based on a scale analogous to that of octane numbers.[2] Mixtures of a fast-burning paraffinic constituent, cetane (*n*-hexadecane), and of a slow-burning aromatic material, α-methylnaphthalene,[3] are mixed to match test fuels in performance in a standardized test engine,[4] and the result is expressed as the percentage of cetane in the matching mixture. At present, diesel fuels may fall in the range of 35 to 65 or 70 in cetane number. Those in the upper range are special products. In practice, the higher-quality diesel fuels generally are in the range of about 42 to 56.

It has been found that some of the physical and chemical properties of a fuel can be used to give an approximate evaluation of its burning properties and suitability for use. Various indices of quality have been proposed, based on such properties as aniline point, gravity, viscosity, average boiling point, and hydrogen content. In the absence of an engine test, they serve as useful guides. A comparison of these indices with the actual cetane ratings[5] of a number of fuels shows a general relationship to hold, no one index having any particular advantage over the other with the exception of the (CFR) Calculated Cetane Index (ASTM D 975, Appendix II). The indices are not reliable when used to estimate the quality of "doped" fuels and have a tendency to show discrepancies in the high cetane range.

1. Aniline point. High aniline points (temperature of critical dissolution with aniline) denote high paraffinic content, as aniline is miscible with the paraffin hydrocarbons only on warming. The figure is relative, as it would not be the same for fuels of the same cetane numbers from California and Pennsylvania stocks. For instance, aniline points were found to be of no significance in evaluating the cetane numbers of various alkylated benzenes.[6]

2. Diesel index.[7] This index is defined as the product of aniline point

---

[1] Cloud and Blackwood, *J. SAE*, **51**(11):408 (1943). Blanc, *Quart. Trans. SAE*, **2**(2):306 (1948). Eltinge, Gray, and Taliaferro, Preprint, SAE Fuels and Lubricants Meeting, Tulsa, November, 1954. Moore and Kent, *Quart. Trans. SAE*, **1**(4):687 (1947). Furston, *Quart. Trans. SAE*, **3**(4):611 (1949). Cadebusch, Preprint, SAE Tractor and Diesel Engine Meeting, Milwaukee, September, 1948.

[2] Rendel, *Trans. SAE*, **38**:225 (1936).

[3] For a discussion of the relationship between hydrocarbon composition and cetane number, see Lee and Woods, *Oil Gas J.*, **39**(35):41 (1941).

[4] CFR diesel test engine. ASTM D 613.

[5] Hubner and Murphy, *Nat. Petrol. News*, **28**(4):22 (1936); (5):25 (1936).

[6] Shen, Wood, and Garner, *J. Inst. Petrol. Technologists*, **25**:695 (1939).

[7] Becker and Fischer, *Trans. SAE*, **35**:376 (1934).

and API gravity at 60°F divided by 100:

$$\frac{\text{Aniline point, °F} \times \text{°API (60°F)}}{100}$$

The diesel index increases with increase in cetane number. It is more commonly used in specifications than the other indices.

3. Viscosity-gravity constant.[1] This index is used extensively in characterizing the paraffinicity of lubricating oils. The following modified form is employed for diesel fuels:

$$G = 1.082A - 0.0887 + (0.776 - 0.72A) [\log \log (KV - 4)]$$

where G is the specific gravity at 60°F, A is the viscosity-gravity constant, and KV is the kinematic viscosity in millistokes at 100°F. The viscosity-gravity constant decreases with increase in cetane number.

4. Boiling point–gravity index.[2] The boiling point–gravity number is expressed in the following empirical equation.

$$G = A + (68 - 0.703A) \log BP$$

where G is the degree API at 60°F, A is the boiling point–gravity number, and BP is the 50 per cent distillation point in degrees centigrade. The boiling point–gravity number decreases with increasing cetane number.

5. Characterization factor.[3]

$$K = \frac{(T_b)^{\frac{1}{3}}}{S}$$

where K is the characterization factor, S is the specific gravity at 60°F, and T_b is the molar average boiling point in degrees Rankine (°F + 460); the 50 per cent distillation temperature (degrees Rankine) is used for diesel fuels.

The factor increases with increasing cetane numbers. The spread of these indices between high and low cetane number is roughly:

Cetane number	Approximate aniline* point, °F	Diesel index	Viscosity-gravity number	Boiling point–gravity number	UOP factor
30	105	20	0.93	200	10.8
70	180	76	0.81	173	12.2

* Would vary with source of fuel.

[1] Hill and Coats, *Ind. Eng. Chem.*, **20**:641 (1928). Moore and Kaye, *Oil Gas J.*, **33**(26):108 (1934).

[2] Jackson, *Oil Gas J.*, **33**(44):16 (1935).

[3] Watson and Nelson, *Ind. Eng. Chem.*, **25**:880 (1933).

The various indices have been correlated more completely by Hubner and Murphy.[1]

Others, such as carbon-hydrogen ratio, heating value in Btu,[2] refractive index, specific gravity, and[3]

$$\text{Parachor} = \sqrt[4]{\frac{\text{surface tension}}{\text{specific gravity}}}$$

have been suggested. A fairly good correlation exists between cetane numbers and octane numbers. A blending value is calculated[4] from the octane number of a mixture of 25 per cent diesel fuel plus 75 per cent reference gasoline. These values may be converted to heptane numbers, based on the percentage of heptane required in mixture with isooctane, to match the diesel fuel. The heptane number does not cover the entire diesel fuel range.

6. Calculated cetane index.[5] As a matter of experience the best results in prediction have been obtained with this number.[6] It is defined by the expression

Calculated cetane index = 97.833 (log mid-bp)^2
+ 2.2088 (API gravity) (log mid-bp) + 0.01247 (API gravity)^2
− 423.51 (log mid-bp) − 4.7808 (API gravity) + 419.59

where mid-bp is the temperature in degrees Fahrenheit at which 50 per cent is recovered at a barometric pressure of 760 mm of mercury in the ASTM Distillation Method D 86. The equation is solved conveniently by means of the nomograph given in the ASTM description. This index gives numerical values practically equivalent to the ASTM cetane number throughout the range encountered in petroleum distillates normally used as diesel engine fuels. It is applicable to straight-run and catalytically cracked fuels and blends of the two, but cannot be relied upon for fuels containing appreciable quantities of residual or thermally cracked oil, extremely volatile fuels (boiling below the kerosene range), coal-tar products, vegetable or animal oils, or "doped" petroleum fuels containing cetane-improver additives.

The significance of fuel properties for engine performance varies with the type of engine. For large, slow-speed units of stationary and marine installations, running at 500 rpm or less, requirements are not critical.

[1] *Natl. Petrol. News*, **28**(4):22 (1936); (5):25 (1936).
[2] Marder, *Angew. Chem.*, **50**:147 (1937).
[3] Heinze and Marder, *Brennstoff-Chem.*, **16**:286 (1935).
[4] Hubner and Murphy, *loc. cit.*
[5] ASTM Standards on Petroleum Products, p. 455, 1955.
[6] *J. Inst. Petrol.*, **30**:193 (1944); Young, *Proc. API*, **30M**(III):238 (1950).

Combustion is relatively slow, and high cetane number (low ignition temperature) is not necessary. The cylinders are large, so that penetrating sprays of heavy, viscous oils may be used. At the same time, a high carbon residue can be tolerated in the fuel, since there is time for the charge to burn completely. It is evident that for such installations, heavier distillates and even residues may be satisfactory. Smaller units, tending to the automotive type, running at 1,000 rpm or more, require fuels of shorter ignition lag, lower carbon residue, and lower viscosity.[1] Table XI-7 gives limiting requirements for several grades of diesel fuel oils.

TABLE XI-7

	Grade		
	No. 1-D	No. 2-D	No. 4-D
Viscosity, 100°F:			
Kinematic, cs:			
Minimum...	1.4	1.8	5.8
Maximum...	......	5.8	26.4
SSU:			
Minimum...	......	32.0	45.0
Maximum...	......	45.0	125.0
Distillation temperature, °F:			
90 per cent point, maximum.........................	......	675	
End point, maximum.............................	625		
Sulfur, weight per cent, maximum....................	0.5	1.0	2.0
Carbon residue on 10 per cent residuum, maximum....	0.15	0.35	
Water and sediment, volume per cent, maximum......	Trace	0.10	0.50
Flash point, °F, minimum..........................	100*	125*	130*
Ash, weight per cent, maximum.....................	0.01	0.02	0.01
Cetane number, minimum..........................	40	40	30

* Or legal.

From ASTM Standards on Petroleum Products and Lubricants, D 975–53T, p. 452, 1956.

The available straight-run oils are often of more value as charge stocks for catalytic cracking than for diesel fuels. Catalytically cracked distillates less volatile than gasoline, however, are in the proper boiling range for diesel use. The olefin and aromatic contents are unfavorable with respect to ignition lag, but viscosity, pour- and cloud-point temperatures,

[1] For a relation between diesel fuel properties and engine performance, see MacGregor and Hanley, *Oil Gas J.*, **36**(36):90 (1938). Mount and Hope, *Trans. SAE*, **46**:100 (1940). Blackwood and Cloud, *Trans. SAE*, **46**:49 (1940). Ainsley, *Trans. SAE*, **49**:448 (1941). Griffith and Williams, *Trans. SAE*, **53**:292 (1945). Thompson and Backey, *Quart. Trans. SAE*, **3**(1):41 (1949).

and gravities are in the right direction.   Their cetane values are about 5 to 15 numbers below those of straight-run distillates but are still about 10 numbers above thermally cracked material of corresponding boiling range from the same crude.

XI-15. Addition Agents.   As the octane number of a gasoline may be increased by the addition of compounds such as aniline or tetraethyllead, so may the cetane number of a diesel fuel be raised (or critical compression ratio be lowered) by various addition agents.   The most efficient of those so far found are classified as follows in order of decreasing effectiveness:

Thionitrites   Amyl nitrates
Chloropicrins   Acetyl peroxide
Amyl nitrites

Various nitro and nitroso compounds, aldehydes, ketones, peroxides, polysulfides, and compounds of oxidizing power have been proposed.   An idea of the elevation of cetane number attainable may be gained from the following,

Additive	*Increase in cetane number*
Isopropyl nitrate	17
n-Butyl nitrate	19
n-Amyl nitrate	23
sec-Amyl nitrate	20
Isoamyl nitrate	21
Mixed amyl nitrates	19
n-Hexyl nitrate	20
sec-Hexyl nitrate	18
Cyclohexyl nitrate	22
Octyl nitrate	19

which shows the results obtained on adding 1.5 per cent of each to a 44 cetane number base fuel.[1]

Amyl nitrate is being used commercially for this purpose.   On the average, four cetane numbers are gained on the addition of 0.1 volume per cent to a series of diesel fuels ranging from 26 to 55 cetane value.[2]   The low-cetane cracked fuels were the least susceptible, straight-run distillates, the most.[3]

The exact mechanism by which cetane improvers reduce ignition delay is not well understood; in one case, however, that of ethyl nitrate, low-temperature instability under pressure has been observed.[4]   It has been

[1] Bogen and Wilson, *Natl. Petrol. News*, **36**(18): R-284 (1944).
[2] Hubner, Panel Discussion, SAE Metropolitan Section Meeting, January, 1954.
[3] Bogen and Wilson, *op. cit.*
[4] See symposium on the subject, National Petroleum Association, Atlantic City, September, 1955.

shown that an additive-bearing fuel starts to release heat energy after a shorter interval of time than the clear fuel.[1] It may be significant that alkyl nitrites[2] and alkyl hydroperoxides[3] both decompose to give ROO· and possibly RO· and OH· radicals, which may serve as chain carriers.

GAS TURBINE AND JET ENGINE FUELS

One of the basic concepts of the early development of diesel, gas turbine, and jet engines was that almost any combustible liquid could be used as fuel. Within limits powdered coal could be employed, at least in theory. This ideal has been attained only in part and only for large, slow, and usually stationary units. Small high-speed diesel engines require very specialized fuels for satisfactory operation, and the same is true of oil-fired gas turbines and jet engines. While engine design has involved a number of compromises influenced by the availability of particular fuel materials, the tendency has been to design for optimum performance, with the consequence of rather stringent requirements as to fuel.[4,5] As mentioned earlier in this chapter, such a tendency results from the great importance of developing as much power as possible from any given piece of equipment. Even when difficulties like flame stability and coke deposition might be alleviated by mechanical alterations, such changes are not favored if performance would be impaired.[6]

Fuels such as straight-run kerosenes are preferred as jet fuels but mixtures with gasoline are widely used because of availability. The early development of gas turbine and jet engine fuels has passed through the following stages in this country.

JP-1: Well-refined, close-cut paraffinic kerosene
JP-2: Essentially aviation gasoline; never widely used
JP-3: Mixture of gasoline and kerosene; vapor pressure 5 to 7 lb, Reid
JP-4: Gasoline-kerosene mixture, vapor pressure 2 to 3 lb; 200 to 500°F boiling range

[1] Hurn and Hughes, *ACS, Div. Petrol. Chem.*, Preprint, The Use of Additives in Petroleum Fuels, p. 157, ACS Meeting, Minneapolis, September, 1955.

[2] Steacie and Shaw, *Proc. Roy. Soc. (London)*, **A146**:388 (1934).

[3] Ubbelohde and Egerton, *Nature*, **135**:67 (1935).

[4] For a comprehensive review of the chemical and physical properties of jet engine fuels and their relation to performance, see Barnett and Hibbard, Properties of Aircraft Fuels, *Natl. Advisory Comm. Aeronaut.*, *Tech. Note* 3276, August, 1956.

[5] For a discussion of the technical requirements for petroleum-derived ballistic missile fuels, see Silverman, Thompson, and Tormey, *ACS, Div. Petrol. Chem.*, Preprints, Chemistry and Technology of Petroleum Fuels of the Future, C-59, ACS Meeting, San Francisco, April, 1958.

[6] Barnard and Eltinge, *Ind. Eng. Chem.*, **46**:2160 (1954).

JP-5: A high-flash point kerosene-like stock for blending with aviation gasoline; 350 to 550°F boiling range

JP:6: Wide-cut kerosene; 250 to 550°F boiling range

Specifications for these fuels are voluminous.[1] The properties covered include distillation range, gravity to indicate paraffinic character, gum, and sulfur content; a low vapor pressure is required to minimize loss at high altitudes, and a low freezing point ($-76°F$) for fear of solidification. To secure maximum range, a minimum heat of combustion is set at about 18,400 Btu per lb and a maximum aromatic content of 25 per cent; this latter to minimize smoking tendency. The fuels must ignite easily under all conditions of temperature and barometric pressure; they must burn steadily without blowout or flash back,[2] and cleanly with minimum deposit in the combustion. The spraying qualities are influenced by viscosity and density, which are specified.[3] Combustion efficiency for all the proposed fuels is about the same when temperature rise in the combustion is high. If temperature rise is low, the more volatile fuels are the more effective.[4]

One of the most serious difficulties experienced with potentially available fuels is their tendency, depending upon volatility and chemical composition, to deposit carbon in the openings in the combustor liner, on the spark plug, and on the fuel nozzle.[5] Carbon deposition appears to

---

[1] Blade, *U.S. Bur. Mines Rept. Invest.* 5132, 1955.

[2] On the relation of fuel structure to spontaneous ignition temperature, critical ignition energy, ignition delay, flammability limits, quenching distance, flame velocity, and smoke formation, see Gibbons, Barnett, and Gerstein, *Ind. Eng. Chem.*, **46**:2150 (1954). Albright, Heath, and Thena, *Ind. Eng. Chem.*, **44**:2490 (1952). Alquist and Scherman, SAE New York Meeting, April, 1955.

[3] Droegemueller, *Symposium on Jet Fuels—Present and Future*, National Petroleum Association, Atlantic City Meeting, September, 1952. Sometimes the properties under conditions of use are required. The density and viscosity of a JP-4 fuel at high temperature and pressure have been measured as follows:

Temperature, °F	Pressure, psi	Density	Viscosity, cp
100	200	0.74	0.52
500	1,000	0.54	0.12

(Greathouse and Smith, *ACS, Div. Petrol. Chem., Gen. Papers*, p. 5, ACS Meeting, San Francisco, April, 1958).

[4] Kuhbach, Ritcheske, and Strauss, SAE Los Angeles Aeronautical Meeting, October, 1954.

[5] Kuhbach, Ritcheske, and Strauss, *Trans. SAE*, **63**:642 (1955). Gibbons, Garrett, and Gerstein, *loc. cit.* Schalla, Clark, and McDonald, *Natl. Advisory Comm. Aeronaut., Rept.* 1186, 1954. Starkman, Cattaneo, and McAllister, *Ind. Eng. Chem.*, **43**:2822 (1951).

increase with rise in the end point of the fuel and is particularly affected by the high-boiling aromatic content (primarily polynuclear). For this reason the specifications for JP-3, JP-4, JP-5, and JP-6 (proposed) fuels limit the aromatic content to 25 per cent. The smoking tendency of hydrocarbon types decreases in the following order: aromatics > alkynes > monoolefins > isoparaffins > n-paraffins.[1] The sulfur content is critical because of its action on rubber, on cadmium coating of fuel tanks, and on parts made of bronze.

Jet fuels burn in a turbulent diffusion flame with a large excess of air. If perfect mixing could be obtained, the fuel would burn cleanly. Since carbon is formed in the combustion, one can assume that localized rich air-fuel mixtures exist and that, when they burn, the relation between carbon formation and air supply is critical. The carbon deposited in gas turbine combustors is of two types: amorphous (soft and fluffy) and graphitic (hard and crystalline),[2] the latter form causing more trouble. The actual mechanism of coke formation in this and a wide variety of other instances has been an object of much study. The fuel may crack as such[3] which does not seem probable, or may dehydrogenate to intermediates which condense to larger molecules or even to droplets.[4] Such secondary products would not be very stable thermally.

A variety of existing test procedures have been tried as indicators of carbon-forming tendency. Among these are

Aniline point
Specific gravity
UOP characterization factor[5]
National Advisory Committee for Aeronautics K factor[6]

[1] Schalla and McDonald, *Natl. Advisory Comm. Aeronaut. Research Mem.* E 52122, 1952; *Ind. Eng. Chem.*, **45**:1497 (1953). Hunt, *ACS Div. Petrol. Chem., Gen. Papers*, Preprint, p. 71, ACS Meeting, Atlantic City, September, 1952.

[2] Clark, *Natl. Advisory Comm. Aeronaut. Research Mem.* E 52126, 1952. Droegemueller, *loc. cit.*

[3] Schalla and McDonald, *loc. cit.; Ind. Eng. Chem.*, **45**:1497 (1953).

[4] Thorp, Long, and Garner, *Fuel*, **30**:266 (1951); **32**:116 (1953). Comerford, *Fuel*, **32**:67 (1953). Hadzi, *Fuel*, **32**:112 (1953). Hunt, *Ind. Eng. Chem.*, **45**:602 (1953). Arthur, Kapur, and Napier, *Nature*, **169**:372 (1952). Parker and Wolford, *J. Chem. Soc.*, 1950, p. 2038.

[5] Watson and Nelson, *Ind. Eng. Chem.*, **25**:880 (1933).

[6] The NACA K factor of a fuel is expressed as follows:

$$K = (t + 600) \ (0.7) \ \frac{H/C - 0.207}{H/C - 0.259}$$

where t = average volumetric boiling point in degrees Fahrenheit and H/C = hydrogen to carbon weight ratio. In general, the carbon depositing tendency of a fuel increases with this K factor.

Per cent aromatics boiling above 400°F

Smoke point[1]

Of these, the smoke point appears to give best correlation with actual carbon deposition in jet engine combustors. It is defined as the height of a diffusion flame at the point of incipient smoking, measured in a conventional test lamp. Modifications of the smoke point are the smoking tendency and the smoke volatility index. The former is the reciprocal of the smoke point multiplied by a factor, usually 320. The smoke volatility index is the smoke point plus 0.42 times the per cent distilled to 400°F; it is incorporated into JP-3 and JP-4 fuel specifications.

Reductions up to about 65 per cent in carbon deposition have been obtained by the addition of 0.1 to 0.5 per cent of clean-burning agents to the fuel. Metallo-organics such as iron carbonyl, tetraethyllead, and triphenyl bismuth, among other compounds, have been found to show this property. Because of the supply situation, use of cracked instead of straight-run distillates is desirable. This raises questions of stability against gum and sludge formation in storage and use;[2] this is particularly true in the light of proposals to employ fuel as a cooling agent for the lubricant and to reduce thermal stresses on aircraft components in high-speed flight.[3]

TRACTOR FUELS

With the increase in compression ratios of tractor engines into the present range of 6.5 to 7.25 the need for special fuels has diminished; most tractors now use motor gasoline or liquefied petroleum gas as fuel. Earlier tractors with low-compression engines utilized relatively non-volatile fuels, of which kerosene, 300 to 500°F boiling range, or thermally cracked distillates (furnace oil), 320 to 560°F, were typical.[4] Such fuels offered difficulties in starting, high oil dilution, poor carburetion and manifold distribution, incomplete combustion, and smoking, as well as preignition and knocking.[5]

---

[1] Krynitsky, Garrett, and McLean, *Naval Research Lab. Rept.* 4068, 1952. See also Eldib, *ACS, Div. Petrol. Chem.*, Preprints, ACS Meeting, San Francisco, April, 1958.

[2] Thompson, *Oil Gas J.*, **53**(5):123 (1954). For discussion of the gum and deposit stability of aircraft turbine fuels, see Johnson, Fink, and Nixon, *Ind. Eng. Chem.*, **46**:2166 (1954). Nixon and Minor, *Ind. Eng. Chem.*, **48**:1909 (1956). See also Nixon and Cole, *ACS, Div. Petrol. Chem., Gen. Papers*, Preprint, p. 5, ACS Meeting, Kansas City, March–April, 1954. Heath, Hoffman, and Reynolds, Preprint, SAE Golden Anniversary Summer Meeting, Atlantic City, June, 1955.

[3] Crampton, Gleason, and Wieland, Preprint, SAE Summer Meeting, Atlantic City, June, 1955. Heath, Hoffman, and Reynolds, Preprint, SAE Summer Meeting, Atlantic City, June, 1955.

[4] Wilson and Barnard, *Trans. SAE*, **35**:359 (1934). Barger, *Kansas State Coll. Bull.* 23, no. 6, *Eng. Expert. Sta. Bull.* 37, 1939.

[5] Their use continues abroad; for properties see *J. Inst. Petrol.*, **40**:242 (1954).

PROPANE AND BUTANE MOTOR FUELS

Since liquefied petroleum gases (LPG) have become widely available, they have been employed as fuels for tractors, trucks, and motor coaches.[1] Advantages claimed include good carburetion, clean burning, and absence of bad exhaust odor; the antiknock values are high. Disadvantages are storage and handling problems, lowered work output per unit volume, and difficulties in maintaining valve stem lubrication. The largest use for LPG materials is as domestic fuel in areas remote from available supplies of heating gas. Liquid propane is stored for stand-by purposes by gas manufacturers and distributors, and has been recommended as an improving addition in water gasmaking.[2] It is a desirable fuel in some industrial operations, particularly metal fabrication.

Normal and isobutane are in demand, the former for manufacture of butadiene and other chemicals, the latter for alkylation of olefins to yield gasoline constituents. As a result the LPG on the market today is composed largely of propane. The NGAA specifications[3] do not exclude presence of propylene in commercial propane or of butenes in commercial butane; however, these olefins are consumed in the refineries for conversion to motor fuel or chemicals. The specifications cover composition, content of water and sulfur compounds, and vapor pressure.

[1] Larson, *Kansas State Coll. Bull.* 38, no. 3, *Eng. Expert. Sta. Bull.* 71, 1954. Samuelson, *J. SAE,* **59**:18 (1951).

[2] Zankl, *Gas u. Wasserfach,* **96**(23):785 (1955).

[3] Natural Gasoline Association of America, September, 1940.

CHAPTER XII

Kerosene, Absorbent Oils, and Fuel Oils

KEROSENE

Kerosene is the general name applied to the group of refined petroleum fractions employed as fuel for lamps and for heating appliances (such as cooking stoves) requiring a uniform, nonviscous fuel less volatile than gasoline. The limited number of uses to which they are put have defined rather closely their properties and nature. They must be closely cut distillates, low in viscosity, of higher flash point than gasoline; they must be so highly refined as to be light and fairly stable in color, free of ill-smelling substances, free of hydrocarbons which burn with a smoky flame, reasonably low in sulfur content, and possessed of properties enabling them to rise freely in the wick of a lamp.

Material with these properties is supplied by the fraction of paraffinic and mixed-base petroleums distilling next after the gasoline fraction. It is ordinarily a material boiling over the range 175 to 275°C (350 to 525°F) and of specific gravity about 0.80. Its viscosity is typically about 2.5 centistokes (cs), and it remains clear down to 0°F (-18°C) and liquid to -20°F or below.

Kerosene commands greater historical interest than other petroleum products, because it was for this material that the entire industry of the discovery period was built up. It is probable that oil from seepages had been employed for torches and lamps long before drilled wells, and perhaps in all parts of the world. As early as 1834, seepage oil was employed for lamps in the valley of the Kanawha River in Virginia (now West Virginia), and it was known that filtration through charcoal improved the odor given off in burning.[1] In 1854, Samuel Kier of Pittsburgh distilled petroleum (from salt-water wells at Tarentum, Pa.) in a 5-bbl still, to yield a lamp oil.[2] The credit for first applying chemical refining probably belongs to Benjamin Silliman, Jr., although he did not practice it on a large scale.

[1] Hildreth, quoted by S. F. Peckham, Tenth U.S. Census (1880), vol. 10, p. 7.
[2] Peckham, *ibid.*, p. 159.

XII-1. Chemical Properties. All the major uses of kerosene involve burning under specified conditions; it follows that the chemical as well as the physical properties of such a material are important as they influence its burning. It might be supposed that since burning conditions will be different in lamps, heating stoves, and tractor engines, different kerosene fuels would be made for these different purposes. For instance, a tractor fuel kerosene can be made from an aromatic or a cracked stock to afford a higher octane number.[1] Actually, special kerosenes are made to only a moderate extent, and general-purpose products are the rule.[2] This is largely because of the economy of storing and distributing one material instead of several.

Chemical composition is important in governing flame type in burning and residue left after burning. The chemical composition of Mid-Continent kerosene distillates was first described by Wagner[3] and has since been worked out in considerably more detail by the American Petroleum Institute Research Project 6 under the direction of Rossini and Mair (see Chap. II). It may be concluded that such materials are made up of high proportions of naphthenes and branched paraffins. The known molecular weights and freezing points of the hydrocarbons concerned make quite unlikely the presence of any large proportion of normal paraffins. The selection of crudes and the refining processes employed will guarantee the absence of significant proportions of aromatics. Where paraffinic distillates are employed, sulfuric acid treating will remove the unsaturated hydrocarbons formed in distillation and the bulk of the aromatics naturally present. When distillates from aromatic crudes—East Indian, Rumanian, California—are at hand, solvent refining serves to remove essentially all but the paraffins and naphthenes (see Chap. IX). Indeed such segregation was the purpose of the original Edeleanu method of liquid sulfur dioxide extraction, the precursor of all modern solvent refining. In other words, commercial kerosene, no matter from what crude it is derived, is very likely to be a mixture of paraffins and naphthenes of the molecular weight indicated by the boiling range, roughly C_{10} to C_{14}.

All this fits in well with what is known of the burning of these several hydrocarbons. In the conventional lamps and stove burners of today, paraffins and naphthenes burn with the yellowish-white smokeless flame to which we are accustomed; aromatics, on the other hand, burn in these same lamps with a red and smoky flame. An interesting demonstration was described by Romp.[4] Six conventional lamps were set side by side

---

[1] See *J. Inst. Petrol.*, **40**:242 (1954), for properties of such special distillates.

[2] Testing methods and specifications are available, however; see ASTM D 1215–54.

[3] *Ind. Eng. Chem.*, **16**:135 (1934).

[4] "Oil Burning," p. 85, M. Nijhoff, The Hague, 1937.

charged, respectively, with:

> Tetrahydronaphthalene, $C_{10}H_{12}$
> Mesitylene, C_9H_{12},—$(C_6H_3(CH_3)_3)$
> Aromatic extract from a kerosene distillate
> Refined kerosene
> Cetene, $C_{16}H_{32}$
> Cetane, $C_{16}H_{34}$

This series represents a progression of increasing paraffinicity. When each lamp wick was turned up to the point of incipient smoking,[1] it was found that the permissible flame height increased from the first to the last of the series. There has been some objection to this viewpoint[2] and it must be admitted that the reagents which remove aromatics also remove cyclic unsaturated and similar reactive hydrocarbons high in carbon content and thus likely to burn with a smoky flame or to leave coke deposits. Furthermore, it has been reported that by the use of specially designed lamps pure aromatics can be burned without smoke trouble.[3]

The importance of using only the relatively stable paraffins and naphthenes can probably be explained on the basis of chemical composition as related to burning qualities. Unsaturated gum-forming substances, sulfur compounds, and salts of sulfonic acids have a negative importance; their absence is beneficial in that their residual products are undesirable. The positive importance of the main constituents lies in the fact that the manner of burning (under given conditions) depends on their constitution. Following Haslam and Russell[4] and Romp,[5] any ordinary combustion involves a race between thermal cracking and the first stages of oxidation; a compound of paraffin or naphthene type, of large hydrogen content, will oxidize and burn under lamp conditions more rapidly than it will decompose to smaller hydrocarbons and free carbon, although some of the latter reaction occurs. It is possible to burn such compounds with a blue flame, and in an ordinary lamp it is possible to use a very high flame, equivalent to a high fuel consumption per minute, without encountering a smoky condition. That is, with hydrocarbons

---

[1] Flame height as a measure of smoking is discussed below. On the relation of constitution to smoking, see Hunt, *Ind. Eng. Chem.*, **45**:602 (1953). Schalla, Clark, and McDonald, *Natl. Advisory Comm. Aeronautics Rept.* 1186, 1954.

[2] Danaila and coworkers, *Petroleum Z.*, **26**(2):47 (1930); **28**(17)1:(1932); **29**(7)1: (1933). Jakubowicz, *C.A.*, **27**:4064 (1933). Grote and Hunsdorf, *Petroleum Z.*, **28**(28)9:(1932). Minchin, *World Petrol. Congr., Proc. 1st Congr., London*, **2**:739 (1933).

[3] Wendt, *J. Gasbeleucht.*, **63**:654 (1920).

[4] "Fuels and Their Combustion," p. 185, McGraw-Hill Book Company, Inc., New York, 1926.

[5] "Oil Burning," p. 73, M. Nijhoff, The Hague, 1937.

of these classes, a conventional lamp can supply air enough for clean burning, at a high rate of fuel consumption. This is not so true of aromatic mixtures, where any attempt to use a high flame immediately encounters smoke, which means incomplete burning. It might be surmised that the paraffin-naphthene type is more resistant to thermal decomposition than are the aromatics; more probably, both types crack at about the same rates at flame temperature, but the aromatics crack to yield more solid carbonaceous residues and the paraffin-naphthenes crack to yield less of these soot-like products. This last statement is analogous to what is true in thermal cracking during refinery processing.

Another factor in the difference in manner of burning of the two types may be the content of hydrogen, considered as water vapor after burning. According to the water-gas reaction

$$C + H_2O \rightleftharpoons CO + H_2$$

carbon in the flame may be converted by an excess of steam into gases which burn nonluminously. Romp says that a smoky lamp flame may be converted to a clean one by saturating the incoming air with water vapor. Since tetrahydronaphthalene, $C_{10}H_{12}$, yields 10 CO_2 and 6 H_2O, while the corresponding decane, $C_{10}H_{22}$, will give the same CO_2 with 11 H_2O, it is evident that there should be a tendency for the presence of less free carbon in the decane flame.[1]

It must not be supposed that the paraffin-naphthene type does not yield any free carbon. The continuous spectrum of the lamp flame indicates radiation by incandescent carbon. It is simply that in the conventional lamp just the right combination (of direct oxidation with colorless flame and of cracking to free carbon which is heated to incandescence and finally burned) will occur, with optimum results as to illumination. Of course, the probability is that the lamp was altered until Pennsylvania kerosene would burn perfectly in it. If Borneo or California kerosene had been produced in large quantities before the paraffinic illuminant, some other type of lamp would have been prevalent.

Summarizing, it may be said that a good kerosene in a conventional lamp does several things in burning:

1. A large proportion burns by a smokeless combustion, to yield a high flame temperature.

2. A limited amount cracks to gaseous hydrocarbons and soot-like material.

3. Part of the coke may react by the water-gas reaction to yield combustible gases.

[1] The smoke-suppressing effect obtained by injecting liquid water into a refinery gas flare is described by Martin, *Oil Gas J.*, **55**(8):116 (1957).

4. Some of the coke is heated to incandescence, yielding the desired light.

5. All the coke is finally burned to carbon dioxide.

An interesting point has been discussed by Minchin,[1] who has called attention to Bancroft's characterization of a luminous flame as a colloidal suspension of carbon in a gas medium. He has found that carbon can be deposited from a flame on the negative element of an electrical system conducting current through the flame; this indicates positive charges on the colloidal carbon particles. Since more is deposited, for a given amount of current, at the top than at the bottom of a flame, it can be assumed that the particles are small at the base and agglomerate to larger units near the top. When they grow too large to burn under the flame conditions, smoking ensues.

It was said above that traces of impurities had a negative importance in the make-up of a kerosene. This is true in the sense that, in their presence, troubles arise which do not occur when they are absent. The chief offenders are sulfur compounds of various kinds and hydrocarbons of the cyclic or unsaturated type likely to form coke deposits on the wick.[2] The chief manifestation of the importance of sulfur in the small proportions likely to occur in a kerosene with any pretension to quality (never over 0.2 per cent) is likely to be the formation on the lamp chimney of a translucent white deposit, known as a "bloom." This may be due to the etching of the glass by sulfurous or other sulfur acids in the flue gases, with the formation of sodium sulfate or sulfonates, or to deposition of corresponding salts of ammonium (from ammonia in the air used by the flame) or of potassium and calcium compounds contained in the wick. In support of the glass-etching idea is the fact that blooming occurs most readily with new lamp chimneys, decreasing with age and use, presumably as the most reactive compounds are removed from the surface by etching and washing.

Compounds of the condensed aromatic and cyclic unsaturated types are undesirable because they contribute to the formation of a deposit of coke or char on top of the wick, where it must inevitably interfere with the flow of oil and the shaping of the flame. Oil-soluble metallic sulfonates or naphthenates surviving the chemical treatment will leave inorganic oxides, sulfonates, or carbonates in the wick to the detriment of oil flow and flame structure.

---

[1] *World Petrol. Congr., Proc. 1st Congr., London,* **2**:739 (1933).

[2] Kewley and Jackson, *J. Inst. Petrol. Technology,* **13**:377 (1927). Moerbeek, *World Petrol. Congr., Proc. 1st Congr., London,* **2**:703 (1933). On the mechanism of coke deposit formation see Thorp, Long, and Garner, *Fuel,* vol. 34, p. 51, April, 1955, Supplement; cracking of hydrocarbons to butadiene, followed by elaboration of fulvenes, is indicated. These polymerize and oxidize to coke-like substances.

XII-2. Physical Properties. Attempts have been made to relate the burning qualities of kerosenes to a variety of their physical properties, chiefly without success because of a lack of rational basis for the relations sought. Some of the proposals have been examined by Kunerth[1] and by Stewart.[2] Burning in an ordinary lamp involves the drawing of the oil up the wick by capillarity; the rate of flow will be governed by the surface tension and viscosity at the equilibrium temperature of the kerosene in the lamp reservoir. Surface tension decreases a little with rise of temperature in the ordinary range and increases slightly with rise in boiling point for the products of a given crude oil,[3] but these changes are not large enough to be important. Stewart observed that two kerosenes widely different in specific gravity differed only 2 per cent in surface tension. Viscosity is much more significant; a lamp will give a full flame soon after lighting, because the entire wick is saturated, but the flame size will drop if the oil is too viscous at reservoir temperature to climb the wick as fast as the flame consumes it. A temporary remedy is to turn up the wick, but this leads to ultimate burning of the wick fabric. This importance of viscosity is likely to invalidate most of the attempts to correlate illuminating power with boiling point or molecular weight. The actual viscosity satisfactory for conventional lamps is apparently of the order of a little above or below 2.0 cs, depending on temperature. Thus, a Mid-Continent kerosene of good quality will show viscosities as follows:

At　0°F.......... 2.50 cs
At 100°F.......... 1.70 cs

Typical inspection tests of two conventional kerosenes are as follows:

	Mid-Continent	Pennsylvania
Specific gravity..............	0.8086	0.7909
Over point, °F...............	360	355
50 per cent point............	436	432
End point...................	544	528
Sulfur, lamp, per cent.........	0.004	0.01
Flash point, °F...............	139	136
Cloud point, °F..............	−38	−26
Copper strip corrosion........	O.K.	O.K.

XII-3. Manufacture. The preparation of kerosene is simple in theory. A crude oil fraction, boiling roughly between 175 and 275°C[4] and defined

[1] *Lighting J.*, **3**:28 (1915).

[2] *Phys. Rev.*, **31**:513 (1910).

[3] Johansen, *Ind. Eng. Chem.*, **16**:132 (1924).

[4] As initial boiling point has been made higher because of demand for gasoline, the end point has become lower to maintain viscosity in the correct range.

more exactly by gravity limits which change with the crude oil being worked, is isolated and subjected to a refining drastic enough to remove all the constituents undesirable according to the preceding discussion. The practice of earlier years was to prepare kerosene only from crudes of paraffinic type, such as those of Pennsylvania and of the better Mid-Continent oils. For these, rather light sulfuric acid treatment—say, 6 lb per bbl of oil, or about 1 per cent by volume—was the maximum of severity. This was followed by alkali washing or doctor treatment (see Chap. VII) and by redistillation or fuller's earth adsorption treatment. Fractions of different gravity and flash and fire points were collected separately, to serve as domestic and export kerosenes and for long-time burning oils to be used in signal lamps. This general scheme is still followed, but the devising of more drastic refining methods has made it possible to employ lower-grade crudes containing higher proportions of undesired reactive constituents. Thus, California kerosene fractions are stated by Van Senden[1] and by McHatton[2] to contain traces of phenols, unsaturated cyclic hydrocarbons resembling cyclopentadiene, nitrogen compounds, and naphthenic acids, all of which contribute to instability, particularly of color. Heavy treatment with sulfuric acid or, preferably, extraction with sulfur dioxide followed by light sulfuric acid treatment will remove aromatics as well as the traces of the aforementioned compounds, which can apparently persist through a mild refining treatment. The principle involved is the destruction or removal of all the hydrocarbons of unstable or aromatic character, all oxygen compounds or all that tend to be acidic or resin-forming, all nitrogen compounds because they tend to color instability, and the bulk of the sulfur compounds because they produce sulfur dioxide in the chimney gases, with consequent blooming of glass chimneys or possibly unpleasant odor. Obviously, it is important to wash out of the kerosene very thoroughly any compounds, such as sulfonic acids, which could hold alkalies or other metals in solution, to deposit later as ash in wicks or burners.

The discoloration in storage likely to occur with kerosenes made from somewhat unstable crudes has attracted attention.[3] Hillman has devised a test involving the extent of discoloration caused by lead peroxide, to predict color stability. This resembles a similar test devised by Jones[4] by which the stability of shale distillates was predicted from the extent of color reaction with sodium peroxide.

---

[1] *World Petroleum Congr., Proc. 1st Congr., London,* **2**:717 (1933).

[2] *Ibid.,* p. 721.

[3] Hillman, *World Petrol. Congr., Proc. 1st Congr., London,* **2**:708 (1933). Moerbeek, *World Petrol. Congr., Proc. 1st Congr., London,* **2**:713 (1933). Allibone, *World Petrol. Congr., Proc. 1st Congr., London,* **2**:725 (1933).

[4] Unpublished work at the Mellon Institute (1922).

XII-4. Testing Methods. The testing of kerosene for suitability and quality involves chiefly the conventional measurements of specific gravity, distillation range, sulfur content, color, and flash point. Suitable methods are described by the American Society for Testing Materials.[1] Cloud point, doctor test, and corrosion of copper strip are applied to control wax content and proportion of harmful sulfur compounds. Flash-point determination, for many years, served as the best means of recognizing dangerously volatile compounds likely to cause lamp explosions. The significance of the flash point and the influence of traces of volatile impurities on flash-point temperature are discussed by Ormandy and Craven[2] and by Craven and Banks.[3]

The viscosity of kerosene can be determined in any good capillary instrument of suitable dimensions. In past years the instrument and scale of units employed in the United States have been the Saybolt thermoviscosimeter and a scale of seconds for efflux of a measured volume of liquid; these readings are convertible into kinematic units. For instance, the limiting values for an ordinary kerosene on the Saybolt instrument may be of the order of 375 to 430 sec.

Testing for illuminating and burning power has been carried on in a variety of ways. At present, ability to burn for a long time without undue decrease in illuminating power is indicated by a long-time burning test.[4] Suitability for lamp use is indicated by measuring the maximum initial height at which a flame will burn without forming smoke. An aromatic kerosene will furnish only a short flame without depositing soot on a white surface, while a paraffinic oil may give a flame four to eight times as long under the same conditions. A test for this purpose was devised in 1923 by R. F. Davis;[5] similar procedures have been studied and standardized in England[6] and in the United States.[7] More recently, the amount of char remaining on the wick of a test lamp after a period of burning has been proposed as a measure of burning quality.[8] Some precautions are necessary; the wick should be extracted with water and a series of solvents to afford the necessary precision.

XII-5. Miscellaneous Uses. Kerosenes have in the past been used extensively as fuels for tractor engines and for the power units of small farm electric power generators. This practice is decreasing largely

[1] ASTM Standards on Petroleum Products, annual edition.

[2] *J. Inst. Petrol. Technologists*, **8**:145 (1922).

[3] *J. Inst. Petrol. Technologists*, **9**:490 (1923).

[4] ASTM D 187–49.

[5] Terry and Field, *Ind. Eng. Chem., Anal. Ed.*, **8**:293 (1936).

[6] *J. Inst. Petrol. Technologists*, **19**:812 (1933); "Standard Methods of Testing Petroleum," 5th ed., p. 299, Institute of Petroleum Technologists, 1942.

[7] Federal Specification VV-L-791e, 1953, Method 2107.

[8] *J. Inst. Petrol.*, **32**:269 (1946).

because of the trouble and expense of maintaining and handling different grades of fuels for different purposes. Where such materials are made and sold, it is often the custom to employ distillates from aromatic crude oils and even from cracked stocks; these latter yield fractions of higher octane number than do the paraffinic crudes suitable for conventional kerosenes.[1] Kerosene or an unrefined kerosene distillate, sold as No. 1 fuel oil, is now widely used for diesel-powered buses in city service; a volatile fuel is required to minimize smoke and odor in the exhaust and coke-like deposits in the engine. It was also customary to prepare such materials so as to be slightly more volatile than ordinary kerosene. The name engine distillates has been applied to such products ("vaporizing oils" in England). They were also quite suitable for use as stove fuels, since calorific value was more important than the luminous flame essential for lamp purposes. However, as stated, it has proved to be more economical to supply only one grade of kerosene for all such purposes.

This simplification has resulted in the practical disappearance of what was known as mineral seal oil, long-time burning oil, or 300° oil. These were all terms for a heavy, less volatile kerosene employed as a lantern fuel, as in railway signal lamps or lighthouses. The product gave a more persistent flame, which was difficult to blow out and was thus more permanent in outdoor use. The term 300° oil probably referred to the requirement of about 300°F as a fire test value, thus reflecting a much higher low limit for molecular weight than that of ordinary kerosene.

Even well-refined kerosene possesses some odor, especially after long storage or after exposure to light and air. This is more or less of an obstacle to many of the miscellaneous uses of kerosene, where a liquid of stable color and odor is desired. Highly refined kerosenes have been produced to meet these objections. Conventional kerosenes so refined, or fractions differing very slightly in volatility, are employed as solvents for hair dressings and hair tonics, certain varieties of liniments, external antiseptics, facial creams, and shampoo preparations. Probably the largest use of such products is that of a high-boiling naphtha fraction a little more volatile than kerosene as a vehicle for widely distributed pyrethrum, derris, and synthetic insecticides. In addition there are many miscellaneous outlets in paints, polishes, cleaning and degreasing compounds, and wherever a low-priced hydrocarbon solvent is required.

It should be noted that the drastic refining applied to render a kerosene or an insecticide naphtha colorless and odorless usually lowers its resistance to oxidation, the latter resulting in development of color and odor[2]

---

[1] See *J. Inst. Petrol.*, **40**:242 (1954), ASTM D 1215–54T; octane number by motor method not less than 35.

[2] Rather and Beard, *Natl. Petrol. News*, **28**(20):34 (1936).

with age.   The practice has therefore spread of adding small quantities of antioxidants which inhibit such deterioration.

ABSORBENT OILS

The absorption process for the recovery of low-boiling gasoline hydrocarbons from natural gas, which consists in scrubbing the gas at a fairly high pressure with a solvent for these hydrocarbons, employs, in general, a material of the type of mineral seal oil, which is a high-boiling-point kerosene fraction.   This product fulfills very well the requirements for the purpose.   Since the dissolved hydrocarbons are driven off by steam distillation, it is important that the solvent be as nonvolatile as is consistent with other properties.   The presence in the absorbent oil of comparatively low-boiling fractions would permit some of these fractions to be distilled over with the recovered light hydrocarbons; this would affect seriously and irregularly the volatility of the gasoline product. By choosing a distillation range for the absorbent oil sufficiently above the final distillation temperature of the usual product of the absorption process, trouble of this kind is minimized.   An interval difference of 50°C is usually sufficient.   A compromise must, however, be effected between the volatility and the viscosity of the absorbent, since the latter must not only be nonviscous enough to circulate freely through the system without excessive resistance but must also allow any condensed and emulsified water to separate out readily.   In general, this ready tendency to drop emulsified water is also dependent on the degree of refining and care of preparation of the absorbent oil.   This applies particularly after the oil has been in use for some time.   Poorly refined oil may contain readily oxidizable constituents which will produce small amounts of asphaltic or sludge-making substances, which are very effective as stabilizers for emulsions.   The use of an oil which will not separate out wax at the lowest operating temperatures (cloud test) is important for two reasons: (1) suspended solid matter may hinder the settling-out of emulsified water, and (2) an oil of high cloud test might solidify in the system if the plant were to stop operation in cold weather.

It has been assumed that, in general, absorbent oils made from paraffinic crudes have better absorbent properties than similar fractions from oils of other types.   From Raoult's law of the lowering of vapor pressures, it follows that of two absorbents, the one of lower molecular weight will be better.   It has been found, however, that Raoult's law is not always followed rigidly;[1] and in a study by Wilson and Wylde, it was noted that for four absorbents, the order of decreasing molecular weight was also the order of increasing deviation from Raoult's law.   The deviations

[1] Matheson and Cummings, *Ind. Eng. Chem.*, **25**:723 (1933).

observed were great enough to neutralize partially the influence of changing molecular weight. Wilson and Wylde[1] used lubricating fractions from California, Gulf Coast, and Pennsylvania crude oils and castor oil, the (approximate) molecular weight increasing in the order given. Hexane exerted a somewhat lower vapor pressure when dissolved in the Pennsylvania oil than when in the Gulf Coast or California oils. These experiments were not strictly comparable with actual practice, but ordinary absorbent oils were used in another study by Wilson and Davis[2] of the vapor pressure of benzene; the same relations were found to apply. Since the hydrocarbons recovered from natural gas are, so far as known, all paraffins, it may be deduced from the work on hexane that a naphthenic absorbent is somewhat less effective than a paraffinic absorbent. It is stated that, in practice, naphthenic absorbents possess only about 75 per cent of the absorbing ability of paraffinic oils of similar properties.

The amount of absorbent oil required for a given volume of gas varies, of course, with the gasoline content of the gas and should be limited to the point where the result secured does not justify further cost of operation. It has been pointed out by Cantelo[3] that the complete removal of any one constituent from a gas depends on the use of such an amount of oil as would give a solution having the same vapor pressure of that constituent as the constituent has partial pressure in the gas. If this condition is met for the most plentiful constituent, the gasoline will be completely removed. The matter is usually approached more empirically, and oil is employed in such quantity as will, after absorption, give a concentration of gasoline hydrocarbons of about 3 per cent, though cases are known where 6 per cent has been reached without a loss of efficiency.

As a matter of practice, absorbent oils of the following characteristics are chosen when available:

Type....................	Paraffinic
Color....................	Not darker than pale yellow
Odor....................	Not offensive
Molecular weight...........	150 to 200 (approx.)
Cloud test.................	Below 32°F
Viscosity.................	40 to 60 or 70 SSU at 100°F
Volatile with steam.........	Less than 0.1 per cent
Initial point...............	Approx. 500°F

---

[1] *Ind. Eng. Chem.*, **15**: 801 (1923). See also Hull, *Petrol. Refiner*, **35**(4):149 (1956). The improvement effected by use of lower-molecular-weight absorbents is about equal to that calculated from theory, at 100 psi; at 500 to 800 psi it drops to 70 per cent of theory and rises to 100 per cent at 1,500 psi.

[2] *Ind. Eng. Chem.*, **15**:947 (1923).

[3] *Can. Chem. Met.*, **6**:197 (1922).

A typical product showed the following inspection tests:

Degrees Fahrenheit

Initial point	520
Boiling range	150
Flash point	255
Fire point	300

Absorption for recovery of benzene and coal-tar light oil from coke-oven gas is also customary. Oils about like those required for gasoline recovery are employed when feasible. Contrary to gasoline practice, oils of cyclic character give theoretically better recovery, and tetra-hydronaphthalene has been reported in use under abnormal circumstances. The objection to using aromatic or naphthenic oils or coal-tar products lies in their instability. In gasoline plants oils do not deteriorate rapidly under ordinary conditions; even so, a good petroleum oil is not used long and, where possible, the once-used absorbent is diverted to other outlets and fresh absorbent is employed. In cycling plants for the recovery of "condensate" crude oils, where fresh absorbent is sometimes not readily available, the oil is carefully reclaimed and kept clean.[1] In benzol recovery plants, long-continued re-use is widespread, and oil thickening with accompanying troubles are customary.[2] These are attributed to the contamination of the oil by sulfur compounds and entrained tar carried by the gas, and the reaction of these materials with themselves or with constituents of the oil, especially when this latter itself is a coal-tar derivative. A naphthenic or aromatic petroleum oil would be less reactive than a coal-tar product, but more so than a paraffinic material. The problem is said to be even more acute in naphthalene recovery; for such purposes it is recommended that the spent oil be used only once and then diverted to fuel purposes or for the carburetting of water gas.

FUEL OILS[3]

Among the advantages which make fuel oils desirable as compared with solid fuels are:

1. The greater heating value of a given weight or volume of oil, with the consequence that a smaller storage space is required

2. The higher chemical efficiencies attained due to better contact between the fuel and air

[1] Grimshaw, *Petrol. Engr.*, **14**(3):80 (1942).

[2] Powell, Merritt, and Byrne, *Gas Age-Record*, **60**:3 (1927). Wilson, *Coke and Smokeless-Fuel Age*, **7**:231 (1945).

[3] For a brief review of the early uses of petroleum oils as fuels, see the second edition of this work, p. 595, 1942.

3. The greater ease of handling the fuel and tending the fires, together with almost complete freedom from ash

4. The considerable increase in the heat input possible in a given combustion space

The fundamental properties required are so simple that the listed advantages are obtainable with a wide variety of oils.

XII-6. Combustion of Fuel Oils. The chemical changes involved in the combustion of fuel oil are as little understood as are those involved in any other combustion reaction. The starting materials are air and a rather complex hydrocarbon mixture of molecular weight ranging from about 300 upward. Where the molecular weight is quite high, as for residual oils, there is usually an appreciable content of oxygen or sulfur compounds of hydrocarbon character, which, in extreme cases, may reach 20 or 30 per cent.[1] The latter are presumably the asphaltic constituents, common in asphaltic crudes; in general, the asphaltenes and the parent hydrocarbons are made up of cyclic nuclei, aromatic and naphthenic, tending somewhat to condensed structure. These compounds are likely to be semisolid or even solid when alone but remain in solution when the mixture is warm enough, say, at room temperature or somewhat above. The final products, depending on the completeness of combustion, are the ordinary flue gases, mixtures of nitrogen, water vapor, and carbon dioxide, with small proportions of carbon monoxide, hydrogen, gaseous hydrocarbons, aldehydes, and acids. Normally, a small amount of unburned carbon (carrying adsorbed tars and hydrocarbon liquids) will appear as smoke or soot. The hydrogen in the fuel oil hydrocarbons, which may have amounted to 12 per cent, will have burned to water, and this passes off as steam, so that its heat of vaporization is lost. This loss is reflected in the difference between net and gross heat of combustion. Sulfur present in the oil as sulfur compounds will end as sulfur dioxide. The lighter fuel oils, kerosene and gas oil, present a simpler picture than the residual oils, but are sufficiently complex in make-up to leave the burning reaction extremely complicated.

It is obviously impossible to trace the combustion reactions for even a few of the constituents of any one oil. Fortunately, the high temperature of the flame has an homogenizing effect, so that the last steps seem to be nearly always the same. Spraying or vaporizing a high-molecular-weight hydrocarbon into a flame zone serves to expose it, in an almost molecular state of division, to temperatures at which no hydrocarbon is stable and all hydrocarbons will ultimately decompose into their elements; but this does not occur directly, taking rather a series of steps. By analogy with the known cracking of oils in gas-

---

[1] Two to three per cent of elementary sulfur or oxygen.

making processes, where the temperatures are somewhat lower (at most 700°C instead of, say, 1200 to 1500°C), the large molecules are broken into the very much smaller ones characteristic of permanent gases (see Chap. IX). Methane, ethane and ethylene, propane and propylene, some butadiene, and presumably some hydrogen are formed. Because not enough hydrogen is available to balance out all the material present as permanent gases of saturated character, carbonaceous residues, coke, and even some elementary carbon are set free. The separate hydrocarbon gases then oxidize individually, as do the carbon-like solids. It might be argued that oxidation of some of the large molecules may occur before the cracking can proceed, but it is not likely that such a step would change the final result. It is known that hydrocarbons which have been oxidized crack more readily, and that the presence of a small amount of oxygen will cause a marked increase in the cracking velocity of such hydrocarbons as propane.[1] In other words, it seems likely that any preoxidation which may occur in the flame of a burning hydrocarbon of high molecular weight will result in a speeding up of the cracking.[2]

The modern theory of combustion has been formulated by a gradual evolution. In view of the cracking process mentioned above, it is possible to confine the study to a consideration (for even a heavy oil) of gaseous reactions.[3] The idea that the initial reaction in burning a hydrocarbon was one of hydroxylation was proposed fifty years ago by Bone,[4] supported and developed by Blair and Wheeler.[5] This was altered by the peroxide theory of Callendar.[6] These later ideas have been worked out energetically by more recent investigators who have employed the technique of studying the more conveniently observable phenomena displayed by low-temperature oxidations and the so-called

[1] Schultz and White, *Ind. Eng. Chem.*, **24**:1277 (1932). Frolich and Wiezevich, *Ind. Eng. Chem.*, **27**10:55 (1935).

[2] It seems unlikely that the cracking and the oxidation can be separated. Soot and carbon are formed by cracking, but the analytical examination of cokes and carbons from combustion [Garner, *Fuel*, **32**:117 (1953); Thorp, Long, and Garner, *Fuel*, **34**:51 (1955)] has supplied evidence of oxygen compounds. Garner speculates that, at the prevailing temperatures, most oils crack to butadiene, which builds up into fulvene complexes; these polymerize, oxidize, and dehydrogenate to carbonaceous residues. Spectral evidence exists [Minkoff, *Fuel*, **35**:135 (1956)] that acetylene occurs near the luminous carbon zone of a flat diffusion flame composed of ethylene and oxygen. Since ethylene is a product of high-temperature cracking of hydrocarbons, the sequence ethylene → acetylene → carbon seems at least possible.

[3] Obviously, the burning of coke or elementary carbon, produced by the cracking, must also be dealt with.

[4] A series of papers; for example, see *J. Chem. Soc.*, **89**:660 (1906).

[5] *J. Soc. Chem. Ind.*, **42**:491T (1923).

[6] *Engineering*, **123**:147, 182, 210 (1927). Contributions have been made by Egerton, *Nature*, **121**:10 (1928); Bone, *Trans. Faraday Soc.*, **30**:148 (1934); and Ubbelohde, *Phil. Trans. Roy. Soc. London*, **A152**:354 (1936).

cool flames.[1]　There is general recognition that much advantage can be gained through considering the complex of phenomena as a series of consecutive reactions, each of which can be analyzed in turn.　The velocity with which the molecules are moving varies widely, and the resulting collisions, chiefly of low-velocity particles, will, to that extent, be elastic, resulting in no reaction.　Those between molecules moving with a velocity higher than a necessary minimum and with a proper distribution of energy may result in reaction, the speed being governed by the temperature.

It is customary to distinguish between a thermal and a chain type of reaction.　In the former, only molecules are involved, and the reaction is produced by a temperature rise resulting from the reacting mixture itself; in the latter, the initial reaction is pictured as being followed by a chain of events, which are triggered by energy-carrying atoms or relatively unstable fragments of molecules known as free radicals.　In chain reactions, the rate of reaction is proportional to the concentration of chain carriers and is therefore affected directly by the rates of formation and destruction of these carriers.　Theoretically, the chain reaction may accelerate without temperature rise.　If one step of the reaction produces more than one carrier, the chain is said to branch, and the rate of the reaction usually rises, with a possible increase to the point of explosion. This may not occur for a variety of reasons; one such may be the contact of the propagating radicals with the walls of the container, resulting in the loss of their energy content.

The initial collision of hydrocarbon molecules with molecules of oxygen is pictured as resulting in the formation of peroxides;[2] these decompose with the ultimate formation of hydroxyl and alkyl radicals.　These latter, combining with unreacted hydrocarbons, may supply still other radicals, so that there is no shortage of carriers for the reaction chain. It must be recognized, however, that the concentration of carriers is less at low temperatures; however, the carriers are plentiful in an actual flame region.[3]　Whether the mechanism assumed is thermal or based

---

[1] For instance, see Gaydon, *Trans. Faraday Soc.*, **42**:292 (1946).　Walsh, *Trans. Faraday Soc.*, **42**:269 (1946).　Spence and Townsend, *Rev. inst. franç. petrole et Ann. combustibles liquides*, **4**:389 (1949).　Norrish and Patniak, *Nature*, **163**:883 (1949). Norrish, *Rev. inst. franç. petrole et Ann. combustibles liquides*, **4**:288 (1949).　Kahler, Bearse, and Stoner, *Ind. Eng. Chem.*, **43**:2777 (1951).　Norrish, *Discussions Faraday Soc.*, **10**:269 (1951).　Bailey and Norrish, *Proc. Roy. Soc. (London)*, **A212**:311 (1952).

[2] Correspondingly, the burning of carbon is represented as starting (in the presence of water vapor) with the formation of highly unstable carbon-oxygen-water complexes, which by decomposition lead to other reactions.　Jones and Townsend, *Trans. Faraday Soc.*, **42**:297 (1946).

[3] The possibly simpler case of the reaction of oxygen with hydrogen has been dealt with by von Elbe and Lewis, *J. Chem. Phys.*, **10**:366 (1942).　For a condensed summary of modern theory of burning of gaseous fuels, see Heiple and Sullivan, *Trans. ASME*, **70**:343 (1948).

on chain propagation, the end result may be the same. Unless the thermal energy or, alternatively, the number of chain carriers is reduced by lowering of temperature or by some influence such as contact with the containing walls, the speed of the combustion may increase in an isolated system to the point of explosion. The burning of gas in a bunsen burner or of kerosene in a lamp does not change in this way because of mechanical arrangements. In a gas burner, gas is supplied and the products of burning are cooled and withdrawn at such a rate that a steady combustion can be maintained at one particular location; the same is true in a lamp or in an industrial fuel oil burner. In these cases, the burning of a hydrocarbon molecule proceeds in an orderly fashion. An adequate supply of oxygen or air will ensure that the radicals and fragments, no matter how diverse, will end as molecules of carbon dioxide and water vapor, after the release of a considerable amount of heat energy.

However, some of the details and conditions of the burning will result in differentiation of flame type. It is customary to discuss at least two kinds of flame, the yellow and the blue. Sometimes a green flame is recognized, but in the case of either the blue or the green, the color is attributed to radiation from certain radicals existing in the reaction zone. The luminous yellow flame, however, is believed to arise from the heating to incandescence of carbon particles set free in the cracking process which breaks large molecules into smaller fragments. The distinction between the conditions bringing about the one or the other flame type was outlined by Haslam and Russell,[1] and developed more fully by Romp.[2] Yellow-flame combustion supplies a continuous spectrum and the blue-flame type a discontinuous one; either type can be converted to the other by a change of conditions only, but a given fuel is likely to produce only one type if the conditions are not altered.

It is known that complete evaporation, thorough mixing of oil and air, suitable preheating to permit preflame oxidation, and little sudden, intense heating (especially by radiation) favor blue-flame oxidation and that sudden cooling, so as to cause incomplete combustion, will produce acrid fumes, containing formaldehyde. Burning of the blue-flame type is characteristic of reversed flames, where air burns in an atmosphere of hydrocarbon gas; certain cookstove burners employ this principle. On the other hand, incomplete evaporation of oil, uneven mixing of oil and air, inadequate preheating, so as to avoid preoxidation, and sudden and intense radiation will encourage yellow-flame oxidation, because the molecules may crack before they are oxidized, thus yielding solid carbon which may become incandescent.

[1] "Fuels and Their Combustion," p. 185, McGraw-Hill Book Company, Inc., New York, 1926.
[2] "Oil Burning," p. 74, M. Nijhoff, The Hague, 1937.

It should be noted that although blue-flame combustion is perhaps more typical for such fuels, a yellow flame can be obtained from low-molecular-weight liquid hydrocarbons, such as in kerosene, or even from gaseous hydrocarbons, by applying some of the conditions just mentioned. The reverse, however, is probably not true because of inherent limitations; it seems likely that a blue flame can only with difficulty be produced with heavy fuel oil hydrocarbons deficient in the hydrogen necessary for cracking to gaseous intermediates. Instead, cracking to some gaseous hydrocarbon material and some solid or semiliquid and totally non-volatile carbonaceous residue occurs. In this case, no matter how intimate the mixing with air, the system cannot approximate true gaseous contact. As a result, some of the carbon burns, while other portions are heated to incandescence, making the flame yellow before it itself burns.

The appearance of a yellow flame from a fuel rich in hydrogen is easy to understand if it is remembered that a hydrocarbon undergoing cracking will supply fragments which may dehydrogenate, isomerize, or polymerize to structures likely to yield carbon. The formation of aromatics from lower paraffins is a commonplace of high-temperature cracking, and the role of cyclics such as aromatics and fulvenes in carbon formation has been indicated by Thorp, Long, and Garner.[1] They observed biphenyl in the flame of burning benzene, and suspected that this compound and the related terphenyls are the intermediates to carbon formation. Later they recovered fulvenes from coke residues[2] of various petroleum fuels; this supports the probable existence of diene intermediates. It appears that in a hydrogen carrier gas, soot formation is restrained by the suppression of the dehydrogenation believed to be the predecessor of cyclization. The fact that the cracking of benzene does not easily form naphthalene and anthracene may indicate that these compounds are not ordinary intermediates to soot formation and again favors the diene-fulvene mechanism.[3]

XII-7. Petroleum Products Used as Fuel Oils. The basic requirements of satisfactory fuel oils are few and simple. The most important

---

[1] *Fuel*, **30**:266 (1951); **32**:117 (1953). Both these investigators and Arthur, Kapur, and Napier, *Nature*, **169**:372 (1953), found evidence of oxygen compounds in the soot solids.

[2] On the action of iron dicyclopentadienyl in reducing coke deposition, see Arimoto, Corzitius, Lamb, and Melby, *Abstr. Papers*, P-17, ACS Meeting, Cincinnati, April, 1955.

[3] For more complete discussion of combustion theory, see Lewis and von Elbe, "Combustion Flames and Explosions," Academic Press, Inc., New York, 1951. Jost, "Explosion and Combustion Processes in Gases," McGraw-Hill Book Company, Inc., New York, 1946. Gaydon and Wolfhard, "Flames, Their Structure, Radiation, and Temperature," Chapman & Hall, Ltd., London, 1953.

requirement, that they must burn with a reasonable degree of completeness, is ordinarily assumed, but is taken care of in specifications by a statement that water and incombustible solid matter shall not exceed a given amount. Many public agencies set the figure at not over a trace to 0.1 per cent for the less viscous, and at not over 1.0 or 2.0 per cent for the more viscous oils. In the latter case, the sediment may be limited to, say, 0.25 per cent, with a deduction of payment for water and sediment in excess of 1 per cent. It is further necessary that the oils be of such viscosity at a convenient temperature that they can be pumped to burners with fair ease, and that they shall be sufficiently free of volatile constituents to have a flash point consistent with safety; this might be, say, above 150°F.

These requirements are such as to be met to a considerable extent by most unrefined and relatively heavy petroleum oils of such character that they cannot be otherwise employed more profitably. These materials fall into a variety of classes, more or less as follows:

Certain Unusual Crude Oils. Crudes so employed are usually low in gasoline and kerosene content and are unfitted by a high proportion of, say, asphalt or sulfur compounds for use as lubricants. Certain of the Mexican and East Indian crudes have at times fallen into this class.

Crude Oil Residua. These constitute much of the available industrial and bunker fuel oils. Since they are the chief products of the simplest refining operations, such as topping (see Chap. VI), in which gasoline or gasoline (perhaps kerosene) and light fuel oils distillate are removed overhead, leaving fuel oil residuum, most of the lower-grade crudes of the

TABLE XII-1*

| Type of crude | Specific gravity 60°/60°F | Engler distillation | | | Coke, per cent by weight | Sulfur, per cent by weight | Calorific value gross, Btu per lb |
		410°F (210°C) per cent	437°F (225°C) per cent	572°F (300°C) per cent			
Ebano, Mexico.....	0.9738	6.0	8.0	16.5	19.3	5.45	17,772
Venezuela, S.A.....	0.9647	3.0	4.0	17.0	10.5	2.62	18,408
Seminole, Okla.....	0.9516	0.0	0.0	8.0	9.4	1.48	18,698
Ventura, Calif......	0.9421	0.0	0.0	2.0	14.0	1.60	18,607
West Texas........	0.9346	0.0	0.0	5.0	7.7	2.03	18,758
Grozny, Russia.....	0.9088	0.0	0.0	1.0	10.2	0.17	19,300
Mixed Kansas......	0.9036	0.0	0.0	10.0	10.0	0.39	19,256
Mid-Continent.....	0.8299	0.0	0.0	40.0	9.0	0.17	19,890

* Faragher, Morrell, and Essex, *Ind. Eng. Chem.*, **21**:933 (1929).

world were, in the past, handled in this way.[1] Such oils contain in concentrated form the sulfur, wax, and asphaltic compounds of the entire crude oil and are most likely to be very viscous and somewhat hard to handle. This is so true that their viscosities are ordinarily rated by separate instruments such as the Saybolt Furol or Redwood No. II viscosimeters. The content of wax and asphalt gives them high congealing temperatures with peculiar hysteresis phenomena, so that the measuring of pour-test temperature requires a special precaution.[2] Table XII-1 shows the properties of some typical uncracked residual fuel oils made at various times in the past. More recent data averaged over the crudes available and refining methods practiced in different regions of the United States are:[3]

Gravity:

    °API...................... 3–5 to 18–20
    Specific.................... 1.10.... 1.03 to 0.93

Viscosity seconds:

    Furol at 122°F.............. 30–50 up to 290

Flash point, °F................ 140–50 up to 420
Pour point, °F................ Zero up to 60–65

Sulfur:

    Weight per cent............. 0.3 up to 2.5 or even 5.0

Water and sediment:

    Volume per cent............. Zero through trace to 1.5

Carbon residue:

    Ramsbottom, per cent........ 1.6 up to 15 or 20

Ash, per cent.................. Zero through trace to 0.2 or even 0.5
Btu per gallon................ 137,000 to a top value of 154,000

With the development of catalytic cracking processes, the need for distillate charging stocks to supply such operations has increased markedly. This need has been met by taking overhead higher and higher proportions of the suitable crude oils, with the result that the residua become more viscous. In order to bring such residua down to suitable viscosities,

---

[1] For the United States these products now make up less than 20 per cent of the yield from the over-all refining operations.

[2] Moerbeek and Van Beest, *J. Inst. Petrol. Technologists*, **21**:155 (1935).

[3] Orr and Van Sant, SAE Detroit Meeting, January, 1957.

the diluting or "cutting" with lighter oils is required. However, this represents an expensive process, to be avoided when possible. The "vis-breaking" processes have been developed to meet this situation. As described in Chap. IX, vis-breaking is a mild cracking process which serves to produce small yields of gasoline and light gas oil, while at the same time reducing the viscosity of the residuum which is the chief product of the operation. As a result, the proportion of uncracked heavy fuel marketed has decreased greatly within the past ten years; it is now less than 20 per cent of the crude oil produced.

Residual fuel oils offer a number of problems in use, connected with their high viscosity and their content of solid material such as asphaltenes. These lead to difficulties in pumping and in flow at low temperatures. Such oils are non-Newtonian liquids when cold, and show variable solidifying temperature, depending on thermal history.[1] The sulfur content, also, may be serious for certain outlets. It always presents the possibility of corroding metals and polluting the atmosphere with sulfur dioxide; however, in the glass industry, for instance, a sulfur content in the fuel oil above about 0.5 per cent may promote the formation of deposits—probably sodium sulfate—on the glass surface. It will be recalled that salt deposits of similar nature on the glass chimneys of kerosene lamps were mentioned earlier in this chapter as being caused by a much smaller content of sulfur in the kerosene. A high sulfur content in a fuel oil has always been a hazard in ceramic manufacture and in most metallurgical operations.

However, within recent years, the nonvolatile ash content of residual fuels has developed a new seriousness. These ash materials often amount to 0.005 up to 0.05 per cent of the original crude, all concentrated into the residuum. While common salt is a major constituent, nickel and vanadium are rather common, particularly in those residua derived from asphaltic oils; the oxides are corrosive at high temperatures, as happens when they impinge on the blades of oil-fired gas turbines, on the refractories used to line the fireboxes of industrial furnaces, and on the tube supports of modern high-pressure boilers. These metals seem to be related to the asphaltene content of the oils and to be removable with them, as by propane precipitation.[2] There seems to be some hope of avoiding much of the damage by the use of additive materials mixed with the oil.[3]

Gas Oils, Distillate Fuel Oils. The name gas oil is derived from the

---

[1] See Gill and Russell, *Ind. Eng. Chem.*, **46**:1264 (1954). Ackroyd and Aubrey, *Proc. Intern. Cong. Rheol.*, 2nd Congr., Oxford, p. 397, 1954.

[2] Evans, *ASTM Spec. Tech. Publ.* 108, p. 59, 1950. Sacks, *Can. J. Technol.*, **29**:492 (1951). Jones and Hardy, *Ind. Eng. Chem.*, **44**:2615 (1952).

[3] Holler and Lee, *Trans. ASME*, **76**:31 (1954).

fact that originally those products were made for the carburetion (enriching) of water gas.[1] When a crude oil of good quality is subjected to a complete refining, the gas oils are the distillates between the kerosene and the lubricating fractions. From a crude oil which is being topped, they represent everything which can be taken off after the gasoline and kerosene—perhaps only the gasoline—without running into operating difficulty. The term is also applied to the somewhat cracked distillates produced in the now-obsolete coking in horizontal shell stills to make wax distillates (see Chap. XIV) and to the volatile products from continuous coking and from vis-breaking. Because of the demand, mentioned above, for distilled oils even of high molecular weight, for charging to catalytic cracking, the term has, then, been broadened within recent years to include oils boiling as high as the heaviest distilled lubricating oils. Within the strict meaning of the term, typical gas oils might have the following properties:

Specific gravity..................	0.80 to 0.85
Viscosity SSU, 100°F............	35 to 40
Distillation, °F:	
10 per cent..................	375 to 450
90 per cent..................	550 to 650
End point...................	625 to 700

Distilled fuel oils have two main uses; as charge to catalytic cracking mentioned above, and employment as fuel for such purposes as will justify paying a premium price. Examples would be domestic furnace (home heating) oil and fuel oil for metallurgical or other manufacturing purposes where close control of conditions is required. Another competing demand which applies only to very light straight-run oils of the kerosene class is that for fuels for small high speed, so-called automotive-type diesel engines (see Chap. XI). The various requirements, both industrial and domestic, are met by the several classes of fuel oils set up by technical societies and public agencies.[2] Among these, the No. 1 and No. 2 oils (see footnote, Table XII-2) may be considered the typical distilled oils. The first, as may be seen from its properties, is essentially a kerosene distillate, while the second comes closer to being gas oil in the narrower sense of the word. The No. 1 oils present few problems in handling or use, but those of the No. 2 class, because of the content of cracked products which they almost always contain, offer some difficulty. Because cracking, and particularly catalytic cracking, produces

---

[1] The name gasoline was also coined because the volatile fractions of the crude were employed in so-called gas machines for illumination.

[2] For example, the U.S. Dept. of Commerce and the American Society for Testing Materials. See Blade, *U.S. Bur. Mines Inform. Circ.* 7762, August, 1956, for characteristics of domestic furnace oils sold in the United States.

TABLE XII-2. DETAILED REQUIREMENTS FOR FUEL OILS*,a

Grade of fuel oil[b]	Flash point, °F Min	Pour point, °F Max	Water and sediment, per cent by volume Max	Carbon residue on 10 per cent bottoms, per cent Max	Ash, per cent by weight Max	Distillation temperatures, °F 10 per cent point Max	90 per cent point Max	End point Max	SSU Universal at 100F Max	Min	Furol at 122F Max	Min	Kinematic viscosity, cs At 100F Max	Min	At 122F Max	Min	Gravity, °API Min	Copper-strip corrosion
No. 1 { A distillate oil intended for vaporizing pot-type burners and other burners requiring this grade of fuel	100 or legal	0	trace	0.15	.....	420	...	625	...	...	...	...	2.2	1.4	.....	.....	35	No. 3
No. 2 { A distillate oil for general purpose domestic heating for use in burners not requiring No. 1 fuel oil	100 or legal	20[c]	0.10	0.35	.....	[d]	675	...	40	...	...	...	(4.3)	....	.....	.....	26	
No. 4 { An oil for burner installations not equipped with preheating facilities	130 or legal	20	0.50	.....	0.10	...	...	...	125	45	...	...	(26.4)	(5.8)	.....	.....		
No. 5 { A residual-type oil for burner installations equipped with preheating facilities	130 or legal	...	1.00	.....	0.10	...	...	...	...	150	40	...	....	(32.1)	(81)	.....		

| An oil for use in burners equipped with preheaters permitting a high-viscosity fuel | No. 6 | 150 | ... | 2.00ᵉ | ... | ... | ... | ... | ... | ... | 300 | 45 | ....(638) | (92) |

* From ASTM Tentative Specifications for Fuels D 396–48T.

ᵃ Recognizing the necessity for low-sulfur fuel oils used in connection with heat-treatment, nonferrous metal, glass, and ceramic furnaces and other special uses, a sulfur requirement may be specified in accordance with the following table:

Grade of fuel oil	Sulfur, max, per cent
No. 1	0.5
No. 2	1.0
No. 4	No limit
No. 5	No limit
No. 6	No limit

Other sulfur limits may be specified only by mutual agreement between the purchaser and the seller.

ᵇ It is the intent of these classifications that failure to meet any requirement of a given grade does not automatically place an oil in the next lower grade unless in fact it meets all requirements of the lower grade.

ᶜ Lower or higher pour points may be specified whenever required by conditions of storage or use. However, these specifications shall not require a pour point lower than 0°F under any conditions.

ᵈ The 10 per cent point may be specified at 440°F maximum for use in other than atomizing burners.

ᵉ The amount of water by distillation plus the sediment by extraction shall not exceed 2.00 per cent. The amount of sediment by extraction shall not exceed 0.50 per cent. A deduction in quantity shall be made for all water and sediment in excess of 1.0 per cent.

olefinic and aromatic hydrocarbons, oils containing appreciable proportions of cracked compounds may, unless air supply is adequate and burner adjustment good, tend to produce more smoke and more deposits of the coke type.[1] They may also exhibit instability in storage, e.g., darkening in color because of formation of insoluble material which will eventually deposit as a gummy sludge threatening to clog filter and burner orifices during use. This latter phenomenon is apparently related to the content of sulfur and nitrogen compounds.[2] Chemical refining and mild hydrogenation are effective against such trouble and one or the other of such treatments is often applied. There is some indication that a mixture of cracked and straight-run materials will show signs of instability sooner and under less severe conditions than will the cracked oil alone.[3] It has in some cases been necessary to apply chemical refining, such as washing with strong sodium hydroxide solution, or treating with sulfuric acid followed by neutralization with alkali solution, to correct this instability; solvent refining with furfural is used to a small extent. Alternatively, oxidation inhibitors and detergent-dispersant additives (see Chap. XIII) are often applied as preventatives.[4] Advance laboratory evaluation of the storage stability of such oils has been attempted in various ways; heating in open beakers at 100°C for 24 hr;[5] amount of sediment obtained by hot filtration; amount of xylene dilution necessary to prevent the formation of a dark ring on filter paper; the last two will be recognized as tests intended to determine the amount of insoluble material present at the time of the examination.[6] It will be evident, from the chemical make-up of blends of cracked constituents, that burning such oils will require a greater supply of air and better mixing of this air with the oil

[1] Sullivan and Glendenning, *Fueloil and Oil Heat*, **4**(1):36, 82 (1945). The burning quality of a catalytically cracked oil is indicated, according to these authors, by the diesel index, API gravity $\times$ aniline point. Unpublished study of this index, however, indicates that the correlation is no better than that with gravity alone.

[2] Williams and Offenhauer, *Ind. Eng. Chem.*, **49**:1259 (1957).

[3] Thompson, Chenicek, Druge, and Simon, *Ind. Eng. Chem.*, **43**:935 (1951). Sauer, Melpolder, and Brown, *Ind. Eng. Chem.*, **44**:2606 (1952).

[4] Hill, *Advances in Chem. Ser.*, No. 5, p. 251, 1951. Bertollete and Rogers, *Refining Engr.*, **28**(12):C-41 (1956). *ACS, Div. Petrol. Chem., Symposium on Additives in Petroleum Fuels*, ACS Meeting, Minneapolis, September, 1955.

[5] Hawes and Miller, *Ind. Eng. Chem.*, **33**:1318 (1941).

[6] Broom, *J. Inst. Petrol.*, **31**:347 (1945); other laboratory evaluation tests are described by Proell and Bolt, *Oil Gas J.*, **44**(47):234 (1946), and by Rescorla, Cromwell, and Milsom, *Petrol. Engr.*, **22**(12):C-31 (1950). A correlation between the smoking tendency of No. 2 oils and the 50 per cent distillation temperature and API gravity has been reported by Reid and Hersberger, *ASTM Bull.* 145, p. 77, 1947. There is sometimes difficulty in confirming the validity of this and similar indices; since they rest on empirical observation, it may be surmised that they do not take in all the necessary facts.

vapor or oil droplets. Improvement can also be effected by providing a greater amount of vaporizing area and by avoiding impingement of the flame on cool surfaces. It is evident that combustion can be improved, with consequent decrease in smoke formation, by securing the proper degree of atomizing.[1] In fact, the phenomena observed in studying smoking tendency are just what would be predicted from a supposition that smoke may be avoided by doing whatever will bring about a more rapid and more complete chemical reaction between the fuel and the combining air. This is brought out by a study of smoke formation and smoke consumption in a bunsen flame;[2] large amounts of smoke can be consumed in a flame if the smoke is finely divided; additional air has little effect in a lean flame, but a marked effect in a rich flame; butane will produce a large, smoky flame if the flow of the reacting gases is stream-like in character, but a proper flame can be secured if aeration is increased by supplying the gases in turbulent flow.

Pressure-still Tars. The pressure-still tars resulting from thermal cracking are less common since that process has given way to catalytic cracking. Because of their exposure to high temperatures cracked tars are rather highly aromatized, but less so than the coal-tar products which they somewhat resemble. They are characterized by a high specific gravity (often greater than 1.0), a low viscosity for a given gravity and boiling range as compared with uncracked products, a low solidifying temperature, and definitely aromatic constitution. They may also carry a content of suspended coke-like material which causes trouble by settling out and which has been observed to assume a gel-like structure in the oil when undisturbed for a long time.[3] Apparently protective colloids such as lime soaps are of some benefit in preventing such structure formation. Correspondingly such tars show a tendency to drop out carbonaceous sediments on standing, on mixing with other oils of poor solvent power (usually paraffinic cutter oils, analogous to the precipitation of asphaltenes by naphtha), or on overheating. The chemical nature of the constituents (oils, asphaltenes, and resins) will govern the peptization of the solid asphaltenes.[4] This effect of overheating is noticeable in preheater units, which may become clogged. The tendency may be related to the content of benzene-insoluble "carboids," but is at present best indicated by an empirical test.[5]

The cracked oils possess some advantages and disadvantages not con-

[1] Joyce, *J. Inst. Fuel,* **22**:150 (1949).

[2] Clark, *Ind. Eng. Chem.,* **45**:2785 (1953).

[3] Sheppard and Eberlin, *Ind. Eng. Chem.,* **16**:832 (1924).

[4] Brierly, *J. Am. Soc., Naval Engrs.,* **46**:199 (1934). van Kerkvoort, Nieustad, and van der Waarden, *Congr. intern. chauffage ind.,* 4-*Congr., Paris,* 1952; Preprint no. 220.

[5] Batchelder, *Proc. API,* **17**(III):17 (1936).

nected with their instability. The low natural viscosity reduces the preheating necessary for easy handling, say, to 125° or 150°F instead of to 300°, as required for an uncracked oil of similar gravity. At the same time the somewhat greater density gives higher Btu values per gallon or per barrel, although not per pound. Against these practical points must be counted the recognition that the aromatic hydrocarbons are slower burning, thus requiring higher furnace temperature, adjustment for long flame travel, and avoidance of sudden chilling before combustion is complete.[1]

Residua Subjected to Slight Cracking to Reduce Viscosity—Vis-broken Residua. Such treatments are equivalent to a partial destructive distillation, effecting a small amount of cracking and producing 5 to 10 per cent of gasoline, together with a relatively nonviscous heavy distillate which can be blended back with the residuum; the residuum itself will have been reduced in viscosity by a measurable and useful amount. A typical operation of this kind[2] will involve heating the charge oil to a temperature of about 900°F at a pressure of, say, 200 lb, for a very short time; the oil, which may have had an extrapolated initial distillation temperature of 950°F, will be so converted that 10 per cent will appear as gasoline, 40 per cent as light and heavy oil, and about 47 per cent as fuel oil residuum. The properties of this residuum (from a Mid-Continent charge stock) may be as follows:

> Gravity, °API.............. 11.5 to 9.5
> Viscosity, furol............ 220 to 380
> Pour point, °F............. 50 to 60

It should be understood that these figures are illustrative. The oil is likely to show a high carbon residua value—10 or 12 per cent; it will have some of the advantages and disadvantages of a cracked oil, the chief gain of the treatment having been the lowering of viscosity.

Miscellaneous Fuel Products. Petroleum refineries sometimes find it necessary to utilize as fuels semiwaste products of their operations. Such materials are sulfuric acid sludges from refining operations, emulsified recovered oils, asphalts, and coke products. These present a variety of technical problems in handling.[3]

XII-8. Oil Burners. The mechanical problems involved in burning oil are in principle the same, no matter for what purpose. It is necessary to supply the oil at a constant and easily controlled rate and to increase

---

[1] Hanlon, *Mech. Eng.*, **57**:241 (1935). Solberg, *Power*, **79**(1):32 (1935).

[2] Allen, Little, and Wadill, *Oil Gas J.*, **50**(6):78 (1951).

[3] See Dunstan, *J. Inst. Petrol. Technologists*, **16**:701 (1930). Mekler, *Natl. Petrol. News*, **22**(46):151; (47):51 (1930). On the burning of undiluted acid sludge containing 50 or more per cent of sulfuric acid, see Kaye and Spencer, *Oil Gas J.*, **48**(40):80 (1950).

its surface so that the area of contact between oil and air may be great enough to permit the rapid combination with oxygen which characterizes burning. In addition, the combustion space must be so arranged in size and shape that the useful heat may be recovered. These requirements are met by supplying the oil to a device for vaporizing it or, more commonly, spraying it into very fine droplets. In most industrial applications, these are dispersed into a more or less cone-shaped volume, with the apex at the orifice of the distributing device. This permits intimate mixing of droplets and air, and the resulting flame will be of the desired form, usually cone-shaped or resembling a cone flattened down into a tongue.

The equipment employed for burning oil may include the necessary storage tanks, which for heavy oils are supplied with steam coils for warming any product too high in wax content or too viscous for easy handling at normal temperatures; pumps, often in duplicate, for supplying oil to the burners (sometimes, to prevent solidifying, the oil is circulated past the burners, only a part being used); strainers to remove suspended foreign matter; and the burners themselves. These last present a complex problem which goes beyond the scope of this discussion. They may be classified briefly as:[1]

Vaporizing burners
Mechanical atomizing
Steam atomizing
Air atomizing

Steam atomizing and air atomizing are used for large industrial installations, where the accessory equipment is available for handling the viscous and often semisolid oils which can be bought at a low price. For cooking stoves and particularly for domestic heating, where the service is variable and where the users are unwilling to give the attention which industrial burner installations receive, kerosene distillates and light gas oils (Nos. 1 and 2 fuel oils), which are relatively volatile and low in viscosity, are employed in vaporizing pot-type, rotary-wall, and mechanical atomizing, so-called gun-type burners. These fuel materials require no preheating, vaporize readily, and do not carbonize to clog the burner orifices; in fact, trouble-free operation is commonplace.

In vaporizing burners, the fuel, commonly a kerosene distillate, is vaporized on a hot surface or by radiant heat and is burned as a gas. If the installation is provided with mechanical draft blowers, a gas oil fuel can sometimes be used. Atomizing burners may function by forcing the fuel under high pressure through an atomizing orifice, or by low-pressure

[1] Romp, "Oil Burning," p. 157, M. Nijhoff, The Hague, 1937.

air atomizing of an oil-air mixture.   Included under the atomizing type
are rotary burners, which form a spray mechanically.   Mechanical spraying or mechanically aided vaporizing together with mechanically induced
draft all render a burner installation more flexible as to the type of oil
which it will burn efficiently.[1]

XII-9.   Property Requirements and Tests.   The tests applied to fuel
oils include:

Flash-point determination as indicative of danger from the explosive
ignition of vapors given off by the oil.

Pour point as indicating the temperature below which the oil may solidify.   This value apparently bears no simple relation to the pumpability.[2]

Water and sediment, because water may cause foaming or flame
extinction, and sediment may clog nozzles, filters, and heaters.

Carbon residue on the oil, or, for a light product, on its 10 per cent
distillation residue, as an indication of tendency to leave coke-like deposits
and heavy tars.

Ash.   This is usually only iron rust and dirt in light oils, but in residual
fuels may be inorganic salts from well brine, as well as the natural content of metals such as vanadium and nickel.   The rust and dirt may
cause clogging and wear, and the vanadium may be corrosive to refractories and turbine blades (see above).

Viscosity.   The viscosity at the temperature to be encountered in
service, or the amount of preheating needed to attain that viscosity, is
important in estimating pumping load and avoiding pump cavitation.

Gravity.   This property has no real importance as an indication of
quality, but when considered with other test figures, can afford a good deal
of information to an experienced observer.   For instance, the gravity of
an oil of given viscosity will give an indication of the nature and origin of
the product; this is the basis of correlations between, for example, gravity
and smoking tendency.   In addition, gravity is significant in calculations
of fuel consumption rates.   Fuel oil is bought and consumed on a volume

[1] See Hill, *Advances in Chem. Ser.*, No. 5, p. 247, 1951, for a discussion of burner
types as related to fuel types.   For a related discussion, see Walsh, *Fueloil and Oil
Heat,* **7**(6):55 (1948).

[2] This latter property will obviously be governed not only by the solid wax present
but also by the rigidity of the wax crystal structure and by the viscosity of the oil at
the prevailing temperature.   There is also the complication introduced by instability
of pour point and the so-called maximum and minimum pour points. See *Proc.
ASTM,* **31**(I):468 (1931); **32**(I):402 (1932); ASTM Standards on Petroleum Products, p. 55, 1953.   Asbach and Ugethoff, *Brennstoff-Chem.*, **24**:67 (1943).   Gill and
Russell, *Ind. Eng. Chem.*, **46**:1264 (1954).   It is, however, a fair assumption that the
pumping of fuel oils at temperatures much below their pour points is likely to involve
a great deal of trouble.   On the relation between viscosity and electrical resistivity
and their relation to maximum and minimum pour points, see Ackroyd and Lowe,
J. Inst. Petrol., **41**:229 (1955).

basis, so that uniform gravity is desirable. However, there is a small decrease in heat of combustion with increase in specific gravity, so that the heavier oils show greater heating value per gallon but less per pound.

Sulfur content. Sulfur offers no difficulty in combustion, since all sulfur compounds come out as sulfur dioxide in the flue gas. It is this fact which is the source of other possible trouble; if the gases are cooled below the dew point of the water vapor in the mixture and in the presence of metal, corrosion may result; furthermore, the presence of sulfur dioxide in the atmosphere to the extent of one or so parts per million is considered by some authorities harmful to animal and vegetable organisms. The danger of such atmospheric pollution arises near industrial cities and large power plants, where high-sulfur fuel (coal or oil) is consumed in quantity.

CHAPTER XIII

Lubrication and Lubricants

The underlying principles of friction between everyday objects of conventional smoothness seem to have been understood clearly by Leonardo da Vinci (ca. 1500).[1] These principles were formulated by Amontons (1700) as follows:

Friction is proportional to the load normal to the rubbing surfaces. It is independent of the area of contact.

The third and less significant rule was formulated by Coulomb (1800):

Friction is independent of the velocity of movement.[2] Even the earliest investigators recognized that friction varies with the material and condition of the surfaces in contact; indeed, it is customary to regard the expression

$$\frac{\text{Resistance to tangential motion}}{\text{Force normal to the surfaces}}$$

as an approximate constant for each surface system; it is called the coefficient of friction. A useful distinction is that when motion between the surfaces is started from rest, the constant is known as the static coefficient; when motion is already established, it becomes the kinetic coefficient of friction.

Friction is an important phenomenon in everyday life, but most of the manifestations with which we are familiar are between soft, rough surfaces rather than the hard, polished ones occurring in the bearings of power-transmitting devices. Thus the high friction between a leather shoe sole and a stone pavement, which enables us to stand or walk without

[1] "Friction produces double the amount of effort if the weight be doubled." "The friction made by the same weight will be of equal resistance . . . although the contact may be of different breadths or lengths." "Notebooks of Leonardo da Vinci," MacCurdy (ed.), vol. I, pp. 615, 621, Reynal & Hitchcock, Inc., New York, 1923.

[2] See below for limitations on these statements. For a review of the early development of the facts about friction, see Palmer, *Am. J. Phys.*, **17**:181 (1949).

slipping, is due to the fact that the irregularities in the floor enter the comparatively soft leather surface pressed down on them. The friction here is due to the irregularities or asperities in the surfaces, which interlock. In a system of this nature, it will generally be found that the coefficient of static friction will increase with the time during which the surfaces have been pressed together and that the kinetic coefficient of friction changes with the velocity of motion. In addition, the static and kinetic coefficients are not the same in value. Where smooth, hard surfaces are employed, the static coefficient for the surfaces at once reaches a steady value, which is not very different from that of the kinetic coefficient. It is obvious that what is involved is the slow change in shape of the nonrigid surface, supplemented by change in the degree of interlocking of asperities.

The general "laws" stated above were derived from observation on relatively smooth, relatively rigid surfaces of ordinary cleanness, thus presumably unlubricated. Actually, all surfaces prepared and handled without elaborate precautions bear, by touch or by condensation from the atmosphere, greasy films of marked lubricating value. For smooth metal surfaces so contaminated, coefficients of friction of the order of 0.1 to 0.3 have been observed. As cleanliness is improved, the coefficients rise to the point where relative sliding without damage becomes impossible and seizure occurs; this is discussed below.

The first and second laws need little change from the form in which they were derived by the early natural philosophers; the third needs restatement as follows·

Friction is practically independent of speed when this latter is above a certain minimum value, and decreases slightly with increase of speed at much higher values.

Any explanation of the nature of friction should offer reasonable opportunity for deduction of these rules. The two explanations which have been most attractive since the earliest days are based, respectively, on the resistance to sliding motion offered by interlocking roughnesses of the two surfaces and on the cohesive attraction, among molecules of the surfaces, across the interface. It is obvious that for rough surfaces such as wood, stone, or unfinished metal castings, gross asperities will be the determining factors.

FRICTION AND LUBRICATION

It has been pointed out that friction between carefully cleaned surfaces is quite high, tending to seizure, while the greasy surfaces of daily life will show coefficients near 0.1 to 0.3. Two further stages, in the progression from full lubrication to no lubrication, are recognizable; these are fluid film, thick film, or hydrodynamic lubrication, and thin film or boundary lubrication.[1]

The mode of occurrence of thin-film and thick-film lubrication in ordinary practice may be indicated by the statement that the latter is regarded as the ideal which should prevail in all well-designed journal bearing systems when in normal motion; the former is a somewhat undesired condition existing when bearing systems are starting, stopping, undergoing oil starvation, or are under extremely severe conditions of duty. The various regions of friction and lubrication may then be listed as follows:

Dry friction of clean surfaces practically never prevails except under experimental conditions; the frictional resistance is high, and seizure occurs with extreme readiness. Dry friction of ordinary surfaces in daily life is lower than that of clean surfaces. Here also seizure occurs readily; the so-called laws of solid friction have been deduced from phenomena observed with surfaces of ordinary cleanliness.

Thin-film lubrication represents a transition stage between greasy dry friction and thick-film lubrication. It is an unstable condition and depends for its existence on what is apparently chemical reaction or secondary valence combination between the metals and the lubricant. It is most likely to prevail at times of low oil supply. In many bearing systems, lubrication is inadequate when the parts are moving at lower speeds than those for which they have been designed, as in starting or stopping. Under these conditions thin-film lubrication may prevail.

Thick-film lubrication represents a stable region in which the moving surfaces are separated by a complete film of lubricant, so maintained in spite of the pressure which constitutes the load on the bearing system. The persistence of the oil film depends on the pumping action of the moving parts (supplemented by the supply pressure usually provided in actual machines), and the ease with which this desirable condition is attained depends on the correctness of the bearing design and the proper choice of oil, particularly as to viscosity at the effective temperature.

Recognition of the dependence of friction in bearings upon the variables of the complete bearing system probably began with the observation by Pétroff[2] in 1883 that an oil of optimum viscosity could be selected for each particular service. The voluminous studies of journal-bearing lubrication since that date have served to extend the list of controlling conditions until it includes:[3]

---

[1] It should be recognized that rolling friction is apparently increased by lubrication; wear, however, is cut down.

[2] *J. Ingenieurs* (St. Petersburg), no. 1, p. 71; no. 2, p. 228; no. 3, p. 377; no. 4, p. 535, 1883.

[3] Wilson and Barnard, *Ind. Eng. Chem.*, **14**:682 (1922); *J. SAE*, **11**:50 (1922).

μ, effective viscosity

n, speed in rpm

p, pressure on the bearing surface

c, clearance between the surfaces

d, diameter of the journal (alternatively the radius)

l, length of the bearing

s, material and condition of the surfaces

m, supply of lubricant and the method of supplying it

o, nature of the lubricant

Presumably other less significant variables could be located, such as end effects.

XIII-1. Hydrodynamic Theory. The potentially very complicated situation was simplified by Reynolds'[1] interpretation of experiments by Tower, performed in 1884. Reynolds set up the theory that bearing friction was a hydrodynamic phenomenon, governed by known laws of fluids. The effort to simplify the phenomena was continued by Sommerfeld,[2] who related the coefficient of friction to the variables:

Viscosity of lubricant

Speed of rotation of journal

Load on bearing

modified by the ratio

$$\frac{\text{Radius of journal}}{\text{Clearance between journal and bearings}}$$

Hersey, applying dimensional reasoning,[3] set up the plot of coefficient of friction against a variable

$$\frac{\text{Viscosity of oil } (\mu) \times \text{ speed of journal } (N)}{\text{Load on bearing } (P)}$$

which has since proved very useful. An ideal bearing system may be considered as one having a perfectly centered journal, absolutely smooth surfaces, no end leakage, no oil grooves, and complete occupation of the clearance space by the lubricant; the frictional resistance is entirely in the oil film and, from the laws of viscous flow, should be directly proportional to the speed of the moving parts and to the viscosity of the lubricant while independent of the load. However, the coefficient of friction is inversely proportional to pressure, and the simplified expression becomes

$$f = K \frac{\mu n}{p}$$

[1] *Phil. Trans. Roy. Soc. London*, **177**:157 (1886).

[2] *Z. math. Physik*, **50**:97 (1904).

[3] *J. Wash. Acad. Sci.*, **4**(19):542 (1914); *Trans. ASME*, **37**:179 (1915); "Theory of Lubrication," p. 62, John Wiley & Sons, Inc., New York, 1936.

Curves illustrating the relationship involved are shown in Fig. XIII-1. Curve I is the friction at the journal surface of a system without end leakage of oil (infinite length), plotted according to Sommerfeld. Curve II is the same calculation for friction at the bearing surface. At high values of $\mu n/p$, the curve approaches a straight line through the origin, but it goes through a minimum and rises again as very low values are attained. Curves of this type have been plotted from experimental data by a number of students of lubrication. Figures obtained by Striebeck[1] and by Lasche and Heimann were replotted by Wilson and Barnard.[2] who also used some of Hersey's experiments. The same was done by Herschel[3] for data of Biel. Barnard, Myers, and Forrest[4] employed their own experimental results. All these reports agree that the experimental curves do not reach the theoretical minimum shown by curve I but take a shape indicated approximately by curve III, characterized by a sharp rise above the minimum and a positive extrapolated intercept on the axis of ordinates. The departure of curve I from the straight line through the origin is attributable to the influence of the eccentric position of the journal in the bearing with consequent change in film thickness and tangential shearing stress. The much more drastic departure of curve III is to be attributed to end leakage of oil, roughness

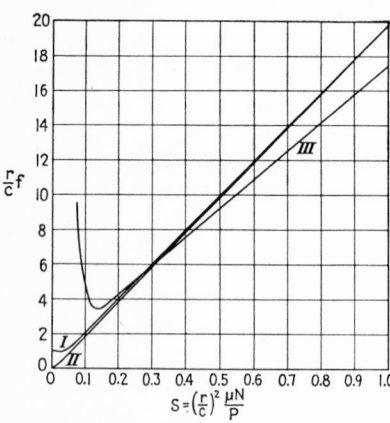

FIG. XIII-1. Theoretical and experimental curves for friction in a journal system. [*From paper by Morgan and Muskat, J. Appl. Phys.*, **9**:394 (1938).]

of surfaces, and similar effects in addition to eccentricity. However, Muskat and Morgan[5] have secured curves of the Sommerfeld type, in which the experimental points fall on a line passing through the origin; this condition prevailed for low values of the Sommerfeld criterion and down to values at which incipient contact of journal with bearing had occurred. Departures from this line at high values of the criterion were attributed to experimental irregularities.

The exact shapes of the curves and the extent of deviation from straight lines through the origin are uncertain for any given case, but the general

[1] *Z. Ver. deut. Ing.*, **46**:1341 (1902).

[2] *Ind. Eng. Chem.*, **14**:682 (1922); *J. SAE*, **11**:49 (1922).

[3] *Chem. & Met. Eng.*, **28**:597 (1923).

[4] *Ind. Eng. Chem.*, **16**:347 (1924); **17**:102 (1925).

[5] *J. Appl. Phys.*, **9**:543 (1938).

relation affords a useful working hypothesis in picturing the mechanism of film lubrication, somewhat as follows.

If a cylindrical journal and bearing, adequately lubricated but in very slow relative motion, are considered, it will be recognized that if the load on the surfaces is increased, the lubricant may be pressed out of the interface to a considerable extent, even completely. When this happens, partially lubricated metal-to-metal contact prevails and frictional resistance is large. It is, however, common experience that as speed increases, frictional resistance becomes less. This is because of the tendency of the lubricant (under the pumping action of the moving surfaces) to build up into a complete film (as speed increases) between the surfaces at the point of nearest approach. With speed and pressure constant, oil viscosity will determine the position of the journal in the bearing; with speed and viscosity constant, pressure will be the significant variable. This is equivalent to saying that at higher speeds, the journal eccentricity decreases. The thicker film so induced will persist even under the pressure of heavy loads on the bearings. The formation of this pressure film is to be attributed to the fact that a more rapidly moving journal carries additional oil into the interface, where it builds up pressure, since there is a period during which oil is not forced out as fast as it is brought in. If one speed is maintained, oil soon begins to escape, as by end leakage, as fast as it enters and equilibrium is then established at some given film thickness. If the load remains constant and the speed is increased, a greater amount of oil is carried into the interface per unit of time, is trapped for a short period, and then begins to escape as fast as it enters. The net result is that the journal now floats on a thicker film of oil. Furthermore, when speed is increased, the load on the bearing may be increased and still leave a lubricant film of the same thickness as before. The magnitude of the influence of speed on the load which may be carried is indicated by an empirical formula cited by Hersey.[1]

$$\text{Permissible load} = K \cdot \text{speed}^{1/3}$$

It will be seen that the increase in carrying power of a film with increase in speed is appreciable though small.

Two interesting applications of fluid film lubrication have been discussed by Fuller. One is the use of air as a lubricant;[2] it has been employed for both journal and thrust bearings,[3] and at speeds up to 100,000 rpm. The equations based on hydrodynamic theory apply up to pressures a few pounds above atmospheric; beyond that rather complicated corrections for the compressibility of the air must be applied.

[1] *J. Am. Soc. Naval Engrs.*, **35**:655 (1923).

[2] *Trans. N.Y. Acad. Sci.*, **II**:15, 83 (1953).

[3] Pigott and Macks, *Lubrication Eng.*, **10**:29 (1954).

The other is hydrostatic lubrication, a system in which a fluid lubricant—oil—is pumped between the surfaces under pressure. A striking example is the system of supporting bearings for the 200-in. telescope on Mt. Palomar in California.[1] The unit weighs about one million pounds, and is carried on three pad systems which are supported by oil pumped under about 300 pounds pressure between the surfaces. The speed of motion is slow and the laws of viscous flow govern the forcing of the oil through the system. The running oil film is about 0.004 in. thick and the coefficient of friction about 0.000004. A $\frac{1}{12}$-hp clock motor moves the assembly and supplies more power than is needed. The oil requirement is small, the pumps supplying about two quarts per minute each. An oil of flat viscosity-temperature curve, good oxidation stability, and favorable antirust properties is required. It should be noted that the system gave appreciably lower friction and torque requirements than those calculated for antifriction bearings designed for the same job.

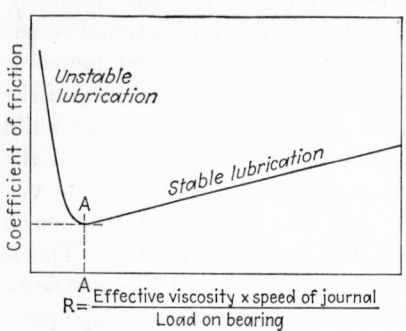

FIG. XIII-2. Fluid film and boundary lubrication; ideal curve. [*From paper by Barnard, Myers, and Forrest, Ind. Eng. Chem.,* **16**:347 (1924).]

The effects upon friction of the sequence pictured is represented by the idealized curve of Fig. XIII-2. The progression from the high friction of starting through a zone of lowered resistance corresponds to the parts of the curve showing unstable lubrication and the minimum values in the region A. As speed is increased still more, and as a thicker oil film is established between journal and bearing, the zone of stable lubrication is entered. Frictional resistance here depends on the mean effective rate of shear, upon viscosity, and upon load or pressure. Thus as speed is increased, oil viscosity increased, or less load imposed, there is an increase in the coefficient of friction at a rate much less than that of the decrease from the high resistance at starting to the low region at A. This is the zone of stable film lubrication, in which all well-designed conventional bearings are presumed to operate except at starting and stopping. It is evident that as the process is reversed, this part of the curve may be retraced. The reduction of oil viscosity or speed and increase of load will cause reductions in coefficient of friction.

[1] McDowell, *Mech. Eng.,* **58**:345 (1936). Karelitz, *Machine Design,* **60**:541 (1938). Fuller, *Machine Design,* **19**:(6) 110; (7) 117; (8) 115 (1947). Burwell, *Ann. N.Y. Acad. Sci.,* **53**:772 (1951). The authors are indebted to B. H. Rule, project engineer of the Observatory, for details of the installation.

It is the effort of bearing designers to achieve the lowering of friction by such means, but they are restrained by the need of maintaining an adequate factor of safety above the minimum point at A; this because the region to the left of A is unstable, with a definite hazard of large increases in friction because of inadequate lubrication and injury to bearing surfaces. In the region to the right of A, the only significant property of the lubricant (so far as frictional resistance at any one time is concerned) is the viscosity. A solution of cane sugar or of glycerol will, theoretically, have as much lubricating value in this region as will an oil of equal viscosity; and this is true so long as a set of complicating and practically very important factors are ignored (stability of the liquid, hygroscopic properties, tendency to crystallize, etc.). Likewise, in the region to the right of A, the materials of which the bearing system is constructed are of no significance. The total value of R ($R = \mu n/p$; illustrated in Fig. XIII-2) may be manipulated by changes in any of the component values. This general relation is confirmed by everyday experience, since large decrease in oil viscosity, decrease in speed, and increase in load all tend toward seizure. It should be recalled that viscosity is increased by high pressures (see page 189, Chap. IV) and that this may account for some of the uncertainties in the application of the $f \cdot \mu n/p$ relation.

XIII-2. Boundary Lubrication. Practical experience with lubrication made evident long ago that under severe conditions—heavy load, high temperature, low velocity of moving parts, low viscosity—a lubricant was required which was more effective than those satisfactory under moderate conditions, i.e., conventional petroleum oils. In popular language, an oilier oil was needed. From this arose the concept of oiliness, an accurate and satisfactory word for use in discussing the kind of lubrication widely prevailing until about 1925. Until then it was possible to recognize that nearly all of the more severe conditions could be met by a lubricant showing under the given conditions a lower coefficient of friction than that shown in the same system by a neutral uncompounded petroleum oil. However, increasing severity of design practice has made necessary lubricants of increasing potency if one is to avoid a succession of failure types going well beyond simple power loss due to high friction. Increase of friction is usually the first phenomenon in this succession, followed by metal wear consequent on scuffing of the surfaces, actual scoring, and finally by seizure; the system is unstable, probably because the heat generated by friction is not conducted away fast enough, and the increase of temperature aggravates the deterioration.[1] It is to be

---

[1] It is true that with oil containing certain additives, high friction and marked wear are encountered without ultimate seizure, but these represent stable systems, operating with heat dissipation adequate to keep temperature safely low.

presumed that the oil film has become so thin (because of inadequate viscosity or expulsion under heavy loads) that metal-to-metal contact begins at isolated spots and increases as the condition becomes more severe.

The region to the left of A in Fig. XIII-2 is, as indicated above, one of unstable lubrication; the coefficient of friction rises sharply with further small reductions of the value $\mu n/p$. In a limited number of cases, the surfaces may become, for a time, more polished, rather than abraded. In other words, the arm of the curve to the right of A is extended to the left, and A moves closer to the origin before the curve turns upward[1] and friction again increases.

The conduct of the lubricant in this region is no longer dependent on its mechanical properties alone, nor is the system independent of the nature of the bearing materials.[2] The chemical properties of the lubricant and to some extent those of the bearing system combine to influence a complex which remains without a good name. It is that property of the lubricant which, under the given conditions, enables it to function in the more severe portion of the $f \cdot \mu n/p$ plot, resisting expulsion by pressure, keeping down friction, and preserving the metallic surfaces against injury by abrasion and wear. It has been proposed that the position of the minimum point (A of Fig. XIII-2) varies with this property of the lubricant.[3] For instance, McKee[4] used in a test equipment several oil blends of matched viscosity containing different proportions of kerosene. The value of $\mu n/p$ at the minimum increased with the proportion of kerosene present. It was also observed that, other conditions being constant, a babbitt bearing gave a lower value of the minimum point than did a bronze bearing.

What happens in a bearing system operating in the unstable region to the left of the minimum point A in Fig. XIII-2 has been discussed briefly above. The outstanding condition is that a completely fluid film no longer separates the metallic surfaces. The amount of lubricant remaining under the conditions prevailing—usually those of very low speed, high temperature, or high pressure—is ordinarily that held by adsorption or more powerful chemical forces; furthermore, the load-carrying surface, under the less desirable but most frequent condition, is likely to be made up of molecules of metal as well as of lubricant. These two conditions will indicate why the materials of the bearing

[1] McKee and McKee, *J. SAE*, **31**:371 (1932).

[2] Not only the composition and physical state of the material and state of oxidation of the surface, but also its metallurgical history are significant. Barnwell, *Proc. Royal Soc. (London)*, **A212**:508 (1952).

[3] Barnard, Myers, and Forrest, *Ind. Eng. Chem.*, **16**:347 (1924).

[4] *J. SAE*, **19**:356 (1926).

surfaces are likely to be of influence (whereas they were not so in the zone of the complete film) and also why abrasion and wear are to be expected. From the latter, it follows that an $f \cdot \mu n/p$ plot followed into the left-hand zone beyond A (Fig. XIII-2) is likely to be difficult to retrace to A, because the surfaces do not remain unchanged during the measurements.

XIII-3. Oiliness. The voluminous literature on the unstable region of lubrication has until recently employed the term *oiliness* to cover a variety of phenomena which may include the following:

Reduction of friction
Resistance to expulsion by pressure or heating
Increase of load required for seizure
Protection against wear
Avoidance of abrasion
Avoidance of welding

No word has been coined to describe such a combination, and the term oiliness should be reserved to cover only the property which reduces friction. The latter concept was introduced by Kingsbury[1] and has been defined by Hersey[2] and others. The definitions boil down to saying that oiliness is the property which causes a difference in coefficient of friction when all the recognizable factors except the lubricants are the same. Various writers have advanced the idea, implied above, that oiliness is a joint property of lubricant and surface lubricated. Hersey suggested that oiliness may be analogous to the consistency of non-Newtonian materials, e.g., soap-oil mixtures, where fluidity depends on rate of shear as well as on previous history. Thus oiliness might need, for its determination in a particular system, a statement of load, speed, and previous history. This seems likely (since nature of a surface can be affected by all these factors) but not obviously useful.

The comparison of lubricants for oiliness, if they happen to differ in viscosity, is not easy. The descriptive facts, however, are familiar. It has been known for many years that fatty oils are superior to mineral oils in lowering friction, and in 1920 Wells and Southcombe pointed out[3] that small proportions of fatty acids in mineral oils would produce the same effect as say 20 per cent of fatty oil. The validity of the proposal seems to have been recognized in New England fifty years before Wells and Southcombe. It is reported that the custom prevailed there of

[1] *Trans. ASME*, **24**:143 (1903).

[2] *Mech. Eng.*, **55**:561 (1933).

[3] *J. Soc. Chem. Ind.*, **39**:51T (1920). The effect is produced by the oxidation of a conventional petroleum oil; for instance, Bowden, Laben, and Tabor, *Trans. Faraday Soc.*, **35**:900 (1939), and Exline, Kramer, and Bowman, *J. Inst. Petrol.*, **29**:295 (1943).

employing by preference highly rancid oils for the compounding of petroleum–fatty oil lubricant mixtures—the so-called compounded oils. Wells
and Southcombe reported prompt and extensive lowering of friction in a
testing machine as soon as the fatty acid blend was introduced, without
cleaning the system. Unpublished work in the authors' laboratory at
the time confirmed the reality of the phenomena. However, the effect
was not as large in magnitude under the conditions used, and required,
in the Kingsbury test apparatus, about 24 hr to reach its full value, and
as long to disappear when an unmixed petroleum oil was substituted for
the blend, also without cleaning.

A satisfactory explanation of the effect on friction of a variety of materials added to mineral oil, for which the higher fatty acids may be regarded
as the typical case, has been based on the adsorption, on the bearing
surface, of layers of molecules of the added substance. This explanation
was first developed extensively by Hardy[1] on the basis of Langmuir's
studies.[2] Much of Hardy's voluminous experimental work seems to
have remained empirical and undigested. For instance, experiments
with glass showed that acetic acid and tripropyl amine reduce friction
markedly; glycerol had little effect and benzene, alcohol, ammonia, and
even water (for clean glass) were quite neutral in action. By contrast,
all liquids tried were good lubricants for bismuth.

Hardy attributed friction to forces of attraction between the surfaces
involved, and lubrication to the saturating, by the lubricant, of these
surface forces of the solids. For instance, a film of oxide or sulfide on a
metal surface acts as a lubricant in this way. The film can be supplied
by adsorption from saturated vapor of the bulk lubricant, which indicated
that the film need not be thick. When polar molecules were used as
lubricants, it was noted that a measurable time period was required to
attain full friction-reducing value. This suggests that orientation of
polar molecules on the surface was required; no such latent period was
observed when nonpolar paraffins were applied. For a homologous
series of compounds, the coefficient of static friction decreased with rise
in molecular weight.[3] When changes in constitution occurred in such a
series, the decrease in friction was irregular, and when friction values
were plotted against temperature, no break was observed at the solidifying
temperatures of the compounds under study. This last point is contra-

[1] *Nature*, **106**:569 (1920); *Proc. Roy. Soc. (London)*, **A100**:550 (1922); **A104**:25
(1923); **A106**:341 (1924); **A108**:1 (1925); **A112**:62 (1926); **A118**:209 (1928); *J. Chem.
Soc.*, **127**:1207 (1925).

[2] Summarized in "Colloid Symposium Monograph," vol. III, p. 48, Chemical
Catalog Company, Inc., New York, 1925. *Nature*, **115**:266 (1925).

[3] Confirmed also by Halder, *Brennstoff-Chem.*, **30**:313 (1949). However, the
incremental effect decreases, as might be predicted. This has been shown by Burwell,
using several homologous series. *Ann. N.Y. Acad. Sci.*, **53**:906 (1951).

dicted by the later work of Bowden, discussed below, who observed changes in friction at the melting points of soaps and similar compounds.

In explaining his results on the basis of layers of adsorbed molecules, Hardy used Langmuir's idea[1] that only the first molecular layer on a surface is exactly oriented, although the zone of influence of the interfacial forces may be many molecules deep. Interesting support for the idea that only the first adsorbed layers are really involved in the reduction of friction is supplied by Greenhill[2] when he noted that if a solution of stearic acid in oil was capable of meeting a lubrication demand, then two or three monomolecular films of the acid, laid down by the Blodgett technic, would do the same job. As the requirement became more severe, more layers would take care of the increase.[3]

The idea of an adsorbed and oriented film involves the assumption that something is present in oils which can be adsorbed. Wilson and Barnard suggested that oils which have lubricating value (oiliness) contain small proportions of active constituents adsorbable at metallic surfaces. Their experiments seemed to indicate the building up of films of such substances of the order of 0.1 mm in thickness and suggested that pretreating of the oil with finely divided iron removed a great part of such film-forming compounds. Later, Rhodes and Lewis[4] obtained confirmatory results on the removal from oil, by powered Wood's metal, of substances which lowered the coefficient of static friction by a limited amount. The surprising thickness for adsorbed films observed by Barnard and Wilson has been rendered doubtful by the work of Bulkley.[5] He found no clogging, by adsorption, of capillaries of diameter down to the order of 0.005 mm when carefully filtered oil was used. At the same time, Ormandy[6] has calculated that an optically true surface can have irregularities forty times as large as the length of a stearic acid molecule, so that an adsorbed film should be at least of that thickness to be effective.

---

[1] *J. Franklin Inst.*, **218**:143 (1934). Blodgett, *J. ACS*, **57**:1007 (1935). See also Adam, Gen. Discussion on Lubrication, *Inst. Mech. Engrs.* (Am. ed.), **2**:197 (1937).

[2] *Trans. Faraday Soc.*, **45**:631 (1949).

[3] There has been some use of the idea that the lubricating value of an oil for a metal can be estimated by measuring the heat of wetting toward that metal. [Bachmann and Brieger, *Koll. Z., Zsigmondy Festschrift, Ergänzungsband*, **36**:142 (1925). Irauth and Neyman, *Petroleum Z.*, **31**(49):4 (1935).] While attractive, the procedure has shown no significant value. Still more used has been the belief that the contact angle —the surface tension balance between air, metal, and oil—will measure the lubricating value of an oil for a given metal. Bartell, Case, and Brown, *J. ACS*, **55**:2769 (1933). Bartell and Hatch, "Colloid Symposium Monograph," p. 11, The Williams & Wilkins Company, Baltimore, 1934. Mack, *J. Phys. Chem.*, **40**:159 (1936). Mack and Lee, *J. Phys. Chem.*, **40**:169 (1936).

[4] *Ind. Eng. Chem.*, **26**: 1011 (1934).

[5] *J. Research Natl. Bur. Standards*, **6**:89 (1931).

[6] *Proc. Inst. Mech. Eng.* (*London*), 1927, p. 291.

Actually, this does not seem to follow, since the adsorbed film, no matter how thin, can conform to the irregularities of the surface.[1]

Trillat believed the oriented layers to be 100 to 200 molecules thick. A value for the upper limit for film thickness may be derived from flow measurements of water solutions by Bowden and Bastow,[2] who found that films down to 10^{-5} cm thick showed no abnormality indicative of orientation influenced by the proximity of a surface.

The application of X-ray technique to the question was apparently first practiced by Trillat[3] and applied by Clark, Lincoln, and Sterrett,[4] who suggested that for certain compounds, the oriented films greatly exceed molecular dimensions in thickness. Electron-diffraction measurement has served to confirm the existence of oriented films[5] and has thrown some light on the arrangement of soap and fatty acid molecules in the surface layers.[6]

While the action of adsorbed films of polar molecules seems to offer an adequate explanation of the phenomena of oiliness, various other theories have been proposed, particularly by Hersey. These include assumption of an increased viscosity in the oil film due to pressures existing locally;[7] increased viscosity due to attractive forces exerted by the metal; a pseudo-crystal structure in the film, and other less probable ideas.

XIII-4. Film Strength. The phenomena which occur in a lubricated bearing system as the conditions become more severe—increased load and higher temperature—are not easy to name accurately. The sequence usually involves rising temperature, scuffing followed by abrasion of the surfaces, and possible seizure; this latter may be a combination of sporadic self-welding and thermal expansion to make the fit of the surfaces excessively close. Whether the temperature rises because the film has failed to keep friction low, or the film fails because the temperature rises is sometimes hard to determine. In popular terms the action of a lubricant in preventing failure is described as depending on its film strength or its extreme pressure (EP) properties. A further stage in the progression is represented by hypoid lubricants, those suitable for the lubrication

[1] But two polished steel plates will make electrical contact long before the intermediate film is reduced to minimum thickness. Ormandy, *loc. cit.*

[2] *Nature*, **135**:828 (1935).

[3] *Compt. rend.*, **182**:843 (1926).

[4] *Proc. API*, **16**(III):68 (1935).

[5] Nelson, *Phys. Rev.*, **44**:717 (1933). Motz and Trillat, *Z. Kryst.*, **91**:248 (1935). Trillat and Motz, *Trans. Faraday Soc.*, **31**:1127 (1935). Andrew, *Trans. Faraday Soc.*, **32**:607 (1936).

[6] Bowden and Tabor, "Friction and Lubrication of Solids," p. 207, Oxford University Press, New York and London, 1950.

[7] See a good summary by Blok, *World Petrol. Congr., Proc. 3rd Congr., Hague*, **8**:305 (1951).

of hypoid gear systems, where the tooth pressure is high and the conditions drastic.[1] Examples of materials possessing the qualities necessary for each type of action, including reduction of friction, might be as follows:

Oiliness agent	Reduction of friction	Fatty oils Fatty acids
Mild EP agent	Resistance to expulsion by pressure and moderate heating; protection against wear	Sulfurized fatty oils Phosphorus compounds
Strong EP agent	Avoidance of abrasion	Phosphorus, sulfur, and chlorine compounds
Hypoid lubricant	Avoidance of welding	Lead soap–active sulfur or chlorine compounds

The nature of the agents suitable for each type of service is evidently such as to interpose between the working surfaces something stable enough to survive the conditions.   This may, for example, be an adsorbed film of fatty acid molecules, a layer of more strongly adsorbed or mildly reactive molecules of an organic sulfur compound, a layer of phosphorus-metal reaction product, or, finally, an iron-chlorine–lead sulfide complex.   It is to be presumed that each of these is in turn a better lubricant under the prevailing conditions than is the one preceding.

As often happens, the information on the action of these and similar materials was obtained empirically long before explanations had been worked out.   The basic concepts of chemical action between metal and lubricant to form new and more potent lubricants developed independently in several places, but the organizing of these ideas, supplying the framework of a physical theory and supporting it by well-conceived experimentation, should be credited to Bowden and his associates.[2] It has long been know that very smooth, clean, flat pieces of metal (Johansen gage blocks) pressed together so as to exclude air may adhere so firmly as to threaten injury to the surfaces on separation.   This attraction is attributable to molecular forces.   Bowden was able to show[3] that clean, thoroughly degassed metal surfaces seized on touching, even at room temperature, and adhered with the bulk strength of the metal.   As slight an intervening layer as an adsorbed gas will prevent the welding action,

[1] On some of the eccentricities of testing hypoid gear lubricants, see Smalheer and Mastin, *J. Inst. Petrol.*, **42**:339 (1956).

[2] Work summarized in Bowden and Tabor, "Friction and Lubrication of Solids."

[3] *Proc. Roy. Soc.* (*London*), **A208**:311 (1951).

and if it can form a chemically attached film a few molecules thick, it will act as an effective lubricant.[1] Oxygen, water vapor, or lower fatty acid vapors act in this way. For comparison, the coefficients of friction for such conditions are about as follows:

Clean degassed metal *in vacuo*................. >100
Unlubricated metal in air..................... About 1
Boundary film of petroleum oil in air.......... About 0.1

Chlorine compounds will reduce the friction if so applied and the action will persist up to about 400°C.[2] Hydrogen sulfide is not as potent as a friction reducer, but the effect persists up to about 800°C.[3] These results indicate the importance of chemical action on the surface to provide a resistant film as a lubricant. Different materials vary in persistence, depending on their properties. Thus a film of solid paraffin will show a decrease in lubricating value as the temperature nears its melting point. A fatty acid which has been allowed to react with the metal of the surface will show this effect only as the (usually higher) melting point of the resulting soap is approached. In agreement, a fatty acid will not show on glass or platinum the effect produced on iron or copper, presumably because it cannot form a soap with glass or platinum. An oxide film on aluminum is not a good lubricant, probably because the oxide is harder than the base metal; copper oxide is a soft material and on copper it acts as a lubricant, at least under moderate loads.

The observation that a film of adsorbed gas on a clean metal surface will prevent seizure but does not lower friction very much agrees with a similar notation that a film of fatty acid on an evacuated metal surface will prevent seizure but leaves the friction high (μ = about 2.5) until oxygen is admitted. A plausible explanation is that the fatty acid does not react to form a soap in the absence of a film of oxide. As load increases or as temperature rises, the protective film may be desorbed and lubrication fails; this may occur with a light mineral oil at about 100°C. That metal contact occurs before damage is apparent has been proved by using a radioactive tracer on one of the surfaces and recognizing its presence on the other after sliding contact, even when very gentle.[4]

Bowden's experiments are significant in understanding ordinary unlu-

[1] Hydrogen sulfide will act as a lubricant for the cutting of aluminum with a steel or molybdenum tool. Bowden and Tabor, *Sci. Lubrication*, **6**(4):29 (1954).

[2] On the lubricating value of chlorinated and fluorinated hydrocarbons, see Murray, Johnson, and Swikert, *Natl. Advisory Comm. Aeronaut., Tech. Note* 3402, 1955. Allen, Buckley, and Johnson, *Natl. Advisory Comm. Aeronaut., Tech. Note* 4316, 1958. Corrosion of metal surfaces is troublesome with such compounds.

[3] Bowden, *Ann. N.Y. Acad. Sci.*, **53**:805 (1951); *World Petrol. Congr., Proc. 3rd Congr., Hague*, **8**:328 (1951).

[4] Sakmann, Burwell, and Irvine, *J. Appl. Phys.*, **15**:459 (1944).

bricated friction.[1] He has been able to show, by electrical conductivity measurements, that the area of actual contact between metal surfaces is very much smaller than the area of apparent contact—perhaps as 1:10,000. Also, the area of real contact will vary with load. For steel surfaces, as load increased from 1 kg to 500 kg, the real contact area increased from 0.00013 to 0.042 sq cm, while the apparent contact area remained the same. Since the contact area supporting the load is small, the metal flows plastically at the contact points until the area has increased enough to support the weight imposed. It will be clear that these ideas are in harmony with the first two laws formulated by Amontons:

1. The friction is independent of the apparent area of contact.
2. It is directly proportional to the load.

Since self-welding occurs readily under pressure, the points of contact may be expected to weld, and friction between metal surfaces may be attributed to the force necessary to shear these metallic junctions. It can then be predicted that friction will approximate the product

Real area of contact × shear strength of junctions

Since the metal at the weld points may be hardened by the working, the breaking necessary to permit sliding will probably occur at points away from the welds, new metal clinging to one surface or the other. This offers a plausible explanation of metal wear and Bowden has shown that copper remains welded on a steel surface after a copper slider has been drawn over it.[2]

According to the above ideas, unlubricated friction of metals, scuffing, wear, frictional pitting, and seizure are all explainable in terms of intersurface welding and the attempts to break these welds. Oiliness agents, EP agents, and hypoid lubricants function by preventing or minimizing the formation of these welded junctions under increasingly severe conditions; such action is presumably due to the interposing of a lubricant film, which may be adsorbed from solution, or, at the more severe end of the sequence, may be formed by chemical attack on the metal.

A useful concept in agreement with the above ideas is that of the chemical polishing agents.[3] Triphenyl phosphine or arsine in a lubricat-

---

[1] *World Petrol. Congr., Proc. 3rd Congr., Hague,* **8**:330 (1951).

[2] Thoma, *Z. tech. Physik,* **24**:78 (1943), makes the point that all bearing metals form welds; a good bearing combination is one for which the weld is weak and breaks where formed. A poor combination gives strong welds, which break somewhere else, thus effecting scoring.

[3] Givens, Beeck, and Williams, *Phys. Rev.,* **57**:247 (1940). Hund, Larson, Beeck, and Vesper, *Mech. Eng.,* **64**:525 (1942). Klaus and Fenske, *ACS, Div. Petrol. Chem.,* Preprints, ACS Meeting, Atlantic City, September, 1956.

ing oil (also some aryl phosphates) will minimize metal wear, apparently because they form (under high pressure and hence at the higher temperature of motion) low-melting phosphides or arsenides on the metal areas involved; the high spots are removed. These compounds are not effective on tin surfaces, perhaps because tin phosphide is a high-melting substance. A small addition of fatty acid will increase the effectiveness of these phosphorus antiwear agents. It should be noted that such antiwear additives are not active in reducing friction.[1]

LUBRICANTS

XIII-5. Service Requirements. The suitability of any material for a lubricating purpose obviously depends on the conditions it must meet and the job it must do. For a steam turbine, a moderately low viscosity and a high chemical stability are necessary; for a worm gear system, a high viscosity and a good deal of EP character are required; but for the lubrication of a railway signaling system in a northern climate, dependability is all-important, and an oil will be chosen which, first of all, remains fluid and effective at the lowest temperature likely to be encountered. For bearings of present-day types, the availability of oils of suitable viscosity can be assumed, since most bearings are designed to operate in the fluid-film region. However, all such systems must start and stop, so that a moderate degree of oiliness–EP property may be necessary. Similarly, even when only a short service period is expected, as with a gasoline engine oil, chemical stability at a high temperature is a requisite. It may be observed that synthetic lubricants can be and are made for specific purposes, where there is an advantage in maintaining conditions which cannot be met by petroleum. But petroleum oils, especially when fortified by additives, are the only materials, possessing the necessary properties, which can be produced (at the present stage of technical development) in the quantity and with the economy required by modern industry. There is literally nothing else available.

Oils for what is known as light duty are ordinarily of quite low viscosity. Typical of such service are spinning and weaving machinery and small electric motors, where speed of moving parts is often extremely high. Oils for lubricating textile machinery are not often exposed to large variations in temperature, so that the properties which change with temperature are not of determining importance. However, resistance to evaporation and to oxidation are major requirements, since corrosion and particularly deposition of gum or varnish are serious for high-speed moving parts. Such stability is more desirable because spinning machinery often operates in atmospheres of controlled high temperature and high-moisture content. Steam turbine oils are called on to meet more

[1] For an interesting compilation on wear, see *Lubrication*, **42**(12):149 (1956).

severe conditions. They are used in forced-feed systems at high speed and usually at high steam temperatures, and are subjected to violent mixing with air and moisture. The environment is thus favorable for oxidation and the forming of emulsions, which sometimes deposit on cooler surfaces and thus choke circulating systems. Removal of insoluble oxidation products by settling, filtering, or centrifuging will serve to prolong the useful life of a turbine oil, but the most striking effects in this direction have been attained by the use of antioxidants. Addition of a few tenths of a per cent of an alkylated phenol or similar antioxidant has resulted in extending the life of turbine oils for times measured in years.[1] A new turbine oil is made resistant to emulsification by refining (e.g., drastic clay filtering after the other usual treatments) which removes surface-active materials. Oxidation tends to produce in the oil more of these surface-active emulsifiers, as well as water-soluble acids of corrosive character. Antioxidants will delay very greatly the formation of such harmful contaminants. The use of antirust agents has also been useful in preventing corrosion of turbine parts; minimal additions of fatty acids or their amine salts will sometimes serve this purpose.[2]

The requirements for automotive engine oils are more varied and in many ways more severe. Service in a radial airplane engine differs from that in a milk delivery van; at the same time, the universal public contact with automotive transportation brings even slight failure of lubrication into unfavorable notice. The functions of a motor oil are as follows:

It must lubricate and cool
It must stay in the engine
It must remain approximately unchanged
It must preserve the lubricated surfaces[3]

The requirement that a motor oil must lubricate means that it must remain a pumpable liquid of useful viscosity in the motor to be lubricated, over the entire temperature range to be encountered, and that it must have a certain minimal "oiliness."[4] As a matter of experience, ordinary petroleum oils have so far been satisfactory from the oiliness standpoint, although it is reported that valve gear trains in automobile engines of

---

[1] Baker, *Power*, **85**:314 (1941). Peterson, *Trans. ASME*, **64**:227 (1942).

[2] Rocchini, U.S. Patents, 2,261,888; 2,399,510; Smith and Cantrell, U.S. Patent 2,400,611.

[3] For a discussion of the tests which have been proposed to show how well oils perform these duties, see Gruse, *Petrol. Engr.*, **25**(13):C-23 (1953); **26**(1):C-9 (1954).

[4] Testing for oiliness and EP properties is done by several friction-measuring devices, such as those of Deeley and Herschel. See Archbutt and Deeley, "Lubrication and Lubricants," 5th ed., p. 412, Charles Griffin & Co., Ltd., London, 1927.

More severe conditions are provided by the Falex [*Refiner Nat. Gasoline Mfr.*, **18**:320 (1939)], Timken (CRC Handbook, Method L-18-545), and Four Ball [*World Petrol. Congr., Proc. 2nd Congr., Paris*, **3**:471 (1937)] devices.

certain types may require lubricants containing additives to minimize wear. Likewise, petroleum oils of intermediate molecular weight, made from wax-free crudes or dewaxed to pour-point temperatures suitable for the prevailing climate (0°F for temperate zones, −30°F for severe northern climates) will remain satisfactorily viscous and fluid at the temperature of service.[1] The cooling quality of a motor oil is important, since a good deal of heat energy produced by the fuel is rejected to the atmosphere via the oil. But it is a property about which nothing much can be done; specific heat and thermal conductivity of oils do not vary widely.

Oil may disappear from an engine by leakage, by evaporation, or by foaming out of the breather openings; the last happens more frequently with radial engines than with other types. Evaporating tendency may be indicated by flash- and fire-temperature measurements, which respond to traces of volatile constituents, or by rather complicated evaporation tests.[2] Actually the customary petroleum motor oils marketed currently are of such molecular weight range as to be satisfactorily nonvolatile in all ordinary service. Foaming of motor oils may be due to volatile materials such as dissolved air or suspended water and is increased by certain additives. It is controlled by addition of traces of silicones.[3]

The requirement that engine oils remain relatively unchanged for reasonable periods of service is tied up with their chemical stability, chiefly to thermal cracking and oxidation, each of which influences the other. Various test results are symptomatic of such deterioration: color change, development of acidic and saponifiable contaminants, increase of coke residue on dry distillation, and accumulation of insoluble material. These may indicate appearance of contaminants, some of them corrosive, accumulation of unstable oxidation products, and the forming of substances which precipitate as varnish and sludge.[4]

Oxidation tests of accelerated character have been employed rather widely in predicting the stability of oils. A few of the better known are the Indiana test,[5] the British Air Ministry test,[6] and that of Underwood.[7]

---

[1] See Table XIII-1 for properties of typical motor oils.

[2] ASTM D 972–48T.

[3] Trautman and Ambrose, *J. SAE*, **53**:373 (1945).

[4] The presence of insoluble sludge in a lubricating oil can be expected to increase friction, since it increases viscosity. An extensive literature has developed on the deposit-forming tendency of motor oils. For an introduction to the subject, see Zuidema, "Performance of Lubricating Oils," chap. V, Reinhold Publishing Corporation, New York, 1952, and Georgi, "Motor Oils and Engine Lubrication," Reinhold Publishing Corporation, New York, 1950.

[5] Rogers and Shoemaker, *Ind. Eng. Chem., Anal. Ed.*, **6**:419 (1934).

[6] Garner, Kelly, and Taylor, *World Petrol. Congr., Proc. 1st Congr., London*, **2**:448 (1933).

[7] *Federal Standard Stock Catalog*, vol. IV, part 5, VV-L-791d; 341.1.1.

In the simpler tests air or oxygen is passed through the heated sample (temperature range from 100 to 175°C) at a controlled rate, and the development of increased viscosity, of acidity, and of pentane-insoluble material is followed.

As to the fourth general requirement, it may be noted that lubricated surfaces may:

1. Wear away due to failure of proper lubrication. This was discussed above.
2. Suffer damage by corrosion.
3. Be covered by deposits.

Corrosion may be that of iron and steel parts by water-soluble acids (the most probable source of these is blow-by gases from the combustion chamber, rather than oil oxidation) usually indicated by rusting, or of alloy bearings—copper-lead, silver alloys—by oil-soluble acids or peroxides resulting from oil oxidation.[1] This latter problem has been encountered chiefly with paraffinic oils operating at high temperatures.

No good laboratory tests have been devised for measuring the tendency of lubricants to cover the important rubbing and heat-conducting surfaces, during operation, with harmful deposits. For one thing, some of the responsible influences may be tied up with engine design and operation. The fact that the fuel may be at least a partial source of trouble was pointed out by one of the authors some years ago,[2] but it appears that the lubricating oil is always involved, either as a source or as a necessary transfer medium for the depositing material. So far, it appears that reliable information on the depositing tendencies of engine oils can best be obtained by direct engine tests under controlled conditions.[3] The mechanisms of formation and deposition are not understood, but presumably include the formation of dissolved or suspended oxidation products which then, through continued heating or further oxidation, come out of solution onto the metal surfaces.[4]

XIII-6. Petroleum Lubricating Stocks.[5] Lubricating oils can be and are made from a wide variety of crudes, depending on availability. Thus

---

[1] Denison, *Ind. Eng. Chem.*, **36**:477 (1944). Prutton, Frey, Turnbull, and Dloughy, *Ind. Eng. Chem.*, **37**:90 (1945). Wilson and Garner, *J. Inst. Petrol.*,**37**:225 (1951). Thomas, Harle, Richardson, and Bowman, *ACS, Div. Petrol. Chem., Symposium Additives in Lubricants*, Preprints, p. 138, ACS Meeting, Atlantic City, September, 1956.

[2] *Ind. Eng. Chem.*, **24**:1298 (1932); *J. SAE*, **45**:324, 334 (1939).

[3] "Coordinating Research Council Handbook," pp. 347, 365, 394, 1946. For tests with the more convenient prototype engines, see *Petrol. Engr.*, **15**(8):196 (1944); **21**(13):C-11 (1949). Georgi, "Motor Oils and Engine Lubrication."

[4] Livingstone and Gruse, *J. Inst. Petrol.*, **26**:413 (1940).

[5] For discussion of the terms employed to describe the various stocks made and used prior to 1935, see the second edition of this work, 1942, pp. 545–554.

a refinery operating on a Middle East crude high in sulfur and asphaltic constituents can do a satisfactory job, thanks to modern refining methods, although not as easily as one which has available some of the sweet paraffinic crudes of North America. Application of solvent extraction and solvent dewaxing has added a great deal to the effectiveness and flexibility of refining operations.

Manufacture from Wax-bearing Crudes. The wax content of typical paraffinic crude oils extends pretty well over the molecular weight range from about 250—roughly the lower limit for lubricating oils—up to the heaviest end of the crude, 1,000 or even higher; the content of normal paraffins, however, does not ordinarily extend to these highest-molecular-weight fractions. To make acceptable lubricants, the wax must be removed. Dewaxing operations for both light distillates, yielding refined wax, and for residua, yielding microcrystalline waxes and petrolatums, are described in Chap. XIV. The paraffin distillates, after removal of wax, are usually rather wide cuts of viscosity near 8 to 15 cs at 100°F (50 to 75 SSU). By redistillation, fractions of increasing viscosity up to final cuts of 60 cs at 100°F (300 SSU) may be obtained. Chemical refining and decolorizing by adsorbents may be applied as required for the intended use, depending also on the degree of refining applied to the distillate before dewaxing.

The dewaxing of heavier oils, as described elsewhere, may be practiced on truly heavy residua in presence of an added diluent or on a somewhat self-diluted "long" residuum. In the former case, only a residual bright stock[1] results, while in the latter a wider range product is obtained which is then distilled into overhead cuts and a residuum. By the latter means, oils of intermediate viscosities—100 to 200 cs (500 to 1,000 SSU)—may be obtained, the lighter ones as distillates. The application of chemical refining to these materials varies; however, it is much easier to refine a long residuum, and within recent years practically all such refining is done with differential solvents (see Chap. VIII). The production of refined wax and paraffin distillates is not essential to the picture, but it usually adds some flexibility. In any case, the refiner can have available a series of paraffinic lubricating oils, which by blending supply the wide range of industrial demand. The inspection properties of typical lubricating oils is given in Table XIII-1.

Manufacture from Wax-free Crudes. This is a somewhat simpler operation, since wax removal is not required. The selection of crude oils sufficiently free of wax to meet the needs of this sort of refining may, however, sometimes be difficult. The crudes and their distillates are characterized by a heavy gravity, a low boiling point, and a low molecular

---

[1] Probably so-called because, in the absence of wax, it remains bright and clear when chilled.

TABLE XIII-1. PROPERTIES OF TYPICAL UNCOMPOUNDED LUBRICATING OILS

Type	Spindle		Turbine	Cylinder stock	Bright stock	Motor oil		
						SAE 10	SAE 30	SAE 30
Gravity, °API	33	28.5	30.0	25.9	25.8	29.0	30.5	26.1
Pour point, °F	−5	−30	0	50	10	0	0	−10
Flash point, °F	375	325	385	550	555	385	450	420
Viscosity SSU:								
At 0°F, extrapolated	3700	3900	8000	700,000	1,100,000	9700	52,000	130,000
At 100°F	105	103	155	2490	2755	168	500	510
At 210°F	39.5	39	43	155	155	44	65	58
Viscosity index	98	85	91	99	92	91	103	61
Color, NPA scale	.....	1.5	1.5	green	6.0	2.0	2.25	4.0
Carbon residue, %	Trace	0.01	Trace	2.50	0.70	0.01	0.09	0.05
Origin	Pennsylvania refined	Naphthenic solvent refined	Mid-Continent solvent refined	Pennsylvania	Mid-Continent solvent refined	Mid-Continent solvent refined	Pennsylvania	Naphthenic solvent refined

For comparison, an SAE 5W-20 oil of viscosity index 150 will show viscosities in seconds as follows:

At 210°F.............. 48
At 100°F.............. 160
At 0°F (extrap.)..... 3,700

weight as compared with paraffinic materials of similar viscosity. The crudes are usually rather high in asphaltic content (asphalt-base crudes), which is left behind in distillation, and usually contain naphthenic acids, kept behind by distilling in contact with caustic soda. The lubricating cuts are separated by distillation; very often these cuts are rather wide, with the expectation that they will be redistilled. Differential solvent extraction has very largely replaced the sulfuric acid–caustic soda process of earlier years. The refined wide cuts are redistilled and, when necessary, may be decolorized by clay contact or clay percolation. The products vary from the very lightest, those intended for low-temperature service, of viscosity about 7 cs at 100°F (50 SSU) to heavy blending stocks of 32 cs at 210°F (150 SSU). Such oils are characterized by lower carbon residue values and less coke-forming tendency than paraffinic oils but are less resistant to oxidation. Table XIII-1 shows typical inspection properties of naphthenic lubricating oils.

XIII-7. Lubricating Oil Additives. Since about 1935 the use of additive materials to help petroleum meet the increasingly severe demands of service as engine lubricants has grown steadily. Those most widely employed are pour-point depressants, viscosity-index improvers, antioxidants and corrosion preventatives, and detergent-dispersants. It is not unusual to encounter compounds which serve two purposes (viscosity-index improver and pour-point depressant, or mixtures which will combine antioxidant and dispersant functions). In fact some commercial detergent additive agents are likely to convey also a fair degree of EP property; this seems most likely for those containing sulfur or phosphorus.

Pour-point depressants are materials which (probably by adsorption) influence the temperature at which the wax content of an oil crystallizes in such a way as to form a gel structure. They presumably have no influence on the failure of oils to flow because of natural increase in viscosity as temperature is lowered. This viscosity pour point is, by calculation, about 25,000,000 SSU when the ASTM test method is used for reference.

Some of the more widely used pour-point depressants are polyalkylated condensed aromatics, the alkyl groups of molecular weight about C_{20}, and alkyl esters of polymerized methacrylic acid, the alkyl groups again being of the order of C_{15} or C_{20}.[1] It should be recognized that pour-point reducers are most effective when compounded with the lighter grades of oils and when employed at low concentrations; under these conditions a pour-point lowering of 15 to 20°F is easily obtained. For oils in the bright stock class the same concentration of additive will cause little shift of the solidifying temperature.[2]

---

[1] U.S. Patents 2,091,637 and 2,100,993.

[2] On the possible failure of pour-point reducers under certain circumstances (pour-point reversion), see McNab, Rogers, Michaels, and Hodges, *Trans. SAE,* **2**:34 (1948).

Viscosity index improvers are often similar materials of higher molecular weight and of rather rod- or chain-like structure; examples are polyisobutylene of such molecular weight as to be semifluid, polymethacrylates, and alkyl polystyrenes.[1] The importance of rod-like molecules in the concept of viscosity was developed by Lewis and Squires[2] on the basis of the theories of Staudinger.[3] Apparently the improver must have a certain optimum solubility in the medium[4] and must, as temperature rises, change readily from a colloidally dispersed to a dissolved state, or must pass (each molecule) from a spiral to an expanded condition; the latter form in each of the above changes has an increased effect on viscosity.

Viscosity-index improvers may suffer permanent degradation by shearing,[5] especially if the molecular weight is much above 25,000 and the rate of shear extremely high; this is not troublesome in ordinary usage. However, when an oil of quite low viscosity index is changed considerably in viscosity by a large proportion of improver, it may not only lose viscosity during use because of shearing breakdown, but may show viscosities in use which deviate considerably from the extrapolated values obtained by application of the ASTM viscosity-temperature chart. A further disadvantage is that all improvers confer increased viscosity on the oil in which they are dispersed. This means that improved oils of relatively low viscosity cannot be made by such compounding without running into the rather high volatility of the lighter petroleum oils which must be used as the base stocks.

The antioxidants effective in petroleum oils under operating conditions fall usually into three classes: phenols, nitrogen compounds, and sulfur derivatives.[6] The most effective phenols are usually of the alkylated hindered type,[7] for example, 2,6,di-*tert*-butyl-4-methylphenol. A typical amine antioxidant is phenylalphanaphthylamine, useful in protecting lubricating greases against oxidative deterioration. A variety of organic sulfides and more recently analogous selenides[8] are recognized

[1] Van Horne, *Ind. Eng. Chem.*, **41**:952 (1949). Glavis, *Ind. Eng. Chem.*, **42**:2441 (1949).

[2] *Proc. API*, **15**(III):69 (1934).

[3] *Angew. Chem.*, **47**:502 (1934).

[4] Evans and Young, *Ind. Eng. Chem.*, **39**:1676 (1947).

[5] Pohl, *Naval Research Lab. Rept.* P-2075, May, 1943. Zisman, *Ind. Eng. Chem.*, **45**:1406 (1953). van Horne, *ACS, Div. Petrol. Chem., Symposium on Additives in Lubricants*, Preprints, p. 26, ACS Meeting, Atlantic City, September, 1956.

[6] This listing does not include anticorrosion compounds, such as reaction products of fatty oils and phosphorus pentasulfide, which have antioxidant value as well. Reaction products of P_2S_5 with terpenes and polyolefins have also been employed for such purposes.

[7] Stevens, *Ind. Eng. Chem.*, **35**:655 (1943). Stillson, Sawyer, and Hunt, *J. ACS*, **67**:303 (1945).

[8] Denison and Condit, *Ind. Eng. Chem.*, **41**:944 (1949).

as effective oxidation inhibitors, but in some cases are believed to operate as deactivators of the catalyzing metal surfaces which are always present in engines. Zisman has pointed out[1] that phenolic antioxidants fail at temperatures near 150°C, amines near 165°C,[2] the selenides at 175°C, and phenothiazine derivatives at 190°C. In other words, effective antioxidants for really high temperatures have not yet been discovered.

Detergent dispersants were first used commercially in oils intended for light, high-speed diesel engines of such design that lubricants of naphthenic type, which leave a soft carbon deposit, were preferred for lubrication. Such oils oxidize readily to oil-insoluble sludges, and the detergents were applied to keep these sludges suspended during the service period.[3] The first detergents were somewhat corrosive to alloy bearings; later products have successfully overcome this difficulty. Typical constituents of detergent formulae are calcium or barium petroleum sulfonates, calcium alkyl (about C_{16}) phosphates, salicylates, or phenyl stearates, barium phenates of alkylated bis-phenol sulfides, and metal salts of organic derivatives of thiophosphates and thiophosphites.[4] It may be observed that large alkyl or similar organic groups (sometimes paraffin wax hydrocarbons) are often present to provide solubility or pseudo solubility in oil. The detergent function is apparently tied up with the presence of metal salts and the action disappears when the metal is removed. Sometimes the residual molecule has another beneficial action. For instance, the alkylated bis-phenol sulfides are themselves possessed of antioxidant properties.

It should be recognized that commercial "detergents" have good dispersing power, but not much detergent action. Synthetic oils such as sebacates and, better yet, polyalkylene oxide oils will, however, not only dissolve some of their own decomposition products, but have been known, under favorable conditions, to remove deposits left by previous operation, provided that not too much baking by high-temperature operation had occurred.

The extent to which dispersant additives can lower the effectiveness with which engine filters can remove solid contaminants from oil streams is an interesting question. Experimental work has indicated[5] that a good detergent will keep normal sludge so well dispersed that it will pass

[1] *Ind. Eng. Chem.*, **45**:1411 (1953).

[2] Amines are reported to be less effective than phenols in preventing formation of insoluble oxidation products.

[3] Electron micrographs indicate that normal dispersants do not dissolve oil deterioration products, but suspend them. McBrian, ASME Preprint, no. 52, p. A40, November 30, 1952. Peri, *ACS, Div. Petrol. Chem., Symposium on Additives in Lubricants*, Preprints, p. 8, ACS Meeting, Atlantic City, September, 1956.

[4] Smalheer and Mastin, *J. Inst. Petrol.*, **42**:342 (1956).

[5] Gadebusch, Karr, and Bassett, *SAE J.*, **60**:33 (1952).

the ordinary filter; in fact, any accumulation of sludge on the filter is sometimes regarded as an indication that the detergent content of the oil may be exhausted. This sounds as though the dispersant were defeating the purpose of the filter. Actually, however, the filter will continue to remove large particles including road dust, while the dispersant will maintain suspended the oxidation and cracking products, some part of which would inevitably escape the filter to plate out, in the absence of dispersant, as harmful deposits on oil screens and piston skirts.

The marked lubricating value of graphite (long used as an additive) and similar materials crystallizing in plates, such as molybdenum disulfide, has always excited interest.[1] The phenomena have been studied from a basic standpoint by Savage,[2] who pointed out that the friction of clean graphite in vacuum is high, and that lubricating action occurs when oxygen is adsorbed. The surface "oxide" then adsorbs water readily, and this so-called graphite particle shows the familiar lubricating action.[3]

XIII-8. Synthetic Lubricants. Synthetic lubricating oils have been produced mainly under the stimulus of wartime scarcity, as in Germany during 1939–1945, or to meet the demands of rapidly advancing technology. It is not unusual to see a natural product replaced by a more controllable synthetic material of superior properties, but natural petroleum oils, especially when reinforced by additives, have so far been satisfactory for all but especially severe requirements.

The qualities in which synthetic oils can be superior to the natural oils, even when compounded with additives, are:

Better consistency-temperature relations
Greater stability at high temperatures
Lower vapor pressure at high temperature

The change of consistency with extremes at both ends of the range of temperatures encountered has been one of the chief difficulties in the use of ordinary petroleum products. Thus in arctic climates or at high altitudes conventional oils are likely to solidify because wax comes out of solution or simply because the viscosity becomes too great for the oil

---

[1] Stuart, *Engineering*, **145**:17, 71, 142, 215, 260 (1938). Smith, *ACS, Div. Petrol. Chem., Symposium on Additives in Lubricants*, Preprints, p. 85, ACS Meeting, Atlantic City, September, 1956.

[2] *Ann. N.Y. Acad. Sci.*, **53**:862 (1951). See also Moreal and Trillat, *Rev. inst. franc. petrole*, **5**:33 (1950).

[3] Graphite is often applied as a dispersion in oil or water. Use of an analogous dispersion of glass in isopropyl alcohol has been described for lubrication of metalworking operations at temperatures where the glass is in a molten condition.

to flow at any reasonable velocity under the available pressure (viscosity pour point). Similarly, at high operating temperatures inside an engine the oil may lose viscosity to the point where it will no longer protect the contacting metal surfaces against wear and scuffing. It is possible to encounter both these difficulties when an oil is required to permit cold-weather starting and to provide adequate lubrication under heavy load in modern heavy-duty internal-combustion engines. Likewise, for extremely high-temperature service, as near furnaces or combustors, petroleum oils may decompose (thermally or by oxidation), the liquid film failing and leaving only objectionable deposits of resinous or coke-like nature. Finally, it may happen that low-temperature operation may prompt the choice of a petroleum oil of such low molecular weight (low viscosity) that it may begin to vaporize when the temperature reaches full operating level.

It is not likely that the synthetic oils known today will excel in all these respects or that even one will be good enough to do so, but some improvement in one or more features has been observed in the synthetics proposed. It must also be recognized that additives will be required for these synthetic products.[1]

The classes of materials of greatest present interest as synthetic lubricating oils are:

Aliphatic esters and di-esters (for instance octyl sebacates)
Polyalkylene oxides or glycols
Silicones
Organic phosphates and silicates
Highly fluorinated hydrocarbons

Zisman has pointed out[2] that the molecules of all these substances are made up of flexible linear chains of atoms, and that they are comparatively free of molecular association. Both these characteristics are favorable to small change of viscosity with temperature. The alkyl silicones excel in this respect, and for practically all the types of compounds mentioned, the addition of branching chains or cyclic groups and the lengthening of branches have an unfavorable effect. However, at least some members of each of the classes listed, except the fluocarbons, are better in viscosity-temperature relations than conventional, uncompounded petroleum oils of similar viscosity range. It is likewise true that the high molecular weight of many of the synthetics provides greater resistance to evaporation than is common for petroleum oils of comparable viscosity. Resistance to oxidation and to thermal degradation cannot be predicted so easily.

---

[1] Zisman, *Ind. Eng. Chem.*, **45**:1407 (1953).
[2] *Ibid.* and *Trans. SAE*, **61**:309 (1953).

Keeping the above statements in mind, the other most obvious strong and weak points of some of the synthetics (without additives) may be listed as follows:

Silicones:[1]
    Limited lubricating value, especially for steel on steel
    Good oxidation resistance
    Good thermal stability at high temperatures
    Good viscosity-temperature slope
    Low protection against rusting
    Limited solvent power

Fluocarbons:
    High thermal stability
    Low inflammability
    Rather mediocre viscosity-temperature relations
    Poor solvent power for oils and additives
    Relatively high pour-point temperatures

Alkyl di-esters:[2]
    Nonsludging, nondepositing
    Self-detergent
    Responding well to additives
    Generally compatible with other materials
    Harmful to rubber and plastics

Polyalkylene oxides:[3]
    Nonsludging, nondepositing
    Not self-detergent, but fair solvents for deposits
    Not affording protection against rusting
    Somewhat corrosive
    Capable of attacking paints

The lubricants produced synthetically in Germany under war conditions are of some interest.[4] Ethylene and longer chain olefins were polymerized (aluminum chloride catalyst) to good yields of oils showing good viscosity-temperature qualities. Paraffinic gas oil from Fischer-Tropsch synthesis was chlorinated and the product condensed with naphthalene to rather mediocre products. Esters of adipic acid were produced, but sebacic acid for sebacates was not available.

[1] Grant and Currie, *Mech. Eng.*, **73**:311 (1951). Currie and Hummel, *Ind. Eng. Chem.*, **42**:2452 (1950).

[2] Zisman, *Trans. SAE*, **61**:319 (1953).

[3] Millet, *Ind. Eng. Chem.*, **42**:2436 (1950). Sweatt and Langer, *Mech. Eng.*, **73**:469 (1951); **74**:162 (1952). Rubin and Glass, *Quart. Trans., SAE*, **4**:287 (1950).

[4] Horne, *Ind. Eng. Chem.*, **42**:2428 (1950). See also Herold, Geiseler, and Runge, *Angew. Chem.*, **66**:208 (1954).

The polymerization of ethylene to lubricants had been studied much earlier,[1] and similar manufacture of lubricants from cracked wax olefins had been commercialized in the United States prior to 1931.[2]

An interesting effect shown by a synthetic hydrocarbon mixture is the flammability-reducing power of hydrogenated polyisobutylene. A 40 per cent addition raised markedly the ignition temperature of several kinds of synthetic lubricants, including esters and polyalkylene oxides.[3]

XIII-9. Lubricating Greases. Until the past ten years lubricating greases were always mixtures of petroleum oil thickened by fatty acid soaps, the common exception being the axle greases made by using a soap of abietic acid (rosin). Recently, however, a wide variety of thickening agents has been employed and it can be specified that a lubricating grease is a system in which a viscous liquid is retained in a semisolid structure of fine particles or fibers held together by the attractive forces of the solid particles.[4] Greases are employed where some difficulty is encountered in retaining lubricant, as in chain drives; wherever highly viscous shock-resisting lubricants are needed, as in heavily loaded gear trains; where heavy pressure and high temperatures are encountered as at the necks of hot rolls for shaping very hot sheet metal; or where a source is needed which will supply, by bleeding or melting, small amounts of liquid to fast-moving systems, such as the "antifriction" ball and roller bearings.[5] Greases are made of both highly viscous and relatively nonviscous oils, and it is probable that those made of heavy oils, which become semifluid in service, actually do the lubricating. However, for greases made with light oils, employed for high-speed moving parts, it may be that, at the operating temperatures, oil exudes from the grease and supplies the liquid for the lubricating film.

The soap-thickened greases still serve all demands except those for a few specialties. The oils employed range from light products of viscosity not much over 100 SSU at 100°F to heavy cylinder stocks of 150 to 200 SSU at 210°F.[6] Oil properties have recognized effects on the properties of the resulting greases.[7] In general, the more naphthenic an

---

[1] For example, Stanley and Bowen, *J. Inst. Petrol. Technologists*, **16**:830 (1930).

[2] Sullivan, Voorhees, Neeley, and Shankland, *Ind. Eng. Chem.*, **23**:604 (1931). See Herold, Geiseler, and Runge, *loc. cit.*, for recent work on the constitution of such polymers.

[3] Frank, Swarts, and Mecklenborg, *Natl. Advisory Comm. Aeronaut.*, PB 112, p. 981, January, 1954.

[4] Klemgard, "Lubricating Greases," Reinhold Publishing Corporation, New York, 1937. Lutz, Ambrose, and Gruse, *Oil Gas J.*, **37**(39):62; (40):49 (1939). Evans, *J. Inst. Petrol.*, **36**:367 (1950). Farrington, *Proc. N.Y. Acad. Sci.*, **53**:979 (1951).

[5] Fogg and Webber, *J. Inst. Petrol.*, **39**:744 (1953).

[6] Lange, *Natl. Petrol. News*, **21**(42):67 (1929). Wilch, *Natl. Petrol. News*, **26**(6):340 (1934).

[7] Boner, *NLGI Spokesman*, **15**(1):7 (1951).

oil, the more stable is the resulting grease dispersion. Likewise, a highly paraffinic oil did not form well-dispersed greases with sodium, calcium, and aluminum soaps.

The soaps employed are derived from the fatty animal and vegetable oils, cottonseed and tallow,[1] etc., while the metals are commonly calcium, sodium, aluminum, and lithium; some work has been done on the soaps of barium and strontium.[2] Conventional cup greases are those made from light paraffin oils plus from 5 to 20 per cent of calcium soaps. They show low melting (dropping) points—not above 100°C—and ordinarily lose structure when heated above that temperature. This last is probably due to the loss of water, which is essential to the dispersion. Higher melting greases are obtained by dispersing sodium or lithium soaps in oils; these sometimes have a well-defined fiber structure. For very high-temperature duty, sodium soaps (sometimes of rosin acids) are dispersed in heavy oils to which stearin pitch, asphaltic residua, or other high-molecular-weight materials of like character have been added.

Aluminum soap greases—oleates or, more probably, stearates—are usually transparent and retain consistency well at high temperatures. Lithium soap greases[3] serve a variety of purposes, can be used from 0 to 150°C, are comparatively stable to oxidation, and do not lose consistency with working or shearing. They do not readily emulsify with water, and will reform if liquefied by heating above the melting point.

Axle greases, so-called, are made by saponifying, and dispersing in a light oil, ordinary rosin with lime; this reaction will occur without heating, and hence the name, cold-set greases.[4] The calcium abietate formed will stabilize the product for service at ordinary temperatures. The making of greases for various purposes has called out a wide variety of expedients. For instance, many of the above product types can be rendered stringy and adhesive by admixing various resins and even rubber.[5]

There is enough variety in the different types of grease to present difficulty for an over-all theory of formation and structure. Lawrence[6] pointed out the existence of a gel phase, succeeded by a crystalline phase as a solution of soap in hot oil is cooled slowly. He also called attention to the need for polar peptizing agents such as water, glycerol, or fatty acids. There is now not much doubt about the fiber structure of most greases and the retaining of the oil between these fibers by either attrac-

---

[1] On the shear strength of such soaps, see White, *Lubrication Eng.*, **10**(2):105 (1954).

[2] Boner, *Ind. Eng. Chem.*, **29**:58 (1937). Worth and McClennan, *Oil Gas J.*, **45**(43):74 (1947).

[3] Meyer, *Petrol. Engr.*, **22**(1):5 (1950).

[4] Kaufman, *Petrol. Engr.*, **2**(5):72 (1931).

[5] Kopp, *Petrol. Engr.*, **4**(1):84 (1932). Licata, *Natl. Petrol. News*, **25**(23):23 (1933).

[6] *J. Inst. Petrol.*, **31**:303 (1945).

tive forces or just mechanical swelling. Browning[1] leached out the oil with hexane, left the soap unchanged, and then replaced the oil with glycerol or a silicone liquid. X-ray diffraction[2] and electron micrography have demonstrated fiber structure for the soaps of nearly all greases, even those of aluminum.[3] The fibers are broken by shearing, and the grease loses consistency, which may be regained (provided no essential constituent, such as water from a calcium grease, is lost in the process) by redissolving the soap and cooling to regrow the crystals. These fibers may be 0.2 to 50 μ long and the ratio length/diameter may vary between 10:1 and 200:1.[4] The particle sizes of some of the dispersed solid grease thickeners are comparable with those of known bacilli and viruses.

The newer greases include both dispersions of soaps in nonpetroleum liquids and of nonsoap thickeners in petroleum oils. Lithium soaps in aliphatic di-esters[5] fall in the first class, and conventional hydrocarbon oils thickened with hydrophobic bentonite,[6] fine silica or attapulgite treated for hydrophobic character, copper phthalocyanine,[7] and carbon black fall in the second class. An example of the third possibility—nonsoap, nonpetroleum—is shown by silicone fluids thickened by alkyl ureas. They are reported as useful over a wide temperature range.[8] Improvements in heat resistance can be obtained by these means, but certain disadvantages of rusting tendency may be encountered. At the present state of development, the correcting of one difficulty is likely to aggravate another.

Grease consistency is ordinarily measured by an empirical penetration test[9] but flow properties and a better rheological picture of grease structure have been obtained by plastometer measurements.[10] It appears that

---

[1] *NLGI Spokesman*, **14**(1):10 (1950).

[2] Vold, Hattiangda, and Vold, *Ind. Eng. Chem.*, **41**:2539 (1949). Farrington, *Proc. N.Y. Acad. Sci.*, **53**:979 (1951). Brown, Hudson, and Loring, *Petrol. Engr.*, **24**(2):C31 (1952). Vold and Vold, *J. Inst. Petrol.*, **38**:155 (1952).

[3] The fibers differ in size and structure from one soap to another. Allred, *Chem. Eng. News*, **32**:713 (1954). Progressive differences in fiber structure and flow orientation for aluminum, lithium, calcium, and sodium soap greases have been shown by X-ray diffraction studies made by Vold, Elersich, Baker, and Vold, *NLGI Spokesman*, **18**(5):8 (1954). The sodium soap greases are the most fibrous.

[4] Farrington and Birdsall, *Oil Gas J.*, **45**(46):268, 275 (1947).

[5] Hain, Jones, Merker, and Zisman, *Ind. Eng. Chem.*, **39**:500 (1949).

[6] Jordan, *J. Phys. & Colloid Chem.*, **53**:294 (1949). Finlayson and McCarthy, *NLGI Spokesman*, **14**(2):13 (1950).

[7] Fitzsimmons, Merker, and Singleterry, *Ind. Eng. Chem.*, **44**:556 (1952).

[8] Swakon, Brannen, and Brumstrum, *NLGI Spokesman*, **18**(1):8 (1954).

[9] ASTM Method D 217–52T.

[10] Porter and Gruse, *Ind. Eng. Chem.*, **17**:953 (1925). Arveson, *Ind. Eng. Chem.*, **24**:71 (1932); **26**:624 (1934). Marusov, *NLGI Spokesman*, **15**(5):11 (1951).

reasonably homogeneous greases are what might be called plastics in the Bingham sense, characterized by a definite yield value and limiting values of viscosity and mobility.

Greases are improved by additives in much the same way as are liquid oils. Thus oxidation and the development of corrosive acids may be much delayed by aryl amine inhibitors; load-carrying ability is increased and metal wear reduced by EP agents as discussed above. These latter are much employed in the semifluid greases known as gear oils, used for lubricating gear systems of power-transmitting devices.[1] In fact, the additives employed to convey the highest degree of EP quality so far known were developed to meet the demands of hypoid gear systems.[2]

XIII-10. Cutting and Drawing Lubricants. The lubricants required for thread cutting, boring, and similar machine work, together with those for drawing wire and the shaping of sheet metal, present special problems. Two functions are expected of such materials: (1) the dissipation of heat generated in the working and (2) the maintaining, under severe conditions,[3] of a lubricating film between the tool, die, or roll and the metal in process.[4]

For cutting operations when cooling is the chief need, water or alkaline solutions (to avoid rusting) may be satisfactory. When, in addition, a little lubrication is required, as in grinding,[5] a dilute emulsion containing, say, 1 part of oil to 60 of water may be necessary.[6] These emulsions are usually made from the spontaneously emulsifiable so-called soluble oils, containing a soap or a sulfonated product like sulfonated castor oil, and sometimes an alcohol.[7] As the lubricating becomes more important and the cooling less so, the proportion of oil in the emulsion

---

[1] For a series of articles on gear lubrication, see *J. Inst. Petrol.*, **38**:607 (1952).

[2] See Sec. XIII-4; see also Mougey and Almen, *Natl. Petrol. News*, **23**(45):47 (1931). Schlesman, *J. SAE*, **36**:147 (1935). Neely, *J. SAE*, **39**:293 (1936). Griswold, *J. SAE*, **40**:194 (1937).

[3] For a discussion of the theory of metal cutting as a lubrication problem, see Bowden and Tabor, *J. Inst. Petrol.*, **40**:243 (1954); this article is the first in a symposium which reviews also the mechanical and testing aspects of metal forming. The character of the lubricants required is indicated by the fact that metal cutting has been used as a means for studying EP lubricants. Shaw, *Ann. N.Y. Acad. Sci.*, **53**:962 (1951).

[4] The significance of maintaining of a film between the operating surfaces is illustrated by the application, to metal drawing, of the principle of hydrostatic lubrication (see Sec. XIII-1). Christopherson, Naylor, and Wells have shown [*Sci. Lubrication (London)*, **6**(5):32 (1954)] that friction and wear may be avoided by supplying an ordinary petroleum oil at a pressure equal to the yield stress of the wire being drawn.

[5] Krekeler, *Oberflächentech.*, **11**:115 (1934).

[6] Oldacre, *Lubrication Eng.*, **4**:162, 181 (1948).

[7] Larson, *Iron Steel Engr.*, **24**(11):73 (1947).

is increased; the oils employed are usually of medium viscosity. As the nature of the cutting becomes progressively more severe, straight mineral oils, these compounded with fatty oils and then with sulfurized organic compounds, must be employed. They are succeeded in the order of effectiveness by unmixed fatty oils and by the same compounds after sulfurization; such products are especially suitable when precision surface finish is required.[1] A high degree of lubricating efficiency is needed where heavy cutting of tough metals is performed, so that the tool and chip do not overheat, fuse, seize, and tear. An attempt to express these relations in general terms has been made by Beaubien and Cattaneo.[2] For this purpose they have employed viscosity, heat of wetting, and chemical activity, with combinations of these, as indices of suitability.

The basic mechanical quantities in metal cutting have been developed by Merchant[3] and the general theory of the operation of cutting oils has been presented in a simple manner by Bingham.[4] The effectiveness of a fine high-pressure jet of lubricant directed at the cutting interface has been discovered by Pigott.[5] This observation serves, as did the application of hydrostatic principles to wire drawing, just mentioned (footnote 4, page 547), to point out the equivalence of mechanical and chemical means of keeping a lubricant where it is needed.[6] Wire drawing and deep drawing of metal shapes are severe operations which present considerable danger of welding and injury of surface. As just indicated for cutting, it is important that the lubricant maintain a film between the work and the die. A variety of expedients is employed;[7] solid materials, such as lime, soap powders, talc, graphite, powdered metals (copper), and mixtures of these in oil suspension or emulsion, are useful for different purposes.[8] Within recent years the application of a phosphate coating, such as zinc phosphate, has been found to increase formability of metals considerably.[9] The phosphate is believed to absorb the conventional

[1] For a review of literature and patents on sulfurized and similar cutting oils, see Sellie, *Petrol. Processing*, **4**:1003, 1116 (1949). On other cutting lubricants, see Kauffman, *Oil Gas J.*, **28**(4):46 (1929). Huffman, *J. SAE*, **35**:463 (1934). Smith, *Can. Chem. Met.*, **19**(3):70 (1935). For choice of lubricants for specific metals, see Fluskey, *Machinery (London)*, **58**:429 (1941).

[2] *Lubrication Eng.*, **10**(2):74 (1954).

[3] *J. Appl. Phys.*, **16**:267, 318 (1945).

[4] *Natl. Bur. Standards Tech. Paper* 204, 1921.

[5] *SAE J.*, **60**(4):45 (1952).

[6] Francis, *Iron Steel Inst. (London), Carnegie Schol. Mem.*, **21**(16):55 (1932).

[7] Kalmer, *Petrol. Refiner*, **35**(7):351 (1946). Pistoles, *Iron Age*, **158**(16):55 (1946).

[8] Lueg and Treptow, *Stahl u. Eisen*, **72**:399 (1952). Brown, *NLGI Spokesman*, **17**(8):8 (1953). On lubricants for tube drawing, see McFarlane and Wilson, *Sci. Lubrication*, **6**(5):33 (1954); also Perry, *J. Inst. Petrol.*, **40**:319 (1954). McFarlane and Wilson, *J. Inst. Petrol.*, **40**:324 (1954).

[9] Overath, *Stahl u. Eisen*, **68**:231 (1948). Stager, *Appl. Mechanics Revs.*, **3**:96 (1950). Spring, *Iron Steel Engr.*, **29**(5):64 (1952).

oil vehicle and then to release it gradually. The problems of wire drawing and deep drawing of metal shapes are complicated by the additional requirements imposed by the desire to produce surfaces of specific nature. Thus the need of turning out a metal surface suitable for direct enameling or lacquering will influence the choice of a lubricant.

XIII-11. Re-refining of Used Oils. Since lubricating oils in service are contaminated from outside and suffer deterioration within, the possibility of reclaiming them has been a subject of continuing interest.[1] Turbine oils gradually develop acidity and in extreme cases deposit sludges, which are sometimes emulsions of oil and water stabilized by solids; these latter may be asphaltenes resulting from oxidation of the oil. Other deposits are gummy solids.[2] Such oils are successfully purified by settling, filtration, or centrifuging. Engine crankcase oils offer greater difficulty, since, because the service units are small and conditions different, the oils are usually widely different. The contaminants are dust and dirt, diluents from unburned and partly burned fuel, water condensed from blow-by gases, together with soluble and insoluble decomposition products of the oil.[3] There is no particular technical reason why such a mixture could not be refined to a usable condition, and it has been done at times. The questions are chiefly whether it has been done well enough, and whether it is economically worth while.[4] The procedures employed have usually involved distilling off the diluent (heavy ends of gasoline— something like kerosene), removing the suspended solids, as by centrifuging or filtering with or without a coagulant, and neutralizing and washing out the acidity.[5] Operations somewhat like the above have been applied with fair success where drainings are uniform as to source and service, as in large fleet installations, and where technical control is adequate. Practice for aircraft engine oils has been discussed by Brower.[6] One obvious difficulty in handling automotive oils is that refining operations are likely to remove additive materials to a variable and not easily controllable extent. When complete removal occurs, a new compounding with additives becomes necessary if the oil is to be restored to something like its original state.[7]

[1] Archbutt and Deeley, "Lubrication and Lubricants," 5th ed., p. 587, Charles Griffin & Co., Ltd., London, 1927.

[2] Salathe, *Ind. Eng. Chem.*, **17**:414 (1925).

[3] Dickinson, *Ind. Eng. Chem., News Ed.*, **11**:187 (1933).

[4] See *Petrol. Processing*, **9**(2):155 (1954), on costs and reclaiming losses.

[5] For the early literature, see Rhoades and Haon, *Ind. Eng. Chem.*, **17**:25 (1925). Flowers, McBerty, and Reamer, *Ind. Eng. Chem.*, **17**:481 (1925). Pidgeon and Tester, *J. Inst. Petrol. Technologists*, **15**:91 (1929). Herschel, *J. SAE*, **27**:671 (1930).

[6] *J. SAE*, **51**:130 (1943).

[7] Alkalinity and dispersancy could be restored by controlled reintroduction of additives, *Chem. Eng. News*, **33**(10):958 (1955). For reclaiming of railway journal box oils, see *Lubrication Eng.*, **14**:382 (1958).

CHAPTER **XIV**

Petroleum Waxes

The paraffin wax employed for the making of candles and the coating of paper is a familiar product;[1] other related materials are less well known. Among these are the microcrystalline, sometimes called amorphous, petroleum waxes melting from 150 to 190°F, and the petrolatums, soft ointment-like products of high oil content.[2] These products have in common a high content of paraffin hydrocarbons, straight or slightly branched in structure, and the differing physical properties may be attributed to variation in the proportions of the two and to the presence of modifying amounts of other hydrocarbon types. It is reasonable to assume that the waxes from different crude oils will differ in composition, especially in the high-molecular-weight fractions. Occasional statements have been made that nonhydrocarbon materials, especially true wax esters, have been recognized in paraffin waxes; these are presumed to have persisted from the source materials of the petroleum and to resemble montan wax in nature; no really good evidence has appeared. The ordinary purification of wax materials for chemical study is likely to remove such compounds.

The origin of the paraffin hydrocarbons in petroleum is quite as uncertain as that of any other group of constituents, but they occur widely

[1] It has been defined as a fusible organic, solid thermoplastic, melting between 50 and 90°C, usually transparent, low in viscosity when melted, incapable of being spun into fibers, and containing long-chain paraffins as characteristic constituents. See *J. Inst. Petrol.*, **29**:361 (1943), for definitions of other wax products.

[2] Microcrystalline waxes are sometimes called petroleum ceresins; it should be remembered that commercial ceresins are often mixtures of true ozokerite ceresins with petroleum waxes. Slack wax and scale wax are manufacturing terms; the former is a first product of cold filter-pressing separation applied to a wax-containing distillate; it is now frequently used, by extension, to describe the wax fractions obtained in the solvent dewaxing of certain lubricating stocks. The latter is a first product of sweating separation applied to slack wax; it is likely to be a crumbly, somewhat colored material containing from 2 to 3 per cent of oil.

in natural plant and animal sources.[1] It should be noted that the paraffins from biological sources are often accompanied by olefins of similar molecular weight, and in some cases the olefins may have been incorrectly identified as paraffins.

XIV-1. Chemical Properties and Composition. Work on the chemical nature of paraffins from a variety of sources goes back to the days of Gay-Lussac; there is general agreement on the broader conclusions that most petroleum waxes are made up largely of paraffin hydrocarbons, normal or branched in structure and of molecular weight sufficiently high to be solid at ordinary temperatures.[2] However, these paraffins rarely occur pure, and it is the nature of the accompanying materials, together with their effect on the physical properties and crystal habits of the paraffins, which remain obscure.[3] The earliest reliable, though not completely precise, work on American petroleum waxes was that of Mabery.[4]

A commercial paraffin wax examined by Mabery contained no compound below $C_{23}H_{48}$, melting at 48°C. He was able to isolate six fractions, which he regarded as individual compounds ranging up to $C_{29}H_{60}$. These represented only 21 per cent of the original sample; moreover, judging from the method of preparation and a comparison with synthetic paraffins made by Krafft, they were not the pure normal compounds that Mabery supposed he had in hand. Mabery's list was extended up to $C_{35}H_{72}$, melting at 76 to 77°C, on an examination of the paraffins in a rod wax, settled out of Pennsylvania crude oil and collected in the well-pumping equipment. In the meantime, Krafft[5] had prepared synthetic paraffin hydrocarbons and had made a similar investigation of a lignite paraffin, obtaining 35 fractions, melting up to 93°C and of indicated composition ranging to C_{48}–C_{50}. Krafft fractionated with some care, but it is doubtful if he really isolated pure compounds. Later

---

[1] Paraffins have been found in rose oil and oat oil, in tobacco, in fruit peels, and rather extensively in the oleoresins of conifers, *Pinus palustris* and *P. pinaster*. The oleoresin of *P. Jeffreyi* contains about 98 per cent of *n*-heptane; this is the most striking case known [Balas, see Palkin and Clark, *Ind. Eng. Chem.*, **26**:720 (1934)]. "Pristane," $C_{18}H_{38}$ or $C_{19}H_{40}$ and a hydrocarbon $C_{44}H_{90}$, exist in the liver oils of sharks and dolphins [Tsujimoto, *Ind. Eng. Chem.*, **9**:1098 (1917). Sorensen, *Acta. chem. Scand.*, **3**:939 (1949); **4**:751 (1951). Kato, *J. Chem. Soc. Japan*, **53**:305 (1950)].

[2] True also of shale oil waxes. Tisot and Horne, *U.S. Bur. Mines Rept. Invest.* 4708, 1950.

[3] For the influence of chemical composition on physical and functional properties of waxes, see Turner, Brown, and Harrison, *Ind. Eng. Chem.*, **47**:1219 (1955); see also Edwards, *Petrol. Refiner* **36**(1):180 (1957).

[4] For example, *Proc. Am. Acad. Arts Sci.*, **37**:565 (1902); *Am. Chem. J.*, **33**:251 (1905).

[5] *Ber.*, **19**:2223 (1886). Krafft and Weilandt, *Ber.*, **29**:1323 (1896).

Francis, Watkins, and Wallington[1] distilled a Scotch shale paraffin, melting point 55°C, very carefully in vacuum, repeating twenty-one times, at which point no further separation was occurring. Eighty-eight per cent of the materials was accounted for, the bulk of it in seven fractions of constant boiling point and the following properties.

Fraction	Per cent original	Boiling point, °C, 0.05 mm	Melting point, °C	Molecular weight	Density, 100°/4°	Solubility, CHCl₃/15°C	Iodine number
B	8.0	150 to 151	44.9	325	0.7453	20.6	3.1
C	13.7	160.8 to 161.3	51.9	332	0.7501	8.38	2.4
D	5.2	169 to 170	53.2	358	0.7532	5.42	
E	17.2	180 to 182	57.3	394	0.7555	3.48	1.6
F	15.7	190.5 to 191	60.9	419	0.7596	2.0	1.4
G	6.8	196 to 198	63.3	449	0.7630	1.1	1.4
H	3.4	217 to 219	66.6	434	0.7678	0.66	

It was observed that fraction G did not match n-dotriacontane, $C_{32}H_{66}$, molecular weight 450, of synthetic origin and that fraction H, which evidently represents a break in the series, does not match synthetic $C_{31}H_{64}$, having a higher specific gravity and a lower molecular weight. Carpenter[2] found, in wax from Burma crude, an entire range of hydrocarbons from C_{21} to C_{34}; some isomers of different melting points for the same molecular weight were encountered. In rod wax from the same crude, a hydrocarbon, $C_{57}H_{116}$, melting at 96.5°C, was recognized.

Buchler and Graves[3] studied wax hydrocarbons from all the wax products of Salt Creek (Wyoming, Rocky Mountain area) crude—paraffin wax, slop wax from an unpressable high-viscosity distillate, petrolatum wax from undistilled residuum, and rod wax. After drastic purification, including crystallization from hot ethylene dichloride to remove soluble impurities ("soft wax"), the distillation fractions from all the materials gave points along one straight line representing the relation of melting point to refractive index—presumptive evidence that all the compounds belonged to one series of homologues. The ranges of melting points of the separated fractions were

Degrees Fahrenheit

Paraffin wax.................	80.5 to 156
Slop wax....................	128.5 to 172.2
Petrolatum wax.............	159.7 to 176.5
Rod wax....................	163.0 to 178.5

[1] *J. Chem. Soc.*, **121**:1529, 2804 (1922).

[2] *J. Inst. Petrol. Technologists*, **12**:288 (1926).

[3] *Ind. Eng. Chem.*, **19**:718 (1927).

Combustion analyses, molecular refractivities, and comparison of properties with those of Krafft's synthetics all supported the belief that these fractions were normal paraffins.

The whole question of wax constitution was reinvestigated by Ferris, Cowles, and Henderson.[1] Paraffin intermediates from a Mid-Continent crude were freed of oil and fractionated through a good column at 1 mm pressure to yield close cuts. Fractions of same boiling point or refractive index but of widely different melting points were recognized. These were sorted by systematic recrystallization, recombining fractions of identical melting points. Eventually six fractions of high purity, as indicated by flat cooling curves, were obtained. These had closely the same 50 per cent boiling points and a maximum difference in molecular weight of not over two carbon atoms, but the melting points covered a wide range. The properties were as follows.

Fraction	A	B	C	D	E	F
Melting point, °C	59.9	55.2	47.1	40.5	35.2	29.4
50 per cent temperature, °C at 10 mm	269.5	269.5	272.0	272.0	272.0	273.0
Refractive index, 80°C	1.4303	1.4306	1.4330	1.4350	1.4359	1.4380
Specific gravity, 80°C	0.770	0.773	0.779	0.783	0.786	0.792
Molecular weight	366	367	379	389	385	377
C_n	26	26	27	27.6	27.4	26.8
Per cent of charge	59	6	7	9.5	9.5	8
Solubility in $EtCl_2$ at 14°C, g per 100 ml	0.115	0.218	0.82	2.4	5.7	70.3

The molecular refraction indicated a saturated structure for all fractions except F, where some doubt existed. This might be due to cyclics, and as a matter of fact, a very careful re-analysis of some of Ferris' fractions by Mair and Schicktanz[2] showed that while the high-melting fraction examined was paraffinic, the low-melting ones were sufficiently low in hydrogen and at the same time low in iodine number to suggest rather strongly that they were cyclic in structure to the amount of 70 per cent C_nH_{2n}, or less of a more hydrogen-deficient formula. The low iodine number precludes structural unsaturation, and the analysis indicates a monocyclic type of molecule. Later, the authors repeated part of the work on a better authenticated Mid-Continent raw material, obtaining similar results, discussed further below. The results of Buchler and Graves emphasize the prevalence of what are probably normal paraffins in the wax products from one particular crude. The purification was,

[1] *Ind. Eng. Chem.*, **21**:1090 (1929); **23**:681 (1931).

[2] *Ind. Eng. Chem.* **28**:1056 (1936).

however, conventional, and the products so removed were more or less ignored. Ferris and his coworkers brought out the nature of the so-called impurities. Since these show a high solubility in the solvent, they would ordinarily be removed in preparation of samples. It should be remembered that this increasing solubility is not due to lower molecular weight, as with the fractions isolated by Watkins, etc., but apparently to a change in constitution, since molecular weight was essentially constant while all the other properties shifted gradually. It may be surmised that the waxes isolated by Buchler and Graves and fractions A and perhaps B of Ferris represent normal paraffins or something very close to them while the fractions of constant molecular weight but of decreasing melting point and increasing solubility may be hydrocarbons of paraffinic nature but of increasingly branched or cyclic structure. Such compounds would always be retained in the mother liquor of an ordinary crystallization and would thus be lost and ignored in the conventional examination. The recent application of mass spectrometric methods has more or less confirmed results obtained by chemical means. The product examined was found by this procedure to be made up of 90 per cent *n*-paraffins, 8 per cent branched paraffins, and the rest naphthene rings.[1]

The only attention given, in any of the foregoing studies, to the waxes of boiling point higher than those of the conventional wax distillates is that by Buchler and Graves, who, by hot crystallization, isolated hydrocarbons melting up to 178°F, and all considered to be of normal structure. The hot solvent would presumably keep in solution whatever compounds corresponded to Ferris' fractions of low melting point and high solubility, so that the failure of Buchler and Graves to note these latter materials is no proof of their absence in the original mixtures.

The sum total of work on the nature of the amorphous wax hydrocarbons in petroleum is rather scanty.[2] The actual truth probably is that, in most cases, the total wax from high-boiling and residual oils is made up to a considerable extent of normal and isoparaffins plasticized by solid or semisolid cyclic hydrocarbons or cyclic-straight-chain molecules, i.e., cyclic nuclei carrying straight-chain groups, not very far in composition from the most paraffinic of the liquid hydrocarbons in lubri-

---

[1] O'Neal and Weir, *Anal. Chem.*, **23**:843 (1951). Turner, *Ind. Eng. Chem.*, **47**:1219 (1955). See also p. 51.

[2] Work on the nature of the higher-molecular-weight paraffins and accompanying hydrocarbons in petrolatums and waxy residua was done by Engler and Böhm, *Dinglers polytech. J.*, **262**:469, 624 (1886). Mabery, *loc. cit.* Gurwitsch, "Erdöl-verarbeitung," p. 394, Springer-Verlag OHG, Berlin, 1924. Muller and Pilat, *J. Inst. Petrol. Technologists*, **21**:887 (1935). Nametkin and Nifontova, *C.A.*, **30**:7829 (1936). Koolwoort, Moser, and Verver, *J. Inst. Petrol. Technologists*, **23**:734 (1937). Robert, Alexanian, and Buzon, *World Petrol. Congr., Proc. 3rd Congr., Hague*, **6**:276 (1951).

cating oils.[1] The relative proportions of the several types probably vary from one crude oil to another, and the whole truth, for even one crude, will not be known until an investigator accounts for 100 per cent of his starting materials.

Some interest attaches to the gradual filling in by synthesis of the empty spaces in the chart of paraffinic hydrocarbons, both normal and branched. Although all the compounds made and many others, no doubt, exist in natural mixtures, this is difficult to prove. Following the early work of Krafft, Gascard[2] made a series of normal paraffins as follows:

	Melting point, °C		Melting point, °C
C_{21}	28	C_{32}	70.5
C_{26}	56	C_{34}	73.2
C_{27}	59.5	C_{54}	95
C_{30}	65.6	C_{62}	100.5
C_{31}	69	C_{64}	102

These melting points are somewhat lower than those found for presumably identical synthetics by Levene, West, and van der Scheer.[3] The latter reported the following.

	Melting point, °C		Melting point, °C
$C_{16}H_{34}$	20	$C_{26}H_{54}$	59 to 60
$C_{18}H_{38}$	28	$C_{28}H_{58}$	64 to 65
$C_{20}H_{42}$	38	$C_{30}H_{62}$	69 to 70
$C_{22}H_{46}$	47	$C_{32}H_{66}$	74 to 74.5
$C_{24}H_{50}$	54	$C_{34}H_{70}$	76 to 76.5

Impure mixtures of molecular weight near 1,000 and melting point to 117°C were isolated by Fischer, Tropsch, and Ter-Nedden,[4] in the course of carbon monoxide–hydrogen syntheses. Later studies of the mixtures[5] indicate *n*-paraffins melting up to 117°C and having compositions near $C_{150}H_{302}$.

By use of a ruthenium catalyst, Pichler[6] was able to synthesize paraffins as follows:

[1] See Minchin, *J. Inst. Petrol.*, **34**:542 (1948), for evidence of this plasticizing action.
[2] *Ann. chim.*, **15**:332 (1921).
[3] *J. Biol. Chem.*, **20**:521 (1915).
[4] *Ber.*, **60B**:1330 (1927).
[5] Koch and Ibing, *Brennstoff-Chem.*, **16**:141 (1935). See also Marsel, *Soap and Chem. Specialties*, **31**(1):149 (1955).
[6] *Bronnstoff-Chem.*, **19**:226 (1938).

Melting point, °C	Average molecular weight	Number of C atoms
123.5	2,100	170
127.0	2,500	290
128.5	4,000	330
130.0	5,000	420
131.5	8,000	670

Definite compounds in this range have been synthesized by Carothers and assistants,[1] who went as far as $C_{70}H_{142}$, melting at 105.5°C.[2] The high point of synthesis to date is probably marked by the preparation of $C_{82}H_{166}$, melting at 110, and $C_{100}H_{202}$, melting at 115°C.[3] It is evident, as would be predicted, that the melting point rise with molecular weight increase diminishes as the molecular weight rises. The predicted melting point of an *n*-paraffin of infinite chain length is 138°C.[4]

The recognition of what seem to be very high melting paraffins suspended rather than dissolved in crude oils is rather interesting. By passing water into contact with a crude oil surface, a variety of materials was adsorbed at the interface.[5] Among these there were identified, on rather sketchy evidence, high-melting paraffins in the range above C_{80}.

Enough syntheses of branched paraffins have been performed to establish the lower melting points and different properties of these compounds; the melting point decreases as the degree of branching increases. For instance, 7, 8-diisopropyl tetradecane, C_{20}, melts at −69°C.[6] It will be recalled that the normal C_{20} melts at 38°. For larger molecules, the following are typical:[7]

Melting point, °C

$(C_{15}H_{31})_2CHCH_3$.................... 32 to 34
$(C_{15}H_{31})_2CHCH_2CH_3$................ 18
$(C_{15}H_{31})_2CHCH_2CH_2CH_3$............ 23
$(C_{51}H_{31})_2CH(C_{16}H_{33})$................ 46

The last compound adds up to $C_{47}H_{96}$, the corresponding normal paraffin should melt near 90°C.

XIV-2. Crystallization of Wax. Study of the crystallization phenomena of paraffin hydrocarbons and petroleum waxes is complicated by

[1] *J. ACS*, **52**:5279 (1930).

[2] See Doolittle and Peterson for syntheses of $C_{64}H_{130}$, mp 102°, *J. ACS*, **73**:2145 (1951).

[3] Stallberg and Steinhagen, *Acta Chem. Scand.*, **6**:313 (1952).

[4] Joliot, *Compt. rend.*, **240**:749 (1955).

[5] Denekas, Carlson, Moore, and Dodd, *Ind. Eng. Chem.*, **43**:1165 (1951).

[6] Petrov and Ol'dekop, *C.A.*, **43**:107 (1949).

[7] Landa and Sliva, *C.A.*, **27**:1611 (1931), for a series of references.

the polymorphism which they show. X-ray techniques were applied rather early; the Scotch shale paraffin fractions separated by Francis, Watkins, and Wallington, mentioned above, were examined by Piper, Brown, and Dyment.[1] They plotted the spacings of the diffracted X-ray images against the number of carbon atoms and found all but one to fall opposite integral values for carbon atoms; the exception was a fraction of doubtful purity. The variability of the long diffraction spacings with rate of cooling through the melting point range was first noted by Clark.[2] The structure of a normal paraffin, C_{29}, was fixed and the dimensions established by Müller,[3] and Hengstenberg[4] observed that a mixture of paraffins showed the same spacing as a single compound. The predominance of normal paraffins in a shale wax was established by this means.[5] The existence of solid crystal transitions at temperatures below the melting point was developed by Seyer[6] and others.[7] There seems to be no doubt that the commercial paraffin wax mixtures show the phenomena displayed by the individual long-chain hydrocarbons.[8] The value of refractive index measurements for recognizing transition points has recently been brought out by Johnson.[9] While some paraffins show more than one transition, Fontana has demonstrated that within the range C_{25} to C_{38}, the normal compounds show only one crystal transition involving any appreciable energy change, between the melting point and room temperature. It appears that for these compounds and above the transition temperature, crystallization occurs in a close-packed hexagonal lattice. Below the transition point, the compounds containing odd numbers of carbon atoms crystallize in an orthorhombic lattice and the even-numbered in either a monoclinic or a triclinic lattice, depending on molecular weight.[10] As stated, the patterns for purified commercial paraffin waxes agree pretty well with those for the hydrocarbons, except that apparently the inclined axis systems do not occur frequently in crystals formed from the melted state.

The crystallization behavior of the commercial waxes is closely related to the operations involved in their manufacture. A satisfactory expla-

---

[1] *J. Chem. Soc.*, **127**:2194 (1925).

[2] *Nature*, **120**:12 (1927).

[3] *Proc. Royal Society (London)*, **A120**:437 (1928); see more recent work by McCrone, Wright Air Development Center, *Tech. Rept.* 54-349, 1954.

[4] *Z. Kryst.*, **67**:583 (1928).

[5] *J. Soc. Chem. Ind. Japan*, **38** (Suppl. Bdg.):677 (1935).

[6] *J. ACS*, **58**:2029 (1936); **61**:1114 (1939); **66**:179 (1944).

[7] See, for example, West, *J. ACS*, **59**:742 (1937); Fontana, *J. Phys. Chem.*, **57**:222 (1953).

[8] Vorländer and Selke, *Z. physik. Chem.*, **129**:435 (1927). See also Templin, *Ind. Eng. Chem.*, **48**:154 (1956).

[9] *ACS, Div. Petrol. Chem.*, Preprints, no. 30, p. 75, 1953.

[10] Edwards, *Ind. Eng. Chem.*, **49**:750 (1957).

nation of the phenomena has been worked out by Ferris, Cowles, and Henderson. The conventional wax separation from light distillates of earlier years involves filter pressing a chilled semisolid wax-oil mixture to isolate an oily product known as slack wax; this is then remelted, and cast into cakes and "sweated" to remove oil by fractional fusion of the softer wax compounds. The success of these operations depends completely on the providing of crystal structures which will permit, first, easy filtration of oil from the chilled distillate, and then, good drainage of melted soft wax and oil from the resolidified secondary product. The views of Ferris on the process are more or less as follows: when a well-prepared and well-fractionated wax distillate (see Sec. XIV-3) is chilled, the wax content separates in hexagonal-plate crystals. It is a matter of observation that these plates form a well-drained, filterable cake. It also seems true that the hexagonal plate is the form obtained when any wax product is drastically purified by recrystallization from solvents to yield the normal paraffin hydrocarbons contained. Under certain other conditions, however, the wax appears in needles rather than plates, and this has contributed to the confusion existing in the field of study. For instance, much of the synthetic preparation of high-molecular-weight paraffin hydrocarbons has resulted in pure products crystallizing in needles.[1] It appears, from the accumulated observations of many workers, that the separation as needles rather than plates may be influenced by:

1. Concentration; plates form in solutions of low concentration.

2. Viscosity; a medium- or low-viscosity solution is likely to deposit plate crystals.

3. State of purity; needles separate from solutions of paraffins contaminated by other hydrocarbons.

4. Temperature; transition points in the temperature range have been discussed above. It should be noted that these transition temperatures are not independent of solvent employed.

5. Cooling velocity; rapid cooling favors the formation of needles.

Many attempts have been made to explain this set of observations, based often on experiments made with widely different materials and different conditions. A plausible hypothesis, however, is available. Buchler and Graves had recognized that a soluble and low melting "soft wax" fraction, separated from the harder, normally crystalline materials, by its presence influenced the formation of needle crystals. Ferris and his assistants followed by recognizing not only two but a series of wax compounds of decreasing melting point for a given molecular-weight

---

[1] For example, Carothers, *J. ACS*, **52**:5279 (1930).

range. These showed, on recrystallization, the presence of plate, badly crystalline, and needle forms.

The needle waxes are more soluble than the plates, for a given molecular weight, so that when a wax-bearing distillate of low average molecular weight is chilled and filter-pressed in the ordinary way, the plate waxes are insoluble enough to separate out while the needle waxes remain dissolved. When a fraction of higher molecular weight is processed, the concentration of needle and mal-crystalline waxes increases, and these may separate out with the normally plate compounds, which, however, will take the shape of needle or mal-crystalline forms when either of the latter comes out of solution simultaneously, the mal-crystalline being apparently the more powerful.

As oil fractions of still higher molecular weight are treated, the transition to the so-called amorphous (really microcrystalline) waxes occurs. They are characteristic of undistilled residua, and their crystallization causes the phenomenon involved in spoiling the crystal structure of a wax cake by failure to fractionate out the high-boiling ends in preparing the wax distillate. The higher-boiling fractions carry poorly crystalline or noncrystalline material which imposes its structure on the otherwise suitable plate or needle wax, and this interferes with filter pressing and sweating. By avoiding the presence of these higher-boiling products, trouble is spared. The chilling and filter pressing of a well-prepared wax distillate will yield chiefly plates because the needle waxes boiling in this range are soluble enough to stay in solution at the separating temperature. However, when the same wax cake, made up of plates, is melted and resolidified for "sweating," it will now come out in needle form. In the original crystallization, much oil was present and the needle-forming compounds remained dissolved. In the remelt, little oil is present in proportion to wax, so that needles separate out and impress their form on the bulk of the normally plate wax. This is fortunate, because a crystal mass made up of needles reacts well to fractional fusion or "sweating."

The work of Ferris does not agree entirely with the list of factors given above as influencing plate or needle form. A plate wax was crystallized from six solvents in turn, one of them an oil of 8,000 SSU viscosity; it remained a plate wax, and similar irreversibility was noted for a needle wax. Only when needle or amorphous waxes were added to plate wax could a change be induced.

Doubt about the exclusively paraffinic nature of petroleum waxes, expressed earlier by Ferris, was confirmed by McKittrick, Henriques, and Wolff.[1] By plotting refractive indices against melting points and com-

---

[1] *J. Inst. Petrol. Technologists,* **23**:616 (1937).

paring the results for waxes with those for pure hydrocarbons, they deduced that a commercial paraffin wax is made up completely of n-paraffins but that waxes as recovered from various wax distillates contained considerable proportions of isoparaffins and even of naphthenes. Residue waxes continued the trend and showed high content of the hydrocarbon classes mentioned and even of aromatics and polynaphthenes. Although these results call for chemical support which the authors do not offer, they are suggestive. The presence of such compounds permits a revival of the idea of Padgett and others that the same compounds may crystallize as either plates or needles, depending on the adsorption of foreign substances at the crystal surfaces; this is discussed below.

The hypothesis of Ferris was supported by later experiments[1] and by a reexamination of the crystal properties of 23 hydrocarbons, all in the molecular-weight range of the typical waxes and falling in the paraffinic, naphthenic, and aromatic classes.[2] Clarke found that all these compounds could be crystallized as plates, needles, or mal-crystals, from the melted condition or from solvents, depending on the rate and temperature of crystallization. There seems to be a little doubt that the formation of needles is encouraged by the presence of resinous impurities. One exception to Clarke's generalization above was that n-hexacosane (C_{26}) could be obtained in needle form only in the presence of added resin material. Likewise, Goldenberg and Zhuze[3] found pure individual normal paraffins always to crystallize, from various solvents, in fine rhombic plates of the order of 50 to 300 μ long. However, the same compounds could be obtained as needles, 5 to 40 μ long, by crystallizing from solutions containing aluminum stearate, typical pour-point depressors, or oxidized petrolatum. These items fit more or less with the observation of Anderson and Talley, who examined the wax precipitated from propane solution in propane dewaxing of a deasphalted Mid-Continent residuum.[4] The precipitated wax proved to be made up of masses of small crystals, needle-like in appearance, held together in popcorn-like clusters by what was believed to be a highly aromatic resin, which had precipitated at the same time.

Some modification of the Ferris hypothesis has been provided in a useful discussion by Edwards.[5] He pointed out that paraffin crystals grow in layers;[6] since the largest molecules have the highest melting

[1] *Ind. Eng. Chem.*, **37**:1054 (1945).

[2] Clarke, *Ind. Eng. Chem.*, **43**:2526 (1951).

[3] *Kolloid Zhur.*, **13**:175 (1951); *C.A.*, **46**:411 (1952).

[4] *Ind. Eng. Chem.*, **29**:432 (1937). Anderson and Talley recognized that apparent needles may be plates viewed edgewise. They found that the more obvious needle structures did not filter well.

[5] *Loc. cit.;* also *Ind. Eng. Chem.*, **47**:2555 (1955).

[6] Dawson and Vaud, *Proc. Roy. Soc. (London)*, **A206**, 555 (1951).

points, they will separate first, while the smaller, more soluble ones will be left to deposit on those already crystallized. Those later deposited will not register properly with the first. A parallel influence will be exerted by the tendency to crystal transition. As temperature drops during crystallization, the transition temperature may be traversed, the preferred crystal form changes, and the structure already formed comes under strain; the net effect of both influences is that the plates already deposited will curl. This mechanism was first invoked by Padgett and by Rhodes, Mason, and Sutton, as an explanation of needle occurrence.[1] Edwards suggests that paraffins do not crystallize in three forms, but in two only—the hexagonal and the orthorhombic plates, depending on crystallization above or below the transition temperature. Any other forms observed are due to distortion caused by the presence of modifying poisons. The refining qualities of waxes he attributes to the size and rigidity of the crystals formed, rather than to crystal habit. Soft, thin plates would pack into an unfilterable mass, which would give an appearance of needle crystals, the more so under the crossed Nicols ordinarily used, and particularly when a transition had already occurred. But soft plates of this kind may curl, especially when formed at higher temperature, to give a stronger mass very needle-like in appearance, which will sweat properly.

It must not be forgotten that nearly each study of the problem has been carried out with different raw materials; conflicting results and opinions are to be expected, since differences in composition and in environment may have a varying share in explaining the phenomena. As far as the matter can be summarized at the present stage of understanding, it appears that:

1. The highly purified commercial paraffin waxes are mostly normal paraffins.

2. They are accompanied in petroleum by compounds of about the same molecular weight and differing in structure; for instance, these soft waxes and nonwaxes may contain chains, naphthenic rings, and aromatic rings; they can be separated by solvent crystallization into viscous oil, soft wax-like materials, and hard dry microcrystalline solids.

3. It is certain that these mixed molecules influence profoundly the physical properties and crystal habits of the normal paraffins.

XIV-3. Industrial Separation of Waxes.[2] Lubricating oil fractions from wax-bearing crudes ordinarily contain enough wax to cause them to solidify when chilled; it is necessary to remove this wax, and the

---

[1] *Ind. Eng. Chem.*, **18**:832 (1926); **19**:935 (1927).

[2] Separation of wax hydrocarbons—*n*-paraffins—by complexing with urea has been used extensively for laboratory study. Bailey and others, *World Petrol. Congr., Proc. 3rd Congr., Hague*, **3**:161 (1951). See also pp. 41 and 341.

removal is so expensive that, whenever feasible, the material removed is worked up into salable products. Moreover, the removal becomes more expensive as it is made more complete. This increases the difficulty and cost of manufacturing oils of very low pour point. Within recent years the availability of crystallization inhibitors or pour-point depressants has made such drastic dewaxing less necessary (see Chap. XIII). Such additives have little effect on residual oils such as bright stocks but for oils of moderate viscosity it is sufficient to dewax to a moderate degree and then to add a pour-point depressant for the rest of the desired lowering of solidifying temperature.

The waxes present in wax-bearing crudes usually boil in the same range as the various lubricating oils manufactured, so that separation of wax and oil by distillation is not possible. The only slight exception lies in the fact that it is sometimes possible to lower the solidifying temperature of a wax-bearing residual cylinder stock by exhaustive noncracking distillation (steam or vacuum). What happens is that the higher melting wax materials are more volatile than the bulk of the liquid hydrocarbons making up the residuum, so that the latter becomes relatively more wax-free by the distillation.

Wax separation is ordinarily applied to the following:

1. Light lubricating fractions from the more paraffinic and asphalt-free crude oils,[1] containing only crystalline wax. These are known as "wax distillates"; they are ordinarily of Saybolt viscosity 65 to 85 at 100°F and boil from roughly 300 to 600°F at 10 mm pressure. They supply the great bulk of the crystalline paraffin wax of commerce. The separation is usually by direct chilling and filter pressing.

2. Heavier lubricating distillates, more viscous than the usual wax distillates, extending into the so-called unpressable cuts. These are ordinarily processed in the presence of the wax distillates; in other words, a wider fraction is taken in the distillation, including both the wax distillate and some of the unpressable fractions, and this whole cut is processed together.

3. Long residua from asphalt-free crudes. The reduced crude is subjected to distillation to remove the light fractions referred to under (1), leaving the higher-boiling and nonvolatile materials which contain microcrystalline and amorphous waxes. The dewaxing is done by chilling in naphtha solution and centrifuging or by filter pressing solutions of the oils in special solvents such as methyl ethyl ketone–toluene mixtures.

4. Cylinder stocks, residual oils from which all readily volatile fractions have been removed. These are usually dewaxed by centrifuging chilled naphtha solutions, or preferably by solvent processing in filter presses.

[1] On the recovery of wax from shale oil distillates, see Tisot and Horne, *U.S. Bur. Mines Rept. Invest.* 4708, 1950.

Dewaxing of Light Oils. For the preparation of crystalline wax from conventional wax distillates by the sweating process, four steps require careful control:

Preparation of wax distillate
Chilling
Filter pressing
Sweating

Wax distillates are made from selected crudes and the range of the fractions taken is controlled by a combination of viscosity and boiling range; these will obviously vary from one crude to another. If poor fractionation or entrainment has permitted a small amount of higher-boiling oil, carrying poorly crystalline or amorphous wax or even asphaltic material, to contaminate the product, the subsequent pressing and sweating will give trouble. The distillation limits are so chosen as to include in the fraction a considerable proportion of lower-boiling gas oil; this serves as a diluent during subsequent processing. In fact, the wax distillate may be pictured as containing the heavier portions of the gas oil and the lighter portion of the lubricating oil in the crude. For average American practice, the wax distillate may comprise 15 to 18 per cent of the crude, and may contain in turn 10 per cent of recoverable wax.[1]

The chilling and pressing operations, while basically the same everywhere, are applied with several variations. Chilling is effected by pumping the distillate through tubes jacketed by cold brine and provided with helical scrapers. The crystal mush which results is pumped to plate-and-frame filter presses set in refrigerated rooms. The effluent pressed distillate is worked up into lubricating oils, and the filter cake constitutes "slack wax." The chilling and pressing may be done in one step at an intermediate temperature, say, 15°F or, with oils of high wax content, in several steps, say, at 35 and 0°F. The pour point of the dewaxed lubricant will obviously vary with the temperature of the last separation. Since a wax distillate usually contains excess gas oil (as diluent) which must be distilled off in making lubricants, the wax in the pressed distillate is concentrated by the distillation, and the pour point of the lubricant recovered is always higher than the pressing temperature. A distillate pressed at 20°F may yield lubricating oils of pour point about 35°F, and a pressing at 0°F may yield an oil of pour point, say, 15°F.

The slack wax separated in the presses is melted and resolidified. At this stage, it is, at ordinary temperature, a fragile, solid mass of needle-like crystals containing 25 to 50 per cent of liquid oil and about equal parts of high- and low-melting waxes. It is markedly thixotropic and

[1] For estimates of wax content of various crude oils, see Nelson, *Oil Gas J.*, **53**(41): 129 (1955).

can be broken into a pumpable fluid, from which nearly all the oil can be removed mechanically.[1]   Apparently none of the oil is in solid solution in the wax, for cold washing with acetone (a fair solvent for oil and a poor one for wax) will remove all the oil, leaving an entirely oil-free wax.[2]

It is not uncommon to apply a sulfuric acid treatment to the slack wax at this stage of the manufacture; in fact, such treatment is sometimes employed for the wax distillate prior to dewaxing, and sometimes to both the wax-containing oil and to the slack wax after separation.   Such an operation, because of the removal of resinous materials, assists the sharp separation desirable for good filter pressing and sweating, makes it easier to obtain stable and light-colored waxes, and reduces the clay requirement in the final percolation which gives commercial waxes their freedom from color, odor, and taste; all these properties depend on complete oil removal.

Separation of the desired hard dry wax from the soft wax and oil can be effected by:

Fractional fusion in air, known as sweating
Similar fractional fusion in contact with water
Fractional crystallization with solvents

Sweating in air has until recently been the preferred practice throughout the industry; the process has been described by Espach.[3]   The theory of fractional fusion and of sweating has been discussed by Bowman and Burk[4] and by Aston and Mastrangelo.[5]

In conventional sweating the slack wax is melted and cast in sheets of varying thickness (about 4 in. in American practice) resting on perforated metal false bottoms in pans 10 by 40 ft or more, arranged in vertical stacks with space for air circulation, and a large number are assembled in one sweating house or oven; the interior air temperature is raised very slowly, 1 or 2°F per hr, thus allowing the liquid oil and low-melting wax to drain off.   As the temperature rises, a series of fractions of different melting point may be obtained; the final temperature will control the melting point of the residual wax; the hardest large-scale commercial product usually has a melting point of 135°F or slightly

[1] Souther and Gruse, U.S. Patent 1,685,008, 1928.

[2] Souther and Gruse, U.S. Patent 1,685,058,1928.

[3] *U.S. Bur. Mines Bull.* 388, 1935.   For a discussion of the technical problems and of the process variables, see Campbell and Wilson, *J. Inst. Petrol. Technologists,* **5**:106 (1918), and Sawyer, Nash, and Hunter, *J. Inst. Petrol. Technologists,* **26**:390, 430 (1940); **27**:1, 143 (1941).   On the preparation of wax for sweating, see Wyant, *Natl. Petrol. News,* **16**(40):73 (1924).

[4] *Ind. Eng. Chem.,* **41**:2008 (1949).

[5] *Anal. Chem.,* **22**:636 (1950).

higher.   One sweating is generally not sufficient to render a wax commercially free of oil and soft wax; the separate fractions and the unmelted residuum (crude scale wax) may be mixed and subjected to several treatments, as required.   The melted wax is finally run through vertical cylindrical filters of fuller's earth or bauxite, heated above the melting point of the wax; the filtered product is then cast into slabs for the market.[1]

Fractional fusion in contact with water has taken various forms.   In one operation, water of controlled temperature was circulated through a wax container of gauze or perforated metal, carrying away melted constituents.[2]   The separation of waxes of different melting point by fractional precipitation—the reverse of sweating—was described by Fleischer.[3] Under ordinary conditions, this operation does not give very clean separation.   A modern process for water separation of oil from slack wax is known as emulsion deoiling.[4]   It involves the mixing of semisolid slack wax with water, some cooling being effected by controlling the temperature of the water, followed by centrifugally separating the emulsified oil and water from the solid wax crystals.   Complete deoiling is not claimed for this process; it seems best suited for preliminary removal of the bulk of the oil from a slack wax which is then charged to a sweating operation.

Fractional crystallization from solvent solutions was developed first for processing of heavy oils; the dewaxing of light oils differs only in minor details, which will be noted below.

In the case of the ordinary crystalline wax prepared by sweating, as just described, the necessary separation into the various melting point grades is effected during the sweating, particularly after the oil has been pretty well worked out.   Solvent separation, however, may provide a wide range product which cannot conveniently be further fractionated by partial crystallization.   Since the differences in melting point rest on differences in molecular weight, fractional distillation serves very well to give a good distribution of melting points.   An example of what can be done is supplied by the following table.   A commercial wax, melting at 132°F, was distilled at 10 mm pressure into 10 per cent cuts.

[1] On attempts at rendering the air-sweating process continuous, see U.S. Patents 1,040,408, 1,070,730, and 1,429,721.

[2] Wild, *Petroleum Z.*, **8**:1182 (1913).   A continuous variant on this, in which the wax in the container is agitated by intermeshing screw conveyors, is described in U.S. Patent 1,663,592.   Oil separation down to 5 per cent was effected.

[3] *Petroleum Z.*, **9**:87 (1913).   A similar process was patented by Winterstein and Nitsch, German Patent 226,137, 1909.

[4] Schutte, *Proc. API*, **21**(III):48 (1940); *Petroleum Engr.*, **21**(5):C-7 (1949).

Number of fraction	Melting point	Number of fraction	Melting point
1	120.2	6	133.3
2	123.3	7	135.8
3	125.7	8	138.7
4	128.2	9	142.2
5	130.6	Residuum	147.8

The proportions vary from one wax to another.   It will be evident that, since oil and wax in the wax-bearing fractions are of about the same molecular weight, separation of oil cannot be effected, and an oil-free charge must be provided.

Dewaxing of Heavy Oils.   In the processing of light oils for wax removal by filter pressing, the recovery of wax is a relatively important part of the operation.   This is not so true for the dewaxing of heavier oils; the crude wax as removed covers a wide range of molecular weights and physical properties, and is likely also to include semisolid resins and other nonwax compounds; some fractionation and refining to yield micro-crystalline waxes and petrolatums is carried on, but in the past a good part of the output has found its way into cracking stock.

The methods used for removal of wax materials from high-viscosity oils are[1] centrifuging of chilled naphtha solutions and crystallization from cold solvents, followed by filtering.

The centrifugal process is the logical successor of the cold settling of earlier years, which involved making a solution of cylinder stock in naphtha, cooling slowly, and allowing settling to occur at a low tempera-ture.   The wax and resin suspension in cold naphtha is a little more dense than the solution of oil in naphtha; a soft layer of these materials contain-ing much naphtha settled out slowly.   The yield was rather poor; and because of inexact separation, the pour-point temperature of the oil was not excessively low.   No doubt much of the improvement resulting from the use of the centrifuge process came from incidental changes which could equally well have been applied in cold settling; but in the end, results are much better.[2]   A solution of the cylinder stock or long residuum in two or two and a half volumes of 60° gravity (average Mid-Continent) naphtha is chilled slowly—a slow rate would be 3°F per hr—

---

[1] The chief difficulty in direct filter pressing of chilled heavy oil distillates containing solid wax or of chilled suspensions of such materials in naphtha is the failure to lay down a crystalline wax cake porous enough to allow drainage of mother liquor on the press.   One remedy proposed has been the admixing of clay filter aids.   Weir, *Natl. Petrol. News*, **18**(13):91 (1926); Gee, *Proc. API*, **14**(III):24 (1933).

[2] Jones, *Natl. Petrol. News*, **15**(41):32A (1923).   Miller, *Natl. Petrol. News*, **18**(9): 37 (1926).   Lederer and Zublin, *Oil Gas J.*, **29**(32):64 (1930).   Nelson, *Petrol. Engr.*, **6**(6):65 (1934).

with some convection circulation. The final temperature for an oil of $+15°F$ pour point should be about $-10°F$ and for a $0°F$ pour, say $-40°F$.

The centrifuge process has been practiced almost exclusively with naphtha as a medium, though it has an appreciable solvent power for wax even at low temperatures; the dissolved wax is concentrated in the oil on distilling off the naphtha, so that the resulting pour point is not so low as it might be. Much thought has been given to other, more selective solvents. One difficulty is that most of these are so much heavier than wax that in centrifuging, the oil-solvent layer flows outside the wax-solvent layer; centrifuge installations are ordinarily built for the reverse operation.

Special solvents for wax separation were apparently tried first by European students interested in recovering waxes from lignite tar and low-temperature coal tar, for instance, the process of Erdmann using acetone[1] and that of Seidenschnur employing a benzene-alcohol mixture.[2] Early attempts to apply these methods to petroleum materials failed, probably because of the sometimes unrecognized differential action of the solvents. Acetone would keep lignite tar oils in solution but was not able to do the same for the rather paraffinic liquid hydrocarbons accompanying paraffin wax. The difficulty has been overcome by modern processes.

The most widely used of these employs a mixture of acetone, or preferably methyl ethyl ketone with benzene, toluene, or blends of the two.[3] The ketone functions as a separating solvent, but at low temperatures will throw out of solution not only the solid paraffin hydrocarbons, but also liquid and semiliquid paraffinic molecules, some of which would be undesirable in the wax and some of which would be useful in the lubricating fractions. This difficulty is corrected by adding an aromatic hydrocarbon; benzene was employed at first, but toluene has proved to be more satisfactory from several standpoints, one of which is its nontoxic character. Admixing the aromatic constituent up to 70 per cent, depending on circumstances, permits effective separation of the wax without undue precipitation of liquid oil.[4] The process is a simple one, in which the wax-bearing oil is dissolved in the appropriate solvent mixture, chilled continuously by pumping through elongated cylinders jacketed to carry refrigerants, and provided with internal scrapers. The slurry of wax crystals in the solvent-oil complex is then pumped to horizontal

[1] Braunkohle, **17**:425 (1918).

[2] Brennstoff-Chem., **2**:49, 73, 81 (1921).

[3] Govers and Bryant, *Proc. API*, **14**(III):7 (1933). Gee, Kiersted, and McCarty, *Oil Gas J.*, **35**(1):50 (1936). David and Huemmer, *Chem. Eng. Progr.*, **43**:174 (1947).

[4] On use of higher ketones—methyl isoamyl, etc., without any admixture of aromatic hydrocarbons—see Tiedje and MacLeod, *J. Inst. Petrol.*, **41**:37 (1955).

rotary drum filters, in which the wax cake is vacuum filtered and washed with additional cold solvent. An atmosphere of flue gas is usually maintained. There are many minor variations on the procedure and it has proved to be quite flexible in handling different wax-bearing stocks and in producing a wide range of waxes.[1] Distillates of wide molecular-weight range and long residua are treated successfully when appropriate adjustments are made. One considerable advantage over the naphtha type solvents is the low solvent power of the mixture for wax; this results in the possibility of making a final oil product of pour-point temperature about the same as the dewaxing temperature. When refined wax of conventional type is desired, it is customary to filter at a rather high temperature, say 30°F, which serves to recover the useful wax, and then to put the remaining oil through the operation again at a lower temperature in order to produce an oil of the desired low pour point. The wax separated in this second filtering falls in the class of slop waxes of doubtful utility. Another approach involves separating a wide range crystalline wax in one operation at a rather low temperature and then recovering the useful crystalline wax from this cake by distillation. Alternatively, the separation can in some cases be effected by sweating. Where solvents are employed to carry out the final deoiling of refined wax, high solvent proportions are necessary—as much as 12 parts of solvent to one of wax in the more extreme cases. Processing of long residua and cylinder stocks requires less dilution, perhaps not more than three or four parts of solvent to one of oil, and can be a very simple operation, in which the solution is chilled to the desired temperature, filtered, and the oil passed on to further refining after the solvent has been recovered by stripping. The wax in such cases may be finished as a petrolatum without any further separation. Alternatively, a cylinder stock solution may be filtered at, say 30°F, to recover a salable microcrystalline wax, and then at a lower temperature to yield a bright stock of low pour point and a slop wax which can be cracked. The slop waxes are sometimes reworked for a content of higher melting usable product.

The discovery that solubility of wax in paraffinic naphthas goes through a maximum as the molecular weight of the naphtha is lowered and then decreases to a low figure for butane and propane made possible the development of the propane dewaxing process.[2] Oil is retained in solu-

[1] Ebner and Mertons, *Petrol. Refiner*, **23**(6):118 (1944); *Lubrication*, **32**:137 (1946). Albright, *Petrol. Refiner*, **26**(7):121 (1947). Reeves and Pattillo, *Petrol. Refiner*, **27**(3):80 (1948). Hinman, National Petroleum Association Meeting, Atlantic City, Sept. 15, 1949.

[2] Bahlke, Giles, and Adams, *Proc. API*, **14M**(III):16 (1933). Anderson, Forrest, and Van Horn, *Natl. Petrol. News*, **28**(21):49 (1936). Anderson and Talley, *Ind. Eng. Chem.*, **29**:432 (1937).

tion in propane at quite low temperatures, while the ordinary waxes come out of solution in readily filterable forms.[1] Because of the high volatility of the propane, self-refrigeration is possible; the solvent is allowed to evaporate by lowering pressure, and control of chilling rate is very easy. Actually, this rate may be quite high, as much as 1°F per min. The separation is effected by pumping the crystal suspension to rotary filters, as with the ketone solvent mixture. The ratio of solvent to oil is not critical as long as it does not fall below a value at which a wax gel is formed; continuous filtration is possible without much trouble.

It should be emphasized that solvent dewaxing is applied in a variety of ways, depending on the stock on hand and the requirements of the refiner. The flexibility of the operation is such that practically all new installations are of that type. While conventional sweating for refined wax and centrifugal naphtha dewaxing for cylinder stocks are still widely used, their replacement seems to be only a matter of time.

The wax discharge removed from the heavy oils by any of the processes described usually contains the bulk of the colored materials in the original stock; highly colored constituents such as resins are often insoluble in the cold dewaxing mixture and come out with the wax. The color can be removed by percolation through or contact treatment with clay or bauxite, or alternatively at least some of the color may have been taken out of the oil stock before the dewaxing. The former is the more statisfactory and is more widely practiced.

The recovery operations described above yield the following:

1. From the light wax distillates, crystalline waxes of varying degrees of purity; the melting points will range from about 125 to upward of 145°F, and the oil content from 2 to 3 to a few hundredths of 1 per cent.

2. From cold centrifuging of heavy stocks dissolved in naphtha, salvelike petrolatums of dark color and high oil content; the actual wax solids are quite mixed in character. These may be refined into petrolatums or deoiled to yield dry microcrystalline waxes.

3. From solvent dewaxing of heavy residua, somewhat drier and higher melting soft waxes, usually lighter in color and higher in actual wax content. These also may be worked up by recrystallization into higher melting dry waxes.

4. Microcrystalline final products melting from 155 to 195°F, varying from a dark chocolate to a pale tan color; they may be plastic and sticky or hard and dry, depending on the extent of oil removal. Such materials result from the reworking of (2) and (3) above by deoiling with solvents and decolorizing with adsorbents.

[1] Chamberlin, Dinwiddie, and Franklin, *Ind. Eng. Chem.*, **41**:566 (1949). The crystal form is influenced by temperature, solvent ratio, amount crystallized, and by crystal poisons acting as dewaxing aids.

General properties of (1) and (4) are given below.

	Refined waxes			
Melting point, cooling-curve method, °F.......	126	131	142	150
Hardness, cone penetration, 77°F............	140	75	14	9
Oil content, per cent......................	0.3	0.25	0.25	0.25
Flash point, °F...........................	.....	410		

	Microcrystalline waxes		
Melting point, drop point, °F.........	165	173	195
Hardness:			
Cone penetration, 77°F...........	11		
Needle.........................	...	15	4
Viscosity, 210°F..................	70	...	85
Oil content, per cent..............	6	2	0.3
Flash point, °F....................	525	565	

It should be noted that higher-melting microcrystalline waxes accumulate in evaporation residues and tank bottoms resulting from the handling of wax-bearing crudes. Earlier in this chapter it was mentioned that Mabery had isolated C_{35} paraffins from a Pennsylvania "rod wax"; more recent studies have extended this range up to C_{81}. Within recent years, it has been profitable to collect and rework tank bottoms from Mid-Continent and Pennsylvania fields, to recover waxes melting up to 190°F; the methods are in general those just described.

XIV-4. Wax Uses. The various petroleum waxes are sold at lower prices than most of the vegetable waxes and synthetic plastics;[1] quantities of the order of 750,000 tons per year are employed for very diverse purposes. The most important may be listed as follows:[2]

Candlemaking	Polishes
Waxing paper and	Medicines and cosmetics
paper containers	Metal-can linings
Laminating papers	Sealing compounds
Sizing paper	Electrical insulation
Protective coatings	Dressing and filling
(antirust)	textiles and fibers
Compounding rubber	Matches and cartridges
Electrotypes	Coating fruits and vegetables

[1] This has not always been true. It is reported that in 1849 the first paraffin recovered from Rangoon petroleum was valued at £200 per ton. Allan, *J. Inst. Petrol. Technologists*, **19**:161 (1933).

[2] Dean, *Petrol. Refiner*, **25**(5):87 (1946). Padgett, *Oil Gas J.*, **36**(38):30 (1938).

Inks and carbon papers   Leather dressing
Coating trees and bushes   Weatherproofing stone
Wax figures and models

The oldest large use of paraffin wax is in the making of candles. This complex industry, dating from classical times, has employed one type of wax after another as each became available. Paraffin wax has succeeded stearin as the cheapest satisfactory raw material. It has high illuminating power and good burning qualities, leaves no ash, and can be molded easily. The chief objections, the tendency to bend on standing in a warm place and to mottle, have been pretty well overcome. Bending has been corrected by additions to the wax—stearic acid and carnauba wax—or by coating the candle with a layer of harder, stiffer wax. Various other minor faults—tendency to stick in the molds, lack of opacity, mottling—are remedied by additions of similar character. Naphthol improves opacity and lead stearate remedies sticking. These prescriptions are likely to fail when tried for a wide variety of waxes. Mottling and opacity are both related to crystal form and orientation and to content of oil and air. In other words, anything which influences crystal structure or the materials between the crystals will affect the optical properties. Thus a bad color may often be covered over by stirring air into the wax while it is cooling. Transparency has been studied extensively; heating over long periods below the melting point induces transparency.[1] This sounds like loss of intercrystalline air, but crystal growth or reorientation may occur; the density and electrical resistance increase at the same time. Candles can be colored by dissolving the dye in stearic acid which is mixed with the wax or is coated on to the candle by dipping.

The largest demands for petroleum waxes come from the manufacturers of waxed paper and waxed-paper containers. While candle making employs only refined crystalline wax, the paper outlets take appreciable quantities of microcrystalline products.

The waxing of paper and the production of the wide variety of waxed-paper products have developed into a complicated technology.[2] A distinction is made between wet-waxed and dry-waxed papers. A paper may be waterproof if the interstices between the cellulose fibers are filled with wax, but it will not be proof against water vapor unless the fibers themselves are covered over by a layer of wax. The latter condition is most readily attained by coating the paper with an excess of wax which forms a continuous film, and the product is exemplified by the familiar bread wrapper paper. The dry-waxed paper contains less wax and very

[1] Pieczalski, *Compt. rend.*, **162**:784 (1916).
[2] Dean, *op. cit.*; Thorpe, *J. Inst. Petrol.*, **37**:275 (1951); *Ind. Paper World*, **27**:1678 (1946).

much less on the surface; an example is that used in making paper drinking cups; the waxed paper is allowed to stand at a fairly high temperature while the wax migrates from the surface to the interstices between the paper fibers.   The same type of material is employed as butcher's paper. Paper milk bottles are ordinarily heavily waxed on the surface, since mechanical strength as well as waterproofness are desired, but packages for frozen foods are more thoroughly impregnated.   While crystalline wax makes up the bulk of that used for paper treating, it is now widely customary to blend microcrystalline waxes and even additives such as polyethylene to attain needed properties.   For instance, the conventional paraffin is too brittle at low temperatures to be satisfactory as an impregnant for frozen-food containers; however, a judicious admixture of soft microcrystalline wax will give desired flexibility.   Partial and less efficient waxing may be effected by adding soft microcrystalline wax to the paper pulp of which containers are made; this obviously can merge into ordinary sizing, the wax being emulsified with the size.

The most heavily waxed papers may contain as much as 30 or 35 per cent of wax by weight; the dry-waxed products probably not over 25 per cent.

Most of the other uses listed for waxes do not require extended comment.   Softer and amorphous waxes and petrolatums are blended as required to give the desired physical properties.   Petroleum waxes are in general not as satisfactory for polishing purposes as the harder vegetable waxes; for medicines and cosmetics the softer, completely odorless, and tasteless products are needed.[1]   Beverage-can linings, because of the low temperatures at which they are stored in use, require flexible microcrystalline products; obviously they must be refined to the point of complete tastelessness.

Waxes for insulating purposes are usually of the microcrystalline variety.   They may be applied as coatings, in which case they serve also a protective purpose; as impregnants for fabric or paper; and either alone or in admixture with asphalt, as "potting" materials.   A rather unexpected application is as an impregnant for ceramic insulators, where they improve moisture resistance.   In all these cases as high melting a wax as possible is used, because of the high local temperatures likely to be encountered and because electrical properties change near the melting point.

There are not many uses for low melting point waxes.   Paper caps for glass milk bottles are impregnated with a low melting point, soft wax which is often mixed with tasteless white oil.   Match sticks are impregnated with wax which may melt as low as 110 to 112°F, and need not be of low

[1] Myddleton, *J. Inst. Petrol.*, **37**:45 (1951).

oil content or highly refined. The waxing of trees, bushes, and nursery stock in handling or under other circumstances in which loss of moisture is undesirable has become rather widespread.[1] The coating of fruits and vegetables for both appearance and preservation is now well established.[2] Wax is compounded into rubber because of its tendency to migrate to the surface of the finished article, where it exerts a protective action against deterioration by light and oxygen. The coating of wooden packages, butter and beer casks, and the dressing of fabrics and leather with waxes are rather familiar. The similar coating of masonry for weatherproofing was practiced many years ago (Cleopatra's Needle in New York) but has been lost sight of in recent years; however, the matter has been the subject of a technical study.[3]

XIV-5. Properties of Waxes.[4] The important chemical properties of the petroleum waxes are those related to the chemical stability of the compounds contained. While it has been customary in the past to regard the paraffin hydrocarbons as quite stable, they possess considerable reactivity (see Chap. III). Alkylation and isomerization of lower paraffin hydrocarbons are standard refinery processes. Attack on higher paraffins by microorganisms is now well known.[5] Stability is a relative term and the rather small departures from complete stability mentioned here can be quite important in application. Prolonged standing at temperatures much above the melting point, as may occur in the shipping of molten wax in insulated tank cars, can cause incipient oxidation, with impairment of taste and odor. Resistance to oxidation is estimated by heating tests followed by observations of odor and taste, or more quantitatively, by determination of peroxide content. Likewise, while well-refined waxes are stable to light, long exposure is undesirable for the same reason.

The physical properties of the component hydrocarbons will determine those of the waxes, except as the influence of mixing may enter. The most widely used physical constant is the melting point; this for refined crystalline waxes is the temperature determined by an extended plateau in the cooling curve, and for the amorphous waxes and petrolatums the

---

[1] *New York Times*, Oct. 23, 1938.

[2] Claypool and King, *Proc. Am. Soc. Hort. Sci.*, **37**:443, 448 (1940); **38**:261 (1941). Mack and Janer, *Food Research*, **7**:38 (1942). Winston, *Ind. Eng. Chem.*, **26**:762 (1944).

[3] Kessler, *J. Research Natl. Bur. Standards*, **14**:317 (1935).

[4] On relations between applications and properties of waxes, see Ferris, "Science of Petroleum," vol. V, pp. 3, 177, Oxford University Press, New York and London, 1955; also Yates, *Paper, Film, and Foil Converter*, **30**(3):21 (1956).

[5] Rogers, *Nature*, **152**:105 (1943). Heitzmann, Girard, and Bouchard, *Compt. rend. soc. biol.*, **142**:815 (1948). Zobell, *Advances in Enzymol.*, **10**:443 (1950). Beerstecher, "Petroleum Microbiology," p. 185, Elsevier Press, Inc., Houston, Tex., 1954.

temperature at which a first drop will fall from a thermometer.[1] The electrical resistivity and the dielectric strength are important in insulating service; petroleum waxes show values in the same range as average synthetic plastics, about 2.5×10^6 volts per cm.[2] The contraction on solidification is important; it is mentioned below. A purely practical related consideration is the tendency to fractional crystallization and the consequent possibility of segregation. This occurs because waxes are made up of compounds melting at different temperatures. A difference of 0.32°C in melting point has been reported for different parts of a large cake of wax.[3] This tendency is more noticeable for lower-melting waxes of high oil content; a barrel of slack wax may solidify with a soft, semiliquid core.

A set of largely empirical but important properties has been recognized as expressing the extent to which waxes meet service requirements. These are:

Color and transparency
Gloss
Hardness
Tensile strength
Sealing strength
Blocking tendency

Color of wax is of course determined by the degree of refining applied; it is usually improved by a final percolation through fuller's earth or preferably bauxite. A transparent wax is preferred, and a good color is necessary for such a product. The content of air and oil is influential, but the rate of cooling is also important; slow cooling is considered desirable. Mottling, as mentioned above, seems to be dependent on both crystal form and content of air. Since the transparency of wax is important chiefly in coated papers, it may be that the index of refraction of the wax should match fairly well that of the paper fiber to be coated. Gloss is also a complex property of both wax and paper. It can be manipulated by the procedure applied in cooling the film on the paper.[4]

Measurement of consistency of waxes is not very well developed; hardness, ductility, flexibility, and similar properties seem to be involved. Hardness has been measured by penetration methods[5] or with the Abra-

---

[1] ASTM D87–42 and D 127–49, respectively.   See Chap. IV.

[2] Austin and Pelzer, *J. Inst. Elec. Engrs.* (*London*), **93**(I):525 (1946).

[3] Breth, *Petroleum Z.*, **7**:196 (1911).

[4] Harrison, *Paint Manuf.*, **20**:277, 293 (1950).   Kinsel and Phillips, *Petrol. Refiner*, **28**(4):147 (1949).

[5] ASTM D 937–49T.   A more recent proposal is the modulus of rigidity, Mazee, *J. Inst. Petrol.*, **43**:21 (1957).

ham consistometer;[1] ductility figures may be obtained by the ASTM apparatus employed for asphalts[2] and flexibility has been estimated by repeated bending, to the break point, of rods of the test material. Obviously these latter tests are applicable chiefly to the microcrystalline products.[3] Tensile strength is closely related to consistency data. It is perhaps the best standardized of the ordinary wax tests.[4] A well-refined wax will show values by the conventional method ranging from 300 to 400 lb per sq in. at 70°F. Without too clear understanding, it is generally agreed that high tensile strength is an indication of desirability for waxes intended for use in coating paper and paper containers. Tensile strength is highly sensitive to oil content, probably because in refined waxes the oil content is apparently all intercrystalline. Additions of microcrystalline waxes and resins like polyethylene raise tensile strength.

Sealing strength and blocking tendency, the tendency for wax surfaces to stick together (the latter when sticking is undesired and occurs during handling or storage), are closely related. Both are influenced by the paper and the method of coating. Sealing is rated by tests in which a seal is pulled apart and the force required is measured.[5] Blocking, or sticking together of waxed surfaces at some time after solidification is similarly affected by the thickness of the wax film and the conditions of waxing. It is measured by empirical methods which attempt to reproduce the conditions of storage. As with tensile strength, there seems to be a rough inverse relation between sealing and blocking on one hand and content of oil on the other.[6]

Some of the confusion about physical properties of paraffin waxes may be caused by the low melting point, with consequently easy change of state. The variations of specific gravity and of coefficient of expansion with temperature and with melting point make it desirable, in all handling operations, to measure the wax by weight or to refer all calculations to the specific gravity of the melted product. Much of the difficulty is of course due to the tendency of the waxes to crystallize in different forms

[1] Abraham, "Asphalts and Allied Substances," p. 668, D. Van Nostrand Company, Inc., Princeton, N.J., 1929.

[2] ASTM D 113–44; see also *Petrol. Refiner*, **27**:334 (1948).

[3] Schindler, *Paper Trade J.*, **126**(13):58 (1948).

[4] Espach, *U.S. Bur. Mines Bull.* 388, 1935; ASTM D 1320–54. For the designing of the briquette mold, see Tappi–ASTM Technical Committee on Petroleum Wax, Section I—Strength Tests. *Report of Activities—Tappi Divisions and Committees*, *Tappi*, **37**(4):154A (1954). *Proc. ASTM*, vol. 52, Appendix VII, pp. 371–376, 1952. *ASTM Bull.* 194, p. 31, December, 1953.

[5] Funk, Davis, Hanson, and Segessen, *Anal. Chem.*, **22**:179 (1950). Capell, Ridenour, and Templin, *Tappi*, **34**:515 (1951).

[6] Other approaches to the problem of measuring the various manifestations of strength in waxes are the test for modulus of rupture [Hoag, *Tappi*, **33**:343 (1950)] and that for breaking strength [McLaren, *Ind. Eng. Chem.*, **42**:2134 (1950)].

under different conditions; inclusion of air has also been blamed.[1]   When melted waxes only are considered, the gravity relations are not different from those of other liquid petroleum fractions; for the solids the variations are greater.   Specific gravity increases with the melting point and of course decreases with rise in temperature.   Typical figures are given by Morris and Adkins:

Melting point, °F	Specific gravity, 60°F	Specific gravity, 130°F
123	0.9068	0.784
127	0.920	
130	......	0.778

The cubical coefficient of expansion, as given in the older literature, extends over a range as wide as 0.0008 to 0.005; the following are for a wax melting at 60°C.

Temperature range, °C	Coefficiency of expansion
0 to 15.5	0.000576
15.5 to 37.7	0.000704
37.7 to 48.5	0.00258
48.5 to 61.0	0.00440
Melting point to boiling point for this melted wax	0.00106

Figures supplied by Carpenter[2] for a variety of waxes vary from 0.001 to 0.009 over the temperature range from 0 to 100°C except at the melting point, where the coefficients are nearer to 0.01 to 0.07.   These variations are not surprising, considering the uncertain purity of the materials and the differences in methods of measurement.   Careful determinations by Templin[3] on refined waxes in the ordinary melting range show:

Coefficients of expansion

Liquid..............	0.0010
A solid*...........	0.0014
B solid*............	0.0008

* The A solid exists between the solidification and the transition; the B solid, below the transition.

Change of volume on melting, per cent..................................	11.0
Change of volume at transition, per cent..............................	3.5
From low-temperature transition to liquid at the crystal point temperature, per cent........................	16.0
Specific volume at the crystal point.....................................	1.2789
Specific volume at transition point.......................................	1.1413

[1] Morris and Adkins, *Ind. Eng. Chem.*, **19**:301 (1927).

[2] *J. Inst. Petrol. Technologists*, **12**:301 (1926).

[3] Made in the authors' laboratory, *Ind. Eng. Chem.*, **48**:154 (1956).

For the corresponding pure paraffin hydrocarbons, Templin found much the same figures:

Liquid coefficient of expansion............. 0.0011
Expansion on melting, per cent...... about 11

However, the expansion on transition for the pure hydrocarbons is greater, namely, about 7 per cent.

The solubility of waxes in various solvents has been a subject of considerable disagreement; this may be caused largely by the failure of investigators to recognize the mixed character of the waxes as a major source of error. Not only will waxes differ in composition, but even with the same wax it is important, in determining solubility, to keep constant the relative amounts of wax and solvent, the time of contact, and similar details. The amount of (perhaps) soft wax dissolved out of a given sample will almost certainly vary with the size of the sample and the time of contact with the solvent. This is indicated by the following figures for one wax:

Approximate concentration hot solution	*Solubility, g per* 100 *g solution*
0.3	0.294
0.9	0.596
1.8	0.818

The solvent was acetone and the temperature 27°C.[1] Approximate solubility figures for a refined wax melting at 124°F are as follows: the concentration of solute was kept constant at 9.8 g per 100 g solvent and the temperature was 27°C.

Solvent	*G dissolved per* 100 *g solution*
Ethylene dichloride..................	1.79
Carbon tetrachloride................	35.8
Benzene...........................	31.7
Ethyl alcohol 95 per cent............	0.2
n-Butyl alcohol....................	3.5

In petroleum fractions such as naphtha solvents, the ordinary waxes are soluble at 0°C to the extent of about 3 per cent and at 20° to about 8 or 9 per cent.[2]

The actual solubility of waxes in the petroleum fractions with which they are associated in the crude oils is difficult to determine, because of the mixed character of both the waxes and the oils. By way of indica-

[1] Determined by B. L. Souther in the authors' laboratory.

[2] Empirical relations between the properties of the wax and the petroleum solvent have been published by Berne-Allen and Work, *Ind. Eng. Chem.*, **30**:806 (1938). A nomograph based on the same figures has been supplied by D. S. Davis, *Ind. Eng. Chem.*, **32**:1293 (1940).

tion, it may be mentioned that the wax distillate prepared from a wax-bearing crude and separated for wax-recovery purposes may contain about 20 per cent of wax; this latter is, however, a wide range product and the distillate will throw wax out of solution on slight cooling.[1]

As indicated above, a small oil content in a refined wax remains between the crystals, affecting the properties in a rather marked way; when oil is added to a microcrystalline wax, it goes into solution, exerting a plasticizing effect.[2]   It is not surprising that a good deal of attention has been devoted to analytical determination of oil content of wax products.   A mechanical pressing at 60°F between linen and blotting paper was practiced quite early.[3]   The earliest recrystallization method was probably that of Holde, with an ether-alcohol solvent; its chief fault lay in a failure to hold in solution the so-called resins.   Acetone was tried by Wyant,[4] and at present good results are being obtained with methyl ethyl ketone, separation and washing of the crystals being effected at 25°F.[5]

The effect of dissolved paraffin on the properties of oils in which it is dissolved has been considered by Dean and Cooke[6] and by Bjerregaard.[7] The former studied only viscosity, finding that the added paraffin acted as would an oil which, at the same temperature, possessed a viscosity equal to that of the melted paraffin; it decreased the viscosity of heavier oils and increased the viscosity of lighter oils.   Bjerregaard found identical results with regard to viscosity; the specific gravity of the oils that he examined was lowered by addition of paraffin, and the freezing point (pour point) was raised.   Two per cent of added paraffin was found capable of causing a rise in freezing point of 30°F.

XIV-6. Petrolatum.   Petrolatum constitutes a salve-like residuum obtained from paraffin-base oils; it is defined and described[8] as a purified

---

[1] For rough figures on the wax content of a variety of crude oils, see Nelson, *Oil Gas J.*, **53**(40):127 (1955).

[2] Nelson and Stewart, *Ind. Eng. Chem.*, **41**:2231 (1949).

[3] Bacon and Hamor, "American Petroleum Industry," vol. II, p. 766, McGraw-Hill Book Company, Inc., New York, 1916.   Hamor and Padgett, "The Examination of Petroleum," p. 176, McGraw-Hill Book Company, Inc., New York, 1920.

[4] *U.S. Bur. Mines Tech. Paper* 368, 1925.

[5] ASTM D 721–53T.   For short-cut methods, see Lee and Kalichevsky, *Ind. Eng. Chem., Anal. Ed.*, **14**:767 (1942).   Wiberly and Rather, *Anal. Chem.*, **20**:972 (1948). Layton, *Anal. Chem.*, **22**:1168 (1950).

[6] *Ind. Eng. Chem.*, **14**:410 (1922).

[7] *Ibid.*, p. 215.

[8] By the U.S. Pharmacopoeia, **XIV**:448 (1950).   It is further described as "insoluble in water, almost insoluble in cold or hot alcohol and in cold dehydrated alcohol.   It is freely soluble in benzene, in carbon disulfide, in chloroform, and in oil of turpentine. It is soluble in ether, in petroleum benzin, and in most fixed or volatile oils, the degree of solubility in these solvents varying with the composition of the petrolatum.   The specific gravity is between 0.815 and 0.860 at 60°C.   The melting (drop) point lies between 38° and 60°C."

semisolid mixture of hydrocarbons obtained from petroleum; it is an unctuous mass, light yellow to amber in color, not more than slightly fluorescent, even when melted; it is transparent in thin layers, amorphous, and practically free of odor and taste. The long list of requirements for a satisfactory petrolatum is necessary because of the practice, more common in Europe than in America, of preparing synthetic petrolatum by mixing high-melting paraffin waxes from lignite tar, etc., with liquid petroleum oils; the resulting materials differ from the genuine product in several respects.

The early method of manufacture from residua of paraffin-base oils is described by Redwood.[1] It is now made exclusively as a by-product of the preparation of dewaxed lubricating oils of high viscosity. The methods by which such oils are dewaxed to low pour points have been described in Sec. XIV-3. The wax discharges from centrifugal dewaxing or the wax cakes from solvent processing are purified, usually by percolation through decolorizing clay or bauxite until the color is sufficiently light and the taste and odor reduced sufficiently for the purpose in mind; obviously the standards for pharmaceutical purposes are higher than for industrial outlets. It can be surmised that petrolatums are made up of normal and isoparaffins of high molecular weight partly dissolved and partly suspended in, in any case plasticized by, semiliquid oils containing substituted naphthenes and aromatics, viscous enough to inhibit any tendency of the waxes to crystallize and thus render the petrolatum grainy. Synthetic petrolatums prepared from crystalline waxes and liquid oils, particularly those of too low viscosity, are likely to assume a granular structure in storage. In addition it is reported that the synthetic products change viscosity more suddenly with change of temperature than do the natural materials. Even a well-refined petrolatum is slightly susceptible to oxidation, especially under exposure to light; it is not unusual to see a layer of dark color extending downward from the top surface of a sample stored without precautions, suggestive of advancing oxidation from the contact with air.

Petrolatums are employed widely as external medicinal agents and as constituents of salves and ointments. They can be emulsified in water by addition of higher alcohols, such as cetyl alcohol, and the resulting stable emulsions are useful for pharmaceutical purposes. The less highly refined grades are employed as rust-preventing coatings for metals or as constituents of antirust agents. They are sometimes applied as impregnants of the paper insulation of power cables and are useful in the mixing and stabilizing of nitroglycerin smokeless powders; here they are believed to react with the oxides of nitrogen given off in small quantities during periods of storage.

[1] "Petroleum," 3d ed., pp. 2, 130, Charles Griffin & Co., Ltd., London, 1913.

CHAPTER XV

Petroleum Asphalts

CHEMICAL AND PHYSICAL COMPOSITION

Asphaltic substances are widely distributed in nature, usually in the form of mineral deposits impregnated with bitumen.[1] Deposits containing less than, say, 10 per cent of mineral ash are, however, comparatively rare; they are found in Venezuela, California, and to some extent in the Middle East, and ordinarily are closely associated with liquid petroleum. The fact that asphaltic materials of various kinds are usually plentiful in petroleum-producing areas suggests rather strongly that asphalts are derived from petroleum or that the two have a common origin.[2] This supposition is strengthened by the fact that asphalts can be manufactured from petroleum by simple processes which could conceivably have occurred in nature.

XV-1. Chemical Composition. A logical arrangement of the natural asphaltic materials gives, as with the coals, a sequence of increasing hardness, insolubility, and nonvolatility; in addition the asphalts become more infusible with this sequence. At one end of the scale are liquid petroleums of asphaltic character, and at the other are materials like albertite, resembling coal and containing not much more than 5 per cent soluble in the most potent solvents. A simple tabulation can be arranged as follows:

Asphaltic petroleum, liquid, entirely soluble in petroleum naphtha, of specific gravity not over 1.0. Examples are Mexican and California crude oils of asphaltic type.

Asphalts, semisolid to solid, melting typically about 150 to 200°F, from

---

[1] See, for instance, Ball, *C.A.*, **38**:1098 (1944). Holloway, *C.A.*, **41**:271 (1947). Wenger and Hubbard, *C.A.*, **46**:6809 (1952). *U.S. Bur. Mines Rept. Inves.* 4817, p. 11, 1952. The name bitumen is restricted in this discussion to solid and semisolid materials of this class.

[2] On chemical differences between natural and petroleum asphalts, see Martin, *Petroleum*, **4**:37 (1941). Grader, *Oel u. Kohle*, **38**:807 (1942). Sartori, *C.A.*, **47**:6642 (1952).

10 to 70 per cent soluble in petroleum naphtha, and 70 to 98 per cent soluble in carbon disulfide; specific gravity 1.0 to 1.10 and exceptionally 1.20. Products of Bermudez and of Trinidad after removal of mineral matter are examples.

Asphaltites,[1] hard solids of melting point well above 250 and ranging, for grahamite, as high as 600°F. The specific gravity is not above 1.20; the solubility in petroleum naphtha lies between 0 and 60 per cent, and in carbon disulfide between 50 and 99 per cent. Examples are gilsonite and grahamite.

The final stage in this series is illustrated by such bitumens as wurtzilite and albertite; these have specific gravities as high as 1.25, they swell and decompose before the melting temperature is reached, are to all intents insoluble in petroleum naphtha and not more than 10 per cent soluble in carbon disulfide.[2]

The chemical composition of these substances remains very uncertain. It is important in this instance because there is much reason to suppose that the artificial asphalts made from petroleum by distillation or by air blowing resemble the natural asphalts closely as to constitution. Elementary analysis yields little information. The carbon content of asphalts, asphaltites, and asphaltic pyrobitumens shows only a slight and irregular tendency to increase in the order given—the extreme range is 80 to 87 per cent—the hydrogen content differs little, and the data on proportions of acids and other oxygen compounds are not complete enough for comparison. The saponification value, however, does show a sharp decrease as the series is ascended. Much of the difficulty, of course, lies in the inadequacy and possible inaccuracy of many of the published analyses. Typical data from Abraham are shown in Table XV-1.

A basic difficulty in such classifications lies in the fact that truly homogeneous asphaltic products probably do not exist in nature. There is inevitably a good deal of overlapping and identity of substance. For example, it was customary in the earlier literature[3] to recognize the presence of several essentially equivalent liquid or semiliquid constituents: mineral oil, petrolenes, and maltenes, each somewhat arbitrarily defined. No distinction between these is now made and a content of petroleum-like mineral oil is assumed; it is likely, however, that such oil is of the type regarded as geologically or chemically young. That is,

---

[1] Name taken from Abraham, "Asphalts and Allied Substances," 5th ed., vol. I, p. 61, D. Van Nostrand Company, Inc., Princeton, N.J., 1954.

[2] This class is named asphaltic pyrobitumen by Abraham; his definition is so worded as to include bituminous and anthracite coal. The name seems unsuitable because it implies the action of heat in the genesis of the substance, whereas what Abraham almost certainly meant is resistance to heating.

[3] Richardson, *J. Soc. Chem. Ind.*, **17**:13 (1898); *Ind. Eng. Chem.*, **8**:493 (1916).

there is ordinarily present a high proportion of aromatics and naphthenes, with more sulfur and nitrogen compounds than are normal for a paraffinic petroleum.[1]

The various proximate constituents of an asphalt may then be defined as follows:

Mineral Oil. This is the material soluble in standardized petroleum naphtha (precipitation naphtha, normal pentane, or isopentane)[2] and not

TABLE XV-1

	Asphalts			Asphaltites and higher			
	Trinidad	Alberta	Ber-mudez	Gilsonite	Glance pitch	Wurtzilite	Albertite
Carbon, per cent......	80 to 82	84.5	83	85	80 to 85	79 to 80	83 to 87
Hydrogen, per cent....	10 to 11	11.2	10.8	8.5 to 10	7 to 12	10 to 12	9 to 13
Sulfur, per cent.......	6 to 8	2.7	5.9	0.3 to 0.5	2 to 8	4 to 6	0.4 to 1.2
Nitrogen, per cent.....	0.6	0.04	0.7	2.0 to 2.8	0 to 2	1.8 to 2.2	0.5 to 3.0
Oxygen, per cent.....	....	......	....	0 to 2.0		....	1.9 to 2.2
Saponification number.	40	......	28	5.6	Trace		
Acids, per cent........	6.4	......	3.5				
Anhydrides, per cent...	3.9	......	2.0				
Asphaltenes, per cent..	33 to 37	......	35				
Resins, per cent.......	23 to 26	......	14				
Oil, per cent..........	31 to 32	......	40				
Soluble in naphtha....	62 to 64	78	60 to 75	10 to 60	20 to 50	0 to 2	0.5 to 2.0
Soluble in CS$_2$.........	56 to 57	97	92 to 97	> 98	> 95	5 to 10	2 to 10

removable from such solution by adsorbents like fuller's earth, active charcoal, or silica gel. As indicated above, this oil is not likely to be very different from any rather cyclic petroleum fraction of similar molecular weight containing the usual constituents, including even paraffin waxes.[3]

Resins. These are considered to be present in true solution when the asphalt is dispersed in pentane or petroleum ether, but are adsorbable by a surface active material, such as fuller's earth; after mechanically held oil has been displaced from the adsorbent by washing with more of the solvent, the resins may be removed by a more powerful desorbent, such as chloroform or carbon disulfide. Physically the resins are stringy semisolids of brownish color, melting below about 100°C, and it may be supposed that they resemble the resins separated from lubricating oil

[1] O'Donnell, *Anal. Chem.*, **23**:894 (1951).

[2] Hillman and Barnett, *Proc. ASTM*, **37**(II):559 (1937). Hubbard and Stanfield, *Anal. Chem.*, **20**:463 (1948).

[3] The latter can be removed by crystallizing from a good dewaxing solvent: methyl isobutyl ketone, Knowles and Levin, *Ind. Eng. Chem., Anal. Ed.*, **13**:314 (1941); acetone–methylene chloride mixture, Hoiberg and Garris, *Ind. Eng. Chem., Anal. Ed.*, **16**:294 (1944).

fractions by extraction with aqueous alcohol.[1] There is no good reason
to doubt that they also resemble the resinous constituents recovered from
oxidized lubricating oil by Garner, who employed a similar adsorption
technique.[2] As indicated, they are desorbed by and soluble in the more
potent solvents, but only slightly in acetone. The content of sulfur and
nitrogen is higher than that of conventional petroleum oils, the molecular
weight varies with that of the oil medium from which they are recovered,
and the ratio of carbon to hydrogen is of the order of 8:1.[3] Elementary
analysis indicates that a typical resin from a distillate might contain:

Per cent

Carbon..............	80–82
Hydrogen...........	9–10
Sulfur..............	1–2
Oxygen.............	5–7

The material soluble in normal pentane and insoluble in liquid propane
from an entire crude oil (Middle East) was observed, in the authors'
laboratory, to have an oxygen content of about 1 per cent and an ebullioscopic molecular weight of the order of 800. As indicated, resins resembling those under discussion can be made by oxidation of gas oil or lubricating oil fractions, and further oxidation of resins from either source
yields materials resembling asphaltenes from authentic asphalts. It is
customary to refer to the asphaltic resins as neutral resins. This is probably because a content of resins can be isolated from an asphaltic material—even though acidic substances had been removed previously—usually by extraction with an excess of ethyl alcohol. When the resins are
recovered by propane precipitation, the product will contain "asphaltic"
or "asphaltogenic" acids and their anhydrides. These can be regarded
as naphthenic acids of high molecular weight and resinous character.[4]
The content of such acids is low in petroleum asphalts, but may reach
10 per cent or more in natural asphalts.[5] Presumably they should influ-

---

[1] Holde and Eickmann, *Petroleum Z.*, **2**:1077 (1907).

[2] *J. Inst. Petrol. Technologists*, **7**:98 (1921).

[3] Usefully summarized by Murphy, *J. Inst. Petrol.*, **31**:475 (1945).

[4] It is perhaps significant that commercial naphthenic acids are isolated from the
lower rather than the higher molecular weight range of petroleum fractions. The
upper limit for molecular weight of the acids themselves is about 400; these latter
are rather viscous and those from still heavier stocks are apt to be rather gummy.

[5] Sachanen, "Chemical Constituents of Petroleum," p. 390, Reinhold Publishing
Corporation, New York, 1945. It has been pointed out by Bogomolov [*J. Appl.
Chem., U.S.S.R.*, **27**:1012 (1954)] that the ratio of neutral to acid increases with age of
asphalt deposit; this seems reasonable, since it may be recalled that decarboxylation
is a conventional reaction of organic acids.

ence the properties of asphalts containing them in about the same way as the neutral resins, except to a greater extent as they are more polar in character.

Asphaltenes. These are quantitatively the most important constituents of ordinary asphalts. They are defined as those substances precipitated from a suspension of the asphalt in a large excess, say 20 volumes, of a standardized petroleum naphtha;[1] a pure chemical is to be preferred as precipitant and normal pentane is now widely used. The definition given is not a rigid one, since it will be necessary later to indicate that the asphaltene precipitate so made can contain other components separable by still other solvents. The asphaltenes melt with swelling and decomposition over the range 180 to 280°C; they are soluble in benzene, carbon disulfide, and chloroform, while almost insoluble in alcohol and paraffinic hydrocarbons of low molecular weight, and only slightly so in ether and acetone. They contain rather high proportions of sulfur and oxygen, and show on analysis a carbon-hydrogen ratio of about 10 to 1. They may be converted by hydrogenation to resinous materials, and, under sufficiently severe conditions, to liquid hydrocarbons. Asphaltenes are apparently not volatile; where they have been found in distillates, they can safely be attributed to entrainment or to subsequent oxidation.

Analyses made by Thurston and Knowles[2] indicate that the asphaltenes from different sources differ little in chemical composition. Typical figures are as follows:

Source	Carbon	Hydrogen	C/H	Sulfur	Ash	O₂ by diff.
Mexican:						
Blown..............	81.3	7.9	10.4	8.0	0.2	2.7
Steam-reduced.......	79.7	7.8	10.2	8.2	0.3	3.8
Gulf Coast:						
Blown..............	83.9	8.2	10 2	1.7	1.2	4.8
Grosny asphaltenes*....	70	7.3	9.5	9.5	...	11.1

* Barisov, Zal'tsman, and Romanva, *C.A.*, **47**:5103 (1953). They also give a figure of 1.7 for nitrogen.

Nellensteyn[3] has reported that asphaltenes, when subjected to destructive distillation, yield a wax tailings, or picene, fraction containing the condensed aromatics formerly produced by the now obsolescent coking distillation of reduced crude oils, and also that chlorination of asphaltenes

[1] Precipitation naphtha, ASTM D 91–52. A material of specified gravity, boiling range, and aniline point, thus of controlled chemical composition and solvent power.
[2] *Ind. Eng. Chem.*, **28**:91 (1936).
[3] *C.A.*, **41**:7088, 7089 (1947).

resulted in rather vigorous reaction, one of the products of which was benzene hexachloride. The force of both arguments apparently is that the asphaltenes contain aromatic nuclei, probably of condensed structure. Similarly Rakovski[1] has suggested that asphaltenes contain rather high proportions of phenols and carboxylic acid groups. On the basis of a supposed relation between the black solids derived from heating of humic acids and the petroleum asphaltenes, Kazakov and Grigor'eva[2] proposed that asphaltenes are made up predominantly of cyclic groups, particularly of high-molecular-weight phenols.

Carbenes and Carboids. Not too much is known about these classes of materials. They are ordinarily defined as those substances insoluble in *n*-pentane but soluble, respectively, in carbon disulfide and chloroform. One concept of their nature may be illustrated by the fact that Sachanen makes carboids equivalent to what he calls "free coke." This is probably going too far, since both carboids and carbenes seem generally to contain less carbon and more oxygen, sulfur, and similar extraneous elements than the "carbons." It is, however, a matter of terminology. Carbenes and carboids apparently occur in quantity only when the asphaltic material has been subjected to prolonged or rather severe heating or other equivalent condensing influences.[3] They can be formed from asphaltenes by oxidation, and in consequence show a rather high oxygen content and a higher saponification value than the asphaltenes. Thurston and Knowles observed that, among the various class constituents of an asphalt, the asphaltenes showed the highest absorption of oxygen. The asphaltenes and the carboids formed from them differed in composition as follows:

Material	Carbon	Hydrogen	Sulfur	Ash	Nitrogen	Oxygen
Asphaltenes............	81.5	7.5	8.6	0.5	1.16	0.7
Carboids..............	74.2	5.1	8.1	0.5	1.10	10.8

The low acid values for both materials and the high saponification figure for the carboids indicate formation of esters on oxidation. It should be noted that from a qualitative standpoint, the carbenes and carboids represent successively the last stages in the progression of insolubility and infusibility in the sequences from liquid oils to the hardest asphalts. They are thus the constituents which are supposed to make up a consider-

[1] *C.A.*, **47**:5663 (1953).

[2] *C.A.*, **47**:3541 (1953).

[3] Work in the authors' laboratory indicates that carbenes and carboids are not present in the conventional crudes well known today, even those of asphaltic character.

able part of substances like grahamite and albertite, and to be responsible for their characteristic properties.

It should be kept in mind that the stages pictured in the progression may have no real existence. By analogy with the changes in the composition and molecular weight of petroleum fractions of increasing boiling point, it would be expected that asphaltic compounds would vary gradually in properties; if a smooth gradation of solvents could be applied, the curves of changing properties of the asphaltic substances might presumably be quite smooth also, without discontinuities.

No good explanation of the changes in chemical composition which probably cause the changes in physical properties has yet been offered. It is known, as mentioned, that the composition of the materials at the liquid end of the series is not far from that of the residuum of an ordinary cyclic petroleum; also that the ratio of carbon to hydrogen rises as the

TABLE XV-2. CRACKED RESIDUA

Fraction		Percentage of original residue	Chemical analyses, per cent							Density, 20°C	Average molecular weight
			Carbon	Hydrogen	Nitrogen	Sulfur	Ash	Oxygen	Carbon–hydrogen ratio		
Isopentane insoluble	Hexane-soluble*	4.2	88.1	7.4	1.8	1.3	0.07	1.30	11.9	1.1 to 1.2	490‡
	CCl₄-soluble†	6.3	83.9	6.2	2.2	0.3	0.10	6.73	13.5	1.18	830‡–850§
	Benzene-soluble	2.0	86.8	6.1	2.3	0.8	0.17	3.75	14.2	1.19	880§
	CS₂-soluble†	1.0	87.1	6.0	2.1	0.9	0.25	3.68	14.5	. . . .	817§
	Pyridine-soluble†	2.0	83.7	5.6	3.2	0.9	0.22	6.31	15.1	1.24	860§

* Semisolids at room temperature.
† Powdery solids; the CCl₄ solubles melt at high temperatures with decomposition and swelling; the benzene-solubles also decompose, although with less swelling; and the carbenes and carboids neither melt nor swell.
‡ In benzene, at the boiling point; and in naphthalene, at the freezing point.
§ In naphthalene, at the freezing point.

substance becomes less like liquid oil; this can most readily be explained by an increase in the proportion of ring structures in the molecules. It has been shown, however, by Hillman and Barnett[1] that this increase in carbon-hydrogen ratio usually occurs at the same time that the proportions of sulfur, nitrogen, and oxygen are rising. The figures in Tables XV-2 and XV-3 show that such rise in foreign elements occurs in all cases studied except for the sulfur content of cracked residua. It should be recognized of course that the analyses were made on asphalt-containing residua rather than on native asphalts, but the figures are still persuasive.

[1] *Proc. ASTM,* **37**(II):559 (1940).

The idea that oxidation[1] may have been responsible for the conversion of petroleum to asphalt rests probably on the observation that in certain well-known cases (Trinidad, for instance) the presence of an asphalt deposit seems pretty well connected with the migration of an asphaltic liquid petroleum from depth to the earth surface; here it became exposed to evaporation and atmospheric oxidation.   Another supporting observation is that the differences in composition between the several asphaltic individuals in the progression to hard insoluble substances can be duplicated fairly well by oxidizing liquid hydrocarbon starting materials in the laboratory.

TABLE XV-3. STRAIGHT-RUN RESIDUA

Fraction	Percentage of original residue	Chemical analyses, per cent							Density, 20°C	Average molecular weight
		Carbon	Hydrogen	Nitrogen	Sulfur	Ash	Oxygen	Carbon-hydrogen ratio		
Isopentane-soluble (Cut number 1)	15.80	86.7	9.7	1.29	0.95	0.03	1.33	8.94	1.0479	616†
Hexane-solubles..	5.6	86.25	8.55	2.03	1.15	0.07	1.95	10.1	1.103	1,630*; 850‡
CCl₄-solubles.....	9.4	84.4	7.6	2.24	1.33	0.97	3.46	11.1	1.116	2,400†; 1,660‡

   * In benzene, at the boiling point.
   † In benzene, at the freezing point.
   ‡ In naphthalene, at the freezing point.

A fairly close analogy can perhaps be assumed for the action of sulfur This is made easier by the fact that elemental sulfur is not uncommon in certain oil-bearing formations, where it could react with hydrocarbons; whereas for the similar action with oxygen, the availability of atmospheric oxygen or that dissolved in ground waters must be invoked.[2]

The oxidation mechanism was developed actively by Marcusson.[3]   He suggested that asphaltogenic acids and their anhydrides were formed from hydrocarbons (of somewhat cyclic character) by the condensing oxidations illustrated.

[1] Sachanen has pointed out (*op. cit.*, p. 406) that thermal cracking can effect many of the condensation reactions attributable to oxidation.   While this is undoubtedly correct and applies to manufactured products, it has less meaning for natural asphalts.

[2] For early work on the chemical reactions of sulfur with hydrocarbons, see Friedmann, *Ber.*, **49**:50, 683, 1344, 1352, 1551 (1916); *Petroleum Z.*, **11**:693, 978 (1916).

[3] Numerous articles; see, for example, *Z. Angew. Chem.*, **31**(1):113, 119 (1918); *Mitt. kgl. Materialprüfungsamt,* **36**:209 (1918); *Chem. Ztg.*, **44**:43 (1920).

$$\begin{array}{c} R\!-\!CH_3 \\ \end{array} \quad \tfrac{1}{2}O_2 \;+\; xs\; O_2 \rightarrow \qquad \begin{array}{c} R\!-\!COOH \\ \\ R\!-\!COOH \end{array}$$

$$\begin{array}{c} R\!-\!COO\boxed{H} \\ \\ R\!-\!CO\boxed{OH} \end{array} \rightarrow \begin{array}{c} R\!-\!C \!\!\!\begin{array}{c} O \\ \diagup\!\!\!\diagdown \end{array} \\ \qquad\quad O \\ R\!-\!C\diagdown \\ \qquad O \end{array}$$

Presumably intermolecular as well as intramolecular anhydrides can be formed. The neutral resins can be pictured as forming by two further reactions.

1. Oxidation of hydrocarbons to hydroxyl derivatives, followed by separation of water to form an ether.

$$\begin{array}{c} R\!-\!O\;\boxed{H} \\ \\ R\!-\!\boxed{OH} \end{array} \rightarrow H_2O + \begin{array}{c} R \\ \diagdown \\ \qquad O \\ \diagup \\ R \end{array}$$

2. Inter- or intramolecular loss of carbon dioxide from an anhydride to yield a ketone.

$$\begin{array}{c} O \\ \| \\ R\!-\!C \\ \quad\diagdown \\ \qquad O \rightarrow CO_2 + \begin{array}{c} R \\ \diagdown \\ \quad C\!=\!O \\ \diagup \\ R \end{array} \\ \quad\diagup \\ R\!-\!C \\ \| \\ O \end{array}$$

The asphaltenes, carboids, and carbenes can be pictured as resulting from continuation of these reactions. If condensation is between different molecules, molecular weight will rise rapidly, and the oxygen or its equivalent sulfur can remain in positions permitting the oxonium type compounds with ferric and mercuric chlorides and sulfuric acid which Marcusson recognized. Just how high the molecular weights of these and members of the series may be is not known. Work in the authors' laboratory on unfractionated pentane-insoluble precipitates suggests maximum figures of the order of 40,000. Other estimates have been as high as 140,000.[1]

The above speculations about the role of oxygen could probably be confirmed or disproved by a careful kinetic study; oxygen distribution in final products has been observed by Knotnerus.[2] Analysis by improved methods for —COOR, —OH, and =CO groups accounted pretty closely for all the oxygen determined separately as the element. This indicated that ether formation was not a major reaction in asphalt formation by air blowing. The magnitude of the figures and separate infrared studies indicated that anhydrides and lactones were not important constituents. A typical set of analyses was as follows:

	COOH	COOR	OH	CO	Total
Oxygen content of asphaltenes from blown residuum..................	0.25	1.15	0.3	0.15	1.85

Esters are thus predominant, but the analyses do not indicate the course of the reaction.

While it has been widely assumed that the hydrocarbon nuclei involved are aromatic and probably even condensed aromatics, there is some question about this. Hillman and Barnett have pointed out that while the high-molecular-weight condensed polynuclear aromatics are rather insoluble in most known solvents, the asphaltic constituents up to and including the asphaltenes are appreciably soluble in a range of solvents. Furthermore, the prevailingly aromatic coal-tar products are soluble in concentrated sulfuric acid, while the asphalts are not soluble; in addition, the condensed polycyclic aromatics analyze to high carbon–hydrogen ratios for rather low molecular weights, while the asphaltic complexes show lower ratios for appreciably higher molecular weights. Thus

	Formula	Molecular weight	C:H
Anthracene.....................................	$C_{14}H_{10}$	178	16.8:1
Carbon tetrachloride–soluble straight-run asphalt...	....	2,400	11.1:1

It can further be observed that when sulfonic acids are formed from asphaltic materials, the calcium soaps of acids derived from substances of a wide range of molecular weight resemble one another closely in soapy quality and high solubility in water. These indications add up to the

[1] Pfeiffer and Saal, *J. Phys. Chem.*, **44**:138 (1940).
[2] *J. Inst. Petrol.*, **42**:355 (1956).

conclusions, first, that the asphaltic nuclei are not completely aromatic in structure and second, that they are probably built up of repeated simpler units strung together in much the same way that amino acids are assembled into proteins. A typical example provided by Hillman and Barnett is as follows:

$(C:H = 12.0)$

$(C:H = 13.5)$

Possible Structures of the Nuclei in Resins and Asphaltenes

The possibility of assembling groups like these by condensing oxidation is easily seen. Sulfur and oxygen atoms can be inserted, so linked as to have predictable properties corresponding to those of these elements in actual asphalts. Also the results of thermal cracking can be predicted to coincide approximately with what actually occurs with real asphalts.

XV-2. Physical Constitution. The rapid growth of the asphalt industry with the spread of the road systems has made necessary a workable method of describing and dealing with the properties of the various bituminous products. The chemical approach has not led to such a method, and the fact that many of the important properties are at least superficially physical in character has given impetus to a study of the physical constitution of the whole range of bitumens. While not as complete as might be desired, the results have been useful.

The idea that asphalts represent colloidal systems is credited to Nellensteyn,[1] but his concept seems to have been narrower than those of later students; he proposed that asphalts are made up of micelles protected by adsorbed resins and hydrocarbon-like materials, all distributed in a hydrocarbon medium. The nuclei of the component particles were supposed to be made up of elementary carbon, and the differences between the various stages in the sequence from petroleum oil to, say, albertite rested on the differences of amount and kind of protective adsorbates.

[1] *J. Inst. Petrol. Technologists,* **10**:311 (1924).

This proposal has not been fruitful and has been almost completely superseded. More workable ideas were developed by Mack.[1] He pointed out in the first place that the observed diffusion of benzene solutions of asphaltenes into aluminum naphthenate gels or the dialysis of similar solutions, performed by Hatschek, did not agree with the Nellensteyn concept. Sachanen has suggested that the relatively easy hydrogenation of asphaltic substances to homogeneous liquid oils is also a rather strong argument against the Nellensteyn hypothesis.

Mack recognized the asphalts as lyophilic colloids, observed the anomalies of flow which have since been used by others to distinguish the different types, and determined that the oils and resins, the adsorbed constituents, are the determining factors in setting up the physical nature of the various products. He did this by showing that the same asphaltene dispersed in various oil-resin combinations yielded different asphalts, while different asphaltenes dispersed in the same medium yielded essentially the same asphalt.

Nellensteyn's proposal has been modified by Dickinson and by Letters.[2] Both have conceived of the micelles of coal-tar pitches and bitumens as consisting of cores of highly cyclic, presumably polyaromatic hydrocarbons of high molecular weight, surrounded by layers of less aromatic compounds grading into naphthenic or even paraffinic structures. The observation that the amount of propane precipitate goes through a maximum as dilution with propane is increased[3] does not fit with an exclusively colloidal picture of structure.

The viscosity of asphalts is high, of the order of 10^3 to 10^{20} poises or greater.[4] Recognition and study of the abnormalities of flow in this high-viscosity range have supplied much of the useful information now available on the physical constitution of these substances.

In general, three classes of material, characterized by differences of flow, have been recognized, but it should be clear that no sudden transition exists, since the divisions merge one into the other. They may be listed as follows:[5]

[1] *Proc. Assoc. Asphalt Paving Technologists*, **5**:40 (1933); *J. Phys. Chem.*, **36**:2901 (1932); *Ind. Eng. Chem.*, **27**:1500 (1935); *J. Appl. Phys.*, **17**:1086, 1930, 1101 (1946).

[2] *J. Soc. Chem. Ind.*, **64**(5):121T (1945). *Bitumen, Teere, Asphalte, Peche*, **3**:284 (1952).

[3] Bogdanov, *API Tech. Abst.*, **2**(47):5 (1955). *Heftyanoe Khoz.*, no. 5, p. 63, 1955.

[4] For discussion of methods of measuring these high viscosities, see Traxler, *Ind. Eng. Chem.* **30**:322 (1938). Romberg and Traxler, *J. Colloid Sci.*, **2**:33 (1947).

[5] Traxler and Coombs, *J. Phys. Chem.*, **40**:1133 (1936). Swanson, *J. Phys. Chem.*, **46**:141 (1942). Dickinson, *J. Soc. Chem. Ind.*, **64**(5):121T (1945). Saal, Baas, and Heukelom, *J. chim. phys.*, **43**:235 (1946). Nellensteyn, *Fuel Abstr.* (NS), **3**(2):79 (1948); *J. Inst. Petrol.*, **35**:302 (1949). Eilers, *J. Phys. and Colloid Chem.*, **53**:1195 (1949). Traxler, *Ind. Eng. Chem.*, **44**:155 (1952).

1. Those showing truly viscous flow, which does not differ essentially from that of ordinary viscous petroleum oils at room temperature. The shear rate under constant stress does not change with time, the deformation or flow per unit of time is proportional to the stress, and there is no observable elastic recovery. Typical asphalts of this class are certain California and Venezuela residua, made by careful noncracking reduction under vacuum or with plentiful use of steam.

2. Viscous flow with elastic effects; this is an intermediate type, in which the application of a constant stress brings about first a decreasing rate of deformation, followed by a period during which the rate becomes constant, as in viscous flow. The decreasing rate of deformation can be pictured as beginning as the elastic recovery begins, opposing the constant rate induced by viscous flow. When the stress is removed, there is a perceptible elastic recovery. The materials of this type are believed to be dispersions of the sol class.

3. Thixotropic; here the application of a constant stress produces a rate of shear which decreases and then increases. This may be pictured as caused by viscous flow overcome by, first, an elastic recovery which slows down the rate of shear, and then reinforced by breakdown of an internal structure, which permits more ready flow. As long as the stress is small, its removal permits an almost complete elastic recovery, because only elastic deformation has occurred. When the stress exceeds a certain "yield value," the recovery is not complete; this is an evidence that a structural deformation has occurred. The rate of shear (under constant stress) may increase with time, but on removal of the stress the original resistance to shear is gradually recovered; this seems to indicate that the breakdown of internal structure is reversible under proper conditions. It is a matter of observation that such asphalts show a considerable amount of what is called age hardening.[1] A Trinidad asphalt has been observed to harden over a period of a year, although the effect was reversed by gentle heating.

The first of the three classes is considered to be made up of viscous liquids without obvious colloidal structure, the second are regarded as colloidal sols, while the third correspond to typical gels. The explanation of the phenomena listed can be presented more or less as follows, keeping in mind that real experimental proof is lacking.

A typical asphalt is made up of asphaltenes and resins, the latter probably adsorbed by the former, the whole dispersed in an oily medium. The nature of the complex is determined by such factors as the nature of the medium (paraffinic or aromatic) as well as the nature and proportion

[1] Traxler and Coombs, *ASTM*, **37**(II):549 (1937). Apparently a loose three-dimensional network formed by asphaltenes and resins. Brown, Sparks, and Smith, *Proc. Assoc. Asphalt Paving Technologists*, **26**:486 (1957).

of the asphaltenes and of the resins, both being polar in character. The asphaltenes can be considered as somewhat lyophobic while the resins are lyophilic; the adsorption of the resins gives them the marked control they seem to exercise on the nature of the end product. The asphaltenes will vary in character, but are of sufficiently high molecular weight to require dispersion as micelles, which are peptized by the resins. If the asphaltenes are relatively low in molecular weight, the resins plentiful, and the medium aromatic in nature, the result may be a viscous asphalt without anomalous properties. If, however, the medium is paraffinic while the resins are scarce and the asphaltenes high in molecular or micellar weight[1] (the latter two conditions are encouraged by such processing as drastic vacuum or steam reduction or air blowing), then the asphalt will acquire an internal structure of gel type and show in marked degree the properties which go with such structure.[2] Among these are typical non-Newtonian flow, tendency to bleed onto an adsorptive surface, low ductility, high elasticity, marked age hardening, and thixotropy. A high content of resins will impart to a product desirable adhesiveness and plasticity; likewise a high content of asphaltenes will cause greater deviation from Newtonian flow properties, particularly if the molecular weight of these latter has been increased by such treatment as drastic air blowing.[3]

Physical Properties and Tests.[4] The most important physical property of asphalts, and the most studied, is that of consistency and its change with temperature. It has been customary for many years to estimate consistency empirically by measuring the depth of penetration of a standard loaded needle in a given time at standard temperature (ASTM Standards 1952, p. 1331, Method D 5–52). These penetration figures have been related to more general flow properties[5] and particularly to absolute

[1] Nellensteyn states that the particle size may vary (electron microscope measurements) from 6μ to 0.1μ. Eilers calculated from the rate of oil separation that the radius of the asphaltene micelles of a blown Mexican product was of the order of 2×10^{-7} cm and the micellar weight about 10^5.

[2] The importance of cyclic—presumably aromatic—constituents in solvent-type structures is supported by analyses presented by Romberg, Nesmith, and Traxler, *ACS, Div. Petrol. Chem.*, Preprints, ACS Meeting, San Francisco, April, 1958.

[3] On differences in the plasticizing action of various asphaltenes, characterized by differences in solubility, see Krenkler, *Bitumen, Teere, Asphalte, Peche*, **9**(6):295 (1955). The more definite gel structure produced by extended air blowing has been shown by electron micrographs. Freund, *Erdöl u. Kohle*, **11**(1):13 (1958). On the application of surface etching with appropriate solvents as an indication of internal structure, see Traxler and Coombs, *Ind. Eng. Chem.*, **30**:440 (1938).

[4] On physical properties and yields of different grades of residual asphalts from a series of asphaltic crude oils, see Stanfield and Hubbard, *U.S. Bur. Mines Tech. Paper* 717, 1949. On relation of properties and tests to uses of asphalts, see series of articles by Barth in the *Petroleum Refiner;* for example, *Petrol. Refiner* **36**(12):124 (1957).

[5] Mill and Harrison, *J. Soc. Chem. Ind.*, **59**:66 (1940).

viscosity.[1] The latter can be measured directly by a variety of methods[2] which are applied only for research purposes. A great deal of ingenuity has gone into deriving basic data from empirical procedures for consistency measurement; for instance, the data for ring-and-ball softening point have been related to absolute viscosity.[3] Also, by making successive penetration measurements in the same spot without changing conditions[4] a good deal has been deduced about the rheology of asphalts.

Viscosity-temperature relations of bitumens are of great practical importance. The simplest approach to such data has been to measure penetrations at different temperatures.[5] An asphalt viscosity index has been devised by Traxler and Schweyer,[6] but probably the best results can be obtained by plotting log of absolute viscosity against log of temperature.

Some interest attaches to recent analyses of mechanical properties of asphaltic substances. Lethersich[7] has made the point that brittleness is a relative term, and that the phenomena depend on the rate of loading; thus nearly all asphalts are brittle if the loading is fast enough. Brittle failure is considered as due to the hydrostatic component of stress, and plastic failure to the shear component. A more general approach is suggested by Thelen.[8] He believes that unfilled asphalts—those containing no mineral aggregates—are never true Bingham plastics; that is, they do not show real mobility and yield value. They manifest only viscous flow and elastic deformation, as is also true of many polymeric materials. These properties change greatly with temperature and with the frequency of cyclic loading. From considerations of this sort it was hoped that a variety of physical phenomena could be predicted. While the approach is undoubtedly useful, determination of its ultimate validity will depend on obtaining further data.

A good deal of attention has been given to the Oliensis so-called spot test, which depends on the stain spreading of a drop of asphalt solution.[9] It was devised to indicate the degree of heterogeneity of a bitumen, and thus to indicate the occurrence of highly heated or otherwise changed materials. It seems to be limited to study of bitumens of the same source of manufacture.[10]

[1] Saal, *World Petrol. Congr., Proc. 1st Congr., London,* **2**:515 (1933).

[2] Broome, *J. Inst. Petrol.,* **25**:509 (1939).

[3] Romberg and Traxler, *J. Colloid Sci.,* **2**:33 (1947).

[4] Rhodes and Volkmann, *J. Appl. Phys.,* **8**:492 (1937). Traxler and Moffatt, *Ind. Eng. Chem.,* **30**:188 (1938).

[5] Bencowitz and Boe, *Ind. Eng. Chem., Anal. Ed.,* **8**:157 (1936). Pfeiffer and van Doormaal, *J. Inst. Petrol. Technologists,* **22**:414 (1936).

[6] *Physics,* **7**:67 (1936).

[7] *J. Soc. Chem. Ind.,* **65**:190 (1946).

[8] *Proc. Assoc. Asphalt Paving Technologists,* **23**:1 (1954).

[9] *Proc. ASTM,* **33**(II):715 (1933); **36**(II):494 (1936).

[10] Winterkorn and Eckert, *Ind. Eng. Chem.,* **33**:285 (1941).

Coefficients of cubical expansion of asphalts[1] are comparable with those for coal-tar pitches:

$$
\begin{array}{ll}
\text{Asphalts} \dots\dots\dots\dots\dots & 0.00062 \\
\text{Coal-tar pitches} \dots\dots\dots\dots & 0.00045
\end{array}
$$

Specific heat values range from 0.425 to 0.612 for products of various types at temperatures from 0 to 300°C. An equation deduced for a relation between density and specific heat of mineral oils[2] holds also for asphalts. Thermal conductivities in kilogram-calories flowing per hour through a cross section of 1 sq m under a differential of 1°C per linear meter ranged from 0.115 to 0.150, and surface tensions in dynes per centimeter from 24 to 34. Figures for permeability to water vapor in comparison with data for a variety of plastics showed that an asphalt was less permeable than most plastics; it was surpassed only by paraffin wax and an ethylene sulfide product.

The sensitiveness of asphalts to light,[3] indicated by a decrease in solubility, is evidently related to a change in degree of colloidal dispersion. Apparently the phenomenon has not been studied in relation to the composition or condition of the materials showing it. It is possible that light may accelerate oxidation and thus influence the colloidal conditions and the solubility.

The black color of most asphaltic materials invokes pictures of suspended coke or carbon particles. Actually Clar[4] has called attention to the greenish-black color of synthetic hydrocarbons, hexacene and heptacene, carrying six and seven condensed aromatic rings. By contrast, water-white "asphalt," residua from drastic purification, have been prepared.[5]

Attempts have been made to generalize the effect of solvents on asphaltic materials. Nellensteyn[6] suggested that a solvent of surface tension above 26 dynes would peptize an asphalt, while one of surface tension below 24 would flocculate the same asphalt. For solvents falling between 24 and 26 dynes, the stability of the asphalt micelles was determining; the rule is only approximate.

The testing of asphalt products is a subject beyond the scope of this

[1] Mallinson, Jacobsohn, and Sarre, *Z. angew. Chem.*, **39**:154 (1926). Saal, Heukelom, and Blokker, *J. Inst. Petrol.*, **26**:29 (1940).

[2] Cragoe, *Natl. Bur. Standards, Misc. Publ.*, 97, 1929.

[3] Errara, *Trans. Faraday Soc.*, **19**:314 (1923). Tycinin, *Neftyanoe Slantsevoe Khoz.*, **4**(1):73 (1923); *C.A.*, **17**:3782 (1923).

[4] *Ber.*, **72**:1817 (1939); **75**:1283, 1330 (1942); cited by Sachanen, *op. cit.*, p. 387.

[5] Gaetz, *Ind. Eng. Chem.*, **27**:647 (1935).

[6] *"Science of Petroleum,"* vol. IV, p. 2760, Oxford University Press, New York and London, 1938; *J. Inst. Petrol.*, **35**:302 (1949).

discussion; the reader is referred to the comprehensive work of Abraham.[1] While all such examination is presumably related to the service to be expected of the product, certain specialized testing, more related to the subject, can be described briefly. It falls into three classes, those connected with:

1. Stability in service, such as weathering
2. Bleeding, or exudation of softer constituents
3. Adherence to mineral fillers or aggregates

The stability tests are mostly of the accelerated oxidation variety, with dependence either on the amount of oxygen absorbed or on the changes in properties of the product during oxidation. Specific methods have been described by Thurston and Knowles,[2] Shattuck,[3] Anderson, Stross, and Ellings,[4] and Ebberts and Ebberts.[5] Examination of specimens aged for periods up to thirty years has been reported by Oliensis.[6] The material may be oxidized in thin films or mixed with a mineral aggregate and then heated. The bitumen may be recovered and tested for some property, such as ductility.[7]

The exudation of soft material from a bituminous mixture is attributed by Rick[8] to incompatibility of constituents, or of constituents with solvents, which leads to flocculation and release of less viscous components. Failure of bitumen to adhere to a mineral aggregate, known as "stripping," can be determined empirically by washing tests.[9] A good deal of attention has been given to additive materials for improving this adherence.[10] The aggregate may be coated with an insoluble soap of a heavy metal or the asphalt may be admixed with a compound such as an amine

[1] *Op. cit.*, vol. II.

[2] *Ind. Eng. Chem.*, **28**:88 (1936).

[3] *Proc. Assoc. Asphalt Paving Technologists*, **11**:186 (1940).

[4] *Ind. Eng. Chem., Anal. Ed.*, **14**:45 (1942).

[5] *Ind. Eng. Chem.*, **34**:1048 (1942). See also van Oort, *Ind. Eng. Chem.*, **48**:1196 (1956).

[6] *ASTM Bull.* 163, p. 59, April, 1950.

[7] A good many attempts have been made to relate the physical and particularly the engineering properties of asphalts to chemical composition; among the properties studied in this manner is durability, as indicated by the several oxidation tests for stability. Composition is ordinarily expressed in terms of the known empirical constituents, such as asphaltenes, resins, wax, paraffinic, naphthenic, and aromatic oils, etc. See *ACS, Div. Petrol. Chem., Program on Chemistry and Composition of Asphalts*, Preprints, ACS Meeting, San Francisco, April, 1958.

[8] *Deut. Farben-Z.*, **6**:478 (1952); *C.A.*, **47**:2999 (1953).

[9] Winterkorn, *Ind. Eng. Chem.*, **30**:1362 (1938).

[10] Swanson, *Ind. Eng. Chem.*, **36**:584 (1944). Snyder and Pavlish, *Ind. Eng. Chem.*, **41**:2649 (1949). Huber and Thompson, *Proc. Assoc. Asphalt Paving Technologists*, **24**:375 (1955.) Lissant and Farr, *Ind. Eng. Chem.*, **47**:2276 (1955). Hoiberg, *Ind. Eng. Chem.*, **43**:1419 (1951).

derivative. In the latter case the thermal stability of the material requires consideration.

MANUFACTURE OF ASPHALT FROM PETROLEUM[1]

Reasonably satisfactory asphalt can be made from almost any crude oil, but desirable properties and economical yields can be secured most readily from selected stocks already quite asphaltic in character. Examples are the very heavy Mexican crude oils, the distillation residues of similar California or Middle East crudes, the relatively nonvolatile tars from thermal cracking, sludges from sulfuric acid treating of lubricating oil stocks,[2] and solvent extracts from refining residua for manufacture of lubricating oils.[3] The processes applied are simple. They involve either (1) controlled removal of volatile constituents by vacuum or steam distillation; or (2) air blowing to induce condensation reactions; a little distillation of lighter constituents will occur also, but it is a minor factor. In both cases controlled high temperature is necessary.

XV-3. Residual or Straight-run Asphalts.[4] These are made up of the nonvolatile hydrocarbons and asphaltic compounds in the charge stock, together with similar materials resulting from the exposure to heating involved in the distillation. This increase may be due to conversion of asphaltic resins—probably polynaphthenic acids or anhydrides, or their sulfur equivalents—to more condensed compounds.[5] Residual asphalts are likely to contain, say, 30 per cent of asphaltenes and 3 or 4 per cent of neutral resins. They are characterized by a comparatively high specific gravity, greater hardness (lower penetration) for a given melting point, and greater change in consistency with temperature, all these in comparison with air-blown products.

Elementary analyses indicate that residual asphalts made from high-sulfur charge stocks are likely to have a comparatively high sulfur content. It is known that many of the sulfur compounds in petroleum are unstable at the temperatures of asphalt manufacture, so that some displacement of sulfur atoms is to be expected, but there is no present evidence that sulfur compounds in the oil charge play a direct part in the reactions involved.

[1] During recent years petroleum-derived materials have constituted about 90 per cent of the United States asphalt consumption.

[2] This is an old idea; see Jenney, U.S. Patent 178,061, 1876. Dean, U.S. Patent 564,975, 1896. Gray, U.S. Patents 923,427, 923,428, 923,429, 1909. The products were quite susceptible to temperature change and not resistant to weathering.

[3] For example, the asphaltic precipitates from the propane deasphalting of cylinder stocks; see Chap. VIII.

[4] *Ind. Eng. Chem.*, **40**:548 (1948).

[5] It should be kept in mind that steam often contains a little air, so that some oxidation of hydrocarbons to asphaltic compounds may occur during steam reduction.

The preparation of residual asphalts is now carried on almost exclusively by continuous vacuum flash distillation. A reduced crude oil is heated by pumping through a heating coil and is discharged into a vacuum tower, where all volatile constituents are taken overhead. The properties of the residuum depend on the temperature and vacuum, which control the proportion distilled and the reactions which occur. Since the time of exposure is short, a temperature of 800°F can be tolerated, while batch methods would permit not over 700°F. A typical Mid-Continent crude flash-distilled in vacuum at 800°F will yield about 6 per cent of asphaltic flux. The yields of harder products by continued reduction of these softer materials are uncertain, because of variations in crude oils.[1]

XV-4. Air-blown Asphalts. The chemistry of asphalt making by air oxidation has been discussed above. The subject was reinvestigated recently by Goppel and Knoterus.[2] Their work indicated that in a typical air-blowing operation, the stock absorbs oxygen to form alcohol, ketone, acid, and ester groups, the esters predominating; these latter are important also in linking up molecules to increase the molecular weight. There was also evidence of condensing oxidation, in which carbon-to-carbon linkages were established; this latter reaction varied with the temperature, reaching a maximum (over 50 per cent of the oxygen consumed) at about 250°F. Mabery and Byerley[3] had characterized the oxidation as predominantly a removal of hydrogen rather than an addition of oxygen;[4] this seems to be only partly true, at least for some charge stocks. The principal overhead products from a charge stock properly stripped of volatile constituents are carbon dioxide and water. If, however, volatile fractions remain in the charge an oxidized condensate may be produced which is both acidic and ill-smelling.

The blowing operation, like the early forms of steam reducing, was originally conducted in cheese-box stills, as many as eight sometimes connected into a cascade battery. Charge flowed into one end of the battery and product from the other, temperature rising along the line from about 400 to 450°F to upward of 600°F. Air was blown into the bottom of each unit; as required to avoid runaway temperatures, steam was mixed with the air current. The charge took about 80 hr to pass through the entire battery. When a batch operation was employed, the blowing rate was about 40 cu ft per min per ton charged. A Mid-Continent residuum of softening point 100°F blown for 8 hr at 475°F yielded 99 per cent of a product softening at 230°F; for a still harder material the yield might be 97 per cent. Very different yields, processing, and products would result

[1] Ziegenhain, *Oil Gas J.*, **32**(29):10 (1933).

[2] *World Petrol. Congr., Proc. 4th Congr., Rome*, III, p. 399, 1955.

[3] *Am. Chem. J.*, **18**:141 (1896).

[4] Also to the same effect, Cudmore and Heyding, *Can. J. Technol.*, **30**:143 (1952).

from different charge materials. Continuous blowing in a vertical reactor
of narrow cross section is described by Hughes and Hardman.[1] Such an
operation would secure efficient use of air and would be suitable where an
equilibrium product of moderate hardness or melting point was desired;
it probably would not easily yield a material blown to extreme properties.

The use of catalysts and promotors for the asphalt-making reactions is
not new. Sulfur as an accelerator for blowing was described by Brooks
and Humphrey in 1917.[2] More recently ferric chloride[3] and phosphorus
pentoxide[4] have been employed. The latter is reported to make possible
a blowing time as short as 5 hr in a vertical batch reactor. Products of
these accelerated methods are said to show less change of consistency with
temperature than those blown without catalysts. Ordinary blown
asphalts are in general softer than are the unoxidized residual products;
they are more resilient, have lower specific gravities, lower ductilities and
tensile strengths, and have flatter consistency-temperature curves. They
are thus desirable for roofing and insulation purposes, where a product is
needed which does not suffer deformation at elevated temperatures.

Asphalts made from cracked tars[5] (residues from thermal cracking)
have at times been regarded as representing a different type. They
resemble coal-tar pitches, being rather aromatic in character, show a high
change of consistency with temperature, and deteriorate quickly under
exposure to weather. They are reported to yield good molded articles
and to be effective in stabilizing soil. This may be in part due to the low
viscosity when melted, making possible a good distribution. The raw
material from which they have been manufactured is disappearing with
the decline of thermal cracking.

The manufacturing process is of considerable importance, but the type
of oil employed is also significant as governing final properties. The
products from typical charge materials may be described as follows:

Asphaltic California crudes...... Rather steep consistency curves; better for satu-
                                  rating than for roofing and paving
Heavy Mexican................ Less susceptible to temperature change; durable
                                  and stable; suitable for roofing and paving
Gulf Coastal.................. Excellent for paving; very durable; intermediate
                                  temperature susceptibility
Mid-Continent................ Quite low temperature susceptibility; thus useful
                                  for insulation, paints, varnishes

[1] *Advances in Chem. Ser.*, No. 5, p. 263, 1951.

[2] *Ind. Eng. Chem.*, **9**:746 (1917). The making of asphalt by reacting heavy oils
with sulfur was patented by Dubbs in 1872.

[3] *Ind. Eng. Chem.*, **40**:549 (1948); chlorine was mentioned for the same purpose by
Pauer and Haruni, *Erdol u. Kohle*, **5**:771 (1952).

[4] *Ind. Eng. Chem.*, **45**:2122 (1953); Eng, Govier, and Quon, *Can. J. Technol.*,
33(5):368 (1955).

[5] Egloff and Morrell, *Ind. Eng. Chem.*, **23**:679 (1931).

The order shown above can be only approximate and may in some cases be changed, because, as just stated, manufacturing techniques will alter results, and because the nature of crude oils varies even within "typical" areas.   This last point is mentioned in Chap. I.   Differences in depth and geological formation will often account for production of quite different crudes.

Correlation between service properties and proximate chemical composition has not been too successful; not much information is available. Krenkler[1] has suggested that the substances insoluble in cyclohexane are mere fillers, with no significant influence on properties; high-molecular-weight asphaltenes, segregated by insolubility in n-heptane, contribute good plasticity and low susceptibility to temperature change; resins of medium molecular weight, those insoluble in n-butanol, contribute tackiness and ductility but have an adverse effect on temperature susceptibility.

USES OF ASPHALTS

Approximately one-half of the asphalt produced from petroleum in the United States is consumed in paving roads and streets.   About one-quarter is employed for roofing and the rest for paints, varnishes, insulating, and rust-protective compositions, cast articles like battery boxes, and for compounding materials which go into rubber products, brake linings, and fuel briquettes.

The specific requirements for asphalts which will serve these various purposes are too detailed for this discussion.   Some general distinctions may be drawn, however.

Paving asphalts may be divided into:

Road oils   Solid asphalts
Cutbacks   Joint fillers
Emulsions

XV-5. Road Oils.   These are, as the name implies, liquid asphaltic materials intended for easy application to earth roads; they do not provide a strong base or a hard surface, but will maintain a satisfactory passage for light traffic.   Their application is described by Padgett,[2] and the oils themselves by Sperry,[3] Milburn and Pauls,[4] and Lewis and

---

[1] *Bitumen, Teere, Asphalte, Peche,* **2**:59 (1951).   On the differences of pentane-insoluble content of straight-run, blown, and thermally cracked asphalts, see Corbett, *Proc. Assoc. Asphalt Paving Technologists,* **23**:14 (1954).

[2] *Natl. Petrol. News,* **16**(12):87 (1924); $\frac{1}{4}$ to 1 gal per sq yd of surface is applied.

[3] *Proc. ASTM,* **25**(II):376 (1925).

[4] *Natl. Petrol. News,* **26**(28):28 (1934).

Welborn.[1] Both straight-run and cracked residua have been employed successfully. Binding quality and adhesiveness are important, as governing the quality of the road produced, while resistance to removal by emulsification has some influence on its permanence.[2] The influence of types of road oils on public water supplies has been considered by Carpenter and Klinger.[3]

XV-6. Cutbacks. These are mixtures in which hard asphalt has been diluted with a lighter oil to permit application as a liquid without drastic heating. They are classified as rapid, medium, and slow curing, depending on the volatility of the diluent, which governs the rate of evaporation and consequent hardening.[4] The diluents employed are discussed in Sec. XVI-2.

XV-7. Asphalt Emulsions.[5] An asphaltic material may be emulsified with water to permit application without heating. Such emulsions are normally of the oil-in-water type. They reverse or break on application to a stone or earth surface, so that the oil clings to the stone and the water disappears. In addition to road and soil stabilization they are useful for paper impregnation and waterproofing.[6]

The emulsions are chiefly (1) of the soap or alkaline type and (2) of the neutral or clay type. The former break readily on contact but the latter are more stable, and probably lose water mainly by evaporation. Good emulsions must be stable during storage or freezing, of suitable fluidity, and amenable to control for speed of breaking.[7]

XV-8. Solid Asphalts. Liquid road oils, cutbacks, and emulsions are of recent date, but use of asphaltic solids for paving goes back to European practice of about 1835.[8] Detailed consideration of asphalt paving is beyond the scope of this discussion. Classification of paving materials

---

[1] *Public Roads,* **17**:89 (1936).

[2] Road oil specifications are discussed in the following references: Staley, *Petrol. Eng.,* **3**(10):35 (1932); Mullins, *Natl. Petrol. News,* **24**(32):25 (1932); Foster, *Natl. Petrol. News,* **24**(42):27 (1932).

[3] *J. Penn. Water Works Operators' Assoc.,* **5**:43 (1933).

[4] For further discussion, see Hubbard, *Proc. Natl. Asphalt Paving Conf., 10th Conf.,* 1932. Also Lewis and Hillman, *Public Roads,* **15**:85 (1934).

[5] Barth, *Petrol. Refiner,* **21**(8):72 (1942). Bierhalter, *Petrol. Refiner,* **30**(8):103 (1951).

[6] On flow properties of asphalt emulsions, see Lyttleton and Traxler, *Ind. Eng. Chem.,* **40**:2115 (1948).

[7] Clayton-Sumner, "Theory of Emulsions," 5th ed., p. 374, The Blakiston Division, McGraw-Hill Book Company, Inc., New York, 1954. For uses and tests, see Kirschbraun, *Chem. & Met. Eng.,* **36**:477 (1929). McKesson, *Proc. ASTM* **31**(II):41 (1931).

[8] Molded articles of asphalt and brick joint filling as well as flooring are known from about 2500 B.C. in the Middle East. Forbes, "Bitumen and Petroleum in Antiquity," p. 66, E. J. Brill, N. V. Leiden, Netherland, 1936.

and method of application are discussed by Abraham.[1] The asphaltic constituents employed may have softening points up to, say, 230°F and hardness measured by penetration down to 10 or 15 at 77°F.[2]

The improvement of asphalt by admixing rubber was discussed in 1936[3] and has recently been revived. Addition of small percentages is reported to increase elasticity, cohesion, and stability and to raise viscosity and softening point temperatures.[4] Synthetic elastomers are considered satisfactory for the purpose.[5]

[1] *Op cit.*, vol. I, p. 633.

[2] The Asphalt Institute has set up specifications for five grades of paving asphalts. The penetration limits, 25 to 200, are the same as those employed in the National Bureau of Standards Simplified Recommendations No. 4, which described nine grades for paving and four for joint filling; the latter included penetration limits 30 to 100. *Oil Gas J.*, **55**(8):110 (1956).

[3] *J. Soc. Chem. Ind.*, **55**:435 (1936).

[4] Fisher, *India Rubber World*, **127**:220 (1952).

[5] Endres, Coleman, Pierson, and Sinclair, *Ind. Eng. Chem.*, **43**:334 (1951).

CHAPTER XVI

Miscellaneous Petroleum Products and Derived Products

MISCELLANEOUS PETROLEUM PRODUCTS

XVI-1. White Oils. For many years, much of the production of white oils came from Russia, chiefly because of the availability of suitable naphthenic stocks. White oils are now prepared from paraffinic, mixed-base, or naphthenic fractions, the choice depending upon the final use; American oils have been found to be entirely suitable for this purpose. Naphthenic crudes give products of high specific gravity and viscosity, properties desired in pharmaceutical use; paraffinic stocks produce oils of lighter gravity and lower viscosity suitable for lubrication purposes.[1] The materials fall into two classes: (1) those known as technical white oils, employed for cosmetics, textile lubrication, insecticide vehicles, paper impregnation, and for many other purposes, and (2) pharmaceutical white oils, employed as laxatives[2] and for the lubrication of food-handling machinery. The colorless character of these oils is, in some cases, important of itself and, in others, as indicating the chemically inert nature of the hydrocarbons contained. Thus textile lubricants should be colorless to prevent the staining of light-colored threads and fabrics; insecticide oils should be free of reactive (probably meaning easily oxidizable) constituents, so as not to injure plant tissues when applied as summer sprays; laxative oils[3] should be free of odor and taste, and should also be free of hydrocarbons unstable enough to develop them in storage. These properties are attained by the removal of oxygen, nitrogen, and sulfur compounds and reactive hydrocarbons by drastic refining, almost universally by sulfuric acid. The refining action of the acid takes place

---

[1] Meyer, "White Mineral Oil and Petrolatum," p. 4, Chemical Publishing Company, Inc., New York, 1950.

[2] Schlagintweit, *C.A.*, **22**:277, 640 (1928). Jackson, *J. Nutrition*, **7**:607 (1934).

[3] These oils are reported to interfere with the assimilation of carotene and vitamin A. Jackson, *op. cit.* Alexander, Lorenzen, Hoffmann, and Garfinkel, *Proc. Soc. Exptl. Biol. Med.*, **65**:275 (1947).

both chemically, through sulfonation and oxidation reactions, and physically, by acting as a differential solvent for resins, asphaltic material, and nitrogen and sulfur-containing compounds.

The crude or fraction chosen for refining may have been subjected to a preliminary refining with a differential solvent.[1] The exact procedure for the acid treatment varies, but a preliminary dose of ordinary 66°Bé acid (chiefly for drying) may be followed by incremental addition of as much as 50 per cent by volume of acid as strong as 20 per cent fuming, or even sulfur trioxide, itself.[2] The reaction sludge is drawn off promptly to limit oxidation-reduction reactions; the time, temperature, and method of application depend upon the type of charge stock and the degree of refining desired. The product is neutralized with alkali and washed with ethyl or isopropyl alcohol or acetone to remove the oil-soluble sulfonic "mahogany" acids. The water-soluble "green" acids are recovered from the alkali washings. The treated oil is further refined and decolorized by adsorption, either by percolation or contacting with fuller's earth, bentonite, etc.

It is evident that this sequence will leave only the most acid-resistant hydrocarbons behind, and since these are roughly the more generally stable compounds, the process is effective. The degree of refining is ordinarily measured by the U.S. Pharmacopoeia test,[3] which involves heating equal volumes of oil and 95 per cent sulfuric acid in boiling water for 10 min, shaking at 30-sec intervals. The color developed in the oil may be measured in terms of standard color solutions or by a colorimeter;[4] the medicinal oils require a test showing minimal change, while, depending on its intended use, a technical oil showing rather marked color change may be satisfactory. The only further distinction between pharmaceutical and technical oils is the approximate one that the former, at least those of high quality, are made as viscous as possible (250 to 350 SSU), while the latter are likely to be made of the less viscous fractions which are easier to refine.[5] Typical technical oils of paraffinic type will show the following general properties:

Specific gravity	0.835 to 0.845
Viscosity, SSU, at 100°F	85 to 110
Pour point, °F	30
Cloud point, °F	40

[1] Archibald, "Science of Petroleum," vol. IV, p. 2838, Oxford University Press, New York and London, 1938.

[2] Gilbert and Veldhuis, *Ind. Eng. Chem.*, **49**:31 (1957). Carlson, Flint, Gilbert, and Nychka, *Ind. Eng. Chem.*, **50**:276 (1958).

[3] U.S. Pharmacopoeia, **XV**:527 (1955).

[4] Hampshire and Page, *Quart. J. Pharm. Pharmacol.*, **7**:354 (1934).

[5] Nugey, *Refiner. Nat. Gasoline Mfr.*, **13**:140 (1934).

When machinery carrying heavier loads is to be lubricated, oils of viscosity near 200 SSU may be required. The broad range of properties of white oils used for all purposes can be outlined more or less as follows:[1]

Specific gravity	0.827 to 0.890
Viscosity, SSU, at 100°F	50 to 350
Flash, closed cup (Pensky-Martin), °F	310 to 375
Cloud point, °F	38 to 52
Pour point, °F	−30 for heavy gravity oils
	+10 to +35 for light gravity oils
Sulfur, per cent	0.05 to 0.10
Refractive index, 26°C	1.46 to 1.48
Iodine number (Hanus)	0.8 to 9.2

The matter of cloud point is of importance only with regard to appearance after standing in cold places. Often, otherwise satisfactory wax-free oils will contain a trace of waxy material insoluble in the oil at the low temperatures indicated. This phenomenon is influenced by choice of crude and degree of refining. It may be mentioned also that the drastic acid treatment causes a very marked diminution in specific gravity and in viscosity. A stock of 400 sec viscosity will end up as a white oil of 250 sec and to obtain an oil of 350 sec requires a stock of 600 or thereabouts.

XVI-2. Industrial Naphtha Solvents. Petroleum naphthas are valuable as solvents because of their essentially nonpoisonous character,[2] good dissolving power, and lower cost. The wide range of naphthas available, from the ordinary paraffinic straight-run to the highly aromatic types and of various degrees of volatility, offers products suitable for many uses. In general, they may be prepared by:[3]

Fractionation of straight-run, cracked, and reformed distillates
Solvent extraction
Hydrogenation of cracked distillates
Polymerization of unsaturated hydrocarbons
Synthesis involving hydrocarbons
Admixture of chemicals (alcohols, ketones) or combinations of these

Their main uses may be classified as:

Solvents and diluents for paints, varnishes, and lacquers
Dry-cleaning media
Solvents for cutback asphalts

[1] Archibald, *loc. cit.*

[2] Gardner, *U.S. Paint Mfrs. Assoc., Circ.* 250, p. 89, 1925.

[3] MacGee, *Paint, Oil and Chem. Rev.*, **113**(10):18 (1950). Frost, *Petrol. Refiner*, **29**(4):137 (1950). For the effect which removing polar compounds from petroleum naphthas has on chemical reactivity and physical properties such as surface activity, association, solubility, vapor pressure, and drying rates, etc., see Allen, *Ind. Eng. Chem.*, **40**:124 (1948).

Solvents in rubber manufacture and rubber products
Solvents in extraction industries

Paints, Varnishes, and Lacquers.[1] Turpentine had always been the accepted solvent for paints until the cheaper petroleum naphthas were found to be equally satisfactory. The differences in application are trifling; naphthas cause a slightly greater decrease in viscosity, when added to some paints, than does turpentine and, depending on the boiling range, may show some differences in evaporation rates.

The boiling ranges of fractions which will evaporate at rates permitting the deposition of good films have been fairly well established.[2] Depending on conditions, products are employed as light as those boiling from 100 to 300°F and as heavy as those falling between 300 and 450°F. The latter are used mainly in the manufacture of baked and forced-drying products.

The solvent power required for conventional paints is possessed by ordinary distillates from paraffinic crudes, which are, in general, the poorest solvents in the class of petroleum naphthas. In addition to solvent power and proper evaporation rate, a paint thinner should be resistant to oxidation to the extent of not developing bad color and odor during use, and should be free of corrosive impurities and reactive materials, such as certain types of sulfur compounds, when employed in paints containing lead and similar metals. These requirements are best met by straight-run distillates from paraffinic (usually Mid-Continent) crude oils, boiling from 250 or 300 to 400°F. The components of enamels, varnishes, nitro-cellulose lacquers, and synthetic resin finishes are not as soluble in paraffinic naphthas as the materials in conventional paints. This situation favors naphthenic and aromatic naphthas, such as those from Gulf Coast and California crudes, solvent extracts, selected fractions of catalytic reformates, or paraffinic naphthas to which accessory solvents such as toluene or the more powerful synthetic solvents- •butanol and butyl acetate—have been added. In certain cases solvent power can be improved by addition of a few per cent of a compound like glyceryl monoleate.[3] The formulation of these special solvent mixtures is a complicated matter, and several special tests have been set up for estimating

---

[1] Stewart, *Prodts. Finishing*, **9**(1):46 (1944). Chittick, *Paint, Oil, Chem. Rev.*, **113**(10):40 (1950). Scofield, *Natl. Paint, Varnish and Lacquer Assoc., Sci. Sec., Circ.* 746, p. 419, 1950. Armsbury, *Offic. Dig. Federation & Varnish Production Clubs*, no. 189, p. 366, 1939. Boggs, *Offic. Dig. Federation Paint & Varnish Production Clubs*, no. 285, p. 719, 1948. Rabek and Johnson, *Offic. Dig. Federation Paint & Varnish Production Clubs*, no. 328, p. 342, 1952.

[2] McArdle and Baldeschwieler, *Ind. Eng. Chem., Anal. Ed.*, **13**:301 (1941). McArdle and Robertson, *Ind. Eng. Chem., Anal. Ed.*, **16**:690 (1944). Tobay, *Ind. Eng. Chem.*, **35**:1044 (1943). Curtis, Scheibli, and Bradley, *Anal. Chem.*, **22**:538 (1950).

[3] *Chem. Week*, **74**(7):78 (1954).

quality. Among these are the dilution ratio test for indicating the solvent power for nitrocellulose,[1] the kauri-butanol test,[2] the aniline point, solubility in dimethyl sulfate, and viscosities of certain standardized resin solutions.[3]

Among the physical tests, evaporation rate is perhaps most closely related to service. Several methods for determining such rates are employed.[4]

Dry Cleaning. This is a well-established industry, and the solvent employed, the so-called "Stoddard solvent," has been carefully standardized. The specifications for this material[5] require a petroleum distillate of the following character:

Color not darker than 21 by the Saybolt chromometer
Flash point not below 100°F by the "Tag" closed tester
No corrosion of a copper strip during 3 hr at 212°F
Distillation test:
   Not less than 50 per cent over at 350°F
   Not less than 90 per cent over at 375°F
   End point not above 410°F
Distillation residue to show no acidity
Doctor test negative (absence of mercaptans and peroxides)
Sulfuric acid adsorption not more than 5 per cent in concentrated acid (93.2 per cent)

These requirements are met by a straight-run naphtha from a low-sulfur paraffinic crude, suitably refined. An aromatic hydrocarbon content is not desirable, since it may cause removal of dyes from fabrics or too efficient removal of natural oils from wool, etc.[6] A product as above described is high boiling enough to be safe from fire risk and is stable enough for extensive reuse and reclaiming.

[1] Davidson and Reid, *Ind. Eng. Chem.*, **19**:977 (1927). Ware and Bruner, *Ind. Eng. Chem.*, **32**:78 (1940).

[2] Baldeschwieler, Troeller, and Morgan, *Ind. Eng. Chem., Anal. Ed.*, **7**:374 (1935). McArdle and Baldeschwieler, *Ind. Eng. Chem., Anal. Ed.*, **13**:301 (1941).

[3] Huff, *Am. Paint J., Convention Daily*, **24**:12 (1939). Kurtz, *Paint Manuf.*, **10**:226 (1940). Ware and Teeters, *Ind. Eng. Chem.*, **31**:738 (1939).

[4] Wetlaufer and Gregor, *Ind. Eng. Chem., Anal. Ed.*, **7**:290 (1935). Lowell, *Ind. Eng. Chem., Anal. Ed.*, **7**:278 (1935). Rubek and Dahl, *Ind. Eng. Chem., Anal. Ed.*, **6**:421 (1934). Lewis, Squires, and Sanders, *Ind. Eng. Chem.*, **27**:1395 (1935). McArdle and Robertson, *Ind. Eng. Chem., Anal. Ed.*, **16**:690 (1944). Curtis, Scheibli, and Bradley, *Anal. Chem.*, **22**:538 (1950).

[5] *U.S. Dept. of Commerce, Bureau of Standards, Commercial Standard* CS3-40, 1940. ASTM Specification D 484–52. For 140 F flash solvent, *U.S. Dept. of Commerce, Bureau of Standards, Commercial Standard* 174–51.

[6] Jackson, *Ind. Eng. Chem.*, **18**:237 (1926).

Cutback Asphalt.[1] A cutback asphalt is an asphalt cement diluted with a petroleum distillate to make it suitable for direct application to road surfaces with little or no heating. An asphalt cement, in turn, is a combination of hard asphalt with a heavy distillate or with a viscous residuum of an asphaltic crude oil. The products are classified as rapid, medium, and slow-curing, depending on the rate of evaporation of the solvent. A rapid-curing product may contain 40 to 50 per cent of material distilling up to 680°F in an assay distillation test, while a slow-curing mixture may have only 25 per cent. There will be differences also in the residuum used. Gasoline, naphtha, kerosene, and light fuel oils boiling from 100 to 630°F are used in different products and for different purposes. It is customary to employ a naphtha boiling from 250 to 450°F for small-scale cutting back by users. Since there are no requirements as to color, odor, and sulfur or gum content, an unrefined cracked distillate would be satisfactory. In a very few cases care must be exercised in selecting materials which will be "compatible." The precipitating of asphaltenes from an overparaffinic medium is not unknown and is the presumable cause of the so-called "livering."

Rubber.[2] Petroleum naphthas are used in the rubber industry for dampening the ply and tread stocks of automobile tires during manufacture so as to obtain better adhesion between the units of the tire. They are also consumed extensively in making rubber cements, which are sold as adhesives or are employed in the fabricating of rubberized cloth, hot-water bottles, bathing caps, gloves, overshoes, and toys. These cements, which are solutions of rubber, were formerly made with benzene, but petroleum naphtha is preferred because of its less toxic character.

Naphthas for the rubber industry must be:

Satisfactory solvents for rubber
Stable to oxygen, moisture, and (for cold-curing) sulfur chloride
Free of objectionable odor and toxic character
Of safe flash point and of proper evaporation rate

The conventional tire-manufacturing naphtha is a straight-run, paraffinic product boiling from about 100 to 300°F. For cements and dipped-goods making, similar products boiling from 150 to 250 and from 200 to 300°F

---

[1] Hubbard, *Roads and Streets*, January–February, 1933. "Specifications for Liquid Asphaltic Road Materials," 3d ed., Asphalt Institute, New York. Hubbard, *Mineral Ind.*, **43**:52 (1934). Mack, *Ind. Eng. Chem.*, **27**:1500 (1935).

[2] Twiss, *Trans. Inst. Rubber Ind.*, **2**:381 (1927). Geer, *Ind. Eng. Chem.*, **19**:1095 (1927). Dodd, *India Rubber World*, **79**(3):68 (1928); **81**(1):59 (1929). Knapp, *Rubber Age*, **31**:473 (1932). Shepard, *Ind. Eng. Chem.*, **25**:35 (1933); **28**:281 (1936); *India Rubber World*, **90**:27 (1934). Steward, *Rubber Age*, **44**:267 (1939). Rubek, *Rubber Age*, **44**:269 (1939). LeBean, *Rubber Age*, **68**:49 (1950).

are employed. Color, doctor test, and copper corrosion test are specified as in the dry-cleaning industry.

Petroleum distillates are also added in amounts up to 25 per cent and higher at the latex stage in the polymerization of butadiene-styrene (GRS) synthetic rubber. Those employed in oil-extended rubber are of the aromatic type; they are generally high-boiling fractions from Gulf Coastal, California, or Venezuela crudes. They preferably contain no wax, boil from 800 to 950°F, have characterization factors of 10.5 to 11.6 (see Chap. IV), a viscosity index lower than zero, bromine numbers of 6 to 30, and API gravities of 3 to 24.[1]

Extraction Industries.[2] Petroleum naphthas are used for extraction on a moderately wide scale. They are applied in extracting residual oil from the press cake of castor beans, soybeans, cottonseed, and wheat germ, and in the recovery of so-called garbage grease from mixed garbage. The latter seems to be a disappearing industry, although as much as 50 lb of grease per ton of garbage can be recovered with less than 0.5 per cent solvent loss. The solvent employed in these cases is known as a hexane cut, boiling from about 150 to 250°F. Where the oils recovered from seed cake are of edible grade or intended for refined purposes, stable solvents completely free of residual odor and taste are necessary. Straight-run products from sweet, low-sulfur, paraffinic crudes are, in general, satisfactory.

The recovery of wood rosin by extraction of the resinous portions of dead trees of the resin-bearing varieties, stumps, etc., by naphtha extraction, is a somewhat larger industry. In several plants, the chipped wood is steamed to distill out the resinous products recoverable in this way and only then extracted with a naphtha solvent. The latter is a well-refined, low-sulfur, paraffinic product boiling from, say, 200 to 300°F. The loss of solvent is less than 1 per cent per cycle. More recent installations are understood to omit the steaming process, proceeding to immediate extraction; the naphtha solution is treated with adsorptive clay or with differential solvents to remove coloring materials. The naphtha for the improved method is preferably of a naphthenic rather than of a paraffinic make-up and of closer boiling range, say, 200 to 250°, rather than 200 to 300°F.

---

[1] Rostler, *Rubber Age*, **69**:559 (1951); **71**:223 (1952). Rostler and Sternber, *Ind. Eng. Chem.*, **41**:598 (1949). Weinstock, Storey, and Sweeley, *Ind. Eng. Chem.*, **45**:1035 (1953). Dunkel, Ford, and McAteer, *Ind. Eng. Chem.*, **46**:578 (1954). Rostler and White, *Ind. Eng. Chem.*, **46**:610 (1954). Taft, Feldon, Duke, Laundrie, and Prem, *Ind. Eng. Chem.*, **46**:396 (1954); **47**:1077 (1955). Kurtz, King, and Sweeley, *Ind. Eng. Chem.*, **48**:2232 (1956).

[2] Palmer, *Ind. Eng. Chem.*, **26**:703 (1934). MacGee, *Oil and Soap*, **14**:322, 324 (1937); *World Petrol.*, **9**(3) 67 (1938). McArdle, *Natl. Petrol. News*, **36**:R-188 (1944). Greenfield, *Oil Gas. J.*, **44**(40):101 (1946).

Miscellaneous. Petroleum distillates of various compositions and volatilities are also employed as solvents in the manufacture of printing inks, leather coatings, textiles (diluents for dyes and degreasing of wool fibers), polishes and waxes, rust and waterproofing compositions, mildew-proofing compositions and insecticides, wood preservatives, and many other products.

XVI-3. Insulating Oils. Petroleum oils for electrical insulation fall into two general classes: (1) those used in transformers, circuit breakers, and oil-filled cables and (2) those employed for impregnating the paper covering of wrapped cables. The first are highly refined fractions of low viscosity and comparatively high-boiling range. They resemble heavy burning oils, such as mineral seal oil, or the very light lubricating fractions known as nonviscous neutral oils. The second are usually highly viscous products, often naphthenic distillates. They are not usually highly refined; in fact, in many cases they are mixed for use with rosin or similar compounds.[1]

The general requirements for oils for transformers are as follows:[2]

1. Light color, to facilitate visual inspection.

2. A flash point of the order of 270 to 280°F and a corresponding low vapor pressure, so that the oil will not evaporate easily or offer a fire risk at service temperatures. Sometimes a maximum rate of evaporation is specified, such as 0.003 g per hr per sq cm exposed surface at 100°C.[3]

3. A viscosity in the neighborhood of 50 sec Saybolt at 100°F, good fluidity at 0°F, and a pour-point temperature as much below 0°F as is required by climatic conditions.

4. A high insulating value, of the order of 25 to 40 kv between parallel disk electrodes spaced at 2.5 mm apart.

5. The oil should have a high degree of stability against chemical changes and against disruptive discharges; it should be free of acid, alkali, moisture, dirt, and harmful sulfur compounds. It must not corrode or injure any metal parts, and must remain free of deposits formed by deterioration. High specific heats, coefficients of expansion, and thermal conductivities are desirable.[4]

The insulating value of fresh transformer oils seems to vary but little with chemical constitution;[5] mechanical purity, however, especially

[1] Sommerman, *Trans. AIEE*, **56**:566 (1937). Finch, *Ind. Eng. Chem.*, **32**:1021 (1940).

[2] *Sci. Lubrication*, p. 18, March, 1921. Rodman, *Elec. World*, **79**:1271 (1922). Stäger, *Schweiz. elektrotech. Ver.*, *Bull.* 16, pp.188, 214, 1925. Ham and Thompson, *J. Inst. Petrol.*, **36**:673 (1950).

[3] Rodman, *op. cit.*, p. 1273.

[4] *J. Inst. Elec. Eng. (London)*, **67**:527 (1929).

[5] For the saturated hydrocarbon gases, electric strength increases with length of the hydrocarbon chain. Devine and Crowe, *J. Chem. Phys.*, **25**:1053 (1956).

freedom from water, is highly significant.   A water content of 0.1 per cent will lower an original dry insulating value from 250 kv per sq cm to about 22 kv; higher water content causes little additional change.[1]

The deterioration of transformer oils in service is closely connected with oxidation by air,[2] which brings on deposition of sludge on the coils and the development of acids, resulting in overheating and corrosion, respectively.   The sludges formed are of three types:[3] (1) those attributed to the direct oxidation of the hydrocarbon constituents to oil-insoluble products, (2) soaps, resulting from the reaction of acidic products of oxidation with metals in the transformer, and (3) the carbon formed by any arc or corona discharge occurring in service.

The first two types of sludge and the simultaneously formed acidic products may be attributable to oxidation of the less refined and the more refined oils, respectively.[4]   Overrefining is undesirable on account of the natural inhibitors removed.   Drastic refining with sulfuric acid has further limitations because the finished oil is characterized by rapid acid development, even though the sludge formation may be low.   This may in part be due to traces of oil-soluble sulfonic acids or salts remaining in the oil after neutralization or contact with solid adsorbents.[5]

The formation of sludge through oxidative processes has received much attention, not only in insulating oils but also in turbine lubricants and automotive oils.   The exact chemistry involved is still somewhat uncertain but apparently polymerization and condensation of oxidation products, such as hydroxy and unsaturated alcohols, aldehydes, ketones, and acids to oil-insoluble products, are involved.   The acids formed are reported to be hydroxynaphthenic[6] together with carbonyl-containing hydroxy acids and their anhydrides.[7]   The oxidation of transformer oils (with or without catalysts, which may be metal salts,[8] or transformer parts other than the metals, such as varnish on the coils, celluosic insula-

[1] Gemant, *Naturwissenschaften*, **13**:726 (1925).   Stager, *Z. angew. Chem.*, **39**:308 (1926).   See also Hockaday and McDonald, *Gen. Elec. Rev.*, **32**:243 (1929).   Evans, Davenport, and Revukas, *Ind. Eng. Chem., Anal. Ed.*, **13**:589 (1941).   Dickson, *J. Inst. Petrol.*, **37**:373 (1951).   Clark, *Ind. Eng. Chem.*, **44**:887 (1952).

[2] Balsbaugh and Oncley, *Ind. Eng. Chem.*, **31**:318 (1939).   Evans and Davenport, *Ind. Eng. Chem., Anal. Ed.*, **9**:321 (1937).

[3] Rodman, *Trans. Am. Electrochem. Soc.*, **40**:105 (1921).

[4] Ford, *Elec. Eng.*, **55**:371 (1936).   Stager, *Petroleum Z.*, **33**(7):1 (1937).   Clark and Raab, *Ind. Eng. Chem.*, **34**:110 (1942).

[5] Mizushima and Yamada, *C.A.*, **25**:195 (1931).   Stadnikov and Vozzhinska, *Petroleum Z.*, **25**:651 (1929).   Wood-Mallock, *J. Inst. Petrol.*, **32**:365 (1946).

[6] Marcusson and Bauerschafer, *Petroleum Z.*, **22**:572 (1926).

[7] Kreulen and Kreulen van Selms, *J. Inst. Petrol.*, **35**:88 (1949).

[8] The metal salts are reported to be of acids in the molecular weight range of C_{12} to C_{32}.   *J. Soc. Chem. Ind.*, **44**:B-161 (1925).

tors, etc.[1]) follows the same path kinetically as indicated for hydrocarbons in other types of service.[2] The chain reaction involved is successfully inhibited commercially by the addition of small amounts of antioxidants, and the useful life of a transformer oil is extended to many times its normal period.[3] The antioxidants normally employed are phenyl-alpha-naphthylamine and alkylated phenols, such as 2,6-di-*t*-butyl-4-methyl-phenol.[4] Selenium and sulfur compounds, benzyl-*p*-anisidine, and alkyl-phenylphosphites[5] are also effective.

The testing of transformer oils for suitability, in addition to the conventional inspection data (flash and pour points, viscosity, etc.) and determination of insulating value,[6] is concerned mostly with accelerated oxidation tests aimed at estimating probable life in service. Various procedures have been suggested.[7] Nearly all involve heating the oil at a temperature near 120°C in air or oxygen, usually in the presence of copper as an oxidation catalyst. The changes followed are color, interfacial tension,[8] acidity development, sludge and water formation, steam emulsion number, and power factor.[9]

Oils used for liquid-filled cables approximate more nearly the properties of transformer oils than of those used for paper-wrapped cables. Moderately refined distillates of viscosity about 100 sec Saybolt at 100°F fill the requirement.

As indicated above, the paper-wrapped, oil-impregnated cables contain heavy distillate oils only moderately refined. These are usually dehydrated and deaerated with care before application. Failures, involving

[1] Norris, *Elec. Times*, **107**:612 (1945). Burlando, *Chim. & ind.*, **60**:461 (1948). Irving and Thompson, *J. Inst. Petrol.*, **37**:67 (1951). Massey, *J. Inst. Petrol.*, **38**:281 (1952).

[2] Ornstein, Janssen, Krijgsman, and terHorst, *Physica*, **2**:201 (1935); *C.A.*, **29**:7060 (1930); *Proc. Acad. Sci. Amsterdam*, **39**:566 (1936); *C.A.*, **30**:5775 (1936). Hurworth, *J. Inst. Elect. Engrs.* (*London*), **95**(3):28, 342 (1948). Irving and Thompson, *J. Inst. Petrol.*, **37**:67 (1951). Massey, *J. Inst. Petrol.*, **38**:361 (1952).

[3] Reamer and Larsen, *ASTM Bull.* 149, p. 58, 1947.

[4] Reamer and Larsen, *op. cit.; Elec. World*, **130**(11):106 (1948). Berberich, *ASTM Bull.* 149, p. 64, 1947. Seabert and Sarchet, *Elec. World*, **133**(19):84 (1950).

[5] Reamer and Larsen, *op. cit.* Berberich, *op. cit.* Seabert and Sarchet, *op. cit.* Mizushima and Yamada, *J. Soc. Chem. Ind. Japan*, **32**:848 (1929). Wood-Mallock, *J. Inst. Petrol.*, **32**:365 (1946).

[6] Balsbaugh, *ASTM Bull.* 149, p. 75, 1947. ASTM D 117–54T.

[7] Staeger, *Ind. Eng. Chem.*, **17**:1272 (1925). Heyden and Typke, *Petroleum Z.*, **21**:1377 (1925); **21**:1553 (1925). Ford, *Ind. Eng. Chem.*, **19**:1165 (1927).

[8] Sommerman, "Science of Petroleum," vol. II, p. 1361, Oxford University Press, New York and London, 1938. Lawrence, *ibid.*, p. 1369.

[9] Balsbaugh, Howell, and Assof, *Ind. Eng. Chem.*, **32**:1497 (1940). Clark, *Proc. ASTM*, **40**:1213 (1940). Baker, *ASTM Bull.* 146, p. 90, 1947. Gerell, *ASTM Bull.* 146, p. 92, 1947. Walsh, *ASTM Bull.* 146, p. 95, 1947; 187, p. 55, 1953. Clark, *Proc. ASTM*, **49**:1041 (1949).

the puncturing of the paper wrapping, presumably by silent discharges, are of some interest. Silent discharges occurring at weak points in the insulation release gas bubbles[1] and waxy polymers, which serve, the former particularly, as loci for further and more destructive discharges. It is interesting to note that aromatic and polyaromatic hydrocarbons not only release no gas themselves but help to suppress gas formation in oil mixtures containing them. Oxidation is of significance for these oils also; electrical conductivity and dielectric losses are increased, and the ability to spread on water increases considerably in proportion to a small increase in acidity.[2]

XVI-4. Petroleum Insecticides. Petroleum oils, as such, usually applied in water-emulsion form, have marked killing power for certain species of insects.[3] For many applications, where their own effectiveness is too slight, the oils serve as carriers for active poisons, as in household and livestock sprays.

The most extensive use of petroleum itself as a killing agent is in fruit-tree sprays. The spraying of swamp waters with an oil film as a method of mosquito control has been practiced to some extent.[4] The fruit-tree spray oils are known to be effective in control of scale insects, leaf rollers, red spiders, tree hoppers, mites, moth eggs, and aphids. Molecular weight and structure appear to be the factors determining insecticidal power of these oils. Olefins and aromatics are both highly toxic to insects but they also have a detrimental effect on the plant. For this reason spray oils generally receive a refining treatment, especially those

---

[1] Schoepfle and Connell, *Ind. Eng. Chem.*, **21**:529 (1929). Nowak, *Petroleum Z.*, **29**(2):1 (1933). Hahnel, *Arch. Electroteck*, **36**:716 (1942); *Chem. Zentr.*, **1**:1967 (1943).

[2] Race, *J. Phys. Chem.*, **36**:1928 (1932). Piper, Thomas, and Smith, *Ind. Eng. Chem.*, **28**:843 (1936). Clark, *Ind. Eng. Chem.*, **31**:327 (1939). Finch, *Ind. Eng. Chem.*, **32**:1021 (1940). Trautman and Arnquist, *Ind. Eng. Chem.*, **32**:1535 (1940). Piper and Kerstein, *Ind. Eng. Chem.*, **36**:1104 (1944). Piper, Treend, and Bevis, *Ind. Eng. Chem.*, **40**:323 (1948).

[3] For general references on petroleum oils as insecticides, see Scoggin, Steiner, and Allen, *Soap Sanit. Chemicals*, **22**(4):149 (1946). Chapman and Pearce, *Agr. Chemicals*, part I, **2**(3):17 (1947); part II, **2**(4):35 (1947). Crafts and Reiber, *Hilgardia*, **18**(2):77 (1948). De Ong, "The Chemistry and Uses of Insecticides," p. 112, Reinhold Publishing Corporation, New York, 1948. Ebeling, "Subtropic Entomology," p. 165, Lithotype Process Co., San Francisco, 1950. *ACS Joint Symposium on the Agricultural Applications of Petroleum Products*, 1950. Shepard, "The Chemistry and Action of Insecticides," p. 191, McGraw-Hill Book Company, Inc., New York, 1951.

[4] MacFie, *Bull. Entomol. Research*, **7** (3):277 (1917). Ryles and Majumder, *Malay. Med. J.*, **2**:144 (1927); *U.S. Publ. Health Eng. Abstracts*, **E-789**:17 (1927). DeRock and Swellengrabel, *C.A.*, **23**:1977 (1929). Ramsay and Carpenter, *Malaria Survey of India*, **3**(2):203 (1923); *Bull. Rubber Growers' Assoc.*, **15**:98 (1933). Lord, *J. Inst. Petrol.*, **27**:73 (1941). Powers and Heedlee, *J. Econ. Entomol.*, **32**:219 (1939). Hensill and Tikenko, *J. Econ. Entomol.*, **32**:36 (1939).

of the summer oil type which come into contact with foliage. In these oils the unsulfonatable residue (with $37N$ sulfuric acid) is generally 90 per cent or higher; for those to be applied in the dormant season it may fall as low as 60 or 70 per cent. Of the paraffins and naphthenes that compose the bulk of the refined spray oil, the former appear to be the more toxic.[1] With both naphthenic and paraffinic hydrocarbons the insecticidal effect increases with molecular weight but becomes constant at about 350 for each;[2] the maximum toxicity has also been attributed to that fraction boiling between 240 and 300°C at 40 mm mercury pressure.[3]

The spray oil emulsions generally contain from 2 to 12 per cent of oil. There is some preference for quick-breaking emulsions, containing little or no stabilizing agent, so that a film of oil may be formed on the plant as soon as possible.[4]

The physical properties of petroleum oils, such as their solvent power for waxy coatings on leaf surfaces and insect bodies, make them suitable as carriers for more active fungicides and insecticides.[5] The additive substance may vary from fatty acids and soaps, the latter intended chiefly to affect favorably the spreading properties of the oil, to physiologically quite active compounds, such as pyrethrum, nicotine, rotenone, DDT, thiocyanates, methoxychlor, chlordane, lindane, etc. Solubility of the chlorine-containing insecticides is often aided by a proportion of an accessory solvent rich in methylnaphthalenes. The hydrocarbon base solvent used in household insecticides is generally a high-flash (150°F) 380 to 480°F boiling naphtha which has been heavily treated with concentrated sulfuric acid. Household and livestock sprays are also made up for application from aerosol containers in which liquefied gases (generally dichlorodifluoromethane and trichloromonofluoromethane) are used as the propelling agents.

Petroleum oils are widely used as weed killers; their effectiveness appears to be in the order of aromatics > olefins > saturates. Dry cleaner's naphtha, a highly refined solvent in the 150 to 200°C boiling range, is used as a selective spray for deweeding vegetable plots, such as those in which carrots are grown.[6]

[1] Pearce, Chapman and Frear, *Ind. Eng. Chem.*, **40**:284 (1948).

[2] *Ibid.*

[3] Green, *Ind. Eng. Chem.*, **19**:931 (1927).

[4] De Ong and Knight, *J. Econ. Entomol.*, **18**:299 (1925). De Ong, *API Bull.*, **7**(27):191 (1926); *Oil Gas J.*, **24**(36):142 (1926); *Calif. Dept. Agr., Monthly Bull.*, **18**:65 (1929). Woodman, *J. Phys. Chem.*, **33**:88 (1929). Spuler, Overley, and Green, *Wash. Agr. Exp. Sta. Bull.* 247, p. 3, 1931.

[5] De Ong, *Ind. Eng. Chem.*, **20**:826 (1928).

[6] Sweet, Kunkel, and Raleigh, *Proc. Am. Soc. Hort. Sci.*, **48**:475 (1946).

BY-PRODUCTS

XVI-5. Petroleum Coke. Petroleum coke is the residue left by the destructive distillation of reduced petroleum.[1] That formed in catalytic cracking operations is nonrecoverable, since it is employed as fuel for the process. The coke collected from thermal processes varies in character. That from the old-fashioned batch coking operation is hard, porous, and brittle; that from continuous and delayed coking processes is more likely to be soft and oily, depending on the time and the temperature to which it has been exposed. Batch-still coke is grey in color and gives a somewhat metallic ring when struck. Cracking-still coke is black and sooty. Heavy refinery residues, not suitable for fuel use, may be heated in specially designed ovens[2] for conversion into gas, gasoline, fuel oil, and coke.

The proximate analysis (air-dry basis) for the several types of petroleum coke are tabulated below.[3] The composition varies with the source

	From cracking still	From coking still	From Knowles oven
Moisture, per cent............	0.1 – 5.0	0.0– 0.5	0.0– 0.5
Volatile matter, per cent.......	3.5 –18.0	4.0– 7.0	1.0– 5.0
Fixed carbon, per cent.........	79.0 –92.0	92.0–96.0	95.0–99.0
Ash, per cent.................	0.05– 1.5	0.2– 1.3	0.2– 1.3
Sulfur, per cent..............	0.2 – 4.0	1.0– 2.5	0.7– 1.6
Btu per lb..................	15,200–16,200	14,800–15,500	14,200–15,000

of oil but, in general, large amounts of high-molecular weight hydrocarbon-like complexes, very rich in carbon and correspondingly poor in hydrogen, make up a high proportion. Chemically combined hydrogen is not lost from such cokes until graphitization temperatures (1000 to 1200°C) are reached.[4] The solubility of petroleum coke in carbon disulfide may be as high as 50 to 80 per cent.[5]

Petroleum coke is employed for a number of purposes but its chief industrial use is in the manufacture of carbon electrodes for the refining of aluminum, which requires a pure carbon, low in ash and reasonably

[1] For formation and composition of petroleum cokes, see Berry and Edgeworth-Johnson, *Ind. Eng. Chem.*, **36**:1140 (1944); **37**:551 (1945).

[2] Knowles ovens. See Ziegenhain, *Oil Gas J.*, **30**(17):16 (1931). Foster, *Natl. Petrol. News*, **25**(10):26 (1933). Thomas, *Advances in Chem. Ser.*, No. 5, p. 278, 1951.

[3] Stroud, "Science of Petroleum," vol. IV, p. 2772, Oxford University Press, New York and London, 1938. See also Nelson, *Oil Gas J.*, **54**(30):117 (1955).

[4] Lowry, *J. ACS*, **46**:824 (1924).

[5] Frolich, *Chem. & Met. Eng.*, **38**:343 (1931).

free of sulfur.   The volatile matter must be removed by calcining.   One such heat-treated (2700°F) coke analyzed 99.26 per cent fixed carbon, 0.35 per cent ash, and 0.64 per cent sulfur.[1]   The ash may contain small amounts of cobalt, nickel, tin, vanadium, and molybdenum.[2]   In addition, the mineral matter in various oils ending as ash in a coke has been reported to contain iron, aluminum, phosphorus, manganese, silica, calcium, magnesium, lead, titanium, sodium, copper, gold, and silver.[3]

In addition to its use as a metallurgical reducing agent,[4] it is employed in the manufacture of carbon brushes, silicon carbide abrasives, and structural carbon (pipes, Raschig rings, etc).   A sizable amount is converted into calcium carbide and then into acetylene.[5]

XVI-6. Sulfuric Acid Sludge.[6]   The sludges produced in sulfuric acid refining are mainly of two types: those from light oils (gasoline and kerosene) and those from lubricating stocks, medicinal oils, etc.   In the treatment of the latter, it is believed that the action of the acid is in part physical, involving the precipitation of asphaltenes and resins and the solution of color-bearing complexes and sulfur compounds.[7]   Sulfonation and oxidation-reduction reactions take place to a relatively minor degree, for much of the acid used can be recovered.   In the desulfurization of cracked distillates, however, chemical action becomes more important, with polymerization, ester formation, aromatic-olefin condensations, sulfonation, etc., taking place.   Nitrogen bases are neutralized and naphthenic acids are dissolved by the acid.   The composition of the sludge is thus very complex, depending largely upon the oil treated, the strength of the acid, and the treating temperature.

Sulfuric acid sludges from isoparaffin alkylation and lubricating oil treating are frequently decomposed thermally with agitation to produce sulfur dioxide (which is returned to the refiner's sulfuric acid plant) and "sludge acid coke."   The latter, in the form of small pea-sized pellets as produced, finds ready use as a substitute for charcoal in the manufacture of carbon disulfide.   Sulfuric acid coke is different from other petroleum coke in that it is pyrophoric in air and also will react directly with sulfur vapors to form carbon disulfide.

XVI-7. Petroleum Sulfonic Acids.   Sulfuric acid treating of petroleum distillates is generally applied to dissolve out unstable or colored sub-

[1] Watkins, *Chem. & Met. Eng.*, **44**:153 (1937).

[2] Shirey, *Ind. Eng. Chem.*, **23**:1151 (1931).   See also Nelson, *op. cit.*

[3] Thomas, *J. Inst. Petrol. Technologists*, **10**:216 (1924).   "Science of Petroleum," vol. II, p. 1053, Oxford University Press, New York and London, 1938.

[4] For discussion of uses of petroleum coke, see Weber, *Oil Gas J.*, **52**(46):151 (1954).

[5] Jones, Parker, and Strobel, *Oil Gas J.*, **52**(52):97 (1954).   Specifications of petroleum cokes for various uses are given by Nelson, *op. cit.*

[6] See also Sec. XII-2.

[7] Weir, Houghton, and Majewski, *Ind. Eng. Chem.*, **22**:1293 (1930).

stances and sulfur compounds as well as to precipitate asphalts. When the conditions become more drastic, as in the treatment of lubricating stocks with large amounts of concentrated acid or when fuming acid is used in the manufacture of white oils, sulfonation becomes important and considerable quantities of petroleum sulfonic acids are formed. Extensive side reactions, mainly oxidation, take place simultaneously, the extent increasing with the proportion of sulfur trioxide in the acid; it is sometimes possible to suppress these by keeping the temperature low. The sludges resulting from acid treating of lubricating stocks presented a disposal problem even in the primitive stages of the industry. The process was suggested by Silliman in 1855, and the discovery of methods for separating out useful by-products came fairly early. The chemistry of sulfuric acid treating has been discussed briefly in Chap. VII. The lower paraffins and naphthenes are comparatively resistant to sulfuric acid if kept cool, and in treating even cracked gasolines (i.e., those containing olefins and aromatics) low temperature and short contact time can effectively control the extent of reaction.[1]

While many of the lower paraffins are physically absorbed by concentrated and fuming sulfuric acids,[2] chemical activity increases with rise in molecular weight; compounds containing tertiary carbons are especially responsive.[3] *n*-Hexane, *n*-heptane, and *n*-octane are essentially inactive in cold fuming acid; but at the boiling point of the hydrocarbons, rapid sulfonation takes place to give mono- and disulfonic acids.[4] The five- and six-membered ring lower naphthenes are stable to cold concentrated sulfuric acid. Fuming acid acts on cyclohexane to give mono- and dinaphthenic and monoaromatic sulfonic acids along with products based on cyclic olefins formed through hydrogen-transfer reactions. With methylcyclohexane oxidation is the more important reaction.[5]

Tendency to reaction with sulfuric acid increases as the molecular weight of the hydrocarbons rises, and this is particularly true of the mixed molecules present in lubricating oil stocks. In fact, both sulfona-

[1] On methods of preparation of individual sulfonic acids, see Hemilian, *Ann.*, **168**:145 (1873). Wagner and Reid, *J. ACS*, **53**:3407 (1931). Nollar and Gordon, *J. ACS*, **55**:1090 (1933). Hallerich and Grünert, *Ber.*, **74B**:1531 (1941). Suter, Malkemus, and Archer, *J. ACS*, **63**:978, 1594 (1941); **66**:1105 (1944); **67**:827 (1945). Lantz, *Bull. soc. chim.*, **12**:1004 (1945). Proell, Adams, and Shoemaker, *Ind. Eng. Chem.*, **40**:1129 (1948). Miron and Richter, *J. ACS*, **71**:453 (1949).

[2] Orndorff and Young, *Am. Chem. J.*, **15**:249 (1893). Mabery, *Am. Chem. J.*, **28**:165 (1902). Ormandy and Craven, *J. Inst. Petrol. Technologists*, **12**:68 (1926). Carpenter, *J. Inst. Petrol. Technologists*, **12**:518 (1926). Tropsch and Dittrich, *Brennstoff-Chem.*, **6**:169 (1925).

[3] Brooks and Humphrey, *J. ACS*, **40**:822 (1918).

[4] Worstall, *Am. Chem. J.*, **20**:664 (1898).

[5] Burkhardt, *J. Chem. Soc.*, 1930, p. 2387. Markownikoff, *Ann.*, **341**:131 (1905).

tion and oxidative degradation are normal accompaniments of acid refining of higher petroleum fractions.

The points of attack by the acid are not known, but it is not difficult to surmise that aromatic rings and tertiary carbon atoms in naphthene rings, both present in the mixed molecules making up lubricating fractions of petroleum, would be quite reactive. Ordinarily, a manufacturer of sulfonates and white oils will prefer a charge stock which has already been refined by solvent extraction with, say, furfural. Since such a solvent removes these more highly aromatic fractions, it can be concluded that the remaining hydrocarbons, which give higher yields of better sulfonates, are those in which aromatic rings are entirely absent or are low in proportion to the naphthene rings and paraffinic chains. It seems likely then that the preferred sulfonic acids of commerce are naphthene sulfonic acids. Work on the constitution, and even the empirical composition, of these products has been quite inadequate. General formulae corresponding to $C_nH_{2n-10}SO_3H$ or $C_nH_{2n-12}SO_3H$ have been suggested; an average composition for a mixture resulting from sulfonation of what seems to have been a medicinal white oil (low aromatics, high naphthenes) was reported[1] as $C_{20}H_{27}SO_3H$. Fractions analyzing $C_{17}H_{21}SO_3H$ and $C_{19}H_{35}SO_3H$ were hydrolyzed to yield hydrocarbons of definitely cyclic nature. Molecular weights[2] of 374 and of 590 with a sulfur content of 5 per cent[3] have been observed. An idea of the general composition of petroleum sulfonic acids is shown by the following analysis:[4]

	Oil-soluble monosulfonic acids	Oil-insoluble monosulfonic acids	Oil-soluble short-chain disulfonic acids	Oil-soluble highly aromatic sulfonic acids
Per cent aromatic rings......	38.8	55.4	66.3	80.8
Per cent naphthenic rings....	18.0	32.2	9.6	19.3
Per cent paraffinic chains.....	43.3	12.4	24.1	0.0

Detergents of the sulfonate type are well known. They are made by sulfonation of alkylated benzenes. The alkylation is achieved by treatment of the aromatic in presence of anhydrous aluminum chloride, with a monochlorinated kerosene or naphtha fraction, or with an olefin polymer such as a butene trimer or a propylene tetramer; for the polymerization

[1] Shestokoff. See Gurwitsch, "Scientific Principles of Petroleum Technology," pp. 391, 461, D. Van Nostrand Company, Inc., Princeton, N.J., 1932.

[2] Berry, British Patent 699,341, 1953.

[3] Schindler, *Petroleum Z.*, **33**(15):1 (1937).

[4] Treffler, *Soap Sanit. Chemicals*, **26**(8):34 (1950).

an acid catalyst is required. The number, size, and structure of the alkyl side chains are important in determining the performance of the finished detergent. Sulfonation is effected at ordinary temperatures.

The alkyl sulfonic acids are quite stable although they can be broken up by either acid[1] or alkaline[2] hydrolysis and they react with aromatic bases to liberate the parent hydrocarbon;[3] the methyl sulfonic acid is the most resistant. The secondary alkyl sulfonic acids are less stable than the normal compounds, and the stability increases with molecular weight.[4] The per cent of decomposition of the sodium salts (sulfite splitting), on treating with $3.7N$ alkali for 3 hr at 341°C, was found to be as follows:[4]

Methyl	1.5	Amyl	13.3
Ethyl	62.7	sec-Amyl	64.2
Propyl	20.2	Hexyl	11.7
Isopropyl	88.6	sec-Hexyl	54.9
Butyl	17.3	Benzene	5.0
sec-Butyl	75.2		

Two general methods are applied for the recovery of sulfonic acids from sulfonated oils and their sludges. In one case, the acids are selectively removed by adsorbents or by solvents (generally low-molecular-weight alcohols); and in the other, by salting out with organic salts or bases.[5] Phenol sulfonic acids may be present, even in highly purified petroleum sulfonic acids.[6] Sulfonic and naphthenic acids may be separated in their aqueous mixtures by the addition of sodium chloride; the naphthenic acids remain in solution, while the sodium salts of sulfonic acids are precipitated.[7]

Petroleum sulfonic acids may be roughly divided into those soluble in hydrocarbons and those soluble in water. Because of their color characteristics the former are referred to as "mahogany" and the latter as "green" acids. The composition of each type will vary with the source of the oil sulfonated and the concentration of the acids produced. In general, those formed during light acid treatment are water-soluble,

[1] Serada, *Ber.*, **68**:1933 (1935).

[2] Wagner and Reid, *J. ACS*, **53**:3407 (1931).

[3] Serada, Nacura, and Udrycki, *Ber.*, **68**:1935 (1935).

[4] Wagner and Reid, *op. cit.*

[5] For a detailed discussion of petroleum sulfonic acid purification and commercial applications, see Ellis, "Chemistry of Petroleum Derivatives," vol. I, p. 1013, Reinhold Publishing Corporation, New York, 1934; vol. II, p. 1070, 1937. Shindler, *op. cit.* Berry, *op. cit.* For analysis of oil-soluble petroleum sulfonates, see Archibald, *Ind. Eng. Chem., Anal. Ed.*, **13**:608 (1941). Koch, *Ind. Eng. Chem., Anal. Ed.*, **16**:25 (1944). Brooks, Peters, and Lyken, *Ind. Eng. Chem., Anal. Ed.*, **18**:544 (1946).

[6] von Pilat and Serada, *Refiner Nat. Gasoline Mfr.*, **19**(2):50 (1940).

[7] von Pilat and Serada, *Fettchem. Umschau*, **41**:171, 200, 237 (1934).

while oil-soluble acids result from more drastic sulfonation.[1] A more specific classification, although still empirical, based upon the solubilities of their calcium salts in water and ethyl ether has been developed.[2] The acids have been classified into four types.

TABLE XVI-1

Sulfonic acid	Solubility in mineral oils	Source	Solubility of calcium sulfonate	
			Water	Ethyl ether
α	Insoluble	Mainly in the acid sludge but partly in the oil phase	Insoluble	Insoluble
β	Soluble	Mainly in oil phase but partly in acid sludge if oleum is used	Insoluble	Soluble
γ	Insoluble	Only in the acid sludge	Soluble	Insoluble
δ	Soluble	Aqueous-alcohol extract of acid sludge and in oil phase if oleum is used	Insoluble	Soluble

Practically nothing is known about the chemical composition of any of the types given above.   It is stated that the nature of the γ-acids is independent of the oil.   A purified γ-sodium sulfonate analyzed $C_{13}H_{13}SO_3Na$.

Another classification has been applied to water-soluble and oil-soluble sulfonic acids, with division into mono- and disulfonic compounds; each of these is subdivided into hydrocarbon, resin, and asphaltene sulfonic acids.[3]

The salts of mixed petroleum sulfonic acids have many commercial applications.   They find use as anticorrosion agents,[4] leather softeners,[5] and flotation agents;[6] they have been used to replace turkey red oil (sulfonated castor oil) in the textile industry.   Lead salts have been employed in greases as extreme pressure agents, and alkyl esters are applied as alkylating agents.   Of possibly greater importance, however, has been the

---

[1] Hetzer, *Chem. Z.*, **64**:160 (1940).

[2] von Pilat, Serada, and Szankowski, *Petroleum Z.*, **29**(3):1 (1930); **31**(10):1 (1935); *Refiner Nat. Gasoline Mfr.*, **19**(2):50 (1940).   Hetzer, *op. cit.* Cherchez, *Monit. pétrol roumain*, **44**:581 (1943).   David, *J. Inst. Petrol.*, **35**:563 (1949).

[3] Sperling, *Ind. Eng. Chem.*, **40**:890 (1948).

[4] Baker, Singleterry, and Solomon, *Ind. Eng. Chem.*, **46**:1035 (1954).   Desnos, *J. usines Gaz.*, **75**:246 (1951); *Chem. Abstr.*, **46**:5827 (1952).   For discussion of adsorption of sulfonates on metal surfaces in rust inhibition, see Hong, Eisler, Bootzin, and Harrison, *Corrosion*, **10**:343 (1954).

[5] Rhodes, *Leather and Shoes*, **115**(13):53 (1948).

[6] Keck and Jasberg, *Eng. Mining J.*, **140**(6):49 (1939).

inclusion of their alkaline earth salts in detergent compositions for motor oils and the alkali salts as detergents in aqueous systems.[1]

CHEMICALS DERIVED FROM PETROLEUM

The manufacture of chemical products from petroleum stocks is based on ample supply and the ready response of the simpler types to basic chemical reactions such as oxidation, halogenation, nitration, dehydrogenation, addition, polymerization, alkylation, etc. The low-molecular-weight paraffins and olefins, as found in natural gas and refinery gases, and the simple aromatic hydrocarbons have so far been of the most interest because it is only with these that individual species can readily be isolated and dealt with. A wide range of compounds is possible and many are being manufactured. Some idea of the scope of the industry is shown in Fig. XVI-1, which gives a general (but by no means complete) picture of the chemicals originating from methane, ethane, propane, and the butanes, and the corresponding olefins. A sizable group of products is also prepared from liquid and even solid fractions from petroleum; sometimes they are used as gross mixtures.

XVI-8. Acetylene. Acetylene is a valuable source material for acetaldehyde, vinyl chloride, vinyl acetate, acrylonitrile, and neoprene rubber.[2] It is still prepared in greatest quantity from calcium carbide, but direct manufacture from natural gas is also employed. Possible methods of doing this are:

1. Partial oxidation of natural gas, producing carbon monoxide and hydrogen as by-products.[3]

2. High temperature short-time cracking of natural gas, ethane, propane, or butane.[4] Cracking of naphtha feed stocks is also reported.[5]

---

[1] For reviews of petroleum or derived petroleum sulfonic acids as detergents, see Pritzker, *Natl. Petrol. News*, **37**(40):R-793 (1945). Weil, *Petrol. Refiner*, **27**(5):126 (1948). Greissinger and Nevinson, *Advances in Chem. Ser.*, No. 5, p. 324, 1951. Davidsohn, *Ind. Chemist*, **28**:198 (1952). Birch, *J. Inst. Petrol.*, **38**:69 (1952). Snell, *Petrol. Processing*, **1**(7):982 (1952).

[2] For chart showing products derived from acetylene, see Lowy, *Ind. Eng. Chem.*, *News Ed.*, **11**:156 (1933). See also, Reppe, "Acetylene Chemistry," Meyer, New York, 1949.

[3] Sherwood, *Erdöl u. Kohle*, **7**:819 (1954); *Petroleum (London)*, **29**(4):135 (1956).

[4] Sherwood, *op. cit.* Bogart and Dodd, *Chem. Eng. Progr.*, **50**:372 (1954). Farnsworth, Manes, McGure, and Bretz, *Ind. Eng. Chem.*, **47**:1517 (1955). Kramer and Happel in "The Chemistry of Petroleum Hydrocarbons," Brooks, Boord, Kurtz, and Schmerling (eds.), vol. II, p. 71, Reinhold Publishing Corporation New York, 1955. Akin, Reid, and Schrader, *Oil Gas. J.*, **56**, **2**:78 (1958).

[5] Linden and Reid, *Petrol. Refiner*, **35**, **6**:189 (1956). See *Chem. Week*, May 18, 1957, p. 112, for treatment of light hydrocarbons in a methane-oxygen flame; also, *Chem. Eng. News*, **35**(24):76 (1957).

XVI-9. Chemicals Derived from Olefinic Hydrocarbons. The olefins present in cracked products and particularly those in cracking-still gases offer promising source materials.   To meet the demand, individual olefins are also produced by cracking the corresponding paraffins or heavier oils. Thus, ethylene is produced from the cracking of various stocks, such as ethane, propane, butane, and liquids such as gas oil, naphthas, and reduced crudes.   Propylene is produced from thermal and catalytic cracking of naphthas and gas oils as well as propane and butane.

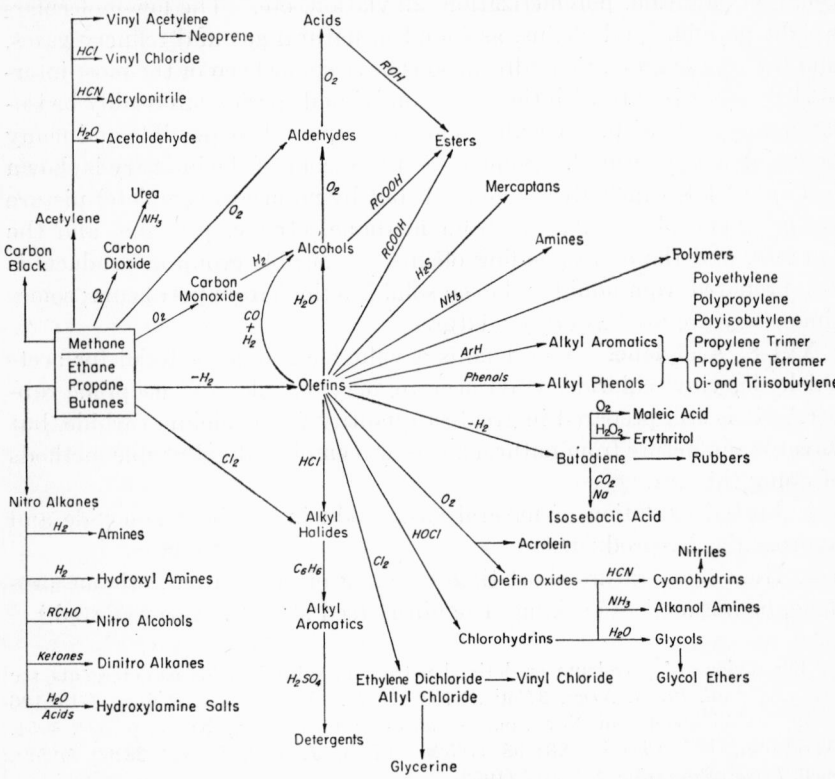

Fig. XVI-1. General types of products derived from C_1-C_4 paraffins.

Alcohols.   The earliest method for conversion of olefins into alcohols involved their absorption in sulfuric acid to form esters, followed by dilution and hydrolysis, generally with the aid of steam; it is still widely used. In case of ethyl alcohol, the direct catalytic hydration of ethylene can be employed.   Higher alcohols are formed by the addition of carbon monoxide and hydrogen to olefins (Oxo process).[1]

---

[1] Some alcohols can be made by methods other than double-bond reactions, such as reaction of carbon monoxide and hydrogen; oxidation of propane and butane; hydrolysis of alkyl chlorides; aldol condensation of aldehydes.

ETHYL ALCOHOL.   Ethylene is readily absorbed in 98 to 100 per cent sulfuric acid at 75 to 80°C.   Higher temperatures cause undesirable oxidation-reduction reactions, and high acid concentrations result in the loss of ethylene to ethionic acid and carbyl sulfate.[1]   Polymer formation is not important in the case of ethylene.   Both the mono- and diethyl sulfates are formed; hydrolysis takes place readily on dilution with water and heating.   A secondary reaction between the neutral ester and the alcohol results in the formation of ethyl ether.

$$(C_2H_5)_2SO_4 + C_2H_5OH \rightarrow C_2H_5OC_2H_5 + C_2H_5HSO_4$$

Ether formation can be minimized, if desired, by separating the diethyl sulfate layer before dilution and hydrolyzing it separately under controlled conditions, removing the alcohol vapors as formed.

The direct hydration of ethylene to ethyl alcohol is practiced over phosphoric acid on diatomaceous earth[2] or promoted tungstic oxide[3] under about 100 psi pressure and at 300°C.   Purer ethylene is required than in the acid absorption process.   Because of equilibrium relations, the conversion per pass is low but high yields are possible by recycling.   Propylene[4] and the normal butenes[5] can also be hydrated directly.

ISOPROPYL ALCOHOL.   One of the first alcohol syntheses practiced commercially was that of isopropyl alcohol from propylene.   Sulfuric acid absorbs propylene more readily than it does ethylene, but care must be taken to avoid polymer formation.   This side reaction is retarded by keeping the mixture relatively cool and using acid of about 85 per cent strength under 300 to 400 psi pressure.   Dilution with an inert absorption oil is also practiced.   Polymerization can further be retarded by maintaining a high partial pressure of propylene, which favors the formation of the neutral ester.   Weaker acid (75 per cent) may be employed at elevated pressures.   Hydrolysis of the diluted ester mixture gives some isopropyl ether as a by-product.   Acetone is readily made from isopropyl alcohol either by catalytic oxidation or by dehydrogenation over metal (usually copper) catalysts.

SECONDARY BUTYL ALCOHOL.   Secondary butyl alcohol is formed on absorption of 1- or 2-butene by 78 to 80 per cent sulfuric acid, followed by dilution and hydrolysis.   Higher acid concentrations cause considerable

---

[1] Plant and Sidgwick, *J. Soc. Chem. Ind.* **40**:14T (1921).   Michael and Weiner, *J. ACS*, **58**:294 (1936).

[2] Bliss and Dodge, *Ind. Eng. Chem.*, **29**:19 (1937).   Paik, Swann, and Keyes, *Ind. Eng. Chem.*, **30**:173 (1938).   Majewski and Marek, *Ind. Eng. Chem.*, **30**:203 (1938).   Schiffler, Holm, and Brooke, *Ind. Eng. Chem.*, **31**:1099 (1939).   Nelson and Courter, *Chem. Eng. Prog.*, **50**:526 (1954).   Sherwood, *Petrol. Eng.*, **28**(1):C-33 (1956).

[3] Mace and Bonilla, *Chem. Eng. Prog.*, **50**:385 (1954).

[4] Rungs, Bankowski, and Hoffmann, *Brennstoff-Chem.*, **34**:330 (1953).

[5] Dale, Sliprevich, and White, *Ind. Eng. Chem.*, **48**:913 (1956).

polymerization. Secondary butyl alcohol is converted into methyl ethyl ketone by catalytic oxidation or dehydrogenation.

TERTIARY ALCOHOLS. Isobutylene is readily absorbed by 60 to 65 per cent sulfuric acid, and by weaker acids under pressure, the amount dissolved depending on the water present rather than on the acid content. For instance, 35.0 per cent sulfuric acid takes up to 7.2 moles of isobutylene for each mole of acid present,[1] the olefin evidently existing in the solution as the alcohol; similarly, five equivalents of trimethylethylene can be dissolved in 46 per cent acid.[2] Because even dilute acid solutions of the tertiary-base olefins yield the olefins on heating, the reaction liquid is generally neutralized before conducting the hydrolysis step.

HIGHER ALCOHOLS. The tendency toward stable ester formation between olefins and acids decreases rapidly as the size of the olefin increases beyond C_6, and the ease of alcohol formation through sulfuric acid absorption decreases accordingly for the higher-molecular-weight compounds. There are several methods, however, for preparing higher alcohols; one is through aldol condensation reactions and another is by the so-called Oxo reaction. The latter involves the direct addition of carbon monoxide and a hydrogen atom across the double bond of an olefin to form an aldehyde; this in turn is reduced to the alcohol. The hydroformylation is brought about by contacting the olefin with synthesis gas (1:1 carbon monoxide–hydrogen) at 75 to 200°C under 100 to 300 atm pressure over a metal catalyst, usually cobalt. The active catalyst is held to be cobalt hydrocarbonyl, $HCo(CO)_4$, formed by the action of the hydrogen on dicobalt octacarbonyl.[3]

A wide variety of olefins enter the reaction, those containing terminal unsaturation being the most active. The hydroformylation is not specific; the hydrogen and carbon monoxide add across each side of the double bond. Thus, propylene gives a mixture of 60 per cent *n*- and 40 per cent isobutyraldehyde. Terminal and nonterminal olefin isomers, such as 1- and 2-pentene, give essentially the same distribution of straight- and branched-chain C_6 aldehydes, indicating that rapid isomerization takes place. Simple branched structures add mainly at the terminal carbon; isobutylene forms 95 per cent isovaleraldehyde and 5 per cent tri-

[1] Deanesley and Engs, U.S. 2,012,785, 1935.

[2] Norris and Joubert, *J. ACS*, **49**:873 (1927).

[3] For a more detailed account of the Oxo reaction, see Orchin in "The Chemistry of Petroleum Hydrocarbons," Brooks, Boord, Kurtz, and Schmerling (eds.), vol. III, p. 341, Reinhold Publishing Corporation, New York, 1955. Bhattacharyya and Subba Rao, *Petroleum (London)*, **19**:119 (1956). Wender, *Petrol. Refiner*, **35**(12):197 (1956). Bartlett, Kirshenbaum, and Muessig, *ACS, Div. Petrol. Chem., Symposium on Recent Developments in Chemicals from Petroleum*, Preprints, B-51, ACS Meeting, San Francisco, April, 1958.

methylacetaldehyde.   Only one product each is obtained from higher-branched olefins such as the dimethylbutenes and the isomeric diisobutylenes.   Double unsaturated compounds undergo hydroformylation at one double bond and saturation at the other; butadiene, for example, forms C_5 saturated monoaldehydes.

Commercial application of the synthesis has been most successful in the manufacture of isooctyl alcohol from a refinery C_3-C_4 copolymer, decyl alcohol from propylene trimer, and tridecyl alcohol from propylene tetramer.   Important outlets for the higher alcohols lie in their sulfation to make detergents and the formation of esters with dibasic acids for use as plasticizers and synthetic lubricants.

GLYCOLS AND GLYCEROL.   Ethylene glycol is prepared by the hydrolysis of ethylene chlorohydrin or ethylene oxide.   Its main use is for antifreeze mixtures in automobile radiators and for cooling aviation engines; considerable amounts are used as ethylene glycol dinitrate in low-freezing dynamites.   Propylene glycol is also made by the hydrolysis of its chlorohydrin or oxide.[1]

Ethylene chlorohydrin is produced by the addition of hypochlorous acid to ethylene, with ethylene dichloride and dichloroethyl ether as by-products.   The latter, once used as a selective solvent in the refining of oils, can be produced in larger amounts by treating the ethylene chlorohydrin with sulfuric acid.

The dehydrohalogenation of ethylene chlorohydrin over lime forms ethylene oxide, but a fair proportion of this compound is now made by the direct oxidation of ethylene over a silver catalyst.   Ethylene oxide is a very useful intermediate in the synthesis of a wide variety of organic compounds.   It reacts with water to give ethylene glycol, diethylene glycol, and on to long-chain polyethylene glycols with molecular weights as high as 6,000.   A useful solvent, dioxane, is prepared by dehydrating diethylene glycol.   Ethylene oxide reacts with alcohols to form hydroxy ethers, which are used as solvents.   It will react also with various amines; with ammonia, for example, it forms mono-, di-, and triethanol amines; the last forms esters with fatty acids, which are used as emulsifying agents.   Mono- and diethanol amines are employed to remove carbon dioxide and hydrogen sulfide from gases.   Ethylene oxide reacts with hydrogen cyanide to form ethylene cyanohydrin; this on dehydration forms acrylonitrile, which is basic to the production of certain synthetic fibers, viscosity-index improvers, and nitrile rubbers.

Glycerol is produced by chlorinating propylene at elevated temperatures (400 to 600°C) to form allyl chloride; this in turn is hydrolyzed to

[1] For a discussion of the chemistry involved in the hydrolysis of alkylene oxides, see Long and Pritchard, *J. ACS*, **78**:2663, 2667 (1956).

allyl alcohol.   The latter is hypochlorinated to the dichlorohydrin, which is then converted into glycerol by alkaline hydrolysis.[1]

Addition of Halogens.   At ordinary temperatures chlorine reacts with olefins by addition.   Thus ethylene dichloride (a constituent of the scavenging agent in tetraethyllead mixtures) is made in this way from ethylene.[2]   At slightly higher temperatures substitution occurs.   In the chlorination of propylene, a rise of 50°C will change the product from propylene dichloride to allyl chloride.[3]

Polymers.   The polymerization of ethylene (over activated aluminum chloride) into lubricating oils was practiced in Germany during wartime (1940–1944); the product was an emergency material and the process is no longer used.   Valuable solid resins are now obtained, however, as the various polyethylenes.   Pressures in the range of 1,500 to 3,000 psi, applied at 110 to 120°C to ethylene in contact with a 1 per cent solution of benzoyl peroxide in methanol, produce a polymer in the 2,000 to 3,000 molecular-weight range.   Polymerization at 15,000 to 30,000 psi and at 180 to 200°C produces a wax melting at 110°C and of 15,000 to 20,000 molecular weight, containing 0.7 to 1.3 per cent oxygen.[4]   The polymer is not linear; the ratio of methyl to methylene groups is about 1:30.[5]   Considerably lower pressures can be used over catalysts composed of aluminum alkyls in presence of titanium tetrachloride,[6] supported chromic oxide,[7] nickel or cobalt on charcoal,[8] and promoted molybdena-alumina,[9] which at the same time give products more linear in structure.   Polypropylenes can be made in similar ways.   Ethylene-propylene and ethylene-butene mixtures can be treated to give high-molecular-weight copolymers of good elasticity.   First interest in polyethylene centered around its excellent electrical insulating properties; its chemical resistance, toughness, machineability, light weight, and high strength make it suitable for many other uses.

Low-molecular-weight propylene and butene polymers, and copolymers

[1] Williams, *Ind. Chem. Eng., News Ed.*, **16**:630 (1938).   Groll and Hearne, *Ind. Eng. Chem.*, **31**:1530 (1939); *Chem. Eng. Progr.*, **44**(10):16 (1948).

[2] Further chlorination yields trichloro- to hexachloroethanes; these are good degreasing solvents.

[3] Groll and Hearne, *op. cit.*

[4] Richards, *J. Inst. Petrol.*, **34**:237 (1948).

[5] Fox and Martin, *Proc. Roy. Soc. (London)*, **A175**:208 (1940).   Cross, Richards, and Willis, *Discussions Faraday Soc.*, **9**:235 (1950).   Rugg, Smith, and Wartman, *J. Polymer Sci.*, **11**:1 (1953).

[6] Ziegler, *Angew. Chem.*, **64**:323 (1952); *Brennstoff-Chem.*, **33**:193 (1952); **35**:321 (1954); Belgian Patent 533,362, 1954.

[7] Clark, Hogan, Banks, and Lanning, *Ind. Eng. Chem.*, **48**:1152 (1956).   Smith, *Ind. Eng. Chem.*, **48**:1161 (1956).   Jones and Boeke, *Ind. Eng. Chem.*, **48**:1155 (1956).

[8] Peters, Zletz, and Evering, *Ind. Eng. Chem.*, **49**:1879 (1957).

[9] Field and Feller, *Ind. Eng. Chem.*, **49**:1883 (1957).

up through C_{12}, are used as such in motor fuels or as wartime hydrogenation stocks for aviation gasolines. These polymers are generally made over a phosphoric acid catalyst. Propylene trimer (mainly dimethyl-heptenes) and tetramer (trimethylnonenes) are applied in the alkylation of aromatic hydrocarbons for the production of alkylaryl sulfonate detergents, and also as olefinic feed stocks in the manufacture of C_{10} and C_{13} oxo alcohols. Phenol is alkylated by the trimer to make nonylphenol, a chemical intermediate for the manufacture of lubricating oil detergents and other products.

Except for motor fuel use, the normal butenes are not subjected to polymerization reactions. Isobutylene, however, forms several series of valuable products. While di- and triisobutylenes make excellent motor fuel components and hydrogenation stocks for aviation gasolines, they can also be used as alkylating agents for aromatic hydrocarbons and phenols, and as reactants in the oxo alcohol synthesis. Polyisobutylenes in the viscosity range of 55,000 (SSU at 100°F) have been employed as viscosity-index improvers in lubricating oils.[1] The high-molecular-weight poly-isobutylenes are elastomers. Butyl rubber is a copolymer of isobutylene with a small amount of isoprene (about 1.5 to 4.5 per cent). The normal butenes enter the polymerization picture by way of butadiene, the dehydrogenation product, which is copolymerized with styrene (23.5 per cent) to form GR-S rubber,[2] and with acrylonitrile (25 per cent) to form GR-N.

Isoprene, polymerized over aluminum alkyls, is reported to produce an elastomer identical with natural rubber.[3]

Oxidation Products. The most striking industrial olefin oxidation is that of ethylene, which is air-oxidized over a silver catalyst at 225 to 325°C to give pure ethylene oxide (there are no by-products other than water and carbon dioxide), in yields ranging from 55 to 70 per cent.[4] Analogous higher olefin oxides can be prepared from propylene, butadiene, octene, dodecene, and styrene through the chlorhydrin route or by reaction with peracetic acid; of these only propylene oxide has a commercial usefulness up to this time. Acrolein is formed on air oxidation of

---

[1] Otto, Miller, Blackwood, and Davis, *Oil Gas J.*, **33**(26):98 (1934). Thomas, Zimmer, Turner, Rosen, and Frolich, *Ind. Eng. Chem.*, **32**:299 (1940). Thomas, Sparks, and Frolich, *J. ACS*, **62**:276 (1940).

[2] It is reported that when the ratio is reversed, i.e., 25 per cent butadiene and 75 per cent styrene, other properties, such as wear resistance, are emphasized.

[3] Stavely and coworkers, *Ind. Eng. Chem.*, **48**:778 (1956). Horne and coworkers, *Ind. Eng. Chem.*, **48**:784 (1956). Mayor, Saltman, and Pierson, *ACS, Div. Petrol. Chem., Symposium on Recent Developments in Chemicals from Petroleum*, Preprints, B-33, ACS Meeting, San Francisco, April, 1958.

[4] McBee, Hass, and Wiseman, *Ind. Eng. Chem.*, **37**:432 (1945). See also Landau, *Petrol. Refiner*, **32**(9):146 (1953). Sherwood, *Petrol. Engr.*, **27**(13):C-14 (1955); *Petroleum (London)*, **19**(6):203 (1956).

propylene over a supported cuprous oxide catalyst.[1]   This unsaturated aldehyde is also prepared by condensing acetaldehyde with formaldehyde.

Air oxidation of the higher olefins has not become practical because of the difficulty in controlling the reactions.   At temperatures between 350 and 500°C, maleic acid is obtained from amylene in 12 to 22 per cent yield per pass over vanadium pentoxide.   Slightly higher yields of the acid are obtained from hexene, heptene, and octene.[2]

One of the newer methods for the production of hydrogen peroxide involves the liquid-phase oxidation of isopropyl alcohol with oxygen at 90 to 140°C; acetone is a by-product.[3]

Miscellaneous Products.   Esters are formed directly by the addition of acids to olefins,[4] mercaptans by the addition of hydrogen sulfide, sulfides by the addition of mercaptans,[5] and amines by the addition of ammonia and other amines.[6]   Terminal olefins react with acid anhydrides to give unsaturated ketones; thus diisobutylene and acetic anhydride give methyl isooctenyl ketone.[7]

XVI-10. Chemicals Derived from Paraffinic Hydrocarbons.   In general, only paraffinic hydrocarbons from C_1 through C_5 are used as starting materials for specific chemical syntheses.   This is because the higher members of the series are less easy to fractionate from petroleum in pure form and also because the number of compounds formed in each particular treatment (oxidation, chlorination, etc.) makes the separation of individual products quite difficult.

Chlorination Products.   The ease with which chlorine can be introduced into the molecules of all the classes of hydrocarbons present in petroleum, together with its cheapness, has resulted in the commercial production of a number of widely used compounds.   With saturated hydrocarbons, the reactions are predominantly substitutions, strongly exothermic, difficult to control, and inclined to become explosively violent.   Moderately high temperatures are used, about 250 to 300°C, for the thermal chlorination of methane,[8] but in general as the molecular weight of the paraffin increases, the temperature should be lowered.   A mixture of chlorinated derivatives is always obtained, and many expedients such as choice of catalyst, dilution with inert gases, and presence of other chlorinating

[1] See Sherwood, *op. cit.*

[2] Faith and Dendurent, *Petrol. Refiner,* **18**(10):393 (1939).

[3] Hatch, *Petrol. Refiner,* **35**(3):197 (1956).

[4] Evans, Edlund, and Taylor, *Ind. Eng. Chem.,* **30**:55 (1938).

[5] Jones, Emmett, and Reid, *J. ACS,* **60**:2452 (1938).   Ipatieff and Friedman, *J. ACS,* **60**:2731 (1938); **61**:71 (1939).

[6] Radakovsky, *C.A.,* **31**:5322 (1937).

[7] Byrns and Doumani, *Ind. Eng. Chem.,* **35**:349 (1943).

[8] Jones, Allison, and Meighan, *U.S. Bur. Mines Tech. Papers* 255, 1921.   Hatch, *Petrol. Refiner,* **33**(12):13b (1954).

agents (antimony pentachloride, sulfuryl chloride, and phosgene) have been tried in an effort to direct the path of the reaction.[1] The refrigerant dichlorodifluoromethane is obtained by reacting carbon tetrachloride with antimony trifluoride.

Ethyl chloride is made by the chlorination of ethane in the presence of ethylene; it is also prepared by the direct addition of hydrogen chloride to ethylene or by reacting ethyl ether or ethyl alcohol with hydrogen chloride. Another path is the reaction of ethyl sulfate with sodium chloride.[2]

The chlorination of *n*- and isopentane does not take place in the liquid or vapor phase below 100°C in the absence of light or a catalyst, but above 200°C, it proceeds smoothly by thermal action alone.[3] The hydrolysis of the mixed chlorides obtained yields all the isomeric amyl alcohols except isoamyl. Reaction with acetic acid produces the corresponding amyl acetates, an important group of solvents.

The alkyl chloride obtained on substituting an equivalent of one chlorine atom in kerosene is used to alkylate benzene or naphthalene in the preparation of a sulfonation stock for the making of detergents and antirust agents. Similarly, paraffin wax can be converted to a mono-chloride mixture containing 10 to 12 per cent chlorine; when this is employed to alkylate benzene, naphthalene, or anthracene, a pour-point depressor is obtained which is effective for retarding wax crystal growth in cold lubricating oils.

Nitration Products. The normally gaseous hydrocarbons[4] (including normal and isopentane) react smoothly in the vapor phase with nitric acid to give a mixture of nitro products.[5] The main side reactions are those of oxidation. Only mononitro derivatives are obtained with the lower paraffins at high temperatures, and they correspond to those expected if a primary scission of each C—C and C—H bond takes place. Ethane, for example, gives nitromethane and nitroethane; propane gives nitromethane, nitroethane, 1-nitropropane and 2-nitropropane. In practice, propane, for instance, is nitrated at 430 to 450°C with 75 per cent nitric acid.

The nitro derivatives of the lower paraffins are colorless and noncorro-

---

[1] See Ellis, "Chemistry of Petroleum Derivatives," vol. I, pp. 465, 686, Reinhold Publishing Corporation, New York, 1934; vol. II, pp. 491, 726, 1937.

[2] Cade, *Chem. & Met. Eng.*, **28**:219 (1923). Giraitis, *ACS, Div. Petrol. Chem.*, Chemicals from Petroleum, Preprints, p. 63, ACS Meeting, Dallas, April, 1956.

[3] Ayres, *Ind. Eng. Chem.*, **21**:899 (1929).

[4] See Chap. III for a discussion of the action of nitric acid on liquid hydrocarbons.

[5] Hass and Riley, *Chem. Revs.*, **32**:373 (1943). Hass and Schechter, *Ind. Eng. Chem.*, **39**:817 (1947). Hass, Riley, and Schechter, "Science of Petroleum," vol. V, part 2, p. 70, Oxford University Press, New York and London, 1953. Reidel, *Oil Gas J.*, **54**(36):110 (1956).

sive. They find use as solvents and as starting materials in a variety of syntheses. For example, treating with inorganic acids and water yields fatty acids and hydroxylamine salts; condensation with aldehydes gives mono- and dihydric nitro alcohols; reaction with ketones gives dinitro hydrocarbons.

Oxidation Products. Partial oxidation of hydrocarbons and their mixtures has always been an intriguing subject for investigation, but has offered great difficulty because of the tendency of the reactions to run away, and in any case because of the mixed character of the products. An application which has been studied extensively is the making of synthesis gas (carbon monoxide–hydrogen) for manufacture of methyl and higher alcohols, aldehydes, and ketones.[1] Commercial methane (natural gas) and 95 per cent oxygen[2] will supply a charge material for the above procedures or will provide hydrogen for ammonia manufacture.[3] Except for the above, direct oxidation to useful products has been rather difficult to operate successfully. Methane and ethane are not generally subjected to direct oxidation; the relatively high temperatures required, even with catalysts, make it difficult to stop the reaction at desired intermediate points. Propane and the butanes, however, have been studied extensively as sources for alcohols, aldehydes, ketones, acids, and esters. Except for the making of mixed products having specific properties, such as fatty acids, hydrocarbons higher than pentanes are not employed for oxidation because of the difficulty of isolating individual compounds. Thus, when propane and butane are oxidized in the vapor phase, generally without a catalyst, at 270 to 350°C and under 50 to 3,000 psi pressure, a wide variety of products is obtained, as is illustrated in Table XVI-2. Other products include C_1-C_4 acids, C_2-C_7 alcohols, C_3-C_7 ketones, ethylene oxide, esters, formals, acetals, etc.[4] The ratios of the compounds formed vary with the operating conditions. The yield of oxygenated materials is highest at reaction temperatures in the range 150 to 250°; higher temperatures provide faster oxidation rates but pyrolysis increases. For example, the formation of butenes reaches a maximum at 375°C and ethylene and propylene at about 700°C (all at atmospheric pressure), the yield of oxidation products falling steadily with temperature rise.[5] A

[1] Schlesinger, Benson, Murphy, and Storch, *Ind. Eng. Chem.*, **46**:1322 (1954); **47**:2104 (1955).

[2] Mayland and Hayes, *Chem. Eng. Progr.*, **45**:452 (1949). Montgomery, Weinberg, and Hoffman, *Ind. Eng. Chem.*, **40**:601 (1948). Munger and Kratzer, *Ind. Eng. Chem.*, **43**:2782 (1951). Eastman, *Ind. Eng. Chem.*, **48**:1118 (1956).

[3] Kelley and Cain, *ACS, Div. Petrol. Chem., Symposium on Petro-chemicals in the Postwar Years*, Preprints, p. 43, ACS Meeting Chicago, September, 1953.

[4] Wiezevich and Frolich, *Ind. Eng. Chem.*, **26**:269 (1934). Powers, *Oil Gas J.*, **54**:(17):74 (1955).

[5] Powers, *op. cit.*

catalyst is generally needed to obtain a suitable reaction rate at temperatures below 230 to 250°C. Increased pressure decreases the olefin content of the product, permits lower operating temperatures or allows higher yields of oxygenated compounds at the same temperature, and gives higher alcohol to aldehyde or ketone ratios. Increases in the hydrocarbon-air ratio, outside the explosive limits, decrease the formation of carbon oxides and increase the yield of alcohols and ketones. Reaction time is held within the range of 0.3 to 10 sec. The process is thus quite flexible with respect to the nature of the products.

TABLE XVI-2

Products	Liquid product distribution, weight per cent		
	Propane	*n*-Butane	Isobutane
Acetaldehyde...........	28.0	30.6	17.0
Formaldehyde.........	26.4	22.9	19.8
Methanol.............	23.8	19.4	13.8
Acetone.............	1.7	4.9	26.0
C$_3$ aldehydes...........	2.9	4.5	3.8
Propylene oxide........	2.5	....	3.0
Butylene oxides........	....	2.8	1.1

From Mitchell, *Petrol. Refiner*, **35**(7):179 (1956). See also, Sherwood, *Petrol. Engr.*, **27**(13):C-14 (1955).

Cyclohexane is the only naphthene oxidized commercially. It responds to air oxidation rather selectively at 150 to 250°C in the liquid phase and in the presence of metal ion catalysts (cobalt acetate) to form cyclohexanol and cyclohexanone as intermediate products, and adipic acid on further oxidation. Maleic and glutaric acids can be prepared by the partial oxidation of cyclohexane and methylcyclohexane over vanadium pentoxide at 450 to 500°C.[1]

As just stated, higher-boiling liquid hydrocarbons are not employed for oxidation because of the difficulty of separating the components of the complex formed. A highly odorous denaturant for industrial ethyl alcohol was at one time produced, however, by air oxidation of kerosene over metal oxide catalysts at 240 to 250°C.[2] Hydrocarbon derivatives in all stages of oxidation were obtained, aldehydes and aldehyde acids making up about 50 per cent of the product. The latter components resinified on saponification.

[1] Milas and Walsh, U.S. Patent 2,118,567, 1938. Nelles, U.S. Patent 2,168,844, 1939.
[2] James, *Chem. & Met. Eng.*, **26**:209 (1922). Bitler and James, *Chem. & Met. Eng.*, **35**:156 (1928).

The making of fatty acids from petroleum, and particularly from paraffin wax, for esterification to fats or neutralization to form soaps has been the subject of a large number of rather early investigations.[1] Wax oxidation has had large-scale application when, as during war, natural fats are scarce. Oxidation with air is comparatively slow at low temperature and normal pressure, very little reaction taking place at 110°C, with a wax melting at 55°C, after 280 hr.[2] At higher temperatures the oxidation proceeds more readily; maximum yields of mixed alcohols and high-molecular-weight acids are formed at 110 to 140°C under 60 to 150 psi; higher temperatures (140 to 160°C) result in more oxyacid formation. A wax oxidized at 160°C to a 50 to 60 acid number and 140 to 150 saponification number is reported to contain 26 to 28 per cent fatty acids, 36 to 40 per cent unsaponifiables, and 6 to 9 per cent hydroxy acids. Catalysts generally employed are salts of iron, manganese, lead, mercury, chromium, vanadium, copper, and nickel.[3]

Not many investigators have identified the individual acids in their products. Generally, small amounts of volatile acids and somewhat larger quantities of water-insoluble saturated acids are produced; yields up to 60 to 70 per cent of the latter and of 250 average molecular weight have been claimed.[4] An idea of the nature of the acids produced on oxidation of a Fischer-Tropsch wax, in presence of 0.5 per cent of manganese stearate, is given in Table XVI-3. Carbon-carbon bond scission appears to take place all along the chain, leading to products of a wide molecular-weight range. The following volatile acids have been identified: formic, acetic, propionic, butyric, valeric, caproic, and on up to the 10 carbon chain. The water-insoluble, nonvolatile acids represent very complex mixtures. In addition to the fatty acids the product may contain hydroxy acids, lactones, anhydrides, aldehyde and keto acids, aldehydes, alcohols, and esters.[5] The wax acids contain over 80 per cent of saturated

[1] For more detailed discussion of the oxidation of gaseous, liquid, and solid hydrocarbons, see Ellis, *op. cit.*, vol. I, pp. 830–960; vol. II, pp. 843–979; Marek, "Oxidation of Organic Compounds in the Vapor Phase," pp. 152–258, Reinhold Publishing Corporation, New York, 1932. Stossel, *Oil Gas J.*, **44**(11):130 (1945); (15):145 (1945); (17):69 (1945).

[2] Francis, *J. Chem. Soc.*, **121**:496 (1922). Stossel, *Oil Gas J.*, **44**(11):130 (1945).

[3] Franck, *Chem. Ztg.*, **44**:309 (1920). Loffl, *Chem. Ztg.*, **44**:561 (1920). Bergmann, *Z. angew. Chem.*, **31**(1):69 (1918). Siebeneck, *Petroleum Z.*, **18**:1193 (1922). Grun, *Ber.*, **53**:987 (1920). Arditti, *Compt. rend.*, **193**:589 (1931).

[4] Schneider, Fischer, and Jantsch, *Ges. Abhandl. Kenntnis Kohle*, **4**:35, 48, 94, 101, 118, 132 (1919).

[5] Burwell, *Ind. Eng. Chem.*, **26**:204 (1934). Salway and Williams, *J. Chem. Soc.*, **121**:1343 (1922). Francis and Gauntlett, *J. Chem. Soc.*, **129**:2377 (1926). Shoruigin and Kreschkov, *J. Gen. Chem. (U.S.S.R.)*, **3**:825 (1933); **4**:988 (1934); *C.A.*, **28**:6106 (1934); **29**:2147 (1935). Sheely and King, *Ind. Eng. Chem.*, **26**:1150 (1934). Nametkin and Zvorykina, *Natl. Petrol. News*, **36** 40, R-702 (1944).

compounds ranging in molecular weight from 145 to 300, probably half corresponding to a content of C_{14} or less per molecule.[1] Myristic, palmitic, stearic, arachidic, lignoceric, and isopalmitic[2] acids have been reported. Dibasic acids are not formed to any great extent, although succinic acid has been recovered.[3] The nonacidic residue resembles beeswax in appearance. Production of fatty acids by this path has not been a success under normal economic conditions.

TABLE XVI-3

Oxidation temperature, °C	Air flow, liters per g per hr	Acid No.	Sapon. No.	Ester value	Hydroxy value	Per cent	
						Unsaponi-fiable	Oxy acids
100	0.05	197.3	231.2	33.9	55.3	5.0	0.2
120	0.10	194.2	237.9	43.7	48.2	6.8	0.4
130	0.50	187.5	238.0	50.5	57.9	7.6	0.2
150	1.0	163.9	209.7	46.8	75.5	12.8	0.6
160	1.0	139.0	221.6	82.6	54.9	13.7	3.1

From Pardun and Kichinka, *Fette u. Seifen*, **49**:441 (1942); see also *Petrol. Refiner*, **22** (11):410 (1943).

XVI-11. Chemicals Derived from Aromatic Hydrocarbons. Catalytic reforming of naphthas has made benzene, toluene, xylenes, and ethylbenzene economically available from petroleum sources. They are generally recovered by solvent extraction (with water-glycol mixtures or liquid sulfur dioxide), by extractive or azeotropic distillation, or by adsorption.[4] Naphthalene and methylnaphthalenes are present in sizable amounts in catalytically cracked distillates but coal-tar oils remain their chief source. A large share of the benzene consumed is now derived from petroleum. It has many chemical uses:

Oxidation to maleic anhydride
Hydrogenation to cyclohexane followed by oxidation to adipic acid

[1] Collin, *J. Soc. Chem. Ind.*, **49**:333T (1930).

[2] Bergmann, *Z. angew. Chem.*, **31**(1):69 (1918).

[3] Burwell, *Ind. Eng. Chem.*, **26**:204 (1934); "Science of Petroleum," vol. II, p. 1028, Oxford University Press, New York and London, 1938.

[4] Bloch and Wackher, *ACS, Div. Petrol. Chem., Symposium on Separation of Hydrocarbons and Related Compounds*, Preprints, p. 149, ACS Meeting, New York, September, 1954. Hirschler and Mertes, *ACS, Div. Petrol. Chem., Symposium on Separation of Hydrocarbons and Related Compounds*, Preprints, p. 5, ACS Meeting, New York, September, 1954. Lindholm and Sarno, *ACS, Div. Petrol. Chem., Symposium on Future of Aromatic Hydrocarbons*, Preprints, p. 21, ACS Meeting, Cincinnati, April, 1955.

Alkylation with ethylene to ethylbenzene which, after conversion to styrene, is employed to make polystyrene plastics and synthetic rubber (GR-S)

Alkylation with propylene to make cumene, an intermediate in the manufacture of phenol

Alkylation with higher olefins to prepare sulfonation stocks for detergents

Chlorination as a step in the manufacture of phenol or insecticides (DDT, methoxychlor, benzene hexachloride, etc.)

Sulfonation for conversion to phenol

Nitration for conversion to aniline and its derivatives

Toluene is usually in great demand during wartime as a source of TNT, but has fewer chemical uses than benzene. Alkylation with ethylene, followed by dehydrogenation, yields methylstyrene, which has possibilities for polymerization; alkylation with propylene tetramer forms a product suitable for sulfonation to a detergent-grade surface active compound. Toluene is sometimes employed as a high-octane constituent of aviation gasolines.

The xylene fraction of catalytically cracked and refined distillates is fairly constant in compositions, roughly as follows:

	Per cent
o-Xylene	17
m-Xylene	40
p-Xylene	17
Ethyl benzene	26

The mixture offers some difficulty in separation. Ethylbenzene and orthoxylene are separated by fractionation through an efficient column; the meta and para isomers, however, are close boiling and are generally recovered by fractional crystallization or selective sulfonation.[1] Metaxylene forms a complex with hydrogen fluoride–boron trifluoride, which is soluble in an excess of hydrogen fluoride.

Aromatics are more resistant to oxidation than the paraffin hydrocarbons, and higher temperatures are necessary; the oxidations are carried out in the vapor phase over a catalyst, generally supported vanadium oxide. Orthoxylene is oxidized to phthalic anhydride, metaxylene to isophthalic acid through an ester intermediate, and paraxylene with nitric acid to terephthalic acid. All the resulting dibasic acids are used in the manufacture of fibers, plastics, and plasticizers. Ethylbenzene, of course, is converted into styrene by dehydrogenation. Maleic anhydride and lesser amounts of fumaric acid are made by air oxidation of benzene over vanadium pentoxide at 400 to 500°C, with yields of the order of 50 to 60

[1] McCauley, Shoemaker, and Lien, *Ind. Eng. Chem.*, **42**:2103 (1950).

per cent. Maleic anhydride is also obtained as a by-product in the manufacture of phthalic anhydride.

Phthalic anhydride of high purity is produced in 70 to 80 per cent yield through air oxidation of naphthalene or, as just stated, orthoxylene.[1] The process is carried out at 400 to 450°C in the vapor phase under about 25 psi pressure over a fixed-bed vanadium oxide catalyst. The time of contact is quite short (about 1 sec) and a large excess of air is used to avoid explosive mixtures and to bring about rapid reaction. Care must be taken to have an inactive catalyst substrate (such as pumice) to prevent large losses to carbon dioxide and water. A silica gel support modified by potassium sulfate is described as effective for this purpose. A fluidized catalyst process, offering some advantages especially with respect to lower air requirements and easier dissipation of the heat released, has been developed.[2] Terephthalic acid is similarly produced from paraxylene, although here the toluic acid intermediate is further oxidized with difficulty. The methyl esters of *m*- and *p*-toluic acids, however, are readily air-oxidized to the methyl esters of iso- and terephthalic acids, respectively.[3]

A small amount of benzaldehyde is made through the oxidation of the methyl group in toluene, but most of it is prepared from benzyl chloride. Benzoic acid is obtained mainly by the decarboxylation of phthalic acid.

A process of interest and importance is the preparation of phenol by the air oxidation of isopropylbenzene (cumene) to cumene hydroperoxide which, on catalytic (acid) decomposition, forms phenol and acetone through an ionic reaction.[4] Alpha-methylstyrene and acetophenone are among the by-products formed through a free radical dissociation. Alkyl-substituted cumenes produce the corresponding cresols, xylenols, etc.

Hydrogen. The availability of large quantities of hydrogen from catalytic reforming operations has made its application economically feasible in a number of petroleum refining operations. Previously, the chief sources of large-scale hydrogen (used mainly for ammonia manufacture)[5] were the cracking of methane (or natural gas) and the reaction

[1] It is reported that other polycyclic aromatic-containing coal tar or petroleum distillates can also be employed as source materials. Kinney and Pincus, *Ind. Eng. Chem.*, **43**:2880 (1951).

[2] Ruthruff, *Petrol. Refiner*, **32**(10):113 (1953).

[3] Albert and Kneisley, *ACS, Div. Petrol. Chem., Symposium on Petrochemicals in the Post War Years*, Preprints, p. 125, ACS Meeting, Chicago, September, 1953.

[4] Franck, *Chem. Revs.*, **46**:155 (1950). Sherwood, *Petrol. Engr.*, **30**(11):C-9 (1958).

[5] A process reported under development is the application of hydrogen for its direct reduction of iron ore. Old, *ACS, Div. Petrol. Chem., Symposium on Recent Developments in Chemicals from Petroleum*, Preprints, B-65, ACS Meeting, San Francisco, April, 1958.

between methane and steam.   In the latter, at 900 to 1000°C, conversion into carbon monoxide and hydrogen results.

$$CH_4 + H_2O \rightleftharpoons CO + 3H_2$$

If this mixture is treated further with steam at 500°C over catalysts, the carbon monoxide present is converted into carbon dioxide and more hydrogen is produced.

$$CO + H_2O \rightleftharpoons H_2 + CO_2$$

The over-all reaction is

$$CH_4 + 2H_2O \rightarrow 4H_2 + CO_2$$

Carbon Blacks.   Carbon blacks are produced by the incomplete combustion and cracking of methane, natural gas, or higher-boiling liquid hydrocarbons, including aromatic gas oils; they are composed of 80 to 95 per cent or more of quasi-graphitic carbon of particle size in the colloidal range.[1]   The quality is very sensitive to the method by which the charge is heated, the nature of the hydrocarbon material, the shape of the flame, the rate of burning, and other more subtle influences.[2]

Fischer-Tropsch Process and Products.   The reduction, by hydrogen, of carbon monoxide is the basis of several syntheses, such as the making of methanol, higher alcohols, and other more complex oxygen-containing compounds.   The syntheses of hydrocarbons, by the Fischer-Tropsch method, have been studied extensively and practiced on a large scale under special circumstances, such as those of wartime.   The production of one or the other of the above materials depends on choice of operating conditions and catalysts.

For the production of hydrocarbon constituents useful as motor fuels, the primary reaction is

$$nCO + 2nH_2 = (CH_2)n + nH_2O$$

This occurs in the temperature range 200 to 350°C, which is sufficiently high for the water-gas shift to take place in presence of the catalyst,

$$CO + H_2O \rightleftharpoons CO_2 + H_2$$

[1] For the composition of carbon blacks and the mechanism of their formation, see Sweitzer and Heller, *Rubber World,* **134**:855 (1956).

[2] Cohan, "Science of Petroleum," vol. V, part 2, p. 78, Oxford University Press, New York and London, 1953.

and the over-all reaction may be written

$$2nCO + 2nH_2 = (CH_2)n + nCO_2$$

The main products are olefins, paraffins, oxygenated compounds, carbon dioxide, and steam.

The carbon monoxide and hydrogen (synthesis gas) used in the above reaction may be obtained from coal, oil, hydrocarbon gases, or any other carbonaceous material. Natural gas may be converted into synthesis gas either by reaction with steam over a nickel catalyst[1]

$$CH_4 + H_2O = CO + 3H_2$$

or by partial direct oxidation, using oxygen[2]

$$CH_4 + \frac{1}{2}O_2 = CO + 2H_2$$

The latter method is probably the more economical; it produces the reactants in about the desired ratio,[3] but seems to give operating difficulties.

As indicated above, a wide range of products is possible. A general picture of the materials produced and the conditions under which they are formed is given in Fig. XVI-2.

In general, the process may be divided as follows:

1. Low and medium pressure synthesis in presence of cobalt catalysts, used in Germany during wartime.[4]

2. Medium pressure synthesis in presence of iron catalysts originated in Germany[5] and further developed in the United States.[6]

3. High-pressure synthesis of branched structures (isosynthesis) in the presence of thoria catalysts; not used commercially.

The products obtained under all these operating conditions contain both hydrocarbons and oxygenated compounds, but their proportions may be varied over a wide range by changing catalysts or their method

[1] Discussed by Lewis, *Chem. Eng. News.*, **25**:2815 (1947). Reitmeier, Atwood, Bennett, and Baugh, *Ind. Eng. Chem.*, **40**:620 (1948).

[2] Mayland and Hayes, *Chem. Eng. Progr.*, **45**:452 (1949). Montgomery, Weinberger, and Hoffman, *Ind. Eng. Chem.*, **40**:601 (1948). Munger and Kratzer, *Ind. Eng. Chem.*, **43**:2782 (1951). Eastman, *Ind. Eng. Chem.*, **48**:1118 (1956).

[3] Keith, *Oil Gas J.*, **45**(6):102 (1946).

[4] Fischer and Tropsch, *Ber.*, **59**:830, 832, 923 (1926).

[5] Fischer and Pichler, Technical Oil Mission to Germany Film, Reel 259, Frames 467–654. French Patent 841,043, 1939.

[6] Arnold and Keith, *Advances in Chem. Ser.*, No. 5, p. 120, 1951.

of preparation, temperature, pressure, and carbon monoxide–hydrogen ratios. The hydrocarbon content may be altered from compositions containing 80 per cent gases and low-boiling liquids (mainly olefins) to those containing up to 60 per cent of high-melting waxes; other compounds (mainly alcohols) may be varied from less than 10 per cent to nearly 80 per cent of the total.[1]

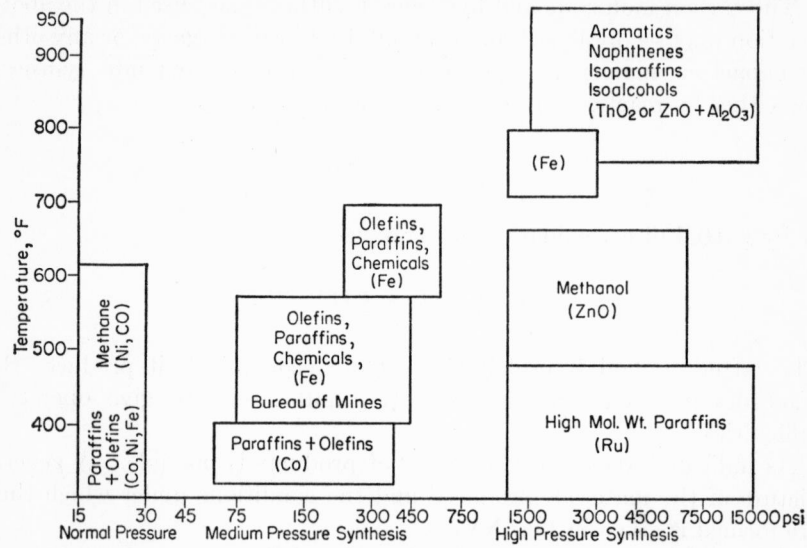

FIG. XVI-2. Pressure-temperature regions for synthesis processes on carbon monoxide and hydrogen basis. (*Adapted from Arnold and Keith, Advances in Chem. Ser., No. 5, p. 128, 1951.*)

HYDROCARBON PRODUCTS.   With the cobalt catalyst, a temperature of about 200°C is employed at pressures varying from atmospheric to 225 psi. A prepared catalyst contains 5 parts thoria, 8 magnesia, and 100 cobalt on 200 parts of kieselguhr (pure cobalt produces mainly methane); its use is somewhat limited to the stoichiometric carbon monoxide–hydrogen ratio of 1:2 for optimum results; the allowable temperature is about 225°C maximum.   The iron-catalyzed process operates at somewhat higher temperatures (280 to 360°C) and pressures (300 to 600 psi).   The main advantages of the iron catalyst (which is generally promoted by a small amount of potassium carbonate or oxide) are low cost, flexibility with respect to permissible carbon monoxide–hydrogen ratios, less sensitivity to overheating, and the wide range of useful compositions that can be produced.   Both the iron and cobalt catalysts require relatively pure reactants, as their tolerance for sulfur compounds is low.   Heat dissipation in the highly exothermic reaction is a critical factor in plant design.

[1] Hall, *Research,* **9**(1):7 (1956).

Difficulties in the separation of product constituents are also encountered.

The hydrocarbons formed are mainly aliphatic.   On a molar basis, the yield of methane is the largest; the amount of higher hydrocarbons, with a possible irregularity reported at C_2, decreases gradually with increase in molecular weight.   The iron catalyst gives a considerably more volatile and olefinic product[1] as shown in Table XVI-4, and also one containing more branched hydrocarbons[2] as shown in Table XVI-5.

TABLE XVI-4

	Cobalt catalyst		Iron catalyst	
	Weight per cent of total	Olefin content, volume per cent	Weight per cent of total	Olefin content, volume per cent
$C_3 + C_4$........ ..	10	40	32	82
Naphtha cut........	30	26	56	85–90
Diesel fuel cut......	33	8	8	75–85
Residue...........	27	...	4	

From Bruner, *Ind. Eng. Chem.*, **41**:2511 (1949).

TABLE XVI-5

	C_5	C_6	C_7	C_8
Cobalt catalyst:*				
n-Hydrocarbons, volume per cent..........	94.9	89.6	87.7	84.6
Monomethyl isomers, volume per cent.....	5.1	10.4	12.3	15.5
Iron catalyst:†				
n-Hydrocarbons, weight per cent..........	....	75.9	60.2	55.4
Monomethyl isomers, we ght per cent......	....	20.0	29.3	36.6
Dimethyl isomers, weight per cent.........	....	0.4	1.7	2.4
Cyclic isomers, weight per cent............	....	3.7	8.8	5.6

* Friedel and Anderson, *J. ACS*, **72**:1212 (1950).
† Bruner, *Ind. Eng. Chem.*, **41**:2511 (1949).

Isoparaffin formation is more extensive over zinc oxide or thoria at 400 to 500°C and under higher pressures.[3]   Paraffin waxes are formed

[1] Bruner, *Ind. Eng. Chem.*, **41**:2511 (1949).   Morrell, Carlson, McAteer, Robey, and Smith, *Ind. Eng. Chem.*, **44**:2839 (1952).   Weitkamp, Seelig, Bowman, and Cady, *Ind. Eng. Chem.*, **45**:343 (1953).
[2] Friedel and Anderson, *J. ACS*, **72**:1212 (1950).   MacDonald, Sweett, and Hall, *J. Appl. Chem.*, **5**:536 (1955).
[3] Pichler, Ziesecke, and Titzenthaler, *Brennstoff-Chem.*, **30**:333 (1949).   Pichler and Ziesecke, *U.S. Bur. Mines. Bull.* 488, 1950.

over ruthenium catalysts at relatively low temperatures (170 to 200°C), high pressures (1,500 psi), and with a high carbon monoxide–hydrogen ratio.[1]

The more highly branched product made over the iron catalyst is an important factor in a choice for the manufacture of automotive fuels. On the other hand, a high-quality diesel fuel (paraffinic character) can be prepared over cobalt. The C_9-C_{19} fraction (380 to 592°F) of a German Fischer-Tropsch fuel made at 200°C under 150 psi pressure, made up of 88 per cent normal paraffins, 1.5 per cent α-olefins, 8.5 per cent internal olefins, and 2 per cent oxygenated compounds, has a cetane number of 80, and of 88 after removal of the polar compounds.[2]

Secondary reactions play an important part in determining the final structure of the product. The olefins produced are subjected to both hydrogenation and double-bond shifting toward the center of the molecule; *cis* and *trans* isomers are formed in about equal amounts.[3] About 40 to 50 volume per cent of the C_5, C_6, and C_7 fractions (iron catalyst) are straight-chain olefins.[4] Some naphthenic and aromatic hydrocarbons are also formed. The C_4 through C_7 paraffins contain all the possible mono- and dimethyl structures except neopentane. The proportions of straight-chain molecules decrease with rise in molecular weight, but even so they are still more abundant than branched-chain compounds up through C_{10}.

The small amount of aromatic hydrocarbons found in the product covers a wide range of isomer possibilities.[5] In the C_6-C_9 range, benzene, toluene, ethylbenzene, xylenes, *n*- and isopropylbenzene, methylethylbenzenes, and trimethylbenzenes have been identified;[6] naphthalenes and possibly anthracenes are also present.

OXYGENATED COMPOUNDS. About 18 per cent of the carbon and 6 per cent of the oxygen in the carbon monoxide converted end up as oxygenated compounds.[7] These may be divided into water-soluble (low molecular weight) and oil-soluble (high molecular weight), with a certain amount of material overlapping the division.

[1] Pichler and Buffleb, *Brennstoff-Chem.*, **21**:257 (1940).

[2] Ward, Schwartz, and Adams, *Ind. Eng. Chem.*, **43**:1117 (1951).

[3] Weitkamp, Seelig, Bowman, and Cady, *loc. cit.* See also Herington, *Chem. Ind.*, **65**:347 (1946). Friedel and Anderson, *J. ACS*, **72**:1212, 2307 (1950). Anderson, Friedel, and Storch, *J. Chem. Phys.*, **19**:313 (1951). Manes, *J. ACS*, **74**:3148 (1952).

[4] Clark, Andrews, and Fleming, *Ind. Eng. Chem.*, **41**:1527 (1949).

[5] Cady, Launer, and Weitkamp, *Ind. Eng. Chem.*, **45**:350 (1953). Clark, Andrews, and Fleming, *op. cit.*

[6] Cady, Launer, and Weitkamp, *op. cit.*

[7] Weitkamp, Seelig, Bowman, and Cady, *loc. cit.*

The chemical types found in the water phase are:[1]

	Average molecular weight	Weight per cent of water stream
Acids...................	65.7	3.1
Alcohols................	51.7	4.3
Aldehydes..............	48.8	0.6
Ketones................	61.4	2.2

The so-called Synol process is adapted primarily to the production of straight-chain alcohols; the product contains negligible amounts of iso or secondary alcohols, some aldehydes, ketones, esters, and lesser amounts of acids. The synthesis is carried out over an alkali-promoted sintered iron catalyst[2] at temperatures in the neighborhood of 170 to 200°C, at pressures of 275 to 375 psi, with carbon monoxide–hydrogen ratios of the order of 1:0.7, and at a higher space velocity than used in the hydrocarbon synthesis.

MECHANISM. Early attempts to explain the synthesis of hydrocarbons through the carbon monoxide–hydrogen reaction were based on the assumption that the carbon monoxide reacted with the metal catalyst to form a carbide (Fe_2C, Fe_3C, Co_2C) and that this in turn was reduced by the hydrogen to form methylene groups, which polymerized to form higher hydrocarbons $(CH_2)_n$.[3] This theory is open to criticism in that it does not explain the formation of oxygenated compounds,[4] and that iron carbide reacts with hydrogen to form methane instead of $(CH_2)_n$ compounds. The theory is further weakened by tracer experiments which show that a mixture of carbon monoxide and hydrogen passed over Fe_2C^{14} formed a hydrocarbon mixture that contained only 10 to 15 per cent as much radioactive compounds as might be expected if the carbide was acting as an intermediate.[5] Also, the free energies of formation of Fe_2C and Fe_3C are of such magnitude as to make their reduction into aliphatic hydrocarbons containing six or more carbon atoms thermodynamically unlikely.[6]

[1] Steitz and Barnes, *Ind. Eng. Chem.*, **45**:353 (1953).

[2] Large amounts of oxygenated compounds are also formed if iron nitride is the catalyst. Schlesinger, Benson, Murphy, and Storch, *Ind. Eng. Chem.*, **46**:1322 (1954). Weitkamp and Bowman, *Ind. Eng. Chem.*, **45**:359 (1953). Morrell, Carlson, McAteer, Robey, and Smith, *loc. cit.*

[3] Fischer and Tropsch, *Brennstoff-Chem.*, **7**:97 (1926). Craxford and Rideal, *J. Chem. Soc.*, 1939, p. 1604.

[4] Elvins and Nash, *Nature*, **118**:154 (1926).

[5] Kummer, DeWitt, and Emmett, *J. ACS.*, **70**:3632 (1948).

[6] Kummer, Browning, and Emmett, *J. Phys. Chem.*, **16**:739 (1948); *J. ACS*, **72**:4211 (1950).

No mechanism proposed has as yet satisfactorily explained the course of the reaction and the variety of products obtained. The early suggestion of a carbon-hydrogen-oxygen complex on the catalyst surface acting as an intermediate[1] has received substantial support. Radioactive methyl, ethyl, n-propyl, isopropyl, and isobutyl alcohols added to a carbon monoxide–hydrogen mixture being treated over an iron catalyst were found to be built into a normal product, strongly indicating that they could serve as intermediates in the reaction.[2]

The Fischer-Tropsch hydrocarbon synthesis has been the object of much ingenious development. However, it is still somewhat wasteful in terms of energy yield, and in any case has not been able to survive in free competition.

[1] Elvins and Nash, *op. cit.* Weitkamp and Drye, *Ind. Eng. Chem.*, **45**:363 (1953).
[2] Kummer, Podgurski, Spencer, and Emmett, *J. ACS*, **73**:564 (1951). Kummer and Emmett, *J. ACS*, **75**:5177 (1953). Emmett, *ACS, Div. Petrol. Chem., Symposium on Mechanisms of Homogeneous and Heterogeneous Hydrocarbon Reactions*, Preprint, p. 79, ACS Meeting, Kansas City, April, 1954.

Author Index

Subject Index